The Good Hotel Guide 1990

The Good Hotel Guide 1990

Britain and Western Europe
–also Morocco and Turkey

Editor: Hilary Rubinstein

Managing Editor and Editor for the British Isles:
Caroline Raphael

Continental Editor:
John Ardagh

Contributing Editor:
Susan Gillotti

Which? Books
Published by Consumers' Association
and Hodder & Stoughton

Which? Books are commissioned by The Association for Consumer Research and published by Consumers' Association, 2 Marylebone Road, London NW1 4DX and Hodder & Stoughton, 47 Bedford Square, London WC1B 3DP

British Library Cataloguing in Publication Data
The Good hotel guide: Britain and Western Europe.—1990
1. Western Europe. Hotels—Directories
I. Consumers' Association
647.94401

ISBN 0 340 51142 7

Editorial assistants: Katinka Ardagh, Pier Bryden, Philippa Carlile, Susan Carlile, Hilary Hodgson

Illustrations by Ray Evans
Cover illustration by Simon Jones

Computer typeset by SB Datagraphics Ltd.,
Colchester, Essex (an Ician Communications Group company)
Printed and bound in Great Britain by
BPCC Hazell Books Ltd,
Aylesbury, Bucks

Contents

A note for new readers

This is an annual guide to hotels and inns in the British Isles and the continent of Europe (with Morocco now included as well as Turkey) that are of unusual character and quality. The entries are based on reports from readers who write to us when they come across an establishment which has given them out-of-the-ordinary satisfaction, and who also send us their comments, critical or appreciative, when they visit places already included in the Guide. Our task is to collate these reports, check and verify them, making inspections where necessary, and select those which we consider make the grade. No cash changes hands at any point: contributors are not rewarded for writing to us; hotels do not pay for their entries. The editor and his staff accept no free hospitality.

We do not attempt to be comprehensive. There are many blank areas on our maps, including many major cities which lack a single entry. We see no point in lowering our standards in order to recommend an indifferent establishment as "the best available". But of course we are always particularly glad to receive nominations for hotels in a town or a region which is poorly represented.

The Guide operates on the same principle as *The Good Food Guide*, but is independently owned and edited. We have no say in the hotels and restaurants chosen by that guide, nor are they involved in our choices. Hotels listed in that Guide carry the notation [GFG] after their name.

The entries in the book cover a wide range. People want different things from a hotel according to whether they are making a single night stop or spending a whole holiday in one place, whether they have young children with them, whether they are visiting a city or staying in the remote countryside, and according to their age and means. We make no claims of universal compatibility, but we hope that our descriptions will help you to find hotels that suit your tastes, needs and purse. If an entry has misled you, we beg you to use one of the report forms at the back of the book and tell us, in order that we can do better next time; and we hope that you will also write to us if you have found the Guide useful and a hotel has fulfilled your expectations: endorsement and criticism are both essential if the Guide is to achieve its purpose. Hotels are dropped unless we get positive feedback on them.

Introduction

"No wonder city tourism chiefs and hoteliers are hopping mad over Nottingham's exclusion from the new Good Hotel Guide. We have some of the best hotels in the country here in Nottingham – yet The Good Hotel Guide 1989 does not include even one of them."
Nottingham Evening Post, 20 October, 1988

This is by no means the first time that the Guide has been castigated by provincial newspapers and radio stations for its failure to recommend a single hotel in a particular town. It has become something of an annual ritual for reporters to ring up on publication and hector us on the subject. Cheer up, Nottingham. You are in good company: Belfast, Birmingham, Bristol, Cambridge, Cardiff, Leeds and Liverpool are similarly disenfranchised.

Are there no good hotels in any of these great cities? We have been asking this question for the past dozen years and are still waiting for an answer. Of course there are plenty of hotels to choose from in any industrial centre. But most large business-oriented city hotels are relatively indistinguishable one from another. They may differ in their architecture and facilities: some will have air-conditioning and double glazing, four-posters and mini-bars, more spacious public areas, more boutiques. And of course their management and service may be smart and spick and span or, alternatively, slack, snooty or sullen. *That* can make a difference. But however good a big corporation-owned city hotel may be of its kind, it will remain the hotel equivalent of convenience food. And some of us want something else when we travel abroad.

This Guide is – and intends to remain – committed to a more personal experience. But why do so few British cities boast small hotels of character? Why is it that Bath can have no fewer than eight entries and Bristol none? Plainly one reason is that the kind of individually owned hotel of character appeals more to tourists than to the business trade, but it is also unhappily the case that the bad – or at least the mediocre – drives out the good. Trusthouse Forte has made a huge contribution to raising the standards of hotel catering in Britain, but it is no accident that the Guide lists no more than one THF hotel. When it acquires an old hotel, THF will certainly improve its facilities, put in baths *en suite* and colour TV, and yet, again and again, its presence is a kind of kiss – not of death certainly – but of half-life. And the same is true about the acquisitions of all the other major chains – Crest, Thistle, Queens Moat, etc – who are in the business of catering more for customers en masse rather than the individual.

We are witnessing a period of astonishing growth in the hotel and catering business. Tourism, it is reckoned, is likely to become the world's biggest single industry within the next decade and conference-ism isn't far behind. Every day we receive PR handouts for new custom-built hotels in cities and extravagant conversions of old country houses, recommending themselves as "the ideal venue for all your conference and banqueting needs". Nearly all the new country house hotel openings we have heard about this year have been of that ilk. And at the same time it is harder and harder for the new individual enterprise, without benefit of economies of scale and corporate promotion, to get adequate recognition of its quieter virtues and to survive its early years. It is no accident that many popular independent small Guide hotels - more this year than ever before - have had to be omitted because they have closed down or changed hands, often having had to sell to a hotel chain.

We give the last word on this subject to Dickens, writing 140 years ago in *The Uncommercial Traveller*. His insights are every bit as true today as they were then:

> We all know the great hotel belonging to the company of proprietors . . . in which we can get anything we want, after its kind, for money; but where nobody is glad to see us, or sorry to see us, or minds (our bill paid) whether we come or go, or how, or when, or why, or cares about us. We all know this hotel, where we have no individuality, but put ourselves into the general post, as it were, and are sorted and disposed of according to our division. We all know that we can get on very well indeed at such a place, but still not perfectly well; and this may be because the place is largely wholesale, and there is a lingering personal retail interest within us that asks to be satisfied.

Are hotels staying tuned?

As we move into the nineties, it is useful to ask how far the hotel industry is adapting itself to the changing needs of its customers. It has certainly moved a long way from 1980 in embracing new appliances: remote control TV, direct-dial telephones, hair-dryers and trouser presses, once the rare exception, are now commonplace bedroom conveniences. And more and more hotels now have fax and computerised accounts which in principle minimise mistakes and make them easier to spot.

But hoteliers have been deplorably slow, we believe, to recognise other less tangible consumer needs. Consider smoking. How few hotels have registered the extraordinary shift in the public's attitude to smoking in the last few years, especially among the main hotel-using classes. According to one recent opinion poll, 85 per cent of the public agree that smoking is a health hazard and 91 per cent think that all restaurants should provide non-smoking areas. Nobody has thought to ask what percentage of people believe hotels should earmark some of their rooms as smokeless zones, but presumably the hotel poll would be similar to the restaurant one. Few hotels yet provide such rooms, few offer smoke-free zones in their restaurant. (No-smoking Guide hotels in the UK are listed under Special Hotels on page 22.)

Hoteliers have been just as tardy to perceive other shifts in public demand. Many are still boasting of five-, six- or seven-course set menus – feasts for Gargantuas – ignoring the evidence that more and more of their customers are looking these days for lighter diets and dishes, and not just the older generation whose appetites diminish with age. At one time we were used to getting complaints about the modest portions of *nouvelle cuisine*. We hardly ever hear from the anti-*nouvelle* faction these days, but correspondents often tell us how they pine for a two or three-course option. We hear plenty these days about the risks of high cholesterol diets, but many hotels continue to boast of their chariots of rich desserts, the mere sight of which give those who know about such things the intimations of cardiac arrest. And how few hotels are putting themselves out to cater imaginatively for the ever-growing brigade who prefer (at least sometimes) not to eat meat or fish.

It is always difficult to predict future trends in eating, but as we become more health and hygiene conscious – and people all over the western world are taking responsibility for their health as never before – the demand for simpler meals, using fresh, not frozen, packaged or cook-chilled, produce, will certainly grow. We believe that many of the smaller hotels would give greater satisfaction to their guests if they were to be less ambitious in their menus and try less hard to imitate (so often lamentably) the bravura performances of the culinary maestros.

Service charges – are they really on the way out?

In 1984 we launched our first broadside on the subject of service charges and tipping – indicting the catering industry for what we called "the arbitrary, antiquated and discreditable practice of charging for service and touting for tips". We wouldn't claim to have been the first in the field: customers have been complaining for centuries against the various forms of exaction or extortion practised by the trade, from the "salt and pepper" tax imposed by Blackpool landladies, to the "optional" service charge added on at the end of the bill, the open bottom line on the credit card voucher and the shameless nudging for tips that goes on in many hotels and restaurants. But for many years past the topic had attracted little public attention, the practice having become so institutionalised that it seemed difficult to imagine any change for the better.

Our campaign had two aims: the first was to persuade hoteliers and restaurateurs to quote an all-inclusive price for service and VAT, as is done in France and many other countries on the continent; and, second, to encourage owners of hotels and restaurants to take an active stand against their employees holding out the metaphorical palm. We had and have no wish to frustrate generous impulses of guests keen to reward particular services, but wanted an end to any automatic demand for the customer to fumble in his pocket for that something extra.

In March 1989 a new Consumer Protection Act became law, making it a criminal offence to mislead customers about goods, service, accommodation or facilities, and at the same time introduced a Code of Conduct recommending that non-optional extras such as service charges should be incorporated in fully-inclusive prices, clearly displayed as such on menus and tariffs.

It would be a cause for celebration indeed if this new law and code of conduct meant that we could hang up our campaigning cudgels. But though we have no quarrel with the Act itself (which authorises fines of up to £2,000 or six months in jail), the Code of Conduct is as full of holes as a colander. The Code is offered as "practical guidance" and "should be followed where practicable". The Department of Consumer Affairs concedes that "it will not always be practical for a restaurant to include service and VAT on every individual item or on à la carte menus". We cannot follow its reasoning since restaurants and hotels in France have no problem about including service and taxes on all their charges. As things stand at present, there will be nothing to stop hoteliers continuing to impose a cover charge or arm-twisting their customers into paying something extra by a prominent display of that demeaning line about service being at guests' discretion – or simply "not included".

We accept that if service charges were outlawed, some employers would have to pay their staff more. But it is time that catering managements accepted their responsibilities: no other industry expects part of its wage bill to be met in the present anomalous way. Meanwhile, we are continuing to ask British hoteliers, when they fill in our annual questionnaire, to tell us their policy on these issues.

For those readers who share our distaste for these practices, we recommend a policy of civil resistance. We would like restaurateurs and hoteliers who still impose these charges or endeavour to shame the customer into leaving a tip to be challenged in a discreet and unprovocative manner. If you are presented with a credit card with the bottom line left open, we suggest that you don't just fill it in, but make a point of politely asking the waiter or receptionist why the voucher has been left incomplete. Since it is clear that the government has given in to the catering lobby, which longs for the status quo to be maintained, things will continue much as at present unless we start to debate these issues on the shop floor.

Department of complaints

Many grouses surface every year: the lack of sufficient shelves in bathrooms, for example, poor lighting or inadequate heating are hardy perennials which should be easy and not impossibly expensive to correct. We are also accustomed to getting complaints about beds: that they are either too soft or too hard. We reckon that these cancel each other out. People who feel strongly about their mattresses should make a point of mentioning their concern when they book.

Other problems are more intractable. We sympathise with the plight of the single person, constantly being fobbed off with inferior accommodation or else made to pay extra (often twice as much) for a double room. It would be a great day for single people in Britain if they could pay a fixed price per person or at least be asked to pay a fair rather than an extortionate single-person supplement. But we doubt whether many hoteliers will find it worth their while wooing these voters except in towns where there is a constant demand for single rooms from business folk – and the latter often don't mind paying more for a double room if the extra cost isn't hitting their own pocket.

We have had a plethora of complaints this year about hotels not honouring guests' bookings despite – in many cases – confirmation by letter, telex or fax, and the payment of deposits. French hotels figure often in these charges, Parisian ones especially. Some hotels, we suspect, like some airlines, operate a deliberate policy of double-booking, hoping that it will work out on the night. Deposits may be returned, with or without an adequate apology, but the customer often loses out on the exchange rate. There is no instant remedy, but we urge readers to make a point of reporting all such incidents to the appropriate bodies – to any Guide which lists the hotel and to the relevant tourist board – unless satisfactory amends are made. It's a boring, time-consuming exercise, but hotels ought not to be allowed to get away with over-booking any more than travellers should be permitted to book themselves into more than one hotel and flagrantly overlook the loss to the innkeeper of a "no show". Readers often criticise hotels for taking credit card numbers when they are making a reservation; it may seem unfriendly, but we sympathise with hoteliers who need that self-protection.

The children's liberation movement

"We are eager that more hotels should welcome small children," we wrote in our Introduction last year, "but we are not prepared to omit hotels that decline to accept them. We consider that hotels are entitled to exercise any reasonable restrictions they wish as it is the customer's right to patronise these places or give them a wide berth."

That is still our line, though it may change. We mind a great deal about the many hotels in Britain, perhaps one-third of those in the Guide, that refuse to allow children through their doors, or do so only under protest - "by special arrangement" is the polite phrase for saying "we would much rather you didn't ask us". Children are declared undesirable at a variety of different ages; quite a number of hotels regard 16 as the earliest tolerable age, and, as we mentioned last year, one country house hotel (though it no longer has an entry in these pages) considers the little nuisances to be insufferable until they reach the age of 18.

Now turn to the second half of the book and you will find no more than ten hotels across the whole of the continent which impose any restrictions whatsoever on children – and of those ten, two have British owners and two are owned by Americans! We confess that until we had carried out this simple exercise, we had not realised just how bizarre our attitude to children must appear to visitors from abroad.

What do parents feel when a hotel says: "Children are tolerated but not encouraged" or "Children accepted if over 12 years or babies which stay in their rooms" or "Small children not really welcome" or "Babies not encouraged" or "Children must be well-behaved" (and the same might be said of adults). Though perhaps these rebuffs are preferable to the simple, brutal "No children".

For the record, it may be of interest that equivalent hotels in our US sibling, *America's Wonderful Little Hotels & Inns,* are even less enthusiastic about children, with many more refusing entry till 16. Motels (still relatively rare in Britain) no doubt cater for many travelling American families, but we are nevertheless aghast at some of the manifestations of child-phobia in American country inns: "Well-behaved children under constant parental supervision welcome" or "Children must have good table manners" or "Children must be disciplined and polite" or "Children under 8 and pets restricted to accommodation in specific areas" or "Children definitely not encouraged".

Dr Peter Rudd, a consultant paediatrician in Bristol with whom we discussed this phenomenon, commented as follows:

"As a father of three children, I have long been aware of the discrimination existing against children entering hotels and restaurants in this country. This hostility against children is unique. I have taken several holidays in France with my family. What was so striking was the welcome and attention given to the children wherever we went.

"Imagine the outcry if black people or women were excluded from our hotels. Why are children treated in this way? Is it thought that they will wreck the furniture or is the management frightened that the other guests may be disturbed by noise that they may generate? One could argue that the same could and does apply to adults. If we make it difficult for children to stay in hotels, we do not give them the opportunity to show and develop the good manners of which they are capable."

Dr Rudd believes that, by including hotels which impose restrictions on children, we are condoning their actions. He would like us to exclude newcomers who discriminate against children and give hotels which are already in the Guide a year to mend their ways. We are not prepared to adopt these draconian measures, and would prefer to win this struggle by persuasion rather than by an ultimatum. We wish that hotels which at present impose a ban on children would try lifting their restrictions and see what happens. Parents, for their part, will have to take responsibility for ensuring that their children don't run wild. Of course hotel owners will fear losing some of their regular customers, just as many of them have been afraid of losing out if they impose restrictions on smokers. But we have yet to hear of regrets from those hoteliers who have had the courage of their anti-smoking convictions. And we believe that, once they have become accustomed to children round the place, child-phobic hotel guests will accept the change as they already perforce accept children in hotels on the continent. And in time they will look back in amazement at the prejudices that still prevailed in the 1980s.

"Give little children a chance" is our campaigning slogan for the nineties.

Animal liberation too?

As usual the dog lobby has been vocal. Here is a heartfelt plea from Joanne Richardson:

"We travel a lot in the UK and would not consider taking a break without our mutt. She has stayed at some of the best hotels in Britain, but I am constantly amazed at the number of establishments that turn away dogs. Our dog is well trained, doesn't annoy our friends or neighbours and doesn't wreck our furniture or carpets. We would not dream of taking her were she badly behaved or disruptive. If it is a question of extra cleaning, we would happily pay a few pounds extra. What possible harm does a hotel think a dog will do? Dogs and children are a way of life, part of what makes a holiday enjoyable and fun."

We have some sympathy with Ms Richardson's *cri de coeur*. Perhaps half the British hotels in the Guide impose restrictions of one sort or another on pets: some allow dogs in bedrooms only, others would confine them to the public rooms and many others of course ban them altogether. But we also appreciate the force of the anti-pet lobby. Rightly or wrongly, we cannot feel that pressing the claims of pets on hotels is as important as changing their attitude to children.

A message to our volunteer inspectors

Everyone who sends a report is helping to enrich or make more accurate the next edition. But we must urge correspondents never under any provocation to reveal that they are planning to write to us, which could be construed by the hotel as an attempt to obtain favours. Total discretion is of paramount importance.

There is also a danger that reporters in their enthusiasm may start to hunt for faults. Some people are incurable nit-pickers, and must be a curse to their hosts as well as not much pleasure to themselves or their companions. We enjoy reading – and printing – Travellers' Tales, which record some of the terrible things they come across, but would urge our correspondents to do their best to travel hopefully and to be as eager to praise as to condemn. There is plenty wrong with our hotels, even the best of them, but the owners do take a lot of stick, and not all of it is deserved. We sympathise with hoteliers who sometimes send us perfectly awful letters they have had from patronising ingrates. One innkeeper this year was provoked into replying to such a complainant, who happened to be a clergyman: "With respect, Reverend, I hope you are not as uncharitable towards your parishioners."

While on the subject of reports, may we say that those of the gushing or bland variety that tell us "everything was simply marvellous, nothing was too much trouble for the staff, the meals were uniformly delicious, the furnishings all in the best of taste" etc, are, alas, of little use to us. What we are looking for are detailed appraisals, reflecting the shade as well as the light. End of message.

HILARY RUBINSTEIN

The César Awards 1990

Our annual awards of Césars – named after the celebrated hotelier, César Ritz – are given for different sorts of excellence among hotels in Britain and Ireland. The categories listed below show the wide range of hotels, inns and guest houses which appeal to us and afford some kind of definition of the scope of the Guide. As before, we have given a César for acceptable eccentricity, but otherwise categories change from year to year. Last year's Césars are indicated in the text by a small laurel wreath.

AWARD	WINNER
Newcomer of the year, city division	The Draycott London Sired by the admirable *Feathers*, Woodstock, *The Draycott* brings to central London the sympathetic comforts of a country house hotel with the life-support systems expected by city visitors.
Newcomer of the year, country house division	The Manor Chadlington, Oxfordshire David and Chris Grant revealed their vocation for innkeeping at *Kirkby Fleetham Hall*. Now, after a year's globe-trotting, they have come to rest in a lush Cotswold pasture. *The Manor* is a true country house hotel, warmly welcoming and mercifully free from pomp or flannel.
Newcomer of the year, restaurant-with-rooms division	The Peat Inn Peat Inn, Fife David and Patricia Wilson's rosetted restaurant has long been a mecca for travelling gastronomes. Now their eight magnificent bedrooms provide fine lodging for the replete gourmet.
Brilliant restoration of a great hotel to former glory	Hotel Portmeirion Portmeirion, Gwynedd Phoenix-like, Clough Williams-Ellis's hotel in his exuberant Italianate village overlooking Cardigan Bay has been brought back to life by his grandson after the great fire of 1981. The new hotel is no mere replica of the old, but equally exotic and extravagant in its own way.

Outstanding hospitality – Lakeland style

The Old Vicarage
Witherslack, Cumbria

The Burrington-Browns and the Reeves have a sure but relaxed touch in their joint enterprise. They cater for the needs of Lakeland walkers comprehensively, and the landscape outside is as beguiling as the welcome within.

Outstanding Irish hospitality

Roundwood House
Mountrath, Co Laois

A pure Palladian house, built in 1742, and furnished throughout in authentic 18th-century style, provides, with Frank Kennan as the owner/host, a quintessentially Irish form of hospitality.

Sturdy independence in doing their own thing with verve

Heddon's Gate Hotel
Heddon's Mouth, Devon

Robert and Anne De Ville's Swiss-Victorian lodge makes no concession to contemporary style. But the whole place has splendid panache, and its glorious gardens and magnificent views heighten the exhilaration of a visit.

Shangri-La of the Outer Hebrides

Baile-na-Cille
Timsgarry, Lewis,
Outer Hebrides

For those who want to get further away from it all without forfeiting civilised pleasures, Richard and Joanna Gollin's 18th-century manse, overlooking a wide sandy bay and surrounded by mountains and islands, has something unique to offer.

Most cosseting guest house

Reeds
Poughill, Cornwall

Margaret Jackson's "oasis of relaxation" offers many of the sybaritic extras which guests expect from five-star hotels. The rooms are as sympathetically furnished, the meals as elegant and as delicious, only the prices are on a quite different scale.

Utterly acceptable mild eccentricity

The Evesham Hotel
Evesham,
Hereford and Worcester

The irrepressible high spirits of the Jenkinson family show themselves in all departments, from the toy ducks in the bathrooms to the preposterously globe-trotting wine list. But they run their hotel with true professionalism, and those who don't care for their fun-loving style can always go elsewhere.

Special hotels

City hotels with luxury and grandeur

England Connaught, London
Scotland One Devonshire Gardens, Glasgow
Austria Schloss Fuschl, Hof bei Salzburg; Schloss Mönchstein, Salzburg; Sacher, Vienna
Denmark Angleterre, Copenhagen
France Cour des Loges, Lyon; Résidence du Bois, Paris; Opéra, Toulouse
Germany Vier Jahreszeiten, Hamburg
Norway Continental, Oslo
Spain San Marcos, León; Reyes Católicos, Santiago de Compostela
Switzerland L'Arbalète, Geneva

Town hotels of character and/or value

England Priory, Bath; Angel, Bury St Edmunds; Suffolk House, Chichester; Evesham, Evesham; At the Sign of the Angel, Lacock; Draycott, London; L'Hotel, London; Portobello, London; Castle, Taunton; Feathers, Woodstock; Mount Royale, York
Scotland Babbity Bowster, Glasgow; Clifton, Nairn
Ireland Arbutus Lodge, Cork
Austria Elefant, Salzburg; Amadeus, Vienna; König von Ungarn, Vienna
Belgium Swaene, Bruges; Ter Duinen, Bruges
Denmark 71 Nyhavn, Copenhagen; Weis Stue, Ribe
France d'Arlatan, Arles; Europe, Avignon; Lameloise, Chagny; Diderot, Chinon; Pullman Beauvau, Marseille; La Pérouse, Nice; L'Abbaye St-Germain, Paris; Vieux Puits, Pont Audemer; Pyrénées, St-Jean-Pied-de-Port; Colombe d'Or, St-Paul-de-Vence
Germany Mönchs Posthotel, Bad Herrenalb; Kleine Prinz, Baden-Baden; Böttingerhaus, Bamberg; Sankt Nepomuk, Bamberg; Westend, Frankfurt-am-Main; Roten Bären, Freiburg; Hanseatic, Hamburg; Bären, Meersburg
Italy Umbra, Assisi; Villa Belvedere, Florence; Villa Mozart, Merano; Cesari, Rome; Gregoriana, Rome; Flora, Venice
The Netherlands Ambassade, Amsterdam; Pulitzer, Amsterdam
Norway Myklebust, Bergen
Portugal Quinta Penha da França, Funchal; Infante de Sagres, Oporto
Spain Parador, Carmona; Hostal América, Granada
Sweden Tidbloms, Gothenberg
Switzerland Florhof, Zürich
Turkey Çeşme Kervansaray, Çeşme; Yeşil Ev, Istanbul

Rural charm and character in the luxury class

England Mallory Court, Bishop's Tachbrook; Buckland Manor, Buckland; Gidleigh Park, Chagford; Manoir aux Quat' Saisons, Great Milton; Hambleton Hall, Hambleton; Hintlesham Hall, Hintlesham; Homewood Park, Hinton Charterhouse; Horsted Place, Little Horsted; Chewton Glen, New Milton; Gravetye Manor, East Grinstead; Stapleford Park,

Stapleford; Ston Easton Park, Ston Easton; Thornbury Castle, Thornbury; Sharrow Bay, Ullswater
Wales Bodysgallen, Llandudno
Scotland Arisaig House, Arisaig; Inverlochy Castle, Fort William; Cromlix House, Kinbuck
Channel Islands Longueville Manor, St Saviour
Ireland Park Hotel Kenmare, Kenmare
Austria Schloss Dürnstein, Dürnstein
Belgium Moulin Hideux, Noirefontaine
Denmark Falsled Kro, Falsled
France Baumanière, Les Baux; Moulin du Roc, Champagnac-de-Belair; Château de Divonne, Divonne-les-Bains; Prés d'Eugénie, Eugénie-les-Bains; Boyer "les Crayères", Reims; Moulin de la Gorce, La Roche-l'Abeille; Mas de Chastelas, St-Tropez; Cantemerle, Vence
Germany Klostergut Jakobsberg, Boppard; Pflaums, Pegnitz
Greece Argentikon, Chios
Italy Villa Cipriani, Asolo; Villa Corner, Cavasagra; Palumbo, Ravello; Certosa di Maggiano, Siena; Condulmer, Zerman
Spain Residencia, Deyá; Bobadilla, Loja; El Castell, La Seu d'Urgell
Sweden Grythyttans, Grythyttan
Yugoslavia Vila Bled, Bled

Rural charm and character at medium price

England Farlam Hill, Brampton; Grafton Manor, Bromsgrove; Uplands, Cartmel; Manor, Chadlington; Chedington Court, Chedington; Summer Lodge, Evershot; Stock Hill House, Gillingham; Congham Hall, Grimston; Field Head House, Hawkshead; Heddon's Gate, Heddon's Mouth; Jervaulx Hall, Jervaulx; Buckland-tout-Saints, Kingsbridge; Hope End, Ledbury; Brookdale House, North Huish; Whitechapel Manor, South Molton; Bridgefield House, Spark Bridge; Plumber Manor, Sturminster Newton; Calcot Manor, Tetbury; Miller Howe, Windermere; Old Vicarage, Witherslack
Wales Tyddyn Llan, Llandrillo; Portmeirion, Portmeirion; Maes-y-Neuadd, Talsarnau
Scotland Invery House, Banchory; Polmaily House, Drumnadrochit; Factor's House, Fort William; Dunain Park, Inverness; Airds, Port Appin; Tiroran House, Tiroran; Knockie Lodge, Whitebridge
Ireland Gurthalougha House, Ballinderry; Cashel House, Cashel Bay; Marlfield House, Gorey; Assolas, Kanturk; Roundwood House, Mountrath; Newport House, Newport; Ballymaloe, Shanagarry
Austria Gams, Bezau
Belgium 't Convent, Renige
Denmark Steensgaard Herregårdspension, Millinge
France Bérard, Cadière-d'Azur; Benvengudo, Les-Baux-de-Provence; Pescalerie, Cabrerets; Marais St-Jean, Chonas l'Amballan; Moulin de Vey, Clécy; Poste, Corps-la-Salette; Cro-Magnon, Les Eyzies-de-Tayac; Relais de la Magdeleine, Gémenos; Cagnard, Haut-de-Cagnes; Bon Coin, Mimizan; Trois Roses, La Petite Pierre; Hospitaliers, Poët-Laval; Cheval Blanc, Sept-Saulx
Germany Töpferhaus, Alt-Duvenstedt; Erbguth's Landhaus, Hagnau; Schönberg, Oberwesel; Zum Ochsen, Schönwald; Wehrle, Triberg
Italy Tenuta di Ricavo, Castellina in Chianti; Saügo, Cavalese; Castello, Gargonza; Sant' Uffizio, Cioccaro; Amorosa, Sinalunga

Norway Utne, Utne
Portugal Quinta das Torres, Azeitão; Abrigo da Montanha, Monchique; Santa Maria, Marvão; Quinta dos Lobos and Quinta da Capela, Sintra
Spain Es Moli, Deyá; Monasterio de Piedra, Nuévalos; L'Hermitage, Orient;
Sweden Åkerblads, Tällberg
Switzerland Eden, Engelberg; Rothorn, Schwanden; Soglina, Soglio

Rural charm, simple style

England Frog Street Farm, Beercrocombe; Tanyard, Boughton Monchelsea; Glebe Farm, Diddlebury; Woodmans Arms Auberge, Hastingleigh; Manor Farm Barn, Taynton;
Scotland Riverside, Canonbie; Glencripesdale House, Glencripesdale
Ireland Coopershill, Riverstown
France Relais de St-Jacques, Collonges-la-Rouge; Vieux Logis, Lestelle-Bétharram; Clos Normand, Martin Église; Équipe, Molines-en-Queyras; Rostaing, Passanens; Pélissaria, St-Cirq-Lapopie; Poids Public, St-Félix-Lauragais; Midi, St-Jean-du-Bruel; Hameau, St-Paul-de-Vence; Vert, Wierre-Effroy
Germany Lipmann, Beilstein
Turkey Turbel Pansion, Çavuşin

Hotels by the sea, luxury style

Scotland Knockinaam Lodge, Portpatrick
France Langoustier, Porquerolles; Maquis, Porticcio; Caribou, Porticciolo; Plage, Ste-Anne-la-Palud
Greece Akti Myrina, Myrina
Italy Luna Convento, Amalfi; Pellicano, Porto Ercole
Portugal Reid's, Madeira
Turkey Kismet, Kuşadasi

Hotels by the sea, medium-priced or simple

England Treglos, Constantine Bay; Crantock Bay, Crantock; Lamorna Cove, Lamorna Cove; Tides Reach, Salcombe; New Inn, Tresco
Wales Porth Tocyn, Abersoch; St Tudno, Llandudno
Scotland Summer Isles, Achiltibuie; Isle of Colonsay, Colonsay; Enmore, Dunoon; Isle of Raasay, Raasay; Scarista House, Scarista
Channel Islands White House, Herm
Denmark Sønderho Kro, Sønderho
France Menez-Frost, Bénodet; Chez Pierre, Raguenès-Plage; Ty-Pont, St-Jean-du-Doigt; Ti al-Lannec, Trebeurden
Greece Aliki, Simi
Italy Casa Albertina, Positano; Nido di Fiascherino, Tellaro
Spain Aigua Blava, Bagur; Mar I Vent, Bañalbufar; Parador, Gomera

Skiing, walking or mountain hotels

England Seatoller, Borrowdale; Scale Hill, Loweswater; Howtown, Ullswater; Wasdale Head, Wasdale Head
Wales Pen-y-Gwryd, Llanberis; Minffordd, Talyllyn
Austria Senger, Heiligenblut; Salome, Lech am Arlberg
France Albert Premier et de Milan, Chamonix
Germany Unterstmatt, Schwarzwald-Hochstrasse
Norway Mundal, Fjærland; Bessà Touristhytta, Øvre Eidfjord
Spain Sant Pere, Soldeu, Andorra
Switzerland Flüela, Davos Dorf; Chesa Grischuna, Klosters; Metropol, Zermatt

Small hotels and inns with outstanding cuisine

England Stock Hill House, Gillingham; White Moss, Grasmere; Mortons House, Corfe Castle; Provence, Hordle; Dinham Hall, Ludlow; Brookdale House, North Huish; Seafood Restaurant, Padstow; Pool Court, Pool-in-Wharfedale; Well House, St Keyne; McCoys at the Tontine, Staddlebridge
Wales Plas Bodegroes, Pwllheli
Scotland Peat Inn, Peat Inn; Altnaharrie, Ullapool
Belgium Shamrock, Ronse
France Côte St-Jacques, Joigny; Alain Chapel, Mionnay; Bretagne, Questembert; Pic, Valence; Espérance, Vézelay; Georges Blanc, Vonnas
The Netherlands De Swaen, Oisterwijk
Spain Ses Rotges, Cala Ratjada; Posada, Gualchos
Switzerland Fischerzunft, Schaffhausen

Friendly informality/hotel run like a private house

England Frog Street Farm, Beercrocombe; Little Hodgeham, Bethersden; Appletree Holme Farm, Blawith; Chilvester Hill House, Calne; Thornworthy House, Chagford; Field Head House, Hawkshead; Huntsham Court, Huntsham; Fallowfields, Kingston Bagpuize; Howe Villa, Richmond; Reeds, Poughill; Old Millfloor, Trebarwith Strand; Tregony House, Tregony
Wales Old Rectory, Llansanffraid Glan Conwy
Scotland Ard-na-Coille, Newtonmore; Baile-na-Cille, Timsgarry
Austria Erike, Kitzbühel
France Parc des Maréchaux, Auxerre; Châtenet, Brantôme; Château de Roussan, St-Rémy-de-Provence; Pontot, Vézelay
Greece Ganimede, Galaxidion
Portugal Villa Hostilina, Lamego; Quinta São Thiago, Sintra

Hotels which are welcoming to families with children

England Woolley Grange, Bradford-on-Avon; Hell Bay, Bryher; Crantock Bay, Crantock; Evesham, Evesham; Penmere Manor, Falmouth; Embleton Hall, Longframlington; Linden Hall, Longhorsley; Dalmeny, Lytham St Anne's; Polurrian, Mullion; Port Gaverne, Port Gaverne; Seaview, Seaview; Innsacre, Shipton Gorge; Bridgefield House, Spark Bridge; Walletts Court, West Cliffe
Wales Porth Tocyn, Abersoch; Cnapan, Newport
Scotland Craigendarroch, Ballater; Isle of Colonsay, Colonsay; Enmore, Dunoon; Glencripesdale, Glencripesdale; Ard-na-Coille, Newtonmore
Channel Islands Sablonnerie, Sark; Stocks, Sark
Ireland Coopershill, Riverstown; Sand House, Rossnowlagh; Ballymaloe, Shanagarry
Austria Madrisa, Gargellen; Erika, Kitzbühel
France Étrier Camarguais, Les Stes-Maries-de-la-Mer
Switzerland Bellevue, Braunwald

No-smoking hotels in the UK

England Haydon House, Bath; Holly Lodge, Bath; Somerset House, Bath; Sydney Gardens, Bath; Old Windmill, Bradford-on-Avon; Woodman's Arms Auberge, Hastingleigh; Walker Ground Manor, Hawkshead; Sugarswell, Shenington
Wales Old Rectory, Llansaffraid Glan Conwy
Scotland Altnaharrie, Ullapool

How to read the entries

As in previous editions, entries are in two parts – a citation, usually endorsed by one or several names, followed by relevant information about accommodation, amenities, location and tariffs.

We must emphasise once again that the length or brevity of an entry is not a reflection of the quality of a hotel. The size of an entry is determined in part by what we feel needs to be said to convey a hotel's special flavour and in part by the character and interest of the commendation. In general, country hotels get more space than city hotels because the atmosphere of the hotel matters more with the former and also because it is often helpful, when a hotel is in a relatively remote or little-known area, for the entry to say something about the location.

The names at the end of the citation are of those who have nominated that hotel or endorsed the entry that appeared in a previous edition. Some entries are entirely or largely quoted from one report; if several names follow such an entry, we have distinguished writers of quoted material by putting their names first. We do not give the names of those who have sent us adverse reports – though their contributions are every bit as important as the laudatory ones.

The factual material also varies in length. Some hotels provide a wide variety of facilities, others very little. But the paucity of information provided in some cases may derive from the fact that the hotel has failed to return our detailed questionnaire or send us a brochure. All hotels in the British Isles have completed our form, but the same is not true for continental hotels, even though we send out our questionnaire in five languages and repeat the operation for any recalcitrants a month later. Around a quarter of the hotels in the second half of the book ignore our form or return it months later when the Guide has gone to press. In these instances, we have to rely on the information available from national tourist offices. The fact that no lounge or bar is mentioned in an entry does not mean that a hotel lacks public rooms – only that we can't be sure. The same applies to availability of parking, which we aim to mention in the case of town and city hotels. As to tariffs, in those cases where we have had no communication with a hotel, or where it was unable to give next year's rates, we print the 1989 tariffs, making it clear that these are last year's terms.

Our italicised entries indicate hotels which we feel are worth considering, but which because of inadequate information or for lack of feedback do not at the moment justify a full entry. A hotel whose entry is in italics, with briefer information about its tariffs and facilities, need not be thought of as a half-good establishment, only as one about which we are eager to have more opinions. We hope that, with the help of such feedback, many will rate full entries next year.

There is a limit to the amount of "nuts and bolts" that can be given in any guide book, and we are against providing, as some other guide books do, a lot of potted information in complicated, hard-to-decipher hieroglyphic form. [GFG] after the hotel's name indicates that the hotel has an entry in the 1990 edition of *The Good Food Guide*. Days and months are abbreviated, but virtually the only other shorthand we use is "B&B" for bed and breakfast and "alc" for à la carte; the "full alc" price is the hotel's estimate per person for a three-course meal and a half-bottle of modest wine, including service and taxes. We try to give as much information as possible (ground-floor rooms, lifts, etc) to enable disabled people to judge whether or not a hotel will be suitable for them. If a hotel tells us it has special facilities for the disabled we give details; if we know it is not suitable we say so. But we do sometimes lack precise information; disabled people should *always* check with the hotel.

Terms are difficult enough to cope with at the best of times. A few hotels have a standard rate for all rooms regardless of season and length of stay, but most operate a highly complicated system which varies from low season to high (and some have a medium-high season as well), according to length of stay, whether there is a bathroom *en suite* and, in the case of most British hotels, whether a room is in single or double occupancy. And, on top of all that, most British hotels offer breaks of one kind or another, but rarely of the same kind. When we can, we give a room rate rather than a rate per person and hope thereby to give a reliable idea of what people, especially those travelling on their own, can expect to pay. When figures are given without mention of single or double rooms they indicate the range of tariffs per person. Lowest rates are what you pay for the simplest room, or out of season, or both; highest rates are for the best rooms – and in high season if the hotel has one. Meal prices are per person. VAT and service are included unless we state otherwise.

There is one crucial point that must be emphasised with regard to the tariffs: their relative unreliability. We ask hotels when they complete our questionnaire in the spring of one year to make an informed guess at their tariffs the following year. There are many reasons why this is a difficult exercise. Please don't rely on the figures printed. *You should always check at the time of booking and not blame the hotel or the Guide if the prices are different from those printed.*

If you are going for two days or more to a hotel in the British Isles, it will pay you to find out the exact terms of any special offers available. Sometimes these bargain terms are amazing value, and can apply throughout the year, not just in the winter, but they may call for some adjustment in your holiday plans in order to qualify. We also strongly advise you to check whether a hotel is open before making a long detour. We try in all cases to give accurate information, but hotels, particularly small ones, do sometimes close at times when they have told us they expect to be open. And hotels on the Continent often have a weekly closing date, but sometimes fail to make this clear when returning our questionnaire. Finally, they do not always give reliable information about whether or not they take credit cards. If it is vital to you, please check.

We end with our customary exhortation: we implore readers to tell us of any errors of omission or commission in both the descriptive and informative parts of the entries. We make constant efforts to improve our information under "Location", especially with the more out-of-the-way places, but would be very grateful if readers would let us know of any cases where they have found our directions inadequate. We recognise what an imposition it is to be asking readers to write us letters or fill in report forms, but it is essential that people do let us know their views if the Guide is to meet consumer needs as well as it can.

Part one

England
Wales
Scotland
Channel Islands
Northern Ireland
Republic of Ireland

England

BROOKDALE HOUSE, NORTH HUISH

ALLENDALE Northumberland **Map 4**

Bishop Field Country House Hotel *Tel* Hexham (0434) 683248
Hexham NE47 9EJ *Fax* (0434) 683830

"Being from America," writes a nominator from Utah who spent no fewer than 29 days at *Bishop Field,* "I was somewhat apprehensive about the type of accommodations which would be available in England. As it turns out these were near perfect for the following reasons:

1. Beds comfortable, and long enough for my six-foot frame.
2. Bathroom, TV, chairs, closet space and other amenities are adequate, though the shower stall could be a little larger for total comfort; plenty of hot water.
3. The country setting is beautiful, quiet, peaceful and conducive to total relaxation.
4. Meals – both dinner and breakfast – are excellent.
5. The price is very reasonable.
6. The proprietors made every effort to provide helpful service – doing

laundry, preparing American-style meals, recommending places to visit, providing transport.
7. Most important of all, they, their family and their dog are very congenial." (*Raymond H Neville*)

The hotel, in converted cattle byres round a cobbled courtyard, stands in 40-acre grounds, and is owned and run by Kathy and Keith Fairless. Bedrooms are simple, with plain white walls; there is a beamed lounge and a conservatory and a full-size snooker table. *Bishop Field* has access to a 6,000-acre estate for shooting, and owns a mile-and-a-half of trout fishing; there are bicycles for hire, and many other sporting activities are available in the area. Food is traditional; vegetarians are catered for.

Open All year except Christmas.
Rooms 1 suite, 10 double, 1 single – all with bath and/or shower, telephone, radio, TV, tea-making facilities. 2 ground-floor rooms.
Facilities 2 lounges (1 non-smoking), conservatory, dining room. 40-acre grounds; trout fishing. Access to 6,000-acre estate with shooting.
Location 10 m SW of Hexham on B6305. From Allendale take Whitfield road; hotel is on right after 1 m.
Restriction No dogs in public rooms.
Credit card Access.
Terms (No service charge) B&B: single £25–£30, double £40–£50. Set lunch £5, dinner £12.

AMBLESIDE Cumbria — Map 4

Kirkstone Foot Country House Hotel [GFG]
Kirkstone Pass Road
Ambleside LA22 9EH
Tel Ambleside (053 94) 32232

Simon and Jane Bateman, helped by daughter and son-in-law Annabel and Andrew Bedford, run this 17th-century white-painted manor house in two acres of pretty garden leading down to a stream. It is sufficiently outside Ambleside to be peaceful and quiet, though the carpark can become congested at times. Guests continue to enjoy the comfortable and spotlessly clean rooms, attractive decor and welcoming service, and to consider it good value for money. Dinner is a fairly formal five-course affair, served punctually at 8 pm. Last year it was criticised, particularly by non-carnivores, for lack of choice; things have changed with the advent of a new chef, Victor Sharratt, and fish or a vegetarian dish is offered as an alternative to the main course roast; there is also a choice of starter. First courses and desserts continue to be praised, though one reader last year felt the latter was served in rather too small portions. The bearded proprietor Simon Bateman knows his wines, offering a reasonably priced list with an unusually good selection of half-bottles, and the hotel holds wine-tasting weekends. Some of the hotel rooms and self-catering units have recently been redecorated. We'd be glad of more reports, particularly on the new kitchen regime. (*D and P Hawkins, John A Hope, and others*) *Note:* Half-board terms only.

Open All year except 2 weeks at beginning Dec, and Jan (after New Year).
Rooms 15 double, 1 single – all with bath and/or shower, telephone, radio, TV, tea-making facilities, baby-listening. 1 on ground floor. Self-catering flats and cottages in grounds.

Facilities Lounge, bar, restaurant. 2-acre garden with croquet. 1 m from Windermere. Fishing, boating etc.
Location At Ambleside turn E off A591 Windermere–Keswick road towards Ullswater.
Restrictions No smoking in dining room. No children under 6/7 in dining room for dinner (high tea available). Dogs in self-catering annexe only.
Credit cards All major cards accepted.
Terms [1989 rates] Dinner, B&B £30–£38. Set dinner £14.75. Spring and autumn breaks; "Wines of the World" weekends. Reduced rates for children sharing parents' room.
Service/tipping: "Tips at guests' discretion (staff box at reception). They are shared among all staff."

Rothay Manor Hotel [GFG] *Tel* Ambleside (053 94) 33605
Rothay Bridge
Ambleside LA22 0EH

The Nixon family's "welcoming and always comfortable hotel" in a handsome Georgian house is half a mile from Lake Windermere; it stands in one-and-a-half acres of garden in a valley surrounded by fine Lakeland mountain scenery. It is a scheduled building, noted for the grace of its design and detail, and retains some of the original features. There are comfortable lounges with antiques and flowers. The elegant dining room, decorated in browns and golds with deep pile carpets, velvety curtains, "ancient polished candle-lit tables, heavy glass and tableware and pretty, traditionally clad serving maids in caps and pinnies" overlooks the well-maintained lawns and gardens. Bedrooms are "bright and clean, with bathrooms filled with innumerable extras". Readers continue to appreciate the "excellent breakfasts" and the "scrumptious tea, everything home-made, from the quiche and savoury pastries, to the fruit bread, scones, strawberry jam and rich cakes". There is a five-course traditional English dinner menu for £21, but the faint of appetite can opt to eat only two courses at a cost of £15.50. "Very good home cooking, service immaculate." (*Mrs A Rooker, Mrs PVA Holland, and others*) There can be disturbance from traffic on a busy one-way system close by; it is worth asking for a quiet room when booking – rooms are double-glazed.

Open Mid-Feb–early Jan.
Rooms Honeymoon suite, 2 family suites (in annexe), 13 double, 2 single – all with bath, telephone, radio, and TV, baby-listening. 1 ground-floor room specially adapted for ♿.
Facilities 3 lounges (1 with bar), 2 dining rooms. 1½-acre garden with croquet. Near river Rothay and Lake Windermere (¼ m). Sailing, water-skiing, fishing, riding and golf.
Location On A593 SW of Ambleside towards Coniston. Garden-facing rooms quietest.
Restrictions No smoking in dining room. No dogs.
Credit cards All major cards accepted.
Terms (Service at guests' discretion) B&B (English) £36–£58; dinner, B&B £48–£78. Set Sun lunch £12, dinner £15.50 (2-course) and £21 (5-course). Off-season breaks; music courses, French regional dinners. 4-day Christmas house party, 3-day New Year programme. 2-night min booking at weekend. Reduced rates for children sharing parents' room; special meals.

Don't trust out-of-date Guides. Many hotels are dropped and new ones added every year.

Wateredge Hotel [GFG] *Tel* Ambleside (053 94) 32332
Borrans Road, Waterhead
Ambleside LA22 0EP

The *Wateredge,* as you might expect, enjoys a choice position at the head of Windermere looking down the length of the lake with views of Loughrigg Fells as well as other famous landmarks. Owned and run by Mr and Mrs Cowap, it consists of a pair of 17th-century fishermen's cottages with some modern additions, still retaining much of its period charm. The lounges are comfortable and welcoming, with old beams and picture windows overlooking the lake. Bedrooms in the original part are also beamed and have period furniture; the newer ones are larger and furnished in pine. There are five spacious suites, with patio and balcony, in an annexe. All have numerous extras – hair-drier, fresh fruit and so on. *Wateredge* continues to receive warm endorsements, many from regular visitors: "As good as ever, excellent food, friendly staff, luxurious accommodation." "Can't be faulted. No chance to repeat my last year's comment about plates not always hot – they now come so hot that the waitress warns you." "Rooms spacious, clean and comfortable; food delicious, healthy, creative." Meals are served in the two dining rooms in the old part of the building, with low-beamed ceilings and old stone painted walls. The menu is short, with five choices of starter and dessert, and two (generally a roast and a fish dish) of main course. (*Mr and Mrs JT Mills, JP Berryman, Patrick Welsh*) Only problem: It can be noisy from the main road behind; lakeside traffic, heavy at weekends, passes close by the hotel.

Open Feb–early Dec.
Rooms 5 suites, 15 double, 3 single – all with bath and/or shower, telephone, TV and tea-making facilities. The suites are across a small courtyard.
Facilities 3 lounges, TV room, bar, 2 dining rooms. 1-acre grounds with patio, lake frontage, private jetty, boats available to guests free of charge; fishing, bathing.
Location ½ m S of town; just off A591 at Waterhead on Kendal/Keswick road (rooms on road can be noisy).
Restrictions Not suitable for ♿. No children under 7. No dogs in suites or public rooms.
Credit cards Access, Amex, Visa.
Terms (No service charge) B&B (English) £29–£49; dinner, B&B £37–£57. Set dinner £17.50. Winter breaks. 1-night bookings sometimes refused. Half rates for children sharing parents' room.
Service/tipping: "All tips are distributed equally to all staff."

ARNCLIFFE North Yorkshire Map 4

Amerdale House Hotel *Tel* Arncliffe (075 677) 250
Arncliffe, Littondale
Skipton BD23 5QE

This former Elizabethan manor house with Victorian additions re-entered the Guide last year after a change of ownership, and readers have written warm endorsements this year: "My third visit in two years further confirmed that it's one of my English favourites. The gentle ambience, total peace, gorgeous setting with instant access to some marvellous walking, friendliness and sense of style of the hotel are some of the reasons why I go there. Another is the food; scrupulous attention to detail, delicately presented English *nouvelle* dishes. And there is absolutely no pressure to drink. Nothing is forced upon you but it's all available if you ask." "Nigel and Paula Crapper are doing an excellent job – welcome and service very good; food very good indeed. Service at dinner has improved." The former manor house is on the edge of a pretty, unspoilt Dales village in lovely, open country; it has been redecorated and refurbished by the Crappers who have added two rooms in converted stables. Nigel Crapper is a former restaurateur; his limited-choice menus "combine traditional and modern styles with extensive use of excellent local produce"; fruit, herbs and vegetables are grown in the hotel's garden, local lamb and cheeses, and fish from the Yorkshire coast are served. Answering a comment last year that the wine is "fairly expensive" Mr Crapper writes, "I have no interest in selling poor quality, low cost wines; I buy good wines and offer them at fair prices; I currently list 58 wines, 26 of which are priced at under £10 per bottle." (*Trevor Lockwood, JD Campbell, and others*) One complaint: heating inadequate in very cold weather.

Open Mid-Mar–mid-Nov.
Rooms 1 suite, 11 double – 5 with bath, 4 with shower; all with TV and tea-making facilities. 2 in converted stable block. 1 on ground floor.
Facilities Lounge, bar, restaurant. 2-acre grounds.
Location 12 m N of Skipton; take left fork off B6160 to Arncliffe.
Restrictions No smoking in dining room. No dogs in hotel; kennels available.
Credit cards Access, Visa.
Terms B&B (English) £24–£36; dinner, B&B £32–£44. Set dinner £15. 1-night bookings refused for bank holidays. Reduced rates for children sharing parents' room; special meals.
Service/tipping: "No mention of a service charge is made in our literature, nor are tips expected by staff. If guests wish to give tips they are gratefully received and shared equally."

ASHBOURNE Derbyshire — Map 4

Callow Hall [GFG]
Mappleton Road
Ashbourne DE6 2AA

Tel Ashbourne (0335) 43403 and 42412
Fax (0335) 43624

A new nomination, a large and impressive 19th-century Derbyshire house in very attractive countryside, quietly located not far from the centre of a small market town. *Callow Hall* "with turrets and twiddles" is approached up a long drive through large grounds with some lovely trees. It has recently been extensively renovated, but many of the original features are left intact. "Public rooms spacious and furnished in a friendly mixture of styles, antique and modern; most have a fireplace." "Beautiful bedrooms, thoughtfully appointed, most with bathroom *en suite* and lots of hot water." "Shoes cleaned, Teasmaid available but early morning tea brought to the room if preferred." "Excellent breakfast and superb dinner." "Mr and Mrs Spencer are kindness itself; the set menu faultless and reasonably priced." The Spencer family have been bakers in Ashbourne for the last five generations and *Callow Hall* has its own bakery and patisserie department. *Patron*/chef David Spencer buys meat by the carcase and all hanging and butchery is done on the premises. The menu is "French-inspired with a few fashionable touches" and has pleased most comers this year. The hotel has private fishing for trout and grayling, with tuition available. (*Margaret Murray Smith, Mrs J Godfrey, CG Hacking, IC Dewey*) More reports please.

Open All year except Christmas and 2 weeks Jan or Feb. Restaurant closed to non-residents for lunch except Tue and Sun, and dinner Sun and Mon.
Rooms 11 double – 9 with bath and shower, all with telephone, radio, TV, tea-making facilities and baby-listening. 1 self-catering suite.
Facilities Lounge, restaurant; functions/conference facilities. 42-acre grounds with garden, woodland, farmland and stables; fishing (tuition available).
Location ¾ m from Ashbourne; take A515 to Buxton; sharp left at top of hill, first right to Mappleton; cross bridge – drive is on right.
Restrictions Not suitable for ♿.
Credit cards All major cards accepted.
Terms B&B single £50, double £75. Set lunch £9–£11, dinner £18–£26; full alc £21.
Service/tipping: "No service charge. It is for the customer to decide if he wishes to leave a gratuity; anything left is shared among all the staff on duty at the time."

ASKRIGG North Yorkshire — Map 4

King's Arms Hotel — *Tel* Wensleydale (0969) 50258
Market Place, Askrigg
Wensleydale DL8 3HQ

This 18th-century coaching inn, Grade II listed, in a beautiful conservation village at the heart of the Yorkshire Dales National Park entered the Guide last year in an italicised entry. Its period character has earned it a place in the BBC Herriot series "All Creatures Great and Small" as the *Drovers' Arms* – it has a high-ceilinged central room with saddle hooks still in place and huge stone fireplace, a low-beamed panelled front bar and a simpler flagstoned back one. "Narrow twisting stairs, uneven floors, doors of unusual size and shape, but fitting. Comfortable period beds, delicious food (you wait 20 minutes after ordering dinner in the bar). Food all home cooked with some exciting sauces. It is run by a very welcoming couple, Liz and Ray Hopwood." "Beautifully furnished bedroom with huge antique canopy bed, antique table and chairs. Hosts friendly without being overbearing." (*Mrs Joan M Marr, Mrs M de Salvo, and others*)

Open All year except 31 Dec.
Rooms 10 double, all with bath and/or shower, telephone, radio, TV, tea-making facilities and baby-listening.
Facilities Lounge, bar lounge, 2 bars, restaurant. Garden. Fishing, sailing and windsurfing nearby.
Location ½ m off A684. 24 m from M6 at Kendal.
Restrictions Bedrooms not suitable for ♿. Dogs in selected rooms only.
Credit cards Access, Visa.
Terms B&B £20–£35; dinner, B&B £32.50–£48.75. Set lunch £7.50, dinner £13.50. Reduced rates and special meals for children.
Service/tipping: "No tips asked for or expected. If customers wish to leave tips they are distributed equally to all staff."

Traveller's tale *We had a half-hour wait before breakfast arrived. We asked for a second croissant; the answer was: "No." On taking the matter up with the management we were told: "Only one per person."*

ASTON CLINTON Buckinghamshire — Map 1

The Bell Inn [GFG]
Aston Clinton HP22 5HP

Tel Aylesbury (0296) 630252
Fax (0296) 631250
Telex 83252 BELINN

Former coaching inn on what is still a busy main road. Now a grand restaurant, with a pavilion across the road for weddings and conferences. Friendly welcome from Michael Harris whose family has run it since 1939. Sophisticated dining room with murals; cooking under Kevin Cape is "much improved – classical French with a modern touch and continually changing vegetarian menu. Long and tempting wine list." Antiques and some four-posters in the original inn bedrooms; the 15 stable ones are spacious and more modern; all have bath and shower. B&B double from £90. Set dinner £16.50–£19.50. Some criticisms of service and upkeep this year. Hence these italics. More reports please.

ATHERSTONE Warwickshire — Map 1

Chapel House
Friar's Gate, Atherstone CV9 1EY

Tel Atherstone (0827) 718949

Small family-run guest house in conservation area of old market town; mainly Georgian, in walled garden. Adjacent to parish church whose striking clock may disturb light sleepers. Recommended for attractive furnishings, comfortable accommodation, helpful and friendly proprietors, David and Pat Roberts, and good food. Closed Christmas. 12 rooms, all with private facilities. B&B double £45. Set dinner £10.50; full alc £22. Recent nomination. More reports please.

BAKEWELL Derbyshire — Map 4

Milford House Hotel
Mill Street, Bakewell DE4 1DA

Tel Bakewell (0629) 812130

This popular small family-run hotel had its first Guide entry last year: "Decor rather 1950s, but spotlessly clean. The furniture reminded me very much of my grandmother's house when I was young, but was all highly polished. The beds were very high, but were comfortable with good sheets and high-quality blankets. There are modern shower units in a shower room and a wash basin in the bedroom; towels were new and of good quality. Water was piping hot. The owners, the Hunts, and their staff could not have been nicer; our cases were carried to the rooms and though our stay was brief and we were out for meals, we were always met with smiles or some cheery remark. The generous breakfast was good apart from slightly strange-tasting butter. A gong announces dinner and breakfast. It would not appeal to all Guide readers as it is by no means sophisticated, but it is very pleasant, and reasonably priced. It is in a charming quiet part of Bakewell, close to the river Wye, with nice gentle walks." (*Padi Howard*) Dinner, which is served at 7 pm, has a traditional English menu, a set meal with some choice. More reports please, including views on the cooking.

Open Easter–end Oct.
Rooms 10 double, 2 single – all with bath and/or shower, TV and tea-making facilities.
Facilities Hall with bar, lounge, dining room. 1¼-acre grounds with croquet.
Location 300 yards from town centre; right turn off A6 to Buxton. Parking.
Restrictions Not suitable for ♿. No children under 10. No dogs.
Credit cards None accepted.
Terms B&B: single £25.30, double £48.30; dinner, B&B: single £35, double £64. Set Sun lunch £9.70, dinner £10.40. Bar snacks available to residents Mon–Sat. Weekly rates.
Service/tipping: "No service charge included. If guests wish to tip they give directly to staff."

BARWICK Somerset **Map 2**

Little Barwick House [GFG] *Tel* Yeovil (0935) 23902
Barwick, Yeovil BA22 9TD

Christopher and Veronica Colley's Georgian dower house restaurant-with-rooms is set in a beautiful garden in a secluded corner of the attractive, minuscule village of Barwick. It looks out across the valley towards the village with its church and outlying obelisks on the skyline. Readers continue to appreciate the unpretentious welcome from the "warm and outgoing" Colleys, and Mrs Colley's "caring cooking". Bedrooms vary in size; they are not large, nor particularly elegantly furnished, but are comfortable, with firm beds, very good linen, good lighting, and individually controlled central heating. The Colleys have now made a new kitchen, an extension to the dining room, and redecorated the lounge. The restaurant is popular with non-residents, and the food "carefully cooked from good ingredients and not too messed about" continues to be praised for the interesting choice of each course, including excellent game, fresh-tasting, properly cooked vegetables, and the variety of desserts (not all highly calorific). "Quite the best breakfast we have had in many a long day in England – fresh orange juice, plate of fresh fruit, *hot* brown wholemeal and white toast, and warm croissants, home-made marmalade, good and plentiful coffee – served in the bedroom." "Excellent value; winter breaks a great bargain."(*HR, Kenneth E Smith; also Dr John Weston, and others*)

Open All year except Christmas and New Year.
Rooms 6 double – all with bath and/or shower, TV and tea-making facilities.
Facilities 2 lounges, cellar bar, dining room. 3½-acre garden.
Location Follow signs from Yeovil to Dorchester (A37). Turn left off A37 at the *Red House* pub. Hotel is ¼ m on left.
Restrictions Not suitable for ♿. Dogs by arrangement only; not in public rooms.
Credit cards All major cards accepted.
Terms Double room: B&B £66; dinner, B&B £97. Vegetarian and special diets catered for. Reductions for 2 nights or more. Winter breaks. 1-night bookings refused on Sun if hotel is empty. Reduced rates for children.
Service/tipping: "Service is included, but any money left is divided among the staff."

> Set dinner refers to a fixed price meal (which may have ample, limited or no choice on the menu). Full alc is the hotel's own estimated price per person of a three-course meal taken à la carte, with a half-bottle of house wine.

BASLOW Derbyshire — Map 4

Cavendish Hotel
Baslow DE4 1SP

Tel Baslow (024 688) 2311
Telex 547150 CAVTEL

Once a fishing inn, the *Cavendish* was rebuilt in the 1970s by the Chatsworth Estate and is now one of the few luxurious hotels in the Peak District. It is on the edge of Chatsworth Park, which all the rooms overlook. The Duchess of Devonshire selected the decor and furnishings, some of which come from Chatsworth House; rooms are named after members of the Devonshire family and the Mitford sisters (the Duchess was born a Mitford). Other Devonshire manifestations are the Duchess's traditional chocolate chip cookies served with tea, and the aristocratic souvenirs sold in the shop. The hotel has been run for years with style by Eric Marsh. Mrs Marsh is responsible for the beautiful flower arrangements in the public rooms. It is very warm – "almost tropical" – throughout. It is worth discussing your requirements when booking; some rooms are described to us as "small and unimaginatively decorated", others as "generous in size, nicely (not quite beautifully) decorated, with a large bathroom"; all are comfortable and spotless. The ones in the new wing have pleased several readers this year. The dining room was enlarged in early 1989; guests may, if they wish, dine in the kitchen itself and discuss the meal with chef Nick Buckingham as it is prepared. Food is "*nouvelle*, with smallish portions, and beautifully presented"; but it is expensive – "overpriced" according to some. Breakfast is charged extra; a reader this year reports chaotic service on a busy Sunday morning. For some the "extremely high standard of accommodation is well worth the high cost". One reader who booked a room for Friday and Saturday one winter weekend was surprised that he could stay for Sunday night at no extra charge; he had not been told this on booking – "it made the stay seem very good value indeed". Service at the *Cavendish* is almost universally commended. The public rooms were redesigned in early 1989, and a garden room created. More reports please.

Open All year.
Rooms 1 suite, 23 double – all with bath and shower, telephone, radio, TV, tea-making facilities, mini-bar and baby-listening. 2 ground-floor rooms.
Facilities Hall/reception, lounge, bar, garden room, restaurant; private dining room, conference room. 2-acre grounds with golf practice; fishing in rivers Derwent and Wye.
Location On A619 in Chatsworth grounds (leave M1 at exit 29).
Restrictions Not suitable for ♿. No dogs.
Credit cards All major cards accepted.
Terms [1989 rates] (No service charge) Rooms: single occupancy £55-£65, double £65–£75. Breakfast from £3.50. Set lunch and dinner from £18; full alc from £28. Winter bonus weekends. Cots/extra beds available for children (£5); special meals by request.
Service/tipping: "If a client wishes to leave a tip for staff it is gratefully accepted and shared among all staff."

Traveller's tale *The waiter on duty during the afternoon was asked to bring some tea to the pool area. He replied that he could not, because if he did so everyone else sitting round the pool might ask him for something.*

BASSENTHWAITE LAKE Cumbria — Map 4

The Pheasant Inn
Bassenthwaite Lake
Cockermouth CA13 9YE

Tel Bassenthwaite Lake
(076 87) 76234

A popular traditional inn, with beamed ceilings, sparkling copper and brassware, crackling fires in the grates and lots of fresh flowers, surrounded by an old-fashioned country garden in magnificent and peaceful scenery. *The Pheasant,* just out of sight of the lake, has kept something of the atmosphere of the 400-year-old farm from which it grew. Mr and Mrs Barrington Wilson have run the hotel for many years; they serve real ale in the bar and "unfancy country cooking" in the dining room which they have refurbished this year. "Our bedroom was attractively decorated, with plain walls and Laura Ashley-type fabrics, good lighting and comfortable chairs; the bathroom was excellent and of a good size, with a hair-drier." Not many extras, however, and no TV, radio or telephone in the bedrooms. Rooms vary in size: it is worth enquiring what is available. (*Susan and Francis Aglionby*) One reader was critical of service and housekeeping; another felt the cooking, both at dinner and breakfast, was not up to the standards set elsewhere in the inn.

Open All year except 24/25 Dec.
Rooms 16 double, 4 single – 18 with bath, 2 with shower. 3 in bungalow annexe, all with tea-making facilities; ramps available.
Facilities 3 lounges (2 for residents), bar, dining room; facilities for private parties and small conferences. 1½-acre grounds. Sailing, fishing, pony-trekking, golf nearby.
Location 7 m NW of Keswick just off A66 (on W side of Bassenthwaite Lake).
Restrictions No smoking in dining room. No dogs in bedrooms or dining room.
Credit cards None accepted.
Terms B&B: single £38, double £68; dinner, B&B: single £52, double £90. Set Sunday lunch £7.75; set dinner £16. Bar snacks available. 3-day rates, weekly rates; winter breaks. 1-night bookings for Sat sometimes refused. Reduced rates for children sharing parents' room; special meals.
Service/tipping: "A 10% service charge is included in rates and distributed on a point system to all staff. The inclusion is appreciated by guests who do not have to search out individuals to tip."

BATH Avon — Map 2

Haydon House
9 Bloomfield Park
Bath BA2 2BY

Tel (0225) 427351 and 444919

Magdalene Ashman's sophisticated B&B in a quiet residential area of the city entered the Guide last year following a warm nomination: "Think of any long-felt hotel want – trouser-press, tea-making equipment, mags, books, cotton wool, smellies, modern shower, thick duvet, colour telly – you are sure to find it here. Very nice, as is the comfortable chintzy lounge, the terrace at the rear for summer sipping, the spaciousness of the Victorian house, the efficiency of the c.h. and the h&c. But most of all, it's the Ashmans' concern for their guests' welfare that pleases. Nothing is too much trouble. They are in the background until needed, and then at your service. How rare. More than full marks for breakfast – in addition to the usual juices, eggs, bacon, mushrooms and so on, there was a fruit platter which included all manner of exotic fruits, arranged with considerable artistry." "Great thought given to the smallest touches; the Ashmans make guests feel pampered and welcome." (*Patricia Fenn, Jodie Emery*) *Haydon House* is a no-smoking establishment. Breakfast is taken communally.

Open All year.
Rooms 4 double (also let as single) – 1 with bath, 3 with shower, all with telephone, radio, TV and tea-making facilities.
Facilities Sitting room, breakfast room. ½-acre garden with sun terrace. Sports and leisure centre nearby. Boats available on river Avon.
Location From Bath take A367 (Exeter) up Wells Road about ½ m. Turn right into shopping area with *Bear* pub on right. At end of short dual carriageway fork right into Bloomfield Road, then take second right turn into Bloomfield Park.
Restrictions Not really suitable for ♿. No smoking. No dogs.
Credit cards Access, Visa.
Terms (No service charge) B&B (English): single occupancy £28–£32, double £40–£50. Reduced rates for long stays and Easter breaks. Reduced rates for children sharing parents' room.
Service/tipping: "Since we are effectively welcoming guests into our home the question of tipping does not arise."

Holly Lodge *Tel* Bath (0225) 24042
8 Upper Oldfield Park
Bath BA2 3JZ

Readers continue to write warmly about Mrs Carolle Sellick's no-smoking bed-and-breakfast hotel, a large Victorian house high up on the slopes opposite the city, with a magnificent view across the valley and rooms delightfully decorated in subtle and restful colours. "Absolutely wonderful, bedroom well furnished and comfortable, breakfast excellent." "Everything spotlessly clean, fresh towels each day. We were given a key to come and go. Croissants out of this world. I asked for (and got) a second helping. The peppermills suggested in the 1989 Guide had duly appeared and were appreciated. Very reasonably priced for Bath." "Carolle Sellick and George Hall provide a luxurious atmosphere and are always ready to go the extra mile for their guests." (*JS Waters, Kate Kelly, Cynthia Blackberg*) One caveat: "Fresh orange juice would have been nice."

Open All year.
Rooms 5 double, 1 single – all with bath and/or shower, telephone, radio, TV and tea-making facilities.
Facilities Lounge, breakfast room. ½-acre garden.
Location ½ m SW of city centre, 1st right off Wells Road (A367). Carpark.
Restrictions Not suitable for ♿. No smoking. No dogs.
Credit cards Access, Visa.
Terms B&B: single £32–£38, double £50–£60. Off-season reductions for 2 nights or more. "Learn to play golf" weeks in conjunction with Sports Council. Reductions for children sharing parents' room. (No restaurant.)
Service/tipping: "Tipping not encouraged. Any contributions shared among staff."

> We asked hotels to estimate their 1990 tariffs some time before publication so the rates given are often arbitrary. Please always check terms with hotels when making bookings.

Paradise House Hotel *Tel* Bath (0225) 317723
Holloway, Bath BA2 4PX

A civilised bed-and-breakfast run by David and Janet Cutting, seven minutes by foot down to the Roman Baths, the Pump Room and the Abbey (rather longer, and a steep uphill slog on the return journey). It is in a quiet cul-de-sac, formerly part of the old Roman Fosse Way. The house itself is *c.* 1720; it has fine views of the Georgian city, and a well-favoured three-quarter-acre garden. It has been carefully restored by the Cuttings; decor is in Laura Ashley/Designers Guild style. "A revelation. B&B yes, because dinner is not served but it shouldn't be thought of as a B&B. It's a fine hotel. We had Room 1 which was enormous, with brass double bed (really comfortable) and Edwardian bath. David Cutting was very helpful and there was a distinct feeling of generosity about the service. Decoration of rooms was thoughtful and period features restored. The garden a boon in fine weather." (*Ian Durant*) The rates include a generous four-course breakfast. Book well ahead.

Open All year except 20–31 Dec.
Rooms 9 double – 7 with bath and/or shower, all with telephone, radio, TV and tea-making facilities. 1 ground-floor room suitable for ♿.
Facilities Sitting room, breakfast room. ¾-acre garden with patios and croquet.
Location From A4 turn left at first main traffic lights onto A36, A367 Wells and Exeter ring road. At large roundabout (bisected by railway viaduct) take first left (A367 Exeter road). Continue up hill, the Wellsway, about ¾ m; turn left at small shopping area near Dewhurst butcher; continue left down hill into cul-de-sac. Hotel is 200 yds on left. Garages (£1 a night) and parking.
Restriction No dogs.
Credit cards Access, Visa.
Terms B&B: single £30–£45, double £37–£55. Reduced rates for 5 nights or more. 1-night bookings refused for Sat. Children sharing parents' room £10. (No restaurant; hotel can make dinner reservations in restaurants.)

The Priory Hotel [GFG] *Tel* (0225) 331922
Weston Road, Bath BA1 2XT *Fax* (0225) 448276
Telex 44612 PRIORY

"For years I have been falling into this hotel for rest and recuperation after long international journeys, and it has become one of my favourite hotels in the world. Its change of ownership in my opinion only improved it; it is now very charming and highly professional. Its restaurant is one of the best in Bath, the heated swimming pool in its garden is a true luxury and the service is beyond criticism." "Very good, but certainly not cheap; rooms are by no means palatial. What makes the hotel is the tranquillity, and the cosmopolitan staff who are attractive, courteous and friendly. Mr Conboy, the manager, knows what he's doing." Commendations from *Jan Morris* and *Simon Small* restore to the Guide this large 19th-century neo-Gothic house which had an entry, under its previous ownership, for many years. It is two miles out of Bath "away from the hustle and bustle". Though close to the road in front it has two acres of grounds at the back. Other readers praise the "high standard of furnishing and decor throughout the hotel. We had a luxury bedroom at £130 [1988]; it was large, well furnished, very comfortable, with excellent bathroom; high quality of fittings throughout. Excellent housekeeping." Not everyone, however, agrees about the food, "competent, but no more; not worth the price", is a dissenting verdict. Two niggles: "Wine by the glass was a staggeringly small measure, and cost £2." "The swimming pool was not being heated 'because the weather has been poor and no-one had wished to use it'." Parking space is limited and can cause congestion.

Open All year.
Rooms 10 deluxe double, 8 double, 3 single – 20 with bath and shower, 1 with shower, all with telephone, radio, TV.
Facilities Drawing room, 2 morning rooms; functions facilities, 2-acre grounds with swimming pool and croquet.
Location 1 m W of city centre, just beyond Royal Victoria Park. Limited parking.
Restrictions Only public rooms suitable for ♿. No dogs.
Credit cards All major cards accepted.
Terms [1989 rates] B&B (English): single £75, double from £105, deluxe double from £140. Set lunch from £15, dinner from £25.
Service included. Tipping at guests' discretion.

The Queensberry Hotel *Tel* (0225) 447928
Russel Street BA1 2QT *Telex* 445628 QNSBRY

A new hotel opened in 1988 by Stephen and Penny Ross, the proprietors of *Homewood Park,* Hinton Charterhouse (q.v.). It occupies three fine period houses with 18th-century stucco ceilings and cornices, and an attractive drawing room. No restaurant, but there is a 24-hour light-refreshment service (no hot meals) or you can use the hotel's courtesy car and dine at *Homewood Park*. "It is extremely attractively furnished. We saw a number of rooms, all well decorated and in immaculate order." "Superbly equipped bedroom and bathroom. It was very quiet. A fresh, light breakfast was served in the bedroom." "Service friendly and excellent." One reader, however, was surprised to be given a relatively small room on the top floor when the hotel was almost empty. "The following morning I asked for a better proportioned room; we were given the run of the hotel and chose a substantial room in the front with beautiful proportions and pleasant plasterwork." (*Alan J Taylor, AJN Lee, and others*)

Open All year except 2 weeks over Christmas.
Rooms 25 double – all with bath, shower, telephone, radio, TV and baby-listening.
Facilities Drawing room. Private meeting room. Small patio garden.
Location 2 mins' walk from centre, above Assembly Rooms.
Restrictions Not suitable for ♿. No dogs.
Credit cards All major cards accepted.
Terms B&B (continental): single occupancy £55–£65, double £75–£115. Winter break 2-night package including 1 dinner at *Homewood Park* £190 per couple [1989]. (No restaurant but 24-hour light meal service).
Service/tipping: "Service charge included in room rate but is not at a fixed percentage. It is to discourage tipping unless guests wish to give something extra."

The Royal Crescent Hotel [GFG] *Tel* Bath (0225) 319090
16 Royal Crescent, Bath BA1 2LS *Fax* (0225) 339401
Telex 444251

A luxurious, lavishly decorated hotel in a Grade I listed building in an incomparable location, at the centre of John Wood's peerless Crescent, with views across the city from the front and the Avon hills from the rear.

It had an entry in earlier editions; now, under new ownership, it is readmitted following a rhapsodic report from American readers, "The most wonderful hotel experience we've ever had. Our room in a recently restored Palladian building behind the main building was *elegant*: sitting area separated by free-standing armoire from bed, which had a partial canopy with glorious side curtains. The bathroom was marble with brass fixtures. All amenities, and sparkling clean. Public rooms could not be more handsome, but are not off-puttingly formal. Works of art and antiques abound. The restaurant is excellent; exceptional cuisine, beautifully presented, served by knowledgeable, courteous staff. Very good, attractively displayed breakfast served in the room, on time." (*Nena P and Jeffrey E Levine, warmly endorsed by Yorick Wilks*) Not everyone, however, is as enthusiastic; a vegetarian was served a disappointing meal, despite advance warning. One reader felt the atmosphere was decidedly money-grubbing, "We were paying £300 for a suite and were charged 50p for newspapers, £3 for a bottle of mineral water and £3 for a short telephone call to London."

Open All year.
Rooms 13 suites, 27 double, 5 single – all with bath and shower, 2 with jacuzzi, telephone, radio, TV and baby-listening. Some in Pavilion and Dower House in garden.
Facilities Lift. Bar, 2 drawing rooms, reading room, garden room, dining room; conference facilities; 1-acre grounds with plunge pool.
Location 5 mins' walk from town centre. Parking.
Restriction No dogs.
Credit cards All major cards accepted.
Terms Rooms: single £85, double £105–£155, suite £205–£300. Breakfast: continental £7.50, English £9.50. Set lunch from £17, dinner from £33; full alc £41. 4-day Christmas programme.
Service/tipping: "Room rates include service. Restaurant service is optional."

Somerset House *Tel* Bath (0225) 466451 and 463471
35 Bathwick Hill
Bath BA2 6LD

"We spend at least three weekends here each year. The high quality of accommodation and the friendly atmosphere owe much to the Seymours' energy and enthusiasm. Breakfasts are particularly good. We know of no place that offers better value for money." "The house is charming, with a lovely light airy feel; one feels immediately at home amongst the books, the grand piano and the family pets. Food not gourmet but totally fresh, from excellent suppliers. An ideal place for a civilised treat in Bath, particularly for 'singles' wanting a friendly atmosphere." (*JM Chandler, Matthew Bartlett*) Other guests, too, express satisfaction with this reasonably priced, non-smoking hotel or up-market guest house in a handsome Regency mansion a short drive or bus-ride or stiffish walk uphill from the city centre. Rooms are immaculately maintained, and all have private facilities. There are attractive public rooms and an agreeable basement dining room. But it is an establishment very much with its own style – wholly congenial to many, irksome to some. There is no TV. Dinner is served briskly and somewhat inflexibly between 7 and 7.30 pm; the food has come in for some criticism this year, and one reader felt the aforementioned pets should be excluded from the kitchen and dining room. The Seymours' son and son-in-law are now doing the cooking and we'd like more comments on the food. Bookings are generally for dinner, B&B.

Open All year except 2 weeks in Jan. Dining room closed Sun evening.
Rooms 8 double, 1 single – 8 with bath, 1 with shower, all with telephone, radio and tea-making facilities. 1 ground-floor room.
Facilities 2 lounges (1 with TV), dining room. 1½-acre garden with 7¼-inch gauge model railway. 5 mins from Kennet and Avon Canal – angling for temporary members at Bathampton Angling Club; canal boat trips. 15 mins' walk from centre.
Location Junction of Bathwick Hill (which leads to Bath University) and Cleveland Walk. Carpark.
Restrictions Not suitable for ♿. No smoking. No children under 10. Small dogs only, not in public rooms.
Credit cards Access, Amex, Visa.
Terms (No service charge) Dinner, B&B: single £19.35–£24, double £38.70–£48. Set Sun lunch £8.95, dinner £16. Vegetarian and simple diets catered for. Mid-week breaks; special interest weekends: e.g. Georgian Bath, Roman Bath, Brunel. Christmas and New Year packages. 1-night bookings sometimes refused in high season. Reduced rates for children sharing parents' room; special meals.
Service/tipping: "If we are forced to take a tip there is a tin for staff's tips."

Sydney Gardens Hotel

Sydney Road, Bath BA2 6NT — *Tel* Bath (0225) 464818 and 445362

A handsome Italianate Victorian villa in a pretty garden, ten minutes from the city centre – just far enough to be peaceful, yet a short walk to Bridge Street. You can park your car in the grounds. It is next to the Kennet and Avon canal; there are good walks along the towpath. The hotel is B&B only, and no-smoking. "Stanley and Diane Smithson went out of their way to be friendly and helpful." "Room large and comfortable. The garden is beautiful, and Mr Smithson's paintings and original clocks add interest to the house. A nice touch is that they keep menus from the local restaurants to help guests select an eating place." "Prettily decorated bedroom and bathroom; most elegant drawing room with lovely views." Breakfasts too are praised, and Mrs Smithson, in answer to the criticisms voiced last year writes, "We have given up wrapped butter and I now make available a choice of marmalades. And we deliberately chose firm beds for all our rooms because they are preferred by the majority, particularly Americans whose first gesture is to poke the mattress. Alas, poor souls, they seem to have traversed Britain sleeping on trampolines." (*Dr JA Clarke, Linda A Wells, Dorothy Brooks; also Patrick Welsh, and others*) Only snag: the hotel is close to a railway line.

Open 26 Jan–16 Dec, 29 Dec–1 Jan.
Rooms 6 double – all with bath, shower, telephone, radio, TV and tea-making facilities.
Facilities Lounge, breakfast room. ⅓-acre garden; private gateway to park with tennis and walk along adjacent Kennet and Avon canal.
Location From A4 turn left onto A36 ring road towards Exeter and Wells. Cross Avon; gateway to Sydney Gardens is directly ahead. Turn right, pass Holbourne Museum on left, turn left. Hotel is 200 yards up slope on left. From South the approach road (A36) takes you past the hotel. Parking.
Restrictions Not suitable for ♿. No smoking. No children under 4. Small dogs by arrangement.
Credit cards Access, Visa.

Terms B&B (English): single occupancy £38–£48, double £58–£60. Extra bed £15. Winter midweek breaks. 1-night bookings sometimes refused at weekend. (No restaurant.)
Service/tipping: "As we run the business ourselves, we do not expect tips. If anything is kindly left for the chambermaids it is shared between staff."

BATHFORD Avon — Map 2

Eagle House
Church Street
Bathford BA1 7RS

Tel Bath (0225) 859946

Eagle House is an imposing listed Georgian building by John Wood the Elder, in a quiet conservation village three miles from Bath. Its young owners, Mr and Mrs Napier, take genuine pride in maintaining the house, set in spacious grounds in a quiet suburban location. All the rooms look out over countryside or the one-and-a-half-acre garden. Last year's readers praised the "cool entrance hall, large, handsome drawing room, with plenty of well-spaced chairs and sofas, tables with magazines, fine marble fireplace and generous landing upstairs with sofas, chests of drawers, etc"; and the "spacious bedroom, bed comfortable, bathroom scrupulously clean. Very well run; nothing seemed too much trouble". This year, however, a reader writes, "While endorsing the comments on the Napiers' welcoming, caring approach and the grandeur of the public rooms, we found our bedroom decidedly pokey. It was described to us as 'one of our oldest rooms' – it might have been honest to add 'and one of our smallest'". No dinner is served, but there are plenty of small restaurants and pubs nearby, and in Bath. A pleasant alternative to staying in Bath itself, provided you have a car.

Open 5 Jan–23 Dec.
Rooms 5 double, 1 single – all with bath and/or shower, telephone, TV, tea-making facilities and baby-listening. 2 more rooms, in the garden, planned for 1990.
Facilities Drawing room, sitting room, breakfast room. 1½-acre garden with croquet lawn, large sandpit for children.
Location 3 m E of Bath on A363. At roundabout immediately after Batheaston follow sign to Bathford; fork left immediately after railway bridge; after 300 yds take Church Street (first on right). Hotel is 200 yards on right behind high stone wall and wrought iron gates. Conservation area, so hotel sign not permitted. Ample parking.
Restrictions Not suitable for ♿. No dogs in public rooms.
Credit cards None accepted.
Terms B&B: single £24–£32, double £35–£47. Winter breaks. 1-night bookings sometimes refused for Sat and bank holidays. Children free in parents' room. (No restaurant.)
Service/tipping: "The only way to end the debate and uncertainty about this is to introduce legislation including a service charge on basic room rates. Tipping should still be permitted."

> Hotels often book you into their most expensive rooms or suites unless you specify otherwise. Even if all room prices are the same, hotels may give you a less good room in the hope of selling their better rooms to late customers. It always pays to discuss accommodation in detail when making a reservation.

The Orchard *Tel* Bath (0225) 858765
80 High Street
Bathford BA1 7TG

The 1989 Guide's entry for John and Olga London's listed Georgian house in a one-and-a-half-acre garden is heartily endorsed: "Elegant sitting room with books and deep, comfortable chairs; antique or period furniture. Attractive bedroom with pastel decor, deep-pile carpet, large windows overlooking the garden. Mrs London and her daughter are warmly welcoming, smilingly serving tea and coffee at various times without extra charge. Breakfast is good, with a choice of local yoghurts and toasted wholemeal bread; it is taken communally at a large table and we have been fortunate in our fellow guests all of whom have shared our delight in this beautiful house, totally tranquil, set well back from an unbusy road a few miles from Bath." (*KA Hickman, Leneta C Appleby*)

Open Mar–Oct.
Rooms 4 double, all with bath, shower, TV. 1 with separate entrance.
Facilities Lounge, dining room. 1½-acre grounds.
Location Under railway bridge; first left at *Crown Inn*, up hill; past village store on left. *Orchard* is 100 yds on right.
Restrictions Not suitable for ♿. No smoking in bedrooms. No children under 11. No dogs.
Credit cards None accepted.
Terms B&B: double £35.50–£49.50. 1-night bookings sometimes refused for weekend. (No restaurant.)
Service/tipping: "We make it clear that our prices are totally inclusive."

BATTLE East Sussex Map 3

Netherfield Place [GFG] *Tel* Battle (042 46) 4455
Battle TN33 9PP *Fax* (042 46) 4024
Telex 95284

"We revisited this hotel for a family weekend. We were fourteen adults and all our children thought *Netherfield Place* the best hotel we have chosen." (*RCJ Gordon*) Other readers, too, praise Michael and Helen Collier's attractive Georgian-style 1920s country house hotel, peacefully situated in large well-kept grounds, for the high standard of decor, welcoming atmosphere, helpful staff and good-value food – French in style, "not *haute cuisine*, but freshly prepared and cooked". The panelled restaurant is popular with locals – Sunday lunch said to be very good value; service is "courteous and efficient". Many of the vegetables, fruits and herbs are grown in the hotel's kitchen garden. Bedrooms vary in size, the doubles on the first floor are said to be particularly attractive; all have flowers, fresh fruit, chocolates and so on, and well-equipped bathrooms. (Listed under Netherfield in *The Good Food Guide*.)

Open All year except 3 weeks over Christmas and New Year.
Rooms 10 double, 4 single – 8 with bath and shower, 6 with bath, all with telephone, radio, TV and baby-listening.
Facilities Lounge, sun lounge, bar, restaurant; conference facilities. 30-acre grounds with gardens, tennis, woodland walks. Golf, fishing, riding nearby.
Location Go S on A2100; turn left towards Netherfield. Hotel is 1½ m on.
Restrictions Bedrooms not suitable for ♿. No dogs.
Credit cards All major cards accepted.

Terms (No service charge) B&B: single £45, double £70–£95. Set lunch £12.50–£13.95, dinner £16.95; full alc £23. 1-night weekend bookings refused Mar–Oct. Children £5 in parents' room; special meals by arrangement.
Service/tipping: "No service charge. Tips completely at guests' discretion."

BEERCROCOMBE Somerset **Map 1**

Frog Street Farm *Tel* Hatch Beauchamp
Beercrocombe, Taunton TA3 6AF (0823) 480430

"The first time I used the Guide I hit the jackpot. We spent three days here recently. Very warm welcome. A complete suite with well-equipped bedroom and large sitting room with facilities for playing music. First rate food. In the evening in the main lounge we met interesting people all of whom had stayed at least once before." "All the comforts of your own home; the best breakfast ever." This large, airy, well-kept and reasonably priced 15th-century farmhouse/guest house stands in a 130-acre working farm, deep in rural Somerset, about 21 miles from the north and south coasts. It has fields and woods on one side, orchards on the other, a heated pool under the cherry trees, and a kind and generous hostess. Three of the bedrooms have private facilities. No licence, so you bring your own wine. Veronica Cole is an excellent straightforward cook: menus include roast lamb, roast chicken, pheasant casserole, with some adventurous starters and "wicked desserts – not a place for dieters or wholefood addicts". (*Alan Lawson, JS Griffiths, and others*) One reader emphasises that this *is* a working farm; the approach could not be described as *soigné*. And we have a report this year of thin walls and a superannuated bed.

Open Mar–Nov.
Rooms 3 suites, 2 double – 2 with bath, 1 with shower, all with tea-making facilities.
Facilities 3 sitting rooms (1 with TV), dining room. Garden with heated swimming pool. On 130-acre working farm with trout stream.
Location 7 m SE of Taunton. Leave M5 at exit 25; take A358 to Ilminster, then turning to Hatch Beauchamp. Turn at *Hatch Inn*, down Station Rd. Then left all way down no through road. Signposted.
Restrictions Not suitable for ♿. No children under 11. No dogs.
Credit cards None accepted.
Terms B&B £16 without bath, £22 with. Set dinner £13 (unlicensed – bring your own wine). Weekly rates.

BELFORD Northumberland **Map 4**

Blue Bell Hotel *Tel* Belford (066 83) 543
Market Place
Belford NE70 7NE

Creeper-covered inn, 18th-century in origin, run by Mr and Mrs Shirley; in centre of quiet village in attractive part of Northumberland, handy for Lindisfarne. Reports speak warmly of the food (local fish, smoked salmon and meat on the menu), good sized, traditionally furnished bedrooms, and value for money. 3-acre grounds. Open all year except Jan. 16 double, 1 single, all with bath and/or shower; 1 adapted for disabled. B&B: £30–£38. Set dinner in Buttery from £7, in restaurant from £14; bar meals also available. More reports please.

BETHERSDEN Kent — Map 3

Little Hodgeham
Smarden Road, Bethersden
TN26 3HE

Tel High Halden (023 385) 323
from early 1990 (0233) 850323

Australian-born Erica Wallace's 500-year-old half-timbered Tudor cottage in the tiny village of Bethersden in Kent, is "typical chocolate box", with roses, honeysuckle, ancient beams, antiques, fresh flowers from the garden, log fires in cold weather. It is set in a flower-filled garden, with a swimming pool, a pond stocked with carp and tench, and – new this year – a water garden. There are three double bedrooms with comfortable beds with lace-trimmed duvets. In the dining room Miss Wallace presides over "delicious" communally served meals elegantly served with fine bone china and crystal. There is no choice of food or wine; guests are asked their likes and dislikes when they book. The private house-party atmosphere of *Little Hodgeham* is appreciated by those who enjoy socialising with their hostess and meeting their fellow guests. Those seeking full hotel amenities should look elsewhere; what *Little Hodgeham* aims to offer is a warmer welcome and better value for money. (*Joan and Lewin Taylor, Anna Cheung*)

Open Mid-Mar–1 Oct.
Rooms 1 family, 2 double – all with bath and/or shower, radio, tea-making facilities and baby-listening.
Facilities Drawing room, TV room, small conservatory, dining room. ½-acre garden with unheated swimming pool, pond, water garden. Tennis and golf nearby.
Location 10 m W of Ashford. From Bethersden, at *Bull* pub, take Smarden road for 2 m.
Restrictions Not suitable for ♿. Small children not really welcome. Dogs by prior arrangement, not in public rooms.
Credit cards None accepted.
Terms (No service charge) Dinner, B&B £35 (£30 for stays of 4 nights or more). Reduced rates for children sharing parents' room, depending on age; special meals with advance warning.
Service/tipping: "The price is, and always has been, inclusive. Anyone who helps out during the season is told never to tout for tips."

BIBURY Gloucestershire — Map 2

Bibury Court Hotel
Bibury
Nr Cirencester GL7 5NT

Tel Bibury (028 574) 337

A splendid Tudor mansion, added to and improved in the 1660s, 1750s and 1920s, with panelled rooms, four-posters and much fine antique furniture. The Coln river – good fishing for trout – forms the boundary of the six-acre grounds. Charles II and the Prince Regent are said to have visited *Bibury Court*, and celebrated litigation over it in the last century is thought to have inspired Charles Dickens' *Bleak House*. A gate leads through from the orchard to the churchyard of St Mary's Church (fine Saxon carvings), and a footpath follows the river to Arlington Row, the 17th-century weavers' cottages now owned by the National Trust, and Bibury's Old Mill Museum. The hotel makes a tranquil base for touring the Cotswolds – owls, they tell us, are the only night-time distraction.

"Excellent location, the building is quite beautiful and the atmosphere pleasant; unfailingly courteous and helpful staff." Sadly the proprietor, James Collier, died in 1988. The hotel is now owned – and still run "on country house lines" – by his daughters Jane Collier and Anne Johnston, and Anne's husband, Andrew. Colin Salmon, formerly of *The Plough*, Clanfield, has joined Mrs Johnston in the kitchen. A new restaurant has been made from what was the public bar; we'd be glad of reports on the food which, we said last year, "is of good quality with a varied menu". "Very good value," says a report endorsing last year's comment. "Not immaculate, fairly casual, but charming." Returning our questionnaire the hotel engagingly writes: "Previous editions have mentioned bumbling service, maiden-aunt-type decoration and laid-back style. The comments have always been fairly true and we hope we continue to attract visitors in search of a little character." (*Moira Jarrett, Adney and Rachel Payne, and others*)

Open All year except week before and week after Christmas.
Rooms 1 suite, 14 double, 2 single – 16 with bath, all with telephone, TV and baby-listening; radio, tea-making facilities on request. 8 with 4-poster. 1 on ground floor.
Facilities Lounge, TV lounge, bar, breakfast room, dining room, conference room. 6-acre grounds with croquet and fishing. Golf nearby.
Location On edge of village on A433 between Burford and Cirencester.
Restriction Not suitable for severely ♿.
Credit cards Access, Visa.
Terms B&B (continental): single £36–£40, double £52–£58, suite £82. English breakfast from £3.50. Full alc £18. 2-day breaks out of season except Cheltenham Gold Cup week. Reduced rates for children in cots; high teas.
Service/tipping: "We do not pretend to offer 5-star services and therefore make no service charge. Any tips given are shared among all members of staff, not management."

BISHOP'S TACHBROOK Warwickshire — Map 2

Mallory Court Hotel [GFG]
Harbury Lane,
Bishop's Tachbrook
Leamington Spa CV33 9QB

Tel Leamington Spa (0926) 330214
Fax (0926) 451714
Telex 317294 MALORY

"The high praise by your readers is thoroughly justified. We spent two nights over the New Year and did not want to go back to work. Our room was very comfortable and the food magnificent. *Not* cheap certainly, but worth saving up for." "Garden lovely, cleanliness magnificent, bedroom near perfect, public rooms immaculate, food very good." "The Blenheim suite, with its spectacular art deco bath and *tromp l'œil* painting on the ceiling is probably the equal of any hotel suite in Britain. Dinner in the oak-panelled dining room first class – well deserving its *Michelin* rosette." "Very comfortable, wonderful fresh and dried flower displays everywhere. Very pleasant, zealous and efficient young waiters and waitresses." (*Mr and Mrs JW Woloniecki, Richard Creed, PH, SM*) Jeremy Mort and Allan Holland's luxurious country house in the Lutyens manner, in a large lovingly maintained formal garden, with fine views, has been consistently praised by Guide readers for many years. Most of the bedrooms are spacious, all are differently decorated with fine fabrics and period furnishings, and sumptuously equipped. The setting is rural, but it is only nine miles from Stratford-upon-Avon, and little more from the

National Exhibition Centre outside Birmingham. A few niggles: "You are tempted to eat at least three courses because you are paying for them. None of us wanted more than two." "After-dinner coffee and cooked breakfast should be included in the very high prices." But the consensus is, "A very well run hotel."

Open All year.
Rooms 1 suite, 9 double – all with bath and shower, telephone, radio and TV.
Facilities Lounge, drawing room, garden room, dining room. 10-acre gardens with unheated swimming pool, tennis, squash, croquet. Golf 2 m.
Location 2 m S of Leamington Spa off B4087. Take left turning to Harbury.
Restrictions Not suitable for ♿. No children under 12. No dogs (kennels nearby).
Credit cards Access, Visa.
Terms B&B (continental): single occupancy £95, double £87–£165, suite £265. Dinner, B&B £80–£170. English breakfast £7.50. Set lunch £16.50, dinner £35. Only half-board terms at weekends. Winter breaks.
Service/tipping: "We actively discourage tipping. It is stated on all our literature that all prices include VAT and service."

BISHOPS TAWTON Devon — Map 1

Downrew House
Bishops Tawton, Barnstaple
EX32 0DY

Tel Barnstaple (0271) 42497 and 46673

This white-painted, slate-roofed Queen Anne country house is set in 12 acres of meadowland and neatly landscaped gardens on the south-facing slopes of Codden Hill, a few miles from Barnstaple. The grounds include a 15-hole golf course, an "idyllic" swimming pool in a secluded garden with palm trees, and tennis and croquet. Indoors are billiards, a games room and solarium. It would be good for a family holiday – provided the children are over seven. *Downrew* had an entry in earlier editions of the Guide but was omitted when it changed hands. Now an inspector's report recommends its reinstatement. "It is owned and run by two very charming couples with no previous hotel experience, the Spencers and the Middletons. Whatever they lack in experience they make up for in enthusiasm." The style of the house is at present slightly unsettled as it is gradually being refurbished, but there are comfortable lounges, and an attractive newly decorated dining room. Bedrooms and bathrooms are well equipped and housekeeping of a high standard. Cooking is English/French, eschewing the *nouvelle*, and somewhat uneven, but with excellent desserts. The wine list is "very interesting". Breakfast "satisfactory, though coffee in somewhat short supply". Only niggle, "The soundproofing between bedrooms could be improved." More reports please.

Open All year except Jan.
Rooms 2 suites, 10 double – all with bath and shower, telephone, radio and TV. 6 in adjacent Coach House. 3 on ground floor.
Facilities 2 lounges, bar, dining room; billiard room, card room, games room, solarium, laundry. 11½-acre grounds with heated swimming pool, tennis, croquet, golf. Sandy beaches 8–10 m. Fishing nearby.
Location 2½ m S of Barnstaple on A377. Take fork just S of Bishops Tawton to Cobbaton/Chittlehampton. Hotel is 1½ m on right.
Restrictions No children under 7. Dogs in Coach House only, not in public rooms.
Credit cards Access, Visa.

Terms Dinner, B&B £47–£53.50. Set dinner £20. Reductions for 2 or more nights. Christmas/New Year breaks. Reduced rates and special meals for children.
Service/tipping: No service charge. Gratuities, at guests' discretion, shared among all staff."

BLANDFORD FORUM Dorset — Map 2

La Belle Alliance [GFG]
Whitecliff Mill Street
Blandford Forum DT11 7BP

Tel Blandford Forum (0258) 452842
Fax (0258) 480054

"One of those rare finds where the accommodation is tasteful and comfortable, the food excellent, the wine list carefully chosen, and the friendliness and hospitality of Lauren Davison a real treat. Yet the prices are well below those of many far inferior establishments." "Happy, capable staff, warm, hospitable atmosphere." (*DF Tooley, Laura Marshall*)
La Belle Alliance is a restaurant-with-rooms run by Lauren and Philip Davison (he is the chef) in a spacious Victorian house on the quiet outskirts of a pleasant market town in the heart of Hardy country. During their five years here they have been upgrading the decor and furniture. Bedrooms are "pretty, restful and well lit", with good bathrooms; breakfasts are "as good as the dinners". Mrs Davison tells us that they are now changing dishes on the menu more frequently. "The style", she says, "remains modern, and the choice short (five or six dishes at each stage)".

Open All year except Jan. Restaurant closed Sun except bank holidays.
Rooms 5 double (also available as single) – all with bath and shower, telephone, TV and tea-making facilities.
Facilities Lounge, restaurant. Small garden. Riding stables opposite.
Location Go through town (1-way system); bear left onto Shaftesbury (Warminster) Road; restaurant is 300 yards on right. Parking for 9 cars.
Restrictions Not suitable for ♿. No smoking in dining room. Children under 7 by arrangement. No dogs in public rooms.
Credit cards Access, Amex, Visa.
Terms B&B (English): single occupancy £38–£42, double £49–£54. Lunch (by arrangement) £12.50, set dinner £19. Gourmet breaks. Special meals for children by arrangement.
Service/tipping: "We do not expect tips as we believe we pay our staff a fair wage for the good service they offer."

BLAWITH Cumbria — Map 4

Appletree Holme Farm
Blawith, Nr Ulverston
LA12 8EL

Tel Lowick Bridge (022 985) 618

Appletree Holme Farm, owned by "welcoming, helpful, but unobtrusive hosts", Roy and Shirley Carlsen, is a secluded old stone farmhouse, with open fires and beamed ceilings, and views of the five acres of carefully tended gardens – "quiet and pleasant to sit in in fine weather" – and orchard with wooded slopes and fells beyond. The four bedrooms are comfortable, clean and well equipped, with lots of hot water. Lounges are "welcoming, with open fires, china, furniture, ornaments all chosen with impeccable taste. Good, simple food is served in ample helpings" – local game, meats and trout and the Carlsens' own garden vegetables appear on the four-course, no-choice dinner menus. There is an extensive breakfast menu including Cumberland sausages, free-range eggs, oak-smoked kippers and goat's milk yoghurt; orders are taken after dinner. The Carlsens' two border collies and cat are said to be as welcoming as their owners. (*J Mandelstam; also Pat Manners*) Only criticism: "Heating in the bedroom comes on at 7.30 am; since the cooked breakfast is served at about 8 this means that you get up in a cold room – but this is a very insubstantial niggle."

Open All year except Christmas/New Year.
Rooms 2 suites, 2 double – all with bath, shower, telephone, radio, TV and tea-making facilities. 1 is adjacent to main building with private entrance and patio.
Facilities Sitting room, library, dining room. 5-acre grounds with gardens, orchards and paddocks. Fishing, shooting, lake bathing nearby.
Location Turn off A5084 up lane opposite Blawith church. After ½ m turn right; after 1 m turn left at farm sign.
Restrictions Not suitable for ♿. Some smoking restrictions. No children under 10. No dogs in bedrooms or public rooms.
Credit card Amex.
Terms Dinner, B&B double £43–£45, suite £46–£48; single supplement £10. Picnic lunches available. Set dinner £15.50.
Service/tipping: "Tipping does not arise – one does not offer gratuities to one's hosts!"
Note: Mrs Carlsen writes, "*Appletree* is a special place with an appeal limited to country lovers and those seeking peace and seclusion. In order to safeguard our guests' privacy, casual/chance callers are not encouraged and all reservations or requests to look around must be made in advance."

BLICKLING Norfolk — Map 3

The Buckinghamshire Arms — *Tel* Aylsham (0263) 732133
Blickling
Nr Aylsham NR11 6NF

This 17th-century inn run by "ebullient, hospitable proprietor", Nigel Elliott, is quietly situated beside – and with fine views of – Blickling Hall, one of the jewels of the National Trust. It calls itself a hotel but it is really an old-fashioned inn, a popular pub with the locals, with just three bedrooms (each with a comfortable four-poster), though with only one bathroom between them. Food is wholesome and generous, there is an excellent range of moderately priced wines; good and reasonably priced bar snacks are available at lunchtime. Don't expect too much from the decor, nor hotellish extras such as help with baggage.

Open All year except Christmas.
Rooms 3 double – all with TV and tea-making facilities.
Facilities Lounge bar, snug bar, restaurant. Garden with slides and swings.
Location 2 m N of Aylsham on B1354, adjacent to Blickling Hall.
Restrictions Not suitable for ♿. No dogs in public rooms.
Credit cards Access, Visa.
Terms (No service charge) B&B (English): single occupancy £36–£38, double £50–£52. Set lunch £12 (bar snacks available); full alc dinner £19. 1-night bookings sometimes refused. Reduced rates and special meals for children.
Service/tipping: "Tips entirely at customers' discretion; distributed among the staff who actually served the guests."

> Always let a hotel know if you have to cancel a booking, whether you have paid a deposit or not. Hotels lose thousands of pounds and dollars from "no-shows".

BORROWDALE Cumbria — Map 4

Seatoller House — *Tel* Borrowdale (059 684) 218
Borrowdale, Keswick CA12 5XN — *[from April 1990:* Borrowdale (076 87) 77218

"I cannot be too grateful to the Guide for introducing us to this exceptional guest house. Each year it seems better than ever and the new private bathroom facilities have added the finishing touch. Staying at *Seatoller* is like being a very welcome guest in somebody's home, with David Pepper the perfect host and his wife Ann producing the most delectable meals. For comfort, good company and sheer value for money it must be hard to beat. Evidence of this is surely in the number of guests who return year after year." (*Mrs JA Jolly*) One satisfied customer expresses the feelings of many regulars who have written to us over the years in appreciation of *Seatoller*'s remarkably modest tariff, attentive service, excellent food, and the house-party atmosphere created by the communal tables where breakfast is served to everyone at 8.30 am and dinner at 7 pm. The house is over 300 years old, and has been run continuously as a guest house for more than 100 years. It enjoys a "breathtaking setting" at the head of the Borrowdale valley, near the Honister Pass, close to the starting point of many spectacular fell walks. "Accommodation comfortable in a homely, rather old-fashioned way, the company usually very congenial, the food marvellous and served in very generous portions. Not an hotel; guests are really expected not to stay on the premises during the day (though they are not actively discouraged or made to feel unwelcome), so there are none of the usual accoutremements – TV lounge, swimming pool, etc. Won't ever appeal to those who like *pot pourri* in the bedroom, colour co-ordinated with the towels – I certainly hope not!" (*Abigail Kirby Harris; endorsed by Gerhard and Gertrude Cohn, and others*)

Open Feb–Nov. Dining room closed Tue evening.
Rooms 9 double – all with bath and/or shower. 1 in converted bakehouse. 2 ground-floor rooms.
Facilities Lounge, library, dining room, self-service tea-bar; small conference facilities; drying room. 2-acre grounds.
Location 8m S of Keswick on B5289. Regular bus service from Keswick.
Restrictions No smoking in bedrooms. Not suitable for severely ♿. No children under 5. No dogs in public rooms.
Credit cards None accepted.
Terms (No service charge) Dinner, B&B £25–£26.50. Packed lunches available. Weekly rates; special rates for parties of 18 or more. 1-night bookings sometimes refused. Reduced rates for children under 12 sharing parents' room.
Service/tipping: "Service at guests' discretion."

BOUGHTON MONCHELSEA Kent — Map 3

Tanyard Hotel — *Tel* Maidstone (0622) 744705
Wierton Hill, Boughton Monchelsea
Maidstone ME17 4JT

A lovingly restored medieval yeoman's house, later a tannery, now a very small country-house hotel owned and run by Jan Davies. It enjoys a secluded position on the edge of the Weald of Kent, looking out over orchards and cottages, and is well placed for Leeds Castle and

Sissinghurst; Folkestone, Dover and Gatwick are all within an hour's drive. There are only five bedrooms, all heavily beamed and furnished with good antique pieces. A magnificent suite occupies the whole of the top floor, with far-reaching views. "A delightful, happy hotel. We had a large, comfortable twin-bedded room. The best breakfasts we have ever had. No choice at dinner, but we were always asked if we would like alternatives. Attractive garden with fishpond and seats." "Jan Davies is an excellent cook and we got high marks for finishing everything put on our plates." "Our stay was little short of idyllic, and we would happily return." "Superb building - apart from a steep flight of stairs; Mrs Davies most hospitable and a very good cook." (*Mrs VG Bateson, Jeremy and Anthea Larken, KA Hickman, Esler Crawford, and others*)

Open First weekend in Mar–mid-Dec. Restaurant closed for lunch.
Rooms 1 suite, 4 double – all with bath and/or shower, telephone, radio, TV and tea-making facilities.
Facilities Hall/reception, lounge, restaurant. 1-acre garden; 4-acre orchard.
Location 5 m S of Maidstone. From B2163 at Boughton, turn down Park Lane opposite *Cock* pub. Take first right down Wierton Lane. Fork right; *Tanyard* is on left at bottom of hill.
Restrictions Not suitable for ♿. No children under 6. No dogs.
Credit cards All major cards accepted.
Terms (Excluding VAT. No service charge) B&B (English): single £42, double £52, suite £72. Set dinner £16. 1-night bookings refused at weekend.
Service/tipping: "Tips are not expected, but if given are distributed to all staff."

BOWNESS-ON-WINDERMERE Cumbria — Map 4

Lindeth Fell Country House Hotel
Bowness-on-Windermere
LA23 3JP

Tel Windermere (096 62) 3286

"A solid, well-built Lakeland stone house in extensive grounds with rhododendrons and azaleas, tennis and croquet, and a small tarn with trout. It is owned and run by Pat Kennedy, ex-RAF, and his wife Diana, who does most of the cooking, assisted by Sarah Churchward. There are two lounges, one with a beautiful Adam-style plaster ceiling and tall, wide windows looking over the treetops to Lake Windermere. There are also lots of books which you are encouraged to borrow. Most bedrooms overlook the lake; they are clean and comfortable, with crisply laundered sheets and well-placed lights and lamps. Good towels and even a choice of toilet paper in the bathroom. Food is good traditional English cooking, with at least two choices for each course. The wine list is extensive and reasonably priced. The outstanding feature here is the atmosphere, mostly due to the warm, outgoing personalities of the Kennedys – who are a mine of information on local walks, climbs and gardens – and the tranquillity of the house, insulated in its gardens from the bustle and activity of Bowness just down the road." "Efficient and relaxed, staff courteous and cheerful." (*Angela and David Stewart, John and Diane Elliott, and others*) One reader felt the bedroom furniture didn't quite live up to the Edwardian style of the house.

Open 10 Mar–20 Nov.
Rooms 12 double, 2 single – all with bath and/or shower, telephone, radio, TV, tea-making facilities and baby-listening. 1 ground-floor room.

Facilities Hall, lounge with dispense bar, 2 drawing rooms, dining room. 7-acre grounds with tennis, croquet, putting, tarn with fishing. Windermere ¾ m.
Location 1 m S of Bowness on A5074.
Restrictions No children under 5. Dogs in grounds only.
Credit cards All major cards accepted.
Terms Dinner, B&B: single £36–£40, double £65–£90. Light lunch £5, set dinner £17.50. 1-night bookings sometimes refused during Easter and bank holidays. Reduced rates for children sharing parents' room; special meals.
Service/tipping: "I disagree with arbitrary service charges. Here it is entirely optional. I tip for good service, and assume my guests feel the same."

BRADFORD-ON-AVON Wiltshire — Map 2

Bradford Old Windmill
Masons Lane
Bradford-on-Avon BA15 1QN

Tel Bradford-on-Avon (022 16) 6842

A converted mill run by Peter and Priscilla Roberts, founders of the Distinctly Different Association of granaries, chapels, oast houses, railway carriages and the like, converted into inexpensive guest accommodation. It made its Guide debut last year as *The Round House*, but the Roberts have now restored the timber gallery on the second floor level, and feel it appropriate to revert to the mill's original name. It stands on a steepish hill overlooking Bradford. "What a pleasant surprise. Not a hotel, but an old windmill tastefully converted into charming accommodations. Delightful round rooms with magnificent views. The no-smoking rule is an added attraction." (*Dr Stephen Durham*) Priscilla Roberts writes, "I am a vegetarian and my husband is an omnivore, so we compromise in our catering. At breakfast (which is communally taken) we provide a wide range of alternatives to suit carnivores, vegetarians, vegans, healthy and unhealthy eaters. Evening meals are vegetarian with an international flavour. The mill is furnished throughout with old pine, and decorated with an eclectic collection of *objets trouvés* acquired during our travels round the world. Our aim is to make our guests feel part of the household – with all the advantages and disadvantages which this entails." More reports please.

Open All year.
Rooms 1 family, 3 double, 1 single – 1 with bath and shower, 2 with shower; tea-making facilities, radio, TV on request.
Facilities Lounge, dining room. Small garden. River Avon 5 mins' walk.
Location In Bradford on A363 find *Castle* pub. Go down hill towards centre. After 100 yds turn left into private drive immediately before first roadside house.
Restrictions Not suitable for ♿. No smoking. No children under 5.
Credit cards None accepted.
Terms B&B £15–£25. Set dinner £12. Reduced rates for children in family room.
Service/tipping: "Service is included in the price. As proprietors we do not expect to be tipped for being nice to our guests. Our payment is in their return visits."

Traveller's tale *When I checked out, the desk clerk went out of her way to criticise American Express (which the hotel advertises as accepting), particularly the commission. She tried to embarrass me into paying in some different way. I was not asked if we had enjoyed our stay or had been comfortable. I insisted on paying by Amex.*

Woolley Grange Hotel and Restaurant [GFG]
Woolley Green
Bradford-on-Avon BA15 1TX

Tel Bradford-on-Avon (02216) 4705
Fax (02216) 4059

Mainly Jacobean manor house, carefully restored by the Chapman brothers with "simple decor and friendly furniture", brass beds and gas fires in many bedrooms. Large dining room; cooking by Anand Sastry highly praised; much local produce used, some of it organic. Large grounds with swimming pool, grass tennis courts, walled kitchen garden. Children welcome – nursery, playroom, full-time nanny and special meals. 20 rooms, all with bath and shower. B&B double (continental) £85–£150. set lunch £16, dinner £24. Opened in May 1989. More reports please. (See under Woolley Green in The Good Food Guide.)

BRAMPTON Cumbria — Map 4

Farlam Hall [GFG]
Brampton CA8 2NG

Tel Hallbankgate (069 76) 234

A regular to *Farlam Hall* writes: "The unique style of the charming Quinion/Stevenson family and the continued excellence of the food should ensure that this establishment keeps its long-standing double billing in both *The Good Hotel Guide* and *The Good Food Guide*, though we sometimes regret that they didn't keep the accommodation simpler and the prices lower – we enjoyed it just as much when they were only beginning to put in private bathrooms. Full marks for the unaffected and un-snooty welcome, extended equally to regulars and casuals. Our ground-floor room was luxurious, though the decor (padded door, flowery wallpaper, frilly cushion on the bed) not to our personal taste. No matter, it was as always extremely comfortable, with 'give-aways' in abundance, and readable bedside books. The grounds are attractively laid out, with trees and a lake; the immediate environs are a bit dull, but more interesting places are easily reached by car. We have some sympathy with the contributors who complained of being rushed for their meal order (dinner is served punctually at 8 pm). Our advice is to arrive in good time, and if necessary take your drink into the dining room. Food is still excellent, well cooked and presented, and satisfying, although portions are not always over-large. House wine good value. Breakfast has some interesting non-run-of-the-mill choices."

Farlam Hall is a part-17th-century Border manor house in rural Cumbria, close to Hadrian's Wall. It has small, cosy front rooms and vast, elegant high-ceilinged back ones. "Visually delightful, with charming *objets d'art* everywhere. Total professionalism combined with the desire to give pleasure." (*Susan Gillotti*) "Breakfast, thank goodness, is now served at 8.30 which allows a reasonable lie-in with early morning tea", says one reader; whereas another wished that an earlier, full breakfast had been available for people travelling on business, of whom there were quite a few. One visitor found the food over-elaborate.

Open Mar–Jan inclusive. Closed Christmas week. Restaurant closed for lunch.
Rooms 12 double, 1 single – all with bath and/or shower, telephone and TV; some with radio. 2 ground-floor rooms.
Facilities 2 lounges, bar, dining room. 4½-acre grounds with croquet. Golf nearby.

Location On A689, 2½ m SE of Brampton (*not* in Farlam village).
Restrictions Not suitable for ♿. No children under 5. Dogs by arrangement only.
Credit cards Access, Amex, Visa.
Terms (No service charge) Dinner, B&B £55–£85. Set dinner £20. Winter and spring breaks.
Service/tipping: "Tipping is optional. Guests who wish to thank the staff should be allowed to do so. Tips are divided among all staff at the end of the season according to the amount of work done."

BRANSCOMBE Devon — Map 1

The Look Out — *Tel* Branscombe (029 780) 262
Branscombe EX12 3DP

On edge of village in lovely valley, new hotel in former coastguard cottages, attractively converted; flagstones, oak beams, antique and period furniture. Comfortable bedrooms, all with sea view; easy access to magnificent cliff walks and vast shingle beach. Recommended for beautiful setting, good food, friendly if sometimes casual service. Peaceful atmosphere sometimes marred by musak and kitchen noises. Closed Christmas week. 6 rooms, all with bath or shower. No children under 6. B&B (English) double £64–£70. Set dinner £16.25–£18.25. New nomination. More reports please.

BRATHAY Cumbria — Map 4

Grey Friar Lodge Country House Hotel — *Tel* Ambleside (053 94) 33158
Brathay, Ambleside LA22 9NE

A small hotel in the heart of the Lake District; a typical Lakeland country house, once a vicarage, built in 1869 of green stone and slate. It is situated on the wooded flanks of Loughrigg Fell and has lovely far-reaching views. Readers continue to enjoy the "eclectic and reassuring" style of the furnishing; the comfortable, clean and well-appointed bedrooms (they vary in size but all have *en suite* facilities); the "sumptuous Cumbrian breakfasts" and packed lunches, and the no-choice, five-course dinners served at 7.30 – "excellent cooking which uses fresh local produce with considerable flair", with special mention of the home-made soups and hot puddings; and, finally, "the tremendous value for money". "A marvellous friendly house, with attentive hosts, Tony and Sheila Sutton, and a welcome that never faded." (*E Hill, Robert Clark, G Selby*)

Open End Mar–end Oct.
Rooms 8 double – all with bath and/or shower, radio, TV, tea-making facilities.
Facilities 2 lounges, dining room. 1-acre garden with patio and sun terrace. River and fishing ¼ m.
Location 1½ m W of Ambleside on A593.
Restrictions Not suitable for ♿. No children under 10. Dogs by arrangement only (£3.50); not in public rooms.
Credit cards None accepted.
Terms (No service charge) Dinner, B&B: £29–£33; single occupancy of small double £6 supplement. Set dinner £12. Packed lunch on request. Special breaks. 1-night bookings sometimes refused if made far in advance. Reduced rates for children sharing parents' room.
Service/tipping: "Good service is an essential part of our establishment. It should be natural and automatic. Therefore we neither levy nor expect tips."

BRIGHTON East Sussex — Map 3

Topps Hotel
17 Regency Square
Brighton BN1 2FG

Tel Brighton (0273) 729334
Telex 877159 BHVTXS ref Topps

"A really well-run small hotel. Everything one needs, but not a lot of stupid extras. Mr and Mrs Collins very visible and couldn't do more for one. Charming bedroom, abundant hot water, good food, limited vegetarian choice, mostly lots of vegetables, but well cooked. They gave me exactly what I wanted to eat, when I wanted it, in my bedroom every day, even if the restaurant was closed. Mrs Collins did my laundry beautifully and I was helped with my car, making telephone calls and so on. I wish all hotels were like *Topps.*" (*Mrs MD Prodgers*) Other readers, too, praise the friendliness, good service and general helpfulness at Paul and Pauline Collins' conversion of two terraced houses in a seafront Regency square in the heart of Brighton. "Double room of a high standard, room and *en suite* bathroom large and well decorated, but also cosy and welcoming." Breakfast, which includes home-made rolls and bread and real muesli, continues to be considered "excellent". Mrs Collins' cooking in *Bottoms,* the basement restaurant, is "very good, and interesting. The restaurant has improved since our last visit two years ago, with better layout and more space; there were several good half-bottles of wine". Last year we reported some dissent about the decor; it doesn't seem to have bothered anyone recently; a reader this year describes the furnishings as "eclectic". (*Dr Deborah Jenkins, John Gunson, Chris and Stewart Kidd, Gerhard Cohn*)

Note When full the Collins recommend *The Dove,* a B&B run by Peter and Deborah Kalinke at number 19, next door (telephone 779222).

Open All year except Christmas/New Year. Restaurant closed Jan, Sun and Wed.
Rooms 7 double, 5 single – all with bath (8 also have shower), telephone, radio, TV and tea-making facilities.
Facilities Lift. Lounge, bar, restaurant. 100 yds from sea, safe bathing.
Location 200 yds from centre, opposite West Pier, but quietly situated. NCP carpark nearby.
Restrictions Not suitable for ♿. No dogs.
Credit cards All major cards accepted.
Terms B&B: single £39, double £65–£85. Set dinner £13.95; full alc £18.50. 20% reduction for any two nights Fri/Sat/Sun except public holidays. Reduced rates for children sharing parents' room; special meals.
Service/tipping: "Service is free."

BROADSTONE Dorset — Map 2

The Fairlight Hotel
1 Golf Links Road
Broadstone BH18 8BE

Tel Broadstone (0202) 694316

No feedback yet on this budget-price hotel run by friendly and hardworking proprietors, Pat and Brian Marshall. Excellently situated for golfing and for touring Dorset's coast and countryside. Comfortable lounge with fires in winter; small garden; children and pets welcomed. Modest but good food: set four-course dinner in no-smoking dining room at 7 pm (alternative dishes provided by arrangement) and good breakfasts. Open 7 Jan–20 Dec. 9 double, 2 single,

8 with bath and/or shower. B&B double £31–£42. Set dinner £11–£14. New nomination in 1989. More reports please.

BROMSGROVE Hereford and Worcester **Map 2**

Grafton Manor *Tel* Bromsgrove (0527) 579007
Grafton Lane *In USA* (800) 544 9932
Bromsgrove B61 7HA *Fax* (0527) 575221

"A lovely country house, decorated in keeping. Large beautifully furnished bedroom. I have never had such a gourmet-style vegetarian meal in a hotel. I could hardly believe how small my bill was in relation to the value received." "First-class meal. Everyone very friendly. Extremely good value all round." "Service in general exceptionally good – intelligent, civilised, friendly, good-humoured." *(Mrs EH Prodgers, Michael and Margaret Crick, and others) Grafton Manor*, owned and run by John and June Morris and their children, is an architecturally splendid early 18th-century mansion, built in stone and pink brick, with just nine rooms; one is an outsize suite occupying half of one wing on the first floor. Decor varies, but all are fitted with appropriate mod cons, including gas-run coal fires, and many extras. It is not far from Birmingham, peacefully located down an isolated lane, but close to the M5. Back rooms which face the motorway have secondary glazing which keeps the traffic out of earshot if not out of sight. But if you like to open your window at night make sure you face the other way. The *Manor* has lovely grounds with a lake and water gardens; the modern herb garden, laid out like a chess-board, provides herbs for extensive use in the traditional and modern British dishes served in the magnificent and fairly formal dining room. Some criticisms this year: the public rooms can be dominated by business visitors; one guest's visit was spoiled by chain smokers in both lounge and dining room, she reported unevenness in the cooking "and the portions varied from over-generous to embarrassingly small". More reports please.

Open All year.
Rooms 2 suites (1 on ground floor), 6 double, 1 single – all with bath and shower, telephone, radio, TV and teletext.
Facilities Lounge, lounge/bar, restaurant. 11-acre grounds with gardens, fishing lake, 2 golf courses nearby.
Location 1½ m S of Bromsgrove off B4091, opposite Stoke turn.
Restrictions Not suitable for ♿. No children under 7. Dogs in kennels only.
Credit cards All major cards accepted.
Terms (Service at guests' discretion) B&B (continental): single from £60, double £84–£97, suite £120–£145. English breakfast £6.95. Set lunch from £11, dinner £23. Christmas package.

BRYHER Isles of Scilly **Map 1**

Hell Bay Hotel *Tel* Scillonia (0720) 22947
Bryher, Isles of Scilly
Cornwall TR23 0PR

Only hotel on the tiny island of Bryher (population 66), owned by Sorrel Atkinson – a converted farmhouse in 8-acre grounds with accommodation in comfortable and recently decorated apartments (also let on weekly self-catering basis) built round a courtyard of subtropical gardens. Particularly suitable for families. Warmly recommended for high standard of traditional cooking, cleanliness, and welcoming attitude towards children. Open mid-Mar–early Oct. 15 apartments, all with bath and/or shower and cooking facilities. Dinner, B&B £30–£46. Set dinner £14. Bar lunches. More reports please.

BUCKLAND Hereford and Worcester — Map 2

Buckland Manor [GFG]
Buckland, Nr Broadway
WR12 7LY
Tel Broadway (0386) 852626

A luxurious manor house owned and run by Barry and Adrienne Berman, both very much in evidence, in a harmonious little Cotswold village built of mellow honey-coloured stone, and, unlike nearby Broadway, an oasis of tranquillity. The ten acres of gardens and grounds are as beautiful as the house; and there is tennis, swimming and croquet. The house is typically Cotswold, much gabled, with mullioned windows. Inside the atmosphere is "stately and traditional with log fires in great old fireplaces, high-backed settees and dark heavy doors and beams. The large public rooms are well furnished with antiques and working fireplaces; there are lovely flower arrangements. Bedrooms are "superbly and very comfortably furnished" with luxurious carpeted bathrooms and many extras. The restaurant is elegant with white-painted panelling, candles, and waitresses in frilly aprons. Cooking, under Martin Pearn, is considered much improved this year: "civilised dishes, using very good raw materials, vegetables good to excellent", but "service can be a bit overpowering at times". More reports please.

Open All year except 3½ weeks from mid-Jan.
Rooms 1 suite (2 intercommunicating twin-bedded rooms), 9 double – 10 with bath and shower, all with telephone and TV; radio on request. Some ground-floor rooms.
Facilities 3 lounges, writing room, dining room. 10-acre grounds with gardens, heated swimming pool, tennis, croquet, putting. Golf, riding nearby.
Location E of A46, 1½ m SW of Broadway.
Restrictions No children under 12 in hotel, under 8 in restaurant. No dogs.
Credit cards Access, Visa.
Terms (No service charge) B&B: double £125–£180, suite £220 for 4. Full alc £25. Winter breaks Nov–mid-Mar (min 2 days), except Christmas, New Year and Cheltenham Gold Cup week when there are special packages. 1-night bookings refused weekends and bank holidays.
Service/tipping: "Entirely at guests' discretion; all gratuities divided among staff."

BUDOCK VEAN Cornwall — Map 1

Budock Vean Golf and Country House Hotel
Budock Vean, Nr Falmouth
TR11 5LG
Tel Falmouth (0326) 250288
Fax (0326) 250892

A resort-style hotel in fine position in 56-acre grounds with sub-tropical gardens, 9-hole golf-course, 2 all-weather tennis courts, large covered swim-

ming pool – open in summer, with log fire in winter – and private frontage on the Helford river. New wing has roomy if rather functional bedrooms; those in original building are prettier but smaller. Recommended for well-kept facilities, excellent and varied food, "exceptionally helpful and friendly staff". Children welcomed. Closed 4 Jan–mid-Feb. 58 rooms, all with private facilities. Dinner, B&B double £80–£125. Was in earlier editions under previous management. More reports please.

BURY ST EDMUNDS Suffolk — Map 3

The Angel Hotel
Angel Hill
Bury St Edmunds IP33 1LT

Tel Bury St Edmunds (0284) 753926
Fax (0284) 750092
Telex 81630 ANGEL

This "lovely old inn" in a delightful small market town is 15th-century in origin with an 18th-century classical facade, now softened by creepers. It is on the main square opposite the great abbey gate, one of Bury's glories, and is very much part of the life of the town; the comfortable public rooms bustle with activity, particularly on market day (Wednesday). *The Angel*'s teas, sometimes accompanied by harp or piano, are particularly popular. It was patronised by Dickens in the 19th century, and nowadays offers occasional literary weekends off season. *The Angel* has been run since 1973 by Mrs Mary Gough and her family with lots of personal attention for guests: a porter helps you to park and carries your luggage; tea is brought to the bedroom rather than do-it-yourself; beds are turned down at night. Readers this year are unanimous in their praise of the "attentive and professional" service. The bedrooms and bathrooms vary greatly in size and shape, as in all old buildings, so it is important to discuss your requirements when booking; some are "huge, with four-poster", others "smallish with small but well-equipped bathroom"; most are attractively furnished with good quality fabrics and some antiques; those at the back are quietest, but front ones are double-glazed. The hotel has two dining rooms; the *Regency Restaurant* is fairly formal, the one in the vaults more modern in style. Food is traditional English – "good but not exceptional, wines very reasonable". "Excellent" breakfasts include freshly squeezed orange juice and hot brown toast.

Open All year.
Rooms 1 suite, 25 double, 14 single – all with bath and/or shower, telephone, radio, TV and baby-listening.
Facilities Lounge, bar, 2 restaurants; small conference facilities. Parking for 20 cars. Abbey gardens opposite.
Location Central, near Information Centre (front rooms double-glazed). Parking.
Restrictions Not suitable for ♿. No dogs in restaurants.
Credit cards All major cards accepted.
Terms Rooms: single £55–£62, double £80–£100, suite £130. Breakfast: continental £4.50, English £6.50. Set meals £11–£14; full alc £22.25. Reduced rates and special meals for children.
Service/tipping: "Service included. Tipping not actively encouraged."

> Deadlines: nominations for the 1991 edition should reach us not later than 1 May 1990. Latest date for comments on existing entries: 1 June 1990.

CALNE Wiltshire — Map 2

Chilvester Hill House — *Tel* Calne (0249) 813981 and 815785
Calne SN11 0LP

This spacious Victorian mansion in seven acres of grounds (with a swimming pool), close to (but out of earshot of) the A4 is run in a relaxed but thoroughly cosseting way by Dr and Mrs Dilley. The house is set in large grounds, with fine views. "Lovely, with large, warm and comfortable rooms and high ceilings; everything is beautifully decorated and in perfect condition. The bedrooms, all traditional, all different in decor, are spacious, with fresh flowers and every modern convenience." Guests eat in the family dining room round one "magnificently set" table (couples may find themselves split up). "Everything fresh and delicious, with vegetables from the garden. There are books everywhere on literally every subject." "The Dilleys' hospitality is exemplary. They are both charming, caring and thoughtful. Cooking is excellent, imaginative and varied." They do not have a brochure; enquirers get a personal letter. No choice of menu, but visitors are consulted about their likes and dislikes and Mrs Dilley keeps records of meals served "so that I do not duplicate – or so that I *can* when guests want to eat the same as last time". When not entertaining their guests, Dr Dilley, a consultant occupational physician, is now after 18 years in the Middle East in private practice; Mrs Dilley breeds beef cattle. (*GF, Dr Noel Russell; also Jeff and Karen Nebel*)

Open All year, except a week off-season (autumn or spring).
Rooms 3 double – all with bath, hand-shower, radio, TV, tea-making facilities.
Facilities Drawing room, sitting room with TV, dining room. 2½-acre grounds with swimming pool; also 5 acres used for cattle; golf and riding locally.
Location ½ m W of Calne; take A4 towards Chippenham, after ½ m take the right turn signposted Bremhill and immediately turn right into the drive marked by gateposts with stone lions.
Restrictions Not suitable for ♿. No children under 12. No dogs.
Credit cards All major cards accepted.
Terms (No service charge) B&B: single occupancy £35–£40, double £50–£55. Set dinner £16–£18; packed lunches or pool snacks available. Reductions for stays of a week or more.
Service/tipping: "Tips not expected; but if anything is left 'for the girls' it is put in a 'kitty' and shared."

CALSTOCK Cornwall — Map 1

Danescombe Valley Hotel [GFG] — *Tel* Tavistock (0822) 832414
Lower Kelly
Calstock PL18 9RY

The *Danescombe Valley Hotel* has a tranquil setting, on the steep wooded slopes of the river Tamar, adjoining the grounds of Cotehele House, 15 minutes' walk away. Martin Smith and his half-Italian wife, Anna bought it in a run-down condition and extensively renovated the house with Laura Ashley country house fabrics, and antique and traditional furniture. Improvements are still continuing, and the garden is next on the list. There are deep carpets, well-placed lighting, flowers, plants, magazines and books, and generally a light, airy feeling about the place. Bedrooms are well equipped with pretty duvets and huge pillows. Big fluffy towels and many extras – including wind-up bath toys – in the bathrooms. *Danescombe Valley* dispenses with many of the things that are expected these days of hotels – no telephones in bedrooms, no TV, no credit cards, for example. Guests are treated more like friends than fee-paying visitors and the Smiths insist on first names all round, which some find odd. Dinner is "at 7.30 for 8"; Anna Smith cooks "delicious, well balanced and very fresh, unfussy" no-choice meals (but you are consulted about likes and dislikes in advance); "properly cooked vegetables, local cheeses – a special feature, very good ice-cream". "Well thought out wine list; Martin is always on hand to advise." No cooked breakfasts; but a generous choice including fresh orange juice, poached fruit, yoghurt. Martin Smith is "an admirable host"; Anna is less visible, spending much of her time in the kitchen. (*Mrs NE Guess, JF Bowes; also Michael Owens, the Very Rev Michael Napier, David Nutt, and others*) A traveller on his own found the single-occupancy rates high and bemoaned the shortage of half-bottles on the wine list.

Open Easter–end Oct. Closed Wed and Thurs.
Rooms 5 double – all with bath; tea-making facilities on request.
Facilities Lounge, bar, restaurant. 4 acres of steep woodland; steps down to river Tamar. Fishing, walking, golf and riding nearby.
Location ½ m W of Calstock village; under viaduct, past Methodist church; turn sharp right; follow road parallel to river Tamar for ½ m.
Restrictions Not suitable for ♿. No children under 12. No dogs in house.
Credit cards None accepted.
Terms Dinner, B&B: single occupancy £74, double £106. 1-night bookings sometimes refused at weekends.
Service/tipping: "Tips refused unless our refusal gives offence."

CAMPSEA ASH Suffolk — Map 3

The Old Rectory [GFG] — *Tel* Wickham Market (0728) 746524
Campsea Ash, Nr Woodbridge
IP3 0PU

Spacious Victorian rectory in peaceful setting (apart from jets at nearby air base, but they are seldom heard). High ceilings, simple decor. Four-acre grounds. Run as a successful restaurant by Stewart Bassett, "an engaging character". Relaxed country house atmosphere with shared tables for dinner and breakfast. Recommended for informal "seedy gentry" air, friendly, informal service and "exceptionally delicious food" (limited choice). Prices reasonable. Closed 2 weeks Mar, 1 week Nov, 25/26 Dec. 6 pretty double rooms with garden view, all with bath and shower. B&B double £43.50–£47.50. Set dinner £13.50. Recent nomination. More reports please.

CARTMEL Cumbria — Map 4

Aynsome Manor Hotel [GFG] — *Tel* Cartmel (053 95) 36653
Cartmel, Grange-over-Sands
LA11 6HH

Attractively located small hotel with cobbled courtyard and ¾-acre garden, run by Varley family. Comfortable and attractive lounge with open fire, smallish bedrooms. Recommended for friendly and courteous service, good 5-course dinner served in panelled dining room (but portions a bit small for some) and excellent breakfasts. Closed 2–26 Jan. 13 rooms, all with bath or shower. Dinner, B&B double £73–£78. More reports please.

Uplands Hotel [GFG] *Tel* Cartmel (053 95) 36248
Haggs Lane, Cartmel
Grange-over-Sands LA11 6HD

"We wanted a quiet retreat in this area to restore sanity and heal bruised spirits and *Uplands* served these aims admirably." "We cannot praise Tom and Di's place too highly – he for his consistently high-class cooking (now tending to more imaginative use of game), she for her friendly courtesy to everyone. Between them they run a very special place and we will make the pilgrimage for many years to come." Tom and Diana Peters (he in the kitchen, she front of house) co-own *Uplands* with John Tovey, a hotel described as "in the *Miller Howe* manner", but less theatrical in style. Prices are considerably less and, unlike *Miller Howe*, it offers limited choice on the dinner menu and more flexible mealtimes. The hotel is on a hillside, in two acres of garden, with views over Morecambe Bay, in the uncrowded southern end of the Lake District. It is attractively decorated and furnished; the lounge and dining room "elegant, in restful pastel greys and pinks"; tables in the dining room are well spaced, and service is quiet and efficient. "Individual soup tureen, mini loaf of home-made granary bread, subsequent dishes never disappointed – flavours are robust and vegetables never boring. Sweets first-class, with judicious use of seasonal, and imported, fruit." "Excellent, generous breakfasts" – each table has its own toaster with a choice of breads. Bedrooms, though not very spacious, are comfortable and well equipped; two have lovely estuary views. (*Francine Walsh, JM Goodger; also Ann Farrow, Sir Douglas Frank, William Rankin, P and C Bevan, and many others*) One criticism, "The food combines too many ingredients and strong flavours at times – but it is cooked and presented with care."

Open 23 Feb–1 Jan. Restaurant closed Mon.
Rooms 4 double – 1 with bath, 3 with shower, all with telephone and TV.
Facilities Lounge, dining room. 2-acre garden. Golf nearby.
Location From Cartmel, with *Pig & Whistle* on right, immediately take left turn; go up Haggs Lane – hotel is on left at top of hill.
Restrictions Not suitable for ♿. No children under 8. No dogs in public rooms.
Credit cards Access, Amex.
Terms (Excluding 10% service charge) Dinner, B&B: single £60, double £106. Set lunch £10.50, dinner £18.50. Mid-week off-season breaks. Christmas and New Year breaks. 1-night bookings refused for Sat. Reduced rates for children sharing parents' room; special meals on request.
Service/tipping: "As we charge 10% for service we refuse tips if offered."

CHADDESLEY CORBETT Hereford and Worcester — Map 2

Brockencote Hall [GFG] *Tel* Kidderminster (056 283) 876
Chaddesley Corbett *Telex* 333431 BROHAL
Nr Kidderminster DY10 4PY

An elegant Georgian house in 70-acre grounds not far from Birmingham, *Brockencote Hall* was converted into a luxury hotel by Joseph Petitjean, who is French, and his English wife, Alison, about three years ago. "Wide rural outlook on all sides; sheep grazing in front, geese and ducks on the lake. Public rooms are large, light and high-ceilinged, furnishing agreeable and not too designerish. Bedrooms (named after birds and flowers) vary in size; ours was large, warm and pleasantly furnished, with good beds. Bathroom quite large, but lacked storage and shelf space. Attractive dining room; food very good – French, and fairly modern. Prices quite high. Wines predominantly French, on a not very long list, also quite expensive. Good continental breakfast; service swift and friendly." (*P and JT*)

Open Jan–end Dec. Closed New Year. Restaurant closed bank holiday Mons.
Rooms 9 double – all with bath and/or shower, telephone, radio, TV and baby-listening.
Facilities Bar, lounge, restaurant, 2 functions/conference rooms. 70-acre grounds.
Location On A448 from Kidderminster to Bromsgrove, just S of village
Restrictions Only restaurant suitable for ♿. No dogs.
Credit cards All major cards accepted.
Terms B&B (continental): single £58–£90, double £68–£90. Set lunch £14.50, dinner £35; full alc £35. Weekend breaks.

CHADLINGTON Oxfordshire — Map 2

The Manor [GFG] — *Tel* Chadlington (060 876) 711
Chadlington OX7 3LX

César award: Newcomer of the year, country house division

A new entry, though the proprietors of *The Manor*, David and Chris Grant, back from a year's globe-trotting, are well known to regular Guide readers – they previously owned *Kirkby Fleetham Hall* in Yorkshire where they attracted a loyal clientele, many of whom are now to be encountered at Chadlington, a "peaceful backwater on the fringe of the Cotswolds". *The Manor* stands beside the church in large grounds overlooking the Evenlode valley, with just a ha-ha separating them from a pasture where sheep and lambs safely graze. From outside it is "imposing"; inside it has been "sensitively and tastefully decorated, carpeted and furnished with an extensive use of beautiful and heavy materials in the now traditional country house style, with some antiques, interesting pictures, and comfortable modern chesterfields and armchairs. Our twin bedroom faced over the courtyard; it was light and airy thanks to its vast proportions and large sash windows; it has a spectacular domed ceiling where cheerful butterflies flutter, echoing those on the curtains. All the little luxuries one has come to expect in the caring country house were there, from fresh fruit to bottled water. The bathroom is modern, with many extras. Colour schemes throughout are adventurous, cheerful and tasteful; many rooms have lovely views. Mrs Grant is the chef; her short menu was interesting, modern English dishes, with simple sauces, vegetables were perhaps undercooked rather than al dente. Delicious leg of lamb en croûte, also sticky-toffee pudding, delectable petits fours with coffee. Magnificent wine list ranges the world with very modest mark-up. Breakfast was generous and altogether satisfactory. David Grant is a congenial and loquacious host, assisted by charming local girls." Our inspectors summed up: "The Grants have succeeded in creating a genuinely homely country-house atmosphere in a lovely setting with stylish decor and good food. It is one of the nicest hotels we have been to this year. Does their previous incarnation deny them a recommendation for a Newcomer of the Year Award? We hope not!"

Open All year. Lunch for residents only except Sun.
Rooms 7 double – all with bath and shower, telephone, TV, baby-listening.
Facilities Hall, lounge, library, dining room, 2 private dining rooms. 20-acre grounds.
Location Beside church in village 3 m SE of Chipping Norton, 17 m NW of Oxford.
Restrictions Not suitable for ♿. No dogs.
Credit cards Amex, Visa.
Terms B&B: single £55–£75, double £85–£110. Set lunch/dinner £21.50.
Service/tipping: "Service is included in our prices, as it is at Marks and Spencer or your local garage; you don't enquire about the cost of labour when buying a pair of socks! We pay our staff well, and the cost of this is built into our prices. I am against tipping in any form."

CHAGFORD Devon — Map 1

Gidleigh Park Hotel [GFG]
Chagford TQ13 8HH

Tel Chagford (064 73) 2367
Fax (064 73) 2574
Telex 42643 GIDLEY

César award in 1989: Most sumptuous traditional country house hotel

Gidleigh Park is now eleven years old and has been in the Guide since its opening as a country house hotel *de grand luxe*. It is set far off the road on the edge of Dartmoor – you need the sign saying "take heart" to keep you going down the single-track lane lined with huge granite boulders, moss and ferns, and overhung with trees. Once you arrive you find yourself in an interior that combines tradition with unostentatious luxury. The aim of American owners Paul and Kay Henderson with their managing director and head chef, Shaun Hill, is to provide total comfort in a private house atmosphere for "affluent connoisseurs". Prices are according to the size of the room and its view. Croquet is taken seriously here: there are four good quality lawns, and *Gidleigh Park* was the first hotel in Britain to be given the three mallet rating by the Croquet Association – the equivalent of a *Michelin* star in the croquet world.

"After 10 years – and with a lower bank balance as a result – we are still hooked! On every visit we find something new: new pictures, new furnishings, improvements on the second croquet lawn and clearance of surrounding woodland. There is now a tiny cottage in the Stockey Furzen woodland the other side of the river Teign. It has two bedrooms, a sitting room and a tiny kitchen and would be ideal for a very wealthy couple to occupy alone, or for two less wealthy couples to share. Shaun Hill's cooking remains robust, visually beautiful and imaginative. He does not follow any trends or fashionable fads and fancies. Desserts were more exciting than on our last visit and the home-made truffles served with coffee are so good you just have to find a tiny space to indulge in sheer greed." And casual callers report: "We were two travel-stained strangers with an equally stained three-month-old baby but were given such a friendly and natural welcome that we felt human again. A glance at the menu was tempting but we were embarrassed to be seen in the dining room. No problem – lunch was arranged for us on the terrace. The food was beautifully presented and lived up to all expectations (and to the prices!). All in all an episode which encapsulates the best qualities of English hotels, in particular the art of being natural, friendly, unstuffy – even when your hotel is grand, famous and expensive." As ever there are some criticisms arising from the high prices charged, viz. "Modest portions of food on massive plates . . . We felt we were paying for ostentation." But the general verdict continues to be: "Very expensive, but worth every penny." (*Padi Howard, Helen and Charles Priday, and others*)

Open All year.
Rooms 16 double – all with bath and/or shower, telephone, radio and TV. 2 in north wing 75 yds from front door; 2 in cottage 350 yds away.
Facilities Hall, lounge, bar, loggia, 2 dining rooms. 45-acre grounds with gardens, croquet lawns and hard tennis court. Fishing, golf, riding and walking nearby.
Location Approach from Chagford, *not* Gidleigh. From main square, facing Webbers with Lloyds Bank on right, turn right into Mill Street. After 150 yds fork right; go downhill to Factory Crossroad. Go straight across into Holy Street; follow lane 1½ m to end.
Restrictions Not suitable for ♿. No dogs in public rooms.
Credit cards Access, Visa.
Terms Dinner, B&B (continental): single occupancy £126.50–£218.50, double £155.25–£247.25. Cooked breakfast £3.50–£7. Set lunch £27, dinner £38. Winter walking holidays. 1-night bookings sometimes refused.
Service/tipping: "We discourage tipping."

Teignworthy [GFG] *Tel* Chagford (0647) 33355
Frenchbeer, Nr Chagford
TQ13 8EX

A Lutyens-style 1920s house, owned and run by John and Gillian Newell on the edge of Dartmoor, built by the same expert craftsmen as Castle Drogo nearby. It stands on a south-facing slope with views of garden and woodland, falling away to a stretch of the south Teign river; there is a grass tennis court and a croquet lawn in the grounds. The lounge has a log fire, books and records; bedrooms – six in the main building, three in the converted hay loft – are quite small but comfortable and warm, with lovely views, good beds, and extras such as a hair-drier. Decor in the bar and dining room is light; David Woolfall's cooking is modern – using excellent local ingredients – with imaginative vegetarian dishes. It is praised by some, regarded as "pretentious and amazingly expensive" by others. Guests are asked "to take trouble with their appearance at dinner, but jacket and tie are not demanded". One reader in early 1989 felt that "more than a hint of complacency" was creeping in, and refurbishment of lounge and bedrooms was overdue. "But the view and the breakfasts remain great attractions; welcome as good as ever."

Open All year.
Rooms 9 double – all with bath, telephone, radio and TV. 3 in converted hayloft, 2 with shared sitting room.
Facilities Hall, drawing room, small bar, dining room; some conference facilities; sauna and sunbed. 14-acre grounds with garden, woodland, tennis and croquet; fishing, golf, riding available. Dartmoor on the doorstep.
Location 3 m SW of Chagford. Follow signs towards Fernworthy, then Thornworthy.
Restrictions Not suitable for ♿. Smoking in dining room discouraged. Children under 10 by special arrangement. No dogs.
Credit cards Access, Visa.

Terms B&B (continental): single £49.50–£59.50, double £88–£100. Cooked breakfast from £2.50. Set lunch £20, dinner £30. Winter rates (2 nights min); 1-night bookings refused for Sat and bank holidays in season.
Service/tipping: "No service charge. Tipping discouraged."

Thornworthy House *Tel* Chagford (064 73) 3297
Chagford TQ13 8EY

A rambling Victorian house which, despite its address, is three miles out of Chagford, down twisting lanes to the very edge of Dartmoor – 1,200 feet up, with lovely views, and exceptionally tranquil. It stands in a country garden, with a tennis court. Philip and Vicky Jevons have lavishly redecorated and refurbished, giving it "the atmosphere of a well-to-do family house", with soft colours, thick carpets, luxurious fabrics, pictures and family photographs. The "very nice, hospitable" Jevons run the hotel as their private home; normally not taking more than six or eight guests at one time. Dinners, served at about 8 pm, offer three choices for each course and are "like having dinner with a friend, albeit a bit more formal, with good, basic English cooking; the wine list is moderately priced and offers a good choice". There are comfortable reception rooms with log fires; bedrooms are spacious, with lovely views; some have private facilities. (*CS-K, Mrs IE Barker, and others*)

Open All year.
Rooms 6 double, 2 single – 4 with bath and shower, all with TV. 1 on ground floor in adjacent barn.
Facilities Lounge, TV lounge, dining room. 2½-acre grounds with tennis and clock golf. Riding, golf, fishing, wind-surfing nearby.
Location 3 m SW of Chagford. From square take road to Fernworthy. After 150 yds fork left to Fernworthy. At top of hill take second turning on right to Thornworthy. Follow signs to *Thornworthy House* and Barn Cottage (not Thornworthy Cottage).
Restriction No dogs in public rooms.
Credit cards None accepted.
Terms (No service charge) B&B £26–£30; dinner, B&B £41–£45. Set dinner £15. Reduced rates for babies.
Service/tipping: "If guests leave tips they go to garden fund."

CHALFORD Gloucestershire — Map 2

Hill House *Tel* Brimscombe (0453) 882673
London Road, Chalford
Stroud GL6 8PP

Small very inexpensive guest house with garden in lovely position in the Golden Valley between Stroud and Cirencester, well placed for touring the Cotswolds. Furnished simply but with taste; excellent breakfasts. Evening meal £7–£8 [1989] sometimes provided for guests by arrangement with proprietors, Mr and Mrs Kingsland. Closed Dec–Feb. 3 bedrooms, all with H&C; *shared shower room. B&B £12–£17 [1989]. Recent nomination. More reports please.*

> We either quote prices per room, or else the range of prices per person – the lowest is likely to be for one person sharing a double room out of season, the highest for a single room in the high season.

CHARTHAM Kent — Map 3

Thruxted Oast *Tel* Canterbury (0227) 730080
Mystole, Chartham
Canterbury CT4 7BX

This converted oast barn near Canterbury, built in 1791, is now a comfortable guest house with three attractively decorated bedrooms; these have stripped pine furniture, patchwork quilts, remote-control TV and other comforts, but still retain evidence of their original use. It was nominated for a Guide entry last year, "Each room has its own bath, built in as a large dolls' house. It could have been a bit cute, but fortunately lands on the charming side thanks to the good taste of the friendly owners, Tim and Hilary Derouet, both of whom have the knack of making one feel at home, not an intruder. The grounds are picturesque with a handsome garden." (*Martin L Borish; also René de Bondt*) The Derouets no longer provide an evening meal. A generous breakfast is served in the large farmhouse kitchen. The oast also houses the owners' picture-framing workshop.

Open All year.
Rooms 3 double – all with shower, radio, TV and tea-making facilities.
Facilities Lounge; gift shop. ¾-acre grounds with terrace and croquet lawn. Whitstable Beach ½-hour drive.
Location 4 m SW of Canterbury. Brochure has map.
Restrictions Not suitable for ♿. No children under 14. No dogs.
Credit cards Access, Amex, Visa.
Terms (No service charge) B&B: single occupancy £45–£50, double £55–£60. 7 nights stay for the price of 6.
Service/tipping: "We have no service charge and no tipping."

CHARTHAM HATCH Kent — Map 3

Howfield Manor *Tel* Canterbury (0227) 738294
Chartham Hatch, Canterbury
CT4 7HQ

Mellow old house near Canterbury on Ashford road, with modern bedroom extension (windows double-glazed). Efficiently and professionally run by the Towns family. Elegant and comfortable public rooms; one dining room has original 12th-century well, bedrooms not large but pleasant and well equipped. Cooking of a high standard, despite off-putting names of dishes. 5-acre grounds. 13 rooms, all with bath and/or shower. B&B double £60–£65. Full alc £25. Was in earlier editions under previous owners. Reports please, especially unsolicited ones.

CHEDINGTON Dorset — Map 2

Chedington Court [GFG] *Tel* Corscombe (093 589) 265
Chedington *Fax* (093 589) 442
Nr Beaminster DT8 3HY

"Our favourite place – all the beauty of an English country house but none of the stuffiness of a hotel. Our bedroom and bathroom were huge with wonderful views of the grounds. Mr Chapman was a friendly host." "Food wonderful with generous portions. Location superb. A marvellous experience." "Rooms couldn't be more comfortable. Beautifully furnished with antiques, and everything works – very hot water, good lighting, comfortable beds."*(Jeff and Karen Nebel, Stella and David Gersh, Alison Rossiter)* *Chedington Court* is a splendid, 1840s country house hotel in the Jacobean style – curved gables, mullioned windows – in a spectacular position high up in the Dorset hills, with panoramic views across Dorset and Somerset. There are ten acres of parkland that match the grandeur of the building: balustraded and terraced gardens, lots of yews, a croquet lawn and a lake down below. Public rooms are "well furnished with lovely curtains and masses of books". It is quite informally run – "more of a home than a hotel", say the Chapmans – with no official reception or registration procedure and not much room service; guests tend to be left to their own devices for much of the time. Limited choice on the five-course dinner menu cooked by Hilary Chapman except for the first course and the "amazing" sweet trolley", but "it is a masterpiece in planning with all tastes accounted for and very skilfully served". There is an extensive wine cellar.

Open All year, except Christmas, 4 weeks Jan and/or Feb.
Rooms 10 double – all with bath and/or shower, telephone, radio, TV, tea-making facilities and baby-listening. 1 with 4-poster and double jacuzzi.
Facilities Drawing room, library, billiard room, dining room; conservatory. 10-acre garden with croquet, putting. Golf, fishing nearby; coast 10 m.
Location 4½ m SE of Crewkerne, just off A356 at Wynyard's Cap.
Restrictions Only restaurant suitable for ♿. No dogs.
Credit cards Amex, Visa.
Terms Dinner, B&B: single £59–£80, double £98–£140; B&B only, 20% less. Set dinner £22.50. Reductions for stays of more than 1 night. 1-night bookings sometimes refused. Reduced rates for children sharing parents' room; special meals.
Service/tipping: "Service is already paid for so no extra is added or expected."

CHELWOOD Avon — Map 2

Chelwood House Hotel
Chelwood
Nr Bristol BS18 4NH

Tel Compton Dando (076 18) 730
Telex 44830 ACCENT

Chelwood House was built in 1681 as a dower house for the Popham family, formerly of Littlecote House; it is now a small hotel, run by Jill and Rudolf Birk. It is on the A37 (windows are double-glazed, back rooms are quietest), almost equidistant from Bath, Bristol and Wells, in a small village with lovely views of open countryside. Readers praise the attractive public rooms, with period furniture and fresh flowers, and the comfortable bedrooms (three have a four-poster) with spacious and well-planned bathrooms. Mr Birk serves good, straightforward dinners, and excellent and generous English breakfasts. The Birk family are "friendly and professional", and the service "impressive". There is angling in Chew Valley Lake nearby, and there are numerous golf courses in the area. (*Mr and Mrs M Antrobus, and others*)

Open All year except Christmas, New Year and last 2 weeks of Jan.
Rooms 7 double, 1 single – all with bath and/or shower, telephone, radio, TV and tea-making facilities.

Facilities Lounge, dining room. 1½-acre grounds. Fishing and golf nearby.
Location On A37 (rooms are double-glazed; back ones quietest) 8 m S of Bristol.
Restrictions Not suitable for ♿. No smoking in dining room. No children under 10. No dogs.
Credit cards Access, Visa.
Terms B&B (English): single £50–£56, double £64–£90. Set lunch £13.50, dinner £18; full alc £23. Weekend breaks Oct–Apr. 1-night bookings refused for bank holidays.
Service/tipping: "We have abolished the service charge. Tips are accepted and distributed amongst all staff."

CHESTER see MOLLINGTON Map 4

Crabwall Manor Hotel

CHICHESTER West Sussex Map 1

Suffolk House Hotel

3 East Row, Chichester PO19 1PD
Tel Chichester (0243) 778899 and 778924

"Exceptionally well run. I have never met a hotelier who tried so hard to provide what his guests wanted – and succeeded. Very pretty bedroom; the four-poster had delightful hangings and matching duvet. My order for breakfast was correctly served in the room, and I had a delicious specially cooked vegetarian dinner." "Serge Paris has put a tremendous amount of thought into the renovation of the house. He is one of those people who put one at ease immediately and chats to his guests as if they were old friends; he is a person of many talents combined with boundless energy. We were again most comfortable and thoroughly recommend the hotel for a short stay – it might be a little cramped for a longer sojourn." "Immaculate, superbly furnished room, very attractive dining room looking onto the pretty garden. Food delicious; presentation excellent." This 18th-century town house, now owned by Serge Paris, a Yugoslav ex-restaurateur, once belonged to the Dukes of Richmond. Some bedrooms are large, all are well thought out, with good beds and linen; some have lovely views of Priory Park. There are no timetables for meals – you eat dinner, breakfast and any snack in between when you want, off an imaginative, varied and reasonably priced menu. There is a charming walled garden where meals are served in summer, a small bar, and arrangements of silk flowers throughout the hotel, even in the bathrooms. (*Mrs EH Prodgers, JH Bell, Christine Kingston*)

Open All year. Restaurant closed Feb.
Rooms 2 suites, 6 double, 4 single – all with bath and shower, telephone, radio, TV, tea-making facilities and baby-listening; some with 4-poster. Some ground-floor rooms.
Facilities Lounge/bar, restaurant. Sauna and jacuzzi planned. ¼-acre walled garden where meals are served in summer.
Location Central. Head for Quadrant; follow 1-way system into Little London for East Row. Parking.
Restriction No dogs.
Credit cards Access, Diners, Visa.
Terms B&B: single £47–£50, double £65–£70, suite £85–£90. Full alc £20. No charge for cot for child in parents' room.

CHIPPING CAMPDEN Gloucestershire — Map 2

The Cotswold House Hotel and Restaurant
The Square
Chipping Campden GL55 6AN

Tel Evesham (0386) 840330
Fax (0386) 840310

Cotswold House, owned by Robert and Gill Greenstock, is a fine Regency building, centrally placed in the Market Square, with a particularly noble central staircase. "The Greenstocks have done a superlative job of refurbishing, rebuilding and redecorating *Cotswold House*: well-selected antiques sit comfortably next to modern upholstery, interesting pictures grace the walls and flower arrangements are beyond criticism. The same flair is to be found in the bedrooms. The bathroom was impeccable, with the usual goodies one has come to expect from places in this price bracket." (*FW*) The better-proportioned rooms face the street; we reported last year that they are liable to some traffic noise; the Greenstocks tell us they have now been sound-proofed. The rooms at the back look over the walled garden. The dining room faces the garden too, and is an agreeably light, airy place to eat. Last year we asked for comments on the cooking by Raymond Boreham who took over as chef in early 1988. "*Very* good selection of imaginative and well-prepared food," reports *KJ Vaughan*. However, service both at dinner and breakfast continues to be somewhat irregular, and the garden was recently reported to be less well manicured than before. More reports please.

Open All year except 24–27 Dec.
Rooms 12 double, 3 single – 14 with bath and shower, all with telephone, radio, TV and baby-listening.
Facilities Reception lounge, sitting room, bar, dining room, coffee house; private dining room. Courtyard/patio, 1½-acre grounds.
Location Central (front rooms sound-proofed). Parking.
Restrictions Not suitable for ♿. No smoking in restaurant. No children under 8. No dogs.
Credit cards All major cards accepted.
Terms (No service charge) B&B £38.50–£52; dinner, B&B £58–£71.90. Set Sun lunch £12.50, dinner £19.50. Winter breaks. 1-night bookings refused at weekends. Special meals for children by arrangement.
Service/tipping: "We are against any form of tipping. But if we have done our job properly our guests will, if they are customary tippers, show appreciation. All tips are given to staff with instructions that everyone receives a share."

CHITTLEHAMHOLT Devon — Map 1

Highbullen Hotel
Chittlehamholt
Umberleigh EX37 9HD

Tel Chittlehamholt (076 94) 561
Fax (076 94) 492

A "wholly individual un-hotel-like hotel, run, very personally and efficiently, by Hugh and Pam Neil". It has lovely views across a Devon valley and many facilities for the sporting and unsporting (listed below) – but the herd of deer, mentioned in earlier editions, has gone. Bedrooms in the main house are traditional; those in the outbuildings are modern. All are well-equipped; many are spacious. *Highbullen* has many loyal regulars (two this year call it their favourite British hotel), who enjoy its restfulness and the laid-back atmosphere – "the Neils leave you alone to enjoy the wonderful facilities". There is now a new dining room, "large and somewhat brash", superseding the one in the cellar which some readers found claustrophobic; others however regret the loss of the "intimate and unique" atmosphere, though they report that there is now a much more varied dinner menu (it is overseen by the Neils' daughter Colette who, with husband Mike Potter, owns and runs *Stumbles* restaurant in nearby South Molton), and portions are larger. "It is fine for breakfast, however, and means that Hugh Neil allows guests to have their newspapers *before* Sunday breakfast – it used to be forbidden, space being so restricted." "Prices have gone up a bit but it is still outstanding value for money. The showers may be eccentric but the service and cooking are not. The relaxed atmosphere is at once infectious and calming. And I have rarely eaten so consistently well for four days. Seriously good wine list with modest mark-up." (*Stephen and Judy Parish, Dave Watts*) In the past we have warned that *Highbullen* is not for everyone. An *aficionado* warns: "'The customer is always right' was never a *Highbullen* motto." For at least one reader this year (as previously) the "take it or leave it approach" was altogether too much. "A mild request for a less spartan room (ours was upstairs in the annexe overlooking the corrugated roof of the squash court) was met with a response unrivalled in many years' experience of using your Guide; the 'take it or leave it' approach was varied only infinitesimally when my wife fell down a long flight of stairs from our room."

Open All year.
Rooms 34 double, 1 single – all with bath and shower, telephone, TV and tea-making facilities. 23 in converted farmhouse and cottages. Some ground-floor rooms.
Facilities Drawing room with conservatory, library, bar with small dance floor, dining room, breakfast room, billiard room; hairdressing and massage facilities; indoor tennis court and swimming pool, sauna, steam room, spa bath, sunbed, exercise room, table tennis room, squash court. 50-acre grounds with 6-acre garden, 9-hole golf course, tennis, croquet lawn, putting green, outdoor heated swimming pool. Golf and tennis tuition. Fishing in river Mole ½ m.
Location Leave M5 at exit 27 – onto A361 at South Molton take B3226 for 5.2 m, turn right to Chittlehamholt; go through village ½ m to hotel.
Restrictions Not suitable for ♿. No children under 10. No dogs.
Credit cards None accepted.
Terms Dinner, B&B £40–£50. Snack lunch. Set dinner £14.50. Midweek breaks Nov–Mar. 1-night bookings may be refused for Fri and Sat. Reduced rates for children sharing parents' room.
Service/tipping: "We make it quite clear that service is included and no tips are expected. Some people insist on leaving tips; they are distributed in proportion to individual staff earnings."

CONSTANTINE BAY Cornwall — Map 1

Treglos Hotel
Padstow PL28 8JH

Tel Padstow (0841) 520727
Fax (0841) 521163
Telex 457959 TGS

A traditional seaside hotel, 400 yards from a sandy beach with rock pools at low tide. It has a sheltered sunken garden for sun-bathing, and an indoor heated pool. The National Trust coastal footpath is nearby; maps of walks are provided by the hotel. Also close by are Trevose golf course, sea fishing and boat trips, tennis, surfing and riding. The hotel has been run for 24 years by Ted and Barbara Barlow and has many devoted regular visitors. Its decor – brick fireplaces, chintzy furniture and patterned carpets – is conventionally English, as is the food. Bedrooms, many with sea views, have light colour-schemes and white fitted furniture; some have a balcony. Men are expected to wear a jacket and tie for dinner. Not a hotel for those in search of elegance or *haute cuisine*, but a friendly, welcoming place for a family holiday. More reports please.

Open Mar–Nov.
Rooms 3 suites (1 on ground floor), 32 double, 8 single – all with bath, shower, telephone, radio, TV and baby-listening. 4 self-catering flats in grounds.
Facilities Lift, ramps. 2 lounges, cocktail bar, bridge room, restaurant; children's den, snooker room, indoor heated swimming pool, whirlpool bath. 3-acre grounds. Sandy beach 400 yds. Golf, tennis, riding nearby.
Location Avoid Bodmin and Wadebridge. From Padstow follow signs to St Merryn, then Constantine Bay.
Restrictions No smoking in dining room. No children under 3 in dining room. Dogs at management's discretion; not in public rooms.
Credit card Access (restaurant only).
Terms Dinner, B&B £42–£69.50. Set lunch £3.95, dinner £14.95; full alc £20.75. 1-night bookings sometimes refused.
Service/tipping: "No service charge; tips at guests' discretion."

CORFE CASTLE Dorset — Map 2

Mortons House Hotel [GFG] — *Tel* (0929) 480988
45 East Street
Corfe Castle BH20 5EE

A new entry, an impressive E-shaped Elizabethan stone manor house, with 17th- and 20th-century additions, just off the main street on a hilltop in "the prettiest of Dorset villages". It has gables, mullioned windows, formal walled gardens, and fine views of the castle and the Purbeck Hills. "The entrance hall is huge and stone-flagged, off it is a large dark-panelled and comfortably furnished drawing room; a fire blazed in the vast fireplace. There is a delightful library on the first floor. Our bedroom in the new wing – a dash through the snow, in February – was not large, but well furnished with comfortable beds and expensive chintzy fabrics; it had a splendid view of Corfe Castle. The bathroom gleamed with cleanliness. Dinner – modern British cooking – was superb, all the dishes immensely pretty, the main course accompanied by side plates with lots of crisp vegetables, excellent desserts; a good selection of wines, some very reasonably priced. The chef, Tim Hughes, previously worked with Marco White at the rosetted restaurant *Harvey's* in London. Breakfast included freshly squeezed orange juice, and a wonderful plate of mixed fruit arranged with as much delicacy and precision as the dishes of the night before. The atmosphere was lovely: quiet, peaceful, caring." (*RAE*) There are two bedrooms with a spa bath; one also has a four-poster. Some of Dorset's finest coast is within an easy drive.

Open All year.
Rooms 3 suites, 14 double – all with bath (16 also have shower; 2 have spa bath), telephone, radio, TV and baby-listening.
Facilities Lounge, bar, restaurant, 2 private dining rooms, conference room. 1-acre garden.
Location In village on A351. Carpark.
Restrictions Not suitable for ♿. No dogs in public rooms.

Credit cards Access, Visa.
Terms [1989 rates] B&B £30–£70. Set lunch £10–£13, dinner £19–£22; full alc £28. Weekend breaks. Reduced rates for children sharing parents' room; special meals.
Service/tipping: "Staff paid above-average wage and would never solicit a tip. However if guests wish to express satisfaction for exceptional service or food it is up to them."

CRANBROOK Kent — Map 3

The Old Cloth Hall — *Tel* Cranbrook (0580) 712220
Cranbrook TN17 3NR

Elizabethan house in "superb" 13-acre gardens noted for rhododendrons and azaleas (open to the public in May and June as part of National Gardens Scheme) with unheated swimming pool and tennis court. Recommended for "home-from-home" atmosphere, good cooking, comfortable accommodation. Only three bedrooms, one with magnificent six-foot-wide four-poster, all with bath and/or shower. B&B double £70–£80. Set dinner £20. New nomination. More reports please.

CRANTOCK Cornwall — Map 1

Crantock Bay Hotel — *Tel* Crantock (0637) 830229
Crantock, Newquay TR8 5SE

This traditional seaside hotel near an old village with an ancient church and thatched cottages has been run for many years by David and Brenda Eyles. It has a stunning and quiet setting facing the Atlantic on the Cornish coast, 200 yards from a sandy beach with rockpools round the edge. There are six golf courses nearby; Newquay is the nearest big town. Food is conventionally English. It's the the sort of friendly place that welcomes your children and your dogs; bedrooms are geared for families and have an intercom system for baby-listening; plenty of entertainments are organised in season. Many guests have been visiting the hotel regularly for years. This year the Eyles have built a large extension with an indoor swimming pool with spa bath, a toddlers' pool, sauna, exercise room and sun patio; the dining room and bar lounge have been extended and redecorated. Because of the new facilities the hotel's season has been extended and a variety of new off-season packages introduced. More reports please.

Open Mar–Nov.
Rooms 27 double, 9 single – 35 with bath and shower, 1 with shower, all with radio, TV, tea-making facilities and baby-listening.
Facilities 2 lounges (1 no-smoking), bar lounge, games room, 2 restaurant areas; indoor swimming pool, exercise room; dancing, table tennis, bar billiards, slide shows, children's parties 2-3 nights a week. 4½-acre grounds with tennis court, putting green, croquet, children's play area. Sea with sandy beach and safe bathing (lifeguard service) 200 yards; tennis, riding, golf nearby.
Location On West Pentire headland, 1 m beyond Crantock; 5 m SW of Newquay. Guests met by arrangement at Newquay and Truro stations.
Restrictions No smoking in dining room. No dogs in public rooms.
Credit cards All major cards accepted.
Terms (No service charge) Dinner, B&B £20–£38.50. Bar lunch from £1.50, set dinner £9.75. 5-day packages; bargain breaks in spring and autumn; half term rates. Reduced rates and special meals for children.

Service/tipping: "We are against a service charge. However, as visitors do tend to show their 'appreciation', I hold a fund distributed to the staff at the end of the summer. An explanatory note appears in bedrooms."

CROYDE Devon — Map 1

The Whiteleaf at Croyde [GFG] — *Tel* Croyde (0271) 890266
Croyde, Nr Braunton EX33 1PN

Croyde is an attractive seaside village with thatched, colour-washed cottages. The *Whiteleaf,* which had its first Guide entry last year, is on the outskirts, in a large garden surrounded by bungalows; the path down to the sweeping sandy beach is through thirties-type wooden chalets. Last year our inspector wrote: "The owners, David and Florence Wallington, describe it as a guest house which is misleading as it offers more in terms of comfort and service. The house itself lacks charm, as does its situation, but we were won over by the hospitality, accommodation and food. We (a family with two small boys) were welcomed most warmly. Bedrooms, though not elegantly furnished, had plenty of storage space, good beds, well-stocked fridge, comfortable little chairs and hair-drier. Good big towels and plenty of extras in the bathroom. The rooms were delightfully warm and would have served as a cosy refuge had fellow guests in the not very large lounge been uncongenial. The dining room is large with well- spaced tables and a view of the garden. Food is David Wallington's real strength. His British-style menus (plenty of choice) show invention and imagination, though he claims to have had no formal chef's training. There is a well-chosen, wide-ranging wine list with a good selection of half-bottles. The full English breakfast, too, was excellent, and included fresh orange juice, and vast quantities of toasted home-made bread and marmalade. The comforts, attention to detail and high standards of service are a triumph in an otherwise gastronomic desert." David Wallington writes, "Our aim is to cater for our guests in a welcoming and relaxing atmosphere. There are no rules and notices and we seem to appeal mainly to the 'Middletons' – middle-aged, middle income, middle class." The North Devon Coastal Path is easily accessible from the hotel. More reports please.

Open All year. Closed 2 weeks Jan, Apr, and July.
Rooms 5 double – all with bath and/or shower, telephone, radio, TV, tea-making facilities and baby-listening.
Facilities Lounge, bar, dining room. ½-acre grounds. Footpath to Croyde beach with sand, rocks, surfing and bathing (life-guard in season).
Location On beach, 3 minutes from village.
Restrictions Not suitable for ♿. No dogs in public rooms.
Credit cards Access, Visa.
Terms B&B £19.50–£27; dinner, B&B £29.50–£42. Set dinner £12.50. Off-season breaks; 3- and 7-night rates; Christmas and New Year packages. 1-night bookings sometimes refused. 50% reduction for children sharing parents' room and taking meals.

Traveller's tale *It used to be a good hotel, but that proves nothing – I used to be a good boy.*
Mark Twain

CRUDWELL Wiltshire — Map 2

Crudwell Court Hotel and Restaurant
Crudwell, Nr Malmesbury
SN16 9EP

Tel Crudwell (066 67) 7194 and 554
Fax (066 67) 7853

"We much enjoyed our two-day winter break. We arrived late but were given a warm and courteous welcome. Dinner was a pleasant experience on both nights. Local waitresses responded quickly to requests; fresh ingredients were cooked with flair and the hot home-made rolls were delicious. Our large bedroom was well heated, properly lit and comfortable." (*Sandra Howard*) An endorsement of last year's new entry for this 17th-century vicarage, set in large walled gardens, in a peaceful Wiltshire setting. It has been extensively restored by Brian and Susan Howe who bought *Crudwell Court* in a run-down condition at the beginning of 1987. The 15 bedrooms are individually decorated with pastel colours and Sanderson fabrics; furniture is mostly modern, with some antiques; there are ornaments and original paintings, all contributing to a genuine country house atmosphere – "restful, calm and unfussy". Rooms on the ground and first floors are large and high-ceilinged, those on the second, up a narrow staircase, are smaller (and cheaper), with lovely views over the surrounding trees and farmland. The Howes have built up a good local restaurant trade thanks to the "very competent and reasonably priced" cooking; Paul Lawrence has now joined them as chef to cope with the increased business. There is plenty of choice on the menu; the price of the main course includes a starter and dessert. "The food is interesting without being over-elaborate," our inspector wrote last year. "The wine list is surprisingly long." Only niggles: the breakfast toast continues to be criticised and "bath towels were on the minimal side".

Open All year.
Rooms 14 double, 1 single – all with bath and/or shower, telephone, radio, TV, tea-making facilities and baby-listening.
Facilities 2 lounges, dining room. Functions facilities. 3-acre garden with heated swimming pool and croquet. River fishing and lake with water sports nearby.
Location On A429, 3 m N of Malmesbury. Front rooms double glazed. Hotel is on green opposite *Plough* pub.
Restrictions Not suitable for ♿. No dogs in public rooms.
Credit cards All major cards accepted.
Terms (No service charge) B&B: single £40–£60, double £70–£90; Set lunch £12 (snack menu also available), dinner approx £16. Off-season 2- and 3-day breaks; 3-day Christmas package. Reduced rates for children sharing parents' room.
Service/tipping: "No service charge. Tips are gratefully received and shared among all staff according to hours worked."

DALLINGTON Sussex — Map 3

Little Byres [GFG]
Christmas Farm, Battle Road
Dallington, Heathfield TH21 9LE

Tel Brightling (042 482) 230

A "restaurant with chalets" on farm at edge of village in lovely countryside, run by young and "most amiable" Chris and Evelyn Davis. Food – French provincial and modern British – served in "impressively simple" 200-year-old spacious beamed and raftered barn, is "outstanding and beautifully presented". Accommodation in half-timbered and prettily furnished outbuildings fairly basic, but comfortable beds and very good breakfasts. 5 rooms, all with shower. B&B double £35–£45; full alc £23. 2 rather more luxurious rooms planned for 1990. New nomination. More reports please.

DEDHAM Essex **Map 3**

Dedham Hall *Tel* Colchester (0206) 323027
Dedham, Nr Colchester CO7 6AD

"Even better than expectations – as good as staying in a comfy, relaxed private house. *Exceptional* breakfast and wholesome dinner. Much nicer than a conventional hotel, and the Slingos are delightful hosts." (*MJ Richardson*) *Dedham Hall* is a pink-washed house in five-acre grounds with a carp pond, just outside the village of Dedham in the heart of Constable country. The river Stour is a short stroll away, and Flatford Mill two miles further on. The house has changed little in outward appearance since it was built in 1400. Mr and Mrs Slingo run a mixture of farm, guest house and, periodically, a residential art school, with dedication. Over the years readers have appreciated the tranquil setting, the comfortable public rooms and spacious, pretty and well-furnished bedrooms – some in converted barns – as well as the home-like atmosphere and food: "everything home-grown, home-reared and home-cooked" – there is no choice until the pudding stage. This year a reader points out that though the Slingos do not accept guests' pets they themselves have two dogs and several cats which are very much in evidence in the sitting room and kitchen.

Open 1 Mar–20 Dec. Closed Christmas and New Year. Restaurant closed for lunch and on Wed.
Rooms 12 double, 2 single – all with bath and/or shower (10 have WC), and tea-making facilities. 7 in converted buildings in yard.
Facilities 2 lounges with TV, bar, 2 dining rooms. 6-acre grounds; studio. River Stour within yards, coarse fishing, boating.
Location Just outside village, but 200 yds from road, so quiet.
Restrictions Not suitable for ♿. Not suitable for children. No dogs.
Credit cards None accepted.
Terms (No service charge) B&B: single £22–£34, double £33–£51. Set dinner £12.50. Painting courses.
Service/tipping: "We make no compulsory charge, but if customers wish to show appreciation, we are happy to distribute tips to the staff."

Maison Talbooth [GFG] *Tel* Colchester (0206) 322367
Stratford Road, Dedham *Fax* (0206) 322752
Colchester CO7 6HN *Telex* 987083 LETALB

Dedham Vale Hotel *Tel* Colchester (0206) 322273
Stratford Road, Dedham *Fax* (0206) 322752
Colchester CO7 6HW *Telex* 987083 LETALB

The entrepreneurial Milsom family – Gerald, with sons David and Paul – run three very attractively situated establishments on or close to the banks of the Stour in Dedham, at which they offer a "Mix 'n Match" stay.

You can sleep in either *Maison Talbooth* or *Dedham Vale*, but the former only serves breakfast; for other meals, residents must take themselves to *Dedham Vale*, half a mile up the road, or to another Milsom offspring, *Le Talbooth*, a quarter of a mile further on. *Le Talbooth*'s chef is now Steven Blake, formerly of the *Meridien*, Piccadilly, in London. *Maison Talbooth* is a luxuriously equipped Victorian house, its ten outsize bedrooms are all kitted out with virtually every pampering extra your imagination can run to; the beds are king-size and the bathrooms are often as opulent as the bedrooms. "I would never have thought it possible to sit in a hot-tub whirlpool, sipping champagne and looking out over exquisite English countryside." "First-floor bedroom splendid, and the beautifully designed and proportioned sitting room is surely one of the most elegant in any British hotel."

Dedham Vale is also a fully modernised Victorian mansion, set in three acres of landscaped garden, close by – but out of earshot of – the A12. The bedrooms are a bit smaller than at *Maison Talbooth*, and the prices considerably lower, but they are furnished with almost as many extras as those at the senior house. Readers appreciate its country-house informal style, pleasant furnishing and friendly service. Sadly the consensus on the meals in the hotel's pretty conservatory-like rôtisserie, *Terrace Restaurant*, is that they are not as good as the accommodation. Food at *Le Talbooth*, too, has come in for criticism this year.

The Pier at Harwich (*tel* (0255 241212), yet another of Gerald Milsom's enterprises, for long a praised restaurant – fish and chips downstairs, *soigné* menu upstairs – has six well-equipped, though less lavish, bedrooms with lovely views of the Stour and Orwell estuaries and the activities of the bustling port. B&B double is £50 to £60. We'd be glad of reports on any of these branches of the Milsom enterprise.

Maison Talbooth
Open All year.
Rooms 4 suites, 6 double – all with bath (2 also with shower), telephone, TV and baby-listening. 5 ground-floor rooms.
Facilities Large lounge. The hotel has 2-acre grounds, the restaurant 3 acres on the banks of the river Stour; fishing. 2 yachts for hire.
Location Off A12. 6 m NE of Colchester. From A12, about 6 m out of Colchester, take Stratford St Mary–Dedham road. After about 1 m take second right-hand turning to Dedham. *Maison Talbooth* is about 1 m down the road on right.
Restriction No dogs.
Credit cards Access, Visa.
Terms (Excluding 10% service charge) B&B (continental): single £75, double £95, suite £125. Cooked breakfast £5. Set lunch at *Le Talbooth* £16–£17 (packed lunch available); full alc £40.00 Sailing holidays May-Sept (book a month in advance). 1-night bookings not accepted for weekends; min 3 nights at Christmas and bank holidays. Reduced rates for children sharing parents' room; special meals.

Dedham Vale Hotel
Open All year.
Rooms 1 suite, 5 double – all with bath, telephone, radio TV, baby-listening.
Facilities Drawing room, bar, restaurant; function facilities. 3-acre grounds; river 100 yards; fishing and sailing locally.
Location 7 m NE of Colchester on A12.
Restrictions Not suitable for ♿. No dogs.
Credit cards Access, Visa.
Terms (Excluding 10% service charge) B&B (continental): single £70, double £80, suite £100. English breakfast £5. Full alc £30. 1-night bookings refused for weekend. Reduced rates and special meals for children.

DIDDLEBURY Shropshire — Map 1

The Glebe Farm — *Tel* Munslow (058 476) 221
Diddlebury, Craven Arms
SY7 9DH

"Truly a delight to stay in the home of the Wilkes family; you are welcomed as a friend and cosseted throughout your stay. The food is excellent, there being a choice of main course, several starters and sweets each evening. All the produce is local; the vegetables served are often from their newly organic garden. A most peaceful setting in an idyllic hamlet; the quality of life here is supreme." "The other guests were convivial, and Mr and Mrs Wilkes encouraged us all to meet and talk." As in previous years, there is praise for this modestly priced half-timbered Elizabethan farmhouse, with oak beams and flagstones, in a pretty garden with a stream, on a working farm. It is near the Saxon village church with its fortified tower (and bell which strikes throughout the night!); well situated for exploring Housman country and the Welsh Marches. There are only six bedrooms, three of which have shower and loo fitted into the old structure. The "simple but generous" dinner is served at 7.45 pm; wine and drinks are reasonably priced; vegetarians are catered for. A full English breakfast is served between 8.30 and 9 am. The private facilities in the garden cottage are rather cramped, and last year we warned that "some of the walls are paper thin"; Mrs Wilkes writes: "unfortunately our house 'forbids' us to do anything about this". (*PA Morgan, Walter Cottingham; also Richard and Elizabeth-Ann Pyle*)

Open Early Mar–Nov. Closed 10 days early June. Dining room closed Mon evening and sometimes on Tue.
Rooms 5 double, 1 single – 3 with shower, all with tea-making facilities. 3 in cottage in garden.
Facilities Sitting room, bar with TV, dining room. 1-acre garden. Fishing, riding, walking nearby.
Location E of B4368, 4 m NE of Craven Arms.
Restrictions Not suitable for ♿. No children under 10. No dogs.
Credit cards None accepted.
Terms B&B (English) £17–£23; dinner, B&B £27.95–£33.95. Set dinner £11.20. Mid-week breaks off-season. Reductions for children.
Service/tipping: "As owners we do not expect a tip. Any gratuities are divided equally among the staff."

DOCKING Norfolk — Map 3

Holland House — *Tel* Docking (048 58) 295
Chequers Street, Docking
Nr King's Lynn PE31 8LH

Mrs Margaret Robinson's extremely inexpensive B&B in a large Grade II listed Georgian house in a Norfolk village entered the Guide last year with an italicised entry; it is warmly endorsed this year, "Everywhere warm and immaculate; our double bedroom was spacious, with comfortable bed, small couch and armchair, flowers and ornaments. Bathrooms spotlessly clean, the whole house welcoming and the atmosphere tranquil and relaxing." (*Vivienne and David Draper*) An inspector adds, "*Holland House* feels like a home and is filled with solid family furniture; the decor is serviceable rather than elegant. Huge choice of drinks sachets in the bedroom, and a jug of fresh milk. Breakfast, continental or English, is ordered the night before, but we changed our minds *and* came down early – and were greeted with smiles. The cooked breakfast, served in a squarish, beautifully proportioned room, included scrambled eggs as good as at home, bacon, mushrooms, rather average sausages. Very good value indeed." Mrs Robinson never accepts more than six people at one time; guests have access to the small walled garden.

Open All year except 2 weeks Christmas/New Year.
Rooms 3 double, 2 single – 1 with shower, all with TV and tea-making facilities.
Facilities Lounge, breakfast room. Small walled garden.
Location In village centre but little traffic at night.
Restrictions Not suitable for ♿. No dogs in public rooms.
Credit cards None accepted.
Terms B&B: continental £12, English £14. (No restaurant.)
Service/tipping: "Tips not expected, occasionally offered, and only accepted to avoid giving offence."

DORCHESTER Dorset — Map 2

Casterbridge Hotel — *Tel* Dorchester (0305) 64043
49 High East Street
Dorchester DT1 1HU

Old hotel in Hardy's "Casterbridge"; central, so front rooms can be noisy. Liked for the friendly welcome from Stuart Turner and his staff and the "excellent and generous breakfasts". Rooms vary in size: some are said to be too small for comfort, ditto the bathrooms. No restaurant, but two well-appointed public rooms, and a conservatory where tea is served in summer. 15 rooms, all with private facilities. B&B: double £40–£48. More reports needed.

DORCHESTER-UPON-THAMES Oxfordshire — Map 2

The George Hotel [GFG] — *Tel* Oxford (0865) 340404
High Street
Dorchester-on-Thames OX9 8HH

Ancient coaching inn with black-and-white facade in tiny village with enormous abbey, once a 12th-century Augustinian priory, also many antique shops. "The glory of the interior is the two dining rooms with heavily beamed and raftered ceiling and brick walls, stylish in best Olde English tradition"; a promising new chef arrived in spring 1989. Service friendly. 17 comfortable, traditionally furnished bedrooms, some beamed, 2 with four-poster, all with private facilities, divided between main house and outbuildings. Closed Christmas. B&B (English) double £68–£90. Set dinner £18.50. New nomination. More reports please.

Traveller's tale *In Zermatt recently we went to the best restaurant in town. On being given the credit card voucher to sign with the total left open, I enquired whether or not service was included. The waiter replied: "Yes, sir, we do include the service charge, but not the tips."*

DORRINGTON Shropshire — Map 4

Country Friends [GFG] *Tel* Dorrington (074 373) 707
Dorrington SY5 7JD

A long-established restaurant is warmly nominated for inclusion in the Guide, "Sybaritic short stays at supermarket prices. Stylish but business-like rooms at £13–£18 per person [1989] for bed and no-choice breakfast of scrambled eggs and smoked salmon, brioche and Bucks Fizz. Top-class restaurant, with very reasonably priced à la carte menu, plus a table d'hôte at £12.50. This is not a house-party hotel and you must not arrive expecting conviviality. It is an unabashed restaurant with rooms. The owners, Charles and Pauline Whittaker, are both chefs and not really interested in people wishing to stay without dining. The main building is large, half-timbered, and dates from the 16th to 19th centuries. The annexe Coach House at present holds three of the four guest bedrooms. The main house has double glazing, the annexe doesn't. But a by-pass is planned; and the traffic noise isn't too bad at present. Glorious walking country all around in hilly, thinly populated Shropshire." The bedrooms are newly decorated, fresh and bright; one has a shower *en suite*, two share a stylish bathroom; all are individually furnished – modern design, wall-to-wall thick carpets, antique furniture. Food is "modern English and light; portions not large. Ridiculously cheap and unusually good bar food served at lunch and on quiet evenings. Very nice owners." (*CS-K*)

Open All year except last week July, first week Aug, last week Oct. Closed Sun and Mon, and Christmas.
Rooms 4 double – 1 with shower, all with tea-making facilities. 3 in annexe across drive.
Facilities Lounge bar, dining room. ¼-acre grounds.
Location 6 m S of Shrewsbury. On A49. 1 room double-glazed.
Restrictions Not suitable for ♿. No smoking in dining room. No dogs.
Credit cards Amex, Diners, Visa.
Terms (No service charge) B&B double £26–£36. Set lunch/dinner £12.50; full alc £20.
Service/tipping: "No policy on tipping. The sooner the practice finishes the better it will be."

DREWSTEIGNTON Devon — Map 1

Hunts Tor House [GFG] *Tel* Drewsteignton (0647) 21228
Drewsteignton EX6 6QW

Drewsteignton is a tiny picture-book village below Lutyens' Castle Drogo, with a Norman church and thatched houses. *Hunts Tor*, new to the Guide this year, is extraordinary in that the original building, built in about 1640, was later extended on all sides so that the present large square house encloses the original building. At the heart of the house is a small low-ceilinged, heavily beamed room, wood everywhere, which is one of the two dining rooms; a few steps away are the lounge and the larger dining room, which belong to the extension. The four bedrooms on the first floor are stylish, but simple – no telephone, TV etc, but new, bright and clean, with an attractive, restrained colour scheme, plenty of storage space, good lights, and private facilities. The house is full of Victorian and Edwardian furniture inherited from the previous owners, to which the present owner, Chris Harrison, who converted *Hunts Tor* into a guest house, has added Art Deco pottery and other collector's items; the resulting decor is "very turn of the century". Not really a house-party atmosphere: guests eat at a communal table in the smaller dining room only if they are very few; there are four tables for separate dining in the other. Dinner is at 7.30, served by Chris Harrison; his wife, Sue, who trained with Keith Floyd, cooks the four-course no-choice meal (the fourth course is cheese). Her style is "homely, quite modern, with a tendency to the healthy. The wine list is recited to guests before dinner. Breakfast excellent, including freshly squeezed orange juice and home-made jam and marmalade. Exceptionally nice owners." "The charming owners try to provide clean, comfortable and interesting surroundings with delicious meals – and succeed." The Harrisons do not take more than eight guests at one time. Dinner is for residents only. (*CS-K, GL Collier*)

Open Feb–end Nov. Dining room closed for lunch.
Rooms 4 double – all with bath.
Facilities Lounge, bar/dining room, dining room. River Teign nearby, with fishing.
Location In village which is 3 m N of Moretonhampstead.
Restrictions Not suitable for ♿. No children under 14. No dogs in dining room.
Credit cards None accepted.
Terms B&B £18–£38, dinner, B&B £30.50–£50.50.
Service/tipping: "No tips expected, but we add an optional 10p per person for the Devon Wildlife Trust."

The Old Inn [GFG] *Tel* Drewsteignton (0647) 21276
The Square
Drewsteignton EX6 6QR

A restaurant-with-rooms in a 300-year-old building in the square, owned and run by Vivien and Rose Chapman, mother and daughter. *The Old Inn* is "inexpensive, unpretentious and in very good taste", with good-sized, attractively decorated bedrooms; no room has private facilities but there are hand-basins with plenty of hot water; rooms are well lit and have good beds with duvet. There is a menu with a limited choice which changes every day according to the season. Rose Chapman explains each dish; you are called to the table when your food is ready. Diners in the "lovely dining room with huge log fire", continue to praise "Rose Chapman's commitment to fresh food." "English country style cooking, everything is local and absolutely fresh, portions are large, vegetables well cooked. Both mother and daughter Chapman are much in evidence and very friendly. Willing, not always very experienced, local girls help." "A real walkers' breakfast, complete with yoghurt and home-made pork and apple sausages – more than ordinary mortals could possible eat. Friendly service, excellent food, and so *cheap*". " (*ULP, Ruth Bloom, and others*) Rose Chapman writes, "We are still a straightforward restaurant offering fresh local food and simple, basic accommodation. We don't have the time or inclination to be flashy, although we are keen that our guests should feel at home and comfortable. The building is a cross between a cottage and a defrocked pub; it is an extension of our home and can in no way be described as a hotel. The atmosphere is informal and, we think, in keeping with the building, the surrounding area and our personal interest in caring for our guests."

Open All year except Christmas and Feb. Restaurant closed Mon and for lunch.
Rooms 4 double, 1 single – all with tea-making facilities.
Facilities Bar, lounge, restaurant. Fishing nearby.
Location In village square. Parking.
Restrictions Not suitable for ♿. No smoking in the restaurant. No small children in restaurant. No dogs in public rooms.
Credit card Access.
Terms B&B £13.50. Set dinner £16. 1-night bookings refused for Easter and bank holidays. Baby in cot free; child in parents' room half-price; special meals by arrangement.
Service/tipping: "We do not charge for service or expect tips."

DULVERTON Somerset — Map 1

Ashwick Country House Hotel and Restaurant [GFG] — *Tel* Dulverton (0398) 23868
Dulverton TA22 9QD

Ashwick House is a small Edwardian country house in a "delightful and quiet" situation, 900 feet up in the Exmoor National Park in six-acre grounds with sweeping lawns, mature trees, water-gardens and lily ponds, overlooking the valley of the river Barle. The hall, with long broad gallery and log fire, still has the original William Morris wallpaper; the lounge and library – decorated in purple – are considered by some "particularly stylish", by others "funereal". Bedrooms are "attractively decorated, bright, with good lighting" and equipped with more than the usual extras including TV with in-house films, changed every day, tape recorder, electronic scales "which announce your weight with malicious delight after the *Ashwick* dinner", magazines, mini-bar and fresh flowers." The one called *Ash* is particularly recommended. For years *Ashwick House* was run by Mr and Mrs Sherwood and their son. Sadly, Mr Sherwood senior died at the end of 1988; his wife and son are carrying on the business. "They do a magnificent job. Service could not be faulted." (*BA Orman*) Mr Sherwood junior is now the chef, continuing the *Ashwick* style of English home cooking: a four-course meal with no choice of main course, and an emphasis on good local produce. Generous breakfasts include freshly squeezed apple juice and good brown toast. Guests are expected to dine in. More reports please.

Open All year.
Rooms 6 double – all with bath, shower, radio, TV; telephone on request.
Facilities Hall, lounge, library, bar, dining room. 6-acre grounds with 2 ponds and croquet.
Location 2½ m NW of Dulverton. Take the B3223 Exford–Lynton road. ½ m after cattle grid hotel signpost directs you left.
Restrictions Not suitable for ♿. No children under 8. No dogs.
Credit cards None accepted.
Terms Dinner, B&B £34.75–£58. £9 added for single occupancy. Set Sun lunch £9.75, set dinner £16.75. Special rates for 2 or 5 nights. 1-night bookings generally refused over bank holidays.
Service/tipping: "No service charge added. We do not expect tips."

> Most hotels have reduced rates out of season and for children, and some British hotels offer "mini-break" rates throughout the year. If you are staying more than one night, it is always worth asking about special terms.

EASINGTON Cleveland **Map 4**

Grinkle Park Hotel *Tel* Guisborough (0287) 40515
Easington
Saltburn-by-the-Sea
TS13 4UB

A fine stone Victorian house in extensive grounds and lawns with a lake, approached by a long drive of rhododendrons. It has been modernised and redecorated by Bass plc to a high standard. There are comfortable lounges and a fine staircase with a half-landing to a huge stained-glass window. Bedrooms are individually decorated: the most elegant, on the first floor, with four-posters, are named after flowers; those on the second floor are simpler and called after moorland birds. All are well appointed with good bathrooms. The dining room is formal in decor, with fresh posies of flowers, quality china, silver and glass, and tables set well apart. It serves "good sound Yorkshire fare at reasonable prices" with the emphasis on local supplies. Game comes from the estate, fish from the fishing village nearby. Mrs Atkinson, who lives on the estate, makes calorific desserts for the trolley. There is an English cheeseboard, plenty of coffee and an affordable house wine. "Service is good. The young head waiter is correct; local girls exude friendly warmth, smiles, willingness to please. Breakfast is what you'd expect from a good Northern hotel – huge fry-up if you want it; kippers oak-smoked." Only qualification: to keep solvent *Grinkle Park* has frequent conferences and functions; holiday guests should discuss accommodation carefully. More reports please.

Open All year.
Rooms 13 double, 7 single – all with bath and/or shower, telephone, TV, tea-making facilities and baby-listening.
Facilities 2 lounges, bar, billiard room, dining room; conference/functions facilities. 35-acre grounds with lake, tennis, croquet. Sea 4 m with safe bathing; fishing, sailing, climbing, walking, shooting nearby.
Location 2 m E of Loftus. Turn N towards Grinkle off A171 Whitby road.
Restrictions Not suitable for ♿. No dogs in public rooms.
Credit cards All major cards accepted.
Terms [1989 rates] B&B (English): single £51.50, double £68–£76. Set lunch £8.95, dinner £13.95; full alc £18; bar meals available. Weekend breaks; 5- and 7-day breaks.
Service/tipping: "Tips at guests' discretion; divided between all staff."

EAST BUCKLAND Devon **Map 1**

Lower Pitt Restaurant and Guest House [GFG] *Tel* Filleigh (059 86) 243
East Buckland, Barnstaple
EX32 0TD

"Fully support this entry. A real find; the Lyons could not have been more helpful and friendly." "Staff friendly and highly professional. Menu thoughtfully selected and carefully prepared – including breakfast, so often a let-down." "Very quiet and peaceful, an ideal spot for walkers; excellent value for money." *Lower Pitt Manor*, owned and run by Suzanne and Jerome Lyons, is a 16th-century white-washed stone farmhouse, once two cottages, now a popular restaurant-with-rooms, in the fold of a hillside in a modest hamlet, surrounded by the walled fields of South

Exmoor. It has a strong following among local gourmets who appreciate Mrs Lyons' "honest home cooking – carefully prepared real food served with style". Residents are allowed to choose from the à la carte menu for the dinner, B&B rate. The three small bedrooms are not luxurious, but thoroughly comfortable, with pine furniture, duvets and electric blankets. Readers continue to praise the food and the rooms as well as the welcoming hospitality of the Lyons. There is no residents' sitting room, everyone uses the lounge bar before and after meals and it can get crowded. Tall visitors should observe the injunction to mind their heads when passing through the doorways, a reminder of *Lower Pitt*'s cottage ancestry. (*J Bowes, Peter Curtis, Dr and Mrs Lovejoy; also Sydney Downs*)

Open All year except Christmas and New Year.
Rooms 3 double – 1 with bath and shower, 2 with shower, all with tea-making facilities.
Facilities Lounge/bar, 2 dining rooms. 2-acre grounds with gardens and terrace for drinks. Sandy beaches and North Devon coast within easy reach.
Location 3 m NW of South Molton. Turn off A361 at *Stag's Head*.
Restrictions Not suitable for ♿. No children under 11. No dogs.
Credit cards Access, Visa.
Terms (No service charge) Dinner, B&B £37.50–£40. Full alc £20. Mid-week reductions (3 nights min).
Service/tipping: "No service charge; tips are at customers' discretion and are divided equally among all staff. As owners, we do not expect a tip."

EAST GRINSTEAD West Sussex — Map 3

Gravetye Manor [GFG]
East Grinstead RH19 4LJ

Tel Sharpthorne (0342) 810567
Fax (0342) 810080
Telex 957239 GRAVTY

An immaculate Elizabethan manor house, with "understated elegance, an exceptional original decor and a cosseting atmosphere". It once belonged to William Robinson, pioneer of the English natural garden, who laid out the beautiful grounds. For the past 33 years – a considerable innings – *Gravetye* has been owned and run by Peter Herbert, recently joined by his son, Leigh Stone Herbert, a graduate of the Roux brothers, who is dubbed chef/*patron;* Mark Raffan is head chef. It has spacious panelled public rooms with fine paintings and fresh flowers, and a renowned restaurant. Bedrooms, all named after trees, are extremely comfortable, with many extras, including good pictures, and books. They vary in size, the best are large with panelling, plenty of storage space and garden views; bathrooms, too, are well supplied. The kitchen uses fruit, vegetables, herbs, spring water and free range eggs from the estate, salmon, venison and duck breasts all smoked in the hotel's own smoke-house, and game obtained locally. "A yardstick to judge all other restaurants by. Consistently high standards. There has been a steady improvement of the food; it is *nouvelle cuisine* kept under very strict control, with no gimmicks. I admire Peter Herbert's courage in banning smoking in the restaurant." "Last year we thought portions rather small. No such complaints this time." (*Jenny Gilbert, B Crymble; also Uwe Kitzinger, and others*) Two persistent niggles, "refusal to take credit cards an eccentric anachronism"; VAT is added to the bills which means that you pay tax on service. One visitor this year found the dining room reserved for a club function and minded having to dine in a small side room. Despite its peaceful setting *Gravetye* is only 20 minutes' drive from Gatwick Airport.

Open All year. Restaurant closed to non-residents on Christmas evening.
Rooms 12 double, 2 single – 12 with bath and shower, 2 with shower, all with telephone, radio, TV and baby-listening.
Facilities 3 sitting rooms, bar, restaurant; private dining room. 30-acre grounds with croquet, trout-fishing.
Location 5 m SW of East Grinstead off B2110 at West Hoathly sign. Glyndebourne 40 mins' drive; Gatwick Airport 9 m.
Restrictions Not suitable for ♿. No smoking in restaurants. No children under 7 except babies. No dogs.
Credit cards None accepted.
Terms [1989 rates] (Excluding VAT) Rooms: single from £70, small double from £85, medium from £105, large from £130. Breakfast: continental £5, English alc. Set lunch £15, dinner £19; full alc £35. 1-night bookings refused Sat except winter.
Service/tipping: "Prices include service; our staff do not expect tips.

EAST STOKE Dorset — Map 2

Kemps Country House Hotel — *Tel* Bindon Abbey (0929) 462563
East Stoke, Wareham BH20 6AL

Kemps featured in earlier editions of the Guide but was omitted last year following a change of ownership. New proprietors, Paul and Gill Warren, have added six bedrooms and done some redecorating. *Robert C Sim* reports, "We booked for only three nights but would have happily stayed longer. The new owners have made worthwhile improvements in decor and housekeeping – daily changes of all towels and unobtrusive cleaning of rooms. Our room in the main building was spacious, with comfortable beds and plenty of hanging space. It faced the A352 but traffic noise did not bother us (we are light sleepers). Meals are back to the original standard, if not better; they appeared to have improved the range of their suppliers, particularly of vegetables. Desserts were excellent but a slimmer's nightmare. Breakfasts were good." Other readers, too, consider it "excellent value". Only niggles: "Dinner good but portions far too large." "We could have done with a chair in the bathroom." (*RAL Ogston, J Bickerdike, and others*)

Open All year except Christmas.
Rooms 14 double, 1 single – 14 with bath and/or shower, 2 with jacuzzi, all with telephone, TV, tea-making facilities and baby-listening. 4 in converted barn 15 yds from house; 10 ground-floor rooms.
Facilities Lounge, bar, study, restaurant. 1½-acre landscaped garden.
Location On A352 between Wareham and Wool.
Restrictions No children under 7 in dining room for dinner (supper at 6 pm). No dogs.
Credit cards All major cards accepted.
Terms B&B £28.50–£38.50; dinner, B&B £38.50–£51.50. Set lunch £6.95, dinner £12.95; full alc £18. 2-night winter breaks. Reduced rates for children sharing parents' room.
Service/tipping: "We do not charge for service. Tips at customers' discretion." .

> Important reminder: terms printed must be regarded as a rough guide only to the size of the bill to be expected at the end of your stay. For latest tariffs, check when booking.

ELTERWATER Cumbria — Map 4

Eltermere Country House Hotel *Tel* Langdale (096 67) 207
Elterwater, Nr Ambleside LA22 9HY

An unsophisticated, clean and comfortable hotel in listed building in 2-acre grounds on edge of small village four miles from Ambleside. "Idyllic", quiet setting 200 yards from head of Elterwater (but no easy access), with hills all around and good walking from the front door. Dinner at 7–7.30 pm; English-style cooking with limited choice; generous portions for hungry fell-walkers. Recommended for friendly helpful proprietors and reasonable rates. Closed last 2 weeks Dec, first 2 weeks Jan. 15 double rooms with bath or shower, 3 singles. Dinner, B&B double £56–£70. No children under 10; dogs by arrangement. Some criticisms of room furnishings. More reports please.

EVERSHOT Dorset — Map 2

Summer Lodge [GFG] *Tel* Evershot (0935) 83424
Evershot DT2 0JR

"Delightful country house with excellent food, efficient cheerful staff, charming host and, Oh! those small, meaningful extras that cost so little but mean so much." "We keep going back. The Corbetts' personalities and the continuing high standards stop it being 'just another hotel'. We stayed in one of the six new bedrooms in the Coach House; it was beautiful, but we missed the lovely views. Dinner is no longer at a fixed time, a great improvement. Food is still good, though still repetitive; but there is now a choice of starter (soup is offered as an alternative) and of main course." "Drawing room pretty as a picture. Welcoming armchairs and sofas. Bedroom included an amazing compendium of local information. Food faultless; breakfast passed the test admirably too. Genuinely cordial service from everyone." (*Mrs WA Collins, Heather Sharland, Susan Gillotti; also Minda Alexander, Mrs MJ Currie, and many others*) Nigel and Margaret Corbett's country house hotel, the Earl of Ilchester's former dower house in a pretty Dorset village, always draws the warmest of compliments. The comfortable furnishings and attractive decor, Mrs Corbett's "exquisite flower arrangements throughout the house", the remembering of guests' likes and dislikes, the Corbetts' personal farewells to departing guests, are all praised. Nigel Corbett has now taken on a chef, Jeffry Condliffe, and a manager, Michael Ash – "this leaves me freer to meet and talk to our guests which I so enjoy." Such is *Summer Lodge*'s popularity that at busy times things can be a bit disorganised in the dining room; but the many regulars regard the occasional lapses with indulgence. Some visitors have commented sorrowfully that prices, particularly at peak times are now quite high, but there are virtually no extras except drinks, as the half-board rates include tea, after-dinner coffee, full breakfast and newspapers.

Open All year, except first 2 weeks Jan.
Rooms 14 double, 3 single – all with bath (6 also have shower), telephone and tea-making facilities; 6 with TV in coach house annexe. 3 ground-floor rooms.
Facilities Drawing room, TV room, bar, dining room. 4-acre garden with heated swimming pool, croquet and tennis. Golf, fishing, nearby. Sea 12 m.

Location 10 m S of Yeovil. (*Note:* the entrance on village street is for pedestrians only; cars must turn left on reaching village into Summer Lane and then right into drive to house.)
Restrictions No children under 8. No dogs in public rooms.
Credit cards Access, Visa.
Terms B&B (English) £40–£60; dinner, B&B £50–£82.50. Set lunch £12.50, dinner £18.50. 3-day breaks. 1-night bookings sometimes refused for Sat and bank holiday weekends. 40% reduction for children sharing parents' room.
Service/tipping: "Tipping is left entirely to our guests' discretion, and is not necessary as our staff are fully and properly paid."

EVESHAM Hereford and Worcester — Map 2

The Evesham Hotel [GFG]
Cooper's Lane
Evesham WR11 6DA

Tel Evesham (0386) 765566
Fax (0386) 765443
Telex 339342

César award: Utterly acceptable mild eccentricity

A high-spirited hotel run by the Jenkinson family, with jokey brochure, toy ducks and boats in the baths and resident teddy bears. Bedrooms and bathrooms are well equipped and comfortable, service professional and friendly. It enjoys a secluded setting but is only a short walk from the centre of town, and is one of the all too small number of hotels which are genuinely welcoming to children. The restaurant overlooks the large garden with a huge old cedar of Lebanon; chatty dinner menus offer exotic dishes from around the world as well as plain grills; lunch is a reasonably priced buffet or a choice of hot dishes; the extensive and informative wine list "encompasses Afrikanerdom to Zimbabwe". "An informal family-run hotel of the kind so many of us are looking for. It is possible that the younger Jenkinson's humour is sometimes a bit off-beat, but never impolite. Note how all the staff are smiling and helpful. The flowers inside, the pictures in every room, the attention to detail and the excellent food: no wonder it always seems full, even in winter." (*Michael Schofield*) John Jenkinson writes: "I have tried to behave, but I tend to see the funnier side of situations and it can be difficult to please some people whom the Good Lord has designed without a built-in sense of humour; but most guests, we hope, find the approach relaxing; please apologise to any who don't."

Open All year except 25/26 Dec.
Rooms 1 family, 33 double, 6 single – all with bath and/or shower, telephone, radio, TV, tea-making facilities and baby-listening.
Facilities Bar, lounge, restaurant; small indoor swimming pool. 2½-acre grounds.
Location 5 mins' walk from town centre, across river
Restrictions Not suitable for ♿. No dogs in public rooms.
Credit cards All major cards accepted.
Terms [1989 rates] B&B (English): single £40–£46, double £56–£62, family £80. Buffet lunch £5.50; alc lunch £10–£12, dinner £15 (excluding wine). Off-season breaks. Reduced rates and special meals for children.
Service/tipping: "Service included, as are sheets, light bulbs, etc."

> We get less feedback from smaller and more remote hotels. But we need feedback on all hotels: big and small, far and near, famous and first-timers.

FALMOUTH Cornwall — Map 1

Penmere Manor Hotel
Mongleath Road, Falmouth
TR11 4PN

Tel Falmouth (0326) 211411
Telex 45608

A family hotel in a well-bred Georgian house, a member of the Best Western consortium, run "with calm professionalism" by the Pope family for many years. It is the kind of unpretentious but dependable hotel that families often look for in vain, and its virtues bring it plenty of loyal regulars. Sandy beaches are a mile away. The hotel has five acres of sub-tropical gardens and woodland, a large walled garden sheltering a heated swimming pool, snooker and games rooms, and a new leisure centre "as clean as a delivery room in a maternity ward. The place sparkles. Pool, jacuzzi, sauna, weights and exercise bikes all included in the price. One of the Popes is always available which gives the hotel very much the atmosphere of a friend's large house. Dinner offers an eclectic mix each night; breakfasts are copious." Not a hotel to please all comers; food is not *haute cuisine* and the atmosphere may be too casual for some, but to *aficionados* it is "a thoroughly professional, warm and friendly place". (*Geoff Barratt; also MR Farley*)

Open All year except Christmas.
Rooms 32 double, 7 single – all with bath and/or shower, telephone, radio, TV, tea-making facilities and baby-listening. Some on ground floor.
Facilities 4 lounges, restaurant, games room, snooker room, leisure centre. 5-acre grounds with heated swimming pool, adventure playground. Sandy beach, golf 1 m.
Location 1 m from Falmouth. Turn right 50 yds beyond traffic lights at Penryn bridge signposted Gweek. After ½ m bear left towards Budock and Maenporth. Hotel sign on left after 1 m.
Restrictions No smoking in dining room. No dogs in public rooms.
Credit cards All major cards accepted.
Terms B&B (English): single £37–£42, double £58–£85; dinner, B&B: single £50.50–£56.50, double £85–£115. Set dinner £14.50; full alc £15. No charge for accommodation for children under 15 sharing parents' room.
Service/tipping: "Our staff are well remunerated for the services they give willingly. There is no further obligation on guests."

FAUGH Cumbria — Map 4

The String of Horses Inn
Faugh, Heads Nook
Carlisle CA4 9EG

Tel Hayton (022 870) 297 and 509

Erik and Anne Tasker's exuberant 17th-century pub was omitted last year when some readers found its kitsch and its prices excessive. Others now urge its readmission: "What it lacks in refinement it more than makes up for in generosity and warmth of style. We enjoyed the uninhibited decadence of the furnishings. Everything worked. Staff efficient. Not for snobs." The menu is eclectic; some dishes considered over-elaborate. Closed 24–26 Dec. 14 double rooms with many fancy features including exotic Bonsack baths en suite. Leisure centre and heated swimming pool. B&B double £54–£78. Set dinner £12.95.

Give the Guide positive support. Don't just leave feedback to others.

FLITWICK Bedfordshire — Map 3

Flitwick Manor [GFG]
Church Road, Flitwick MK45 1AE

Tel Flitwick (0525) 712242
Fax (0525) 419422
Telex 825562 FM

A Grade II early 18th-century listed building, approached down an avenue of huge trees, set in a 50-acre park (though only seven acres of well-tended gardens belong to the hotel). Flitwick itself is "not a tremendously inspiring place" but the *Manor* is well out of eyeshot of the village. Readers this year offer conflicting views, though most praise the welcoming, helpful staff. There is a huge, high-ceilinged Gothick lounge "well lit with comfortable seats and an amazingly comprehensive collection of sardine dishes", and a "delightful library, with *real* books". Bedrooms vary considerably; satisfied customers approve the lavish furnishings and numerous extras: flowers, fresh fruit, bath-robe, slippers, shampoos, aftershave. "Marvellous ground-floor suite with beautiful sitting room and views of the grounds". But other rooms are less satisfactory: one reader felt he was charged too much for a small bedroom, another complained of "uncomfortable bedheads, uncomfortably short and narrow bath, no full-length mirror, early-morning dustbin noises. Limited choice of newspaper". *Flitwick Manor* is owned and run by former restaurateurs, Somerset and Hélène Moore, and the restaurant does a busy non-residential trade. Tables are close together, making private conversation difficult. Conferences and functions sometimes impair the service or affect the atmosphere. Meals are a mixture of classic French and modern British, with an emphasis on fish, and a good choice of vegetarian dishes; some readers find them extremely good: "expertly cooked, presented and served"; others are more critical: "vegetables so al dente they were almost raw; service, by chatty local ladies, willing but rather unsophisticated". More reports please.

Open All year except 24–28 Dec.
Rooms 2 suites, 10 double, 3 single – all with bath and/or shower, telephone, radio, TV and baby-listening. 1 suite with spa bath, 1 with sauna. 3 ground-floor rooms, 1 equipped for ♿.
Facilities Drawing room, library, morning room, restaurant; private dining room. 7-acre grounds with lake, tennis, croquet, 12th-century church and helipad; bicycles available. Set in 50-acre park (not hotel's).
Location Take exit 12 from M1, then A5120 towards Bedford. Hotel is on outskirts of Flitwick.
Credit cards Access, Amex, Visa.
Terms [1989 rates] (Service at guests' discretion) B&B: single £65–£125, double £100–£130, suites £150 and £160. Set lunch/dinner £16.50–£27.50. Reduced rates for children sharing parents' room; special meals.

FOSSEBRIDGE Gloucestershire — Map 2

Fossebridge Inn [GFG]
Fossebridge, Nr Cheltenham
GL54 3JS

Tel Fossebridge (0285) 720721

Handsomely proportioned house, part Tudor, part Georgian, in large grounds with lake on banks of river Coln in a steep-sided valley. Recent enterprise self-styled as a "country inn hotel" – a hybrid of a country pub and a country house. Best bedrooms in the main building, with lovely views (but one is small);

cheaper ones in stable annexe. Recently renovated, notable for lovely fabrics. Popular locally for both restaurant and large oak-beamed Bridge Bar which serves similar but cheaper dishes as well as bar food. Meals can be good, especially desserts, but some evidence of portion control; service good, though can be over-pressed in restaurant on Saturday; fewer problems in the bar. Closed 25/26 Dec. B&B double £55–£75. Set meals £18.50, £21.50, £23.50. New nomination. More reports please. (See under Northleach in The Good Food Guide.)

FOWEY Cornwall **Map 1**

Marina Hotel *Tel* Fowey (0726) 833315
The Esplanade, Fowey PL23 1HY

This "very reasonably priced hotel offering excellent value for money, and caring hospitality in an outstanding setting" is introduced to the Guide this year by a Devon hotelier: "The town itself is charming, tumbling down to the water's edge on the Fowey river; it is relatively free of tourist clutter, with minimal traffic, as all vehicles must be left in the carparks on the edge of town. You can drive down the 1-in-6 hill to the hotel to unload your luggage: pre-arrival organisation with David Johns, the proprietor, is essential – unloading in front of the hotel blocks the Esplanade. And the altitude problem is not confined to the streets of Fowey; from the beach at the end of the *Marina*'s small and charming garden to third and top floor there are 101 steps, of which 60 are inside the hotel from the dining room to the top landing. The listed Georgian building, originally built as the summer retreat of the Bishops of Truro, is more like an elegant and well-maintained home than a hotel. It has a spacious entrance lobby, a curved staircase lit from above by an overhead oval window, and an almost semi-circular first-floor landing. Moulded ceilings and arches add a finishing touch. Some bedrooms overlook the river, four of these have a balcony. Furnishing is simple; our rooms had flowery wallpaper and curtains, individual pictures and decorations, firm beds with good linen; towels a little skimpy. Housekeeping of a very high standard. The dining room has a panoramic view and mealtimes are a picture show of riverscapes and boats. There is plenty of choice on the menu and fresh local fish is normally offered; the cooking is slightly variable but soups are good, and desserts good and abundant. Breakfasts nicely cooked; you get what you ordered." (*David Wallington*) More reports please.

Open Mar–Oct inclusive.
Rooms 11 double – all with bath, telephone, radio, TV and baby-listening.
Facilities 2 lounges, bar lounge, dining room. Small walled garden with steps to water; moorings available to guests.
Location 1-way circuit, turn right at start of shops.
Restrictions Not suitable for ♿. No dogs in public rooms.
Credit cards All major cards accepted.
Terms B&B (English) £21–£30. Single room supplement £5. Bar snacks £2–£3; packed lunches available. Set dinner £13; full alc £18. 2-day and weekly breaks. Reduced rates for children sharing parents' room; high tea.
Service/tipping: "No service charge. Tipping at guests' discretion at end of stay; shared by all staff."

GILLAN Cornwall — Map 1

Tregildry Hotel — *Tel* Manaccan (032 623) 378
Gillan, Manaccan TR12 6HG

New to the Guide this year, enthusiastically nominated as "a small, relaxed, unpretentious and carefully renovated hotel, well situated with superb views. Rooms are light and comfortable with exceptionally good bathrooms. Bar and lounge attractive and spacious enough to make even a really wet day enjoyable. Food, on a fixed menu (with limited choice) is much better than routine, especially when accompanied by the unusually good, and comparatively cheap, choice of house wines (Mr Norton was in the wine trade for almost 20 years). This hotel is exceptional value." Mr and Mrs Norton's white-painted family-run hotel stands in a tranquil setting in four acres of grounds with a private footpath to the cove below, which is good for fishing, bathing, windsurfing and boating. Most bedrooms have fine views over the bay or creek.

Open Easter–mid-Oct.
Rooms 10 double – all with bath and/or shower, radio and tea-making facilities; TV and baby-listening on request.
Facilities Bar, lounge, TV room. 4-acre grounds. Private path to beach – bathing, sailing, fishing, windsurfing.
Location 12 m NE of Helston. From A3083 take B3293. Left at New Town St Martin, follow signs to Manaccan, then Gillan. Hotel sign at T junction.
Restrictions Not suitable for ♿. No dogs in public rooms.
Credit cards Access, Visa.
Terms B&B £23–£27; dinner, B&B £28.50–£34. Bar lunch £6.50, set dinner £11.50. 3-day breaks except in high season. 1-night bookings sometimes refused in high season.
Service/tipping: "Tipping not encouraged. If guests leave tips they are distributed to all staff members."

GILLINGHAM Dorset — Map 2

Stock Hill House Hotel [GFG] — *Tel* Gillingham (0747) 823626
Wyke, Gillingham SP8 5NR

"A delightful setting and first-rate comfort. Top quality food and attention to detail from a chef who cares. The day's exertions, be they walking on windy hills or touring the region, are properly balanced by the evening's and night's relaxation. Fresh, perfectly ripe, fruit in the bedroom is a splendid touch, as is the music that comes from Austrian-born Peter Hauser's zither once he has prepared the evening meal. The decor, and the embellishments of the food, show that the Hausers share a touch of whimsy; strange, but not tasteless, antiques surround you, and you eat tiny animals, birds and other exotica hand-made from chocolate, puff-pastry or meringue." Peter and Nita Hauser's Victorian manor house is quietly situated in ten acres of parkland, with old and rare trees and lots of wildlife. Since coming here four years ago they have made many improvements, and all the bedrooms have now been refurbished. They vary in size; the large four-poster room with sofa and armchair, huge bathroom, plenty of storage space, and many extras, is particularly commended. Beds, except the four-poster, have duvets, but you can ask for conventional bedding if you prefer it. Peter Hauser's cooking, always of a high quality, and in earlier days described as Austrian Baroque, has recently become much simpler, concentrating on fresh locally produced ingredients and home-grown herbs and vegetables, but a Viennese accent remains. The wine list is reasonably priced, and readers appreciate the choice on the menu (six starters, six main courses). Men are expected to wear jacket and tie at dinner. The welcoming hospitality and professionalism of the hard-working Hausers, helped by Nita's sister Lorna, and the high standard of accommodation continue to be applauded by many readers. (*A Dearing; also K and J Beal, BA Orman, and others*)

Open All year. Closed Sun evening and Mon.
Rooms 1 suite, 4 double, 2 single – all with bath and/or shower, telephone, radio, TV.
Facilities Foyer with small bar, lounge, breakfast room, restaurant. 10-acre grounds with stream, lake, croquet lawn.
Location On B3081 1½ m from Gillingham, just S of A303.
Restrictions Not suitable for ♿. No smoking in dining and breakfast rooms. No children under 7. No dogs.
Credit cards Access, Visa.
Terms (No service charge) Dinner, B&B: single £70, double £130–£140. Set lunch £18, dinner £25. Mid-week reductions in winter. Reduced rates and special lunches for children.
Service/tipping: "Tipping is between the guest and staff; we are very much against service charges."

GITTISHAM Devon — Map 1

Combe House Hotel — *Tel* Honiton (0404) 42756 and 43560
Gittisham, Nr Honiton EX14 0AD

A grand and historic manor house with five acres of secluded gardens in a 3,500-acre estate not far from Dartmoor. It has one-and-a-half miles of dry fly fishing on the river Otter. *Combe House* has panelled rooms, moulded ceilings, a fine Italian fireplace in one dining room, and a mirrored overmantle in the other, and ancestral portraits. There are fifteen bedrooms, most of them spacious, with antique or reproduction furniture. "Feels like a country house hotel should. Our room was individually furnished and decorated, with adequate space. Public rooms are not just for show – you feel *expected* to stretch out and relax. Real open fires and a prowling cat. Food extremely good, service professional but discreet. Strongly recommended!" "Vast room, heavenly views, service immaculate, food and comfort wonderful." *Paul and Deirdre McDonald, Katie Wood.* Dinners are à la carte; cooking, under *chef de cuisine* Caroline Prescott, is basically French, with much use of local produce, some of it home-grown; you can ask if you want your food simply cooked. Children are welcome here, but the very young are expected not to eat in the restaurant at night; they have a special menu for supper, which is served in the bedrooms.

Open 2 Mar–end early Jan.
Rooms 2 suites, 13 double – all with bath and shower, telephone, TV; baby-listening on request.
Facilities Bar, 3 lounges, 2 dining rooms. 5-acre grounds. Fishing, golf, riding nearby.
Location Just off A30, 3 m W of Honiton.
Restrictions Not suitable for ♿. No dogs in restaurant at mealtimes.
Credit cards All major cards accepted.

Terms B&B (English): single £52–£76.50, double £80–£103.50, suite £112. Bar lunches Mon–Sat; set Sun lunch £15. Full alc £23.30. Winter rates. 1-night bookings sometimes refused. Reduced rates and special meals for children.

GRASMERE Cumbria — Map 4

Lancrigg Vegetarian Country House Hotel

Tel Grasmere (096 65) 317
Easedale, Grasmere LA22 9QN

A new entry – and our only vegetarian hotel – a listed building in the beautiful and quiet valley of Easedale, just outside Grasmere. It stands in large grounds with fine trees, streams, deer, and good walks and, says the proprietor, Robert Whittington "most guests are in fact not vegetarian, but the majority return". Our nominators, *Lilian and Donald Brown,* are among the loyal followers: "We have now had three visits of a week each and plan to go again next year. *Lancrigg* is a beautiful building, and has associations with Wordsworth, Tennyson and many other writers. There are splendid walks of all levels of difficulty all around, and at our ages (totalling 140) the comfort and good dinner on return were extremely welcome. The decor is in reasonable taste, and not fussy, with some interesting pieces of furniture. Our room had a triangular bath big enough for two, a magnificent view of Silver Howe and Sour Milk Gill, television and a four-poster. The lounge has plenty of comfortable furniture, arranged so one doesn't have to sit looking at the other guests, and a good fire. The dining room verges on the elegant, although a little redecoration would not come amiss. The food is good and imaginative, and served in very generous portions. There is a fair choice of wines, mostly organic. Breakfasts also were good – eggs, mushrooms, tomatoes – as were the packed lunches. There is a friendly, cosy air about the place; staff are helpful without being a nuisance. *Lancrigg* can be recommended to all, vegetarian or not." More reports please.

Open All year. B&B only 2 weeks in June.
Rooms 10 double, 1 single – 6 with bath and shower (some with whirlpool), all with radio, TV, tea-making facilities and baby-listening. 1 on ground floor.
Facilities Lounge, dining room. 27-acre grounds with woodlands and streams.
Location ½-m along the Easedale road from Grasmere.
Restriction No dogs in bedrooms or public rooms.
Credit cards None accepted.
Terms [1989 rates] Dinner, B&B £25–46. Set dinner £12.50. Midweek reductions in low season. 1-night bookings refused over bank holidays. Reduced rates for children sharing parents' room; special meals.

White Moss House [GFG]

Tel Grasmere (096 65) 295
Rydal Water, Grasmere LA22 9SE

White Moss, formerly three 18th-century cottages owned by Wordsworth's family – his descendants lived there until the 1930s – is now owned and run by Susan and Peter Dixon. There are five rooms in the main house on the A591 (heavy lorries banned), and two up a steep footpath in Brockstone cottage. They are smallish, with small bathrooms, but are extensively kitted out with cosseting extras – trouser press, sewing kit, hair-drier, bath essence, dried *White Moss* lavender, Crabtree and Evelyn soaps, and so forth. The lounge, too, is small and comfortable, and conducive to after-dinner fraternisation. Peter Dixon is the chef; dinners, served at "7.30 for 8", are five-course affairs – good local ingredients, unpretentiously cooked, with fresh herbs; lots of vegetables; no choice until the dessert; there is a good selection of English cheeses and a long and varied wine list. "The high standard of cuisine continues. Prices reasonable by Lake District standards. And *White Moss* is superbly situated for fell walking." (*Richard Osborne*)

Open Mar–Nov. Restaurant closed for Sun dinner.
Rooms 1 suite, 5 double – all with bath and shower, radio and TV. 2, let as a unit, in cottage on hillside (10 mins by car or direct footpath).
Facilities Lounge, bar, dining room. 1-acre garden with terrace. Near Rydal Water and river Rothay; swimming and fishing.
Location On A591 between Ambleside and Grasmere.
Restrictions Not suitable for ♿. No smoking in dining room. No dogs.
Credit cards None accepted.
Terms (Service at guests' discretion) Dinner, B&B £51–£61. Set dinner £19.95. Reduced rates for stays of 3 nights or more Mar, Apr and Nov. 1-night bookings sometimes refused, especially Sat and bank holidays. 25% reductions in July and Aug for children 10–18.
Service/tipping: "Tipping is not expected. Sometimes guests insist on leaving something, which we put in a staff box."

GREAT LANGDALE Cumbria — Map 4

Long House — *Tel* Langdale (096 67) 222
Great Langdale
Nr Ambleside LA22 9JS

17th-century Lakeland house in two-acre grounds; low beamed ceilings, open fires. Excellent base for climbing Langdale Pikes and exploring the valley. Clean, comfortable, good simple meals: British cooking, using local specialities; bring your own wine. Unobtrusive but helpful hosts, the Wilkinsons; very reasonable rates. Recommended for a relaxed break in beautiful surroundings. Book well ahead. 3 bedrooms, all with bath. B&B (English) £15–£16.50. Set dinner £7.50–£8. New nomination. More reports please.

GREAT LONGSTONE Derbyshire — Map 4

The Croft Country House Hotel — *Tel* Great Longstone (062 987) 278
Great Longstone, Nr Bakewell
DE4 1TF

Unpretentious country house hotel, run by Clive and Rosemary Sheridan, in 4-acre grounds on edge of village three miles north of Bakewell, in beautiful walking country. Victorian building with imposing galleried hall, spacious well-equipped bedrooms "delicious, freshly cooked meals", friendly and professional service. Open 1 Mar–23 Dec. 9 rooms, 7 with private facilities. B&B: double £45–£59. Set 4-course dinner (no choice of main dish, but special diets and vegetarians catered for) £13.25 [1989]. Guide dogs only. More reports please.

> Hotels are dropped if we lack positive feedback. If you can endorse an entry, please do so.

GREAT MILTON Oxfordshire Map 1

Le Manoir aux Quat' Saisons [GFG]
Great Milton OX9 7PD

Tel Great Milton (0844) 278881 and 278751
Fax (0844) 278847
Telex 837552 BLANC

"Perfection. How do they do it?" "We have stayed here several times this year. A wonderful away-from-it-all treat. The atmosphere, the decor of the rooms, the service and the food are of equal excellence." "Triumphant combination of English country-house style and quality French restaurant. It is so much better than most equivalent places in France that the very high prices can be justified and brought into perspective." "One of the best meals we have ever had." (*Mrs JA Patterson, Michael and Elena Emmerson, David Wooff, HR*) Raymond Blanc's serene country mansion, 15th- and 16th-century in origin, in 27 acres of garden and parkland near Oxford, with its famous restaurant, double-rosetted in *Michelin*, continues to draw a large and almost entirely favourable postbag from our readers praising the well-equipped and comfortable bedrooms – even the smaller rooms are considered "very special" – the "immaculate" housekeeping and the "excellent" breakfasts which include fresh croissants and rolls, and quality yoghurt. The public rooms are beautifully decorated with fresh flowers, fine fabrics, antique and period furniture, there is a "lovely garden, with a particularly well-laid-out herb garden". Winter breaks for two continue to offer "outstanding value". A further ten bedrooms will be opened in March 1990, and the restaurant, conservatory and kitchen are being extended.

Open All year except 20 Dec–21 Jan. Restaurant closed Mon and Tue lunch, only open to residents on Mon night with a restricted menu.
Rooms 3 suites, 7 double – 2 with bath and shower, 8 with bath, all with telephone, radio, TV; some with whirlpool bath; baby-sitters available.
Facilities 2 sitting rooms, 2 restaurants; 2 rooms for private functions. 27 acres of landscaped garden and parkland with heated swimming pool and stables.
Location 1 m W of M40/A40, 8 m SE of Oxford. From London take M40: exit 7, 1 mile, 2nd right. From Oxford, take A40, then A329 at Milton Common towards Wallingford, 2nd right.
Restrictions Not suitable for ♿. No children under 7. No dogs in building – free kennel facilities in grounds.
Credit cards All major cards accepted.
Terms B&B: double £150–£220, suite £300. Single rates by negotiation. Set lunch £23–£48, dinner from £48; full alc £77. Midweek breaks on certain dates between 1 Oct and 30 Apr £200 per night for 2 half board (1, 2 or 3 nights). 1-night bookings may be refused for Sat. Reduced rates and special meals for children. *Service/tipping: "Tips are optional and distributed amongst staff."*

GREAT SNORING Norfolk Map 3

The Old Rectory
Barsham Road, Great Snoring
Fakenham NR21 0HP

Tel Fakenham (0328) 820597

"Incomparable rural setting – the historic church is almost in the garden – in an unspoilt village well away from main roads." "A welcoming, gleaming home full of flowers, warmth, friendliness – and a high degree of efficiency in all departments." "Our room was spacious and well heated with good antique furniture and a pleasant view over the garden. Very friendly atmosphere. Food, good plain English cooking with all the trimmings and plenty of vegetables." *The Old Rectory* is a listed building set in a walled garden, and considerably grander than the average country parsonage. First built in 1500, it is now an architectural mixture of Elizabethan, Georgian and Victorian Gothic. Inevitably in such a venerable house the bedrooms vary in size; readers have reported "wardrobe doors with a propensity to come open because of the uneven floor" and a shortage of hanging space in some rooms, but they are comfortable, with good lighting and well-provided bathrooms. The dining room has mullioned windows, heavy oak beams and "excellent silver, plate and glass". Food (no choice of main course) is substantial, but not *haute cuisine*. Early morning tea is brought to the bedroom at no extra charge. *(JJW, PM Stephens, Tom and Rosemary Rose)*

Open All year except 24–27 Dec. Dining room closed for lunch.
Rooms 6 double, 1 single – all with bath, telephone and TV.
Facilities Sitting room, dining room. 1½-acre walled garden. 6 m from north Norfolk nature reserves.
Location Great Snoring is 3 m NE of Fakenham off A148 Fakenham by-pass. *Old Rectory* is behind church on Barsham road.
Restrictions Not suitable for ♿. Children under 12 not encouraged. No dogs.
Credit cards Amex, Diners.
Terms (No service charge) B&B (English): single £39.50–£46, double £68–£70. Set dinner £15.
Service/tipping: "If a guest wishes to tip this is given to the staff concerned."

GRIMSTON Norfolk — Map 3

Congham Hall Country House Hotel [GFG]
Lynn Road, Grimston
King's Lynn PE32 1AH

Tel Hillington (0485) 600250
Telex 81508 CHOTEL

Two 1989 visitors are enthusiastic: "The Guide entry fully endorsed. We stayed in one of the newly converted attic rooms – plenty of space, attractively decorated in the usual Laura Ashley style. The bathroom too was splendidly spacious – only drawback the positioning of the light over the mirror which made shaving injuries inevitable. How is it that someone appears like magic to welcome you on arrival? A detector strip at the drive entrance activates a bell in reception. This illustrates the Forecasts' thoughtfulness." "Lovely hotel, beautifully appointed, with caring host and hostess, Christine and Trevor Forecast. Splendid welcome, lots of help on departure. The best dinners we have eaten for some time; breakfast also extremely good."

Congham Hall is an elegant Georgian manor house, with 40 acres of velvety lawn, country garden, paddocks, orchards and parkland, and its own cricket pitch. The "large and beautiful drawing room", the hall and bar are "all pleasant places to be". Bedrooms, including one with a four-poster, are generally well appointed though they vary in size; the suite is "beautiful, with a super-size bed". Visitors appreciate the old-fashioned service and excellent housekeeping – beds turned down at night, fresh towels provided twice daily, early morning tea delivered with a newspaper to the bedroom. There are two dinner menus: a gourmet "Hobson's Choice" menu "with eight light courses incorporating many different tastes", which changes twice weekly, and a four-course menu offering six choices for each course; both include coffee and petits fours. (*Dr JEM Whitehead, Heather Sharland; also Mr and Mrs DJ Snow, Jean and Tom Campbell*) A few minor complaints: public rooms not quite warm enough on a winter's afternoon, lighting "too dull in the bedroom, too bright in public rooms", the swimming pool out of use in August. And one visitor was severely critical of her attic room which had a poor outlook and was "claustrophobic, unattractively furnished and over-priced". There is also a plea for pictures or mirrors to add interest to the dining room decor. But even the carpers agree: "Delightful hosts and grounds, herb garden (and gardener)."

Open All year.
Rooms 1 suite, 9 double, 1 single – 10 with bath and shower, 1 with shower, all with telephone, radio and TV.
Facilities Hall, lounge, bar, restaurant; boardroom for private parties and meetings. 40-acre grounds with heated swimming pool, jacuzzi, tennis court, cricket pitch, parklands and orchards; stabling for visiting horses. Coast with sandy beaches 10 m; nature and bird sanctuaries, fishing, golf, riding nearby.
Location 6 m NE of King's Lynn. Turn right off A148 to Grimston; *Congham Hall* is 2½ m on left. Do not go to Congham.
Restrictions Only restaurant suitable for ♿. No smoking in restaurant. No children under 12. Dogs in kennels only.
Credit cards All major cards accepted.
Terms B&B (light English): single £65, double £85, suite £130. Full English breakfast £2 added. Set lunch £12.50, 5-course dinner £25; "Hobson's Choice dinner £32. Weekend breaks (Fri–Sun) all year; 3-day Christmas break.
Service/tipping: "All our tariffs carry the statement: 'No service charges are added to your account for any facilities offered in the hotel.' If guests do leave a tip it is all passed on to the staff who share it out."

GULWORTHY Devon — Map 1

The Horn of Plenty [GFG] — *Tel* Tavistock (0822) 832528
Gulworthy, Tavistock PL19 8JD

A long-established restaurant in a lovely setting, with extensive grounds, trees and flowers, and views over the Tamar valley. The six relatively new bedrooms in converted stables are simple and modern in style and furnishing, and well equipped, with fridge, telephone, lights in the right place, plenty of towels in the bathroom, and good beds; but don't expect such hotel-style service as the tidying of rooms in the evening. Sonia Stevenson, a Master Chef of Great Britain, has run the *Horn of Plenty* for 22 years, and her style of cooking has not changed much in that time – it is classic, rather than "inventive", and not in the least *nouvelle*. An *aficionado* writes, "Once again, though a restaurant-with-rooms, a wonderful place to stay; our room was spacious and beautifully furnished in Provençal-style colours and fabrics; views from the rooms and the restaurant are lovely. Dinner is superb, and so is the continental breakfast served in the bedroom – on the balcony in fine weather (a full English breakfast is available in the restaurant). *The Horn of Plenty* is extremely well run, with a perfect mixture of professionalism and personal warmth from all the staff." (*Lydia Lim*) Other visitors, however, regret the lack of a residents' lounge – "there is nowhere to go after dinner, except back to your bedroom"; consider the restaurant is over-rated, and point out that this is not a place for a long stay as the dinner menu does not change much.

Open All year except 25/26 Dec. Restaurant closed Thur and Fri lunchtime.
Rooms 6 double – all with bath and/or shower, telephone, radio, TV, tea-making facilities. All in annexe adjacent to restaurant. 4 on ground floor.
Facilities Hall, restaurant; small conference room with TV; terrace. 5-acre garden. Fishing nearby.
Location 3 m W of Tavistock; follow roadsigns off A390.
Restrictions Children under 12 discouraged at dinner. Dogs by arrangement only, not in public rooms.
Credit cards Access, Amex, Visa.
Terms B&B (continental): single occupancy £52–£59, double £71–£79. English breakfast £9.50. Set lunch £17.50, dinner £24 and £34; full alc £33. Winter and summer breaks. Cookery courses Oct–Mar. Reduced rates for children sharing parents' room; special meals
Service/tipping; "We do not encourage tipping by bedroom guests. Tipping in the restaurant is optional."

HAMBLETON Leicestershire — Map 4

Hambleton Hall [GFG] — *Tel* Oakham (0572) 756991
Hambleton, Oakham LE15 8TH — *Telex* 342888 HAMBLE

Among the half-dozen most luxurious English country house hotels, *Hambleton Hall* is a stately Victorian mansion overlooking Rutland Water, on what is almost an island. Its gardens are manicured, with lovely mature trees; the interior has been beautifully decorated by Nina Campbell, and is always full of lovely arrangements of fresh flowers. The owners, Tim and Stefa Hart, are dependably welcoming, and visitors continue to express their satisfaction: "Magnificent setting, excellent food and lovely atmosphere. Service first class but not fawning." "The external beauty of the gardens and surrounding countryside is complemented superbly by the exquisite internal decor. Bedroom comfortable and quiet." "Totally cosseting. My room was beautifully furnished with efficient individually controlled heating." Only criticism (as last year): "No vegetarian dish on the menu." (*Diane and Keith Moss, David Heather, Mrs EH Prodgers*)

Open All year.
Rooms 15 double – all with bath, shower, telephone, radio, TV, baby-listening.
Facilities Lift. Drawing room, bar, dining room; small conference facilities, private dining room. 17-acre grounds overlooking lake with trout-fishing, wind surfing, sailing; tennis court. Riding, shooting by arrangement.
Location Off A606 Stamford Road 1 m E of Oakham.
Restrictions No children under 9. Dogs by arrangement; not in public rooms, or alone in bedrooms.
Credit cards All major cards accepted.
Terms B&B (continental): single £85, double £95–£180. Set lunch £20, dinner £29; full alc £33. Off-season discounts for stays of 3 nights or more. 1-night bookings generally refused for Sat.
Service/tipping: "No service charge. No additional payment expected."

Do you know of a good hotel or country inn in the United States or Canada? Nominations please to our sibling publication, America's Wonderful Little Hotels and Inns, PO Box 150, Riverside Avenue, Riverside, Conn. 06878, USA.

HASTINGLEIGH Kent Map 3

The Woodmans Arms Auberge [GFG] *Tel* Elmsted (023 375) 250
Hassell Street
Hastingleigh, nr Ashford
TN25 5JE

"It is a constant source of amazement that they maintain the same high standards year in year out without variation," write *Roger and Jean Nicholls* of this 1988 César winner. Other readers praise "the quality of the rooms, food and service and the social environment created by Mr Campion. It is something like being a guest in a Japanese home; the host did everything he could to make us comfortable while the hostess spent her time in the kitchen." "Just like staying in someone's home and getting the same attention one would among friends. Lots of thought put into the minutest details." "The garden room has its own private charming garden with deck chairs; you can also use the rest of the garden, and on fine days you can breakfast and dine out of doors." "The packed lunch was a cordon bleu meal in itself." This very small and not at all hotel-like establishment has only three double rooms and the restaurant can seat no more than ten. It has no staff, only the owners Gerald Campion and his wife Susan, and is the kind of place where you are likely to end up on first-name terms with the proprietors. An inn since the 17th century, the *Woodmans Arms* stands on a small lane leading to nowhere except the Downs, guaranteeing total peace and seclusion. Without the hotel's directions it can be difficult to find. For those with cars there is no shortage of showplaces in the neighbourhood: Leeds Castle, Chilham Castle, Dover Castle – Canterbury is only ten miles away. It is conveniently situated for the Channel ports. This is a no-smoking establishment; children and dogs are not accommodated. Though the rooms are of a good size, some ceilings are low – tall guests will need to mind their heads, and they might find the mirrors a bit low-hung. (*Susan B Hanley, Barb and Jim Harvey, Ralph Blumenau, David G Felce; also IM Ziar, and many others*)

Open All year except 18–24 April, 1 Sept–1 Oct. Restaurant usually closed to non-residents.
Rooms 3 double – all with bath (2 also have shower), telephone, intercom and TV. 1 has private outside entrance and small garden.
Facilities Lounge, dining room. Large grassed garden and paddock. Near sea at Sandgate and Hythe.
Location Off A28 Canterbury road. Hotel will send directions.
Restrictions Not suitable for ♿. No smoking. No children under 16. No dogs.
Credit cards None accepted.
Terms B&B: single occupancy £50, double £65; dinner, B&B: single £65, double £90. 1-night bookings refused for Sat.
Service/tipping: "We do not expect tips."

HATCH BEAUCHAMP Somerset Map 1

Farthings Country House Hotel *Tel* Hatch Beauchamp
Hatch Beauchamp TA3 6SG (0823) 480 664

"Wonderful hotel. Fantastic food, rooms very comfortable – *fresh* milk in a thermos for morning tea *and* a tin with biscuits," runs a warm endorsement for Mr and Mrs Cooper's small Georgian house which entered the Guide last year. It is in a quiet Somerset village not far from Taunton, and well placed for exploring Somerset, Devon and Dorset. Public rooms are comfortable and welcoming, with plenty of magazines; bedrooms are mostly large, light and spacious, two have spiral staircases leading to private bathrooms. The Coopers have now employed "a talented young chefess, Wendy Bate"; they offer an imaginative four-course dinner menu and whenever possible fresh local produce is used. "Mr Cooper is an amusing and knowledgeable host. There were many pleasing small touches. We felt like privileged house guests all weekend." (*Holly R Howard, J Brandli*) Only niggle: "We could not have the *cooked* breakfast in our bedroom, but a small price to pay."

Open All year except part of Jan. Possibly also Christmas and New Year.
Rooms 5 double, 1 single – all with bath, shower, telephone, radio, TV and tea-making facilities.
Facilities Lounge, bar, 2 dining rooms. 3-acre grounds.
Location In village 6 m SE of Taunton; 4 m from M5, Junction 25.
Restrictions Not suitable for ♿. Dogs by arrangement, not in public rooms.
Credit cards Access, Visa.
Terms (No service charge) B&B £41–£78. Lunch by arrangement. Set dinner £20.50. Special breaks. Reduced rates and special meals for children.
Service/tipping: "Gratuities are neither anticipated nor necessary."

HAWES North Yorkshire — Map 4

Simonstone Hall — *Tel* Hawes (096 97) 255
Hawes DL8 3LY — from late 1989 (0969) 667255

Former home of Earls of Wharncliffe, now a comfortable family-run country-house hotel with lovely views of upper Wensleydale. 1½ miles north of Hawes. Panelled drawing rooms with antiques. Local produce (including Wensleydale cheese) served in portrait-hung dining room. 3½-acre grounds. Dogs welcomed. 10 spacious bedrooms, all with private facilities. B&B double £62–£77. Set dinner £16.50. New nomination. More reports please.

HAWKRIDGE Somerset — Map 1

Tarr Steps Hotel — *Tel* Winsford (064 385) 293
Hawkridge, Dulverton TA22 9PY

This former Georgian rectory on Exmoor, 12 miles from the coast, is now a sporting hotel *par excellence*. It offers guests three miles of salmon and trout fly-fishing, 500 acres of rough shooting, stabling for their own horses, and fox- or stag-hunting. It is 800 feet above sea level, in eight-acre grounds, with lovely views down the river valley; the famous Tarr Steps bridge – made from unhewn stone, probably in the Bronze Age – over the river Barle is 200 yards away. Indoors the hotel is "very fishing-y and relaxed – all white and green with sporting pictures, carpeted corridors, various public rooms with dark wood and chintzy sofas." There is no television, either in public rooms or bedrooms, no tea- or coffee-making facilities and only one telephone for guests. The guest is made welcome as if to a private house. Last year a reader wrote, "Long may the slightly run-down air last, untouched by so-called 20th-century improvements!" *Anne Laurence* adds, "We very much like the relaxed, slightly shabby comfort. The proprietor is extremely affable but doesn't press his attentions on you. In the past we've stayed in the adjoining cottage which we found a bit cold and dank. This time we had a room in the main building with a nice view over the valley." Some readers have been critical of the cooking; Mr Keane tells us that a new cook arrived at the beginning of the 1989 season, and we should be glad of readers' opinions. Cooking is traditional English, with some choice of each course. The hotel's gardens have in the past have been described as "slightly wild"; he says, "We are trying to tidy them up; we have a bit of a battle on Exmoor, but I hope your readers will notice the difference."

Open Mid-Mar–after Christmas.
Rooms 12 double, 3 single – 8 with bath. 3 in cottage annexe. 1 ground-floor room with bath and access for ♿.
Facilities Sitting room, bar, dining room. 8-acre grounds with garden; rough and clay-pigeon shooting, fishing, fox and staghunting; stables and kennels for guests' horses and dogs. River bathing 100 yds.
Location Take Hawkridge road from Dulverton. From Hawkridge follow signs to Tarr Steps and hotel.
Restriction No dogs in public rooms.
Credit cards Access, Amex, Visa.
Terms (No service charge) B&B: £26. Set Sun lunch £13.50; dinner £14.50. Bar lunches available. Midweek breaks. 1-night bookings refused over bank holiday weekends. Children under 8 sharing parents' room, half price; high teas.
Service/tipping: "Anything left goes direct to staff and is shared equally."

HAWKSHEAD Cumbria — Map 4

Field Head House [GFG] — *Tel* Hawkshead (096 66) 240
Outgate, Hawkshead LA22 0PY

"Staying here is a memorable experience: the van Guliks achieve a rare combination of professionalism and amateurism – you genuinely do feel like a friend of the family without any of the forced bonhomie that term so often implies." "It has the atmosphere of a good-tempered *pension*. The owners clearly love their house and having people in it." *Field Head House* is owned and run by a Dutch couple, Bob and Eeke van Gulik. It stands in six acres of woodland, old orchards, rhododendrons and azaleas. The decor is nothing special: public rooms are not over-large and bedrooms vary in size; rooms 1 and 2 at the front are particularly spacious – the small one with narrow double bed, criticised in the past, has been replaced by a bathroom; and Mr van Gulik tells us that earlier problems with heating and hot water have now been remedied. Guests gather in the drawing room for a drink before dinner "at 7.30 for 8" and are introduced to each other, though Bob van Gulik says "if anyone objects to such contact, there is always the other lounge – or a book – to escape into", and they eat at separate tables. Since *Field Head House* made its Guide debut three years ago readers have written warmly to praise "the calm and civilised atmosphere", the "friendly and courteous service", the excellent value for money, and the good food cooked by Bob van Gulik. There is no choice on the five-course menu until dessert which is usually "a choice between something substantial for Lake District appetites whetted on the hills, e.g. marmalade bread pudding, and a lighter alternative". Main courses tend to be locally produced fish or meat – Eskdale trout or Cumbrian ham, for example. Portions are not over-large.

On the subject of children (see the Introduction) Mr van Gulik writes, "Our policy has not changed: we think it unfair to set an age limit, but we are careful in accepting them, and try to establish that parents are in full control, as there always seem to be one or two couples who are escaping their offspring for a few days." (*Daphne de Moubray, AB, R Wise, SM Batty, and others*)

Open All year except week before Christmas and last 2 weeks Jan. Lunch not served except by special arrangement. Restaurant closed Tues (bookings elsewhere made for residents or cold snack provided).
Rooms 7 double – 4 with bath, 3 with shower, all with radio, TV tea-making facilities.
Facilities 2 lounges (one with dispense bar), dining room. 6-acre grounds with gardens, croquet. Fishing, water sports, walking, golf nearby.
Location From Ambleside take B5286 towards Hawkshead. ½ m past *Outgate Inn* take right turn signposted *Field Head*. From Hawkshead take B5286 towards Ambleside. *Field Head* signposted 1 m N of Hawkshead.
Restrictions Not suitable for ♿. No smoking in bedrooms or dining room.
Credit cards None accepted.
Terms B&B £25–£28; dinner, B&B £41–£44. Surcharge: £8 for single occupancy of double room, £5 for 1-night stay. Set dinner £18. 5% discount for regulars. Off-season rates; Christmas and New Year breaks. 1-night bookings sometimes refused if far in advance or for weekend. Children sharing parents' room £10; special meals (but not outside dinner time; simple snack can be served in bedroom).
Service/tipping: "Tips are not solicited, but if given are shared by all staff."

Highfield House Hotel *Tel* Hawkshead (096 66) 344
Hawkshead Hill, Hawkshead
LA22 0PN

Traditional Lakeland stone building, a century old, on high ground in 2½-acre grounds; particularly well sited for walking and rambling. Recommended for reasonable rates, comfortable accommodation, spacious lounge with beautiful view and, above all, caring proprietors Jim and Pauline Bennett. 11 rooms – 8 with private facilities. B&B £16.50–£22. Set dinner £10.50. More reports please.

Walker Ground Manor *Tel* (096 66) 219
Hawkshead LA22 0PD

"Must be one of the best family-run guest houses in the Lake District, fantastic welcome, excellent company and superb home cooking. We were free to use the garden and conservatory. All in all still highly recommended." Thus the original nominator, on a return visit to Dennis and Wendy Chandler's informal guest house in a 16th-century Lakeland stone building, with original panelling and priest hole, "inexpensive antiques", pictures, ornaments, fine china and crystal. It stands in large and peaceful grounds with lawns and waterfalls. There are only three guest bedrooms; two have four-poster beds, two have private bathrooms, and there are two other bathrooms in the house. No TV to disturb the peace. Food is "traditional – good and wholesome" with vegetables from the garden, local meat and fish etc. Guests dine with the hosts, by a log fire in the dining room or in the conservatory by candle-light; dinner is "a long, relaxed affair at one big table, but is not an organised party". "A lovely spot, properly equipped with daffodils, wooden coat-hangers, good linen, inexpensive wine and plenty of good food. There's a warm welcome and a genuinely friendly atmosphere in this obviously popular hotel. Everything one could wish for – at a sensible price. Like General McArthur, we shall return". (*Imogen Mottram, David Gadsby*) The *Manor* is strictly no-smoking; there are cats in the household, but if guests do not like them they are not permitted beyond a certain area. There is a self-catering cottage whose occupants can dine with the Chandlers when disinclined to cook for themselves. More reports please.

Open All year.
Rooms 3 double – 1 with bath and shower, 1 with bath, all with tea-making facilities. Self-catering 4-bedded holiday cottage adjacent.
Facilities Drawing room, study, dining room, conservatory. 18-acre grounds with gardens, lawns, waterfalls. Coniston Water 3 m, Windermere 4 m; river fishing nearby.
Location 300 yds from village centre; take lane beside garage, marked with T-sign for Barnfield leading to Vicarage and *Walker Ground* through bungalow estate, sharp right up lane, do *not* bear left at the top. Go straight ahead on rough path; manor gates are on left.
Restrictions Not suitable for ♿. No smoking. Adults only except by special arrangement. No dogs.
Credit cards None accepted.
Terms B&B £18–£30. Packed lunches available. Set dinner £10–£15. Christmas/New Year packages. 1-night bookings sometimes refused.
Service/tipping "As this is a private house there is no service charge. We dislike tipping."

HAYTOR South Devon — Map 1

The Bel Alp House — *Tel* Haytor (036)46) 217
Haytor, Nr Bovey Tracey
TQ13 9XX

An Edwardian house, once the home of tobacco millionairess Dame Violet Mills; peacefully set in large grounds on edge of Dartmoor, with lovely views. Carefully restored by "hospitable" owners, Roger and Sarah Curnock. Recommended for personal attention, cleanliness and excellent food: five-course set dinner (but alternatives available) served in no-smoking dining room. Closed Christmas, New Year, 1 week July. Traditionally furnished public rooms with bay windows; nine spacious, light and comfortable bedrooms, all with bath and/or shower. B&B £45–£69. Set dinner £27.50. New nomination. More reports please.

HEDDON'S MOUTH Devon — Map 1

Heddon's Gate Hotel — *Tel* Parracombe (059 83) 313
Heddon's Mouth
Parracombe, Barnstaple
EX31 4PZ

César award: For sturdy independence in doing their own thing with verve

"As we followed Mr De Ville through a doorway framed with bobble-fringed drapes, and along a passage past Victorian prints, a vase of coloured pampas grass, and a 1920s mannequin in dressing-gown, cap and curlers, we wondered what sort of bedroom lay ahead. We needn't have worried: it was light and airy, with unobtrusive modern curtains and wallpaper, and so large that the massive Victorian bed and chest of drawers were not out of scale; the bathroom too was spacious and modern, with every comfort. And Anne De Ville's dinners really impress with the loving care and attention to detail shown in her cooking and presentation of every course." "Service and accommodation of a standard rarely found in far more expensive hotels." "Decor witty and sophisticated, inspired by the *Lucia* stories by EF Benson. Staff always helpful, never obsequious. Although our comfortable bed lacked style in its coverings and our bath was easier to enter than to leave, it was a joy to find a flask of milk provided every night beside the tea-making machine." (*JP Berryman, CA Jones, Cliff and Jean Michelmore, and many others*) *Heddons Gate* is a turn-of-the-century Swiss-Victorian lodge with various extensions and steeply terraced gardens, looking over a luscious valley, with views over miles of moorland and wooded hills. The large grounds are surrounded by National Trust and Exmoor National Park land, and several private paths thread through the gardens – one directly on the South West Peninsular coastal path. The hotel has been owned by Robert and Anne De Ville for the past 22 years. Conflicting opinions of the decor have been voiced over the years, but no-one has ever disputed the generosity of the hospitality and the value for money. Mr De Ville writes this year, "Most of our furniture, pictures, ornaments and books have a sentimental or humorous value, and we feel this element of fun is needed to counter the very serious and disciplined business of running a successful hotel. The dining room has been extravagantly redecorated – all peacocks, lace and candle-light. We still supply a full help-yourself afternoon tea free, and charge only the standard call-box rate for telephone calls made from your room."

Open 6 Apr–5 Nov.
Rooms 4 suites, 9 double, 1 single – all with bath and/or shower, telephone, radio, TV and tea-making facilities. 3 terraced cottage suites with wheelchair access 70 yards from main building.
Facilities Sitting room, library, bar, card room, dining room. 20-acre grounds with terraced gardens. Access to sea (¾ m) and river (¼ m) by footpaths. Riding, pony-trekking, fishing nearby.
Location 6 m W of Lynton; from A39 3 m W of Lynton take Martinhoe/Woody Bay road; turn left towards Hunter's Inn; hotel sign is at next crossroads.
Restrictions No children under 10. Dogs by arrangement, not in dining room.
Credit cards None accepted.
Terms Dinner, B&B £32.20–£52.95. Set dinner (at 8 pm) £16.50. Reductions for stays of 3 or more days; weekly rates. 1-night bookings sometimes refused. 50% reduction for children sharing parents' room.
Service/tipping: "We never make any service charge and staff do not solicit tips; any that are given are collected, taxed and shared out among staff on basis of hours worked."

HENLEY-IN-ARDEN Warwickshire — Map 2

Ashleigh House — *Tel* Henley-in-Arden (056 42) 2315
Whitley Hill
Henley-in-Arden B95 5DL

"Infinitely preferable to staying in Stratford! We stayed in the annexe which was all you would expect of a first-class hotel. Francisco Garcia, painter and charming conversationalist, makes you feel like an unpaying guest. His taste in antiques ranges from the exquisite to the kitsch. We loved it – and so cheap!" "Notice has been taken of the criticisms in the 1989 Guide. Breakfast was fine, with a large selection of cereals, muesli and dried fruits and a substantial cooked breakfast with limitless supplies of brown and white toast, fresh tea and coffee." "Owners, Francisco Garcia and Colin Eades, were helpful and kind in every way." *Ashleigh House* is an Edwardian house in one-and-a-half acres of grounds in quiet open country, with views over the Warwickshire countryside towards the Cotswolds. The spacious bedrooms are furnished almost entirely with Victorian and Edwardian antiques. Only 15 minutes by car from Stratford-upon-Avon, eight miles from Warwick and 14 from the National Exhibition Centre. Light snacks can be provided, but there are many good restaurants close by. (*Braham Murray, Tanya Morris, Mrs Jane Indreland; also Gertrude and Gerhard Cohn*)

Open All year.
Rooms 10 double – all with shower (2 also have bath), telephone, TV, radio and tea-making facilities. 4 in coach-house annexe.
Facilities Sitting room with TV, reading area, dining room. 1½-acre garden.
Location On B4095 Warwick Road, 1 m from A34 traffic lights in Henley.
Restrictions Not suitable for severely ♿. Babies not encouraged. Dogs by arrangement only, not in public rooms.
Credit cards Access, Visa.
Terms B&B: single occupancy £28–£35, double £38–£45. No restaurant; snacks available. 1-night bookings sometimes refused. Reduced rates for children sharing parents' room.
Service/tipping: "Our staff appreciate tips but they are not expected."

HINTLESHAM Suffolk — Map 3

Hintlesham Hall [GFG]
Hintlesham, Ipswich IP8 3NS

Tel Hintlesham (047 387) 268 and 334
Fax (047 387) 463
Telex 98340

"Country-house hospitality at its best. You pay for it – but it's worth it." "Full marks again! I could not fault it: caring staff, great attention to detail, immaculate, beautiful rooms. Fine food." Two typical encomia for this grandly beautiful mansion, dating from the 15th century but mainly Georgian, run by Ruth and David Watson. It is sumptuously decorated in gentle pastels – mostly peach, white and grey – which set off the panelling and glorious plaster mouldings. Bedrooms have antique furniture, chintz curtains and covers, lots of ruching, magazines and books, excellent bathroom and "peaceful green views from the windows". Rooms vary in size and grandeur; some are huge and exceedingly opulent; you should discuss options when booking. There is a high ratio of staff to guests. The kitchens were taken over in August 1988 by Alan Ford, from the *Dorchester*; his cooking is "modern-classical, with a strong Mosimann influence". It is served impeccably in the beautiful dining rooms. Most comments are favourable, but one *Hintlesham* regular felt the food was now over-rich and the portions somewhat large. The English breakfasts continue to please. (*Martin L Dodd, Ian C Dewey, and others*)

At the time of writing the Watsons are in the middle of a major development programme to be completed by the autumn of 1989. The number of bedrooms will be almost doubled and conference and meeting facilities increased. We should like to hear from readers what the effect of this expansion is on the hotel.

Open All year. Restaurant closed for lunch Sat.
Rooms 3 suites, 30 double – all with bath, shower, telephone, radio, TV and mini-bar; some with baby-listening. 18 in stable block adjoining main building. Some ground-floor rooms.
Facilities 3 lounges, bar, 2 restaurants; private dining room, conference/functions room. 175-acre grounds with tennis, riding, fishing, shooting.
Location 4 m W of Ipswich on the A1071 to Hadleigh. Parking.
Restrictions No smoking in dining rooms. Children and dogs by arrangement; no dogs in public rooms.
Credit cards All major cards accepted.
Terms B&B: single occupancy £80–£95, double £80–£160, suite £250–£300. Set lunch £18.50, dinner £35; full alc £45. Special breaks summer and winter; Christmas package. 1-night bookings refused for Sat.

HINTON CHARTERHOUSE Avon — Map 2

Homewood Park Hotel [GFG]
Hinton Charterhouse
Nr Bath BA3 6BB

Tel Limpley Stoke (022 122) 3731
Fax (022 122) 3820
Telex 444937 HOMWOD

Homewood Park stands in a lovely ten-acre garden on what was probably the site of the abbot's house for the now-ruined Hinton Priory. Mainly 18th-century, the house was much added to in Victorian times, and again in the present century; it is now "a gem of a country-house hotel", with luxurious bedrooms and well-furnished public rooms. It does not entirely escape traffic noise from the A36 but the rooms affected have double-glazed windows. As for many years past, most readers appreciate the "elegant, clean and comfortable bedrooms" and the attentive and friendly young staff. Food is described as *cuisine anglaise* at its best, "original and well presented"; the menu is wide and changes daily, and the Rosses offer the choice of a two- or three-course dinner menu. The restaurant caters for outside diners and can be overstretched at peak times. And some readers feel that, in view of the tariff, a full breakfast or a more generous continental one should be included, with better orange juice offered. But "consistently good" or "improves with each visit" is the consensus view.

Note: The Rosses' new luxury hotel, *The Queensberry*, in Bath receives its first Guide entry this year; it has a courtesy car service for those of its guests who wish to eat at *Homewood Park*.

Open All year except 23 Dec–6 Jan.
Rooms 15 double – all with bath and shower, telephone, radio, TV and baby-listening. 2 ground-floor rooms.
Facilities Bar, lounge, 2 dining rooms; private dining room, conference room. 10-acre grounds with tennis court, croquet and arboretum.
Location 5½ m S of Bath opposite Hinton Priory. Turn left off A36 at village of Freshford. Some traffic noise; rooms double-glazed.
Restrictions No smoking in dining room. No dogs.
Credit cards All major cards accepted.
Terms B&B (continental): single occupancy £65–£105, double £95–£135. Set lunch £17.50, dinner £27.50. 2-night winter breaks. 1-night bookings refused for weekends. Special meals for children by arrangement.
Service/tipping: "All our staff are on monthly salaries plus a bonus scheme based on turn-over. Service is included in our prices. Nothing further is expected."

HOCKLEY HEATH West Midlands — Map 2

Nuthurst Grange [GFG]
Nuthurst Grange Lane
Hockley Heath B94 5NL

Tel Lapworth (056 43) 3972
Fax (056 43) 3919
Telex 333485 NUT

"An exciting and worthwhile newcomer, worthy of encouragement", said our inspector last year, commending this new venture by David and Daryll Randolph who formerly ran *Randolph's* restaurant in Warwick. "You approach by an immaculate drive through attractive English parkland. From outside its architectural merits are undistinguished but it commands superb views, is tucked away from noise and bustle (though only five miles from Birmingham airport) and is totally silent at night. Inside it is elegantly furnished in modern but traditional style. Plenty of comfortable sofas and stylish flower arrangements in public rooms. All the bedrooms are delightful, they differ in colour scheme while maintaining a unity of design. We occupied one immediately above the busy restaurant (slightly cheaper than the other rooms) but no noise penetrated through the deep-pile carpet." Numerous extras in the bedroom included a bowl of fudge, a tin with petits fours and a spectacular crystal bowl of fruit. "The bathroom was another experience, with even a jacuzzi; only bathrobes were missing. Bedside lights with dimmers, lighter-than-air duvets. We slept like logs. A delightful place, without a shadow of a doubt exactly right for the Guide." The cooking is warmly approved too, "David Randolph is to West Midlands gastronomy what Simon Rattle is to West Midlands music. There is a similar combination of excellence and integrity. Standards consistently high, food of excellent quality, but a happy lack of pretentiousness in both menus and service, and an unusual degree of helpfulness." (*Robert B Fairweather, and others*) Only niggles: "The cheeseboard is not always in the peak of condition and the service – although very friendly and willing – is sometimes a little less professional than the food deserves."

Open All year except 1 week over Christmas and New Year.
Rooms 8 double – all with air-spa bath (4 also have shower), telephone, radio, TV, safe and baby-listening.
Facilities Reception lounge, lounge, restaurant; private dining room. 7½-acre grounds with croquet, helipad. Riding, hunting, tennis, clay pigeon-shooting, golf, canal boating nearby.
Location Off A34 between Stratford and Birmingham. Go S through Hockley Heath, ignore right turn to Redditch. Take next right turn (Nuthurst Grange Lane).
Restrictions Not suitable for ♿. "Children must be well-behaved." No dogs.
Credit cards All major cards accepted.
Terms B&B (continental): single occupancy £75, double from £95. Set lunch £15.50, dinner £24.50 and £29.50. Weekend breaks. Reduced rates and special meals for children.
Service/tipping: "We do not encourage tipping. Our employees' wages and pride in their work are payment in full."

Traveller's tale *The food was very good, even if I did get severe food poisoning from the fish. I wish they had been a little more concerned the next day when I had to be carried to the car.*

HORDLE Hampshire Map 2

Provence at the Gordleton Mill [GFG] *Tel* Lymington (0590) 682219
Silver Street
Hordle, Lymington SO41 6DJ

"A typical French restaurant-with-rooms that has wandered across the Channel and settled in Hampshire." This creeper-covered former mill has an idyllic setting beside a stream in five-and-a-half acres of grounds. Jean-Pierre Novi's "memorable, modern French cooking" is of a piece with the small, simple but stylish and comfortable dining room – "definitely worth the drive from London", service is "discreet and attentive but unobtrusive". "Food probably the best we have had this year." There is a list of well-chosen French wines, with all the regions well represented and a reasonable mark-up. Rooms are "not over-elaborate nor over-large, but ours was spotlessly clean with very comfortable beds and thoughtful extras – mineral water, sherry, well-appointed toilet kit"; smallish bathroom, beautifully appointed; masses of hot water. One has a small sitting area which could be welcome as there is no residents' lounge. There is a road nearby but readers report that they were not disturbed by traffic during the night; you can ask for a side or back room. There is some difference of opinion about the breakfast: two readers enjoyed their "very good continental breakfast, including fresh orange juice and sweet rolls"; another was critical of the rolls "but the omelettes, filled with diced tomato, and the coffee were excellent". (*Sarah Molloy, Ivor Hall; also EH Whitaker*) One visitor in early 1989, however, reported lack of maintenance in the bedroom and felt the accommodation was "functional rather than enjoyable" and one double bed is reported to be extremely small. More reports please. (See under Lymington in *The Good Food Guide*.)

Open 1 Feb–31 Dec. Closed Sun evening and Mon.
Rooms 5 double, 1 single – 4 with bath and shower, 2 with bath, all with telephone, radio, tea-making facilities and baby-listening; doubles have TV.
Facilities Bar, restaurant. 5½-acre grounds with stream.
Location 2 m NW of Lymington on C430. Take A337 Brockenhurst Road to *Toll House Inn* on outskirts of Lymington. Turn left on C430 towards Sway. Mill is 2½ m along on right just past *Wheel Inn* pub.
Restrictions Not suitable for ♿. No children under 8. No dogs (kennel facilities nearby).
Credit cards All major cards accepted.
Terms B&B (continental): single £35, double £55. Cooked breakfast £2.50 extra. Set lunch £13, dinner £21.50; full alc £35–£40.

HORTON Dorset Map 2

Northill House *Tel* Witchampton (0258) 840407
Horton, Wimborne BH21 7HL

"We chose *Northill House* from the Guide because it looked cosy and unpretentious. It turned out to be just that – but comfortable and welcoming too. Big bedroom, lovely log fires in public rooms, nice simple dinner (no choice except dessert) cooked by Joy Garnsworthy, served at 7.30 in the spacious dining room. Very reasonable." Courtney and Joy Garnsworthy's 19th-century former farmhouse down a track in one-acre grounds entered the Guide in 1989 in italics. Since then readers have written enthusiastically about this "miniature *Plumber Manor*" (q.v.), with "happy family atmosphere, delightfully furnished bedrooms with fine views and good bathrooms", comfortable lounge and "excellent English cooking, the ingredients, usually local, chosen with care. Faultless management. First class value." (*Hamish McRae and Frances Cairncross, Vincent Shaw, Harry Shepherd*) One hazard: "Unclear signs at road end."

Open Mid-Feb–20 Dec.
Rooms 9 double – all with bath and/or shower, telephone, radio, TV and tea-making facilities. 4 in annexe. 1 suitable for ♿.
Facilities Lounge, bar, dining room, conservatory. 2-acre grounds.
Location 7 m N of Wimborne, ½ m from B3078.
Restrictions No children under 8. No pets.
Credit cards Access, Visa.
Terms B&B (English) £23. Snack lunches. Set dinner £10. 3- and 7-night breaks.
Service/tipping: "Tips not expected or solicited; but shared among staff if given."

HUNTSHAM Devon — Map 1

Huntsham Court
Huntsham Valley
Nr Tiverton EX16 7NA

Tel Clayhanger (039 86) 210
Fax (039 86) 456

Huntsham is a a Grade II listed building, a choice example of high Victorian architecture, with huge rooms, massive fireplaces, impressive panelling and marble pillars, in a secluded setting in rural Devon, roughly halfway between Taunton and Exeter. It is run by Mogens and Andrea Bolwig with the aim of making guests forget that they are in a hotel at all. There are no locks on bedroom doors, no TV or telephone. The furniture is varied, with Victorian sideboards and outsize armchairs of the twenties and thirties. The whole place is dedicated to music: there is a baby grand piano in the hall, uprights in the drawing room and bar, a pianola in the dining room, and a collection of over 6,000 records and cassettes, mostly classical with a leaning towards the operatic, which guests are free to play on a high hi-fi. The bedrooms are named after composers. Most have a huge bathroom *en suite*. Beethoven has two free-standing old bathtubs with silver claws side by side in the middle of the bathroom, a log fire, a seven-foot wide bed and a piano. All the bedrooms have pre-war radio sets; two now have organs. The five-course dinner is eaten communally at a single large table. Tea and coffee are free for guests to help themselves to night and day in the butler's pantry. The bar can be help yourself, too, on the honour principle. There are a sauna, a mini-gym, tennis, croquet and lots of bicycles and the Bolvigs are hoping to build a swimming pool in late 1989. It is often taken over by groups, professional during the week, and private parties at weekends. *Huntsham* was the winner of a César in 1988 for "utterly acceptable mild eccentricity". "Food great, atmosphere brilliant", runs a recent endorsement; but we also have a report this year of an excessively hard bed in Bach, and some lapses in housekeeping.

Open All year, except 2 weeks Jan/Feb. Lunch by arrangement only.
Rooms 4 suites, 10 double – all with bath and shower, and pre-war wireless.
Facilities Hall, drawing room, library with snooker table, music room, bar, dining room; sauna, mini-gym, table tennis room. 8-acre garden with croquet, bicycles, tennis courts, barbecue. Trout-fishing in private lake, riding, golf and shooting nearby.

Location M5 to Taunton, then A361 towards Bampton; turn left to Huntsham when signposted. Or take exit 27 off M5, turn sharp right on bridge in Sampford Peverell and continue for 4 m.
Restrictions Not suitable for ♿. No dogs (kennels 2 m away).
Credit cards Access, Amex, Visa.
Terms B&B: single occupancy £60–£70, double £77.50–£85, suite £95. Set dinner £22. House parties; mid-week and weekend breaks; occasional jazz, opera and special weekends; Christmas and New Year programmes. 1-night bookings sometimes refused for weekend. Reduced rates for children sharing parents' room.
Service/tipping: "When guests have been particularly happy with service and staff we accept tips in the spirit in which they have been given. Not to do so would offend."

JERVAULX North Yorkshire — Map 4

Jervaulx Hall
Jervaulx, Masham
Ripon HG4 4PH

Tel Bedale (0677) 60235

An early Victorian mansion with much solid, reassuring Victorian furniture, on the site of one of the famous Cistercian abbeys. These ruins are less well known than Fountains and Rievaulx, but nonetheless impressive. The *Hall* adjoins the ruins, separated only by a ha-ha, and enjoys the run of the substantial abbey park. It makes an admirable base for a touring or walking holiday in the Yorkshire Dales. The public rooms are comfortable, with antiques, paintings and displays of china; bedrooms, though quite simple (no telephone or TV) are comfortable and warm. Dinner is at 8 pm – guests are asked to come down for at least half an hour before to place their orders. The wine list is short, but of good quality. Food, cooked by Mr Sharp's daughter, Elizabeth, is "simple but excellent, served in a friendly atmosphere"; there is a limited choice for each course on the menu. "Puddings excellent; delicious white and blue Wensleydale cheeses to finish." "Excellent English breakfast table"; "John Sharp was an ideal host, affably mixing with guests, yet unobtrusive." "The atmosphere is one of hospitality from the moment one enters." (*Gillian Evans, Stella Scott, Nicholas Crawley*) One reader this year felt her room was small and too basic for the prices charged, and found the food disappointing; another commented, "towels a little small". More reports please.

Open Mid-Mar–mid-Nov.
Rooms 8 double – all with bath (4 also have shower) and tea-making facilities. 1 ground-floor room.
Facilities 2 lounges (1 with TV), dining room. 8-acre garden adjoining abbey ruins; fishing by arrangement in nearby river Ure.
Location On A6108, 12 m N of Ripon, next to Jervaulx Abbey.
Restriction Dogs not to be left unattended in bedrooms.
Credit cards None accepted.
Terms Dinner, B&B £43–£52. Set dinner £14. Reduced rates and special meals for children.
Service/tipping: "No service charge. Tipping is optional; tips shared between all staff."

> Set dinner refers to a fixed price meal (which may have ample, limited or no choice on the menu). Full alc is the hotel's own estimated price per person of a three-course meal taken à la carte, with a half-bottle of house wine.

The Old Hall *Tel* Bedale (0677) 60313
Jervaulx Abbey, Jervaulx,
Masham, Ripon HG4 4PH

Formerly the servants' quarters of Jervaulx Hall, now a relaxed country guest house, run by Ian and Angela Close. Recommended for friendly welcome, "delicious no-nonsense home-style cooking" (meals taken with the Closes) and "exotic decor" – antiques and period furniture, strong colours, lots of flowers. 3 comfortable bedrooms, each with en suite *bathroom. 5-acre grounds. 2 self-catering cottages also available. B&B £25; set dinner £14. New nomination. More reports please.*

KINGSBRIDGE Devon — Map 1

Buckland-Tout-Saints Hotel [GFG] *Tel* Kingsbridge (0548) 3055
Fax (0548) 6261
Kingsbridge TQ7 2DS *Telex* 42513 attn BTS HOTEL

A "comfortable and welcoming" hotel in an elegant Queen Anne manor house peacefully set in the rolling hills of the South Hams, surrounded by manicured lawns, rhododendrons, camellias and low stone walls. You approach it along narrow country lanes – the hotel sends directions. It is a family concern, owned by Victor and Diana Shephard and run with their son David. "Restful, comfortable, excellent food and attentive, friendly but unobtrusive service. High standard of decor and cleanliness." The best bedrooms are large and high-ceilinged, all are individual in colour, size and shape, and have comfortable beds, good bedside lights, efficient heating and garden views. Bathrooms, some quite small, have been cleverly fitted in; some are on a separate level reached by a small stairway. There is a "relaxing lounge, with roaring log fire, books, magazines and fresh flowers". The dining room is "attractively panelled, with generous tables, well-starched white linen, highly polished glass, cutlery – and service – by friendly young girls"; men are expected to wear jacket and tie. Cooking, by Alastair Carter, is "difficult to fault – well-balanced menus with reasonable amount of choice, good local ingredients and well-cooked vegetables" – though these are not always quite hot enough. The cheese-board, with some unusual local produce, is a special feature. Breakfasts are "good and generous". (*Jane Turner, T Mayland, and others*)

Open All year except 2 weeks in early Jan.
Rooms 2 suites, 9 double, 1 single – all with bath, shower, telephone, radio, TV.
Facilities 2 lounges, bar, dining room; conference facilities. 6-acre grounds with putting, croquet and helipad. Beaches, fishing, riding, golf, bird-watching nearby; chauffeur-driven tours available.
Location 2½ m NE of centre of Kingsbridge. Hotel will send directions.
Restrictions Not suitable for ♿. No smoking in restaurant. No children under 8. No dogs.
Credit cards All major cards accepted.
Terms B&B (English): single £85–£115, double £95–£125, suite £145. Set lunch £14, dinner £23.75. Half-board rates (min 2 days). Champagne breaks; wine weekends; Christmas package. 1-night bookings sometimes refused over busy weekends and bank holidays.
Service/tipping: "10% included in the rates and the full amount is paid out to staff; they therefore do not expect tips."

KINGSTON BAGPUIZE Oxfordshire — Map 2

Fallowfields
Southmoor, Kingston Bagpuize
Nr Abingdon OX13 5BH

Tel Oxford (0865) 820416
Telex 83388 KINGS T Attn FALLOWFIELDS

Fallowfields, once the home of the Begum Aga Khan, is nowadays a "private house taking in paying guests" who appreciate the "personal and kindly welcome" of its attractive and energetic owner, Alison Crowther. It is very much a home, full of good Victorian pictures, decent china and glass, and masses of books. There is an immaculate garden with a small swimming pool and a hard tennis court. One front room suffers a bit from the traffic on the nearby main road, but a bypass is due in 1990. "The spacious bedrooms are splendid and emphasise the home-not-an-institution aspect. Ours faced south over the croquet lawn and vegetable gardens. Twin beds draped in expensive blue glazed chintz, piped and swagged with dull pink. Similar treatment for the big windows, no expense spared. Pink frilly draped lampshades, deep-piled fitted carpets, furniture a mixture of antique and repro, books everywhere. Some of the paintings were by our hostess, others collected by her late husband. Bathroom the size of a small bedroom with instant hot water, masses of towels, frills on the cistern, and every conceivable extra. Very good lighting in both bathroom and bedroom." Dinners (four courses, with some choice, served at 8) are lavish, with lots of good vegetables grown on the premises, and a sweet trolley laden with high-cholesterol goodies. "Nice warm home, delicious dinner by candle-light. We felt very comfortable." (*HR, PF, Jeff and Karen Nebel*)

Open 1 Apr–30 Sept. Winter weekend house parties for min 4 people – advance booking only. Dinner not served Wed.
Rooms 3 double – all with bath and/or shower, radio, TV and tea-making facilities; telephone available.
Facilities Lounge, TV lounge, dining room. 2-acre garden, 10-acre paddock; tennis, table tennis, croquet, heated swimming pool. Riding, golf, river and lake fishing, wind-surfing, water-skiing at Stanton Harcourt Leisure Centre nearby.
Location On A420 8 m SW of Oxford, 6 m from Abingdon. Light sleepers may be disturbed by traffic on A420, in 1 north room.
Restrictions Not suitable for ♿. No children under 10. Dogs at management's discretion, not in public rooms.
Credit card Access.
Terms [1989 rates] B&B: single occupancy £31, double £42–£48. Set dinner £14. 5% discount to regular visitors.
Service/tipping: "We do not make a service charge, a fact made clear to clients. If they regard service as exceptional they may hand contributions to the proprietor for distribution to the staff."

KIRKOSWALD Cumbria — Map 4

Prospect Hill Hotel
Kirkoswald, by Penrith
CA10 1ER

Tel Lazonby (076 883) 500

Small hotel owned by John and Isa Henderson, a conversion of old farm buildings on remote road in untrippery area north of Penrith easily reached from the M6. Old beams, open fires, brass beds, "a mixture of good old furniture and interesting junk". Recommended for friendly owners, clean and comfortable bedrooms, inexpensive à la carte dinners (vegetarian menu available), and generous breakfasts. "Good value for money." Closed Feb and 25 Dec. 11 bedrooms, 4 with private facilities. B&B double £35.50–£37.50. Full alc £14. Readmitted last year. More reports please.

LACOCK Wiltshire — Map 2

At The Sign of the Angel [GFG] — *Tel* Lacock (024 973) 230
Church Street, Lacock
Chippenham SN15 2LA

César award in 1989: Inn of the year

This 14th-century half-timbered inn in the heart of the ancient wool village of Lacock, now preserved by the National Trust, has been run by the Levis family for 36 years. It is "quintessentially English" with low doorways, oak panelling, polished brass and silverware, antique furniture, open fires, comfortable sofas and easy chairs in the lounge. Food in the candle-lit dining room is "archetypal good honest English cooking"; much of it comes from local suppliers. A written dinner menu has been introduced this year, with more choices of starter than hitherto, and a fish dish and vegetarian alternative to the main-course roast. Breakfasts include home-made bread and thick-cut marmalade. Last year we reported early-morning noise by cleaning ladies; the Levises tell us that in response to this, "staffing arrangements have been completely reorganised to restore peace and quiet; also there is no longer TV in the lounge – all bedrooms now have television sets (but no bedroom has a communal wall with any other bedroom)". Notwithstanding the attentions of the cleaning ladies, we continue to receive some grumbles about housekeeping in the bedrooms. *The Angel* may not be immaculate – but it has other graces to compensate.

Open All year except 22 Dec–6 Jan. Restaurant closed for Sat lunch; also Sun dinner to non-residents.
Rooms 8 double – all with bath, telephone, TV and tea-making facilities; 2 in cottage across garden.
Facilities Lounge, 2 dining rooms. ½-acre garden with stream.
Location 7 m S of M4 (exit 17); E of A350 between Chippenham and Melksham. Limited off-street parking.
Restrictions Not suitable for ♿. No children under 8. No dogs in public rooms.
Credit cards Access, Amex, Visa.
Terms (Service at guests' discretion) B&B: single £55, double £80. Set lunch £16.50, dinner £20. Winter breaks 1 Nov–1 Apr; mid-week breaks 1 Apr–31 Oct.

LAMORNA COVE Cornwall — Map 1

Lamorna Cove Hotel — *Tel* Penzance (0736) 731411
Lamorna Cove
Nr Penzance TR19 6XH

"We subjected this hotel to what must be considered a severe test: our party consisted of a 72-year-old lady with arthritis and strong views, an eight-year-old and a five-year-old (they have strong views too) and two mild parents. We booked for six nights in the first week of August 1988, decided to stay a seventh and shipped in a further family member for two of the nights. They coped with charm and efficiency. The position is idyllic – lovely view with the sea framed between the cliffs; the hotel is down a leafy glen and seems to float in the trees. Its grounds are superbly kept – beautiful swimming pool, attractive gardens on the rocky slope above the terrace. Undoubtedly the best accommodation is the suite, which has a wonderful sea view. The dining room is immaculate, with great attention given to detail – napery, flowers, candles. Excellent meals offering a balance between some of the richer French dishes, local specialities and also something in the plain steak line for those wanting simpler food. Our party could all eat from the same menu without anything special having to be provided. Good range of desserts too including the familiar, the rich, the light and the adventurous. Excellent home-made croissants for breakfast which in general was very good. Service couldn't be faulted. They will bring you anything anywhere at any time, including early morning tea and breakfast in bed, and really want you to enjoy it. Children are *welcome,* not tolerated. And because they know they are welcome the children are all beautifully behaved. It is a *wonderful* hotel; and remarkable value." (*Helen Watanabe, endorsed by Minda Alexander, and others*)

The hotel, which has been owned since 1987 by the Schlemmer family, lies at the foot of a long leafy valley on the sheltered southern coast of the Penwith peninsula – the rugged toe of Cornwall between Penzance and Land's End; much of the surrounding land belongs to the National Trust. It was originally a quarry-owner's house and an old chapel, and has a modern extension. Bedrooms are individually decorated, clean and comfortable; some overlook the sea, as does the dining room. There is a rocky beach with some sand at low tide, access to the Cornish coastal path and surfing at Sennen Cove ten miles away. A minor niggle: "There is muzak (albeit quiet) in the restaurant." There was also a thumbs-down by a visitor in April 1989: he was not given the two rooms with sea view he had requested for single occupancy, and was severely critical of the food. More reports please.

Open All year.
Rooms 1 suite, 17 double – all with bath and/or shower, telephone, radio, TV and baby-listening.
Facilities Lift. 3 lounges, cocktail bar, dining room; patio. 6-acre grounds with garden, woodland, heated swimming pool. Sandy beach at low tide; safe bathing, fishing. Golf nearby.
Location 4 m SW of Penzance. Take B3315 towards Land's End.
Restriction No dogs in public rooms.
Credit cards Access, Amex, Visa.
Terms (Service at guests' discretion) B&B £40–£70, dinner B&B £45–£75. Set dinner £14.50. 3-night bookings min over bank holidays. Reduced rates and special meals for children.

LANGHO Lancashire — Map 4

Northcote Manor [GFG] *Tel* Blackburn (0254) 40555
Northcote Road, Langho *Fax* (0254) 46568
Nr Blackburn BB6 8BE

Northcote Manor is a restaurant-with-rooms in a slightly dilapidated converted manor house with its back to the A59, 15 minutes from the M6.

The manor is "all olde worlde atmosphere – beams, oak panelling, roaring fires, handsome staircase". It is owned by two young men, Craig Bancroft and Nigel Haworth; the latter, who is also the chef, has rapidly acquired a high reputation for excellent food, modern Anglo-French in style, with the emphasis on the fresh and seasonal. Redecoration and renovation are in hand, all the bedrooms will be revamped by the end of 1989. There are only six, of varying sizes, all with private bathrooms or showers. "Our room was full of huge Victorian furniture in keeping with the house; very comfortable, high bed, huge wardrobe; the bathroom similarly huge, with beautiful tiles, pretty towels, a bath big enough to drown in." (*Karen Trinder; also JR, and others*) The emphasis is definitely on the restaurant side of things. The entrance leads straight into the bar, which can be disconcerting to arriving guests laden with suitcases; there is no residents-only lounge; service can sometimes be casual and housekeeping haphazard. Some confusions over bookings are reported this year. Comments on breakfast range from "superb" to "very poor"; it seems to depend on who is around to serve it.

Open All year except 25/26 Dec.
Rooms 6 double – all with bath and/or shower, telephone, radio, TV and tea-making facilities; baby-listening by arrangement.
Facilities Bar, lounge, restaurant; private dining room. 2-acre grounds.
Location From M6, Junction 31, take A59 towards Whalley. Hotel is on left at sign for Old Langho.
Restrictions Not suitable for ♿. No dogs in public rooms.
Credit cards All major cards accepted.
Terms (Service at guests' discretion) B&B: single occupancy £49, double £59. Set lunch £8.95, full alc dinner £30. Weekend rates.
Service/tipping: "Tipping is not necessary as service should always be good. If guests insist, money is shared equally by all staff."

LASTINGHAM North Yorkshire — Map 4

Lastingham Grange — *Tel* Lastingham (075 15) 345
Lastingham, York YO6 6TH

"I endorse all that is said in your 1989 report. It is difficult to find anything to criticise concerning this superbly run hotel. Very helpful and friendly owner and staff. Attractive garden in peaceful setting." "Staff very good, exemplary host. Most comfortable bedroom and good food." "One of the nicest hotels we have stayed at in England, Dennis Wood is the perfect example of what a hotelier should be. He seemed to be on duty all the time." "The breakfasts large and delicious; dinners (four courses with a reasonable amount of choice) were always good and sometimes very good." (*Edward Hibbert, Dr R Freeman, JRE Sedgwick, Mary and Rodney Milne-Day*) Plenty of approval this year for this modest country hotel, thoroughly traditional in both decor and style of cooking, which has appeared in the Guide since the first edition. *Lastingham Grange* was opened as a hotel in 1946 by the father of the present proprietor, Dennis Wood. It is an old stone creeper-covered house with a courtyard, large grounds with a carefully tended garden, fine old trees and fields, in a particularly tranquil setting in the heart of the North Moors National Park. The only criticism this year came from a reader who felt the room allocated to him (No 11) was altogether too small for a double, with a very small bathroom and no outlook – "but it was spotlessly clean, with a posy of fresh flowers on the dressing table, and the bed was turned down at night. Very good value for money."

Open Mar–Dec.
Rooms 10 double, 2 single – 10 with bath (2 also have shower), all with telephone, radio, TV, tea-making facilities and baby-listening.
Facilities Hall, lounge, dining room; terrace. 10-acre grounds with garden, croquet, swings, slides, adventure playground. In National Park, near moors and dales; riding, golf, swimming nearby.
Location Off A170, 5 m N of Kirkbymoorside. Turn N towards Appleton-le-Moor 2 m E of Kirkbymoorside.
Restrictions Not suitable for ♿. Dogs by arrangement only, not in public rooms.
Credit cards Amex, Diners.
Terms [1989 rates] B&B (English): single £41.75, double £77; dinner, B&B: single £50.50–£52.75, double £93–£97.75. Set lunch £9.75, dinner £16.25. Picnic lunches available. Reduced rates for long stays and winter breaks. Children under 2 sharing parents' room free; special meals.
Service/tipping: "No service charge. Tipping is discouraged."

LAVENHAM Suffolk — Map 3

The Great House Hotel and Restaurant [GFG]
Market Place, Lavenham
CO10 9QE

Tel Lavenham (0787) 247431

A hybrid: a restaurant-with-rooms, American-owned, French-run, in a quintessential well-preserved English medieval house (with a Georgian facade) in a lovely old market town. There are only four bedrooms, all spacious, all with a sitting room or sitting area, bathroom (quite small), gas fire, TV and antiques. They are attractively decorated, though – as you might expect in a building of this age – some windows are on the small side and some do not shut properly. Squeaking floorboards are another period feature. But what matters here is the food produced by Régis Crépy in the oak-beamed, candle-lit dining room with the original inglenook fireplace. "The menu", says the Good Food Guide, "is French, with nods towards *nouvelle cuisine*"; set meals are reasonably priced. "A welcome contrast to the luxurious and expensive hotels. Plenty of solid comfort. Food good – we had one lunch and two dinners and enjoyed them all. Service friendly, if over-stretched. Generally very good value." (*David Felce, and others*) More reports please.

Open All year except Jan. Restaurant closed Mon in winter.
Rooms 4 suites – all with bath and/or shower, telephone, radio, TV, tea-making facilities and baby-listening.
Facilities Bar/lounge, restaurant; patio. 5-acre grounds with children's play area.
Location Take Market Lane in High Street. Hotel is behind Market Cross. Parking.
Restrictions Not suitable for ♿. No dogs in public rooms.
Credit cards Access, Visa.
Terms B&B: single occupancy £45–£60, double £56–£76. Set lunch £7.50, dinner £12.75 (except Sat); full alc £25. Reduced rates for children sharing parents' room. 2- and 3-night breaks. Single-occupancy bookings not accepted Sat or bank holidays.
Service/tipping: "No service charge. Tips at guests' discretion, shared among staff."

Please make a habit of sending a report if you stay at a Guide hotel.

LEAMINGTON SPA Warwickshire — Map 2

The Lansdowne Hotel *Tel* Leamington Spa (0926) 450505
Clarendon Street *Telex* 337556
Leamington Spa CV32 4PF

César award in 1989: Best town house hotel

David and Gillian Allen's elegant Regency town house is near the centre of this once fashionable and still delightful watering place, convenient for Warwick Castle, the National Exhibition Centre (25 minutes by car) and the National Agricultural Centre (10 minutes). Over the years many guests have praised the warmth of welcome, the "bright and cheerful" bedrooms – "comfortable, spotless and well equipped" the "straightforward and tasty" meals – "generous helpings of delicious English food, complemented by excellent wine" and the good value for money. "The *Lansdowne* combines the best of both worlds – the cosy atmosphere of home with the luxury of a good quality hotel. The Allens and their staff work together to ensure that each guest is made to feel special." (*Sue Wildman; also Jean and Joe Carolin*) The Allens have acquired an adjacent house, which will enable them to add five *en suite* bedrooms by the end of 1989. This year one reader found herself in a very small room, and was refused a light evening meal on the grounds that only the four-course menu was served at night.

Open All year. Limited food service 24 Dec–7 Jan.
Rooms 10 double, 5 single – 5 with bath and shower, 7 with shower, all with telephone, radio and double glazing; TV, baby-listening by arrangement.
Facilities Residents' lounge with TV, bar, restaurant. Small garden. Discounts for guests for local attractions such as Ragley Hall, Warwick Castle, Coventry Cathedral crypt,
Location Central, on A425 (rooms are double-glazed). Parking.
Restrictions Only restaurant and bar suitable for ♿. No children under 5. No dogs.
Credit cards Access, Visa.
Terms (No service charge) B&B £19.65–£27.95; dinner, B&B £32.95–£38.95. Set lunch £10.95, dinner £12.95. 2-night packages. Reduced rates for children sharing parents' room; special meals by arrangement.
Service/tipping: "We have always felt this to be an unnecessary impost. However, if guests ask to recognise a particular service we try to get the member of staff together with the guest for a few personal words."

LEDBURY Hereford and Worcester — Map 2

Hope End Country House Hotel [GFG] *Tel* Ledbury (0531) 3613
Hope End, Ledbury HR8 1JQ

"As expected from the Guide a visit of absolute peace and tranquillity. The house and surroundings are lovely. Every room a delight, the food excellent, with very fresh ingredients used expertly to create original dishes. Breakfasts also very good. All in all a superb break, and not that expensive when one considers that dinner, bed and breakfast were all top class." (*Karen Trinder*) Many other readers appreciate equally warmly the quite special kind of hospitality that John and Patricia Hegarty offer – for those who have a taste for it. *Hope End* celebrated its tenth anniversary as a hotel in 1989. It is all that remains of Elizabeth Barrett Browning's childhood home. Once a Moorish fantasy, most of the original was pulled down by later owners, leaving one lone minaret and huge stable gates. It is in a beautiful hidden valley with big trees – a place of great serenity. The hard-working owners tend a vast walled organic vegetable and fruit garden, and keep chickens and goats. The unpretentious bedrooms, mostly pine-clad, are pleasantly furnished, with woven covers on the beds. "A dream-like retreat for city dwellers who wish to escape from the superficialities of 'sophisticated' city life. The Hegartys offer only the minimum of formalities, and some guests may be put off by the unusual lack of eagerness to flatter and please, and find Mr Hegarty a trifle aloof. The food is both healthy and mouth-watering. No lashings of cream, no large pats of butter to disguise any inadequacies in the quality of cooking or ingredients. It is not a typical luxurious hotel – one feels like a guest in the Hegartys' private home." (*Karen Trinder, V Tan; also HR, Barbara Rieck, and others*) To some visitors the Hegartys' "un-unctuous" approach is inhibiting. And not all readers are enthusiastic about the five-course meals with no choice of main course. But those it pleases are mightily pleased.

Note: Patricia Hegarty's just published *An English Flavour* contains 130 *Hope End* recipes.

Open Mar–Nov inclusive. Closed Mon and Tue nights. Restaurant closed for lunch.
Rooms 9 double – all with bath, telephone and tea-making facilities; 1 in cottage, 1 in minaret.
Facilities 3 sitting rooms, dining room. Walled garden; 40 acres parkland.
Location 2 m N of Ledbury, just beyond Wellington Heath.
Restrictions Not suitable for ♿. No smoking in dining room. No children under 14. No pets.
Credit cards Access, Visa.
Terms [1989 rates] Dinner, B&B £58–£86. Set dinner £25. Reduced rates for 2 or more nights; special breaks Mar and Nov. Advance bookings only for weekends. *Service/tipping: "Our prices are fully inclusive. No tipping expected."*

LEW Oxfordshire — Map 2

The Farmhouse Hotel and Restaurant — *Tel* Bampton Castle (0993) 850297, *Telex* 83242 FARMHOUSE
University Farm
Lew, Nr Bampton OX8 2AU

"Tremendous value and a comfortable, welcoming place to stay." "Warm, relaxed and friendly atmosphere. No unnecessary frills in hotel or restaurant, but it is not plain or boring. Excellent five-course dinner (with limited choice and sorbet in the middle)." A modernised farmhouse run by the Rouse family, well set back from the road, attached to a 216-acre working farm in a village with fewer than 60 inhabitants. It is unpretentious – more a farm guest house than a hotel, though the bedrooms are characterful, comfortable and well equipped (telephone, TV etc); one, on the ground floor has been adapted for disabled guests. The atmosphere is informal (for some too informal) – do not be surprised to find a dog on the sitting room sofa. The restaurant is made up of three rooms of varying size, including the original farmhouse dining room, with inglenook fireplace and beamed ceiling, and a Victorian-style garden room overlooking a terrace with pool and fountain. Few guests have been put off by its proximity to Brize Norton airfield, "all is quiet at night". (*Christine White, Mrs K Parsons, and others*)

Open All year except Christmas and New Year. Restaurant closed to non-residents Mon–Thurs in Jan.
Rooms 6 double – all with bath and/or shower, telephone, radio, TV and tea-making facilities. 1 ground-floor room equipped for ♿.
Facilities Lounge, lounge bar, restaurant. ½-acre garden with sun terraces.
Location On A4095, 3 m SW of Witney on Bampton road.
Restrictions No children under 5. No dogs.
Credit cards None accepted.
Terms (No service charge) B&B £18.50–£25; dinner, B&B £32–£38.50. Set dinner £13.50. 1-night bookings sometimes refused on Sat and bank holidays. Reduced rates for children sharing parents' room.
Service/tipping: "If tips are left the staff share them according to hours worked."

LEWDOWN Devon — Map 1

Lewtrenchard Manor [GFG] *Tel* Lewdown (056 683) 256 and 222
Lewtrenchard
Nr Okehampton EX20 4PN *Fax* (056 683) 332

This splendid manor in a peaceful Devon valley eight miles from Tavistock featured in earlier editions of the Guide, under different owners and the name *Fox's Earth*. It is Elizabethan in origin, E-shaped with mullioned windows: the interior is a mixture of styles, owing to Victorian embellishments and alterations. Public rooms have decorated plaster ceilings and dark oak panelling, with ornate fireplaces in the lounge and drawing room; the small dining room is hung with oil paintings and family portraits; there is a grand staircase, and a long gallery. The manor stands in 11-acre grounds with impressive formal gardens, a dovecote, and a private lake with fishing. The "most charming, convivial and civilised" hosts, James and Sue Murray took over *Lewtrenchard* in 1988 and have redecorated and refurbished, and added heating in the bathrooms. They have kept the "excellent" chef, David Shepherd, whose cooking is "ornate, in keeping with the manor, sophisticated and very professional, though portions are a bit over-generous". More reports please. (*Major and Mrs Garrett, and others*)

Open All year except 2 weeks in Jan. Restaurant closed for lunch except Sun.
Rooms 1 suite, 7 double – all with bath and shower, telephone, radio, and TV.
Facilities 2 lounges, bar lounge, dining room. 11-acre grounds with fishing lake, croquet lawn.
Location 8 m N of Tavistock. Just S of A30 at Lewdown.
Restrictions Not suitable for ♿. No children under 8. Dogs by arrangement, not in public rooms.
Credit cards All major cards accepted.
Terms (Service at guests' discretion) B&B: single £50–£65, double £75–£98, suite £110. Set Sun lunch £14.50, dinner £23; full alc £30..
Service/tipping: "We feel the guests should decide if a tip is warranted or not."

> Hotels often book you into their most expensive rooms or suites unless you specify otherwise. Even if all room prices are the same, hotels may give you a less good room in the hope of selling their better rooms to late customers. It always pays to discuss accommodation in detail when making a reservation.

LICHFIELD Staffordshire — Map 4

Oakleigh House Hotel
25 St Chad's Road
Lichfield WS13 7LZ

Tel Lichfield (0543) 262688 and 255573

Small hotel ten minutes' walk from centre of city of Dr Johnson's birth, overlooking Stowe Pool. Recommended for "charmingly furnished rooms with thoughtful touches, delightfully appointed conservatory restaurant with straightforward food and unpretentious wine list, friendly and welcoming owners and cheerful staff". Half-acre garden. Closed 26 Dec to early Jan, 2 weeks about July. 10 rooms (5 in converted stable block), 3 with private facilities. B&B double £48. Residents' set dinner at 7 pm £8.50, full alc £19.75. New ncmination. More reports please.

LIFTON Devon — Map 1

The Arundell Arms [GFG]
Lifton PL16 0AA

Tel Lifton (0566) 84666

This creeper-covered stone building, on the A30 (front rooms are soundproofed and ventilated), formerly a coaching inn, has had a Guide entry for many years. It is very much a sportsperson's hotel, and is particularly popular with the fishing fraternity – it has 20 miles of salmon, trout and sea-trout fishing on the river Tamar and its tributaries and a three-acre stocked lake. It offers fishing courses of all kinds; there are two full-time fishing instructors. In winter there are shooting packages, and the hotel also fills its rooms with bridge and golfing holidays, cookery courses and gourmet weekends; meetings and conferences too are catered for. Last year the *Arundell Arms* had an italicised entry, following little feedback and serious criticisms of service in the restaurant, though the cooking under the new chef Philip Burgess was reported much improved. Ann Voss-Bark who has owned and run the hotel for over a quarter of a century tells us that the service problems have been sorted out and recent reports confirm this: "No complaints at all. Food remarkably good by any standard, accommodation comfortable, general atmosphere most friendly." (*DW Mullock*) Another reader is even more positive: "There is no finer base in England to fish or hunt from, but there is plenty to do if you don't fish or hunt. . .the hotel gives out a warmth and hominess that makes one immediately comfortable. It makes you want to forswear forever all those overly fussy hotels with choreographed dinners." (*Miss AM Bennett*)

Open All year except 4 days over Christmas.
Rooms 19 double, 10 single – all with bath and/or shower, telephone, TV and tea-making facilities; baby-listening in main building. 5 rooms in annexe.
Facilities Lounge, cocktail bar, 2 restaurants; 3 conference rooms.
Location 3 m E of Launceston on A30 (front rooms soundproofed).
Restrictions Not suitable for ♿. No dogs in restaurant.
Credit cards All major cards accepted.
Terms B&B £33.50–£46. Set lunch £12, dinner £20; full alc £30. Fishing holidays all year; shooting, bridge, cookery holidays, gourmet weekends in off-season. Children under 16 accommodated free in parents' room; special meals on request. *Service/tipping: "No charge is made for service, nor are tips expected. I feel strongly that this is a service industry and there should be no obligation either mandatory or morally on*

guests to tip. Any gratuities given are pooled and distributed monthly and equally to all staff."

LINCOLN Lincolnshire — Map 3

D'Isney Place Hotel
Eastgate, Lincoln LN2 4AA

Tel Lincoln (0522) 538881
Fax (0522) 511321

A Georgian B&B hotel with a garden, with some bedrooms overlooking the nearby cathedral. It has neither reception nor breakfast room; breakfast, continental or English – mostly approved this year – is served in the bedrooms which vary in size and style. Most readers have had "comfortable beds in which it was possible to read" and appreciated "the do-it-yourself tea and coffee-making facilities with real milk" and "spacious bathroom, a *proper* room with a window and separate shower cabinet." One, however, had a four-poster with a mattress "with a ditch in the middle", which did not quite compensate for the luxurious bathroom with double jacuzzi. Back rooms are peaceful, those on the street side get some traffic noise, particularly on weekdays (but the windows are double-glazed). There is a carpark but it is "small and awkward to manoeuvre out of". Some housekeeping slip-ups are again reported: two couples found only one set of towels in the bathroom, for example; and the fresh fruit promised in the brochure was not always forthcoming. More reports please.

Open All year.
Rooms 1 suite, 14 double, 2 single – all with bath and/or shower, 2 with jacuzzi, all with telephone, radio, TV, tea-making facilities and baby-listening. Also 2 cottages, each with 2-double bedrooms, lounge, dining room, kitchen.
Facilities No public rooms. 1-acre garden.
Location By cathedral. Rooms double-glazed. Carpark.
Restriction Not suitable for ♿.
Credit cards All major cards accepted.
Terms B&B: single £38–£46, double £55–£65. Weekend breaks. No charge for children in parents' room.
Service/tipping: "No service charge. No tipping; but guests do leave gifts for staff."

LITTLE HORSTED East Sussex — Map 3

Horsted Place
Little Horsted
Nr Uckfield TN22 5TS

Tel Uckfield (0825) 75581
Fax (0825) 75459
Telex 95548 HORSTD

"A hotel *de grand luxe* in a remarkably fine 19th-century building, after the style of Pugin. It formerly belonged to Lord Rupert Nevill who had the courage to paint the ubiquitous panelling and the magnificent carved staircase white so that the atmosphere is not only grand but also light and welcoming. Public rooms are pleasantly proportioned, well lit and delightfully furnished; there is a striking long gallery. Nearly all the rooms are suites; ours, Tower, was faultlessly luxurious and comfortable: large bowl of fresh fruit, bottles of mineral water in the sitting room, remote-control TV in both sitting room and bedroom, bathroom extras, including bathrobes, all of a piece. Shoes left outside the room were polished overnight. Dinner was a very *soigné* affair, impeccably served, but alas was a major disappointment; nearly all the dishes lacked flavour.

Breakfast, criticised in past editions of the Guide, was by contrast thoroughly satisfactory." (*HR*) Other readers were luckier with dinner: "Food excellent, vegetables lightly cooked, served separately, and ample." (*Joy and Raymond Goldman*) There are major changes afoot outdoors: the original garden is intact but much of the grounds have been converted into an 18-hole golf course. Further away, out of sight and earshot, another 18-hole golf course and a 200-bed hotel, the *Golf Hotel*, are being constructed and are due to open in 1990. We are assured that these new golfing enterprises will not impair the pleasures of *Horsted Place* for non-golfers. We should welcome reports, particularly from the latter.

Open All year except first week Jan. Restaurant closed for Sat lunch.
Rooms 14 suites, 3 small double – 16 with bath and shower, 1 with bath, all with telephone, radio and TV. Some ground-floor rooms.
Facilities Lift, ramps. Drawing room, morning room, library, restaurant; indoor heated swimming pool. 23-acre grounds with 7-acre gardens, golf, tennis and croquet. Adjacent to small lake with fishing rights.
Location 2 m S of Uckfield by junction of A22 and A26.
Restrictions No children under 7. No dogs.
Credit cards All major cards accepted.
Terms B&B double £80–£265. Set lunch £15, dinner £25. Champagne breaks.
Service/tipping: "We have no service charge; staff are guaranteed a minimum wage to compensate them for the loss of the service charge; tipping is no longer expected or encouraged."

LITTLE SINGLETON Lancashire — Map 4

Mains Hall Hotel
86 Mains Lane, Little Singleton
Nr Poulton-le-Fylde FY6 7LE
Tel Poulton-le-Fylde (0253) 885130

"I stayed here while at the Democrats' conference and was the *only* person I met in Blackpool who was happy with their accommodation. An attractive, comfortable, easy-going place; staff most obliging about out-of-hours requests for sustenance. As it is only about 15 minutes' drive from Blackpool centre it is ideal for anyone who has business there, but wants to avoid the town as much as possible (and who could blame them?). Excellent value." *Ann Laybourn* endorses our entry for this small, friendly, old manor house in a pastoral setting, with rooms looking over meadows to the river Wyre and a pleasant garden in front. It is a house of character and history, too: the Hesketh lived here in Elizabethan times, and George IV, when Prince of Wales, courted Maria Fitzherbert in these rooms. And the owners, Bob and Beryl Owen, are as unpretentiously sympathetic as their hotel. Dinner is a home-cooked three-course no-choice event at 7 pm, (mention your allergies, state your preferences when you book). "Delicious dinners, excellent bar meals." "More like visiting a private house than a commercial establishment. It is quiet, and our bedroom was interesting and comfortable." (*Mrs C Curtis, Dr JV Boothman*) Except by special arrangement, no evening meal is served on Sunday or during the Owens' own holidays.

Open All year. Restaurant closed for lunch, on Sun and during owners' holiday (dates unspecified).
Rooms 9 double – all with bath and/or shower, telephone, radio, TV, tea-making facilities and baby-listening; 1 4-poster, 2 half-testers. 2 ground-floor rooms.
Facilities Lounge with TV, bar, dining room. 4-acre grounds with games room. Access to tidal river with fishing; bird-watching.

Location 5 m NE of Blackpool. Leave M55 at exit 3; take A585 N following signs to Fleetwood. Hotel is ½ m past 2nd set of traffic lights.
Restriction No dogs in public rooms.
Credit cards Access, Visa.
Terms B&B: single occupancy £22–£33, double £32–£53. Set dinner £11. 10% reduction for weekly bookings. Reduced rates for children sharing parents' room; special meals by arrangement.

LONDON — Map 3

Abbey Court Hotel — *Tel* (01) 221 7518
20 Pembridge Gardens — *Fax* (01) 792 0858
W2 4DU — *Telex* 262167 ABBY CT

A small, expensive, luxuriously equipped B&B which opened in 1988, in a relatively quiet street near Notting Hill, convenient for transport to the West End and the City. Outside are window boxes, bay trees and carriage lamps, inside antique and period furniture, and flowers. Bedrooms are not large; they vary in style, some have grand four-posters, others are more cottagey. There are marble bathrooms with whirlpool baths. "Attractively furnished, staff friendly." There is no restaurant, but light meals and tea are available, served in the bedroom or the conservatory. Their 1989 brochure advertises an English breakfast but in fact only continental is served; this is said to be "excellent, with freshly-squeezed orange juice and good brioches". Not for the infirm, as there is no lift.

Open All year.
Rooms 16 double, 6 single – 21 with bath and shower, 1 with shower, all with telephone, radio, and TV.
Facilities Reception lounge, conservatory.
Location Central, near Notting Hill Gate tube station. Meter parking.
Restrictions Not suitable for ♿. No children under 12. No dogs.
Credit cards All major cards accepted.
Terms Rooms: single £75, double £105–£130. Continental breakfast £6. (No restaurant, but light alc meals – about £20 – and teas served.)
Service/tipping: "No service charge. Tips at guests' discretion."

The Academy Hotel — *Tel* (01) 631 4115
17–21 Gower Street — *Fax* (01) 636 3442
WC1E 6HG — *Telex* 24364

A sympathetic conversion of two Georgian houses in Bloomsbury, with some original features retained; handy for the British Museum and Law Courts. Convivial bar, agreeable library, patio garden. Front rooms noisy (but double-glazed), back ones overlook the garden. Recommended for comfortable beds, warmth, cleanliness, good breakfast served in light and spacious basement room, and friendly service. No lift and not much porterage. Paid parking nearby. 27 double rooms, 5 single, 25 with shower (2 also have bath), all with TV. *Rooms: single £58.50–£64.50, double room £74.50–£79.50. Breakfast: continental £4.25, English £6.25. Weekend rates. New nomination. More reports please.*

> The dialling codes for central London will change at the end of May 1990 to 071.

The Alexander Hotel
9 Sumner Place, SW7 3EE

Tel (01) 581 1591
Fax (01) 589 5530
Telex 917133

A reasonably priced hotel in a residential area, made from three 19th-century town houses, which has been extensively refurbished in the last few years with much attention to detail. The decor is traditional, with restful colours, floor-to-ceiling drapes and thick carpets, good pictures, expensive door-knobs and light fittings. At the rear is a large paved flowery patio garden with chairs and tables, which guests are encouraged to use. It is overlooked by the Garden Restaurant – "very attractive, with green-and-white decor, comfortable chairs, larger than average circular tables, serving well-cooked dinners, and first-class breakfasts". Pre-theatre dinners are served from 6 pm; there is also a room-service menu including soups, cold meats and salads. Bedrooms are clean and comfortable, with good beds; they vary in shape and size, ones on the middle floor are probably the best bet (there is a lift). "Everything worked, and you didn't need a course in electrical engineering to work the shower". "Much improved. Highest standard of decor and cleanliness; room lacked nothing and everything functioned." (*EB, AWT Fuller*) The adjoining *Prince Hotel* is under the same ownership as the *Alexander*.

Open All year.
Rooms 1 suite, 36 double – all with bath and/or shower, telephone, radio, TV and baby-listening. 6 on ground floor.
Facilities Lift. Lounge, lounge bar, TV room, restaurant. Garden.
Location Central; garden-facing rooms quietest. No private parking. (Underground South Kensington.)
Restriction Dogs by prior arrangement only.
Credit cards All major cards accepted.
Terms [1989 rates] B&B: single occupancy £65–£85, double £85–£130, suite £165. Set dinner £14.50; full alc £17.75.

Athenaeum Hotel
116 Piccadilly, W1V 0BJ

Tel (01) 499 3464
Fax (01) 493 1860
Telex 261589 ATHOME
Reservations in US (800) 223 5560

The *Athenaeum* is the flagship hotel of the Rank chain. It has an enviable position overlooking Green Park (jogging maps and suits available for the energetic), and all the trimmings that one would expect from a de luxe West End hotel There are no-smoking bedrooms and all are double-glazed; quietest ones are on the side, but they lack the view of the park. Food is excellent, if expensive. Parking, shared with the adjacent hotel, costs £14.50 a day. For those who prefer to self-cater the hotel rents apartments in an adjacent building on a quiet side street. All our correspondents are enthusiastic about the place. Only one minor complaint: the hotel writes in our questionnaire "there is no service charge and tips are not expected". But a visitor on an all-inclusive weekend package told us that the waiter delivering breakfast to the bedroom patently sulked because he was not tipped.

Open All year.
Rooms 22 suites, 80 double, 10 single – all with bath and shower, telephone, radio and TV; free in-house films; double-glazing, air-conditioning; 24-hour room service. 33 1- and 2-bedroom apartments in adjacent building.

Facilities Lifts. Lounge, cocktail bar, restaurant; conference and function facilities.
Location Central; valet parking (£14.50 per day). (Underground Green Park.)
Restriction Guide dogs only.
Credit cards All major cards accepted.
Terms [1989 rates] Rooms: single £145, double £155–£170, suite £210–£250. Breakfast: continental £7, English £9.50. Set lunch £17.50 and £19.50 (including wine), dinner £25. Weekend packages. Reduced rates and special meals for children.

Basil Street Hotel
8 Basil Street
Knightsbridge, SW3 1AH

Tel (01) 581 3311
Fax (01) 581 3693
Telex 28379

A traditional and generally well-regarded hotel in a lane leading off Sloane Street (convenient for Hyde Park and Harrods); it is an Edwardian building, furnished with antiques, mirrors and paintings, and has numerous public rooms, including a panelled restaurant serving French-oriented food, a coffee shop, a cellar wine bar and a ladies' club. The impressive room on the left of the entrance was once a booking hall for the London Underground. The 94 bedrooms include suites and family rooms; many have a private bathroom. They vary greatly in size, style and position so it is worth trying to specify what you want; some of them can be surprisingly quiet for central London. One reader this year had "a magnificent suite with a large bathroom and double-glazed windows, overlooking the Brompton Road". Many visitors continue to praise the "modern comfort in an elegant old atmosphere", the "helpful staff", and the attentive manager, Stephen Korany. One reader, returning after a long interval reported, "It has much improved, particularly the food, which is now excellent. I was surprised to find that some of the old staff were still there and even more surprised that they still remembered me. All the service was excellent." (*GF Outland, RA Dubery, Richard Creed, and others*) However, as in the past, there are also criticisms: some rooms not good enough for the prices charged, some muddles in room service, and not all staff as friendly as those praised above.

Open All year.
Rooms 1 suite, 45 double, 48 single – 70 with bath and/or shower, all with telephone, radio and TV.
Facilities 3 lounges, coffee shop, wine bar, dining room; ladies' club; facilities for conferences, functions and private meals.
Location Central; public carpark nearby. (Underground Knightsbridge.)
Restrictions Not suitable for ♿. No dogs in public rooms.
Credit cards All major cards accepted.
Terms [1989 rates] (Service at guests' discretion) Rooms: single £45–£85, double £69–£110, family £155, suite £179. Breakfast: continental £4.30, English from £7.30. Set lunch £12.75, dinner £17.50; full alc £29.50. Weekend reductions Nov–Mar; 3-night Christmas stay. No charge for children under 16 sharing parents' room; special meals.

The Beaufort Hotel
33 Beaufort Gardens, SW3 1PP

Tel (01) 584 5252
Fax (01) 589 2834
Telex 929200

An elegant and pricey hotel, owned and run by former television reporter Diana Wallis, with the aim of providing "an English country-house atmosphere in the heart of London". It enjoys an excellent location on a quiet square. Guests continue to appreciate the pretty decor, the well-equipped bathrooms with many extras, the cleanliness and the friendly staff. This year's innovation is videos with a large library of tapes for use (free) by guests, and portable telephones for anyone wishing to receive incoming calls after 11 pm. Residents are given keys; light meals are served in the bedrooms between 7 and 9 pm; you can ask for tea-making facilities. Guests are entitled to free membership of a nearby health club. As is usual in buildings of this kind, some of the top rooms are quite small.

Open 2 Jan–22 Dec.
Rooms 9 junior suites, 16 double, 3 single – all with bath and/or shower, telephone, radio and TV/video; tea-making facilities available. Some ground-floor rooms.
Facilities Lift. Lounge with honour bar. Free membership of nearby health club.
Location Central, near Harrods. Meter parking; public carpark nearby. (Underground Knightsbridge.)
Restrictions No children under 10. Dogs by arrangement only.
Credit cards All major cards accepted.
Terms B&B (continental): single £135–£215, double £135–£215, junior suite £225. No charge for extra bed in suite. (No restaurant but light meals served in bedrooms 7–9 pm.)
Service/tipping: "Tipping is an indignity to both staff and guest. Our staff is properly paid."

Blakes Hotel *Tel* (01) 370 6701
33 Roland Gardens, SW7 3PF *Telex* 8813500

A trendy establishment despite a prim Victorian exterior, a few minutes' walk from South Kensington Underground. Its decor, theatrically stylish with a pronounced Oriental accent, is by the proprietor, former actress, now designer, Anouska Hempel who is constantly refurbishing and last year created new de luxe bedrooms in an adjoining building. Antiques, paintings and rare silks abound. All rooms are different; some are opulent, with heavy drapes and dark colours, others are plainer and lighter but equally stunning; it is best to discuss the style of room you prefer when booking. Some have tape deck and stereo among the extras. Reception is laid-back which won't suit all comers. No one would dream of asking men to wear jackets and ties in the black and mirrored dining room in the basement (tables have alternate black and white cloths). Last year we asked for comments on food produced by the new chef, David Wilson, who offers a cosmopolitan and pricey menu. We are told, "The quality of the cooking has returned to its standard of four or five years ago, and the service, too, has become outstanding." Not everyone, however, considers that it quite lives up to the prices charged. Breakfasts are said to be "delicious, with carrot juice, good croissants and decent thick brown toast". More reports please.

Open All year. Restaurant closed Christmas/Boxing Day.
Rooms 10 suites, 30 double, 10 single – all with bath and/or shower, telephone and TV; 20 with radio.
Facilities Lift. "Chinese Room" (lounge – light refreshments served), bar, restaurant.
Location Central; meter parking. (Underground South Kensington or Gloucester Road.)
Restrictions Not suitable for ♿. No dogs.
Credit cards All major cards accepted.

Terms (15% service charge for restaurant and room service) Rooms: single £115–£140, double £165–£245, suite £200–£510. Breakfast: continental £7.50, English £11. Full alc £70. Special meals for children on request.
Service/tipping: "We do not levy a service charge on accommodation; tips are at guests' discretion. We add a 15% charge to restaurant and room service bills which is included in the waiting staff's wages."

Capital Hotel [GFG]
22-24 Basil Street, SW3 1AT

Tel (01) 589 5171
Fax (01) 225 0011
Telex 919042

The *Capital* is a smallish, thoroughly modern, sophisticated hotel owned by David Levin who also owns *L'Hôtel* (below). The bedrooms have fabrics by the American designer, Ralph Lauren; they are double-glazed, air-conditioned and elegant in a country house sort of way, though with many urban extras, including full sound and vision service. What appear to be bookshelves turn out to be a deep, walk-in hanging cupboard; bathrooms are lavishly marbled and comprehensively equipped with bubble baths, toothbrushes and the like, as well as "wonderfully fluffy towels". Over the years the number of rooms has been reduced to make them more spacious. The *Capital*'s restaurant, with its "gentle Nina Campbell interior", has long been a mecca for London gourmets. Since June 1988 Philip Britten, the chef, has provided a menu which offers "simple combinations, without over-embellishment"; service is "courteous and efficient".

Rooms 8 suites, 28 double, 12 single – all with bath and shower, telephone, radio, TV and baby-listening; 24-hour room service.
Facilities Lift. Lounge, bar, restaurant; 2 private dining rooms. Business facilities available.
Location Central. Rooms double-glazed. Garage for 12 cars (£8 per night). (Underground Knightsbridge.)
Restriction Dogs at management's discretion, not in public rooms.
Credit cards All major cards accepted.
Terms B&B: single £141.50, double £173, suite £253. Set lunch £16.50 and £18.50; full alc £40. Children sharing parents' room free; special meals.
Service/tipping: "Service included. Tips not required nor expected."

Colonnade Hotel
2 Warrington Crescent W9 1ER

Tel (01) 286 1052
Fax (01) 286 1057
Telex 298930

A family-run hotel in a rambling Grade II Victorian listed building in a quiet residential area, but only fifteen minutes by bus or underground (Warwick Avenue station) to centre. Recommended for agreeable location, clean, well thought-out bedrooms (they vary in size and style), and reasonable rates. A new restaurant was recently opened. 52 rooms, most with private facilities (some spa baths). B&B (English) double £66–£77. Set dinner £11.50. New nomination. More reports please.

The 1991 Guide will appear in the autumn of 1990. Reports are particularly useful in the spring, but need to reach us by May 1990 if they are to help the 1991 edition.

The Connaught [GFG] *Tel* (01) 499 7070
Carlos Place, W1Y 6AL

"I thoroughly endorse the Guide's recommendation. The best hotel I have ever stayed in. Service almost beyond compare and the value surprisingly good when you consider the prices charged in fairly mediocre London hotels for an overnight stay." Many others concur. *The Connaught* is one of London's most exclusive hotels; it has no brochure, rates are "on application"; the 90 bedrooms are usually booked months in advance. It is in the heart of Mayfair, a strolling distance from Piccadilly and Oxford Street, in a relatively unbusy street. The decor is sophisticated; flowers abound. The restaurant, *Michelin*-rosetted, is formal with gleaming panels, arched windows and glittering chandeliers. Meals, under *maître* chef Michel Bourdin, are "classic and classy, with great luxury at every turn, you get the quality you pay for". One reader, however, reported "Worst and slowest service I can remember in any restaurant".

Open All year.
Rooms 114, including 24 suites – all with bath, telephone and TV; 24-hour room service. Some rooms suitable for ♿.
Facilities Lounge, cocktail bar, grill/restaurant (jacket and tie required; no jeans).
Location Central. No private parking. (Underground Bond Street.)
Restriction No dogs.
Credit card Access.
Terms On application.

Cranley Place Hotel *Tel* (01) 589 7944
1 Cranley Place SW7 3AB *Fax* (01) 225 3931

Recently refurbished "intimate little B&B hotel, Victorian, with a slightly modern flavour" in residential area a few minutes' walk from South Kensington station. Small garden. Recommended for quiet setting, friendly staff, stylish and pretty decor. Breakfast "adequate but not exceptional". 10 rooms, 3 with sitting area, all with bath and/or shower. Single £75–£80, double £90–£120. Breakfast: continental £3.50, English £6. Teas and sandwiches available. VAT *extra. Readmitted to the Guide under new owners. More reports please.*

The Draycott *Tel* (01) 730 6466
24–26 Cadogan Gardens *Fax* (01) 730 0236
SW3 2RP *Telex* 914947 DRAYCT

César award: Newcomer of the year, city division

This new star, a younger sister to *The Feathers*, Woodstock (q.v.), only opened in early 1989, but soon became known to hotel *cognoscenti*. "It consists of two large *fin-de siècle* houses in a miraculously quiet street a stone's throw from Sloane Square, overlooking gardens at the back. It successfully brings the country-house hotel *genre* to London, offering style and comfort somewhere between an extremely upmarket B&B and the *Connaught*. Our first-floor room was virtually a suite, with a sofa'd and armchaired sitting room at one end and a bedroom at the other, a corridor-like little hall and a bathroom beyond, generously equipped with luxury soaps, shampoos, dressing gowns and things of that sort. It was furnished with grandly draped twin beds, miscellaneous antiques and still more miscellaneous works of art. It was further enriched by a bogus coal fire, gas-fuelled, which overcame my prejudice against such shams by being extremely cosy. The *Draycott* has no restaurant but offers an enterprising and original room service menu, ranging through ordinary or champagne breakfasts to salads, sandwiches and steaks, and a useful wine list. There are also mini-bars in the rooms. You can breakfast in bed or downstairs in either of the two agreeable public rooms, a jolly nice drawing room looking onto the garden, and a resolutely Pall-Mall-like chamber, leathery and portrait-hung, which is unsurprisingly called the Club Room. Parking is rather a problem – one is dependent upon finding a free meter somewhere, and the staff in the uncomfortably cluttered reception area need some determined coaching in the hotelier's arts. Otherwise I have no criticism to make of this very comfortable and well-run hotel whose home-like rooms would provide an admirable base for a few days' stay in London and would not indeed disgrace anyone Coming Up To Town For The Season." (*Jan Morris*)

Warnings: "The *Draycott* is somewhat difficult to find thanks to the eccentric numbering system introduced by Victorian planners and the barely visible plaque that just whispers the hotel's name." Also one single room (No 21) is singularly small and faces the lift shaft.

Open All year.
Rooms 5 suites, 15 double, 6 single – all with bath, shower, telephone, radio, TV, baby-listening, mini-bar and 24-hour room service.
Facilities Lounge, Club Room, bar. ½-acre garden.
Location Between Pavilion Road and Draycott Avenue, behind Peter Jones. Meter Parking. (Underground Sloane Square.)
Restrictions Not suitable for ♿. Dogs by arrangement.
Credit cards All major cards accepted.
Terms (Service at guests' discretion) Rooms: single £75, double £165, suite £185. Breakfast: continental £4.95, English £7.50, champagne £12. Light meals available.

Durrants Hotel
George Street, W1H 6BJ

Tel (01) 935 8131
Fax (01) 487 3510
Telex 894919 DURHOT

A traditional, well-bred and relatively inexpensive hotel encased in a late 18th-century shell; it has been added to during the years which creates a quaint, rambling effect. In summer flowery window-boxes stretch the width of its facade. Formerly a coaching inn, it is one of the oldest privately owned hotels in London. It is convenient for Oxford Street, Harley Street, Marylebone Road and the Wallace Collection. Readers appreciate its old-fashioned comfort, "courteous service, fair prices and unpretentious hospitality. It is charming and pleasant without being stuffy." Bedrooms are individually decorated and well equipped; most are quiet, especially those at the rear. "Many have been recently refurbished – *beautifully*. I occupied several and they were all delightful." The panelled dining room can be an agreeable place to eat, but it is not inexpensive; there are plenty of other restaurants in the area. *Judith Trent; also David Lodge, and others*) A new manager, Mr Speed, has recently arrived.

Open All year. Restaurant closed over Christmas holiday period.
Rooms 3 suites, 3 family, 70 double, 19 single – 86 with bath and/or shower, 74 with WC, all with telephone, radio and TV; baby-sitting by arrangement. Some ground-floor rooms.
Facilities 3 residents' lounges, bar, snug room, restaurant, breakfast room, afternoon tea room; conference facilities.
Location Central (some front rooms could be noisy). Public carpark 5 mins' walk. (Underground Marble Arch.)
Restriction No dogs.
Credit cards Access, Amex, Visa.
Terms [1989 rates] (Excluding 12½% service charge added to restaurant bills) Rooms: single from £47, double from £72, family room from £121, suite from £160. Breakfast: continental £4.75, English £7.50. Full alc £25.
Service/tipping: "By showing the service charge separately we give the customer the chance to deduct the amount if he feels he has not been properly served."

Ebury Court *Tel* (01) 730 8147
26 Ebury Street, SW1W 0LU

An institution: a friendly old-fashioned hostelry run for over half a century by Diana and Romer Topham in five adjoining houses conveniently near Victoria Station. Cluttered corridors, rooms mostly small, furnishings varied. Some rooms have functional bathrooms en suite but queues for public loos in the morning can build up as many are in the shared bathrooms. Traditional English fare served in small basement restaurant, all corners and crannies. Many old Eburians wouldn't dream of going elsewhere, but this year, more than before, readers criticise shabbiness, poor food, indifferent housekeeping. Hence these italics. 39 rooms, 13 with private facilities. B&B (continental) double £67–£77; full alc dinner from £12. More reports needed.

Elizabeth Hotel *Tel* (01) 828 6812
37 Eccleston Square, SW1V 1PB

Welcoming, clean, comfortable and reasonably priced five-storey B&B in quiet residential square in Victoria, convenient for the station. Victorian decor. Guests have access to the attractive private garden (with tennis court) in the square. 24 bedrooms including some for families, a few with private facilities. More bathrooms and a lift to be installed by spring 1990. B&B (continental or English): single £28–£30, double £43–£64, family from £54. More reports please.

The Goring Hotel *Tel* (01) 834 8211
15 Beeston Place, SW1W 0JW *Fax* (01) 834 4393
Telex 919166

A traditional and dependably comfortable hotel built in 1910 by the present Mr Goring's grandfather. The bedrooms, in pastel colours, with good quality furniture, and provided with thoughtful extras, are frequently checked by the present owner, Goring the Third, who sleeps in each one looking for weak spots. A third of the bedrooms are totally redecorated each year. The standards of service and cleanliness are scrupulously maintained. There's a high return ratio: guests appreciate the Englishness of the place as well as its useful location just round the corner from Buckingham Palace. There is a large relaxing bar which overlooks an inner courtyard garden and lawn (not, however, accessible to guests). Reports on the food vary; restaurant service is said to be "quiet and professional".

Open All year.
Rooms 6 suites, 48 double, 36 single – all with bath and shower, telephone, radio and TV; some with air-conditioning. 24-hour room service.
Facilities Lift. Lounge, bar, restaurant; 5 function rooms. 1-acre garden (no access for guests).
Location Central, near Buckingham Palace (front rooms are double-glazed). Garage and mews parking. (Underground Victoria.)
Restrictions Not suitable for ♿. No dogs.
Credit cards All major cards accepted.
Terms (No service charge for hotel; 10% added to restaurant bills) Rooms: single £105, double £150, suite £190. Breakfast: continental from £5.50, English from £8. Set lunch £18, dinner £21; full alc £32. Special meals for children on request.

Hazlitt's — *Tel* (01) 434 1771
6 Frith Street W1V 5TZ — *Fax* (01) 439 1524

Hazlitt's, formerly a nurses' home, was created from three terrace houses built in 1718. It takes its name from the essayist who died in one of the houses a century later; the 23 bedrooms are named after famous residents and visitors to the house. Rooms are light and airy; at the top of the house they are quite small, lower down they have high ceilings; all have agreeable prints and plants, firm beds and decent linen. The hotel is furnished throughout with mahogany, oak and pine. A continental breakfast is served in the bedrooms, and light refreshments and cream teas are available in a sitting room. "A pleasure to stay here. All wood-panelled, quaint nooks and crannies, antique prints and furniture, and a Victorian bath (modern plumbing though!). I'd recommend it to anyone," writes *Ann Victoria Roberts* endorsing last year's comment, "Good value for money in an excellent location. Pleasant and clean; staff very friendly."

Open All year except Christmas.
Rooms 1 suite, 18 double, 4 single – all with bath and/or shower), telephone and TV. 2 ground-floor rooms.
Facility Lounge.
Location Central. NCP nearby. (Underground Tottenham Court Road.)
Restriction No dogs.
Credit cards All major cards accepted.
Terms Rooms: single £69, double £79, suite £128. Breakfast £4.50. (No restaurant.)
Service/tipping: "Service charge not added; all tips optional."

Knightsbridge Green Hotel — *Tel* (01) 584 6274
159 Knightsbridge, SW1X 7PD — *Fax* (01) 225 1635

"We have stayed here about ten times in the last two years and consider it our home in London. If you require room service, a doorman and someone to carry your luggage it is not for you, but if you are looking for lots of space, pleasant decor, great location, spotless housekeeping and brilliant plumbing, this is it. Best of all, the three or four ladies who run the front desk are at all times helpful, efficient, friendly and charming. The entrance hall has just been redecorated and the effect is bright and welcoming (it used to resemble a shadowy entrance to an opium den)." In the past two years this small hotel close to Harrods and Hyde Park, has been completely refurbished and refurnished, first the bedrooms, then the public areas. It is unusual in having mostly suites, each with a double room, reception room and bathroom; they are decorated with "taste and style unusual for a lower-priced hotel. Walls painted white and cream, furnished in shades of tan and blue. Bathrooms have been completely refitted, lighting is good. Full English breakfast, perfectly cooked, was delivered to our door each morning." Front rooms are double-glazed to keep out traffic noise; those at the back are quiet. Though prices have risen due to the refurbishment, the hotel remains excellent value for this part of London. No restaurant, but tea and coffee are available all day in the Club Room on the first floor. (*Sharon Gutman, Carol Barnes; also Dr AJ Pearce, Paul Hoffstein, and others*)

Open All year, except 5 days at Christmas.
Rooms 16 suites, 4 double, 2 single – all with bath and shower, telephone, TV and tea-making facilities; baby-listening by arrangement.
Facilities Lift. Club Room on first floor with complimentary coffee and tea.
Location Central (bedrooms overlooking Knightsbridge double-glazed). NCP in Pavilion Road nearby. (Underground Knightsbridge.)
Restrictions Not suitable for severely ♿. No dogs.
Credit cards Access, Amex, Visa.
Terms [1989 rates] Rooms: single £65, double £80, suite £95. Breakfast: continental £5.50, English £7.50. (No restaurant.)
Service/tipping: "Our rates include a service charge; guests are discouraged from further tipping by a notice in the bedroom."

L'Hotel
28 Basil Street, SW3 1AT

Tel (01) 589 6286
Telex 919042 HOTCAP attn L'HOTEL

A centrally located B&B in the upper-price bracket, owned by the Levins, who also own the neighbouring *Capital* (q.v.). Rooms are decorated in French country style. *L'Hotel* dispenses with such extras as porterage, hair-driers, and a multiplicity of bathroom accessories to maintain prices at a reasonable level for central London. Rooms are all different, but each has fabric-lined walls, fashionable window blinds and curtains, a tiny but well-thought-out bathroom, pine chairs, chests and cupboards, efficient heating, attractive lighting, lots of hot water at all times and a mini-bar. The staff are relaxed and pleasant, and there is a choice of eating arrangements for those not wishing to eat out – the admirable restaurant of the *Capital Hotel* next door or the good-value food in the *Métro*, the busy wine bar in the basement where the food is straightforward but interesting, (it has a Cruover machine, which dispenses good wine by the glass, and a reasonably priced wine list). Breakfasts, also served in the *Métro*, include fresh orange juice, good croissants and coffee. You need to book well ahead to have a choice of rooms: some are smaller than others and lack the cosy benefit of a gas coal-fire; rooms above the wine bar can be noisy until late into the night; the suite at the top is quietest. Parking is not easy. (*David and Kate Wooff*)

Open All year. Wine bar closed Sat evening, Sun and some public holidays, except for residents' breakfasts.

Rooms 1 suite, 11 double – all with bath and shower, telephone, radio, TV, tea-making facilities and mini-bar. 1 ground-floor room. (*Note:* no room service.)
Facilities Lift. Wine bar/brasserie.
Location Central. NCP opposite. (Underground Knightsbridge.)
Restriction Dogs at management's discretion.
Credit cards Amex, Visa.
Terms B&B: double £100 (single occupancy £100), suite £135. Extra bed in room £10. Alc meal in wine bar about £10; light meals also available.
Service/tipping: "Service included. Tipping at guests' discretion."

The Portobello Hotel *Tel* (01) 727 2777
22 Stanley Gardens, W11 2NG *Fax* (01) 792 9641
Telex 268349 PORT

"Excellent, in a good location on a quiet residential street. Singles on the upper floor are small but well-appointed. Staff more than willing to help with bags, then serve your dinner." "Relaxed and discreet. Prices reasonable for central London." "Eccentric and pleasantly surprising. The food was straightforward and good with friendly service in the cosy summer garden-style basement." The *Portobello* is a six-floor Victorian terrace house, within strolling distance of the Portobello Road market and a little further to Kensington Gardens. It has a distinctive decor of palms, Edwardiana, cane and wicker furniture and beige upholstery. Some of the rooms, called cabins, are poky, even if they have essential elements of life-support like colour TV, tiny fridge and micro-bathroom. But there are also, as you work downwards, normal-sized rooms and ritzy suites – the Bath Room has mirrors above the bed and painted clouds on the ceiling, the Round Room has a round bed and free-standing Edwardian bath. There is porterage and room service between 8 am and 4 pm, but reception, as well as bar and restaurant staff, are on duty day and night and happy to help with theatre or restaurant advice or bookings. (*John D Jones, Iain Elliott, Hugo and Sarah Cassirer*) Some critical reports as usual: "Continental breakfast packaged and disappointing". "Our bedroom had been nicely furnished but the 'micro' bath should have been discarded. It doesn't work for most bodies. The restaurant should be avoided."

Open 2 Jan–24 Dec.
Rooms 7 suites, 9 double, 9 single – 4 with bath and shower, 21 with shower, all with telephone, radio, TV, tea-making facilities and fridge; baby-sitting arranged.
Facilities Small lift. Lounge, bar/restaurant (open 24 hours a day to residents).
Location Central. Meter parking. (Underground Notting Hill Gate.)
Restriction Not suitable for ♿.
Credit cards All major cards accepted.
Terms [1989 rates] B&B (continental): single: £52.90–£54.05, double £97.75–£142.60, suite £142.60. Full alc £22. Special meals for children.
Service/tipping: "No service charge added to bill. Tipping not encouraged."

Swiss Cottage Hotel *Tel* (01) 722 2281
4 Adamson Road, NW3 3HP *Fax* (01) 483 4588
Telex 297232 SWISCO

Conversion of four Victorian terraced houses in quiet residential street in north-west London, conveniently placed for transport to centre. Filled with attractive antiques and paintings; delightful Tea House suite in cottage in garden. Recommended for comfortable bedrooms, good bathrooms, friendly and helpful service. 64 rooms, most with private facilities. B&B (continental) double £66–£96. Set dinner £13.50 [1989]. More reports please.

LONGFRAMLINGTON Northumberland — Map 4

Embleton Hall
Longframlington
Nr Morpeth NE65 8DT

Tel Longframlington (066 570) 249 and 206

A small family-run country house hotel in an early 18th-century stone building with Victorian additions. Only 30 minutes from Newcastle; also "an excellent base from which to explore this magnificent coastal stretch of Northumbria". Public rooms and bedrooms attractively furnished in traditional style. Recommended for courteous, friendly atmosphere, excellent and carefully served food. Children welcome. 5-acre grounds with tennis and croquet. 10 bedrooms, all with private facilities. B&B double £48. Set dinner £16. New nomination. More reports please.

LONGHORSLEY Northumberland — Map 4

Linden Hall Hotel
Longhorsley
Morpeth NE65 8XF

Tel Morpeth (0670) 516611
Fax (0670) 88544
Telex 538224

"A rare find – a luxury hotel which welcomes and caters for children; our labrador also recommends *Linden Hall*!" "*Linden Hall* has kept a large proportion of its staff for several years, unlike many hotels we have stayed in; they are ever-present but never intrusive, every request is dealt with courteously and efficiently." The hotel is a mansion of considerable grandeur, built in 1812 in the classical style, and set in 300 acres. There are many sporting facilities (see below) and the hotel also caters extensively for conferences, banquets and so on. Accommodation is extremely luxurious. Visitors appreciate many cossetings and kindnesses: thoughtful facilities for small children, bath gel and shampoo replenished *twice* a day, fresh fruit in bedrooms every day, Bendicks mints left at night when beds turned down, etc. But there have been two changes of chef during the past year – Keith Marshall took over the restaurant in March 1989. First reports, while appreciative, suggest that the restaurant falls a little short of "the impeccable standards of the rest of this beautiful hotel". Can we have more reports please, particularly on the food?

Open All year.
Rooms 5 suites, 44 double, 1 single – all with bath and shower, telephone, radio, TV, tea-making facilities and baby-listening. 10 ground floor-rooms, 2 equipped for ♿.
Facilities Lift. 2 lounges, 2 bars, conservatory, TV room, pub, restaurant; functions/conference facilities; billiards, table tennis, sauna, solarium. 300-acre grounds with tennis, putting, croquet, clay-pigeon shooting, adventure playground.
Location 4 m N of Morpeth on A697; 1 m N of Longhorsley off A697.
Restriction No dogs in public rooms.
Credit cards All major cards accepted.

Terms [1989 rates] B&B: single £70, double from £82.50, suite £125. Set lunch £14.50, dinner £17.50; full alc £30. Special breaks throughout year (Fri–Mon only Mar–Oct); special breaks. Sporting holidays. Children under 14 sharing parents' room free; special meals.
Service/tipping: "Tipping is up to the customer."

LOWER BRAILES Oxfordshire — Map 2

Feldon House [GFG] — *Tel* Brailes (060 885) 580
Lower Brailes
Nr Banbury OX15 5HW

A small country guest house with a good restaurant, run by Maggie and Allan Witherick, with a friendly dog and a couple of cats, in an early 19th-century house set back from the Shipston-on-Stour–Banbury road. It makes a good base for touring the Cotswolds and is convenient for Stratford-upon-Avon, which does not have many recommendable hotels. *Feldon House* is reasonably priced, quiet and welcoming, and furnished with taste and style; "books everywhere". There is a panelled drawing room and a small dining room with a conservatory extension; bedrooms are well appointed and warm; those in the main house have basins; two new ones, in a converted coach house, have bath and shower. Allan Witherick cooks "very English meals, with good bespoke ingredients and no fancy tricks"; lots of fresh vegetables, very generous portions; no choice – three courses for lunch, four for dinner; they are served in the dining room and a conservatory extension. Breakfast, a large Victorian table, is "wonderful" – a cooked, help-yourself affair. Some readers report a degree of regimentation about *Feldon House* – "we like our beef very rare but were not consulted about the fillet, which we thought overcooked"; "we were hurried through the end of our dinner because coffee was waiting in the lounge"; "we were not asked what we wanted for breakfast". But "despite these gripes it is well worth an entry, especially at these prices". More reports please.

Open All year.
Rooms 4 double – all with bath and shower, and telephone; some with TV and tea-making facilities. 2 in converted coach house.
Facilities 2 lounges, TV room, 2 dining areas. Terrace. ⅔-acre garden with croquet.
Location In middle of village on B4035 between Shipston and Banbury. Near church. Parking.
Restrictions Not suitable for ♿. No children under 11. Dogs by arrangement, not in public rooms.
Credit cards Access, Visa.
Terms B&B (English): single £25–£35, double £35–£45. Set lunch £13.50, dinner £16.50. 3-day bargain breaks. Reduced rates for children sharing parents' room.
Service/tipping: "Tips not solicited. If guests leave something it is distributed to all staff."

LOWER SWELL Gloucestershire — Map 2

Old Farmhouse Hotel — *Tel* Cotswold (0451) 30232
Lower Swell, Stow-on-the-Wold
Cheltenham GL54 1LF

16th-century stone farmhouse in secluded walled garden in unspoiled Cotswold village. Recommended for informal atmosphere, warm, clean and comfortable accommodation, welcoming proprietors – Rollo and Rosemary Belsham – and good food. Bedrooms individually decorated; some in stable block, other (smaller) ones in main building, 13 rooms, 11 with private facilities. B&B £21.75–£29.50. Set dinner £11.25. More reports please.

LOWESWATER Cumbria — Map 4

Scale Hill Hotel — *Tel* Lorton (090 085) 232
Loweswater, Nr Cockermouth
CA13 9UX

This 17th-century coaching inn has been owned by the Thompson family for several generations; currently it is run by Michael Thompson, his wife Sheila and daughter Heather – the latter being responsible for the food. It is in a secluded position between Crummock and Loweswater, in one of the least trippery parts of the Lake District, and has spectacular views of the hills to the north-west. The National Trust land at Crummock Water is half a mile through the woods. It is "a self-confident establishment, run with a slightly military efficiency and bonhomie". "Pleasant and comfortable, clever flower arrangements, Mr Thompson very much 'mine host'. More like a private house in the country than a hotel. We enjoyed every second of our stay. The cats are quite a feature of the place." Rooms vary – it is best to discuss options when booking, "ours was spacious and well furnished with much appreciated extras – nail-brush and hair-drier in bathroom, electric blankets. No telephones or radios in the bedroom, no television anywhere – just peace, comfort and beautiful scenery". "We liked the food very much. It was on the plain side, which suits us, vegetables imaginative and well cooked; good packed lunches." (*Ruth West, Paul and Deirdre McDonald; also Chris and Dorothy Brining, JRE Borron, and others*) Other visitors consider the food "good, but with some lapses"; and one minded not being forewarned that Sunday night supper was a cold meal apart from soup, felt that vegetarians were not properly catered for and would have preferred that breakfast was available earlier than 9 am.

Open All year except 3 weeks early Dec; also Jan, Feb.
Rooms 12 double, 5 single – all with bath and/or shower. 2 doubles in annexe 10 yards from main door. 2 ground-floor rooms.
Facilities Entrance hall, 2 residents' lounges (1 non-smoking), 2 public lounges, bar, dining room; laundry, drying room. Small grounds. Walking and climbing, golf, pony-trekking nearby, also 3 lakes with boating, fishing, swimming.
Location 12 m W of Keswick, just off B5289.
Restriction No dogs in public rooms.
Credit cards None accepted.
Terms B&B: single £30–£40, double £40–£72; dinner B&B: single £40–£54, double £60–£100. Set dinner £14; bar lunches. Reduced rates for long stays; winter rates; Christmas and New Year packages. 1-night bookings sometimes refused. Reduced rates for children sharing parents' room; high tea provided.
Service/tipping : "Service is included in the rate; we do not expect anything extra."

Traveller's tale *A request for cheese before pudding met with the response worthy of Basil Fawlty: "Cheese isn't my job, it's my husband's. We're not in France now, you know."*

LUDLOW Shropshire **Map 2**

Dinham Hall [GFG] *Tel* Ludlow (0584) 6464
Ludlow SY8 1EJ *Fax* (0584) 6019

"A new hotel, opened in late 1988, and amazing to find in the middle of Shropshire. It aims at the highest standards and triumphantly succeeds. We had a charming and extremely comfortable room and a meal that would have been exceptional anywhere. What it is *not* trying to do is to smother you in unwanted luxuries or impress with astronomical prices. It is too sophisticated for that. What it does give you are *real* luxuries like a huge jug of freshly squeezed orange juice at breakfast." (*Diana Rothenstein*) An inspector adds, "Paul and Marian Johnson have changed this former school (it is an 18th-century listed building) into a very high class hotel and restaurant. Welcome most cordial. Our room, Lacy, overlooked the castle and was spacious with comfortable beds, well-stocked mini-bar, fresh milk for morning tea, bowl of exotic fruit. Spotless and well-equipped bathroom. Much attention to detail. The house is warm, the staff young and willing. Pretty dining room with lots of fresh flowers. *Dinham Hall* has quickly become a popular restaurant. Chris Galvin's cuisine distinctly *nouvelle*; every dish a picture; small portions. Puddings slightly disappointing, but the clementine and lime sorbet in the middle of dinner was *brilliant* – sharp and pungent. We were sent away with an excellent picnic." For those in need of exercise the hotel has a gym; and it can arrange shooting, clay-pigeon shooting, fishing, gliding, riding and hot-air ballooning for guests. The off-season breaks are said to be very good value.

Open All year except 24–26 Dec. Restaurant closed to non-residents Sun evening.
Rooms 9 double, 1 single – 5 with bath and shower, 5 with shower, all with telephone, radio, TV, mini-bar and tea-making facilities.
Facilities Lounge bar, residents' lounge, restaurant, private dining room; gym, sauna. ¾-acre garden with terrace. Shooting, clay-pigeon shooting, fishing, riding, gliding, hot-air ballooning nearby.
Location Near castle. Parking.
Restrictions Not suitable for ♿. No children under 4. Dogs by arrangement, not in public rooms.
Credit cards Access, Diners, Visa.
Terms [1989 rates] Rooms: single £40–£45, double £55–£82. Breakfast: continental £3, English £6. Set lunch £10.95, dinner £16–£22.50; full alc £30. Off-season breaks. *Service/tipping: "No service charge. Tipping at guests' discretion, not encouraged by staff."*

The Feathers *Tel* Ludlow (0584) 875261
Bull Ring, Ludlow SY8 1AA *Fax* (0584) 876030
Telex 35637

The Feathers, owned and run personally by Osmond Edwards and his family, has been an inn since the 17th century. It has a spectacular half-timbered front elevation, carved mantelpieces and elaborately ornamented plaster ceilings, panelling and original fireplaces. Bedrooms are traditionally furnished but thoroughly modern in the comforts they offer; most are of a good size, and all have private bathrooms; some suites have fires and four-posters. *The Feathers* featured in earlier editions of the Guide but fell by the wayside after criticisms of the decor and the food. After a change of chef and considerable refurbishment it is brought back by warm commendations from several readers: "There is now a lift, and they have added a very nice patio from the dining room which will make a vast difference since there is no garden. The bedrooms are extremely good, with every comfort and mod con. The service is as friendly and efficient as we have ever encountered and the food superb and faultlessly served." "We had a well-equipped room; service was better than when we were there a few years ago. It is true there is an element of *nouvelle cuisine* in the dinner menus, but with the help of a co-operative head-waiter we managed to avoid the worst excesses and had a very good dinner." (*Sir Robert Lusty, HF King, and others*) *The Feathers* is the premier hotel of the town as well as a showplace in its own right. Be prepared for lots of passing trade – also conferences, banquets and coach parties. Not ideal for the disabled as owing to its venerable age there are lots of steps.

Open All year.
Rooms 6 suites, 24 double, 10 single – all with bath, shower, telephone, radio, TV, tea-making facilities and baby-listening.
Facilities Lift. Lounges, 2 bars, restaurant. Conference facilities.
Location In town centre. Carpark.
Restrictions Not suitable for severely ♿. No dogs in bedrooms.
Credit cards All major cards accepted.
Terms (No service charge) B&B (English): single £49–£54, double £78–£92, suite £92–£106. Set lunch £9.50; full alc dinner £20.

LYNTON Devon — Map 1

Waterloo House Hotel — *Tel* (Lynton) 0598) 53391
Lydiate Lane
Lynton EX35 6AJ

An early 19th-century building in a Victorian resort on a cliff, well situated for exploring Exmoor and the North Devon Coast. It is warmly nominated this year: "Simply phenomenal. A dolls' house of a hotel with ten bedrooms (some with private bath). The most comfortable bed I've slept in in a hotel. Everything spotless – table linen changed for each meal – fresh, and redolent of pot pourri. The furnishings are rather over-draped and ruched for my taste but it's fun for a while. It's owned and run by Stephen Blue and Peter Clover. Stephen does front of house and serves meals with friendly formality, playing the piano during the main course; Peter looks after the food – and *what* food!. Dinner is a four-course affair with no choice apart from pudding, delicious and imaginative. Breakfast is either beautifully presented full English or continental with croissants, warm Danish pastries and wholemeal toast. All this and unpushy advice on where to drive and walk for £25 per person [1989]. Miraculous value – we shall certainly return." (*Rod Hall*) Given notice special diets and vegetarians are catered for. More reports please.

Open All year. Dining room closed for lunch.
Rooms 1 suite, 7 double, 1 single – 2 with bath, 3 with shower, all with TV and tea-making facilities.
Facilities Bar lounge, non-smoking lounge, dining room. Small garden, courtyard.
Location 5 mins from village centre.
Restrictions Not suitable for ♿. No children under 14. No dogs.
Credit cards None accepted.
Terms B&B £15.50–£23.50. Set dinner £10.50. 3-day breaks.
Service/tipping: "Tips not expected, but accepted graciously, as refusal can sometimes offend."

LYTHAM ST ANNE'S Lancashire — Map 4

Dalmeny Hotel — *Tel* St Anne's (0253) 712236
19-33 South Promenade
Lytham St Anne's FY8 1LX

There are far too few recommendable seaside hotels for parents with young families: the *Dalmeny*, run by the energetic enterprising Webb family certainly is one – though it does have one restaurant, *C'est la Vie*, and a large lounge by the pool where children are not allowed in the evening. It is a cheerful, bustling establishment on the seafront of St Anne's, well endowed with sporting facilities, and offers plenty of entertainment in season (see below). There are three restaurants: *C'est La Vie*, which is French in style, *The Barbecue*, offering an à la carte menu which changes daily, and *The Carvery* open for breakfasts (substantial English) and lunch (joints and salads); as well as the *Buttery Bar* for sandwiches, salads, coffees and teas. The hotel also caters for conferences and meetings. The Webbs, who have owned the hotel since 1945, claim that the *Dalmeny* is unique in its flexible approach to the needs of families: their tariff is for rooms only so that families can choose their own "package" from any of the restaurants or use the small kitchens in the suites especially designed for families with babies or small children. Visitors appreciate these facilities, good value for money and the efficient and friendly staff at the *Dalmeny*. More reports please.

Open All year except 24–26 Dec.
Rooms 20 suites, 71 double and family – all with bath (7 also have shower), telephone, radio, TV, tea-making facilities and baby-listening; some with balcony; suites have kitchenette. 8 ground-floor rooms. 10 more rooms planned for 1990.
Facilities Lifts, ramps. Lounge bar, no-smoking lounge, sun lounge, TV room, 2 bars, Buttery Bar, 3 restaurants; indoor heated swimming pool, solarium, squash court, games room; organised crèche and family entertainments in holiday periods, live music, discos; children's outdoor play area. 4 championship golf courses nearby.
Location On seafront, 200 yards S of pier; 300 yards from town centre. Carparks and garages.
Restriction No dogs.
Credit cards Access, Visa.
Terms (Service at guests' discretion) Rooms: single occupancy £25–£32, double £32–£52, suite £50–£82. Breakfast from £3 (£2 for children). Lunch from £4.55, dinner from £7.75; full alc £16. Special breaks; weekly rates in high season. 1-night bookings refused in high season. Reduced rates and special menus/meals for children.

MAIDEN NEWTON Dorset — Map 2

Maiden Newton House — *Tel* Maiden Newton (0300) 20336
Maiden Newton — *Telex* 417182 ENEL
Nr Dorchester DT2 0AA

A honey-coloured antique-filled 15th-century Tudor mansion (rebuilt in the early 19th century) with mullioned windows, beautiful chimneys, high-ceilinged hall, elegant lounge and individually styled bedrooms. It is set in 11 acres of secluded parkland and gardens overlooking the river Frome, and is part hotel, part private house taking guests – log fires, warm bedrooms in winter, agreeable colour schemes, books and maps, dogs and cats, all adding to the home-like atmosphere. Bryan and Elizabeth Ferriss, "warm and generous hosts", introduce guests to each other in the lounge, then sit down to dinner with them, one at each end of the table, an arrangement people find either fun or tiresome. No choice on the four-course dinner menu but you are given notice in case a dish is not to your liking, and special diets are happily catered for. It is "all real food, fresh vegetables and much variety and ingenuity"; fish dishes are a speciality. This is the heart of Hardy country – Maiden Newton is the Chalk Newton of *Tess of the D'Urbervilles* – and there is good walking in the area. "Excellent standards of food and service maintained. We had one of the most recently refurbished bedrooms; it was truly sumptuous." (*Julia Norman; also Hugh and Elsie Pryor*)

Open Feb–Dec.
Rooms 6 double – 5 with bath, 1 with shower, all with radio and TV; tea-making facilities on request.
Facilities Drawing room, library, dining room; functions facilities. 11-acre grounds with stabling for visiting horses, croquet, $\frac{3}{4}$ m trout-fishing on river Frome. Golf, sailing, riding, hunting, walking nearby.
Location From A356 in centre of village take road signposted Yeovil. Entrance gates 200 yards on left near church.
Restrictions Not suitable for ♿. No children under 12. Small dogs only; not in public rooms.
Credit cards Access, Visa.
Terms B&B: single £55–£70, double £76–£120. Set dinner £21. Lunches and packed lunches on request. 1-night bookings for weekends sometimes refused if made too far in advance. Weekly half-board rates; house-party rates.
Service/tipping: "No service charge is added to bills and we discourage tipping."

MALVERN WELLS Hereford and Worcester — Map 2

The Old Vicarage — *Tel* Malvern (0684) 572585
Hanley Road
Malvern Wells WR14 4PH

This "rather splendid defrocked Victorian vicarage" in a lawned garden on the slopes of the Malvern Hills overlooking the Severn Vale, has again drawn many favourable comments from readers: "Marvellous value, very clean, best hotel breakfast we have had at any hotel of any price"; "Pleasant welcome; two good double rooms; neat, minute bathroom. Lots of fascinating books everywhere; pleasant to walk from. Excellent value – but not a place for a wild carouse." "It is like someone's much loved home." (*Diana Blake, Mrs J Godfrey; also Mrs James, IS Jones, and others*) Rooms are large, light, freshly redecorated and full of period character; there is lots of stripped pine. The dining room has pale pink walls and traditional Victorian prints. All the above readers also praised the dinners but proprietor Michael Gorvin writes this year, "we can no longer justify the commitment of time and energy involved in providing freshly prepared individual dinners for guests", so the *Old Vicarage* is now B&B only. Some consolation, especially for those in search of gastronomic excitement: the *Michelin*-rosetted *Croque-en-Bouche* restaurant is just up the road.

Open All year except Christmas and New Year.
Rooms 6 double – 3 with bath, 3 with shower, all with TV and tea-making facilities; baby-listening by arrangement. 1 ground-floor room.
Facilities Lounge, dining room. $\frac{3}{4}$-acre garden.

Location From Malvern take A449 Wells Road; turn left down B4209 Hanley Road – *Old Vicarage* on the right just before Green Lane turn-off.
Restriction Dogs by arrangement only, not in public rooms.
Credit cards None accepted.
Terms B&B (English): single occupancy £25–£30, double £34–£44. Reduced rates for children.
Service/tipping: "Owners are rarely tipped, fortunately avoiding embarrassment on both sides."

MANCHESTER — Map 4

Etrop Grange — *Tel* Manchester (061) 437 3594 and 499 0500
Bailey Lane, Etrop Green
Ringway, Manchester Airpost
M22 5NR

"A small, friendly hotel. The staff are very welcoming. Good fresh food, essentially British with modern refinements. Comfortable, attractive bedrooms with good finishing touches such as fresh fruit." "Charming service from young staff. Good atmosphere throughout. Well-furnished bedroom with four-poster bed, at least four armchairs and a sofa! All in all a happy and pleasant stay." Still our only Manchester entry, a small Georgian Grade II listed country house down a leafy lane, 12 minutes' drive from the city centre and half a mile from the airport, run by John and Susan Roebuck. Since last year the top floor has been converted to provide five more bedrooms, all with *en suite* bathrooms. The decor is traditional, with period furniture. Imaginative English food is served in the panelled dining room "with festoons and drapes matching lace tablecloths, and heavy cut glass". Only cavil: "Proximity to the airport does make the rooms slightly noisy" – but secondary glazing was recently installed. We'd welcome more reports.

Open All year.
Rooms 7 double, 1 single – 7 with bath, 1 with shower, all with telephone, radio, TV and tea-making facilities.
Facilities Lounge, conservatory, dining room; private dining room. 1.2-acre garden. Courtesy airport car.
Location 12 minutes' drive S of city centre. Leave M56 motorway at junction 5 to airport.
Restriction Not suitable for ♿.
Credit cards Access, Amex, Visa.
Terms [1989 rates] B&B: single £58, double £68. Breakfast: continental £2.95, English £4.95. Set lunch £10.50, dinner £18.95. Weekend reductions. Special meals for children if advance warning is given.
Service/tipping: "We do not encourage guests to leave tips as good levels of service should not be especially rewarded."

MATLOCK Derbyshire — Map 4

Riber Hall — *Tel* Matlock (0629) 582795
Matlock DE4 5JO — *Fax* (0629) 580475

A partly Elizabethan country manor, high above the town, with heavy oak beams, thick stone walls, public rooms full of period furniture in the main building, and well-modernised bedrooms across a steep gravelled courtyard (not recommended for the disabled). "Easy to reach from the

M1. Very pleasant welcome. Four-poster bed and genuine antiques of all periods. Books and magazines, complimentary sherry and chocolates – almost too many goodies. Super bathroom with whirlpool bath and bidet as well as everything else. Good food, very good wine list with a whole page of half bottles. Staff considerate and genuinely seem to want to please." (*Mrs MD Prodgers*) "Excellent meal; expensive but exceedingly good value for money. Plenty of choice and 'different' dishes, especially game. Home-made sorbets worth trying." (*Mrs Jane Cooper*) Another correspondent, however, found the food unexceptional, and conversation in the sitting room difficult because of the close proximity of others; one reader called the atmosphere "less than sympathetic". More reports please.

Open All year.
Rooms 11 double – all with bath and shower (5 have whirlpool bath), telephone, radio, TV, tea-making facilities and mini-bar. All rooms round courtyard.
Facilities Lounge, restaurant; conference/function facilities. 4-acre grounds with tennis court; clay-pigeon shooting. Fishing, golf nearby.
Location W of M1, exit 28. 1 m off A615; turn S at Tansley.
Restrictions Not suitable for ♿. No children under 10. No dogs.
Credit cards All major cards accepted.
Terms [1989 rates] (No service charge) B&B (continental): single £53–£65, double £70–£105. Set lunch £11; full alc dinner £25 Hideaway breaks in low season.
Service/tipping: "Tipping is discretionary and not expected; distributed to all staff at end of month."

MAWNAN SMITH Cornwall — Map 1

Meudon Hotel
Nr Falmouth TR11 5HT

Tel Falmouth (0326) 250541
Fax (0326) 250543
Telex 45478 MEUDON

Meudon is an old Cornish mansion, a mellow stone building with massive granite pillars and mullioned windows onto which has been grafted a modern bedroom wing. Its chief glories are its location, in 200 acres of protected Cornish coastline between the Fal and Helford rivers, at the head of a lovely valley leading down to its own private beach – and its eight-and-a-half-acre sub-tropical garden, laid out in the 18th century by Capability Brown, with rare flowering shrubs and plants, and still carefully maintained. *Meudon* has been run for many years by Harry Pilgrim and his family and offers old-fashioned service – beds turned down at night, shoes cleaned, early morning tea brought to the room (though there are tea-making facilities for those who prefer them) – of a kind which has long since disappeared from many pricier establishments. The hotel had an entry in earlier editions of the Guide but dropped out following criticisms of food, service and decor, and poor insulation between some rooms. While the latter may not be easily remedied, it has not bothered the visitors who have written to us this year urging *Meudon*'s reinstatement: "Our room, recently redecorated, was immaculate and well equipped; we would have cheerfully stayed in it for the entire week." "The dining room is pleasant; one side is entirely glass, overlooking the lovely gardens. Dinner menus changed daily – imaginative starters, well-cooked main dishes including local salmon and lemon sole; vegetables were cooked properly. Puddings were good, without too much imagination, generally based on fruit with lashings of Cornish cream. For breakfast there was a wide choice. Service was excellent, speedy, friendly, helpful, willing but discreet. A memorable holiday hotel." (*Adrian Nimmo, Roy and Mary Bromell*) Only niggles: "sliced bread at breakfast; food generally under-seasoned." More reports please.

Open Feb–Dec.
Rooms 2 suites, 26 double, 4 single – all with bath and shower, telephone, radio, TV, tea-making facilities. 18 on ground floor.
Facilities 3 lounges, bar, sun loggia, restaurant; laundry, hair-dressing salon. 8-acre grounds leading to private beach. Free golf at Falmouth Golf Club.
Location 4 m S of Falmouth. From Truro take A39 for 7 m, follow signs for Mabe and Mawan Smith. Bear left at *Red Lion*. Meudon is on right in 1 m.
Restrictions No children under 5.
Credit cards Access, Diners, Visa.
Terms [1989 rates] B&B (English) £40–£55, dinner, B&B £55–£70. Set lunch £12.50, dinner £19.50; full alc £29.50. Reductions for long stays. 3-day spring and autumn breaks. Reduced rates for children; high teas.
Service/tipping: "No service charge. Tips left by guests distributed evenly among all staff including gardeners."

MIDDLETON-IN-TEESDALE County Durham — Map 4

The Teesdale Hotel — *Tel* Teesdale (0833) 40264
Middleton-in-Teesdale
Nr Barnard Castle DL12 0QG

A modernised Grade II listed coaching inn, family-run, in the market square of a village in the heart of the High Pennines. Comfortable public rooms; bedrooms recently refurbished. Pretty dining room serving good traditional food; high standard of service. 14 bedrooms, 10 with private facilities. Also 4 self-catering cottages. B&B double £48–£50. Set dinner £12.50. New nomination. More reports please.

MILTON-UNDER-WYCHWOOD Oxfordshire — Map 2

Hillborough Hotel — *Tel* Shipton-under-Wychwood (0993) 830501
The Green
Milton-under-Wychwood
OX7 6JH

A new venture by Wendy Jones, opposite the green in one of the less picturesque Cotswold villages. Renovated Victorian house, "new, clean and pleasant throughout". Attractive public rooms, well-appointed bedrooms and bathrooms. Recommended for friendly and efficient service, good food and very reasonable prices. Small grounds. Closed Jan. 6 rooms, all with private facilities. B&B double £38. Set dinner from £10.50 [1989]. New nomination. More reports please.

> The success of this guide in North America has led to a sister publication on American and Canadian hotels based on the same principles. Readers with recent experience of good hotels in North America are urged to send their nominations to Sandra W Soule, America's Wonderful Little Hotels and Inns, PO Box 150, Riverside Avenue, Riverside, Conn. 06878, USA.

MINCHINHAMPTON Gloucestershire — Map 2

Burleigh Court Hotel
Minchinhampton, Nr Stroud
GL5 2PF

Tel Brimscombe (0453) 883804
Fax (0453) 886870

This 18th-century Pevsner-listed Cotswold house, owned and run by the Benson family, stands in a specially attractive five-acre garden designed by Clough Williams-Ellis on an extremely steep hillside; from the front there are magnificent views across the Stroud valley. The interior is "pleasant and comfortable, rather than stylish, and very English". "Our bedroom was large and comfortable, but not grand. What makes the hotel is the service; we were welcomed, served in a friendly but unobtrusive way at dinner, offered brochures and maps of the area, and generally made to feel that the staff were there to help whenever needed." The style of cooking is varied: "standard English hotel dishes offered alongside classic French provincial, modern British and vegetarian, as well as a 'health menu'". Readers' verdicts vary from "adequate" and "good" to "pretentious, with the mandatory sorbet between courses"; one is severely critical of the dessert trolley; the wine list is "reasonably priced". "Not for those in search of a luxury weekend with luggage-toting porters and 24-hour room service, but highly recommended for a restful and good-natured weekend". "Good value for money".(*Richard Spence, Peter Hall, and others*) One weekend visitor, however, was given a sub-standard bedroom – "admittedly the last one available", found the general standards of cleanliness somewhat lacking, and the restaurant noisy due to parties of non-resident diners. More reports please.

Open 24 Dec–approx 7 Jan.
Rooms 17 double – all with bath and/or shower, telephone, TV, tea-making facilities and baby-listening; some with radio. 6 ground-floor rooms in stable block adjoining main building.
Facilities 3 lounges, bar, 2 restaurants. 5-acre grounds with terrace, heated Victorian plunge pool and putting green. Golf, riding nearby.
Location ½m S of A419 at Brimscombe; follow signs for Minchinhampton and *Burleigh Court.*
Restrictions No smoking in dining room. No dogs.
Credit cards All major cards accepted.
Terms B&B (English): single occupancy £47–£49, double £62–£75. Set lunch from £8 (bar snacks also available); dinner £16–£24; full alc £22. 1-night bookings sometimes refused.
Service/tipping: "Tips not expected. There is, however, a box and money given is shared between the staff."

MOLLINGTON Cheshire — Map 4

Crabwall Manor Hotel and Restaurant [GFG]
Parkgate Road, Mollington
Nr Chester CH1 6NE

Tel Chester (0244) 851666
Telex 61220 CRAWAL

Luxurious new country house hotel in historic castellated building in 11-acre grounds (rather stark at present), two miles from Chester. Public rooms and bedrooms stylishly and comfortably if somewhat impersonally decorated. Two non-smoking bedrooms; two "for ladies". Large, fairly formal split-level dining room; cooking by Michael Truelove, formerly of The Box Tree *restaurant, Ilkley "has moved back to a heavier style, probably in response to customer demand". The emphasis on corporate entertaining and functions has diminished the pleasure of some private visitors in 1988/9; service and meals can be patchy. A leisure complex is planned for 1990/91. A new manager, Julian Hook, arrived in early 1989 from* Horsted Place, *Little Horsted (q.v.). 6 suites, 42 doubles, all with bath and shower. B&B double £110–£125, suite £140–£190. Set dinner £21. More reports please.*

MORETON-IN-MARSH Gloucestershire — Map 2

The Redesdale Arms Hotel
Moreton-in-Marsh GL56 0AW

Tel Moreton-in-Marsh (0608) 50308
Fax (0608) 51843

This 18th-century coaching inn had an entry in early editions of the Guide. Now, under new management and much refurbished, it is brought back by a warm commendation, "Public rooms are large, the bars particularly attractive with elegant panelling, stone walls and great old fireplaces with log fires in winter. Good real ale. Modernisation has been achieved in many areas without spoiling the original charm. Recently a delightful conservatory has been built and reception much improved. There is a respectable table d'hôte and some decent dishes à la carte. Much use is made of fresh herbs and vegetables. We were in 'cottage'-type accommodation in the courtyard. Full private facilities, excellent heating, free from smoke and noise. Private parking immediately adjacent. Moreton is in the north Cotswolds on the Fosse Way – superb countryside." (*Peter Rea*) One caveat, "It would be even better if smoking in the dining room was actively discouraged." In summer drinks and snacks are served in the courtyard.

Open All year.
Rooms 2 suites, 14 double, 2 single – all with bath and/or shower, telephone, radio, TV, tea-making facilities and baby-listening. Suites in rear courtyard. Some ground floor rooms.
Facilities Ramps. Reception, 2 bars, lounge, conservatory lounge, restaurant. Conference facilities.
Location Central. All rooms double-glazed. Parking.
Restriction Guide dogs only.
Credit cards Access, Amex, Visa.
Terms (No service charge) B&B (English): single £39.50–£42.75, double £57.50–£63.75, suite £75–£82.50. Set lunch £9.95, dinner £13.85; full alc £18.50. Mini-breaks. Christmas programme. Reduced rates and special meals for children.

MOULSFORD-ON-THAMES Oxfordshire — Map 2

The Beetle and Wedge Hotel [GFG]
Moulsford-on-Thames OX10 9JF

Tel Cholsey (0491) 651381 and 651376

An old hotel on an attractive stretch of the Thames, but new to the Guide this year, the *Beetle and Wedge* is celebrated in *Three Men in a Boat* and HG Wells's *Mr Polly*. It was taken over in 1988 by Richard and Kate Smith of the *Royal Oak*, Yattendon (q.v.) and the restaurant, overlooking the river, has rapidly acquired a reputation for very good food at reasonable prices without pretentious presentation or price-raising gimmicks. In summer it does a busy bar trade and can be crowded at times. The Smiths have refurbished the public rooms and created a new bar and riverside terrace. Bedrooms, too, have been redecorated; they are simple but well appointed and clean, with comfortable new beds, TV, and bathroom. Further improvements are planned for 1990. Breakfasts are good with fresh orange juice, fresh fruit, warm rolls and the choice of hot dishes. More reports please.

Open All year.
Rooms 9 double, 4 single – all with bath or shower, telephone, radio, TV, tea-making facilities and baby-listening.
Facilities Lounge, 2 bars, 2 restaurants; conference facilities. ⅓-acre grounds. Boating, fishing.
Location On river, on edge of village 8 m NW of Reading.
Restrictions Not suitable for ♿. Dogs by arrangement, not in restaurant.
Credit cards Access, Amex, Visa.
Terms B&B: single £50, double £65. Bar meals. Set lunch £17.50, dinner £18.50. Reduced rates for children sharing parents' room; special meals on request.
Service/tipping: "We like to leave tips to guests' discretion. They are distributed evenly among staff after deduction of tax."

MULLION Cornwall — Map 1

Polurrian Hotel
Mullion TR12 7EN

Tel Mullion (0326) 240421
Fax (0326) 240083
Telex 94015906

A family hotel in a stunning position on cliffs on the Lizard Peninsula, overlooking Polurrian Cove. The National Trust owns most of the surrounding land and there are marvellous walks in both directions; even in August it is relatively quiet. The two lounges have lovely views over Mounts Bay towards Land's End. The *Polurrian* is one of the few hotels we know that is really welcoming to and geared for children as well as their parents, with many facilities, both indoors and out, (see below) for their entertainment. Bedrooms are mostly quite simply furnished but for regulars what counts is: "the outstanding friendliness and concern of the staff plus Richard Francis's imaginative vision and ability to concern himself with every detail of the running of this family hotel. The food at dinner, particularly the vegetables, can be disappointing especially when the chef has an evening off, but during our week every breakfast and four of seven dinners were of good standard, with fresh fish predominating. Mrs Francis senior still plays the piano at dinner twice a week. Of all the hotels we know this is the one where we feel we are staying with friends. The big question mark will be how the *Polurrian* fares now that Mr Francis also has the only hotel permitted on the Scilly Island of St Martin." (*Gwen and Peter Andrews*) A critic, however, "while agreeing that the hotel caters admirably for children with the excellent leisure facilities", was disappointed: "The much-vaunted friendliness was lukewarm at best, any sort of complaint was met with complacency. The food, though extravagantly described in the menu, was bland and badly prepared." The 24-bedroomed *St Martin's Hotel* built to a design personally approved by Prince Charles (he is Duke of Cornwall), opened in the spring of 1989. Our first report is highly favourable. We'd be glad to hear more both on the new venture and the *Polurrian*.

Open 1 Mar–7 Dec.
Rooms 4 suites, 34 double, 1 single – all with bath and shower, telephone, radio, TV, baby-listening and 24-hour room service. Some ground-floor rooms. Also self-catering apartments and bungalows.
Facilities 4 lounges, 4 bars, 2 restaurants; toddlers' playroom, hair salon, laundry facilities. 12-acre grounds with tennis, croquet, toddlers' playground; Indoor Leisure Club with 2 swimming pools, squash, sauna, solarium, snooker room, teenage centre (there are small charges for the use of some of these facilities). Beach at cliff bottom. Wind surfing, golf nearby.
Location ¼ m from Mullion village; go towards harbour, pass cricket field on left; hotel is on right.
Restriction No dogs in public rooms; must be on lead in grounds (£1.50 a day plus £1 for meals).
Credit cards Access, Diners, Visa.
Terms [1989 rates] B&B £33–£52.50; dinner, B&B £38–£64.50. Set lunch £11, dinner £16. Children under 6 free of charge in parents' room.

MUNGRISDALE Cumbria — Map 4

The Mill Hotel — *Tel* Threlkeld (059 683) 659
Mungrisdale, Penrith CA11 0XR

Reports continue to be warmly in favour of this simple but civilised small mill cottage in a lovely setting. Dating from the 17th century, it has been owned and run by Richard and Eleanor Quinlan for the last seven years. Mungrisdale is only a dozen miles from the Penrith exit of the M6, but well away from the tourist pack, and at the foot of the fells. It stands in two acres of grounds with a mill race, waterfall and trout stream, and offers attractive accommodation, warmth, friendly service and imaginative food. Dinner is a set menu with some choice, served at 7 pm; there is a small, carefully selected wine list. "Very well run." "Friendly welcome. We liked the way it is furnished like a private home." "Delightful. Room well equipped – far better than many much more costly places. Food good and in general very well cooked." "Excellent value. I wish I had had more time to browse through their collection of interesting books." This is not a hotel for misanthropes; public rooms are small, and can be crowded at busy times – "old-fashioned conversation after dinner with fellow guests" is one of the pleasures here. (*Jane Spokes, PE Carter, Gabriel Hart, GR Holliday, and many others*) One niggle: "A pity tasty fresh food was let down by tinned grapefruit for breakfast."

Not to be confused with a nearby pub with rooms, *The Mill Inn* at Mungrisdale, though this might be a useful standby if *The Mill* is full.

Open Feb–Nov.
Rooms 9 double – 5 with bath and/or shower, all with tea-making facilities; 5 with TV; radio on request.
Facilities Lounge, TV lounge, sun lounge, dining room; games room; drying room. 2-acre grounds with mill-race, waterfall and trout stream. Ullswater 5 m with fishing, sailing etc; hang-gliding, golf nearby.
Location 2 m N of A66. Leave M6 at Penrith (exit 40); turn off midway between Penrith and Keswick.
Restrictions Not suitable for ♿. Dogs at owners' discretion, not in public rooms.
Credit cards None accepted.
Terms (No service charge) B&B: single £24.50–£30.50, double £39–£53; dinner, B&B: single £31.50–£40.50, double £52–£71. Set dinner £13.50. Weekly rates. Reduced rates for children sharing parents' room; special meals.
Service/tipping: "Tipping not required or looked for."

NEW MILTON Hampshire — Map 2

Chewton Glen Hotel [GFG] — *Tel* Highcliffe (0425) 275341
Christchurch Road — *Fax* (042 52) 72310
New Milton BH25 6QS — *Telex* 41456 CHGLEN

"Very expensive but worth every penny. I have not encountered a better hotel in the United Kingdom and know of very few to equal it abroad." Thus *WE Parker*'s endorsement for this sumptuous country hotel with an international clientele on the southern fringe of the New Forest. Once the home of the writer, Captain Marryat, author of *The Children of the New Forest*, for whom the restaurant is named, *Chewton Glen* has long been one of the most expensive country house hotels in Britain. Decor is impeccable, with antiques and luxurious fabrics as well as modern comforts. The hotel has 30-acre grounds with lovely gardens, walking and jogging trails, a nine-hole golf course, swimming pool, tennis, croquet, and a helipad for affluent guests in a hurry; a chauffeur-driven car is available to collect those who arrive by air at Heathrow or Gatwick. For 23 years Martin Skan, with a large staff, has run the hotel with almost obsessive attention to detail. Food, under Pierre Chevillard, has earned the restaurant a *Michelin* rosette; it is "modern French", generally praised as "varied and imaginatively presented". This year, however, the restaurant comes in for criticism: rushed and poorly served meals, many of the half-bottles of wine listed were not available, breakfasts "ordinary, and badly served". One reader was shown to a bedroom which was cold because the radiator had not been turned on, and had squeaking doors; and "an atmosphere is generated by the staff that guests should consider themselves fortunate to be permitted to stay there". We hope these are temporary falls from grace. More reports please.

Open All year.
Rooms 13 suites, 33 double – all with bath and shower, telephone, radio and TV. Some suites in coach house. Some ground-floor rooms.
Facilities Ramps. Lounge, sun lounge, bar, private dining room, 3 restaurants. 5 conference/banqueting rooms; pianist in lounge most evenings, snooker room, shop, terrace. 30-acre grounds with tennis court, croquet lawn, putting, jogging course and heated swimming pool; helipad. Sea 1 m walk through grounds with safe bathing from shingle beach; New Forest to the north. Fishing, riding, sailing nearby; sea ½ m; 12 golf courses within radius of 20 m. Chauffeur service.
Location Do not follow New Milton signs. From A35, take turning to Walkford and Highcliffe; go through Walkford, then left down Chewton Farm road. Entrance is on right.
Restrictions No children under 7. No dogs; kennel facilities nearby.
Credit cards All major cards accepted.
Terms B&B: single occupancy £146, double £154, suite £218. Set lunch £17, dinner from £36; full alc from £46. Off-season rates 1 Nov–31 Mar; Christmas and Easter 4-day packages. 1-night bookings usually refused for Sat.
Service/tipping: "Our prices are fully inclusive and all our guests are made aware of this."

NEWLANDS Cumbria — Map 4

Swinside Lodge — *Tel* Keswick (076 87) 72948
Newlands, Nr Keswick CA12 5UE

"Nestling at the foot of Cat Bells, peaceful, yet within reach of other beauty spots and amenities, this Victorian house is one to which guests return again and again. The welcome is always welcoming, every corner looks spotless. None of the regulars we spoke to could recall ever being served a repeat menu." "Lambert and Jeanne Dickinson are always the same, they genuinely enjoy having guests and give them all equal care and attention. I know of no other place which offers better value for money." The Dickinsons' unassumingly friendly guest house, among the cheapest in the Guide, is a double-fronted Victorian lodge three miles from Keswick, the hub of northern Lakeland, in an idyllically beautiful location. Everything is maintained immaculately: the bedrooms are well if simply decorated (hot-water bottles, electric blankets and hair-driers available on request) and the food (four-course dinners, no choice) is straightforward cooking in the complimentary sense; vegetarians are well catered for. No licence, but guests can bring their own bottles, with no charge for corkage. (*E and D Blackburn, The Archdeacon of Dorking, and others*) *Note*: The Dickinsons no longer take children under 12.

Open Feb–Nov. Restaurant closed to non-residents.
Rooms 8 double – 3 with bath, the rest with basin.
Facilities Lounge with TV, dining room. ¾-acre garden. Derwentwater 5 mins' walk .
Location 3 m SW of Keswick on A66. At Portinscale follow road to Grange.
Restrictions Not suitable for ♿. No children under 12. No pets.
Credit cards None accepted.
Terms (No service charge) B&B £15–£17.50; dinner, B&B £23–£25.50. Weekly rates. 1-night bookings for B&B refused in high season. Packed lunches on request.

NORTH HUISH Devon — Map 1

Brookdale House [GFG] — *Tel* Gara Bridge (054 882) 402 and 415
North Huish
South Brent TQ10 9NR — *Reservations* in USA (800) 323 5463

"An excellent hotel, improving from already high standards," writes *Richard D Creed* after yet another visit to *Brookdale House*, "The bedroom wattage is now fully acceptable." "The hotel comes pretty well at the top of my price range so expectations were high. In no significant way were they disappointed. The first hurdle was to get there and an OS map was an invaluable companion in the Devon lanes. First impressions were good – a Victorian rectory of irreproachably faded gentility at the head of a wooded valley (floodlit after dark). A cordial welcome from the friendly receptionist followed swiftly by a pot of tea. Our room was a delight, large, well proportioned, thoughtfully equipped and immaculate in a way which was sympathetic to the mid-nineteenth century structure (and its creaky floors). The *en suite* bathroom was positively stuffed with goodies, plumply expensive towels and bathrobes and such a choice of soaps, bath gels, razors etc that one's sponge bag was almost redundant. The dining room was repro-Regency with extravagant displays of real and artificial flowers, and the food was good, with much emphasis on the organic nature of the ingredients. The young French waiter was helpful and charming as was the proprietor, Charles Trevor-Roper, when we came to meet him in order to settle our debt. Legal documents and other historical aspects of Mr Trevor-Roper's family are framed on the landings and give a comforting sense of stability and continuity which is reflected in the whole enterprise, young though it may be." (*WH Bruton*) "I have had over 40 years experience in staying in hotels, and *Brookdale* is the best yet." (*Sir Douglas Frank*) Many other readers comment in similar vein. And Mr Trevor-Roper writes, "The kitchen is now in the hands of Terry Rich who trained at *Gravetye Manor* (q.v.), *Paris House* and *Le Gavroche*. He is providing continually changing set-price dinner menus in a light style that we feel is necessary for a hotel where most guests dine every night." Regarding the "raffish music" emanating from his office he says, "As I am on duty nearly every night of the year I will play the music I enjoy. In general I receive very favourable comments on my choice." And from one of the readers who commented on the music last year we hear, "Now quieter, and more acceptable." Though not far from the Plymouth to Exeter road (A38) *Brookdale House* is in a secluded situation, set in large wooded grounds with a waterfall. The rooms, of course, vary in size – prices depend on their size and position – but even the smaller ones meet with almost unqualified approval. The rates include a full English breakfast (served in the dining room) with exotica such as raspberry porridge on offer along with more traditional items.

Open All year except 3 weeks in Jan.
Rooms 8 double – all with bath and shower, telephone, radio, TV and tea-making facilities. 2 (cheaper) rooms in cottage 25 yds from main building.
Facilities Reception, lounge, bar, dining room. 5-acre grounds with garden, stream, waterfall. Beaches 15 minutes' drive, also S edge of Dartmoor.
Location 7 m SW of Totnes. Off A38 take Avonwick, South Brent exit. In Avonwick turn right opposite *Avon Inn*, then first left to North Huish. Go up lane to top of hill, turn right, signposted *Brookdale House*; at bottom of hill turn right, hotel is first on left.
Restrictions No smoking in dining room. Not suitable for ♿. No children under 10. No dogs.
Credit cards Access, Visa.
Terms B&B: single occupancy £60–£70, double £70–£100. Set dinner £23. Bar lunches available. Christmas, New Year and winter breaks. 1-night bookings sometimes refused at busy weekends.
Service/tipping: "No service charge added to bills, but if tips are offered they are not refused. We assume our customers are intelligent enough to decide whether to leave tips for staff. If they have made this decision it would be churlish to refuse."

NORTON ST PHILIP Avon — Map 2

Bath Lodge Hotel [GFG] — *Tel* Bath (0225) 723737
Norton St Philip
Nr Bath BA3 6NH

Splendid castellated former gatehouse on A36, 7 m S of Bath, lovingly converted by John and Pam Morris. Oak-beamed ceilings, large log-burning fireplaces; furnishings in period. 4 bedrooms with 4-poster or half-tester bed, and balcony overlooking 1-acre gardens with stream and waterfall; all have private facilities. Recommended for charming ambience and good food. No smoking except in conservatory. No children. No dogs. B&B (English) double from £85. Alc dinner £22. New nomination. More reports please.

Please never tell a hotel you intend to send a report to the Guide. Anonymity is essential for objectivity.

NUNNINGTON North Yorkshire — Map 4

Ryedale Lodge — *Tel* Nunnington (043 95) 246
Nunnington
Nr Helmsley, York YO6 5XB

Once Nunnington railway station, *Ryedale Lodge* is now a welcoming hotel in the hands of Jon and Janet Laird. The setting is peaceful, with no other houses visible across the rolling farmland; there is an agreeable half-mile walk along the defunct railway track to the river Rye. The dining room, with conservatory extension, does a busy non-resident trade – "food and service beyond complaint". Bedrooms are well equipped, with fresh fruit, sweets, television and good bathrooms, though not a great deal of storage space for luggage. "We were impressed that they sent us information on the hotel and the surrounding area when we booked." (*Susan B Hanley, and others*) A few niggles this year: "service pretty non-existent; breakfast was good but there was only one girl to wait on us"; "We ordered different meals but were both given the same"; "though we had asked for a cot they did not supply cot linen; 'baby-listening' consisted of the owner listening at the bottom of the stairs". Perhaps more a restaurant-with-rooms than a fully fledged hotel.

Open All year except 3 weeks in Jan. Restaurant closed for lunch.
Rooms 1 suite, 6 double – all with bath (1 also has shower), telephone, radio, TV and tea-making facilities.
Facilities 2 lounges with bar service, restaurant, conservatory. 4-acre grounds. River Rye 10 mins' walk; trout-fishing.
Location 1 m due W of Nunnington towards Oswaldkirk. Pass Nunnington Hall on left; after 400 yards turn right at crossroads. Pass church on right; hotel is 1 m further on right.
Restrictions Not suitable for ♿. No smoking in the dining room. No dogs.
Credit cards Access, Visa.
Terms (No service charge) B&B £32.50–£45. Set dinner £21. 2-day breaks; weekly rates. Christmas and New Year packages. Reduced rates and special meals for children.
Service/tipping: "Tipping at guests' discretion. Tips are shared weekly between all staff."

OTLEY Suffolk — Map 3

Otley House — *Tel* Helmingham (047 339) 253
Otley, Ipswich IP6 9NR

"An exquisitely furnished guest house with an elegant atmosphere. Dinner is a wonderful experience – a chance to practise the art of conversation while enjoying superb food." (*Veronica Stuart*) *Otley House*, owned and run by Mike Hilton and his Danish wife Lise, belongs to the Wolsey Lodge group of guest-taking private houses. It is a "fine, plain, square country house" in rural Suffolk, Grade II listed, with a Grade I staircase, in three acres of mature peaceful grounds with a small lake. Tea is served in the billiard room – there is an "excellent" billiard table – and guests gather for coffee and conversation in a Regency drawing room after dinner. The four-course dinners taken communally, with silver and crystal on the tables, are "delicious, varied, well presented and served". There is no choice of menu; the owners like to be warned in advance of special diets or preferences; and Mrs Hilton is delighted to cook Scandinavian dishes for those who ask. The large light bedrooms, furnished with antiques, are "comfortable and sparkling clean with small extras such as pot-pourri, tissues, and a hair-drier." (*Ray and Angela Evans, PJ Forrest, JS and F Waters, and others*) One niggle, bedrooms can be on the cold side in winter.

Open 1 Mar–1 Nov. Dining room closed for lunch and on Sun.
Rooms 4 double – all with bath (3 also with shower), and radio; 2 with TV.
Facilities Hall, drawing room, TV/billiard room, dining room; tea terrace. 3-acre grounds with small lake, croquet. Golf, fishing, riding nearby.
Location In Otley village, 7 miles N of Ipswich, on B1079; opposite small road to Swilland.
Restrictions Not suitable for ♿. Smoking in billiard room only. No children under 12. No dogs.
Credit cards None accepted.
Terms B&B (English): single occupancy £32–£34, double £38–£46. Set dinner £14; vegetarian meals by arrangement. 1-night bookings sometimes refused for Sat.
Service/tipping: "Service included; any tips are given to the girls to share."

OXFORD Oxfordshire — Map 2

Cotswold House — *Tel* Oxford (0865) 310558
363 Banbury Road
Oxford OX2 7PL

B&B recently opened by Jim and Anne O'Kane, 2 miles north of centre, with frequent buses. Immaculate, warm and comfortable. Recommended for spacious, well-lit and equipped bedrooms with TV. Small garden; parking. Traditional and vegetarian breakfasts. Closed Christmas. 4 double rooms, 1 single, all with shower. B&B: single £18–£19, double £34–£37. New nomination. More reports please.

PADSTOW Cornwall — Map 1

Seafood Restaurant [GFG] — *Tel* Padstow (0841) 532485
Riverside, Padstow PL28 8BY

Don't be put off by the name. This is a very superior example of a restaurant-with-rooms. It may lack public lounges and grounds, but run by Rick and Jill Stein, it "captures all the best things of France and puts them into a lovely English setting". Readers praise the comfortable bedrooms – most of them spacious – particularly room 4 which has a sitting room and a view over the garden towards the estuary, and room 5 with a large balcony and a view over Padstow. They are well equipped and simply decorated in light colours, with "pieces of old furniture and nice prints". Most have *en suite* facilities, but two (smaller and much cheaper) share a shower and toilet. In the restaurant, with similar decor, wicker chairs, plants, prints on white walls, there is plenty of choice on both table d'hôte and à la carte menus. "Rick does wonderful things with fish; the staff is first class." The room price includes breakfast, either continental, with fresh orange juice and home-made croissants, or full English; the former is served in the bedroom on request, the latter only in the conservatory. (*Lydia Limm, Roger Aspin*) One reader this year wished that at least part of the dining room had a no-smoking rule.

Open Mar–Dec. Closed for lunch and on 1 May.
Rooms 10 double – 8 with bath and shower, 2 sharing shower and WC, all with telephone, radio, tea-making facilities, mini-bar and baby-listening; 8 with TV.
Facilities Restaurant, conservatory.
Location Central, overlooking harbour. Carpark.
Restriction Not suitable for ♿.
Credit cards Access, Visa.
Terms B&B: single occupancy £22.50–£45, double £35–£80. Set dinner £19.50; full alc £35. Reduced rates for children sharing parents' room.
Service/tipping: "We do not encourage or discourage tipping; it is a popular incentive with our staff and many customers like to leave tips; anything given is shared amongst all staff on a points system."

PAINSWICK Gloucestershire — Map 2

The Painswick Hotel — *Tel* Painswick (0452) 812160
Kemps Lane, Painswick GL6 6YB — *Fax* (0452) 812160

A "very beautiful" Georgian former vicarage, now a welcoming hotel in the back lanes of a picturesque Cotswold village, well placed for touring Gloucestershire. The main drawback is that there are lots of steps and the "fairly formal" public rooms are on different levels: reception, with ornate ceiling and arched windows, is on the first floor as is the panelled bar with leaded windows and open fireplace; the small lounge, with a baby grand piano, is on the second floor. The smart dining room, on the ground floor, was once the vicar's billiard room. Bedrooms vary in size, some are in the main building, others in a new wing, built in the same style. The hotel is run by Jacqueline Ash and her mother Kay Hardy. "Tasteful, traditional decor with a well-kept garden and a superb view. The proprietors were charming and welcoming and their staff friendly and caring." "We had a very large bedroom with a splendid bathroom. I feared that chef Phillipe Brilliant's menu (French, with unusual combinations) was over-ambitious for such a simple place, but all was well – and it has parking, a rarity in Painswick." (*Dr Noel Russell, Peter Little, and others*) Children are welcome. Only criticisms: "The menu didn't change in the two nights we were there"; some housekeeping oversights.

Open All year.
Rooms 13 double, 2 single – all with bath and/or shower, telephone, radio, TV, tea-making facilities and baby-listening.
Facilities Drawing room, bar, dining room. Garden with croquet.
Location On outskirts of village. Parking.
Restrictions Not suitable for ♿. Dogs at management's discretion; not in public rooms.
Credit cards All major cards accepted.
Terms B&B: single from £39, double £60. Set dinner £15.50; full alc £25. Reduced rates for children sharing parents' room; special meals.
Service/tipping: "No service charge. Tips, at guests' discretion, go into a pool."

PENCRAIG Hereford and Worcester — Map 2

Pencraig Court Hotel — *Tel* Ross-on-Wye (098 984) 306
Pencraig, Nr Ross-on-Wye HR9 6HR

An unassuming, friendly and "remarkably reasonably priced" Georgian country house, comfortably modernised, is nominated by a regular correspondent, "The site is lovely, overlooking the Wye just downstream from Ross – a pleasant sloping garden with benches and tables and fine copper beeches. The room we had was one of the most comfortable we have ever enjoyed, very spacious, with a double and a single bed, sofa and two armchairs, more than adequate hanging and drawer space, well-equipped bathroom. There are two pleasant sitting rooms and a comfortable dining room. Alas, the dinner does not live up to the promise of the specimen menus (English cooking, with some choice), but breakfast was excellent, with a large selection of cereals and home-made porridge. The owners, Mr and Mrs Sykes, are friendly and welcoming. The hotel is on the A40, but our room overlooked the garden so it was quiet." (*Mrs RB Richards*) More reports please.

Open Apr–Oct inclusive.
Rooms 2 suites, 7 double, 2 single – all with bath and TV.
Facilities 2 lounges, bar, restaurant. 4-acre grounds.
Location 3 m SW of Ross-on-Wye, on the A40.
Restrictions Not suitable for ♿. No dogs.
Credit cards All major cards accepted.
Terms B&B (English) £17–£32, Dinner, B&B £26–£42. Bar snack lunches, set dinner £11.50. Special breaks. Reduced rates and special meals for children.
Service/tipping: "Our prices include tax and service. Gratuities are not expected by our staff."

PENZANCE Cornwall — Map 1

The Abbey Hotel — *Tel* Penzance (0736) 66906
Abbey Street
Penzance TR18 4AR

A 17th-century house of character in one of the narrow streets that run down from the centre of Penzance towards the harbour. There are magnificent views across Penzance Bay from the front; rear rooms look out over an attractive walled garden. The *Abbey* is filled with flowers, magazines and a varied collection of objects and curios, paintings and photographs. There are patchwork quilts, floral canopies and sprigged wallpaper in the bedrooms, some of which are very large, and at least one bathroom is attractively wood panelled, bath and all. "Charming old hotel with lots of style, comfortable and relaxed." "Not to everyone's taste perhaps, but a lovely casual atmosphere, delightful room overlooking the harbour and excellent meals." "One of the most romantic places we have ever stayed in." "My favourite hotel in the UK. But it's the sort of place that either you fall in love with or else it leaves you completely cold. I doubt that anyone would have mixed feelings." (*T Horgan, MA George, Christopher Walls, and others*) Housekeeping has never been the *Abbey*'s strong point, but most visitors feel its charms more than compensate. One reader this year found the wine list "poor, and outrageously expensive". More reports please.

Open All year.
Rooms 1 2-bedroomed apartment, 6 double – 3 with bath, 4 with shower, all with TV and tea-making facilities. Apartment on first floor in adjoining building.
Facilities Drawing room, dining room. Small rear garden.
Location Take road for sea front; after 300 yards, just before bridge, turn right, after 10 yds turn left. Hotel is at top of slipway. Courtyard parking for 4 cars.
Restrictions Not suitable for ♿. No children under 5. No dogs in public rooms.

Credit cards None accepted.
Terms (No service charge) B&B (English): single £40–£45, double £50–£80; apartment £75–£90. Set dinner £15. Winter breaks Nov–Mar; 3-day Christmas package. Reduced rates for children sharing parents' room; special meals.

POOL-IN-WHARFEDALE West Yorkshire — Map 4

Pool Court Restaurant with Rooms [GFG]
Otley LS21 1EH

Tel Leeds (0532) 842288
Fax (0532) 843115

"Fully lived up to expectations. But it *is* a restaurant-with-rooms, not a hotel; it would not be a place for more than one night, but that one night was complete luxury." "Room large, immaculate and beautifully furnished, bathroom spotless, beds turned down at night. Staff courteous, efficient and friendly; far better than many exorbitant hotels we've stayed in." "Food is perfection, or as near as one can get." "We kept the restaurant staff up very late but they brushed aside our apologies with charm. Standards in all departments were of the highest order." (*Barbara Hill, John Day, J Teale, GN Levy*) Michael Gill's restaurant-with-rooms in a fine Georgian mansion continues to receive high praise for its "splendid interior, attractively decorated throughout" and "excellent French food, served in the elegant soft gray dining room, sparkling with candle-light and beautiful crystal". In addition to the fairly pricey à la carte menu a no-choice three-course dinner is offered for only £10. There are no public rooms apart from the bar, and the coffee lounge which is used by diners in the evening. There are only six bedrooms, but they have been fitted out, each differently, with "consummate flair and style", and have fresh flowers, a fridge with wines and soft drinks, a tray with fruit, dates, raisins and nuts, books, even a little safe behind a picture on the wall. The continental breakfasts are "generous and delicious".

Open All year except 25 Dec–8 Jan, 2 weeks in summer. Closed Sun and Mon except when there is a trade fair in Harrogate. Lunch served only to pre-arranged parties of 10 or more.
Rooms 5 double, 1 single – all with bath and/or shower, telephone, radio/alarm, TV, bar, fridge, wall-safe and double-glazing; baby-listening by prior arrangement.
Facilities Bar, coffee lounge, restaurant; private dining room. ½-acre grounds.
Location 3 m N of Leeds airport on A658. Equidistant (9 m) from Leeds, Bradford and Harrogate.
Restrictions Not really suitable for ♿. No dogs.
Credit cards All major cards accepted.
Terms (Service at guests' discretion) B&B (continental): single £60, double £75–£93. Set dinner (3 courses, no choice) £10; full alc £35. Weekend rates. 1-night bookings sometimes refused during Harrogate trade fairs.
Service/tipping: "10% service charge added to bills for large private parties. Apart from that we feel that tipping is entirely up to the guest. We don't ask for or expect it, but if a guest wishes to give something it is gratefully received."

POOLE Dorset — Map 2

The Mansion House Hotel
Thames Street, Poole BH15 1JN

Tel Poole (0202) 685666
Telex 41495 SELECT

"An enjoyable week's stay. Food very good, with a wide choice. Prices reasonable." (*Harry McCann*) *The Mansion House* is a well-run hotel in a handsome Georgian town house in a quiet cul-de-sac near the old parish church and Poole's bustling quay. It has a grand sweeping staircase leading up from the hall to a comfortable and stylish residents' lounge; well-equipped, individually designed bedrooms with many extras – books, magazines, sherry and so on. Nine more doubles are due to be completed by autumn 1989. The restaurant is also a fashionable dining club; residents are automatically made temporary members. Chef Tony Parsons offers a long, traditional menu. Experiences of meals can be variable; the restaurant is often very busy. There is also a limited room meal service. One criticism this year, bedrooms less carefully cleaned than public rooms. More reports please.

Open All year.
Rooms 1 suite, 17 double, 9 single – all with bath and shower, telephone, radio and TV.
Facilities Lounge, 2 bars, breakfast room, restaurant; private dining room. Dinner-dances once a month. Poole Quay 100 yds; fishing, boating, sailing.
Location Follow signs for town centre and quay. Thames St is off quay, between Fisheries Office and Maritime Museum – signposted to the parish church. 2 private car parks either side of hotel.
Restrictions Not suitable for ♿. No dogs.
Credit cards All major cards accepted.
Terms (Excluding 10% service charge) B&B: single £65, double from £85. Set lunch £12, dinner £17; full alc £21.50. Weekend rates. Free single room at weekend for child visiting with parents.
Service/tipping: "10% is added to bill and shared among all staff at end of month."

PORT GAVERNE Cornwall — Map 1

Port Gaverne Hotel
Port Gaverne
Nr Port Isaac PL29 3SQ
Tel Bodmin (0208) 880244
Fax (0208) 880151

This unpretentious 17th-century coastal inn enjoys a splendid position in a sheltered cove in an isolated village not far from Port Isaac. Just a small road separates it from a safe bay with sand, shingle and rock; there are good walks along the coast. Some rooms are in an annexe and some in cottages which are also let on a self-catering basis. It has been run by Frederick Ross and his wife for over twenty years and "manages to combine the atmosphere of an ancient inn with that of a comfortable small hotel". It is welcoming to families, many of whom have been visiting it for years. They praise it for the "courteous reception, friendly and prompt service at all times", and the comfortable and well-appointed bedrooms (even the singles!) with "comfortable beds, plenty of hanging space and an air of generosity – boiling hot water at all times, bath cap, flannels, gels, tissues supplied in the very nice bathrooms". Dinner is "good value" with three courses, each with three or four choices. The English breakfast is generous and good. Do not expect an elegant decor or five-star facilities – Frederick Ross says, "Our aim is to be the best of what we are, an elderly Cornish coastal inn, in a particularly beautiful and rugged location, providing pleasant, comfortable accommodation, well-above average food and a happy, relaxing atmosphere". In the eyes of *William Ritchie, Dr and Mrs B Fleshler and Olivia Snow* he is clearly succeeding. More reports please.

Open Closed 7 Jan–17 Feb.
Rooms 7 suites, 16 double, 3 single – 13 with bath and shower, 6 with bath, all with telephone, TV and baby-listening. 3 in annexe, 15 in cottages which are also let on a self-catering basis.
Facilities Residents' lounge, TV lounge, 4 bars, dining room. Cottages have a garden courtyard, annexe has a garden.
Location Take B3314 from Delabole or Wadebridge, then B3267.
Restriction No dogs in dining room.
Credit cards All major cards accepted.
Terms (Including 10% service charge) B&B £27.50–£36. Dinner, B&B (min 2 nights) £66–£78. Snack lunches about £4; alc dinner £15.80. Weekly rates; Christmas and New Year packages. Reduced rates and special meals for children.
Service/tipping: "The service charge is distributed to staff in the form of a service bonus at Christmas and Easter. Guests dissatisfied with service are of course entitled to withhold the 10%."

POUGHILL Cornwall — Map 1

Reeds [GFG] — *Tel* Bude (0288) 2841
Poughill, Bude EX23 9EL

César award: Most cosseting guest house

The aim of Margaret Jackson's highly civilised guest house is "to create an oasis of relaxation for the weary traveller", and over the years many readers have attested to her success in achieving this goal. *Reeds* is a turn-of-the-century house quietly situated in a large garden in a little village (its name is pronounced poffil) close to the dramatic north Cornish coast. The National Trust owns much of the coastline and there are many fine walks in the area. Once again this year *Reeds* is highly praised – in many cases by guests on return visits: "The house is large and very attractive, in a lovely garden. Our bedroom was spacious and restful, decorated in soft pastel colours. Lots of storage space. The whole place is spotless." "A jewel of a hotel. Everything just as before – great welcome, old-fashioned service, wonderful food and wine." "Mrs Jackson dedicates herself to her guests totally; nothing appears to be too much trouble. Not only the usual goodies in the bedrooms – hair-driers, shampoos, magazines, but also fruit, biscuits, and *fresh* milk in a little thermos for early morning tea. Mercifully, however, no television (but there is one downstairs). Meals are in the private-household dinner-party style, with elegant linen, silver and candles. There are no choices, but the menu is always displayed early in the day so that any dissenters can ask for an alternative; also you are asked your culinary preferences on booking." (*Ruth West, Marilyn Logsdon, Jean Willson; also PE Carter, and others*) Last year we said that as there are only three bedrooms you get to know your fellow guests and hostess quite intimately if you stay for any length of time. *Padi Howard* comments: "Though this is a very small concern, you don't feel on top of other guests and need not really be sociable unless you want to; Mrs Jackson respects the fact that you may want to be left to your own devices." Mrs Jackson writes, "There are no hidden extras. Coffee or tea is available at any time with no charge. Everyone has complete freedom to use all the house. I try to serve dinner promptly at 8 pm as I don't like to keep dishes hot long after they are cooked."

Open All year Fri pm–Tues am. Closed Christmas.
Rooms 3 double – all with bath, shower, tea-making facilities; radio on request.
Facilities Drawing room, hall with bar facilities, TV room. 4-acre grounds. Sea 1 m – sandy beaches and coastal walks. Fishing, golf nearby.
Location Take Poughill Road from Bude. Turn left at Post Office towards Northcott Mount. *Reeds* is about 400 yards on left beyond garden centre.
Restrictions Not suitable for ♿. No children under 16. No pets.
Credit cards None accepted.
Terms B&B: single £35, double £60. Light lunch (cheese and fruit) on request £2.50. Set dinner £17.50.
Service/tipping: "I am totally opposed to the idea of tipping and actively (and I hope, politely) discourage it."

RICHMOND North Yorkshire — Map 4

Howe Villa [GFG]
Whitcliffe Mill
Richmond DL10 4TJ

Tel Richmond (0748) 850055

César award in 1989: Perfection in the guest house division

"Once again I write in praise of *Howe Villa* – and of the Guide for its discernment in awarding it a *César*. Why such an honour? Go and see for yourselves. Feast your eyes on the setting of autumn colours bordering the winding Swale. And there is beauty indoors too. *En suite* bedroom an oasis of matching peace, from the beautiful flower arrangement to the smallest box of safety pins. Dinner satisfies all the senses!" (*Olive H Charlton*) "The most pleasant and friendly place, without any 'side'." (*Joan Williamson*) Once again readers write in varying styles but invariably with warm appreciation of this Georgian house with a large garden, bounded by trees on one side and, on the other, a glorious stretch of the river Swale. Again the very reasonable prices, and Tom and Anita Berry's kindness and friendliness are praised. The approach to *Howe Villa* is not particularly salubrious, but the house itself has been restored "with taste and charm"; it has large elegantly proportioned rooms and fine views. There are only four bedrooms, all very comfortable and furnished to a high standard. The four-course menu offers a choice of starters, desserts and cheeses, and a substantial main course, often a roast with vegetables in the middle – "English cooking at its very best, beautifully presented, small but good selection of wine."

Open Feb–Nov.
Rooms 4 double – 2 with bath and shower, 2 with shower, all with radio, TV and tea-making facilities.
Facilities Large drawing room, dining room. ½-acre garden on river Swale.
Location ½ m from centre of Richmond – take A6108 signposted Leyburn and Reeth; at the ATS Tyre service station turn left, keep left following signs to Richmond Cleaners and *Howe Villa*.
Restrictions Not suitable for severely ♿. No children under 12. No dogs.
Credit cards None accepted.
Terms (No service charge) Dinner, B&B £32.50. Set dinner £13.50. Reduction for stays of 3 days or more. Reduced rates and special meals for children.
Service/tipping: "Guests do like to say thank you, perhaps with a small gift. I accept, enjoying the pleasure it gives them, but do not like service charges."

We need feedback on all entries. Often people fail to report on the best-known hotels, assuming that "someone else is sure to".

ROLLESTON ON DOVE Staffordshire — Map 4

The Brookhouse Inn
Brookside, Rolleston on Dove
Nr Burton upon Trent DE13 9AA

Tel Burton upon Trent (0283) 814188
Fax (0283) 813644

A 17th-century listed building in three-acre grounds, attractively converted, taken over in late 1988 by Fiona and John Westwood who inherited the staff and the "excellent" chef David Bould. In a pretty, untouristy Staffordshire village, a convenient stopover off the M1 or M6. Meals highly praised, but niggles about some bedrooms and bathrooms – "scrupulously clean", however, but perhaps too reliant on business trade. New bedrooms and a conservatory planned for 1990. Closed 24 Dec–1 Jan. 16 rooms, all with private facilities. B&B double £65–£70. Full alc dinner £22. More reports please.

ROSEDALE ABBEY North Yorkshire — Map 4

The Milburn Arms Hotel
Rosedale Abbey
Nr Pickering YO18 8RA

Tel Lastingham (075 15) 312

A friendly family-owned stone inn, part 14th-century, in the middle of the North Yorkshire moors. It is popular locally for its good bar meals, and had an italicised entry in the Guide last year. This has brought a series of favourable reports: "Stephen and Frances Colling's first attempt in the hotel business (he is from the wine trade) has now been going for five years. Improvements, including new bedrooms with *en suite* bathrooms in the old stable block, have taken time but do not spoil this old inn set in the most beautiful countryside (could be crowded in summer). Warm welcome from hosts and staff. Restaurant meal well presented, bar meals excellent value, traditional English breakfast a good start to the day. Wine list with over 100 selections reasonably priced with classic items for special occasions. Excellent walks start right from the door." "Food is good dinner party standard. Pleasant lounge for pre-dinner drinks with interesting mixture of books. We much appreciated the comfortable sofa in our annexe bedroom." (*G Benjamin, Caroline Burton, and others*)

Open All year except Christmas.
Rooms 14 double – 12 with bath and shower, 2 with shower, all with telephone, radio, TV, tea-making facilities and baby-listening. 8 in annexe.
Facilities Lounge, bar, bistro, restaurant. Garden.
Location In centre of village; approach through Cropton from Wrelton, off A170 W of Pickering. Ample parking.
Restrictions Not suitable for ♿. No dogs in public rooms.
Credit cards Access, Visa.
Terms B&B £23–£39.50. Full alc £11–£19.50. Off-season breaks; mini-breaks all year. 1-night bookings refused for bank holidays. Reduced rates for children sharing parents' room; special meals on request.

If you have had recent experience of a good hotel that ought to be in the Guide, please write to us at once. Report forms are to be found at the back. Procrastination is the thief of the next edition.

ROSEVINE Cornwall — Map 1

Roseland House Hotel — *Tel* Portscatho (087 258) 644
Rosevine, Nr Portscatho TR2 5EW

Small family-owned hotel in quiet position on lovely Roseland Peninsula. Recommended for high standards of cleanliness and comfort, good food (6-course dinners with fresh ingredients), and reasonable prices. Vegetarians catered for. 6½-acre grounds with terraced gardens and private beach. 18 rooms, most with private facilities, some suitable for disabled. Open Mar–end Nov and Christmas. Dinner, B&B £25–£32. No children under 5. No dogs. New nomination. More reports please.

ROSTHWAITE Cumbria — Map 4

Hazel Bank Hotel — *Tel* Borrowdale (059 684) 248
Rosthwaite — from 1990 (076 87) 77248
Nr Keswick CA12 5XB

"A simple hotel, modestly furnished, serving wholesome food; spotless, fresh new decor, excellent taste," writes *Eileen Broadbent* endorsing last year's new entry for this "charming old house in large, beautifully landscaped grounds; decorated inside with period furniture, with modern facilities". The resident owners, Gwen and John Nuttall, have restored and modernised their 125-year-old house over the past nine years without sacrificing any of the Victorian atmosphere. The bedrooms, each named for the Fell it dramatically overlooks, are attractively furnished and decorated, with immaculate facilities. The dining room is light and airy; meals are served at set times. (*Dr and Mrs AC Trueblood*) Many visitors to *Hazel Bank House* are returnees; it is generally booked up months ahead. The Nuttalls cater for a large proportion of walkers, ramblers, etc; there is a drying room, and packed lunches are provided.

Open 17 Mar–10 Nov.
Rooms 8 double, 1 single – 3 with bath, 5 with shower, 4 with TV, all with tea-making facilities. 2 ground-floor rooms.
Facilities Residents' lounge, bar, dining room; drying room. 4-acre grounds with lawn and woodlands. Derwentwater 4 m.
Location 7 m S of Keswick on B5289. Turn left up drive just before village.
Restrictions Not suitable for ♿. No children under 6. Dogs by prior arrangement only (60p); not in public rooms.
Credit cards None accepted.
Terms (No service charge) Dinner, B&B £27–£29. Weekly rates. 1-night bookings sometimes refused if requested far in advance.
Service/tipping: "Tipping is not expected; regulars know this but some people like to show their appreciation. Tips are distributed to all staff."

RYE East Sussex — Map 3

Jeake's House — *Tel* Rye (0797) 222828
Mermaid Street TN31 7ET

Jeake's House, named after the Jeake family who built it – a later occupant was the American writer, Conrad Aiken – had its first entry in last year's Guide. It is a beautiful old listed building on one of Rye's cobbled streets and is now a very reasonably priced B&B owned by Francis and Jenny Hadfield. Bedrooms, some with brass or mahogany bedsteads, look over the old roof-tops of Rye or face south across the marsh to the sea; most have private bath or shower. Our nominators enjoyed their "small, pretty bedroom, decorated in the Victorian manner, pale pink walls with stencil border, attractive pale pink and blue curtains, lined and of good quality, sprigged Laura Ashley duvet, with some nice old bits of furniture". "Beds are extremely comfortable, with *proper* sheets; excellent bathroom, with lots of hot water. The whole house is charmingly arranged." There is a Victorian parlour with upright piano, sheet music of the period and armchairs with antimacassars. A good and generous breakfast is served in the adjoining converted chapel which was once a Quaker meeting house: "A large galleried white-painted room with high windows and some good paintings; a welcoming fire, books, plants, small pieces of china, some very good; separate tables with white laundered linen and napkins." Parking is a slight problem, but there is a carpark at the end of the road. (*Heather and Roy Sharland, Claire Jacquier*) Vegetarian as well as traditional breakfasts are on offer; the Hadfields keep a stock of menus from local restaurants and help guests make dinner reservations. More reports please.

Open All year.
Rooms 1 suite, 7 double, 1 single – 5 with bath, 2 with shower, all with TV and tea-making facilities.
Facilities Sitting room, dining room. Payphone in hall. Beaches nearby.
Location In centre of Rye; carpark nearby.
Restrictions Not suitable for ♿. No dogs in public rooms.
Credit cards None accepted.
Terms B&B: single £17, double £34–£42, suite £54. 1-night bookings sometimes refused for Sat in high season. Reductions for stays of 4 or more days. Reduced rates for children sharing parents' room. (No restaurant.)
Service/tipping: "We neither expect nor encourage tipping, but our staff always appreciate it."

ST ANNE'S ON SEA see LYTHAM ST ANNE'S — Map 4

Dalmeny Hotel

ST AUSTELL Cornwall — Map 1

Boscundle Manor — *Tel* Par (072 681) 3557
Tregrehan
St Austell PL25 3RL

Andrew and Mary Flint's manor house hotel, medieval in part, 18th-century in the main, lies in a bosky setting about a mile from the sea at Carlyon Bay; it has a particularly attractive garden with a heated pool. The Flints spend much time making improvements in the grounds – at present work is proceeding on a practice golf course. Public rooms "are not opulent but have a country charm. The conservatory is bright and inviting for breakfast. Bedrooms are comfortable, every piece of furniture and print chosen with loving care" (but some are small). *Boscundle Manor* has "mildly eccentric" characteristics, as we have said in the past; its informality is not universally approved, but those in favour report "a wonderful combination of easy cordiality and comfort with understated luxuriousness; it is like visiting considerate, generous and discriminating friends, guests are made to feel comfortable and free to enjoy themselves." The food: "fresh and well-chosen ingredients, handled with respect and perfectly served". More reports please.

Open Easter and mid-Apr–mid-Oct. Restaurant closed for lunch, and Sun evening to non-residents.
Rooms 1 suite, 8 double, 2 single – all with bath and/or shower (4 with spa bath), telephone, radio and TV. 3 in cottage in garden.
Facilities Sitting room, cocktail bar, dining room, private dining room, conservatory; exercise room. 9-acre grounds with 2-acre gardens, croquet, practice golf course and heated swimming pool, woodlands, old tin mine. Beaches 1 m and 6 m; riding, coastal walks, fishing nearby; .
Location 2 m E of St Austell, 100 yds off A390 on road signposted Tregrehan.
Restrictions Not suitable for ♿. No dogs in public rooms.
Credit cards Access, Visa.
Terms B&B (English): single £50, double £75–£90, suite £130. Set dinner £18. Special meals for children by arrangement.
Service/tipping: "All rates include service. We actively discourage anyone from leaving extra money."

ST KEYNE Cornwall — Map 1

The Well House [GFG] — *Tel* Liskeard (0579) 42001
St Keyne
Liskeard PL14 4RN

Nicholas Wainford's "delightful Cornish Victorian country house hotel" has a secluded setting in three-and-a-half-acre grounds with tennis court, swimming pool and croquet lawn in a pretty, unspoilt spot in the Looe valley; it is reached by a winding one-track road. It entered the Guide last year and is now warmly endorsed, "David Pope's cooking is superlative; the food is equal to many meals eaten in France in the better two-rosette restaurants. The bedrooms are charmingly and thoughtfully decorated, each one different, all well lit, with pretty bed covers, fresh flowers and gleaming, well-appointed *en suite* bathrooms. Public rooms, decorated in cool colours, "have a '20s/'30s atmosphere" the dining room tables impeccably set and welcoming". Continental breakfasts, served in the bedroom, are "really good, especially the home-made croissants". English breakfast is available too, served in the dining room. Service is "courteous and attentive – staff seek out guests, not vice versa". *Well House* offers all the amenities one would expect in the most prestigious country house hotels, but at much lower prices and in a more congenial atmosphere." One niggle from a couple who found their bedroom (No 5) "a little confined", with the dressing-table awkwardly placed for applying make-up in the evening.

Open All year. Restaurant closed Mon to non-residents.
Rooms 7 double – all with bath and shower, telephone, radio and TV.
Facilities Sitting room, bar, restaurant. 3½-acre grounds with tennis, croquet and heated swimming pool. Walking, fishing, riding, golf nearby.
Location Take B3254 from Liskeard. St Keyne is 3 m S; at the church take the sign to St Keyne Well; *Well House* is ½ m further on left.
Restrictions Not suitable for ♿. No children under 8 in dining room at night. Dogs by arrangement.

Credit cards Access, Amex, Visa.
Terms (No service charge) B&B (continental): single occupancy £42.50–£47.50, double £65–£92.50. Cooked breakfast £6.50 extra. Set lunch £15 and £24, dinner £24. 1-night bookings refused at Easter, Christmas and New Year.
Service/tipping: "I make it clear that any tips given are entirely at clients' discretion. Credit card slips are always filled in without service so the tip would have to be cash."

ST LAWRENCE Isle of Wight — Map 2

The Lawyers Rest Hotel — *Tel* Ventnor (0983) 852610
Undercliff Drive
St Lawrence, Ventnor PO38 1XF

Victorian house overlooking sea, recently extensively refurbished, in village on south coast of island. Recommended for quiet, warm, comfortable bedrooms, good food, including "the most perfect breakfast croissants north of Eugénie-les-Bains". English menu can include sausage and mash, steak and kidney pie and spotted dick, as well as more sophisticated alternatives. Well chosen and reasonably priced wine list. Wine bar serving snacks. Small, mature garden. Open Mar–Oct. 8 rooms, all with bath or shower. Dinner, B&B £28–£29.50. Was in Guide as the Woody Bank Hotel *under earlier owners. Now, owned by Ann Dex and ex-solicitor Geoffrey Phillips (hence the name), warmly recommended for readmission. More reports please.*

ST MARY'S Isles of Scilly — Map 1

Star Castle Hotel — *Tel* Scillonia (0720) 22317
St Mary's, Isles of Scilly
Cornwall TR21 0JA

St Mary's is easily reached by boat or helicopter from the mainland and is an excellent base for an island-hopping Scillonian holiday. The *Star Castle* is a modest but welcoming hotel, originally – 390 years ago – an Elizabethan fortress against a possible Spanish invasion after the defeat of the Armada. Built in the form of an eight-pointed star, with a dry moat and 18-foot wide ramparts, it enjoys a spectacular position overlooking the town, harbour and neighbouring islands; it has extensive grounds, with lawns enclosed by tall hedges forming welcoming suntraps. There is a covered heated swimming pool and a tennis court. Some of the bedrooms are in the old building (one, popular with honeymooners, is in a guard-house on the ramparts); other, larger ones are in a modern annexe in the garden. There is a dungeon bar where snack lunches are served, and the dining room is the former officers' mess. Public rooms can be a bit cramped when the hotel is full. "Mr and Mrs Reynolds, the resident owners are pleasant and efficient hosts, and their staff as friendly a bunch as one could wish to meet." (*Bob Welham, also R and C Nisbet*) Food is variously described as "very acceptable, but not gourmet" and "mundane and predictable". More reports please.

Open 2 weeks before Easter–mid-Oct.
Rooms 5 family, 16 double, 3 single – 23 with bath and/or shower, all with telephone, radio, TV, tea-making facilities and baby-listening. 16 in 2 blocks in garden.

Facilities 2 lounges, games room, bar, restaurant. 4½-acre grounds with grass tennis court and covered heated swimming pool; croquet and bowls available. Sandy beaches, safe bathing and fishing nearby.
Location Central, overlooking town and harbour, but in large grounds so not noisy. Regular boats and helicopter flights to Scilly Islands from Penzance.
Restrictions Not suitable for ♿. Dogs in garden rooms only (£1.25 per day).
Credit cards None accepted.
Terms (No service charge) Dinner, B&B £32.50–£40. Set dinner £11.50. Packed and bar lunches available; vegetarian meals on request. Reduced rates for children sharing parents' room; high tea.
Service/tipping: "Tips are not expected – but gratefully received if given!"

SALCOMBE Devon — Map 1

Tides Reach Hotel — *Tel* Salcombe (054 884) 3466
South Sands, Salcombe TQ8 8LJ

"This is how a family hotel should be run. Young energetic staff, well-maintained public areas. Top floor rooms well equipped and brightly decorated. Good, well-prepared food including local Dart salmon. Good selection of English cheeses. Sound, reasonably priced wines. Can't wait to go back." (*T Hodge*) The *Tides Reach* is a cheerful modern family-run hotel, with a huge range of activities available for sporting folk, both outdoors and in the hotel's own leisure complex (see below). It has a choice location: South Sands is a mile to the south of Salcombe itself, well away from the crowded summer scene, facing across the estuary, and surrounded by National Trust land. Visitors regularly commend the friendly attentive staff, the bright attractive bedrooms (many with balcony), lounges and restaurant – though, bad news for some, the public rooms have muzak. Some shortcomings in bathrooms – mirrors very high, no shelving; but good housekeeping. Snacks are available at lunchtime.

Open Mar–Nov.
Rooms 3 suites, 36 double, 3 single – all with bath and/or shower, telephone, radio and TV; some with sea view and balcony.
Facilities Lift, ramp to entrance. Lounge, sun lounge, reading lounge, cocktail bar, pool bar, restaurant; health and beauty salon, hairdressing salon, sauna, whirlpool bath, gym, games room, squash court with spectator lounge, snooker; heated swimming pool with sliding doors to make it open in summer. 2-acre grounds with garden, pond, tea lawn. 10 yds from beach with safe bathing, wind surfing school, sea fishing, sailing.
Location 1 mile S of Salcombe; follow signs to Bolt Head and South Sands.
Restrictions Access to some facilities and movement outside hotel may be difficult for ♿. No children under 8. No dogs in public rooms.
Credit cards All major cards accepted.
Terms Dinner, B&B (English): single £44–£72, double £88–£142, suite £100–£150. Light lunch £3.25–£8.50. Set dinner £19.50; full alc £39. Bargain breaks, off-season breaks. 50% reduction for children sharing parents' room.
Service/tipping: "Service is included in our prices. Tipping is at the discretion of the customer, should he wish to show appreciation."

> Our italicised entries indicate hotels which are worth considering, but which, for various reasons – inadequate information, lack of feedback, ambivalent reports – do not at the moment warrant a full entry. We should particularly welcome comments on these hotels.

SALTFORD Avon — Map 2

Brunel's Tunnel House Hotel — *Tel* Saltford (0225) 873873
High Street, Saltford
Nr Bristol BS18 3BQ

A Grade II listed Georgian building in a conservation village between Bristol and Bath, this is one of three tunnel houses in Britain. It was bought by the famous 19th-century engineer, Isambard Kingdom Brunel, so that the Great Western Railway line he designed could be excavated underneath; several of the broad-gauge locomotives of the GWR were assembled in the tunnel before the line opened in 1839. Trains have been running underneath the house ever since. "There is a slight rumble when a train passes but it does not impinge on conversation or sleep." The accommodation is comfortable, clean and co-ordinated with the feminine touch of the owners, Muriel Mitchell and her daughter Sarah, "who combine efficiency with charm and consideration; bedrooms are individually decorated and have canopied beds, mineral water, fruit and sugared almonds. There is no choice on the three-course dinner menu, but the food was excellent. There is an attractive marina nearby." More reports please.

Open All year. B&B only at Christmas and New Year. Dining room closed for lunch.
Rooms 7 – 1 with bath and shower, 6 with shower, all with telephone, radio, TV and tea-making facilities.
Facilities Lounge/bar, dining room. ½-acre garden. River Avon with marina 15 mins' walk; golf nearby.
Location Midway between Bath (5½ m) and Bristol (6½ m). At Saltford Motor Services turn up Beech Road off A4; hotel is at bottom of Beech Road.
Restrictions Not suitable for ♿. No children under 10. Dogs by prior arrangement only; not in public rooms.
Credit cards Access, Amex, Visa.
Terms B&B: single £40, double £48; dinner, B&B: single £51, double £70. Set dinner £11. Weekend discounts.
Service/tipping: "There is no service charge since we feel that excellent service is implicit in the way we work. We feel that tipping should be left to the discretion of customers – it is neither expected nor encouraged, but if offered is not refused."

SANDPLACE Cornwall — Map 1

Polraen Country House Hotel — *Tel* Looe (050 36) 3956
Sandplace, Nr Looe PL13 1PJ

18th-century Cornish stone building in secluded setting outside Looe (which gets crowded in summer). "Well kept and dignified exterior, interior expressive of comfort and common sense." Peter and Joyce Allcroft are welcoming hosts; food is "traditional English with interesting variations". Small grounds. Good cliff walks. Closed end Dec, 2 weeks end Feb/early Mar. 5 rooms, all with private facilities. B&B double £38–£40. Set dinner £11.25. New nomination. More reports please.

> We invite British hotels to tell us of their policy on service charges and tipping. Many hotels ignore this request. Replies, when given, are printed at the end of an entry.

SANDY PARK Devon **Map 1**

Mill End Hotel *Tel* Chagford (064 73) 2282
Sandy Park, Chagford TQ13 8JN

Converted mill on river bank at head of Teign Gorge, on edge of Dartmoor. Recommended for comfortable lounges with log fires, luxurious bedrooms – "some modern, some old and chintzy" – good dinners (traditional English cooking) and breakfasts. 2-acre grounds. Private salmon and sea-trout fishing; excellent walking nearby. Closed 10 days before Christmas. 17 rooms, all with private facilities. B&B double £49–£80. Set dinner £18–£20. New nomination. More reports please.

SCALBY North Yorkshire **Map 4**

Wrea Head Country Hotel *Tel* Scarborough (0723) 378211
Scalby, Nr Scarborough YO13 0PB

Personally run hotel in 19th-century building in quiet situation three miles north-west of Scarborough on edge of North Yorkshire National Park. "Expensively furnished in good taste", warm and comfortable. Bedrooms and bathrooms vary in size; some are large, with lovely views. 14-acre wooded and landscaped grounds. Breakfasts recommended, but some criticisms of dinner. Good service. A drawback could be the hotel's reliance on group trade. 21 rooms, all with private facilities. B&B double £60–£67.50. Set dinner £15.95. New nomination. More reports please.

SEAVIEW Isle of Wight **Map 1**

Seaview Hotel [GFG] *Tel* Seaview (0983) 612711
High Street, Seaview PO34 5EX

César award in 1989: Comprehensively satisfactory seaside hotel

Nicholas and Nicola Hayward's seaside hotel is one of the all too small class of reasonably priced seaside family hotels that offer unusually good food and wine. It is an unassuming three-storey bay-windowed Edwardian house at the foot of the High Street and near a quiet beach in an old-fashioned and picturesque sailing village. Bedrooms vary in size, front rooms have a fine view of the sea and coast. The drawing room is delightful with warm lighting and a gas fire. *Seaview* is very much a family affair – this year we learn that Stephen King, formerly the chef, has now become manager and married the assistant manageress; Charles Bartlett has succeeded him in the kitchen which Mrs Hayward continues to supervise. Plenty of enthusiastic reports again this year: "First impression is of a licensed maritime museum. Fine paintings and artefacts of ships everywhere." "Spotless and charming bedroom with all facilities." "Excellent food and good service – the latter due to the lead given by the proprietor." "The management is relaxed, friendly, yet always professional. Rooms simple but comfortable, food straightforward but excellent. Standards high in all departments." "Menu quite small, a deliberate policy I suspect to ensure that superb quality is maintained." "Excellent local seafood prepared to a very high standard." "Breakfasts very good, as much tea and fresh toast as one could consume." Families are welcome, though – reflecting the dilemma of many hotels which have no age restriction on children – Mrs Hayward writes, "The structure of the hotel does not enable us to have many facilities for them; as a family hotel we have a fair proportion of elderly guests. I do hope they will not be put off by the image of a hotel specialising in children. That is not our aim at all." Small children are not allowed in the restaurant after 7.30 pm; a "very good" high tea is served for them at 5.45 pm or they are served in a special room if dining later. The dining room can get very busy; at certain times of year there are two sittings. (*Mr and Mrs AG Hewett, Mary Lawson, Basil Devonshire, The Hon. Julian Fane, Mrs E Stuart-Clarke, and many others*)

Open All year.
Rooms 4 suites, 12 double – all with bath and/or shower, radio, TV and baby-listening. 2 with patio on ground floor.
Facilities 2 lounges (1 non-smoking), cocktail bar, public bar, restaurant; Sunshine Room for private dining, conferences, early suppers for small children. Patio and courtyard. Sea and sandy beaches nearby with sailing, fishing, windsurfing, etc.
Location In centre of village, near sea. Follow signs for sea front.
Restrictions Not suitable for wheelchairs. No dogs in public rooms. No small children in dining room after 7.30 pm.
Credit cards Access, Amex, Visa.
Terms [1989 rates] B&B £25–£44; dinner, B&B (2 nights min) £33–£54. Full alc from £15. Breakaway, weekend and weekly tariffs all year. Reduced rates and special meals for children.
Service/tipping: "We do not make a service charge, or expect our guests to tip."

SHARPTHORNE see EAST GRINSTEAD — Map 3

Gravetye Manor

SHELDWICH Kent — Map 3

Barons Hotel and Restaurant — *Tel* Sittingbourne (0795) 539168
Sheldwich, Nr Faversham
ME13 0LT

Regency Grade II listed manor house with original features, in large grounds, three miles south of Faversham on Ashford road, carefully restored and redecorated. Comfortable lounge, "exceptionally attractive dining room serving some of the best food in Kent". Elegant large bedrooms with period furnishings; front ones double-glazed to cut out traffic noise, back ones overlook gardens and country. Stables for visiting horses; swimming pool planned for 1990. 9 rooms, all with bath and shower. B&B double £75–£125. Set lunch £14.50, dinner £26.50. New nomination. More reports please.

> There are many expensive hotels in the Guide. We are keen to increase our coverage at the other end of the scale. If you know of a simple place giving simple satisfaction, please write and tell us.

SHENINGTON Oxfordshire — Map 2

Sugarswell Farm
Shenington, Nr Banbury
OX15 6HW

Tel Tysoe (029 588) 512 and 8188

A new nomination, in rural Oxfordshire: "I think GHG readers would enjoy *Sugarswell Farm*. It is a working dairy farm – we watched 100-plus black and white cows passing our bedroom window morning and evening. The house is quite new, built of stones from a demolished cottage, and Rosemary Nunneley is a delightful hostess. There are only three bedrooms. Ours had two armchairs *and* a sofa, and spectacular views across fields and hills – not another building in sight! Very comfortable beds, ample drawer space, large and well-equipped bathroom. The dining room, like the hall and staircase, is papered in dark red with crisp white paint. Guests (never more than six) eat round a large table, though vegetables etc are served in individual tureens. This worked very well during our stay; all our fellow guests were compatible. Food is excellent – starters included salmon soufflé, melon salad and a tasty hot 'beef pot' served with crudités; main courses were veal in a creamy, garlicky sauce and perfectly cooked fillet steak; good sweets and coffee too. *Sugarswell* is an ideal holiday centre: Stratford, Warwick, the Cotswold villages and many other attractions are in easy reach." (*Heather Kirk*) This is mostly a non-smoking establishment, but there is one room where the desperate can go for a puff.

Open All year.
Rooms 3 double – all with bath, TV and tea-making facilities.
Facilities Drawing room, dining room. 350-acre farm.
Location 2¼ m NW of Banbury on Edge Hill road, W of A422.
Restrictions No smoking. No children under 12. No dogs.
Credit cards None accepted.
Terms B&B: single £25–£30, double £36–£40. Set dinner £14.

SHERBORNE Dorset — Map 2

The Eastbury Hotel
Long Street, Sherborne DT9 3BY

Tel Sherborne (0935) 813131
Telex 46644 EASTBY

A dignified Georgian town house close to the Benedictine Abbey and the old and new castles, in a peaceful one-acre walled garden. It belongs to a small group called Clipper Hotels (who recently bought *Hunstrete House*) and is managed by Mr Portet. The pretty bedrooms, with floral decor and named after flowers, are a good size and well equipped, with modern bathrooms. The conservatory restaurant serves good traditional English cooking. Visitors appreciate its "unpretentious charm and unobtrusive service". "I stayed with great pleasure and in great comfort at the *Eastbury*." (*Jan Morris*) More reports please.

Open All year.
Rooms 8 double, 4 single – all with bath and shower, telephone, TV, tea-making facilities and baby-listening.
Facilities 2 lounges, bar, restaurant; private dining room, functions room. 1-acre walled garden.
Location 2 mins' walk from centre. Carpark.
Restrictions Not suitable for ♿. No dogs.

Credit cards Access, Visa.
Terms B&B (English): single £49.50, double from £70. Set lunch £10.50, dinner £16.50. Christmas and New Year rates. Reduced rates and special meals for children.
Service/tipping: "An individual transaction between customer and staff."

SHIPTON GORGE Dorset — Map 2

Innsacre Farmhouse Hotel [GFG] — *Tel* Bridport (0308) 56137
Shipton Gorge, Nr Bridport
DT6 4LJ

Innsacre is a 17th-century farmhouse with a beamed lounge complete with log fire, books and games for the whole family ("pets are also welcome", says the brochure). The restaurant is in the former barn, with stone walls and quaint windows. Ducks, pigs and chickens remind visitors that it was not long ago a working farm. Readers again comment on *Innsacre*'s happy atmosphere, created by the Smith family, the warm welcome and good value for money. Last year's entry was critical of housekeeping; the Smiths tell us they now have a new housekeeper. *DF Tooley*, visiting in March 1989, shortly after a new chef had also arrived, reports, "The whole place was spotless. There were fresh flowers and a bowl of fresh fruit in our bedroom. The restaurant is very attractive; delectable food is served with a good selection from a menu changed fortnightly. The Smiths and their staff looked after our every want throughout our stay." An earlier visitor wrote, "Our room was small but very comfortable. Crisp cotton bedlinen and an electric heater which we could control ourselves. Our host, Mr Smith was charming but very laid back, quietly but kindly looking after our needs. We woke to look out onto budding trees and primroses, no traffic noises, just birdsong and ducks quacking. Only complaint was that the portions of food were too big!" (*Wendy Keen*) Other guests in a room over the bar were kept awake by convivial noises from below, but even they summed up: "A very good place to get away from it all but not feel isolated." We'd like more reports please, particularly on the food.

Open All year.
Rooms 7 double – 5 with bath and shower, all with TV, tea-making facilities and baby-listening.
Facilities Chair lift. Bar lounge, TV lounge, restaurant. 10-acre grounds with orchard and gardens. 2 m from Chesil Beach with pebble beach, fishing, safe bathing.
Location 2 m E of Bridport; second turning to Shipton Gorge off A35 Dorchester–Bridport.
Restriction No dogs in restaurant.
Credit cards All major cards accepted.
Terms (No service charge) B&B (English) £22–£32; dinner, B&B £38.75–£48.75. Set lunch £10.50, dinner £17.75. Weekly rates. Reduced rates for children sharing parents' room; special meals.
Service/tipping: "We discourage tipping."

> We asked hotels to quote 1990 prices. Not all were able to predict them in the late spring of 1989. Some of our terms will be inaccurate. Do check latest tariffs at the time of booking.

SIMONSBATH Somerset **Map 1**

Simonsbath House Hotel *Tel* Exford (064 383) 259
Simonsbath, Nr Minehead
TA24 7SH

This 17th-century hunting lodge returned to the Guide last year in an italicised entry following a change of owners. "We are very glad to see it back. The welcome is friendly, the cooking superb and the general ambience very comfortable country house style. But not a hotel for those in search of excitement. (*Major and Mrs Garnett*) *Simonsbath House* is in two-acre grounds in the heart of Exmoor National Park; most rooms have lovely views over the river Barle. There is a panelled lounge and library bar and plenty of books; log fires burn in cold weather. Bedrooms have period furniture and smallish bathrooms. There are three choices of starter and main course, and four of dessert on the menu, which changes daily; you choose your food and wait about 30 minutes while it is prepared. It is served in generous portions. The hotel is run by Mike and Sue Burns who, aiming for that "not-a- hotel-more-like-visiting-friends" effect, rather coyly call their brochure "An invitation". Only criticisms: the decor isn't to everyone's taste, and "for those of mature years wanting to do the crossword in the evening the light could be a bit brighter."

Open 1 Feb–end Nov.
Rooms 7 double – all with bath (4 also with shower), telephone, ratio, TV .
Facilities Lounge, library, dining room. 2-acre grounds. Riding, shooting, fishing nearby.
Location 7 m SE of Lynton.
Restrictions Not suitable for ♿. No children under 10. No dogs.
Credit cards All major cards accepted.
Terms B&B £31.50–£38. Set dinner £15; full alc £18.25.
Service/tipping: "We make no service charge. Tips discretionary."

Traveller's tale *Monlucon, July. I was looking for rooms in a hotel near the railway. As the landlady and I went along a corridor upstairs, I said I hoped the noise of trains could not be heard in the bedrooms. "One hears nothing," she answered positively. She opened the door of a room and a tremendous engine-shriek met us, seeming to drive us both back from the threshold. She shut the door, and tried another one, and we were met instantly by another tremendous engine-shriek. She burst out laughing. I laughed too. If she had not proved her sense of humour, I might have walked straight out of the hotel. But her sense of humour kept a customer with a sense of humour. I got quiet rooms at the back.*
Arnold Bennett (Journals, 1929)

SLAIDBURN Lancashire **Map 4**

Parrock Head Hotel [GFG]
Slaidburn, Clitheroe BB7 3AH

Tel Slaidburn (02006) 614

Much praise again for *Parrock Head*, owned and run by Richard Umbers, ex-Cambridge rugby blue and ex-brewing, and his wife Vicky. The former farmhouse has been almost entirely refurbished since they took it over three years ago; it is now somewhat upmarket, though prices are still reasonable. It has a remote and beautiful location at the foot of Bowland Fells, on the Lancashire–Yorkshire border, with dales on one side, majestic moorland on the other. Three bedrooms are in the main building, six are in two blocks of garden cottages. "Beautiful peaceful surroundings, attentive service, excellent imaginative cuisine." "Limited menu but all freshly cooked. We liked Mrs Umbers' policy of introducing guests to each other before dinner; it encouraged a relaxed, friendly atmosphere. Decor attractive, everything spotlessly clean." "The two bedrooms in the main house spacious and comfortable. First-class picnic lunches." *Parrock Head* is warm and comfortable, even in the depths of winter; there are log fires in the large sitting room on the first floor and a library filled with books and magazines, maps and tourist information. In the spacious dining room, which also caters to non-residents, the Umbers offer a reasonably priced à la carte menu, cooked by extremely young chefs, with four choices of starter and main course and three of dessert – "English cooking with French touches"; breakfasts are "king-size". (*Dr TC and Mrs IE Barker, CG Clapshoe, The Marchioness Conyngham, and many others*) Rooms in the annexe – "jokingly called 'The Shed'" – may be quieter than those in the main house which are directly off the bar and lounge.

Open Mid-Feb–mid-Dec.
Rooms 1 suite, 8 double – all with bath, shower, telephone, TV, tea-making facilities and baby-listening. 6 rooms in 2 blocks of garden cottages. 3 ground-floor rooms.
Facilities Reception, bar, 2 lounges, library, restaurant. 1-acre grounds; reservoir fishing 2 m; bird-watching.
Location 9 m N of Clitheroe. Take B6478 to Slaidburn; hotel is 1 m NW on unsignposted road.
Restriction Dogs in garden cottages only.
Credit cards Access, Amex.
Terms (No service charge) B&B: single £30–£32, double £44–£48, suite £44 for 2, £65 for 3. Full alc £14. Light lunches on request, packed lunches available. 3-night mid-week breaks. 1-night bookings refused for Sat if the reservation does not include dinner. Reduced rates for children sharing parents' meals; special meals.
Service/tipping: "We do not solicit tips, but payments, if any, are made to the proprietors and distributed to staff."

Deadlines: nominations for the 1991 edition should reach us not later than 1 May 1990. Latest date for comments on existing entries: 1 June 1990.

Always let a hotel know if you have to cancel a booking, whether you have paid a deposit or not. Hotels lose thousands of pounds and dollars from "no-shows".

SOURTON Devon **Map 1**

Collaven Manor Hotel *Tel* Bridestowe (083 786) 522
Sourton, Nr Okehampton
EX20 4HH

Collaven Manor was new to the Guide last year: it's a partly creeper-covered 15th-century manor house, all beams, inglenook fireplaces and stone walls, in large grounds on the edge of Dartmoor. It was praised for the friendly hosts, Mr and Mrs Buckley, and the "beautiful ambience and the stylish design of our spacious room (No 1). Chintz curtains and other fine fabrics contrasted nicely with white walls divided by dark old beams; two armchairs of remarkable elegance looked comfortable. The luxurious bathroom, *en suite*, was splendid. Every detail of the decor in the public rooms – fresh flowers, shiny copper, fine old china plates above the inglenook fireplace – was carefully thought out. English breakfast included delicious freshly smoked haddock and four types of home-made jams and marmalade, served in pretty little bowls. We were treated like royalty." Of the food we are told this year: "No haste, but service just when required. A memorable meal, beautifully presented. Wine list well chosen, with an excellent house wine." You dine in one of two restaurants; the *Hamilton* is considerably pricier than the *Inglenook.* (*Gabriele Berneck and Christine Herxheimer, GS Smith, and others*)

Open All year.
Rooms 7 double, 2 single – all with bath and/or shower, telephone, radio, TV and tea-making facilities. 1 with 4-poster.
Facilities Lounge, bar, 2 restaurants. 5-acre grounds with pitch and putt golf, bowls, croquet, clay-pigeon shooting.
Location 8 m S of Okehampton on A386 to Tavistock.
Restrictions Not suitable for ♿. No children under 12. No dogs.
Credit cards Access, Visa.
Terms (No service charge) B&B (English): single occupancy £35–£50, double £55–£95. Set lunch £10.95 (packed lunch available); dinner £10.95 in Inglenook Restaurant, £18.95 in Hamilton Restaurant; alc grill menu available. Special breaks; 4-day Christmas package.
Service/tipping: "We do not feel guests should be obliged to tip; it is left entirely to their discretion."

SOUTH MOLTON Devon **Map 1**

Whitechapel Manor [GFG] *Tel* South Molton (076 95) 3377
South Molton EX36 3EG *Fax* (07695) 3797

This fine Grade I listed Elizabethan manor in 12-acre grounds in an isolated setting near the Exmoor National Park came into the Guide last year in an entry which is now warmly endorsed, "We cannot praise highly enough the way in which the Devon-born owner John Shapland and his wife Patricia run this beautiful small hotel. Their approach was warm, friendly and extremely helpful. Every comfort was considered: large bedroom, lovely views, huge, comfortable bed, gleaming bathroom. Dinners and breakfasts of superb quality." "The interior is substantial, graceful and restful; it has been brought gently into the 20th century without losing its original charm. The entrance hall is dominated by a magnificent carved oak Jacobean screen. The rooms have high ceilings, some with intricate plaster carvings and mouldings, and deep recessed windows. Furnishings and fabrics throughout are of the highest quality. It is totally quiet – the walls are so thick that you cannot hear a sound from either side or above." "A must for the Guide – but no point in going if you don't want to get away from it all; and it would not suit a family with teenagers in search of action." The talented young chef, Thierry Lepretre-Granet, has worked at *Mallory Court* (q.v.) and in France; cooking is "of a very high standard; excellent quality ingredients, nicely cooked vegetables, exciting desserts. Breakfast also very pleasant – fire and fresh flowers in the dining room, newspapers laid out. The service is totally personal – the Shaplands do almost everything themselves, apart from some very charming young local people who help with the bar and dining room". (*Maggie Hunt, Padi and John Howard, CS-K*) One would-be guest took umbrage at being warned on booking that she would be liable for the full room charge if she cancelled less than 21 days in advance and the room could not be relet. . .

Open All year.
Rooms 1 suite, 7 double, 2 single – all with bath and shower, telephone, radio, TV.
Facilities Bar, 2 lounges, restaurant. 2-acre garden with croquet. Fishing, golf, riding nearby. Exmoor 2 m. Sea 18 m.
Location From M5 motorway, junction 27, follow signs to Barnstaple. Do not turn left to Tiverton. Join A362 to Barnstaple at *Black Cat*. 3 m before South Molton pass Woodside Garage on left and Q8 garage on right. Take next right turn; ¾ m to Whitechapel. If you reach the *Mill Inn* at Bish Mill you have gone too far.
Restrictions Not suitable for ♿. Children under 12 by arrangement. Dogs by arrangement; not in hotel.
Credit cards Access, Visa.
Terms B&B (English): single £49.50–£55, double £67.50–£105, suite £112.50–£125. Set lunch £17.50, dinner £27.50. Packed lunch available. Winter rates.
Service/tipping: "Service included. No stated policy about tipping; it is not encouraged but we do not offend guests who want to say a special thank you to staff."

SOWERBY North Yorkshire — Map 4

Sheppard's Hotel and Restaurant — *Tel* Thirsk (0845) 23655
Church Farm, Front Street
Sowerby, Thirsk YO7 1JF

Creeper-covered family-run restaurant-with-rooms on former farm in lovely countryside. Attractive and comfortable public rooms and bedrooms. Adventurous menu in restaurant in converted stable block. Open all year except 1–5 Jan. 7 double rooms, 5 with bath or shower. B&B (English) £19–£40. Set dinner £12.75. Warmly recommended for friendly and professional service and reasonable rates. More reports please.

SPARK BRIDGE Cumbria — Map 4

Bridgefield House [GFG] — *Tel* Lowick Bridge (022 985) 239
Spark Bridge
Nr Ulverston LA12 8DA

Spark Bridge is on the banks of the river Crake, a short drive to the fells and the lakes themselves; the scenery is beautiful if less dramatic than further north, and it is well away from the tourist hordes. *Bridgefield House*, a late 19th-century gentleman's residence, is on a quiet country lane. Since coming here nine years ago, David and Rosemary Glister have been continually upgrading things. This year all five bedrooms have been redecorated and recarpeted, and telephones, new radios and alarm clocks installed. The drive has been relaid, and the gardens are next on the agenda. Guests continue to enjoy *Bridgefield House*'s quiet location on a back road overlooking Coniston Water, the warmth of every room in cold weather – fires in drawing room and dining room and individually controlled radiators in bedrooms – the home-like atmosphere and the very good value for money, particularly for long stays. There is no supplement for single people or one-night stays. Children are welcome; no charge is made for their high tea, and laundry service for children and babies is free. As before, Rosemary Glister's six-course dinners have won warm approval: "Beautifully presented, imaginative, with a varied choice. Other comments: "Lots of hot water for walkers' squeaking joints." "The Glisters remembered from our last visit that I like decaffeinated coffee." "Rooms comfortable, with all one could reasonably require. It is such a small place you are liable to bump into the Glisters quite a bit. They are extraordinarily nice, and could not be more welcoming." (*Mrs J Godfrey, Moira Jarrett, JA Gallimont; also PE Carter*)

Open All year, but only for lunch on Christmas Day.
Rooms 5 double – all with bath and shower, telephone, radio and baby-listening; tea-making facilities on request.
Facilities Drawing room, bar, dining room. 3-acre garden with swings and see-saw. Sea bathing 3 m; fishing, walking nearby.
Location Off A5092 on back road from Spark Bridge to Lowick Bridge.
Restrictions Not suitable for ♿. No smoking in dining room. No dogs in public rooms.
Credit card Access.
Terms [1989 rates] (No service charge) B&B £30. Packed lunches available on request; set dinner £15.50 (£18.50 to non-residents). Spring and autumn breaks. Children 3 and under free, under 12 50% reduction; high teas; free laundry service for children and babies.
Service/tipping: "The inclusion of a service charge is iniquitous and should be banned by law. Let's face it, it is only an extra increase in the tariff."

SPREYTON Devon — Map 1

Downhayes — *Tel* Bow (036 33) 378
Spreyton, Crediton EX17 5AR

A traditional Devon farmhouse dating from the 16th century, standing in its own 15 acres in deep countryside high in the mid-Devon hills, 20 miles west of Exeter – a car is essential. "The aim of Wolsey Lodges is to make the visitor feel like a guest in a private house," *WH Bruton* reported last year. "This is well realised at *Downhayes*. We were met by our hostess, Prue Hines, with unforced cordiality. Offers of refreshment were immediately forthcoming and we were shown to our room which, like the rest of the house, was centrally heated, immaculate and comfortably furnished. Plenty of storage space. The guests (no more than six at a time can be accommodated) have a lounge with log fire, books, parlour games and TV. Punctually at 8 pm we were called to dinner (no choice of courses except dessert) and ate by candle-light a most acceptable meal with stuffed chicken breasts in vermouth as the high point supported by an imaginative selection of vegetables. A large cafetière kept us going well into the night. Breakfast was ample and delicious and we left our charming temporary home with genuine regret." Subsequent readers endorse this report, "One of our most enjoyable stays in a 'hotel' ever. Most welcoming. Attention to detail good. Food top class – brilliant tastes and presentation; puddings lavish and too plentiful for slimline figures. No licence but our wine was decanted and served at room temperature. Bliss all round." (*Mr and Mrs Tydeman, and others*) Only criticism: "Alas, the breakfast orange juice was not fresh."

Open 1 Jan–20 Dec; also New Year.
Rooms 3 double – 2 with bath. 1 ground-floor room.
Facilities Sitting room with TV, dining room. 15-acre grounds with flower garden and pasture.
Location 9 m SW of Crediton. Leave A30 at Whiddon Down, follow signs to Spreyton. *Downhayes* is on left 1½ m N of Spreyton on Bow Road.
Restrictions Not suitable for wheelchairs. No children under 12. No pets.
Credit cards None accepted.
Terms (Not VAT rated) B&B: single occupancy: £26.25 without bath, £32 with, double: £37 without bath, £45 with. Light lunch on request £6. Set dinner £12.50. Weekly half-board rate. 1-week embroidery courses. Unlicensed – bring your own drink.
Service/tipping: "We do not impose a service charge, nor do we expect tips."

STADDLEBRIDGE North Yorkshire — Map 4

McCoys at the Tontine [GFG] — *Tel* East Harlsey (060 982) 671
Staddlebridge
Northallerton DL6 3JB

César award in 1989: Utterly acceptable mild eccentricity

This characterful establishment run by the three McCoy brothers – Tom is the chef, Eugene cooks for and runs the bistro downstairs and Peter runs the restaurant and accommodation; other members of the family all play active roles – entered the Guide last year with an encomium from *Janet Street-Porter*, backed up by an inspector, "A unique place. The restaurant is small, holding just 43 people, and furnished with giant parasols, odd chairs, potty little 1930s lamps and 1920s net curtains. You eat food as fine as any in London, exquisitely presented but unpretentious, with 1940s music tinkling in the background." The cooking is "good though expensive, with a liking for luxuries such as foie gras, langoustines, lobster and smoked salmon". The bistro downstairs is more simply furnished and cheaper, with blackboard menus; food is straightforward but stylish. Many weekenders eat in the latter on Friday and the former on Saturday. *McCoys* is a stone Victorian house on a busy main road, but with effective double glazing. No grounds to speak of, but good views. Bright floral wallpapers and fabrics in the bedrooms; bold flowered fabrics and large squashy sofas in the lounges; furniture "a mix of antiques, bamboo and junk. Breakfast is served all morning until lunchtime – a long, leisurely meal with exotic fruits, eggs and bacon and tomato, excellent coffee and tea, and newspapers. The place has style and warmth, is efficiently yet flexibly managed." Endorsed this year, "Rooms extremely pleasant, if a little frayed at the edges. The owners are genuinely nice people and very professional. The ambience in the sitting rooms and restaurant unique and great fun. Breakfast deserves an award of its own."

Open All year except 25/26 Dec. Restaurant closed Sun and Mon (but bistro open 7 days a week).
Rooms 6 double – all with bath and shower, telephone, radio and TV.
Facilities 2 lounges, breakfast room, bistro, restaurant.
Location On A19 (rooms double-glazed). 6 M NE of Northallerton.
Restriction Not suitable for ♿.
Credit cards All major cards accepted.
Terms (Service at guests' discretion) B&B (English): single £65, double £80. Set meals in bistro: lunch £10, dinner £22; full alc in restaurant £40.

STAMFORD Lincolnshire — Map 3

The George of Stamford [GFG]
71 St Martin's, Stamford PE9 2LB
Tel Stamford (0780) 55171
Fax (0780) 57070
Telex 32578

"Stamford and *The George* complement each other wonderfully. A really relaxed stay – beautiful room, excellent dinner, superb breakfast." "Fine old coaching inn with obviously ancient parts: comfortable sofas abound in the public rooms, and the dining room is very fine; the bedrooms are in keeping, and housekeeping very good." Stamford is a remarkably unspoilt medieval town, and *The George* is its historic coaching inn, preserving plenty of innish features such as a flower-tubbed cobbled courtyard, but neither prettified nor self-conscious. Bedrooms are comfortable with well-appointed bathrooms, the towels are changed daily; even the smaller rooms are approved. Good food of the trencherman sort has always been a feature of the *George* and again pleases most readers. Unfortunately we continue to get reports, even from the writers quoted above, of poor and often unfriendly service, "and as too often happens, the first sound on waking was not birdsong but cleaners' extremely loud gossip."

Open All year.
Rooms 1 suite, 34 double, 12 single – all with bath and/or shower, telephone, radio, TV (with teletext) and baby-listening; 24-hour room service.
Facilities 3 lounges, bar, 3 restaurants; 4 private dining rooms, business centre. 1-acre grounds with patio and monastery garden. Golf ½ m; fly fishing and sailing at Rutland Water 5 m.
Location In town centre (front rooms double glazed; rooms overlooking courtyard are quietest). Parking for 190 cars.
Restriction Only restaurant suitable for ♿. No dogs in restaurant.
Credit cards All major cards accepted.
Terms B&B: single £59.50–£64, double £86–£120, suite £130. Bar lunches; full alc £24. Christmas package; weekend breaks. Reduced rates for children sharing parents' room; special meals.
Service/tipping: "Service included. Gratuities are at guests' discretion and distributed between all staff on a points basis."

> Most hotels have reduced rates out of season and for children, and some British hotels offer "mini-break" rates throughout the year. If you are staying more than one night, it is always worth asking about special terms.

STAPLEFORD Leicestershire — Map 4

Stapleford Park
Stapleford, Melton Mowbray
LE14 2EF

Tel Wymondham (057 284) 522
Fax (057 284) 651
Telex 342319

César award in 1989: Most exciting newcomer of the year

"A memorable experience indeed! We found the whole place quite fascinating. One quickly establishes a relationship with the staff that is unlike anything previously experienced in a hotel. They are told to make you feel as if you were guests at their dinner party, and they do." "The scale of the house and the quality of the furnishings make all other country-house hotels seem modest by comparison. Bob Payton's casual bonhomie belies a highly professional attention to detail. The bathrooms are the best I've seen; the 'signature' bedrooms all so different that everyone must like some, if not all. The less expensive top rooms, with stunning views, are a real bargain at £95 [1989]." (*DNK McLeod, Stephen Ross*) *Stapleford Park* is a Grade I listed building in 500 acres of woods and parkland – a mixture of periods and styles saved from Disney eclecticism by the beauty of the ivory-coloured stone and the gentleness of the lakeside setting. Inside are stone arches, lots of dark mahogany, magnificent wood carvings attributed to Grinling Gibbons in the dining room, a "clubby" library, and a 19th-century Elizabethan-style wing. The "signature bedrooms" referred to above have each been designed by a "famous name" – Lady Jane Churchill, Lindka Cierach, Liberty, Tiffany etc. Turnbull and Asser has men's shirting fabric on the wall, tweed-covered chairs, framed bow-ties, and pictures hung by braces; Crabtree and Evelyn has hundreds of pictures of wild flowers and herbs; Max Pike has a free-standing bath in front of the window in the bedroom. The restaurant has had its ups and downs in its first year, but Colin White, formerly of *White's* in Cricklade, and a George Perry Smith graduate, took over in May 1989. We look forward to reports on his regime. Breakfast, with home-made bread, blueberry muffins and good coffee, takes place in the vaulted 16th-century refectory – "a delight, eaten off Peter Rabbit china, everything completely fresh; the orange juice squeezed to order". *Stapleford*, while clearly belonging to the country house species, also has elements of an American resort hotel. Its full title is *Stapleford Park Country House Hotel and Sporting Estate*, and there are many outdoor pursuits on offer, including basketball and a jogging track, and an impressive stable block half a mile from the house – "the finest stables in the country still in use", Payton claims; he opened an equestrian centre in mid-1989.

Open All year.
Rooms 3 suites, 27 double – all with bath and shower, telephone, radio, satellite TV and baby-listening.
Facilities Lift, ramps. Library, drawing room, salon, 3 sitting rooms, dining room, breakfast room. 500-acre parkland with church, lake with fishing, tennis, mini-golf, basketball, croquet, clay-pigeon shooting, jogging track.
Location 4 m E of Melton Mowbray. From A1 turn off at Colsterworth; take B676 for 9 m, turn to Stapleford.
Restrictions No smoking in dining room. Children under 10 by prior arrangement only. No dogs in bedrooms (kennels in grounds).
Credit cards All major cards accepted.
Terms [1989 rates] (Service at guests' discretion) B&B (continental): single or double room £95–£175, suite £175–£325. English breakfast £8. Full alc £30.

2 night min stay at weekends. Christmas programme. Special meals for children on request.

STON EASTON Somerset **Map 2**

Ston Easton Park
Ston Easton, Nr Bath BA3 4DF

Tel Chewton Mendip (076 121) 631
Fax (076 121) 377
Telex 444738

"To say that we were well looked after during out five-day stay is a wild understatement. We were totally cosseted and mollycoddled. Our shoes were cleaned, our cars valeted. We ate in every day; the food, while not of the highest level, lived up to expectations." "We have been visiting the hotel over a period of four years and have never been disappointed. This time we had their most princely main bedroom, the Ludlow room, with regal four-poster, enviable antiques, stunning prospect. *Ston Easton Park* performed like a star." "Our favourite English hotel. Like staying with friends (although we don't claim to have friends who live in such grand surroundings). The staff are a credit to the Smedleys, always charming and willing to help." "Staff one hundred per cent attentive, and very welcoming. Food as good as one could command in any hotel. The garden is, sadly, Humphrey Repton; there is never a lot to see in a Repton garden except vistas of trees and water; these are there, and beautifully placed as one would expect from the Master and they are being renovated exactly as his original plans indicate." (*GN Levy, Sharon Gutman, Helen and Charles Priday, Cyril Fletcher*) Hardly a critical murmur this year on Peter and Christine Smedley's grand, immaculately restored Palladian house, in 28 acres of parkland; the river Norr, which runs through the grounds, still flows over Repton's flight of shallow cascades. The public rooms are high-ceilinged and imposing, with many distinctive architectural features, but are also welcoming with log fires and spectacular flower arrangements. Rooms, individually designed by Jean Monro, an expert on 18th-century decoration, are elegant in different ways. Those on the first floor have the huge windows and fine proportions of the original master bedrooms, those on the floor above are smaller. *Ston Easton* is a decorous place: jacket and tie *de rigueur* at dinner, no children under 12. But the open friendliness of the owners and their staff help to dispel any tendency towards stuffiness so often found in the grander sort of hotel. The tariff is naturally high: the upkeep of such a seat must be enormous, and there is no stinting on service or appointments.

Open All year.
Rooms 5 suites 14 double, 1 single – 19 with bath and shower, 1 with shower, all with telephone, radio and TV.
Facilities Drawing room, salon, library, 2 restaurants; private dining room; billiard room, servants' room for chauffeurs etc. Recitals, entertainment groups occasionally. Terrace. 28-acre grounds with croquet, bowls, archery, riding, ballooning, helipad, river with fishing.
Location On A37 from Bristol to Shepton Mallet.
Restrictions Only restaurant suitable for ♿. No children under 12. No dogs in building (kennels on premises).
Credit cards All major cards accepted.
Terms [1989 rates] B&B (continental): single £60, double £105–£220, suite £185–£260. Set lunch £19.50, dinner £29.50. Vegetarian and low-fat meals on request. 4-day Christmas programme; winter breaks.
Service/tipping: "No service charge is included or gratuity expected."

STORRINGTON West Sussex — Map 3

Abingworth Hall
Thakeham Road
Storrington RH20 3EF

Tel West Chiltington (079 83) 3636
Telex 877835 AHOTEL

"A solid, virtuous Edwardian country house hotel" quietly situated in large grounds, well placed for touring the South Downs and only 28 miles from Gatwick Airport. "It has large public rooms; a handsome conservatory has been added to the main drawing room and makes a very agreeable room for pre-dinner drinks, especially since it is a smokeless zone. The dining room is handsome and fairly formal (jacket and tie required for men); food good, but a bit rich. Staff universally pleasant." "Modern British cooking at close to its best. All dishes beautifully presented, vegetables perfectly cooked. No such thing as a skimpy portion." (*HR, Howard Cohen*) Set in ten acres of grounds including a well-tended ornamental lake, *Abingworth Hall* has undergone major refurbishment and upgrading during recent years. Most readers praise its cleanliness and "consistent standard of accommodation, particularly in the main building". Some have found the owner, Philip Bulman, lacking in bonhomie. This year's improvements include the first non-smoking bedroom. One reader minded that the à la carte menu didn't change during his two-day visit and reported some minor housekeeping deficiencies; another pointed out a certain "starkness" due to unexciting decor and lack of pictures.

Open All year.
Rooms 2 suites, 18 double (1 non-smoking) – all with bath and/or shower, telephone, radio and TV. Some on ground floor.
Facilities Drawing room, cocktail bar, restaurant; functions room. 8-acre grounds with heated swimming pool, putting green, croquet, tennis, lake, 2 helipads.
Location On B2139, 2 m N of Storrington.
Restrictions Not suitable for ♿. No children under 10. No dogs.
Credit cards All major cards accepted.
Terms [1989 rates] B&B (English) £36–£52; dinner, B&B £57–£71. Set lunch £14–£15, dinner £23; full alc £30. Special breaks. Christmas house party. 1-night bookings sometimes refused for Sat in summer.
Service/tipping: "No service charge added; our staff are instructed not to solicit for tips. But we do not actively discourage tipping – our staff receive substantial gratuities which are paid out to them twice a year after deduction of tax and though we pay well over the average rate for the job we could not afford to increase the wages bill to the level reached with the help of the tip fund."

STRETTON Leicestershire — Map 4

Ram Jam Inn
Great North Road
Stretton LE15 7QX

Tel Castle Bytham (078 081) 776
from Jan 1990 (0780) 410776
Telex 342888 HAMBLE

Old coaching inn on the Great North Road converted into a motel with a difference by the owners of Hambleton Hall *(q.v.). Warmly praised in earlier editions for attractive decor, large and beautifully furnished bedrooms, and snack bar serving original and interesting food including very good teas. Service "unservile, charming and English". 2-acre grounds. 7 rooms, all with bath and shower. B&B double £45. Closed after a fire in late 1988; reopened after complete refurbishment in June 1989. More reports please.*

STURMINSTER NEWTON Dorset — Map 2

Plumber Manor [GFG] — *Tel* Sturminster Newton (0258) 72507
Sturminster Newton DT10 2AF

A handsome Jacobean house, filled with antiques and family portraits, in the heart of Hardy countryside. It has been the home of the Prideaux-Brunes since the early 17th century and for the past 17 years has been run as a restaurant-with-rooms by brothers Richard and Brian Prideaux-Brune. Brian cooks, Richard waits and does reception and bar. There are six bedrooms in the house and six in a converted stable block 50 yards away; the latter are large and very well appointed, the older rooms in the main building are smaller and less modern. *Plumber Manor* contrives to be professional while maintaining a laid-back air and guests are treated as visitors to a private house – those in search of comprehensive cosseting would probably be happier elsewhere. The dining room is spacious and "refreshingly un-designerish; food excellent, wines reasonably priced." "Food not especially imaginative, but very well prepared and served, with excellent vegetables. Atmosphere elegant but casual. We were never made to feel unwelcome because we were not as dressed up as the other guests." "Lovely setting with well-tended lawns on which play two labradors. Typical that balls are provided with the tennis court. Very much a family operation which bursts into life for the evening dinner, which is what *Plumber Manor* is all about." (*NM Mackintosh, Jean L Woy, Ian Durant; also RA Dubery, and others*)

Open 1 Mar–1 Feb. Restaurant closed for lunch.
Rooms 12 double – all with bath, shower, telephone, TV, tea-making facilities. 6 ground-floor rooms in stable block 50 yds from main building.
Facilities 2 lounge bars, portrait gallery, restaurant in main house; sitting/meeting room in converted barn. 4-acre gardens with tennis, croquet, trout stream.
Location 2 m SW of Sturminster Newton; on A357 to Haselbury Bryan.
Restrictions No children under 12. No dogs.
Credit cards Access, Visa.
Terms [1989 rates] B&B (English): single occupancy £50–£60, double £65–£85. Set dinner £17 and £20. Reductions for stays of 7 or more days in high season; winter bargain breaks. 1-night bookings refused at Easter and Christmas.

TALLAND-BY-LOOE Cornwall — Map 1

Talland Bay Hotel — *Tel* Polperro (0503) 72667
Talland-by-Looe PL13 2JB

A 16th-century Cornish country house in two-and-a-half acres of carefully tended sub-tropical gardens, overlooking an unspoilt bay. Rooms are agreeably furnished in traditional style; some are small – best discuss your requirements on booking. Out of season the owners, Major and Mrs Mayman, fill the hotel with bridge, bird-watching, painting, archaeology, geology and yoga holidays. Several readers have written appreciatively of the four-course dinners: "A choice of four imaginative starters, followed by a choice of four main courses including a truly gourmet vegetarian dish, then a mouthwatering sweet trolley – a choice of at least eight delicious concoctions all offered with an enormous dollop of clotted cream. Breakfast starts with a buffet of cereal, muesli etc;

disappointingly, the juices are not freshly pressed, but the cooked dishes are carefully prepared and generous." "Most impressed – the maid offered to do laundry on a *Sunday*, such a help." A buffet lunch is offered by the pool in summer. Service is said to be friendly and willing but a bit untrained at times. Children and the disabled are catered for. (*Margaret and John Goulding, Jean and Bertram Fleshler, and others*) One reader this year was highly critical of food, reception and ambience. More reports please.

Open Mid-Feb–end Dec, Christmas and New Year.
Rooms 1 suite, 17 double, 5 single – 21 with bath (8 also have shower), all with telephone, radio, TV and baby-listening. 2 in hotel grounds, 2 across lane. 2 ground-floor rooms specially adapted for ♿.
Facilities Lounge, non-smoking lounge, bar, dining room. 2½-acre grounds with swimming pool, putting and croquet. 5 mins' walk to beach with safe swimming.
Location 2½ m SW of Looe, Turn left at hotel sign on Looe-Polperro road.
Restrictions No children under 5 in dining room at night. Dogs in certain rooms only; not in public rooms.
Credit cards All major cards accepted.
Terms (No service charge) Dinner, B&B £36–£65. Set lunch £7, dinner £14.50; full alc £25. 1-night bookings refused in high season. Bridge, bird-watching, painting, archaeology, geology, yoga, honeymoon, Christmas and New Year packages. Reduced rates for children sharing parents' room; high teas.
Service/tipping: "We do not encourage tipping; it is left entirely to guests' discretion."

TAUNTON Somerset — Map 1

The Castle Hotel [GFG]
Castle Green
Taunton TA1 1NF

Tel Taunton (0823) 272671
Telex 46488
Reservations in USA (800) 223 5581

This luxurious 300-year-old hostelry, owned by the Chapman family, stands wistaria-covered and castellated, in the centre of the town, though in a quiet oasis of higher ground on the site of the old castle and with pleasant moated gardens at the back. Readers continue to be delighted with their accommodation but there are still differences of opinion about the restaurant. "The weekend break was excellent value. We were welcomed and cosseted with genuine interest and friendliness by a young and keen staff – present but never oppressive. Our bedroom was well appointed and pleasant though not over-large whereas the bathroom was huge and rather bare and poorly lit; but house-keeping was exemplary. Food and wine were outstanding and the dining room has all the elegance and style one would expect from a *Michelin*-rosetted restaurant. Excellent choice on the menus." "Lovely room with spotless bathroom, very quiet. Quick and courteous room and bar service. On the second night we asked for a more substantial and traditional meal rather than the *nouvelle cuisine* offered on the menu and it was no problem." "Food good but not exceptional. But I liked the lack of pretension; the service, surroundings and consistently high standards made it good value for the fairly high prices." (*Ann Thornton, Mrs Victor Isenberg, Nicola Hayward*) Other diners, however, have suffered disappointments again this year: criticisms include variable meals – good one day, poor the next – inept service, mean portions, and problems about vegetarian meals even when ordered in advance. More reports please.

Open All year.
Rooms 1 suite, 21 double, 13 single – all with bath and shower, telephone, radio, TV and baby-listening.
Facilities Lift. 2 lounges, bar, public bar, restaurant; private dining/meeting rooms. ½-acre grounds with Norman moat, keep and well. Riding and balloon trips in summer; Exmoor safaris. Trout fishing and clay-pigeon shooting nearby.
Location Central (follow signs for castle), but quietly situated. Garages and parking.
Restrictions Guests asked not to smoke in dining room while meals are being served. Dogs by arrangement only, not in dining room.
Credit cards All major cards accepted.
Terms (Service at guests' discretion) B&B (continental): single from £52, double from £89, suite from £165. Set lunch £11.50, dinner £21; full alc £35. Weekend and mid-week breaks; 4-day Christmas package; musical weekends. Special meals for children.

TAYNTON Oxfordshire — Map 2

Manor Farm Barn — *Tel* Burford (099 382) 2069
Taynton, Burford OX8 4UH

A welcoming, comfortably modernised Cotswold stone farmhouse run by Mr and Mrs Florey in a rural setting in an unspoilt hamlet near Burford, which has a lovely old church, but no shop, pub or post office. Tranquillity is guaranteed by the extensive grounds, and adjoining pastures down to the river Windrush. It has only three bedrooms, all with beamed ceiling and private bathroom, "beautifully kept, with every conceivable extra, books, magazines, toiletries laid out in the bedroom as if home from home". There is a good-sized lounge with fires in winter. Breakfasts are taken communally at an elegant mahogany table; "they were lavish, and Mrs Florey's skills as hostess came to the fore in getting sluggish strangers talking among themselves. We understood why some guests had gone back and back over many years." An excellent base for touring the Cotswolds, but you will need a car. (*Martin L Dodd, and others*)

Open All year, except Christmas, New Year, late Jan–mid-Feb.
Rooms 3 double – all with bath and shower, radio, TV and tea-making facilities. 1 self-catering cottage.
Facilities 2 lounges with TV, dining room. 8-acre grounds with garden and paddocks.
Location 1½ m NW of Burford; from Burford, take A361 towards Stow-on-the-Wold; turn left towards Taynton at roundabout, then left by church.
Restrictions Not suitable for ♿. No children under 10. No dogs.
Credit cards None accepted.
Terms B&B double from £40. 1-night bookings refused Sat. (No restaurant.)
Service/tipping: "Tipping not required or looked for."

Traveller's tale *Mr X tries to sell his dessert wine and port to his guests every night after dinner in a very insistent manner. He comes round with glasses asking if we'd care to be "civilised" and have some port or dessert wine, making us feel very "uncivilised" if we decline. By the third night we made a point of leaving before he could pounce on us with his civilised port offer.*

TETBURY Gloucestershire Map 2

Calcot Manor [GFG]
Beverstone
Nr Tetbury GL8 8YJ

Tel Leighterton (066 689) 391
Fax (066 689) 394
Telex 437105

"An enjoyable weekend. We slept in the stable block which was very comfortable. Excellent food, served with pride." "Accommodation and facilities good but not outstanding; service is prompt, courteous and friendly without being familiar and nobody is looking for tips, which creates a pleasant environment." "First rate. Hospitality and service very warm-hearted." (*Ann Farrow, Ian M Ziar, Lord Evans of Claughton*) *Calcot Manor*, owned and run by Brian and Barbara Ball, with son Richard and a pair of decorous labradors, is a timeless mellow Cotswold house with a range of venerable outbuildings, including a fine 14th-century tithe barn. There is also a heated outdoor pool. Bedrooms, all with private bathroom, have been cleverly fitted into the old building and there are some newer ones in a converted stable block. The rooms vary in size; some have a large and luxurious bathroom (four have a whirlpool bath). No errors of taste, though the choice of furnishings could be more adventurous. The restaurant, with innovative cooking by the young chef Ramon Farthing, boasts a *Michelin* rosette which nearly all reports agree is well deserved: "superb food, served in a lovely peach-coloured restaurant, nice flower arrangements, pianist tickling the ivories, rather 30s"; "*nouvelle* cooking with *ancienne* portions". The wine list is catholic, and well-described, with an unusually modest mark-up though one reader wished there were more half-bottles. Some readers, however, are less satisfied than those quoted above. There are reports of excessively long waits in the restaurant during a busy weekend, with residents feeling that outside diners were getting preferential treatment; too much "show" in the presentation of food; disorganised, sometimes amateurish service; a small room in the house which was noisy due to the kitchen's extractor fan; and a visit marred when the manor was overrun by conference visitors. More reports please.

Open All year except 2–10 Jan. Restaurant closed to non-residents Sun night.
Rooms 13 double – all with bath and shower (4 have whirlpool bath), telephone, radio and TV. 5 ground-floor rooms in courtyard,
Facilities Lounge with dispense bar, drawing room, dining room; private dining room, conference facilities. 4-acre grounds with croquet lawn, outdoor swimming pool (heated May–Sept). Fishing, golf and riding nearby.
Location 3 m W of Tetbury on A4135. Parking.
Restrictions No smoking in dining room. No children under 12. No dogs.
Credit cards All major cards accepted.
Terms (No service charge) B&B: single occupancy from £65, double £85–£120; dinner, B&B: single £90, double £145–£180. Set lunch £15 and £25, dinner £27.50 and £35. Reduced rates for longer stays. Weekend or mid-week breaks; Christmas package; gourmet and wine weekends in Autumn. 1-night bookings refused during Badminton, Gold Cup week, Gatcombe horse trials and some bank holidays.
Service/tipping: "We do not make a service charge and tips are not expected."

The length of an entry does not necessarily reflect the merit of a hotel. The more interesting the report or the more unusual or controversial the hotel, the longer the entry.

THORNBURY Avon — Map 2

Thornbury Castle [GFG]
Thornbury
Bristol BS12 1HH

Tel Thornbury (0454) 418511
Fax (0454) 416188
Telex 449986 CASTLE

An imposing building, mostly dating from the early 16th century. The castle as such was never finished, but the remains, luxuriously renovated, make an impressive hotel; baronial public rooms have huge fireplaces, mullioned windows, antique furniture and tapestries. Bedrooms vary considerably in size; all have a well-appointed bathroom and the extras to be expected of this class of hotel; some are palatial with oriel windows overlooking the walled gardens; many have a magnificent four-poster. *Thornbury Castle* was taken over four years ago by an American, Maurice Taylor who recently spent a small fortune restoring a formerly derelict wing to add five bedrooms "in a style Henry VIII would recognise, but with modern conveniences". Readers are almost unanimous in praising the new regime: "There is a lovely feeling of being genuinely cared for rather than chased after to please. We have occupied three different rooms, all elegant and comfortable and a friend had a charming little single room with a balcony." The kitchens, under executive chef Colin Hingston, have earned a red "M" in *Michelin* denoting a carefully prepared good-value meal. "Food in the delightful dining room is much improved under the new owner; less rich than before, choice more varied, quality and presentation superb. There is an extensive list including good-value wines from all over the world." (*Marcia Layton, Nigel Cant; also Mr and Mrs T Hodge, and others*)

Open All year except 2–11 Jan.
Rooms 1 suite, 15 double, 2 single – all with bath and shower, telephone, radio and TV. 5 across small courtyard.
Facilities 2 lounges, 2 dining rooms. 12-acre grounds with walled Tudor garden, vineyard and farm. Clay-pigeon shooting.
Location 12 m N of Bristol, at N edge of Thornbury, just off B4061; lodge gate beside St Mary's parish church.
Restrictions Not suitable for ♿. No smoking in dining room. No children under 12. No dogs.
Credit cards All major cards accepted.
Terms B&B (continental): single £64–£70, double £80–£170, suite £150–£170. Full alc £28.50. 2-night stay min for Sat.
Service/tipping: "All our prices include vat *and service. In a service industry it is unreasonable to expect customers to pay extra for service."*

TREBARWITH STRAND Cornwall — Map 1

The Old Millfloor
Trebarwith Strand
Tintagel PL34 0HA

Tel Camelford (0840) 770234

No hotel, but a small secluded guest house – three rooms in the house and a couple of self-catering chalet/bungalows in a picturesque location by a mill-stream. Not for the disabled or infirm, since there is a steep path down from the road (best to take the minimum of luggage), but perfect for families: lots of pets, ten acres of grounds and the beach ten minutes' walk away; and the prices are ridiculously modest. "A wonderfully relaxing place, set in a fern-filled glen by an old mill-stream. Very romantic atmosphere: old beams, gleaming wood and fresh flowers everywhere. Janice Waddon-Martin is a delightful and enthusiastic hostess. She creates a welcoming feeling with clever use of fabric, light and colour. Dinner by candle-light in the small dining room with different crystal each night! Lovely food: home-made soups, ice-creams and lots of home baking (e.g. breakfast croissants), fresh vegetables, boozy sauces and lashings of clotted cream; excellent tea and coffee. No TV, radio or papers (except Sunday) – a real treat! Cats and books available by the fire for wetter days. Rooms very comfy with friendly touches like supplies of tissues, cotton wool, bath 'smellies' etc. We loved everything about it (except the plumbing which was unpredictable) and thought it excellent value." No licence, bring your own wine. Little feedback this year. More reports would be welcome.

Open Easter–Nov.
Rooms 3 doubles with H&C and TV. 2 self-catering bungalows.
Facilities Restaurant with lounge. 10 acre grounds with garden, orchard, paddocks and stream. Beach 10 mins' walk. Riding centre 2½ m.
Location 2 m S of Tintagel.
Restriction Not suitable for ♿.
Credit cards None accepted.
Terms [1989 rates] (No VAT) B&B £13.50. Dinner £9.50 (unlicensed – bring your own wine). 1 child sharing parents' room free; special meals.
Service/tipping: "No service charge. Tips not expected."

TREGONY Cornwall — Map 1

Tregony House — *Tel* Tregony (087 253) 671
Tregony, Truro TR2 5RN

Once again readers have pulled out all the stops in praise of this friendly, simple and reasonably priced little hotel, a converted part 17th century, part Victorian, village house, run by Mario and Verna Marin. Tregony is an inland village "of charm and distinction" at the entrance to the Roseland Peninsula, about six miles from the sea. Bedrooms are comfortable with adequate lighting and storage. Only two have private facilities, but the communal bathrooms are immaculately clean. Public rooms are comfortable and homely – good decor, pretty flower arrangements, attractive beamed dining room. Cooking is "extremely intelligent in balancing courses. Satisfying but not overfacing. No choice of main course but plenty for starters – including extremely imaginative home-made soups – puddings and cheeses. Vegetarians catered for. Good wine selection at moderate prices. Staff are "outstandingly friendly and helpful – their heart is really in the job of making you welcome and comfortable". "Welcome could not have been warmer. Perfect traditional breakfast." "Being small and intimate it was ideal for a woman on her own." "The Marins come out tops. We have yet to find anything to match *Tregony House* for friendly quiet efficiency, good comfortable rooms, good food and drink – and you are not bankrupt at the end of the holiday." (*Sydney B Downs, JR and H Pickup, Mrs DC Dudley, DF Tooley; and many others*) Tregony is a peaceful village, and the front rooms are double-glazed to cut out traffic noise.

Open Mar–Oct inclusive.
Rooms 5 doubles (2 can form a family suite), 1 single – 1 with bath, 1 with shower.

Facilities Lounge with TV, dining room with bar area and seating. Cottage garden with seats on terrace. Beaches and Cornish coastal path 6 m.
Location In centre of village main street. Private carpark. Front rooms double-glazed.
Restrictions Not suitable for ♿. No children under 7. No dogs.
Credit cards None accepted.
Terms (No VAT or service charge) Dinner, B&B £24. Reduced rates for stays of 7 days or more. 1-night bookings sometimes refused in high season if made very far in advance. Half price for children 7-12; special meals on request.
Service/tipping: "No automatic service charge, neither is tipping expected or encouraged."

TRESCO Isles of Scilly — Map 1

The Island Hotel — *Tel* Scillonia (0720) 22883
Tresco, Isles of Scilly
Cornwall TR24 0PU

Tresco is a private island, two miles by one, renowned for the Abbey Gardens, filled with exotic plants from all over the world. No cars are allowed – there are bicycles for hire, and guests of *The Island Hotel* are met on arrival (by boat or helicopter) by a tractor and trailer – so Tresco (day trippers apart) is exceptionally peaceful. The hotel is a modern building with five acres of grounds beside the sea, and a private beach. It enjoys dramatic views of the rocky coast and other islands, and a peaceful and beautiful setting. It is a favourite of many readers who have written again to endorse last year's verdict of "Expensive but worth it." "Our eighth visit. The food and environment continue to improve every time. One guest was on his thirty-fifth visit! It is now necessary to book two years ahead for summer visits as so many people want to go back." (*GB Harris*) There is an extensive dinner menu, always featuring one low-fat dish; the Sunday evening buffet, with lobsters and crabs, gets a special mention, as well as "the very efficient system for ordering alfresco lunch in all parts of the garden". "One of the very best hotels I have stayed in." (*Derek Cheesbrough, KB Mowle, and others*) But not everyone is as delighted with *The Island*; there have been complaints about the decor and poor fittings; some feel the food is pretentious ("surely many people would prefer two plain and decent courses to six over-cooked, sloppily sauced ones?"). The management and staff, found welcoming and helpful by some, have appeared officious to others. It's one of those places which evoke strong loyalties in those who "belong" and leave some outsiders wishing they were elsewhere.

Open Mid-Mar–mid-Oct.
Rooms 1 suite, 25 double, 4 single – all with bath and shower, telephone, radio, TV and baby-listening; 7 with tea-making facilities. 3 ground-floor rooms.
Facilities Lounge, bar, bar lounge, TV room, dining room, adults' games room, children's playroom; laundry facilities. 5-acre grounds with terrace, heated swimming pool, bowls, croquet, badminton; private beach with safe bathing. Boats, sailing dinghies for hire.
Location Scheduled helicopter flight (British International Helicopters Ltd – approx 20 minutes) or boat (approx 2½ hours) from Penzance; not Sun. Advance booking essential.
Restrictions Island not suitable for ♿. No dogs allowed on Tresco.
Credit cards None accepted.
Terms (Prices according to season, type of room, view, etc) Dinner, B&B £56–£99. Set lunch £11, bar lunches available, dinner £21. Discounts for pre-booked stays

of over 5 nights; Tresco gardeners' 7-day spring/autumn holiday. Reduced rates for children in bunk beds or cots; 6 pm high tea.
Service/tipping: "No service charge made or tips expected. If guests wish to reward courtesy and good service or a particular person for some extra service it is entirely up to them."

The New Inn *Tel* Scillonia (0720) 22844
Tresco, Isles of Scilly
Cornwall TR24 0QQ

A much cheaper alternative to *The Island Hotel*, "more than a restaurant-with-rooms or a country pub, but not a luxury hotel either", *The New Inn*, run by Chris and Lesley Hopkins, offers friendly hospitality and good food, with simple but adequate accommodation. The only public rooms are the bars and a lounge with TV, bedrooms are fairly small but have a pretty floral decor and good lighting; many have "lovely sea views"; the bathrooms have good fluffy towels but lack "freebies". There is a small garden and a swimming pool, "The food is of a high standard, combining fresh ingredients, skilful cooking, imaginative ideas and excellent presentation; there is plenty of choice on the menu; fish dishes are particularly good. The staff are friendly and helpful." "Food good, at times excellent, we appreciated the simple but imaginative set menu which always contained pleasant surprises. Good bar snacks for lunch." Breakfasts, too, are praised. (*Margaret Carr, Abigail Kirby Harris, Alexander and Susan Korda; and others*)

Open All year.
Rooms 10 double, 2 single – 10 with bath, all with radio, tea-making facilities and baby-listening.
Facilities Public bar, lounge bar, TV lounge, restaurant. Garden with swimming pool. Sandy beaches with safe bathing and fishing.
Location As for the *Island* above. Hotel will make travel arrangements.
Restrictions Not suitable for ♿. No dogs allowed on Tresco.
Credit cards None accepted.
Terms [1989 rates] (No service charge) B&B (English) £15. Bar lunches. Set dinner from £10.50. Special breaks. Christmas and New Year packages. Reduced rates and special meals for children.
Service/tipping: "It is time to face up to the truth. Pay and conditions in the industry are not as good as employers make out so tips are a necessary evil. I have yet to visit an average hotel or restaurant in any country that was pompous enough to say they didn't accept gratuities, so why should British hotels be expected to refuse what is often one of the best reflections of the standards offered by a hotel? My staff do very well for tips which are pooled and shared equally between them."

TROUTBECK Cumbria — Map 4

Mortal Man Hotel *Tel* Ambleside (053 94) 33193
Troutbeck, Nr Windermere
LA23 1PL

A modest Lakeland inn peacefully set on a hilltop above the Troutbeck Valley which celebrated its tricentenary in 1989 makes its Guide debut: "We meet the guests time and again who, like us, return to this delightful inn for the following reasons:
a. The proprietors, Annette and Christopher Poulsom, provide friendly, efficient but unobtrusive service, ably supported by a small staff.

b. The recently redecorated dining room with excellent views of the Troutbeck Valley adds to the enjoyment of the imaginatively planned, beautifully prepared and generously served five-course English dinner. Excellent home-made desserts including at least one fruit pie. The cheese course always included well-kept Stilton with crisp celery. The breakfast sets you up for a full day's walking.
c. All 12 rooms have *en suite* facilities. They are well appointed and comfortable, although sizes do vary. All have views down the valley towards Lake Windermere.
"Dogs are welcome – there are two resident – but not children under five. The oak-beamed residents' lounge has an open fire in winter. Old hunting prints on the walls, comfortable easy chairs, gleaming brass-topped tables. There is a welcoming public bar, also beamed, with good bar food from a separate kitchen – imaginative and very reasonably priced. All in all for us it is home from home." (*Mr and Mrs NG Sedgwick*)
More reports please.

Open Mid-Feb–mid-Nov.
Rooms 10 double, 2 single – all with bath and/or shower, radio TV and tea-making facilities.
Facilities Lounge, lounge bar, public bar, restaurant. 1-acre grounds.
Location 3 m N of Windermere.
Restrictions Not suitable for ♿. No children under 5.
Credit cards None accepted.
Terms Dinner, B&B £40–£45. Set lunch £8.50, dinner £15. Reductions for longer stays.
Service/tipping: "No service charge. Tipping discouraged."

TRURO Cornwall — Map 1

Alverton Manor [GFG] — *Tel* Truro (0872) 76633
Tregolls Road, Truro TR1 1XQ — *Fax* (0872) 222989

A splendid Grade II listed sandstone building, once a convent, in an attractive hillside setting in walking distance of town centre. Recently extensively refurbished, but original features retained; heavy hangings, period furniture, sumptuous flower arrangements in public rooms. Large, comfortable bedrooms. Food – nouvelle *in style, using Cornish ingredients – inventive and sophisticated. Slightly impersonal, perhaps business-oriented atmosphere. 25 rooms, all with bath and/or shower. B&B double £85–£120. Set lunch from £11.95, dinner from £21.95. New hotel, newly nominated. More reports please.*

TWO BRIDGES Devon — Map 1

Cherrybrook Hotel — *Tel* Tavistock (0822) 88260
Two Bridges
Yelverton PL20 6SP

John and Susan Reynolds' welcoming, comfortable and modestly priced hotel, formerly a farmhouse, with splendid views, is centrally placed for a Dartmoor holiday. It was built in the early 19th century by a friend of the Prince Regent, which doubtless accounts for its rural elegance. Today it is pleasantly and comfortably furnished, warm and clean, and much praised by Guide readers, many of them on return visits. The lounge and bar have beamed ceiling and slate floors; the bedrooms are quite small but warm and comfortable. The generous four-course dinner menu (with some choice) is "really excellent as long as you don't hanker after fancy *nouvelle cuisine*. To my mind the excellent relatively plain cooking cannot be bettered." (*RF Warner, Dr KR Norton, and others*) At *Cherrybrook* you order your food by 7.15, eat promptly at 7.30 and "have to be matey before and after dinner or go to your room; a great deal therefore depends on your fellow guests."

Open All year except Christmas and New Year.
Rooms 6 double, 1 single – 7 with shower, 6 with WC, all with TV and tea-making facilities.
Facilities Lounge, bar, dining room. 3½-acre grounds with access to moor. Golf, trout-fishing, riding and pony-trekking nearby.
Location On B3212, ½ m NE of Two Bridges crossroads.
Restrictions Not suitable for ♿. No smoking in dining room. No dogs in public rooms.
Credit cards None accepted.
Terms [1989 rates] B&B (English) £18.50; dinner, B&B £27. Set dinner £8.50; packed lunches £1.50. Reduced rates for stays of 3 days or more; weekly rates. Reductions for children sharing parents' room; special meals.
Service/tipping: "No service charge. No tips."

ULLINGSWICK Hereford and Worcester — Map 2

The Steppes Country House Hotel — *Tel* Hereford (0432) 820424
Ullingswick
Nr Hereford HR1 3JG

"Our second visit, even more successful than the first two years ago. We had a spacious and beautifully decorated room in the recently converted cottage. The mini-fridge and two comfortable armchairs were a boon after a long day out. Good beds, reading lights, large bathroom. Henry Howland waited at table with his usual speed, silence and deftness. He and Tricia are a charming couple who aim to please, and certainly succeed. The new bar in the cellar is very attractive and well appointed and the whole house charmingly furnished with antiques." "One of those rare places where a return visit feels like coming home; Tricia Howland is a superb cook." (*Moira Jarrett, Heather Kirk*) Ullingswick is a tiny Domesday-old hamlet quietly situated in the Wye valley, and the *Steppes*, a Grade II listed 17th-century country house, rich in exposed beams, ingle-nook fireplaces and other period features, is a highly personal guest house which pleases some guests mightily but does not suit those in search of hotel-type service. The four-course dinners, no choice except by prior arrangement, are served at 7 pm by candle-light with classical music. They tend to the high cholesterol end of the scale unless otherwise requested, and are generally, but not universally, appreciated. (There is also an à la carte menu offering "less adventurous" food, and vegetarian dishes.) One guest found his bedroom in the main building in need of some attention and the shower tiny.

Open All year except 2 weeks before Christmas and two weeks after New Year.
Rooms 5 double – all with bath and/or shower, telephone, radio, TV, refrigerator and tea-making facilities.

Facilities 2 lounges (1 non-smoking), bar, dining room. 1½-acre garden with duck pond, sheep, rabbits and chickens; riding and fishing nearby.
Location 7 m NE of Hereford off A417 Gloucester to Leominster road.
Restrictions No children under 10. No dogs in public rooms.
Credit cards None accepted.
Terms Dinner B&B double £56–£76. Bargain breaks available throughout the year; Christmas and New Year 3-day house parties.
Service/tipping: "Service included. We do not ask for or expect any form of gratuity. However there are always guests who genuinely wish to give a bit extra for a job well done. Sometimes this takes the form of a little gift but our staff often find tips left in the bedroom."

ULLSWATER Cumbria — Map 4

Howtown Hotel — *Tel* Pooley Bridge (076 84) 86514
Ullswater, Penrith CA10 2ND

This comfortable family-run old farmhouse on the unspoilt southern shore of Ullswater has long been a favourite of Guide readers, particularly walkers and climbers. It is in complete contrast to the luxurious and sophisticated *Sharrow Bay* (below) two miles away. *Howtown* is a long low building set 100 yards back from the road. Few of the bedrooms have private facilities; furnishings are comfortable and homely rather than elegant, the food generous rather than sophisticated – dinner, with limited choice, is at 7; cold and packed lunches are available. The atmosphere is relaxed and the tariff astoundingly low. The hotel has its own private foreshore on Ullswater. Sadly Michael Baldry, who had run *Howtown* with his wife Jacky for many years, died in January 1988; the hotel is now in the hands of Mrs Baldry and their sons – the fourth generation of the family to be involved. Regular visitors report that things have not changed and a first-timer adds, "What a find! Everything spick and span, meals excellent and beautifully served. Astounding value for money and we enjoyed indulgences like having the bed turned down during dinner." (*Sally Saysell, EB*) *Howtown* is not easy to get into, having a very high return rate, and visitors tend not to write to us because they would like to keep it to themselves, but we'd like more reports please.

Open End Mar–1 Nov.
Rooms 13 double, 3 single – 4 with private facilities in 2 annexes in grounds. 4 self-catering cottages.
Facilities 4 lounges, 2 bars, TV room, dining room. 2-acre grounds. 300 yds from lake with private foreshore; walking,climbing, riding, golf nearby.
Location On E shore of lake 4 m S of Pooley Bridge.
Restrictions Not suitable for ♿. No children under 7. Dogs at management's discretion (£1 a day); not in public rooms.
Credit cards None accepted.
Terms Dinner, B&B £23.25. Set lunch: cold table on weekdays from £4.75, table d'hôte on Sun from £6, set dinner £8. 1-night bookings sometimes refused. Reduced rates for children sharing parents' room.
Service/tipping: "No service charge. Any gratuities offered are distributed equally amongst the staff."

> Important reminder: terms printed must be regarded as a rough guide only to the size of the bill to be expected at the end of your stay. For latest tariffs, check when booking.

Sharrow Bay Country House Hotel [GFG]
Ullswater, Penrith CA10 2LZ

Tel Pooley Bridge (076 84) 86301 and 86483

"An exceptional hotel in every way, but what a shame it isn't more spacious, though it would probably fill up anyway. Our room, *Beatrix*, reminded me of a cabin on a Cunarder – clever use of available space. Bed, sheets, pillow all perfect. Food just wonderful. I dream of sticky toffee pudding." "Lovely room in the Lodge, huge bathroom, beautiful bedroom and pretty sitting room. So quiet and peaceful, with glorious views." "Still one of the best. The team of Sack and Coulson has lost none of its qualities. The welcome is as friendly and efficient as ever, the food still superb, the rooms as full of bits and pieces that add up to a sense of being at home in somebody else's house. The fact that it poured with rain for the twelve hours I was there did nothing to dampen my enthusiasm for *Sharrow Bay*." Typical encomiums from this year's postbag for Brian Sack and Francis Coulson's celebrated country house hotel on the beautiful, less-crowded eastern shore of Ullswater where they have been for over forty years. *Sharrow Bay* is renowned for the prodigal generosity of the meals (breakfasts and afternoon teas being of the same scale and quality as lunches and dinners) and a similar prodigality in the furnishings in the bedrooms, filled with innumerable cosseting extras. Throughout the house, too, there is a profusion of *objets d'art*, collected over the years. Some of the bedrooms, particularly those in the main house, are small; those in the annexe, Bank House, a mile away, are larger. Public rooms can get crowded when the restaurant is busy, but the addition of a conservatory has relieved much of the pressure. There is still privacy in the dining room, even though the tables are close together. An unusually large staff copes with the residents and the casual diners. (*Daphne de Moubray, C Roberts, Mrs H Swenson; also Pat and Jeremy Temple, Susan Mullins, and many others*)

Open Mar–Nov inclusive.
Rooms 6 suites, 17 double, 7 single – 26 with bath and/or shower, all with telephone, radio and TV; 6 with tea-making facilities. 17 in cottages, Lodge annexe and Bank House, at varying distances from main building. 5 ground-floor rooms.
Facilities 4 lounges, breakfast room, 2 dining rooms. 12-acre grounds at Sharrow, 5 at Bank House; garden, woodlands; ½ m of lake shore, private jetty and boathouse; fishing, boating, walking, climbing.
Location On E shore of Ullswater, 2 m S of Pooley Bridge. Turn by small church in Pooley Bridge and take Howtown Lane. (M6 exit 40.)
Restrictions No children under 13. No dogs.
Credit cards None accepted.
Terms [1989 rates] (No service charge) Dinner, B&B: single £63–£100. Set lunch from £14.50 (light lunches also available weekdays), dinner from £30.50. 10% mid-week reductions Mar, Nov.1-night bookings sometimes refused, especially weekends.
Service/tipping: "We and our staff give our services freely and do not expect to be rewarded by clients directly. If a particularly persistent client wishes to impose his will upon us we say (we hope without causing offence) that tipping is a feudal system and degrades both giver and receiver."

If you are nominating a hotel, please err on the side of saying too much. Many suggestions have to be rejected only because they are too brief.

UNDERBARROW Cumbria — Map 4

Greenriggs Country House Hotel [GFG]
Underbarrow, Nr Kendal LA8 8HF
Tel Crosthwaite (044 88) 387

A converted, mainly 18th-century house, ecclesiastical in parts, in the secluded Lyth Valley, three miles west of Kendal in a specially peaceful location – "Not easy to find", say several readers. *Greenriggs* is "comfortable without being plush. Public rooms small, intimate and comfortable, owners, Doug and Sarah Smithson extremely pleasant and helpful, went out of their way to find maps, retrieve lost belongings and deal with serious dietary quirks. Food on the whole well thought out and prepared, though occasionally lacking subtlety. Vegetables good, desserts imaginative. Good cheeses. Wine list relatively short and reasonably priced but interesting. English breakfast fine, continental a little sparse. Very good value." This opinion is endorsed by other readers with frequent mention of the "excellent and reasonably priced dinner, served punctually at 8, in the attractive Victorian dining room with superb views. Two choices for each course". Two readers, however, felt that given the isolated situation and inflexible mealtime there should have been an alternative to eating the full dinner. Another found the bedroom, though very clean, altogether too spartan.

Open All year except Jan and Feb. Closed Mon–Thurs Nov, Dec, Mar.
Rooms 12 double, 1 single – 9 with bath, 2 with shower, all with tea-making facilities; baby-listening by arrangement. 2 in cottage adjoining hotel.
Facilities Bar, bar lounge, TV lounge, dining room. 1½-acre grounds with children's play area and croquet.
Location 3 m due W of Kendal on road to Underbarrow. Turn left at a sharp bend before Underbarrow village. Known as Thorns Villa on Ordnance Survey maps.
Restrictions Not really suitable for ♿. No dogs in public rooms.
Credit cards Access, Visa.
Terms [1989 rates] B&B £25–£32.50; dinner, B&B £37.50–£45. Set dinner £14.25. 3-day Christmas package; New Year break; winter breaks. Reduced rates for children; high tea at 6.
Service/tipping: "We state on our terms that there are no service charges. We do not encourage tipping, but if anything is left we accept and distribute it to all staff."

UPPINGHAM Leicestershire — Map 1

The Lake Isle Restaurant with Rooms [GFG]
16 High Street East
Uppingham, Rutland LE15 9PZ
Tel (0572) 822951
Fax (0572) 822951

"Excellent. Everything just as in the 1989 report. Our room was beautifully decorated and very clean, with extras far better than in most hotels. Dinner and breakfast lavish and superb; the whole experience delightful, excellent value." Claire and David Whitfield's unpretentious restaurant, run with the help of Liam and Christine Tinney, is in the main street of this attractive small market town. It is an 18th-century building which has had many uses in its time: it was last known as "Sweeney Todd's", the hairdressers – Uppingham School boys had their hair cut in what is now the bar. It offers good French cooking "in a country-style decor", "Simplicity combined with quality in all aspects". There is a short menu with a choice of three or five courses. Portions are large, bread home-made – you are given a whole loaf and a knife. Excellent wine list with a good selection of half-bottles. Bedrooms (and a lounge) are in a building at the rear and an adjacent cottage; they vary in size and character, from first-floor rooms with large windows to cottage-style ones on the second floor, and are named after the wine regions of France – Dom Perignon has a whirlpool bath. Last year's nominators, on a return visit, comment, "A lesson to many other establishments. Extremely reasonably priced, very friendly, very comfortable." (*A Sheppard and GJ Nichols, Pat and Jeremy Temple; also Rena Prozzer, IC Dewey, and others*) Rutland Water is six miles away; there are many stately homes worth a visit in the area, such as Belvoir Castle, Burghley House and Belton House. Only niggles: "Bath towels too small and the bathrobes promised in last year's entry failed to materialise." "We felt that we should have been offered an alternative to a duvet on a warm night."

Open All year except bank holiday Mon. Restaurant closed Sun evening and Mon lunch (light meals available to residents).
Rooms 9 double, 1 single – all with bath and/or shower (1 with whirlpool), telephone, radio, TV and tea-making facilities.
Facilities Lounge, bar, restaurant; private dining room, meeting room. Walled garden. Rutland Water with fishing, bird-watching, sailing and wind surfing 6 m.
Location "Our restaurant-with-rooms is reached via Reeve's Yard, a small passage just past front of property. Most guests find us on foot and then we give details. Map on brochure."
Restrictions Not suitable for ♿. No dogs in public rooms.
Credit cards All major cards accepted.
Terms (No service charge) B&B (English): single £34–£38, double £51–£55. Set lunch: £9.50–£12, dinner £15.50–£19. Wine evenings 4 times a year. Reduced rates for weekend stays.
Service/tipping: "We most certainly do not agree with service charges; gratuities left to staff at our guests' discretion."

UPTON SNODSBURY Hereford and Worcester — Map 2

Upton House
Upton Snodsbury
Nr Worcester WR7 4NR

Tel Upton Snodsbury (090 560) 226

"A Grade II listed house set in large gardens next to the Norman church in a village six miles from Worcester. Accommodation in three very pretty double bedrooms, chintzes, floral prints, towelling robes and all the extras one could want. Bathrooms excellent. Comfortable sitting and dining room, both with antiques, log fires, beams and magazines. Dinner at a large table – guests dine together. Delicious food, well cooked and imaginative. Four courses plus cheese. We were made very welcome by the owners, Angela and Hugh Jefferson. A thoroughly delightful place to spend a few days." "The most fantastic English house I have seen, black and white, beautifully decorated. I would recommend it to anyone looking for a traditional English country home with good food." *Upton House*, new to Guide, belongs to the Wolsey Lodge consortium of private houses offering accommodation. No choice of meals; you advise your hosts of likes and dislikes when booking, and there is no obligation to dine in, the Jeffersons are happy to advise you about the good restaurants in the area. No licence; bring your own wine. (*Brenda Michelson, SL Dance*) More reports please.

Open All year except Christmas. Dining room closed for lunch.
Rooms 3 – all with private bathroom (2 *en suite*), telephone, radio, TV, tea-making facilities.
Facilities Lounge, dining room. 2-acre grounds.
Location 6 m E of Worcester on A422. In village turn towards Pershore. House is 150 yds on right.
Restrictions Not suitable for ♿. No children under 12. Dogs in car or kennel only.
Credit cards None accepted.
Terms B&B £22.50–£24; dinner, B&B £37.50–£39. £10 surcharge for single occupancy. Set dinner from £15. Bring your own wine.
Service/tipping: "This is run as a home; there is very little tipping."

WALKINGTON Humberside — Map 4

The Manor House — *Tel* Hull (0482) 881645
Northlands, Walkington
Hull HU17 8RT

This recently converted 19th-century manor house entered the Guide in an italicised entry last year. It is an imposing yellow-brick building with mock-Tudor black and white gabling, quietly situated in three-acre grounds "in a delightful location" not far from Kingston-upon-Hull. "The view of the grounds from the dining room and bedrooms", writes an inspector, "lightens the heart on a spring afternoon: a manicured lawn, encircled by mature trees, with rolling fields beyond. My bedroom – The Windsor Room – was one of the most relaxing and cheering I've ever stayed in. 18 foot square, decorated in champagne and white, with huge bow window, china lamps controlled seemingly by every switch in the room. Everything huge: king-size bed, dressing-table that looked about ten feet long, a profusion of flowery china. Bathroom luxurious, but the corner bath a bit cramped. Breakfast was acceptable, though tea was standard blend and orange juice not freshly squeezed." The blue dining room is "luxurious, and French in style, not in the period of the house". Our inspector did not dine, but other visitors much appreciated the cooking of the "extrovert" chef-*patron* Derek Baugh, whose "fairly flamboyant style of cooking was in character with everything else". "*Nouvelle* in Yorkshire-sized portions" was one reader's pithy comment. The menu (French with English subtitles) is extremely flowery; a meal might consist of Symphonie de naissances profondes de la mer au pistil de safran, followed by Rendez-vous de viandes effleuré de saveurs campagnardes, and ending with Le Délice de ces Dames, and Le tour de fromages de France et les fromages Anglais. The set price includes café aux harmonies de chocolats (coffee and chocolates). (*Pat and Jeremy Temple*)

Open All year except Christmas and New Year's Days. Restaurant closed bank holidays.
Rooms 5 double – all with bath, telephone, radio, TV, tea-making facilities and baby-listening.
Facilities Drawing room, restaurant, conservatory. 3-acre grounds.
Location 3 m SW of Beverly. Take Newbald Road off Beverley Westwood York Road.
Restrictions Not suitable for ♿. No children under 12.
Credit cards Access, Visa.
Terms B&B: single £61.50, double £86. Set dinner £21.50. 2-night half-board package.

Service/tipping: "No service charge. Service at guests' discretion, shared among staff on basis of hours worked."

WASDALE HEAD Cumbria — Map 4

Wasdale Head Inn *Tel* Wasdale (094 67) 26229
Wasdale Head, Nr Gosforth
CA20 1EX

"Arriving at this hotel soaked to the skin and deadbeat, I was given the warmest welcome and an offer to put my clothes straight into the washing machine. There followed two very cosy evenings. The bar with its log fire and splendid selection of beers, the dining room with its authentic old furnishings, superb breakfasts, following peaceful sleep with the elements locked out. Atmosphere very relaxed. No dress rules because the clientele were genuine walkers and climbers. Not a frock in sight! Very satisfying dinners, served early at 7.30. I'm going back!" "Wonderful location at the foot of Pillar, Great Gable and Scafell mountains. Excellent breakfasts which set you up for the day, interesting packed lunches. Staff very helpful and cheerful." "Dinners, with limited choice, mostly very good, and adequate in quantity. Puddings very 'more-ish'." (*Trevor Lockwood, DA Cash, and others*) This unsophisticated inn, in an isolated and magnificent setting not far from Wastwater, is famous in the annals of British mountaineering, and popular among walkers and climbers. It has a panelled and comfortably old-fashioned residents' bar and lounge. The main bar is named after the inn's first landlord, Will Ritson, reputed to be the world's biggest liar; in his memory liar competitions are held once a year. The pine-panelled bedrooms are simple and not large, but clean, comfortable and well lit, all with private facilities, plenty of hot water and lovely views. "Telephone, but no TV, praise be!" There is a jolly snug bar serving "good home-made food".

Open Open mid-Mar–mid-Nov, 2 weeks over New Year.
Rooms 9 double, 2 single – 9 with bath, 2 with shower, all with telephone, tea-making facilities and baby-listening. 3 self-catering units nearby.
Facilities Residents' lounge, residents' bar, public bar, restaurant; drying room. ½-acre grounds.
Location Follow signs for Wasdale Head from Gosforth or Santon Bridge.
Restrictions Not suitable for ♿. No children under 8 in dining room at night (high tea available). No dogs in public rooms.
Credit cards Access, Visa.
Terms Dinner, B&B (English) £38–£40. Bar lunches. Set dinner £13. Reductions for stays of 4 nights or more.
Service/tipping: "No service charge. We do not accept tips."

WATERHOUSES Staffordshire — Map 4

The Old Beams [GFG] *Tel* Waterhouses (0538) 308254
Waterhouses ST10 3HW

A new nomination on the edge of the Peak District National Park, *The Old Beams*, a small 18th-century house, heavily beamed, as its name implies, is on the Ashbourne to Leek road. All rooms are double glazed. It is a restaurant-with-rooms, "but the rooms are very comfortable, and immaculately kept, though small. Furnishings and fabrics are top quality and the limited space carefully and cleverly used; we had magazines, sewing kit, and delicious chocolate truffles which were replaced – of course we had tried them on arrival – while we were having a drink in the conservatory and then – again! – during dinner when the bed was turned down. Very good bathroom with good lighting, potted plants and plastic duck as well as the usual oils, shampoos etc. Dinner, served in a pleasant, comfortably furnished conservatory, was excellent, "*nouvelle*-ish, but with generous portions, and carefully cooked by Nigel Wallis; his wife, Ann, efficiently and exuberantly looks after front of house and makes the desserts. Excellent wine list, and very good house wines. There is a lovely garden, floodlit at night. The atmosphere is relaxed and welcoming, and *The Old Beams* would be a good base for exploring the area, or an excellent overnight stop." (*Pat and Jeremy Temple*)

Open All year except 1st 2 weeks Jan. Restaurant closed Mon, Sat lunch, Sun evening.
Rooms 6, all with bath, telephone, radio, TV. All in annexe opposite restaurant. 3 on ground floor.
Facilities Lounge, bar, restaurant, conservatory/restaurant, private dining room. ½-acre garden.
Location On A532 between Ashbourne and Leek. All rooms double-glazed.
Restrictions No children under 4. No dogs.
Credit cards All major cards accepted.
Terms B&B: single £45, double £60. Set lunch £10.75, dinner £17.50; full alc 26.
Service/tipping: "No service charge. Tips at guests' discretion; staff divide among themselves."

WATERMILLOCK Cumbria — Map 4

Leeming House Hotel
Watermillock
Penrith CA11 0JJ

Tel Pooley Bridge (085 36) 622
from late 1989 (076 84) 86622
Telex 64111 LEEMNG

An early Victorian house in magnificent, well kept grounds with mature trees, running down to Ullswater. The views, particularly from the first-floor bedrooms, are superb. It has warm comfortable lounges and a cosy panelled bar. Readers this year, as last, are enthusiastic: "Our third visit. We confirm our earlier comments. Its consistency in all departments is much to be commended: upkeep of grounds, housekeeping, professionalism of manager and staff – they maintain a friendly but discreet presence. It is warm and welcoming in winter. Beds are turned down and bathroom cleaned during dinner and breakfast. The hotel is run for the benefit of its visitors – no rigid mealtimes, no house party atmosphere. The restaurant, with lovely views of the garden, maintains a very high standard." "Bedrooms, though not large, are tastefully decorated. Bathrooms have thick towels and generous allocations of soaps, shampoos replenished daily. Service exceptional, especially the delightful young waitresses." "Outstanding breakfasts with home-made jams and honey." *Leeming House* is the only Guide hotel belonging to the Trusthouse Forte chain. Some new rooms may be added, bringing the total in 1989 to 38, but we are assured by the manager, Christopher Curry, that they will be in keeping with the rest of the house. " (*Alan Greenwood, FW, Helen and Charles Priday, and others*)

Give the Guide positive support. Don't just leave feedback to others.

Open All year.
Rooms 22 double, 3 single – all with bath and/or shower, telephone, radio and TV. 7 doubles with tea-making facilities in cottage annexe 50 yards from main building. 2 ground-floor rooms.
Facilities Drawing rooms, library, cocktail bar, dining room; conference facilities. 20-acre grounds with lake frontage (fishing, sailing etc), arboretum and helipad. Pony-trekking, golf, shooting.
Location On west shore of Ullswater on A592.
Restrictions No smoking in dining room. No dogs in public rooms.
Credit cards All major cards accepted.
Terms [1989 rates] Rooms: single £55–£60, double £65–£98. Breakfast: continental £5, English £7. Set lunch £11.50 (£13.50 on Sun), dinner £27. 2-day breaks all year. Christmas and New Year packages. Winter pheasant shooting parties for groups of 8 or more. 1-night bookings sometimes refused at bank holiday weekends. Reduced rates for children sharing parents' room; special meals by arrangement only.
Service/tipping: "All prices include service; any gratuities are collected and distributed to all staff."

The Old Church Hotel — *Tel* Pooley Bridge (085 36) 204
Watermillock, Penrith CA11 0JN — *from late 1989* (076 84) 86204

"A superbly managed small hotel in an incomparable lakeside position. There seems to be a conscious effort to cater for those who want a get-away-from-it-all break – no radio or TV in the bedrooms; there's a cabinet-concealed TV in one of the lounges which we did not see switched on during our visit. The cheerfulness and efficiency of the staff and willingness of our hostess to stop at any time for a chat about some point of interest also made for a memorable stay. We would not agree with the previous comments that the hotel is run more for the owners than the guests, though they do have young children who can preoccupy parents at times." "Bedroom and bathroom beautifully planned which gave a spacious feel to what was actually quite small. Good firm bed. The personal attention is quite remarkable and the staff follow the lead set by the owners." *The Old Church Hotel,* owned and run by Kevin and Maureen Whitemore is an 18th-century house built on the site of a 12th-century church, in a spectacular setting on Ullswater, reached by a long private drive off the A592. Its gardens go down to the water and there are fine views. The comfortable lounges are decorated in soft colours and there is plenty of evidence throughout of Mrs Whitemore's flair for soft furnishings – she runs upholstery courses in the hotel twice a year in low season. English food is served in a pretty dining room with old wooden tables and fresh flowers; the four-course dinner menu with four choices of starter and main dish changes daily. (*Countess of Malmesbury, Barbara Hill, and others*) Rooms vary in size and style, so it is worth discussing the accommodation you want when booking.

Open Mar–Nov inclusive.
Rooms 10 double – all with bath, telephone and baby-listening.
Facilities Hall, lounge, TV lounge, bar, dining room. 4-acre grounds on lake with mooring and fishing; windsurfers and rowing boat available.
Location 3 m S of Pooley Bridge; 5 m from junction 40 on the M6.
Restrictions Not suitable for ♿. No smoking in dining room. No dogs.
Credit cards None accepted.
Terms [1989 rates] Dinner, B&B £65. Set dinner £19.50 to non-residents. 1-night bookings sometimes refused for bank holidays. Reduced rates for children in cots; special meals. Soft furnishing courses Mar and Nov.

Service/tipping: "We hope service charge and tipping will disappear. We normally suggest that money offered should be spent on the guests' next visit."

WATERROW Somerset — Map 1

Hurstone Farmhouse Hotel — *Tel* Wiveliscombe (0984) 23441
Waterrow, Wiveliscombe TA4 2AT

John Bone's far-off-the-beaten-track Georgian farmhouse hotel has fine views down the combe and up the far hillside. Visitors have enjoyed the relaxing atmosphere, the simple style, the comfortable but not luxurious bedrooms (though all have bath, telephone and TV), and the "plain and homely no-choice menus". This year Mr Bone is making considerable changes, particularly on the eating front. He has appointed a manager and introduced four or five choices of each course to the menu; a new chef arrives as we go to press. By 1990 there will be a new restaurant serving 35. "It will be nicely appointed with good china, silver plate, etc, and the style of cooking will tend towards modern English," says Mr Bone, "our chef will do what he can to meet special requests and will cook vegetarian, vegan, etc dishes by arrangement. We will maintain our most important asset – low-key, friendly service, no set times, no rush, just relax and enjoy." There will also be four new bedrooms above the restaurant. Quite how the new arrangements will affect this "quiet, unpretentious farmhouse hotel" is hard to predict. Can we have reports please?

Open All year.
Rooms 1 suite (1 double, 1 single), 4 double – all with bath and shower, telephone, TV, tea-making facilities and baby-listening. 4 more planned for 1990.
Facilities Sitting room with TV, dining room. Terrace and gardens; 65-acre farmland with small trout river. Riding, tennis, golf nearby.
Location ½ m off B3227 at Waterrow (council sign); 3 m SW of Wiveliscombe.
Restrictions Not suitable for ♿. Dogs by arrangement only.
Credit cards Access, Amex, Visa.
Terms B&B £24.50–£36.25; dinner, B&B £37.50–£48.25. Set dinner £14.50. Weekend and midweek breaks all year except public holidays; 5% discount for stays of 7 nights or more; Christmas and New Year programmes. Reduced rates and special meals for children.
Service/tipping: "No service charge. We do not ask for nor expect tips. We consider it ridiculous to be paid twice for enjoyable work done."

WELLAND Hereford and Worcester — Map 2

Holdfast Cottage Hotel — *Tel* Hanley Swan (0684) 310288
Welland, Nr Malvern WR13 6NA

Holdfast Cottage, approached by a tree-lined drive, stands in large gardens in a quiet situation, facing Little Malvern Priory and the Malvern Hills on one side and Bredon Hill and the Cotswolds on the other. It is fronted by a delightful garden and shrubbery, which partially screens the house from the road. The building is 17th-century at heart; additions have been made as required; public rooms and bedrooms are on the small side, but there are log fires in winter and one can sit on the terrace outside in warm weather. The bedrooms are simple but comfortable. This year we hear that Dennis and Diana Beetlestone have handed over the management to Philip Harris (front of house) and Diane Brown (in the kitchen) who in earlier editions of the Guide gained warm reports for *Esseborne Manor* in Hampshire. First reports on the new setup praise the "helpful host, first-rate, imaginative à la carte menus and interesting wine list". The hotel has been redecorated and all bedrooms now have a private bathroom.

Open All year except Jan.
Rooms 6 double, 2 single – all with bath and/or shower, radio, TV; tea-making facilities on request.
Facilities Lounge, conservatory, bar, 2 dining rooms. 1-acre grounds with garden and croquet.
Location 4 m SE of Malvern on A4014 mid-way between Little Malvern and Welland.
Restriction Not suitable for ♿. No children under 10 as residents. No pets indoors.
Credit card Access.
Terms B&B: single £34–£48, double £72–£86. Full alc £24.
Service/tipping: "We do not charge for the service we offer. Tips are shared equally between all staff contributing to guests' enjoyment."

WEST BAGBOROUGH Somerset **Map 1**

Higher House *Tel* Bishops Lydeard
West Bagborough (0823) 432996
Taunton TA4 3EF

Plenty of warm approval this year for William and Jo Beaumont's reasonably priced country house in three acres of garden and paddocks on the south side of the Quantocks, with lovely views over the Vale of Taunton towards the Brendon Hills and Exmoor. It is a 17th-century farmhouse with later additions, built round two courtyards, one of which now contains a heated swimming pool, the other a herb garden. "An attractive small hotel in a beautiful location with superb views and a most welcoming home-like atmosphere. Bedrooms are spacious and well maintained. William Beaumont is a wonderful host." Substantial evening meals, eaten communally with no choice until the end, generally find favour, with special praise for the desserts. Breakfasts, served between 8 and 10 am, offer a wide choice and are considered "especially good". "Home-made bread and jams, plenty of well cooked vegetables, lots of home baking. Two comfortable lounges, almost always with a fire. Excellent walks from the village leading up to the Quantocks." (*S Lloyd Jones, S Saysell, Judith A Heywood, and others*)

Open All year except Christmas.
Rooms 1 family suite, 5 double – 4 with bath and/or shower, all with telephone, TV, tea-making facilities and baby-listening.
Facilities Hall with bar, drawing room with snooker table, TV room, restaurant. 3-acre grounds with heated swimming pool and paddock.
Location Take A358 from Taunton to Minehead. After about 8 m take road on right signposted West Bagborough; *Higher House* is at end of village.
Restrictions Not suitable for ♿. No dogs in dining room.
Credit cards Access, Visa.
Terms B&B £16–£27; dinner, B&B £27–£45. Discounts for 2 or more nights. Weekly rates.
Service/tipping: We don't refuse tips if offered, but as this is a family-run place we don't have too many problems."

If you have difficulty in finding hotels because our location details are inadequate, please help us to improve directions next year.

WEST CLIFFE Kent — Map 3

Wallett's Court Country House Hotel [GFG] — *Tel* Dover (0304) 852424
West Cliffe, Dover CT15 6EW

A manor house, bits dating back to Domesday, restored in the 17th century, the home of Prime Minister William Pitt in 1804, and entirely renovated in recent years by Lea and Chris Oakley. It is set in rural surroundings on the white cliffs of Dover, a mile from St Margaret's Bay and is a convenient stop-over before or after a channel crossing, but there is plenty to see and do in the area. Inside there are intricately carved honey-coloured beams, huge open fireplaces, plenty of good antiques, flowers everywhere. Four of the bedrooms, small and fairly basic but well equipped, are in a converted barn at the back of the house. Chef-*patron*, Chris Oakley, trained with the Roux brothers at *Le Gavroche* and was then chef at *Le Poulbot* in London. On weekdays there is a three-course dinner at £12.50, and on Saturday a more expensive gourmet meal – with a small amount of choice on each menu. "Continues to provide good-value overnight accommodation and very enjoyable Saturday dinner served in comfortable surroundings and a friendly relaxed atmosphere. We had a large bedroom, pleasantly furnished, with a good modern bathroom. Good breakfast, served promptly." (*Rosamund Hebdon; also MJ and AR Russell*) However, readers continue to complain of poor insulation in the annexe – no joke if your neighbour has to rise before dawn for the Channel crossing; some have been disappointed by the dinner and found the house wine over-priced. And we have two complaints that "Service is at your discretion" or "Service not included" was written in ballpoint at the bottom of the bill. "Don't hoteliers and restaurateurs reward their staff adequately?" asks an irate correspondent. "Do you tip the shop assistant who sells you a shirt, or the dentist's receptionist? One should not have to pay extra for attention that should be there in the first place." (See under St Margaret's at Cliffe in *The Good Food Guide*.)

Open All year except Christmas. Restaurant closed Sun.
Rooms 2 family suites, 10 double – all with bath and shower, radio, TV and tea-making facilities. 4 in converted barn 12 yards from main building.
Facilities Lounge, bar, dining room, private function room; games room. 5-acre grounds. 1 m from St Margaret's Bay with bathing, windsurfing, tennis club.
Location 3 m N of Dover, 1 m down B2058 off A258 Dover–Deal road. Hotel is on right opposite church.
Restrictions Not suitable for ♿. No dogs.
Credit card Access
Terms (Service at guests' discretion) B&B £19–£45. Set dinner on weekdays from £12.50; gourmet dinner on Sat £20.00. Reduced rates for children sharing parents' room; special meals.

WHITEWELL Lancashire — Map 4

The Inn at Whitewell — *Tel* Dunsop Bridge (020 08) 222
Whitewell, Nr Clitheroe BB7 3AT

A long low stone house by a church, surrounded by rolling hills, with lawns down to the river Hodder (the inn has six miles of fishing rights). "Inside," says our sister publication, *The Good Pub Guide*, "the atmosphere is more that of a country house than a pub, with sonorous clocks, heavy curtains on sturdy wooden rails, antique settles, oak gate-leg tables, old cricketing and sporting prints and log fires." The inn, which is owned by the Duchy of Lancaster, comes new to the Guide this year, recommended by *Anne Laurence* after a February visit, "Slightly scruffy in a very soothing way with the most wonderful views over the river and the foothills of the Pennines. It's warm at a time of year when many hotels are freezing. I was staying on my own; my room was huge and old-fashioned, but comfortable. Service was friendly and the food good. I had a bar meal for dinner and an excellent breakfast with good coffee and, most unusually for a hotel, good sausages." The inn also houses an art gallery and wine merchant (so an unusually good range of wines is available with meals). More reports please.

Open All year.
Rooms 11 double – 6 with bath, 6 with telephone; TV available in most rooms (£2 per day).
Facilities Residents' lounge with TV, 2 bars, restaurant. 3-acre grounds; 6 m fishing rights on river Hodder.
Location 6 m NW of Clitheroe. Take B6246 from Whalley or road through Dunsop Bridge from B6478.
Restrictions Bedrooms not suitable for ♿. No dogs in dining room; no Alsatians in public rooms.
Credit cards All major cards accepted.
Terms B&B (English): single £25–£32, double £39–£45. Bar lunches, set dinner £14.50; full alc £21. Reduced rates and special meals for children.
Service/tipping: "Service included. Our policy is to deter politely and with humour any form of tipping."

WICKHAM Hampshire — Map 2

The Old House Hotel [GFG] — *Tel* Wickham (0329) 833049
The Square, Wickham PO17 5JG

"A delightful hotel with excellent rooms and service" in a creepered early-Georgian Grade II listed house with an attractive garden in a picturesque, part-medieval–part-Georgian village square, which is itself a preservation area. It was converted by Richard Skipwith and his French-born wife Annie 18 years ago into a comfortable small hotel with a good, unpretentious restaurant specialising in regional French cooking, in what was once the outhouse and stables. There are panelled rooms on the lower two floors and bedrooms with beams higher up. Bedrooms vary in size but all have private bathroom and TV; furniture is antique or period. A new annexe added three bedrooms in 1989. It is a useful stop-over to or from the ferry. More reports please.

Open All year, except 2 weeks Christmas, 2 weeks Easter, 2 weeks July/Aug. Bedrooms closed Sat and Sun; restaurant closed Mon and Sat lunch, all day Sun.
Rooms 9 double, 3 single – all with bath and shower, telephone, radio, TV and baby-listening. 2 double, 1 single in annexe.
Facilities 2 lounges, bar, breakfast room, restaurant; private dining/conference room. Small garden. River Meon nearby.
Location In village centre (front rooms double-glazed). Parking. Wickham is at junction of A333 and A32, 3 m N of Fareham.
Restrictions Only restaurant suitable for ♿. No dogs.
Credit cards All major cards accepted.
Terms B&B: £60–£70, double £80–£90. Full alc £29.50. Reductions for children according to age; special meals.

Service/tipping: "We feel that in a service industry it is not right to ask for extra payment for service. The tariff should cover the amount we need to run our organisation satisfactorily. However, we print on the menus 'service included' even though no extra amount is added."

WILLITON Somerset — Map 1

Curdon Mill — *Tel* Stogumber (0984) 56522
Lower Vellow
Williton TA4 4LS

"We have just returned from a three-day stay and highly recommend *Curdon Mill*. The Criddles are welcoming and attentive and take a personal pride in everything. Super five-course dinners, the emphasis is on simple English cooking, helpings are generous with lots of fresh vegetables. Second helpings of pudding are encouraged. The large English breakfast is delicious." "Delightful setting. Accommodation imaginatively and tastefully created. Dining room and lounge both comfortably furnished. Garden well laid out with a swimming pool. A good example of a well-run small country hotel, moderately priced." (*Mrs Lucy Slater, DL Baxter; also Mrs DA Wilkinson*) *Curdon Mill* is an attractively converted water mill, part of Richard and Daphne Criddle's 200-acre working farm at the foot of the Quantocks. The mill's water wheel still works, and the mill shaft hangs across the ceiling of the dining room. The large restaurant is open to non-residents; it serves a no-choice meal to residents but also has an extensive à la carte menu which is sent in advance when bookings are made, inviting guests to browse and choose their meals before they arrive. A few niggles: some slightly neglectful housekeeping, inadequate heating on a cool summer night, a disappointing breakfast.

Open All year.
Rooms 6 double – 1 with bath and shower, 5 with shower, all with TV and tea-making facilities.
Facilities Bar, lounge, restaurant. Large garden with stream in 200-acres of farm and woodland. Outdoor heated swimming pool available to guests in morning and late afternoon; stabling for visiting horses; trout-fishing. Coast 3 m.
Location Take A358 from Taunton. After 12 m turn left for Vellow and Stogumber. Mill is 1 m on left.
Restrictions Not suitable for ♿. Dogs outdoors only (kennels provided).
Credit cards None accepted.
Terms (Service at guests' discretion) B&B £18.50–£27.50; dinner, B&B £30.50–£39.50. Set dinner £12; full alc from £20. 4-day Christmas package.
Service/tipping: "No service charge. Tips optional and are shared amongst staff."

The White House Hotel and Restaurant [GFG] — *Tel* Williton (0984) 32306
Williton TA4 4QW

Dick and Kay Smith have been the proprietors of *The White House Hotel* for over 21 years and have had an entry in the Guide almost continually since our first edition in 1978. The hotel is well placed for exploring Somerset, particularly the Quantocks. It does not offer a house-party atmosphere or sybaritic luxury; the decor is the product of taste rather than money. Not all the bedrooms have a private bathroom (and not all the private bathrooms are *en suite*), nor are they filled with 'extras', but each one has been individually thought out. Some are on the road, so are noisy; courtyard ones are quiet. Most guests continue to appreciate Dick Smith's cooking "a version of French provincial using Somerset produce beautifully prepared, nicely balanced and excellently presented". There is a choice of four dishes at each course except soup. Breakfasts are "as good as dinner". This year, however, as sometimes happens when a hotel has previously had exceptionally good coverage, criticisms have been voiced: careless upkeep of the bedrooms, "unwelcoming" public rooms, uncomfortable seating and long delays at times in the dining room. One reader concludes, "All the tender loving care seems to go into the preparation of the food; it should be regarded as a restaurant-with-rooms." More reports please.

Open Mid-May–Nov. Restaurant closed for lunch.
Rooms 1 family suite, 11 double, 1 single – 9 with bath (3 also have shower), all with TV. 5 in courtyard annexe, some on ground floor.
Facilities Lounge, bar, dining room. 2 m from coast; shingle beach 2 m, sandy beach 8 m.
Location On A39 in centre of village (some traffic noise). Parking in courtyard.
Restriction Dogs by arrangement, not in public rooms.
Credit cards None accepted.
Terms [1989 rates] B&B £23–£34; dinner, B&B £41–£52. Set dinner £21. 3- and 4-day breaks. Reduced rates for children.
Service/tipping: "We do not make a service charge. If guests add anything to the bill it is given to the staff involved."

WINDERMERE Cumbria — Map 4

Miller Howe [GFG] — *Tel* Windermere (096 62) 2536
Rayrigg Road
Windermere LA23 1EY

This year, as last, we have a mixed postbag for John Tovey's celebrated hotel perched above Windermere with a magnificent view to the great peaks across the water. Plenty of readers jump to the defence: "The enthusiasm and dedication of the staff were exceptional. I must take issue with your suggestion that the standard suffers when the maestro is absent. This is manifestly untrue and a quite unjustified criticism of the staff." "Just as memorable as a previous visit three years ago. We can remember nowhere else in the land where a good dinner has such a sense of occasion, where (as in the theatre) artists who have worked hard want you to enjoy their best, and often inspired, efforts. Quite the nicest small hotel we know – allowing a dog too." "Food delicious. They went to great lengths to provide vegetarian dishes in place of the ones I could not eat." Breakfasts (with Bucks Fizz) continue to receive full marks, as do the "stupendous cream teas", and there is repeated praise for the friendliness and helpfulness of the staff. As previously, some readers find the whole Tovey dinner show – prompt starting time for everyone, dimmed lights, the joint solemnly carried round the tables, "the exhausting range of taste sensations" – excessive; some would prefer a shorter menu or simpler food. And it is clear from our postbag that such is *Miller Howe*'s reputation that at busy times, particularly the weekend, things can become rushed and impersonal. Some of the cheaper bedrooms and bathrooms are considered too small, and readers mind being charged £3 extra for morning tea. (*Dr Brian Webb, Patricia J Orchard, PG Jones, and many others*)

Open Second Thurs in Mar–first Sun in Dec.
Rooms 13 double – all with bath and/or shower, telephone and radio; TV on request.
Facilities 4 lounges, 2 dining rooms; terrace. 4-acre grounds with landscaped garden. Walking, climbing, tennis, sailing, fishing and water sports nearby.
Location On A592 N of Bowness. Lake-facing rooms quietest.
Restrictions Not suitable for ♿. No children under 12. No dogs in public rooms.
Credit cards Access, Amex, Diners.
Terms (Excluding 12½% service charge) Dinner, B&B £58–£105. Set dinner £26. Packed lunches £9. Bargain breaks, residential cookery courses Mar and Nov. 1-night bookings sometimes refused.
Service/tipping: "A surcharge of 12½% is added to all final accounts in lieu of gratuities."

WITHERSLACK Cumbria — Map 4

The Old Vicarage [GFG]
Witherslack
Grange-over-Sands
LA11 6RS

Tel Witherslack (044 852) 381
Fax (044 852) 373
Telex 668230

César award: Outstanding hospitality – Lakeland style

"Our second visit to this delightful hotel and we thoroughly endorse its Guide entry. It is so comfortable, there is always a warm welcome, nothing is too much trouble – like providing milk for our puppy. The bedrooms have everything one might need from Kendal mint cake to shoe-cleaning material. The atmosphere is cosy and warm; you can mix with other guests or keep to yourself. Scrumptious food." "I loved it. All-day walks followed by this sort of pampering is paradise. Your comfort is checked all the time." (*Mr and Mrs H Stirrat, Braham Murray*) And there are similar eulogies from other readers for this little Georgian hotel in the less dramatic but still attractive walking country south of Lake Windermere, and though only 15 minutes from the M6, quiet and secluded, away from the heart of the village. It is run by Roger and Jill Burrington-Brown and Stanley and Irene Reeve. There are William Morris curtains, Heal's lampshades, lots of pine and cane in the bedrooms, ample reading light. All rooms have baths (some of them half-size) or showers, and duvets, but you can ask for traditional bedding. The five-course set dinner (served "at 7.30 for 8") offers no choice except for hot or cold desserts, you are warmly encouraged to have both. Cooking is English; portions very generous. Breakfasts are "excellent, everything freshly cooked – delicious home-made brioche; toast made from home-made bread." The partners have acquired an orchard in adjoining grounds where they are constructing an all-weather tennis court and an annexe in traditional Lakes style, built round a courtyard, with five double rooms all with a sitting area and *en suite* facilities, due to open by the end of 1989. There is nothing solemn or flash or unctuous about *The Old Vicarage*'s style of hospitality, but it offers an unaffected warmth of welcome which most of us yearn for on our travels, and find less often than we would like.

Open All year except Christmas week. Restaurant closed for lunch.
Rooms 12 double, 1 single – all with bath and/or shower, telephone, radio, TV and tea making facilities. Some on ground floor.

Facilities 2 lounges, bar lounge, restaurant, private dining room. 5-acre grounds with tennis, lawns and woodlands. Sea 3 m, Lake Windermere 8 m, river fishing 5 m. Fell-walking.
Location From M6 take exit 36; follow route to Barrow-in-Furness. Turn off A590 signposted Witherslack and take first turn left past phone-box. Hotel is ½ m along this lane on left.
Restrictions Not suitable for ♿. Children under 10 by arrangement only. Dogs by arrangement only; not in public rooms.
Credit cards All major cards accepted.
Terms [1989 rates] (Service at guests' discretion) B&B single from £40; double from £63; dinner, B&B: single from £54.50, double from £100. Set dinner £19.50. 3-day breaks all year except bank holidays. Reduced rates for children; special meals.
Service/tipping: "We do not encourage or expect tips. However, it would be dishonest to say that we do not appreciate the extras we occasionally receive."

WOODSTOCK Oxfordshire — Map 2

The Feathers Hotel [GFG]
Market Street
Woodstock OX7 1SX

Tel Woodstock (0993) 812291
Fax (0993) 813158
Telex 83147 VIA ORG

"Wins our all-time accolade. A heavenly hotel. Wonderful food, flawless, non-self-abasing service, comfortable and beautifully decorated rooms with never a trace of what I would call the Love Life of an Edwardian Lady syndrome, in other words, no phony nostalgia, no brass warming-pans, no serving-maids in starched pinnies dropping little curtseys. It's very expensive, at any rate by our standards, but it's wonderful." "Ceaseless unashamed comfort. The food a delight, the staff ace. The bedroom. . .we collapsed into its all-encompassing quiet and left very reluctantly." "Good firm mattresses, pretty wallpaper and cut flowers, deep fluffy towels in the bathroom." The restaurant "that glows with soft colour and sparkles next morning at breakfast" offers imaginative modern British food, courteously served in comfortable surroundings. "Having a dog almost always creates problems; *The Feathers* was the exception to the rule; my dog was treated as a guest!" *The Feathers*, owned and run by Gordon Campbell-Gray, is in the centre of the show-place town, a few minutes' stroll from Blenheim Palace – you can walk round the lake before breakfast. It started life as a coaching inn and has expanded over the years to include neighbouring buildings. Bedrooms vary in size, and not all are as well equipped as those occupied by the enthusiasts we have quoted. It has low beamed ceilings, small but comfortable lounges with log fires, interesting furniture, books, flowers, and a relaxed atmosphere. Light meals are served in the Country Bar and, in summer, in its garden. *The Feathers* would be a good base for visiting Oxford, only eight miles away. (*Angela Lambert, Tony Price, Susan Gillotti, RC Ballance, Jan Morris*) Note: Gordon Campbell-Gray has now opened a second hotel, *The Draycott* in London, winner of a 1990 César.

Open All year.
Rooms 14 double, 1 single – all with bath and/or shower, telephone, radio and TV; 24-hour room service. Baby-listening on request.
Facilities 2 lounges, bar, restaurant. Courtyard garden where drinks and lunches are served. Fishing in Blenheim Park lake ¼ m.
Location In town centre, but quiet at night. Street parking; public carpark nearby.
Restrictions Not suitable for ♿. Dogs by prior arrangement; not in public rooms.
Credit cards All major cards accepted.

Terms B&B: single £60–£65, double £80–£110. Set lunch £13.50, dinner £20.50; full alc £28.50. Bar lunches available. Winter breaks; Christmas and New Year packages. Reduced rates for children sharing parents' room.
Service/tipping: "No service charge. We feel tipping should be totally optional and leave it entirely to guests."

WOOLER Northumberland — Map 4

Ryecroft Hotel [GFG] — *Tel* Wooler (0668) 81459
Ryecroft Way, Wooler NE71 6AB

A modest small hotel run by Patricia and David McKechnie in a Northumbrian market town at the foot of the Cheviot Hills, in an area rich in historical sites and good for walking, bird-watching, cycling, angling and gliding. The red-brick exterior is nothing special, nor is the interior decor, but it is spotlessly clean, with fresh flowers, log fires in winter and a relaxing atmosphere; staff are friendly and helpful. The bar serves real ale. Mrs McKechnie, who now has a new assistant, Paul Hibbin, cooks imaginative, unpretentious and highly praised English meals served in generous portions; there is a five-course dinner menu, with some choice, which changes daily. Wines are reasonably priced. Breakfasts are "splendid". Since last year private facilities have been added to all the bedrooms; a conservatory extension has been added to the bar to provide more space for bar lunches, (the prices have risen as a consequence). Readers point out that some bedrooms are small and some face a road which can be noisy, especially on market day, but the McKechnies tell us that all rooms are now double-glazed.

Open All year except first 2 weeks Nov, 24–30 Dec.
Rooms 7 double, 2 single – 6 with bath, 3 with shower, all with telephone, tea-making and baby-listening.
Facilities Lounge, TV lounge, bar/conservatory, restaurant. ½-acre garden.
Location Central (some rooms near main road, but all are double-glazed). Parking.
Restrictions Not suitable for ♿. No smoking in dining room.
Credit cards Access, Visa.
Terms B&B £26–£29; dinner, B&B £41–£44. Bar lunches; set dinner £15. Walking and bird-watching breaks; reduced rates in low season. No charge for accommodation for children under 13 sharing parents' room; meals half price.
Service/tipping: "No service charge. Tipping left to guests' discretion."

WORFIELD Shropshire — Map 1

The Old Vicarage Hotel — *Tel* Worfield (074 64) 497
Worfield — *Telex* 35438 TELCOM
Nr Bridgnorth WV15 5JZ

This red brick Edwardian country rectory is quietly situated on a hill just outside the pretty village of Worfield with extensive views over the Worfe Valley, but is conveniently near the M54 and the confluence of the M5 and M6. It has two-acre grounds, a "very attractive conservatory with glorious views" for pre-dinner drinks and coffee, and an unpretentious restaurant with a regularly changing menu of honest English dishes. Readers continue to appreciate the "restful colour schemes, beautifully furnished bedrooms, sympathetically converted to include bathrooms with carefully blended furnishings even down to matching soaps, towels and bathrobes, TV in a discreet cabinet, electric overblankets and a bowl of fruit", and the "comfortable and welcoming atmosphere created by the owners, Peter and Christine Iles. The staff seemed happy, which indicates good management. The food was varied and cooked with flair." "Food excellent, staff 'homely' in the best sense, pace unhurried. Lots of comfort, lots of hot water, lots of tranquillity." (*JM Chandler, Brian Wicks; also Frank and Doreen Attwood, and others*) The Iles tell us they have converted a coach house to add four non-smoking luxury rooms, with jacuzzi, one of which is fully equipped for disabled guests. There are some criticisms of the food – lamb served well done when it had been ordered rare, some dishes not quite hot enough, a plethora of many high-cholesterol desserts, but the peaceful rural situation, the warmth of welcome, and the excellence of the bedrooms in most readers' view, more than compensate.

Open All year except a few days between Christmas and New Year. Lunch by arrangement only.
Rooms 2 suites, 13 double – all with bath and/or shower, telephone, radio, TV, tea-making facilities and baby-listening. 4 non-smoking doubles, with jacuzzi, in converted coach house; 1 specially adapted for ♿.
Facilities Bar, conservatory lounge, dining room; private dining room. 2-acre grounds. Near river; fishing can be arranged.
Location 1 m N of A454 from Bridgnorth to Wolverhampton.
Restrictions Not suitable for ♿. No smoking in dining room. Children under 8 at management's discretion. No dogs in public rooms.
Credit cards All major cards accepted.
Terms B&B (English): single occupancy £42.50, double £62.50, suite £68.50. Set dinner £17.50 (3 courses) and £23.50 (5 courses). Leisure breaks (credit cards not accepted).
Service/tipping: "We leave it entirely to guests. A surprisingly large number do leave a tip."

YATTENDON Berkshire — Map 2

The Royal Oak Hotel [GFG] — *Tel* Hermitage (0635) 200440
The Square
Yattendon, Nr Newbury
RG16 OUF

A picturesque creeper-covered old building in a pretty village, cosy, informal, but also sophisticated, with young owners, Kate and Richard Smith. It comprises a pub, a restaurant and five smart bedrooms. No formal reception – "and staff can be hard to find at times". The lounge has comfortable sofas, a log fire and magazines; the restaurant is small – only eight tables – but discreetly elegant, with polished wood tables, thick curtains and stencilled walls. Mr Smith's Anglo-French cooking is ambitious and interesting, but not too fussy: he worked with Richard Shepherd at *Langan's Brasserie*, and the influence shows. Desserts can be very rich. The kitchens also serve the pub – "spruce and inviting with red-tiled floors, open brickwork and newspapers hanging on sticks" – where you can have a drink and a snack, or a full meal, in comfort and at lower prices than in the restaurant. There is a wider choice of food in the pub, but many dishes are similar to those served in the restaurant; menus for both change several times a week. Guests in search of simpler food would probably be happier in the pub. The staff is young and friendly. Bedrooms light, spacious, smart with antique furniture and well-equipped bathrooms "but lights a bit dim". Problems with hot water, reported in earlier editions, have now been sorted out. Some bedrooms look onto the walled rose-garden at the back; those above the pub can be noisy until late at night. Lavish breakfasts are cooked to order. (*AP Collett, David Thibodeau*) The Smiths now also own the *Beetle and Wedge* at Moulsford on the Thames not far away, which receives its first entry in this edition; they divide their time between the two establishments. More reports please.

Open All year.
Rooms 5 double – all with bath (1 also has shower), telephone, radio, and TV; baby-listening on request.
Facilities Lounge, bar, 2 restaurants. ⅓-acre garden.
Location Just N of M4 between exits 12 and 13.
Restrictions Only restaurant and bar suitable for ♿. Dogs by arrangement only.
Credit cards Access, Amex, Visa.
Terms [1989 rates] B&B: single from £48, double from £58. Full alc £18.50 in bar, £28.50 in restaurant. Winter weekend breaks except Christmas and New Year. Reduced rates for children sharing parents' room; special meals on request.
Service/tipping: "We feel it is much nicer to leave tips to guests' discretion. All tips are distributed evenly among all full-time staff after deduction of tax."

YORK North Yorkshire — Map 4

Hobbits
9 St Peter's Grove
Clifton, York YO3 6AQ

Tel York (0904) 624538 and 642926

"We totally endorse the comments in the 1989 Guide. The accommodation, furnishings and friendly service would put to shame many larger and classier establishments." write *Mr and Mrs G Benjamin*, endorsing last year's new recommendation for Rosemary Miller's reasonably priced B&B in a quiet suburb, a good ten minutes' walk or an easy bus ride from the centre of York. *Hobbits* has only a few rooms; Mrs Miller has an eye for detail and the decorations and furnishing are stylish and attractive. She runs it as a family home; it includes two children, a cat, a dog and canaries. Guests normally share a table at breakfast, but there is a separate small table for those wanting more privacy. "Breakfasts are excellent, everything in pots, not a trace of plastic anywhere." "Attic-dormer rooms at the top of an attractive red-brick Victorian house, edged with flower beds. Our room was large and spotlessly clean, with a fridge stocked with drinks, chocolates and so on. We had a lovely view of York Minster." (*Richard Pinner, Carolyn Zinke*)

Open All year except 3 days over Christmas.
Rooms 1 double or family, 3 double, 1 single – 1 with bath and shower, 4 with shower, all with radio, TV, tea-making facilities and fridge; baby-sitting arranged.
Facilities Lounge, TV lounge, breakfast room. Small garden with patio. River Ouse 5 minutes with fishing and boating.
Location Just off A19 from the North. Private parking.
Restrictions Not suitable for ♿. No dogs in public rooms.
Credit card Visa.
Terms B&B £15–£22. Reduced rates for children. (No restaurant.)
Service/tipping: "No service charge. We don't expect tips but if guests kindly leave something it is given to the member of staff who has looked after them."

Middlethorpe Hall [GFG]
Bishopthorpe Road
York YO2 1QB

Tel York (0904) 641241
Fax (0904) 620176
Telex 57802 MIDDLE

This noble house with imposing facades in large grounds near York racecourse was rescued from decay by Historic House Hotels Ltd, who also restored *Bodysgallen Hall,* Llandudno (q.v.) and are now doing a rescue job on *Hartwell House* at Aylesbury in Buckinghamshire, due to open in 1990. Built in the reign of William III and subsequently the home of the diarist Lady Mary Wortley Montagu, *Middlethorpe Hall* is a pedigree mansion with gardens and parkland appropriate to its grandeur. "Professionally and thoughtfully run, interior decoration in excellent taste; public and private rooms comfortable and quiet. Very good continental breakfast." This year readers all praise the friendly and helpful staff; a visitor on a weekend break is enthusiastic about the "large, comfortable and well decorated suite" to which he was promoted at no extra cost because the hotel was fairly empty. (*JC Thackray, and others*) The consensus on the food, however, is that it lets the place down. And one reader, allocated a small double room in the courtyard, reported that it was too small for two, and in need of sprucing up.

Open All year.
Rooms 5 suites, 21 double, 5 single – all with bath and shower, telephone, radio and TV; 2 suites in cottages; 19 courtyard rooms.
Facilities Lift. Drawing rooms, library, bar, 2 restaurants; private dining facilities. 27-acre grounds with croquet, walled garden and lake. Racecourse, golf nearby.
Location 1½ m S of city, by racecourse.
Restrictions Not suitable for ♿. No children under 8. No dogs.
Credit cards All major cards accepted.
Terms [1989 rates] Rooms: single £75–£85, double £98–£110, suite £150–£175. Breakfast: (continental) £5.50, (English) £8.50. Set lunch £12.90–£14.90, dinner £20.50–£23.90; full alc £31.10. Champagne breaks Nov–Mar; 4-day Christmas package.

Mount Royale Hotel
The Mount, York YO2 2DA

Tel York (0904) 628856
Fax (0904) 611171

"Thoroughly endorse the good things said about this excellent small hotel." "A lovely, comfortable house, complete with dogs and cats – a real home. I was most impressed to see the same staff as two years ago. Owners who care about their staff and guests command loyalty like this." Praise from two readers for Richard and Christine Oxtoby's characterful hotel, Gothic in appearance, William IV in the main though with modern extensions. It is near the racecourse, a few minutes' walk from Micklegate Bar and three-quarters of a mile from the Minster. Front rooms get traffic noise though this is mitigated by double-glazing, back ones overlooking the attractive garden with a swimming pool are quiet. The new ones in the garden annexe, connected to the main building by a covered walkway, are "thoroughly recommended; ours was spacious, with dressing room and bathroom, and an attractive view of the garden. Breakfast and dinner of a high standard, and substantial. Staff friendly and helpful." (*KW Barker, Dr JR Backhurst, Mrs Victor Isenberg*) Other readers, however, long for more modest servings of food; some are critical of the cooking, especially of vegetables, and dislike the muzak at breakfast. The bedrooms, with their trouser-presses, hair-driers and so forth offer solid comfort, but some of the older ones are said to be in need of refurbishment. The carpark can be congested at times. More reports please.

Open All year except 23–30 Dec.
Rooms 6 suites, 15 double, 2 single – all with bath and shower, telephone, radio, TV, tea-making facilities and baby-listening. 4 rooms in garden annexe connected by covered walkway to main building. Some ground-floor rooms.
Facilities 2 lounges, TV room, bar, dining room with conservatory. $1\frac{1}{2}$-acre grounds with swimming pool heated May–Oct.
Location On A64 from Tadcaster (front rooms have secondary glazing). Hotel is on right just before traffic lights at junction with Albemarle Road opposite sign to Harrogate (A59). Parking for 24 cars.
Restrictions Not suitable for ♿. Small dogs only, by arrangement.
Credit cards All major cards accepted.
Terms (Service at guests' discretion) B&B (English): single £62.50–£67.50, double £67.50–£85, suite £85–£95. Light lunches available; set dinner £18.50. 2-day breaks (excluding bank holidays). 1-night bookings refused over some bank holiday periods. Reduced rates for children sharing parents' room; special meals by arrangement.
Service/tipping: "Very few staff anywhere seem to be embarrassed by being tipped. What our staff collect themselves is their affair, anything added by credit cards etc is divided and added to their wages weekly."

Traveller's tale *At this restaurant-with-rooms, our lavish suite had a separate entrance, as in a motel, but we were not told that we should hang onto our key, so we left it at the reception desk. When we came back at 10.30 pm the restaurant was closed and locked and no-one answered the bell. We tried forcing the door, to no avail. We were about to go to the police when a local resident told us where to find the night-watchman of the adjacent marina, who had a key to the restaurant. But he, when summoned out of bed, refused to believe that we were not interlopers. He referred us to his son, who lived down the road. Finally the son did persuade his stubborn father to go into the restaurant and use the direct private line to the owners (they lived elsewhere) to seek their authorisation to give us our key. With a very ill grace he did so, muttering to us about "the frightful organisation" of the restaurant, which was always landing him in muddles of this sort. Eventually we got to bed, deprived of 90 minutes of sleep before our very early morning start.*

Wales

HOTEL PORTMEIRION,
PORTMEIRION

ABERSOCH Gwynedd **Map 4**

Porth Tocyn Hotel [GFG] *Tel* Abersoch (075 881) 3303
Abersoch LL53 7BU

"The welcome from Nick Fletcher-Brewer was warm and genuine. The rooms, with a good sprinkling of antique furniture, are well equipped. The view from Room 19 must rank as one of the best hotel room views in Wales. Our meal was of a very high standard; the hotel clearly deserves its entry in *The Good Food Guide*. Very good breakfasts too. There is a lovely sandy beach a short walk away. Mrs Fletcher-Brewer (mother of Nick) keeps the staff to high standards. Long may *Porth Tocyn* continue!" (*Steven Parsons*) Last year's encomium has been warmly endorsed by more recent satisfied guests at this consistently popular hotel in a choice position on a headland overlooking Cardigan Bay and Snowdonia. "Wonderful food and atmosphere." "Wine list particularly commendable for variety, length, quality and lack of fierce mark-up. It's not a luxurious hotel: so much the better. It has that easy hospitality which hides great care and toil." Other plus points: the two-course dinner (including coffee and petits fours) offered as an alternative to those unable to cope with five courses, the impressive Welsh cheeseboard, the "old-fashioned 'nursery' puds", the lack of music in the dining room, the imaginative self-service buffet lunch on Sunday and "fresh flowers, everywhere; the atmosphere of a family home but professional standard of service". (*Kathy Alston, AJ Bowen; also Peter and Christine Watkinson, Amy and Stephen Pratt, and others*)

Open Week before Easter–mid-Nov. Possibly Christmas and New Year.
Rooms 14 double, 3 single – all with bath, shower, telephone and TV; radio and tea-making facilities on request; some baby-listening facilities. 3 ground-floor rooms.
Facilities 6 lounges, bar, TV room. Garden with tennis court and swimming pool (heated May–end Sept). Set in hotel's 25-acre farm; sea a few mins' walk, Heritage coastal walk, water sports, fishing, golf, riding nearby.
Location 2½ m S of Abersoch, through hamlets of Sarn Bach and Bwlchtocyn; follow three signs marked "Gwesty/hotel".
Restrictions No children under 7 in dining room at night (high teas available until 6.30 pm). Dogs in bedrooms only – bring dog basket.
Credit card Access.
Terms (No service charge) B&B £26–£41.80. Buffet lunch Sun £10.25; set dinner £13.50 (2 courses), £19 (5 courses). Bargain breaks out of season. 1-night bookings sometimes refused. Reduced rates and special meals for children.
Service/tipping: "Tipping is fast dying out here. We do not promote tipping, but if someone wants to leave something by way of appreciation that is fine."

BRECHFA Dyfed — Map 1

Tŷ Mawr Country House Hotel [GFG] — *Tel* Brechfa (026 789) 332
Brechfa, Nr Carmarthen
SA32 7RA

16th-century house in small village on edge of Brechfa forest. French windows lead to garden and stream. Oak beams, quarry stone floors, pretty dining room with natural stone walls, white lace tablecloths and curtains. Recommended for delightful countryside, friendly owners the Flaherty family, warm and comfortable bedrooms, good food with innovative dishes, extensive, good-value wine list, lack of background music. Bread baked on premises, sold in adjacent shop. Open all year. 5 double rooms, all with bath and shower. B&B double £45–£55. Dinner approx £14. New nomination. More reports please.

CRICKHOWELL Powys — Map 1

Gliffaes Country House Hotel — *Tel* Bwlch (0874) 730371
Crickhowell NP8 1RH — *Fax* (0874) 730463

Bouquets and brickbats fly, as always, around the *campaniles* of this imposing Italianate mansion, with its magnificent gardens in the valley of the Usk, midway between the Brecon Beacons and the Black Mountains. It's an unashamedly traditional country hotel, run for more than 40 years by the Brabner family. Lots of fishing tackle everywhere – the hotel has two stretches on the Usk and there are eight fishable reservoirs in the vicinity. Here are two comments from the rose-tinted "our-*Gliffaes*-right-or-wrong" faction: "We are, avowedly, among those who find *Gliffaes* addictive (and the knowledge that it is still there a reassuring fact of life in an uncertain world). The polished Victorian furniture must be contemporary with the house, and the upgrading of the rooms during the last few years should satisfy all but the sternest critics. Mealtimes are wonderfully elastic, not to mention the time-honoured teas." "Despite our having the smallest and most uncomfortable bedroom, because of booking late, we enjoyed the place immensely for its setting, its comfortable public rooms, the friendliness, and the high standard of its very reasonably priced dinner." (*Mr and Mrs J Wyatt; L and H Fowler, and others*) Criticisms are often delivered in good spirit: "Still a stimulating air of uncertainty on minor points of logistics, but the end result is as good as ever – and that is very good." "Bedrooms could be inspected for cleanliness, beds were untidy, and towels ghastly colours. But this delightful hotel feels like home. The Brabners are charming and unobtrusive." "The restaurant is distinctly boring and the service abysmal (yet friendly). Forget about wines – a 1984 Beaujolais on the wine list. But there's a nice feel to the place." Only one reader this year has had a really bad time, "Grounds and garden idyllic, as the Guide describes, but surly staff, shabby uncared-for interior – urgent redecoration and maintenance required – what a shame!" *Gliffaes* has loyal fans who will tell you that the lack of urgent redecoration is exactly what attracts them.

Open mid-Mar–end Dec.
Rooms 22 double (4 normally let as singles) – 17 with bath, 5 with shower, all with telephone, radio, tea-making facilities, and baby-listening. 3 (with TV) in lodge annexe.
Facilities 2 sitting rooms, bar, TV room, billiards room, sun room, dining room. 29-acre grounds with 6-acre gardens, croquet lawn, putting green. Brown trout and salmon fishing in river Usk.
Location 2½ m W of Crickhowell. Turn left off the A40 at "Gliffaes" sign and drive 1 m to Gliffaes gates.
Restrictions Not suitable for ♿. No dogs in hotel (kennels available).
Credit cards All major cards accepted.
Terms B&B £28; dinner, B&B £41; full board £46. Set lunch £8.25, dinner £13; full alc £21. Reduced rates and special meals for children by arrangement.
Service/tipping: "We say service is included – service is an integral part of the equation in calculating charges. We are in the 'service' business and as such do not make an 'extra' charge. We have abandoned the monthly distribution of a 10% service charge and have adjusted our wage rates accordingly. If guests insist on leaving a gratuity, it is accepted gracefully."

GLAN CONWY see LLANSANFFRAID GLAN CONWY Map 4

The Old Rectory

LLANBERIS Gwynedd Map 4

Pen-y-Gwryd Hotel *Tel* Llanberis (0286) 870211
Nantgwynant LL55 4NT

Well known to mountain climbers, *Pen-y-Gwryd*, now run by Chris Briggs with his daughter Jane and her husband Brian, has been an inn since the early 1800s. It stands in the middle of the Snowdonia National Park, and in 1953 was used as a training base for the successful Everest team. *James Seely* captures its style in the following report, "What the P-y-G. has to offer is solid comfort, a well-stocked bar and cellar, plentiful and appetising nursery cooking and, above all else, old-fashioned hospitality and good fellowship. Charles Kingsley – of *Water Babies* fame – called this mountain inn 'the divinest pigsty under the canopy'. The act has been cleaned up since then, but it is good to think of our Victorian forbears enjoying the same relaxed conviviality that exists here today. It's a perfect centre for walking and climbing, and for exploring some of the most lovely countryside in the British Isles." Other readers have echoed this praise: "Provides meals designed to suit the kind of hunger generated while mountaineering in North Wales." "If the visitor appreciates hot baths in Victorian tubs the size of swimming pools, the dinner gong at 7.30 followed by an excellent five-course meal, and lively, often intellectual, conversation, this is the place." "The beds are big and solid and very comfortable. The furniture in the games room has been left as it was, and it shows! This adds to its character and charm – where else could you find a proper (i.e. non-electronic) games room these days?" (*Roger Beeson, R Hogg, J Adams, and others*)

Open Mar–Nov, New Year, weekends only Jan and Feb.
Rooms 17 double, 3 single – 1 ground-floor room with bath across courtyard.
Facilities Lounge, 3 public rooms, residents' bar, games room, dining room. 1-acre grounds; lake swimming, river fishing nearby.
Location From Nantgwynant signposted to Pen-y-Gwryd.
Credit cards None accepted.
Terms [1989 rates] (No service charge) B&B £15 (£1 extra with bath). Bar and packed lunches from £2; set dinner £9.50. Reduced rates and special meals for children.
Service/tipping: "There is a staff gratuity box available for guests who wish to contribute. They usually do!"

LLANDRILLO Clwyd — Map 4

Tyddyn Llan Country House Hotel and Restaurant [GFG] — *Tel* Llandrillo (049 084) 264
Llandrillo, Nr Corwen LL21 0ST
César award in 1989: Welsh hotel of the year

Bouquets continue for Peter and Bridget Kindred's lovingly restored 18th-century grey stone country house hotel in tranquil countryside in the Vale of Edeyrnion. Refurbishment and redecoration continue (four bedrooms this year) and musical and entertainment evenings are becoming a feature of the hotel. "Set in a quiet valley, *Tyddyn Llan* is furnished with great attention to detail; each bedroom has a style of its own. In drizzly March, the hotel was warm, with a huge log fire in the lounge. Peter Kindred looked after us all very well and his wife produced excellent meals – imaginative with plenty of choice." (*Dorothy Brining*) "We stayed in room 9 at the top of the house – it was wonderfully cosy, and our greatest disturbance – which was no disturbance at all – was from the house martins nesting in the eaves above our bedroom window. The comfortable room and good food made *Tyddan Llan* a terrific place to return to after long and strenuous walks in the Berwyn Mountains." (*Michael and Judith Silverberg, Laura Berish, H ap R, and others*) Only complaints: delays at dinner when the house was full and disappointment with some vegetarian dishes.

Open All year except Feb. Restaurant closed to non-residents Mon and Tue Nov–Mar.
Rooms 9 double – all with bath and/or shower, telephone, radio, TV, baby-listening.
Facilities Lounge with TV, bar, dining room; drying room. Jazz and madrigal evenings, theatrical events. 3-acre grounds with croquet. Private fishing in river Dee behind hotel, ghillie available; guided walks.
Location Through Corwen on A5 take B4401 to Llandrillo.
Restrictions Not suitable for ♿. Small dogs by arrangement, not in public rooms.
Credit cards Access, Visa.
Terms (No service charge) B&B: single £33.75–£37, double £53.50–£60; dinner, B&B: single £46–£51.50, double £83–£89. Set dinner £15.50. Special interest weekends; mini-breaks (2 or more nights); Christmas and New Year house parties. Reduced rates and special meals for children.
Service/tipping: "If guests wish to offer tips to the staff, it is divided amongst them."

LLANDUDNO Gwynedd — Map 4

Bodysgallen Hall [GFG]
Llandudno LL30 1RS

Tel Deganwy (0492) 584466
Fax (0492) 82519
Telex 617163 HHH

Bodysgallen Hall is a Grade I listed house standing in its own parkland on a hillside about a mile away from the Victorian seaside resort of Llandudno. The house is mainly 17th-century with skilful later additions, including nine cottages grouped around a secluded courtyard bright with flowers. Among its delights are a 17th-century knot garden and an 18th-century walled rose garden. Two of its finest rooms are the large entrance hall and first-floor drawing room, both with oak panelling, splendid fireplaces and stone-mullioned windows. The bedrooms are spacious and elegantly furnished with many extras, such as bottled Welsh spring water and home-made biscuits; bathrooms are Edwardian-style with handsome fittings. The hotel is run by a private company, Historic House Hotels, dedicated to restoring and bringing to life buildings of architectural merit. Writers this year have praised the "idyllic grounds and courteous, willing and efficient staff" and "the superb, peaceful location". The food, under the direction of chef Martin James – modern in style with impeccable ingredients – continues to please (though one visitor was disappointed not to be able to have his Dover sole "on the bone"). One addicted couple confessed they had spent 150 breaks at the hotel in the past seven years. "16 so far in 1988." (*RD and MM Whittaker, Garth Drinkwater; also RO Marshall, Philip Carter, David Wooff, and others*)

Open All year.
Rooms 9 cottage suites, 18 double, 1 single – all with bath and/or shower, telephone, radio and TV; tea-making facilities in cottages. 1 cottage with ramps for ♿.
Facilities Hall, drawing room, cocktail bar, library, dining room; conference centre. 200-acre parkland with gardens, tennis and croquet. Sandy beaches 2 m. Riding, shooting, fishing nearby.
Location SE of Llandudno on A470; 1 m on right.
Restrictions No children under 8. Dogs in cottages and grounds only.
Credit cards All major cards accepted.
Terms Rooms: single £75–£105, double £95–£136, suite £130–£150. Breakfast: continental £4.40, English £6.60. Set lunch £13.75, dinner £23.50. Off season Champagne, Winter and Spring breaks.
Service/tipping: "Our prices include a mandatory service charge. It is given to all staff at the end of each month according to length of service, tax being deducted at source."

The St Tudno Hotel [GFG] *Tel* Llandudno (0492) 74411
North Parade, Llandudno *Telex* 61400
LL30 2LP

An enterprising, stylishly decorated hotel on the seafront of this delightful Victorian seaside resort, run in a personal style by Martin and Janette Bland. Most readers continue to praise the young friendly staff, the comfortable bedrooms, and the pretty decor in the dining room: "Its green-and-white trellis wallpaper and greenery make you feel you are eating in a garden." The restaurant, too, is commended in many reports – both the five-course set menu (plenty of choice) and the extensive à la carte. But breakfasts have continued to disappoint. And the size of some of the rooms is also the subject of complaints: "We had the 'four-poster' and had to take it in turns to move round the room!" "Room 12 would have been small before they created a bathroom out of part of it, and then amazingly managed to shoe-horn in a single and a 'double' bed." Mrs Bland tells us that she has revised her breakfast menu, putting more emphasis on healthy eating, and that she warns guests if they are reserving one of the less favoured rooms. More reports please.

Open Mid-Jan–23 Dec.
Rooms 1 suite, 19 double, 1 single – all with bath and/or shower, telephone, radio, TV, tea-making facilities and fridge, baby-listening. 1 ground-floor double room with shower.
Facilities Lift. No-smoking residents' lounge, coffee lounge, lounge bar, restaurant; indoor heated swimming pool; small front patio. Safe sandy beaches, pier, boat rides, fishing, sailing, wind surfing; 3 golf courses close by.
Location Central, opposite pier. Limited free promenade parking and small carpark at rear of hotel (£3 per night).
Restrictions Not suitable for ♿. No children under 5 at dinner. No dogs.
Credit cards Access, Amex, Visa.
Terms (No service charge) B&B: single £37.50–57.50, double £56–£90. Set Sun lunch £10.25, dinner £17.25; full alc £22–£25. Bar lunches. 2-night breaks all year; winter weekend breaks. 1-night bookings sometimes refused for bank holidays and Sat in winter. Reductions according to age for children sharing parents' room; high tea.
Service/tipping: "If customers enjoy kind, considerate and personalised service and feel inclined to tip they should be allowed to do so. As hoteliers, we would never dream of adding a service charge automatically."

LLANRWST Gwynedd — Map 4

Meadowsweet Hotel [GFG] *Tel* Llanrwst (0492) 640732
Station Road, Llanrwst LL26 0DS

Victorian establishment on outskirts of tiny market town with river Conwy 200 yards away, and Snowdonia a few miles up the road. Continued praise for the enterprising menu and magnificent wine list: "no fewer than 70 half-bottles". Breakfast highly praised, too. But continued criticism of reception and of service in the restaurant, also of decor in some bedrooms. Hence these italics. 10 rooms, all with shower. Double room £34–£44. Breakfast: continental £4, English £6.50. Set dinner £17.75 [1989]. More reports please.

> We get less feedback from smaller and more remote hotels. But we need feedback on all hotels: big and small, far and near, famous and first-timers.

LLANSANFFRAID GLAN CONWY Gwynedd — Map 4

The Old Rectory
Llanrwst Road
Llansanffraid Glan Conwy
LL28 5LF

Tel Glan Conwy (0492) 580611
Telex 987067 WOLSEY

Georgian in origin, *The Old Rectory* stands up a steep drive in secluded grounds, with views over the river Conwy estuary to Conwy Castle and Snowdonia. The owners, Wendy and Michael Vaughan, have worked hard on restoring and extending it. "The warmth and friendliness of the Vaughans' welcome made us feel immediately at home, and our delightful room was as well furnished and equipped as a country house bedroom should be. Lashings of hot water, gloriously comfortable (and dramatic-looking) bed, two armchairs set to look out over the small garden to the estuary and mountains in the distance: what more could one want? Dinner is, in effect, a dinner party, with guests introduced to each other over cocktails in the sitting room – no hotel lounge, this, with masses of delightful pictures and other objects and beautiful flowers – before sitting down together at a large table. Michael Vaughan serves unobtrusively and Wendy's food is outstanding: there is a fixed starter, a choice of main course (organised earlier in the day), and a choice of puddings or Welsh cheeses. Unexpected as the house-party atmosphere was, I can only say that we found *our* companions very good company and no one went to bed before midnight!" The village is a convenient stop on the way to the Holyhead crossing to Ireland. The *Old Rectory* is a non-smoking establishment. (*Michael Thomas; and others*) One visitor this year, while warmly endorsing all the tributes to the Vaughans' hospitality, would have liked to have been warned in advance about the communal dinners – he was less fortunate than Michael Thomas in his fellow guests. An American reader reported a disagreeable dispute over a deposit when he cancelled two months before his planned visit.

Open 1 Feb–18 Dec. Dining room closed for lunch and occasionally for dinner (guests warned when booking).
Rooms 4 double – all with bath and/or shower, radio and TV.
Facilities Drawing room, dining room, morning room. 2-acre grounds. Sea with safe bathing 3 m; fishing, golf, riding, sailing nearby.
Restrictions Not suitable for ♿. No smoking. No children under 12. No dogs.
Credit card Access.
Terms Dinner, B&B: single occupancy £62.50, double £95. Set dinner £17.50. 50% reduction for children sharing parents' room.
Service/tipping: "If tips are given for staff we accept for them."

NEWPORT Dyfed — Map 1

Cnapan Restaurant and Country House [GFG]
East Street, Newport SA42 0WF

Tel Newport (0239) 820575

A friendly place in an attractive small town (a good bookshop, a couple of art galleries, and nice little houses on hilly streets), *Cnapan* is a pink-washed listed house in the centre, owned and run by John and Eluned Lloyd and their daughter and son-in-law, Judith and Michael Cooper. "It is where we'll stay when we go back to Newport", wrote a recent visitor.

"The owners are welcoming and accomplished, and the food was excellent." In previous editions we have described *Cnapan* as "more than a guest house, and less than a hotel" – the atmosphere is that of a happy and busy establishment where lots of things are going on. There are bookcases full of maps, local information, magazines and games, and the five bedrooms are comfortably cluttered with whatever a guest might want. Much entices nearby as well: you can be exploring the rock pools on Parrog beach after a ten-minute walk, or picking up the spectacular coastal path towards Cwm-yr-Eglwys in fifteen. Mother and daughter cook the meals: there is lots of choice; vegetarian dishes are a speciality. Breakfasts are serve-yourself-as-much-as-you-like, with home-made bread. (*Brigid Avison, HR*) *Note:* There is another Newport, in Gwent; do not go there for *Cnapan*.

Open All year except 25/26 Dec and Feb. Restaurant closed Tue Mar–Oct and to non-residents at weekends Nov–Jan.
Rooms 5 double – all with shower, TV, tea-making facilities and baby-listening.
Facilities Lounge, bar, restaurant. Small garden. 10 mins' walk to estuary and sea; fishing.
Location In centre of small town (but quiet at night). Parking.
Restrictions Not suitable for ♿. No smoking in dining room. Children not encouraged. No dogs.
Credit cards Access, Visa.
Terms (No service charge) B&B £18; dinner, B&B £28. Full alc £15.
1-night bookings refused for bank holiday weekends.
Service/tipping: "No stated policy; if customers wish to show extra appreciation we accept tips which are distributed amongst staff."

PENMAENPOOL Gwynedd — Map 4

George III Hotel [GFG] *Tel* Dolgellau (0341) 422525
Penmaenpool, Dolgellau LL40 1YD

Colourful old inn in one-and-a-half-acre grounds on banks of Mawddach estuary, complete with inglenook fireplace and lots of exposed beams, polished brass and fishing nets. Popular for lunch, particularly at weekends in summer. Best bedrooms (all with bathroom en suite*) are in the Lodge, formerly a railway station, 50 yards from the main building. Fine views, excellent location for walks and bird watching. Closed 2 weeks Christmas/New Year, and May Day bank holiday dinner. 12 rooms, 11 with private facilities. B&B £60–£70. Full alc £15. In italics for lack of feedback. More reports please. (See under Dolgellau in* The Good Food Guide.)

PORTMEIRION Gwynedd — Map 4

Hotel Portmeirion [GFG]
Portmeirion LL48 4ER

Tel Penrhyndeudraeth (0766) 770228
Fax (0766) 771331
Telex 61520 PORTM

César award: Brilliant restoration of a great hotel to former glory

The *Hotel Portmeirion* was welcomed back to the Guide last year after its seven-year closure following a fire. It stands on the edge of an estuary in

Cardigan Bay, surrounded by a spectacular Italianate village complete with piazza, campanile, pavilions and colonnade. In summer as many as 3,000 visitors a day may come to gawp, but the hotel itself is protected against this invasion. Surrounding the village are acres of woodland and miles of sandy beaches. Here is last year's inspector's report written shortly after the hotel re-opened:

"This is the resurrected central hotel of Portmeirion, the folly-village built by the late Sir Clough Williams-Ellis, on its private wooded peninsula above Tremadog Bay. Cottages in the village can be rented separately; but the hotel itself is a new persona of truly phoenix-like burnish. The exterior remains that of a comfortable and unpretentious early Victorian Welsh *plas;* the interior has been refurbished in an exuberant mixture of oriental dazzle and overblown *World of Interiors.* There is a Chinese Room, an Indian Room fit for maharajahs and a Frenchified Peacock Room of wonderful vulgarity; also a Jaipur Bar that glitters with silver and ought to be incensed. No expense has been spared – even the fire doors are elegant – and there is any amount of ruching and draping and gilding and silking. Set against the heightened exotica of Portmeirion village, and contrasted with its incomparable setting above a wide sandy estuary, where herons stalk and cormorants dive immediately outside the hotel windows – the building triumphantly brings off its decor. While some clients may find its taste suspect, others will enjoy it for its very extravagance." Robin Llywelyn, grandson of Sir Clough, is in charge; Hefin Williams, who was head chef before the fire, is once again wearing the *toque* – *nouvelle cuisine* is no longer served, having proved unpopular. Many of the teething troubles noted last year appear to have been rectified, and our postbag has mostly been full of compliments: "One of the finest hotels in the area; could hold its own in any part of the country. I visit hotels world-wide and the *Portmeirion* is to my mind a little jewel." "The restaurant has become perceptibly more professional, and the decor, settling down like the equipment of a ship after its shake-down cruise, has been graced by time with a slight patina of moderation." "Food much, much better (and cheaper) than it was when the hotel appeared in the Guide in the old days." "We were only able to spend 24 hours there but we found it to be one of the most delightfully situated and uniquely furnished hotels of our experience." Also praised has been the reasonable cost of such luxury. (*TG, The Marquess of Anglesey; also DR AJ Allen, CA Cuttress, and others*)

Open All year.
Rooms 1 suite, 13 double in hotel; 9 suites, 15 double in village – all with bath, shower, telephone, radio, TV, tea-making facilities; baby-sitting by arrangement.
Facilities Lounge, 2 bars (harpist or pianist in 1 most nights), dining room; functions room. 5-acre garden with swimming pool (heated end May–mid-Sep), tennis; free golf at Porthmadog Golf Club.
Location SW of Penrhyndeudraeth, SE of Porthmadog, off A487 at Minffordd.
Restrictions Not suitable for ♿ (but 4 village rooms have no steps and are accessible by car). No smoking in dining room. No children under 7 in main hotel bedrooms or in dining room in evening. No dogs.
Credit cards All major cards accepted.
Terms [1989 rates] (No service charge) In house: double £65–£85, suite £100; in village: double £45, suite £50. Breakfast: continental £2.50, Welsh £5. Set lunch £10, dinner £16.50. Off-season breaks. Min 2-night bookings at weekend in high season.

Service/tipping: "We do not encourage tipping. If a credit card is used we fill in the bottom line before asking for a signature. If guests insist on leaving tips they are banked and shared equally among staff at Christmas."

PWLLHELI Gwynedd — Map 4

Plas Bodegroes [GFG] *Tel* Pwllheli (0758) 612363
Pwllheli LL53 5TH

This grade II listed Georgian manor house in a peaceful setting in the Lleyn Peninsula, was recently converted by Welsh-born Chris Chown and his Faroese wife Gunna á Trødni into a restaurant with rooms. "It's amazing", wrote our inspector, "to find cooking of this calibre in such an out-of-the-way spot. The house is stylish without being grand, soothing in layout and well proportioned; with pleasing views of lawns and beeches, and utter silence except for rookery noises and other more melodious birdsong. And the cooking is exceptionally fine. The menu is written in English but is *nouvelle* cooking with inspired sauces and the flavour of real food. Courses are individually priced and you may eat fewer than the five on the set menu if you prefer. Service, by young girls, is intelligent, efficient and self-effacing. Though Chris Chown calls this a restaurant-with-rooms, bedrooms are well equipped and clean (front ones are the larger, they have four-posters and the best views). There is also a comfortable sitting room. We took breakfast in a small, east-facing room in the sunshine – freshly-squeezed orange juice, real porridge, perfectly-poached eggs. Worth a long detour from anywhere." Pwllheli is a quiet seaside resort; there is golf nearby, and lots of interesting sight-seeing. More reports would be welcome.

Open Mar–31 Dec.
Rooms 5 double – all with bath, shower, jacuzzi, telephone, radio, TV and baby-listening; 2 with mini-bar. 3 more rooms planned for 1990.
Facilities Bar, lounge, restaurant, breakfast room; indoor swimming pool planned for 1990. 6½-acre grounds. Safe, sandy beach 1 m. Golf nearby.
Location On left on Nefyn road (A497) W of Pwllheli.
Restrictions Only restaurant suitable for ♿. Dogs by arrangement; not in public rooms.
Credit cards Access, Visa.
Terms (No service charge) B&B £25–£45; dinner, B&B £40–£60. Set Sun lunch £8.50, dinner £17.50. One night bookings refused bank holidays.
Service/tipping: "Service charges are a 'con' and should be abolished. One may as well write 'prices include heating'. We try in all departments to exceed the guest's expectation for the price. If the guest wishes to acknowledge with a tip, we accept."

REYNOLDSTON West Glamorgan — Map 1

Fairyhill Country House Hotel and Restaurant [GFG] *Tel* Gower (0792) 390139
Reynoldston, Gower
Swansea SA3 1BS

A creeper-covered Welsh manor, inland from the Gower peninsula, standing in 24 acres of park and woodland, with half a mile of trout stream meandering through its grounds. Reception not effusive, but helpful and pleasant. Food "of the very best home dinner party kind" mostly appreciated though some have found it over-ambitious. Reservations also expressed about the furnishings.

Closed 25/26 Dec. 11 rooms, all with private facilities. B&B double £65–£75. full alc £23. More reports welcome.

TALSARNAU Gwynedd — Map 4

Hotel Maes-y-Neuadd [GFG]
Talsarnau LL47 6YA

Tel Harlech (0766) 780200
Fax (0766) 780211

Maes-y-Neuadd (pronounced Mice-er-Nayeth and meaning the mansion in the meadow), is tucked into a wooded hillside smothered in rhododendrons, looking out across Snowdonia National Park and reached by a narrow lane which climbs a one-in-five hill. Dating originally from the 14th century, it was enlarged in the 16th and 17th; there are oak beams, decorated plasterwork and an ingle-nook fireplace. Seven-and-a-half acres of lawns, orchards and paddocks surround it, the renowned Royal St David's golf course is only three miles away, and Portmeirion village and magnificent Harlech castle are nearby. The two couples who own it, the Horsfalls and Slatters, have completely restored this attractive grey granite and slate mansion, furnishing it with good antique and modern furniture; plain clear colour-washed walls show the pretty patterned chintzes to advantage. In the elegant dining room traditional Welsh dishes are offered alongside French and English ones (each day Welsh lamb is served in some form); Trevor Pharoah is now in complete charge of the kitchen and has been winning praise for his talents. Once again reports are almost unanimously favourable: "I have booked my whole family in for Christmas, due to withdrawal symptoms suffered immediately on leaving." "The most remarkable combination of professional management, friendly attention, comfortable public rooms, beautiful site, and quite excellent and interesting food. By far the best hotel overall that we can remember." "Sumptuous bedroom awash with draped chintz. Exceptional hosting by the Slatters and the Horsfalls – unintrusive but always friendly and perceptive." (*Braham Murray, MJN Barnett, P and J Lively, IC Dewey; Dr W Murdoch, AA Bent, Marcia Layton, and others*) Just a few complaints: a bathroom with a loo "reminiscent of British Rail", and a ground-floor bedroom visited (apparently often) through the window by a local cat.

Open Feb–3 Jan. Lunch by reservation only Mon–Sat.
Rooms 1 suite, 13 double, 1 single – all with bath and/or shower, telephone and TV. Suite in Coach House 10 yds from main building, 2 rooms in cottage 30 yds away. 1 ground-floor double room suitable for ♿.
Facilities Lounge, bar/lounge, restaurant; small conference room/private dining room. 8-acre grounds with sun terraces, landscaped lawns, orchard and paddock. Sea, golf, riding, sailing, fishing, climbing nearby.
Location Off B4573, 3 m NE of Harlech. Hotel sign at junction.
Restrictions No smoking in restaurant. No children under 7. Dogs at management's discretion, not in public rooms.
Credit cards All major cards accepted.
Terms B&B: single £32–£36, double £63–£100, suite £83–£110; dinner, B&B: single £50–£56, double £100–£140, suite £120–£150. Set lunch £12.50, dinner £20. 2-day breaks; winter breaks; 3-day Christmas house party. 1-night bookings refused at Christmas and Easter. Reduced rates for children sharing parents' room. *Service/tipping: "No service charge. Tips not solicited in any way. If a guest adds a gratuity it is divided among restaurant and kitchen staff."*

TALYLLYN Gwynedd **Map 4**

Minffordd Hotel [GFG] *Tel* Corris (065 473) 665
Talyllyn, Tywyn LL36 9AJ

An exemplary small family hotel in the medium-price range, at the head of one of the most peaceful and little known valleys in Wales, the Dysynni Valley. The footpath to the top of Cader Idris starts by the front gate, Talyllyn lake is half a mile away, and some of Wales's most beautiful scenery lies all round this former coaching inn (its name means "roadside"). Mr and Mrs Bernard Pickles have owned the hotel for 12 years, and their son Jonathan is the excellent chef. They have preserved the old-world atmosphere of the rambling building while comfortably modernising it. Everything is spick and span. It is not a hotel for the misanthrope: guests are introduced to each other and the smallness of the public rooms makes socialising inevitable, though tables in the dining room are well spaced. Visitors continue to sing its praise: "Mrs Pickles came out to greet us as we parked our car and, as the day was warm and sunny, immediately served us tea on the terrace by the fishpond with a view of the garden and Cader Idris beyond. This set the tone for the friendly, family atmosphere which continued throughout our stay. Everything is done well, with great care but without apparent effort." Another enthusiast asks, "Can I add anything to all the gentle praises that have appeared in the Guide? Only this: when you go, stay at least three days. Any shorter stay would be cheating yourself." Bernard Pickles encourages guests to choose demi-pension by making dinner, bed-and-breakfast not much more expensive than just bed-and-breakfast: "Bed and breakfast guests" he says, "are as ships that pass in the night, never to enjoy what we have to offer them." (*Dr BS Hoyle, Patrick Welsh*)

Open Mid-Mar–end Oct, weekends only Nov–mid-Dec, 3 days at Christmas. Restaurant closed lunchtime, and to non-residents Sun and Mon.
Rooms 1 triple, 5 double – all with bath and/or shower, telephone, radio and tea-making facilities; 1 (with H&C) for 2 children, let in conjunction with adjoining room. 2 ground-floor rooms.
Facilities Sun room, lounge bar, parlour, dining room; laundry facilities. 3 acres paddock and garden with river. Talyllyn lake ½ m – fishing by arrangement.
Location 8 m SW Dolgellau. At junction of A487 and B4405.
Restrictions Not suitable for severely ♿. No smoking in dining room. No children under 3. No dogs.
Credit cards Access, Diners, Visa.
Terms [1989 rates] B&B £28–£38; dinner, B&B £33–£48. Set dinner £14; packed lunches on request. Off-season breaks; reductions for long stays; Christmas package. 1-night bookings refused at peak times. Reduced rates and special meals for children.
Service/tipping: "Service is free and part of the caring family-run atmosphere. Tips are not part of our arrangements."

THREE COCKS Powys **Map 1**

Three Cocks Hotel [GFG] *Tel* Glasbury (049 74) 215
Three Cocks, Nr Brecon LD3 0SL

Inn dating from 15th century in Brecon Beacons National Park, half a mile from river Wye. Cobbled forecourt, ivy-clad walls, worn steps, great oak beams and log fires. All rooms refurbished to high standard. Excellent restaurant, French with Belgian overtones (closed Tues). Open mid-Feb–end Nov. 7 double rooms, all with private facilities. B&B double £46. Set dinner £17. Was in earlier editions under different owners. More reports please.

WHITEBROOK Gwent **Map 3**

The Crown at Whitebrook
Whitebrook, Nr Monmouth
NP5 4TX

Tel Monmouth (0600) 860254

Cosy 17th-century inn in steeply wooded valley a mile from the Wye. Bedrooms small, but "beds extremely comfortable and bathrooms gleaming". Recommended for lovely setting and good restaurant with ambitious menu – "just on the right side of not being too fancy". "Delicious cooked breakfast, 3-course dinner good value." 12 double rooms, all with bath and shower. Closed Christmas and two weeks Jan. B&B £28–£36; Dinner, B&B £39.50–£49.50. Set lunch £10.95, dinner £19.95. In previous editions; re-nominated with new owners. More reports please.

Traveller's tale *This small country hotel deserved all the accolades your entry accorded it. A sumptuously furnished room, an imaginative dinner with service which even the* Ritz *in Paris would have found hard to match. Refreshed after a night of great tranquillity, we breakfasted quietly and then sauntered out across the new-mown lawn towards the park beyond. Turning a corner, we espied a small boy instantly recognised as the proprietor's youngest son. The lad looked up at us glumly. "What have all you people come here for? I don't want you here. Why don't you all bugger off?"*

Scotland

ACHILTIBUIE Highland **Map 5**

Summer Isles Hotel [GFG]
Achiltibuie, by Ullapool
Ross and Cromarty IV26 2YG

Tel Achiltibuie (085 482) 282

One of Britain's most remote hotels, reached by a 15-mile single-track road, the *Summer Isles* is a splendid base for bird-watchers, walkers and fishermen (it holds fishing rights in the area), and has spectacular views over the sea and a great scattering of little islands. Guests are advised to bring wellingtons, sensible shoes, binoculars, paint boxes, comfortable old clothes – and midge cream. But this relaxed demeanour during the day changes in the evening. Most guests change for dinner, served promptly at 8, a serious and sophisticated five-course meal. Mark and Geraldine Irvine took over the running of the hotel four years ago from Mark's father Gerald, and have maintained high standards in the kitchen and made many improvements in the bedrooms – though one reader commented this year on the absence of pictures and flowers. Reports continue to sing the hotel's praises: "*Summer Isles* goes from strength to strength. The Irvines manage to combine professional efficiency with a personal interest in and warmth towards their guests. The food is good: soups are subtle and unusual; the main courses preserve the purity of flavour of the first-class meat and fish; the pudding trolley is a delight, there is a fine range of cheeses including local ones, and the wine list is interesting, with a good selection of inexpensive bottles as well as dearer ones." (*Mrs MH Box*) Rooms in the Loghouse suite are recommended for families: "spacious, comfortable and finished to a high standard. We appreciated the fresh milk in the fridge and the bowl of fruit, which was topped up during the week we stayed. The hotel food was stunningly good." (*Dr CJH Kelnar; and much more in the same vein from Joan and Derek Jennings, Pat and Brian Lloyd, Mr and Mrs C Freeman, Conrad Dehn, Alan Dean, and others*)

Open Easter–end Oct.
Rooms 2-roomed suite (sleeps 2–5; available for self-catering Oct–May), 11 double – all with bath and/or shower. Suite and 7 rooms in Loghouse annexe 3 yds from main building. Some ground-floor rooms.
Facilities Lounge with TV, sun lounge with bar, cocktail lounge, dining room, café for teas and light lunches. Sea nearby, sandy beach 4 m; fishing, walking, bird watching.
Location 10 m N of Ullapool; take twisting single-track road skirting Lochs Lurgain, Badagyle and Oscaig for 15 m. Hotel is a few hundred yards past post office.
Restrictions Not suitable for ♿. No children under 8. No dogs in public rooms.
Credit cards None accepted.
Terms B&B (Scottish): single occupancy £23–£44, double £54–£66, suite £80 (for 2), £120 (for 5). Set dinner £22. Spring breaks.
Service/tipping: "Service is included in all prices; we do not expect our customers to tip. If guests insist on showing special appreciation, the money is divided evenly among all staff."

ARDUAINE Strathclyde — Map 5

Loch Melfort Hotel
Arduaine, by Oban, Argyll
PA34 4XG

Tel Kilmelford (085 22) 233
Fax (085 22) 214

"The situation must afford one of the most superb views from any hotel, not just in Scotland, but in the entire world." So began one recent report on the *Loch Melfort*, a characteristic loch-side house converted into a small modern hotel with a motel-like extension. It lies on the coast road between Oban and Crinan, with views towards the islands of Jura and Scarba. Another reader describes her return from a blustery, wet walk, "The heating was on, there were plenty of hooks by the door for wet clothes, plenty of hot water, and all was bliss." She liked the modern wing – "light, spacious, all rooms with huge picture windows facing the sea, comfortable beds, two good easy chairs, modern simple furnishings, good lighting, and an unusual number of mirrors." Colin and Jane Tindal have run the hotel for more than twenty years, and it is popular with the yachting fraternity. Guests enjoy the Chart Room bar with its nautical flavour "very good bar meals, very reasonably priced" and the "quietly luxurious dining room – beautifully warm with huge log fires; enormous picture windows run its entire length, local girls wait at the tables, all beautifully set with great attention to detail – good silver, apricot linen napkins which match the candles – there are comfortable, modern chairs." Dinners (some choice on the menu) come in for warm praise as do the good-value picnic lunches. Five donkeys and a horse graze on extensive "wildish grass" which runs down to the seashore. (*Stephanie Sowerby, Mr and Mrs Paul May, Mrs M McRae*)

Open Easter–late Oct.
Rooms 23 double, 1 single - 23 with bath (1 also has shower), all with radio, TV, tea-making facilities, baby-listening. 20, with balcony/patio, in cedar wing. Ground floor rooms.
Facilities Portable ramps. Lounge, cocktail lounge, TV lounge, bar, dining room. 30-acre grounds; on sea with safe bathing. Arduaine Garden adjacent.
Location 19 m S of Oban off A816.
Restriction No dogs in public rooms.
Credit card Access.
Terms B&B £29–£40. Bar meals; picnic lunches. Set dinner £17, full alc £20. Off-season breaks. Reduced rates for children; special meals on request.
Service/tipping: "Tipping at guests' discretion. Distributed weekly among all staff."

ARDVASAR Skye, Highland — Map 5

Ardvasar Hotel — *Tel* Ardvasar (047 14) 223
Ardvasar, Sleat, Isle of Skye
Inverness-shire IV45 8RS

An unassuming hotel, a mile from the Armadale Ferry, built as an inn in the 18th century and still serving the needs of visitors from over the water as well as locals. Some bedrooms have views over the Sound of Sleat to the mainland. Bill and Gretta Fowler's aim is a friendly and informal atmosphere; there is nothing special about the decor, but visitors continue to appreciate the hotel's hospitality, especially the cooking, "Excellent food – beautiful fresh-caught lobsters." "Wonderfully fresh prawns, delicious braised pheasant." "Accommodation, although simple, was comfortable, and our spacious room had a wonderful view across the Sound of Sleat. The four-course menu changed daily and offered a good choice." (*Robin and Kathleen Murray, April Young, John and Moira Cole, Mrs Margaret Swain, and others*)

Open Mar–Nov.
Rooms 1 suite, 8 double, 2 single – 8 with bath and/or shower, all with tea-making facilities; TV on request.
Facilities Lounge, TV lounge, cocktail bar, public bar, dining room. Small garden. Safe but rocky bathing ½ m.
Location In tiny village. 2 ferries to island, Kyle of Lochalsh–Kyleakin and Mallaig–Armadale, operate all year round but latter will not take vehicles in winter. Also car ferry Glenelg–Kylerhea in summer.
Restrictions Not suitable for ♿. Dogs at management's discretion.
Credit card Visa.
Terms (No service charge) B&B: single, £18–£25, double £38–£55; dinner, B&B: single £32–£39, double £66–£83. Set dinner £15; picnic lunches and bar meals available. Children sharing parents' room charged for meals only.
Service/tipping: "Tipping not expected but if anyone is pleased enough to want to tip, we are pleased to thank them personally!"

> Most hotels have reduced rates out of season and for children, and some British hotels offer "mini-break" rates throughout the year. If you are staying more than one night, it is always worth asking about special terms.

ARISAIG Highland — Map 5

Arisaig Hotel [GFG]
Arisaig, Inverness-shire
PH39 4NH

Tel Arisaig (068 75) 210

Continued praise for this reliable, comfortably old-fashioned hotel, an early Jacobite inn, on the seashore at Arisaig village, on the Road to the Isles. Do not confuse the *Arisaig Hotel* with *Arisaig House*, below. It is a small family enterprise, with George and Janice Stewart, "a really splendid couple with lots of humour and bags of resilience", and their son Gordon sharing nearly all the work; the tariff is accordingly modest. Some bedrooms are quite small and not all have private facilities, but they are spotlessly clean and there is plenty of hot water. The decor is functional – "somewhat stark" said one report this year – but all readers speak of the genuine warmth of the Stewarts' welcome, the lavish breakfasts and packed lunches, and the good, honest cooking, particularly the "freshly caught fish in all forms – excellent". Readers who hoped last year for more variety in the fresh vegetables will be pleased to learn the Stewarts now have variations "running to 20 or 30 – a far greater range than most hotels". One reader this year concluded, "a real find! a gem of a place at a modest price"; another reported, "an enjoyable stay once again; we have already booked for next summer". (*Dr CJH Kelnar, Dr John Batty, Alan Dean, and others*) The Stewarts tell us that the seashore opposite the hotel, long an eyesore, is to be cleaned up during 1989.

Open All year.
Rooms 1 suite, 12 double, 2 single – 6 with bath, all with telephone, radio, tea-making facilities and baby-listening.
Facilities Residents' lounge, TV lounge, lounge bar, public bar, dining room; ceilidhs and music some weekends in public bar. ½-acre garden. Rocky beach by hotel; sandy beaches 5 mins' drive away, with safe bathing, yachting. Fishing permits arranged. Cruises to Hebrides from village.
Location Take A830 for Mallaig, which is off A82 just N of Fort William. Hotel is on edge of village.
Restrictions Not suitable for severely ♿. No dogs in public rooms.
Credit cards None accepted.
Terms (No service charge) B&B £19.50–£37; dinner, B&B £33–£51.25. Bar lunches, packed lunches; set dinner £18.50; full alc £22.50. 5% reduction for stays of a week or more. Reduced rates for children under 14; special meals.
Service/tipping: "Wish it would stop!! If guests wish to do so, then please give it to reception for distribution to all."

Arisaig House [GFG]
Beasdale, Arisaig
Inverness-shire PH39 4NR

Tel Arisaig (068 75) 622
Telex 777279 ARISAI

A complete contrast with the *Arisaig Hotel*, above, this distinctly grand 19th-century mansion stands in large grounds in a location of outstanding rugged beauty. The exterior is traditional country-house Victorian, the interior a perfect thirties period piece. There are lovely grounds in which to walk, and tranquil vistas to induce a mood of complete relaxation. "The only criticism I have is that it was almost too perfect," wrote a reader this year. "The food, service and facilities were uniformly excellent." *Arisaig House* is owned by Ruth and John Smither and their son-in-law, David Wilkinson, is chef. The dining room has panelled walls and sparkling crystal on polished wood tables; in recent years the standard of cooking has much improved, though we still get occasional murmurs of discontent, and criticisms of the restaurant service. From an earlier report, "The *House* is very well appointed in every respect; the standards of room servicing are second to none; housekeeping of a very high order. The large airy bedrooms with antiques, flowers and other extras are comfortable and have plenty of wardrobe space and well-equipped bathrooms. The public areas are spacious and elegant." (*MJ Hartnall, and others*)

Open Easter–end Oct.
Rooms 13 double, 1 single – all with bath, shower, telephone and TV.
Facilities Reception, 2 lounges, lounge bar, restaurant. 20-acre grounds with gardens, terraces, croquet lawn, woodland, clay-pigeon shooting. Helipad. Sea 10 mins' walk with rock and sandy beach; day cruises by prior arrangement; loch, sea and river fishing.
Location On A830 3 m S of Arisaig.
Restrictions Not suitable for ♿. No smoking in dining room. No children under 10. No dogs.
Credit cards Access, Amex, Visa.
Terms Dinner, B&B (Scottish): single from £72, double £165–£220. Bar lunches; set dinner £27.50. 10% reduction for 5-day or longer bookings made direct and settled by cash or cheque (except Aug/Sept).
Service/tipping: "We are a service industry and therefore do not charge for service. If a guest leaves a gratuity it is divided amongst all staff."

AUCHENCAIRN Dumfries and Galloway — Map 5

Balcary Bay Hotel
Auchencairn, Nr Castle Douglas
DG7 1QZ

Tel Auchencairn
(055 664) 217 and 331

A modernised 17th-century smugglers' inn, "which retains much of its old character and atmosphere". Unpretentious and reasonably priced, it is owned and run by Ron and Joan Lamb and their son Graeme, and is quietly situated on the shore road just outside the village of Auchencairn. It had an entry in early editions of the Guide but dropped out for want of feedback. It is brought back by two warm nominations: "Our third visit within a year. All accommodation is of a high order; central heating throughout, well-appointed, light and airy bedrooms, most with bathroom *en suite*, comfortable public rooms. Service throughout is highly attentive but unobtrusive – this clearly stems from the close involvement of the Lamb family. We were made to feel completely free to come and go; there was no pressure on us to be out of the building or grounds. The hotel stands in well-tended mature gardens and has extensive views; sporting interests – golf, fishing, riding – are well catered for in the area, and there are numerous good walks." "Charming flower arrangements and attractive colour schemes throughout. Dogs are welcome (under control). Very friendly atmosphere." There is a limited-choice menu using local produce, and an extensive wine list; bar meals are available as an alternative. (*Mr and Mrs JA Simms, Trevor and Mary Holley*) More reports please.

Open Early Mar–early Nov.
Rooms 11 double, 2 single – 12 with bath and/or shower, all with telephone, radio, TV, tea-making facilities.

Facilities 2 lounges, 2 bars, restaurant. 3½-acre grounds on bay with sand/rock beach; safe bathing, fishing.
Location Off A711 Dumfries/Kircudbright road, 2 m S of Auchencairn on shore road.
Restrictions Not suitable for ♿. No dogs in public rooms.
Credit cards Access, Visa.
Terms B&B £22–£35. Set dinner £13; full alc £18. Bar meals available. Early season rates; reductions for 3- and 7-night stays. Child sharing with parents half price; special meals.
Service/tipping: "Payment for service not expected or encouraged. Gratuities are shared among all staff."

BALLATER Grampian — Map 5

Craigendarroch Hotel and Country Club [GFG]
Braemar Road, Ballater
Aberdeenshire AB3 5XA

Tel Ballater (033 97) 55858
Fax (033 97) 55447
Telex 739952

A sophisticated hotel in the Scottish baronial style and an elaborate sports complex are part of an ambitious time-sharing enterprise in Royal Deeside. The residents of the hotel and the occupants of the lodges surrounding it have the run of the extensive facilities. 21 new bedrooms have been added this year, also a third restaurant, and a crèche. The hotel's *soigné* restaurant, *The Oaks Room*, under Bill Gibb, provides excellent food, *nouvelle cuisine* in style, in elegant surroundings, with crystal, bone china and silverware; the *Café Jardin* shares the chef and kitchens and provides simpler meals at much lower prices. A visitor this year has been full of praise, "The rooms are super and the food excellent, and the mainly young Scots staff do everything they can to please. Furthermore they welcomed us and our 16-month old toddler without reservation. There aren't many hotels where young children are so warmly received." (*Jane Stevens-Smith*) The new manager, Nick Holmes, formerly at *Gleneagles*, has had experience in running leisure facilities and hotels, a combination that should stand him in good stead here. We would welcome more reports.

Open All year.
Rooms 2 suites, 48 double (including 8 family) – all with bath and shower, telephone, radio, TV, tea-making facilities and baby-listening.
Facilities Lift, ramps, toilet for ♿. 2 lounges, 2 bars, 3 restaurants. Guests have use of Club facilities including swimming pool, squash, snooker, children's room with games and pool table, health and beauty salon, sauna and solarium. 29-acre grounds with tennis courts, curling, putting green and dry-ski slope. Bowls and golf at Ballater Golf Club; fishing, climbing and winter sports nearby.
Location On A93 ½ m W of Ballater.
Restrictions No smoking in *Oaks* restaurant. No dogs.
Credit cards All major cards accepted.
Terms (No service charge) B&B: single occupancy £69–£75, double £85–£95, suite £130–£235. Set lunch £10.50, dinner £15–£26. Reduced rates for children sharing parents' room; special meals.
Service/tipping: "We have a no-tipping policy. Service is complimentary."

> Set dinner refers to a fixed price meal (which may have ample, limited or no choice on the menu). Full alc is the hotel's own estimated price per person of a three-course meal taken à la carte, with a half-bottle of house wine.

Darroch Learg Hotel *Tel* Ballater (033 97) 55443
Ballater, Aberdeenshire AB3 5UX

In 4-acre grounds on the side of a wooded mountain a few minutes' walk from Ballater, the Darroch Learg Hotel, *in two pink-and-grey granite houses, offers a quiet setting and lovely scenery. Spacious public rooms, well-furnished bedrooms, Swedish-style with modern pine furniture. Food is "plain, rather old-fashioned, but freshly cooked and plentiful, and the staff, all wearing tartan, friendly and pleasant." Open Jan–Nov. 19 double rooms, 4 single, 20 with bath or shower, 1 suitable for ♿. B&B £17–£32. Set dinner £14. New to the Guide this year. More reports please*

BANCHORY Grampian Map 5

Banchory Lodge Hotel *Tel* Banchory (033 02) 2625
Banchory, Kincardineshire
AB3 3HS

A well-bred white-painted Georgian building, filled with Victorian and Edwardian furniture and bric-à-brac lovingly collected over the years by the resident owners (since 1966), Mr and Mrs Jaffray. The house has a felicitous position near the confluence of the Water of Feugh and the Dee, and the hotel has fishing rights on the water directly opposite. It is naturally popular with the fishing fraternity, but also with golfers (three courses close by). Traditional hearty British fare, with good local products such as Dee salmon, Aberdeen beef, and game. The house has a friendly feel to it, with lots of flower arrangements, and open fires. It has had its share of criticism in the past, chiefly about the cooking and standards of housekeeping, but this year reports are mostly positive: warm welcome, comfortable rooms, decent food, and service at breakfast "much improved". (*Mary and Rodney Milne-Day, RCJ Gordon*) But we'd still welcome more reports.

Open Feb–Dec.
Rooms 24 – all with bath and/or shower, telephone, radio, TV, tea-making facilities and baby-listening.
Facilities 2 lounges, cocktail bar, dining room, private dining room. 12-acre grounds with salmon and trout fishing (book well in advance).
Location 5 mins' walk from centre.
Restriction Not suitable for ♿.
Credit cards All major cards accepted.
Terms (Service at guests' discretion) B&B single £40, double £75. Reduced rates and special meals for children.

Invery House *Tel* Banchory (033 02) 4782
Bridge of Feugh, Banchory *Fax* (033 02) 4712
Kincardineshire AB3 3NJ *Telex* 73737

"A truly superb hotel, outstanding in every way. Beautiful bedrooms and bathrooms. Impeccable service. Incredible setting." "The food is fantastic – *nouvelle cuisine,* but good-sized helpings. The hotel is superbly furnished and delightfully decorated. The owners collected paintings and pictures for years." These two recent reports confirm our own inspector's commendation last year, following the opening of this new hotel less than 20 miles from Aberdeen. She wrote, "A pale pink mansion set in a wood full of bluebells and snowdrops [in March]. As you approach from the south you pass over the rushing river Feugh. White boulders guide you to the house. The flagstoned porch is liberally filled with antiques, flowers and stuffed birds, as is the main hall, warm underfoot, mostly peach with green velvet, and dark Edwardian furniture. Our bedroom, Rokeby, (all the bedrooms are called after novels by Sir Walter Scott who is said to have visited the house) was a riot of designer chintz – blowsy pink roses cascaded everywhere: on the twin frilled beds, the canopy above, the big comfy armchairs. We enjoyed our complimentary sherry and fruit; I put on my complimentary bathrobe and ran a bath full of complimentary Crabtree and Evelyn essence. The bathroom had everything, even a telephone, but the bath was awkward to use, approached up two steps, and with the taps in the middle. The room had satellite television as well as everything imaginable in the way of knick-knacks. Drinks were served in the peach and pale-blue drawing room where we chose our dinner and consulted the vast wine list – over 400 wines, 36 halves, between 150% and 200% mark-up. In the sage-green dining room we sat in huge upholstered armchairs, so enormous we were miles away from each other across the table." Our inspector's dinner was good, though not outstanding; service, by a very young team, was pleasant and efficient. "Well worth including," was her verdict. "It would appeal to the rich fishing set." (*Invery House* has a mile of private fishing on the river Feugh.) A third reader (he wrote to praise the improving food) cautioned, "But don't make a mess with your green wellies." (*Fiona Burkeman, J Samson, and others*)

Open All year.
Rooms 2 suites, 11 double, 1 single – all with bath and shower, telephone, radio, TV, and tea-making facilities.
Facilities Bar, drawing room, dining room; 2 private dining/conference rooms. 30-acre grounds with 1 mile fishing, croquet, putting, helipad. Chauffeur-driven car available for guests' use. Golf nearby.
Location 18 m W of Aberdeen. Take A93 to Banchory then A974 S to Fettercairn for 1 m. Look for green and gold sign.
Restrictions Only restaurant suitable for ♿ (ramp). No children under 8. Dogs in kennels only.
Credit cards All major cards accepted.
Terms (Service at guests' discretion) [1989 rates] B&B: single £70–£105, double £95–£145, suite £195. Set lunch £13.50, dinner £25.50. Special meals for children on request.

BEATTOCK Dumfries and Galloway — Map 5

Auchen Castle Hotel
Beattock, Moffat
Dumfriesshire DG10 9SH

Tel Beattock (068 33) 407
Fax (068 33) 407
Telex 777205 (specify *Auchen*)

As you drive north from Beattock in the beautiful Scottish borders, you can see *Auchen Castle* off the A74 on the left. Built in sandstone in 1849, it has an impressive tower and porticoed entrance; there is a fine terraced garden, and beautiful views over the upper Annandale. It is a hotel in the traditional style run by Bob Beckh with his wife, Hazel. They continue to please most readers. A visitor for many years writes, "The Beckhs are a delightful couple, very welcoming, as are all their staff. The bedrooms have been redecorated to a high standard, and the food, too, is good. The grounds are magnificent at all times of the year and carefully looked after." Another writer says, "I have stayed here on a dozen occasions in the past 12 months and *Auchen Castle* continues to provide a mellow and friendly atmosphere within its granite walls." A general verdict: "A haven in the desert of this part of South West Scotland," though we continue to receive criticisms of some of the rooms ("basic") and breakfasts. (*Keith Davy, John Bacharach, Diana Gates*)

Open All year except 3 weeks over Christmas and New Year.
Rooms 22 double, 3 single – 13 with bath, 12 with shower, all with telephone, radio, TV, tea-making facilities, baby-listening. 10 in Cedar Lodge annexe.
Facilities Lounge, bar, dining room; conference room. Sat dinner-dance Oct–Mar. 50-acre grounds with trout-stocked loch; boat. Fishing on river Annan. Golf, riding, tennis, sailing nearby.
Location 1 m N of Beattock village with signed access from A74 (east-facing rooms could get traffic noise).
Restrictions Not suitable for ♿. No dogs in dining room.
Credit cards All major cards accepted.
Terms (No service charge) B&B: single £36, double £39–£55 (lower rates in annexe). Set dinner £11–£14; bar lunches. Discounts for stays of more than 1 night. Special breaks; golf holidays. Reduced rates and special meals for children.

BLAIRGOWRIE Tayside — Map 5

Kinloch House Hotel [GFG]
By Blairgowrie
Perthshire PH10 6SG

Tel Essendy (025 084) 237
Fax (025 084) 333

An ivy-covered country house hotel with an oak-panelled hall and bar, and a magnificent gallery, in a 25-acre estate, complete with Highland cattle. It is popular with shooting parties, having a game larder, drying facilities and kennels for the gun-dogs, and also with fishermen and golfers (there are 40 golf courses within an hour's drive). It has one of the best restaurants in the area. "A country house hotel of real warmth and character where one immediately feels welcome and relaxed. The presence of family portraits, *objets d'art*, fresh flowers and books adds to the impression of staying in a very comfortable home rather than a hotel. Housekeeping standards are high." There is also praise for the views from the bedrooms, and for the peaceful setting – "often the only sounds to be heard are the cries of wild geese and ducks". (*TS Stephens, IC Dewey, Mrs Jean Dundas, Dr JR Hamilton, Captain MH Tobey*) David Shentall presides over things in an unobtrusive manner, but this year there have been mixed reports about his style. "He is a charming, courteous man, informative about his food, a superb host" and "a restaurateur who knows his business". But more than one reader found his attitude "disconcerting at times" and felt that service in the restaurant was "somewhat amateur – even if willing". No-one criticises the food, however – "mainly fish/game/beef, cooked as perfectly as these can be", "excellent wines", "puddings lovely", "port and prune ice cream exceedingly good". The Shentalls are adding eight new double or twin rooms this year, two with sitting rooms.

We depend on detailed fresh reports to keep our entries up-to-date.

Open All year except 7–29 Dec.
Rooms 2 suites, 14 double, 5 single – all with bath and/or shower and tea-making facilities, 15 with telephone, 2 with radio, 4 with TV.
Facilities Lounge, TV lounge, cocktail bar, conservatory, dining room. 25-acre grounds with highland cattle and croquet lawn. River and loch fishing, shooting, stalking, golf nearby.
Location 3½ m W of Blairgowrie on A923 Dunkeld road.
Restrictions Not suitable for ♿. No children under 7 in dining room. Dogs by arrangement; not in public rooms.
Credit cards All major cards accepted.
Terms B&B single £38.50, double £60–£68, suite £88. Bar lunches available; set Sun lunch £10.50, dinner £17.50. Reductions for stays of 3 or more nights. 1-night bookings occasionally refused in peak season. Reduced rates and special meals for children by arrangement.
Service/tipping: "All prices inclusive. Tipping not encouraged. If people insist the money is distributed among staff."

BRIDGE OF MARNOCH Grampian — Map 5

The Old Manse of Marnoch — *Tel* Aberchirder (046 65) 873
Bridge of Marnoch
Huntly, Aberdeenshire AB5 5RS

On the banks of the river Deveron, a 19th-century guest house new to the Guide this year, warmly recommended for its friendly welcome, good food, immaculate bedrooms (perhaps rather dainty for some tastes), and reasonable price. It is much used by fishermen, though shooting and stalking can also be arranged. There are wooded walks down to the river, and five-acre grounds with old-fashioned roses, a formal herb parterre, and a walled kitchen garden. The decor reflects the many years the proprietors, Patrick and Keren Carter, spent in the Far East. Bold colours predominate in the public rooms; the dining room, where dinner is served communally, is dark green with nautical prints. Our inspector reports, "*The Old Manse* lifts itself effortlessly from the 'guest house B&B level' by virtue of its food: £7 [1989] for mackerel and orange pâté with home-made brown toast, stuffed neck of beef with tomatoes, mashed potatoes, cauliflower cheese, tomato salad with basil, blackcurrant ice-cream and afterwards – feet up on a buttonback leather Chesterfield in the lounge – coffee, the remains of my half-litre of Côtes du Rhône (£3.50), a plate of shortbread, and a few nutty and spicy truffles. A well-run and friendly small hotel in an interesting part of Scotland." Vegetarian cooking is a speciality of the house.

Open All year.
Rooms 4 double – 1 with bath, 1 with shower, 2 sharing 1 bathroom, all with radio and tea-making facilities.
Facilities Lounge, dining room. Garden with walks to river. Fishing, stalking and shooting arranged. Cookery workshops in off-season.
Location On B9117 less than 1 m W of A97 Huntly-Banff route.
Restrictions Not suitable for ♿. No dogs in dining room.
Credit cards None accepted.
Terms (No service charge) B&B £15–£25. Lunch £4, dinner £8. Reduced rates for children sharing parents' room; special meals on request.
Service/tipping: "It is not expected that guests tip their hosts."

> Hotels are arranged alphabetically under the nearest village following Bartholomew's *Gazetteer*.

BUNCHREW Highland — Map 5

Bunchrew House — *Tel* Inverness (0463) 234917
Bunchrew, by Inverness IV3 6TA

Nominated last year, now under the new ownership of Alan and Patsy Wilson; pink sandstone Scottish baronial concoction set around 15th-century tower in 18-acre grounds on shores of Beauly Firth. Dark panelling, thick carpets, attractively decorated bedrooms. A visitor to Bunchrew *under the new regime praises the "superb meals, welcoming fireplaces" and calls it "the highlight of two weeks in Britain". Closed mid-Nov–mid-Dec. 6 rooms, all with bath and shower, B&B double £47–£95. Set lunch £8.50, dinner £18.50. More reports please.*

BUNESSAN Mull, Strathclyde — Map 5

Ardfenaig House — *Tel* Fionnphort (068 17) 210
Bunessan, Isle of Mull
Argyllshire PA67 6DX

A haven of quietly polished civilisation, *Ardfenaig House* stands at the head of a small loch where only the sound of sheep, curlews and sea birds disturb the silence. The grounds give directly onto the moor and there are many pleasant walks for birdwatchers and sketchers. Mull is an enchanting island, full of wild flowers, and the roads (you must adjust to single-track driving and blind corners) lead through beautiful scenery, especially round the coastline. The house, built in the 1700s and formerly belonging to the Duke of Argyll, is full of books, as well as antiques. It has a real country atmosphere, with wellington boots by the door, portraits on the stairs, decent but not lavish bathrooms and no fewer than three grand pianos; also a friendly Cavalier King Charles spaniel. There are only five rooms for guests; they share three bathrooms, which contributes to the house-party atmosphere as do the four-course, no-choice dinners (with wines that are "excellent and not overpriced"). Reports this year have been warmly enthusiastic about the welcome given by the proprietor, Ian Bowles, his helpful advice about places to visit, and the relaxed but attentive service at all times. Not for everyone, perhaps, because of the remote setting and maximum of six guests at any one time, but readers continue to be highly appreciative of *Ardfenaig*'s hospitality. (*Dr and Mrs AF Cowan; also Lady Bingen, MW Atkinson*)

Open May–Sept inclusive. Restaurant closed for lunch, and to non-residents on Sun.
Rooms 4 double, 1 single – all with tea-making facilities.
Maximum 6 guests at a time.
Facilities Lounge, bar, music room, sun room, dining room. 18-acre grounds sloping down to loch with shingle beach (plenty of sandy beaches nearby). Fishing, safe bathing.
Location 3½ m W of Bunessan on Iona ferry road. The hotel's long drive is on the right.
Restrictions Not suitable for ♿. No children under 12. No dogs in public rooms.
Credit cards None accepted.
Terms Dinner, B&B £60. Set dinner £19. Discount for 3 or more nights' stay.
Service/tipping: "Our prices are structured to include a service charge which is distributed each week to the staff."

CANONBIE Dumfries and Galloway — Map 5

Riverside Inn [GFG]
Canonbie
Dumfriesshire DG14 0UX

Tel Canonbie
(038 73) 71295 and 71512

Robert and Susan Phillips' 17th-century fisherman's retreat on the banks of the Esk is well placed for touring Hadrian's Wall and the Solway coast, and as a staging post on long-haul journeys. Readers this year continue to praise the meals in the "pretty dining room" which are uncommonly enterprising, with much use of local fresh ingredients: "Food excellent and imaginative – avocado correctly ripe, poached salmon very fresh, vegetables beautifully cooked and prettily presented." Breakfasts are perhaps even better; a reader who travels often writes, "the breakfast menu is more comprehensive than anywhere I know; one can have absolutely anything one wants and several things one wouldn't think of having." Bar lunches, too, are well above average, "every bit as good as the restaurant menu. There's a good selection of malt whiskies too." Rooms vary in size (it is wise to discuss your requirements on booking) but all are well equipped – "everything that a good hostess would put there from fruit to needle and thread, and books." Many readers like the rooms in the cottage annexe with a garden running down to the Esk. ("They have large umbrellas for use if it is raining at dinner time.") All seem to agree "the accommodation is much more comfortable than the word 'inn' might suggest". (*Dr and Mrs RM Phillips, Stephanie Sowerby; also Uwe Kitzinger, Christopher Davy, and others*) To the criticism last year that mealtimes were too rigidly imposed Mrs Phillips replies, "Early breakfasts are possible by arrangement, and for guests arriving after 9 pm hot or cold suppers are served in the bar until 11 pm. They only have to ask!"

Open All year except 25/26 Dec, 1/2 Jan, 2 weeks Feb, 2 weeks Nov. Restaurant closed for lunch and Sun night (bar suppers available).
Rooms 6 double – 4 with bath, 2 with shower, all with radio, TV and tea-making facilities. 1 ground-floor room.
Facilities Reception/coffee lounge, lounge bar, residents' lounge, dining room. Small garden. Park opposite with children's play area. River Esk 100 yds; salmon and sea-trout fishing (permits from hotel).
Location M6 exit 44. 12 m N on A7; turn off A7 into Canonbie. Inn is at bottom of hill by river Esk bridge.
Restriction No dogs.
Credit cards Access, Visa.
Terms (No service charge) B&B: single £40, double £50. Set dinner £17. Bar lunches. 2-day winter breaks Nov–Apr. Weekly rates.
Service/tipping: "We don't charge for service. Tipping is discouraged. Our staff are paid well over average rates."

COLONSAY Strathclyde — Map 5

Isle of Colonsay Hotel
Argyllshire PA61 7YP

Tel Colonsay (095 12) 316
Fax (095 12) 353

As the ferry makes its two-and-a-quarter-hour journey to Colonsay only three times a week at present, you are marooned on the island for at least two days. But this is why visitors come – to enjoy the golden beaches, dramatic rocky cliffs, woods, heathland and lochs; the island is particularly good for cycling. The 250-year-old *Isle of Colonsay Hotel*, the most isolated registered hotel in Britain, is run by red-bearded Kevin Byrne, a man of formidable energy, and his wife Christa. The hotel overlooks Scalasaig harbour and is the social centre of the island; people gather to chat, drink, and eat the excellent and inexpensive bar lunches. A new Seafood Bar (open 15 May–30 September) has proved popular; this year the other two bars have been much improved, with "noise, hubbub, and smoke all under control". The restaurant, too, is warmly commended. Bedrooms vary in size, are conventional in decor and some have views; public bathrooms serving the single rooms have been rebuilt. Readers have been warmly enthusiastic about the hotel over the years. A recent visitor extols the "miracle of organisation and good management, and the generous spirit of the Byrnes, from the low price of renting golf clubs and balls to the reasonable prices on the interesting wine list." (*Sharon Gutman*) We had one stinker, however, from a guest who arrived late at night, delayed by storms, found herself in an underheated, poorly-maintained chalet though she had confirmed a room in the inn. She was unable to obtain even a hot drink. More reports would be welcome.

Open 1 Mar–5 Nov and 2 weeks New Year.
Rooms 8 double with bath and shower, 3 single – all with radio and tea-making facilities; TV, telephone and baby-listening on request. 1 garden bungalow with shower for family accommodation.
Facilities Residents' lounge, sun room, cocktail bar, public bar, Seafood Bar (May–Sept), restaurant. 1-acre grounds with garden, burn, sandpit, vegetable gardens. ½ m to sandy beach and lochs.
Location 400 yards W of harbour. Car/passenger ferry from Oban Mon, Wed, Fri; (37 m crossing: 2¼ hours); additional ferries in high season; hotel courtesy car to/from all sailings.
Restrictions "Handicapped guests welcome but facilities not perfect." No dogs in public rooms.
Credit cards All major cards accepted.
Terms Dinner,B&B £38–£50. Set dinner £14. Reductions for long stays; special rates off season. Children charged only for meals when sharing parents' room, except in high season.
Service/tipping: "No service charge; our staff are properly paid. Gratuities are shared equally by our domestic staff amongst themselves."

CRAIGHOUSE Jura, Strathclyde — Map 5

Jura Hotel — *Tel* Jura (049 682) 243
Craighouse, Isle of Jura
Argyllshire PA60 7XU

Jura's only hotel, next to distillery in main village, on island's sheltered east coast. Most public rooms and many bedrooms (some quite small) have sea view. Recommended for simple comfort and food and welcoming hospitality. Closed three weeks Christmas and New Year. 17 rooms, 4 with bath, 1 with shower. B&B £19.50–£25. Set dinner £11.25–£12. New nomination last year. More reports please.

> Hotels often book you into their most expensive rooms or suites unless you specify otherwise. Even if all room prices are the same, hotels may give you a less good room in the hope of selling their better rooms to late customers. It always pays to discuss accommodation in detail when making a reservation.

DERVAIG Mull, Strathclyde — Map 5

Bellachroy Hotel *Tel* Dervaig (068 84) 225 and 314
Dervaig, Isle of Mull
Argyllshire PA75 6QW

Andrew and Anne Arnold's stone-built white-washed drovers' inn is "a Scots example of the sort of place quite easily found in France but almost non-existent in Britain: well cooked, imaginative food, and simple but comfortable and clean bedrooms – with electric blankets, good reading lights over beds, towels changed daily. There are no bathrooms *en suite*, but plenty to go round. The four-course dinner uses fresh local produce, including fish and game, vegetables are lightly cooked, and a there is help-yourself cheeseboard, including the local Mull cheese. Plenty of choice for breakfast, including Loch Fyne kippers, home-made jams and freshly baked bread." Visitors this year have been equally pleased, praising the warmth and comfort of the hotel and the proprietors' "untiring efforts to ensure the happiness of their guests. The obviously good relationship which exists between them and their staff ensures a very pleasant atmosphere." But one correspondent complained about "dinner firmly at 7 pm, breakfast at 9 am, no argument, and if one is ten minutes late for either, there are signs of impatience." Mrs Arnold cooks her four-course dinner for residents first, and then cooks for the bar; despite the degree of inflexibility that this causes, all reports rate the hotel and its food "good value for money". (*James M Aitken, and others*) There is a comfortable sitting room for bad weather; the bars are popular with island characters.

Open All year except Christmas week. Bars open all year.
Rooms 8 double, all with H&C.
Facilities 2 lounges with TV, 2 bars, dining room. Folk music on Thurs May–Oct. 2-acre grounds. Sea and loch fishing, golf and pony trekking nearby; sandy beach 5 m.
Location 8 m W of Tobermory.
Restrictions Not suitable for ♿. Dogs by arrangement.
Credit cards None accepted.
Terms B&B £14.50–£15.50; dinner, B&B £23–£24. Bar meals: lunch £2.50–£5, supper £5–£8; set dinner £11. Children under 12 ½-price in parents' room; special meals.
Service/tipping: "We don't get many tips or solicit/encourage them. Any we do get go into a jar for cold drinks for staff during bar sessions."

DRUMNADROCHIT Highland — Map 5

Polmaily House Hotel [GFG] *Tel* Drumnadrochit (045 62) 343
Drumnadrochit
Inverness-shire IV3 6XT

A rambling Edwardian mansion in 18-acre grounds, a few miles to the west of Loch Ness – a tranquil rural setting, though the dramatic landscape of Glen Affric is only a short drive away. There is very little about the house that suggests a hotel, and it is, for many, a refreshing change from the baronial-style castles and shooting lodges that so often characterise a Scottish grand tour. The bedrooms are individually decorated and furnished; "comfortable beds with plain white wooden bedheads like a superior convent school; the carpets were ecstasy to the feet and the bathroom well equipped". Many visitors have commented on the relaxed, lived-in atmosphere. Alison Parsons' menus combine enterprising starters (fresh mussel, turbot and saffron broth, Scottish smoked cheese soufflé) with more traditional local fare (sautéed venison fillet with chestnuts, grilled Aberdeen Angus sirloin steak). Most guests continue to be appreciative of *Polmaily* hospitality: "My personal favourite: our hosts were delightful, the room was as comfortable as if we were in the home I would like eventually to own" and "Just as agreeable as we remembered it. . .Breakfasts as one expects and hopes for in Scotland but often does not receive." One correspondent, however, complained of a shabby bedroom and another of "wrapped bread at breakfast and no porridge". (*Deborah Hogan Ross, Prof. Sir Alan and Lady Cook*)

Open April–mid-Oct.
Rooms 7 double, 2 single – doubles with bath, all with radio; baby-listening on request.
Facilities Drawing room, bar, reading room with TV (residents only), restaurant. 18-acre grounds with tennis, croquet, unheated swimming pool; fishing, shooting, stalking and pony trekking available.
Location 2 m W of Drumnadrochit on A831 Cannich road.
Restrictions Not suitable for ♿. No smoking in dining room and bar area. No dogs in hotel.
Credit cards Access, Visa.
Terms B&B (Scottish) £35–£38.50. Set dinner from £15. Discounts for long stays. Reduced rates for children sharing parents' room; high teas on request.
Service/tipping: "No service charge. Tips are not solicited."

DUNBLANE see KINBUCK — Map 5

Cromlix House

DUNOON Strathclyde — Map 5

Enmore Hotel — *Tel* Dunoon (0369) 2230 or 2148
Marine Parade, Kirn
Dunoon, Argyllshire PA23 8HH

Dunoon was a popular seaside resort in Victorian times; today it makes a useful base for exploring the Isles of Arran and Bute, and the Mull of Kintyre. The *Enmore* overlooks the Clyde Estuary a mile out of town; its setting and comforts have been pleasing readers since it entered the Guide in 1984. The enterprising proprietors, David and Angela Wilson, have transformed this "rather ordinary Victorian villa" into a small, quite luxurious hotel. "The ultimate in spacious comfort is achieved with imagination and taste; bedrooms are filled with creature comforts: bowls of perfect fruit, well-chosen books, electric blankets"; many have views of the sea, garden, or mountains in the distance. "Every corner seems to have been designed with taste and consideration", wrote a reader this year. The Wilsons are keen on beds – there are five four-posters and a water-bed, and two bathrooms have jacuzzi. Luxury breaks are popular and include "complimentary flowers, 'bubbly', even a heart-shaped box of chocolates and breakfast in bed". A recent report from a parent, "Our three children under five posed no problem; they were charged for their separate room at a nominal rate and catered for admirably. There is an excellent baby-listening system, but as our nine-week-old baby was playing up somewhat the management happily served our dinner in the bedroom." The food and wine list come in for praise, also the "exceptionally helpful and cheerful staff". (*Dr G Smyth, GJ Feldway, Gillian Cave, and others*)

Open Mid-Jan–mid-Dec
Rooms 1 suite, 8 double, 3 single – all with bath and/or shower, telephone, radio, TV, baby-listening; 1 with water-bed, 2 with whirlpool bath; tea-making facilities on request. 2 ground-floor rooms.
Facilities 2 lounges, games room, cocktail bar, dining room; 2 squash courts. 1-acre grounds with private shingle beach across road; safe but cold bathing, boating. Golf, swimming pool, tennis and pony trekking nearby.
Location On Marine Parade between 2 ferries, 1 m N of Dunoon.
Restrictions Not suitable for ♿. No smoking in dining room. Children under 7 not encouraged at dinner.
Credit cards Access, Diners, Visa.
Terms B&B £32–£40; dinner, B&B £45–£56. Set dinner £15. Winter, spring 3- and 7-day breaks. Reduced rates and special meals for children.
Service/tipping: "If tips are are offered they are distributed amongst staff at end of season."

ELGIN Grampian — Map 5

The Mansion House Hotel
The Haugh, Elgin
Moray IV30 1AW

Tel Elgin (0343) 48811
Fax (0343) 7916

An imposing 19th-century Scots baronial mansion, complete with castellated tower and stair turret, in five acres of grounds with many fine trees, overlooking the river Lossie, a quarter of a mile from Elgin. It was rescued from demolition by Fernando Oliveira, who comes from Portugal, and his Scottish wife. Since last year it has moved with the times and acquired a new indoor pool complete with jacuzzi, sauna, Turkish bath and "comprehensive gymnasium". Our inspector this year gave the *Mansion House* a general seal of approval: she noted the warm reception, the dining room softened by pretty pink tablecloths and with new tulip-shaped wine glasses, and the fairly priced set-menu dinner for £12.50. The wine list, with nearly 100 wines, included many bottles at £6–£10, and 20 half-bottles. The hotel caters for many local functions, and is popular with visitors on business. Grampian is a rewarding untouristy area – and the *Mansion House*, is well worth seeking out.

Open All year.
Rooms 18 double – all with bath and shower, telephone, radio, TV, tea-making facilities and baby-listening.
Facilities Residents' lounge, bar, bistro, dining room; conference/function room. 5-acre grounds with children's playground. Near river with fishing.
Location Coming E from Inverness or W from Aberdeen on A96 turn off Elgin High St into Alexandra Rd; take turning into Haugh Rd, then first turning on left. Parking.
Restrictions Not suitable for ♿. No dogs.
Credit cards All major cards accepted.
Terms B&B: single £45–£55, double £70–£85; dinner, B&B: single £55–£60, double £90–£100. Set lunch £7.50, dinner £15; full alc £20. Weekend and weekly breaks. Reduced rates for children; special meals.
Service/tipping: "Service included. Tipping not expected."

Nominations for good Edinburgh hotels would be welcome.

ERISKA Strathclyde — Map 5

Isle of Eriska Hotel [GFG]
Eriska, Ledaig, Connel
Argyllshire PA37 1SD

Tel Ledaig (063 172) 371
Telex 777040 ERISKA

An imposing Victorian mansion on a small private island off the west coast, one mile wide and a mile-and-a-half long, linked by a bridge to the mainland. The island is rich in flora and fauna. The hotel is owned by Robin Buchanan-Smith, a minister of the Church of Scotland, and his wife Sheena, and run on private house lines. For many years the hotel has had a devoted following of those who love its old-fashioned, fairly formal (jackets and ties at dinner) style of hospitality. "This is our favourite place in Great Britain," wrote one recent visitor, "service, food, rooms and facilities exactly as we like them, and the *Isle of Eriska* one of the few places where things should stay exactly as they are." Another wrote, "Our 12th holiday here: seclusion, peace, comfort and quiet. Sophistication is the key note. Magnificent views from the rooms, especially looking down the Lynn of Lorne to Mull." The hotel has tennis, croquet and ponies. But our post continues to deliver grumbles – especially about the price and the cooking. We would welcome more reports.

Open Mid-Mar–Nov.
Rooms 1 suite, 15 double – all with bath and shower, telephone, radio, TV, tea-making facilities and baby-listening. 2 ground-floor rooms with access for wheelchairs.
Facilities Ramp. 2 halls, drawing room, library, dining room. 320-acre grounds with tennis, croquet, putting green, water sports, ponies. Loch 5 mins.
Location 12 m N of Oban. 4 m W of A828.
Restrictions No children under 10 in dining room at night (high tea at 6 pm). No dogs in dining room.
Credit cards Access, Visa.
Terms [1989 rates] (No service charge) B&B: single £59.80–£103.50, double £103.50–£119.60, suite £181. Set lunch from £7, dinner £29. Off-season rates. Reduced rates for children sharing parents' room; high teas.

FORT WILLIAM Highland — Map 5

The Factor's House [GFG]
Torlundy, Fort William
Inverness-shire PH33 6SN

Tel Fort William (0397) 5767
Fax Fort William (0397) 2953
Telex 776229 attn FH

Built in the early part of the century for the factor (estate manager) of what is now *Inverlochy Castle, The Factor's House* is owned and run by Peter Hobbs, son of *Inverlochy*'s owner, Grete Hobbs, as an entirely independent enterprise and at half the prices of the *Castle*. The house has a fresh, light, airy feeling. Bedrooms are furnished in white-painted bamboo with cool Designers Guild wallpaper, but are on the small side and somewhat spartan in feeling. Perhaps they lack a woman's touch? The lounges, too, are small which makes private conversation difficult. However, the simplicity of the decor has not diminished readers' praise for the hotel, "I absolutely endorse the comments in the 1989 Guide. After five days in October, with rain all day on four, we can't wait to return and are planning a long weekend (1,100 miles round-trip) in early December." Another visitor liked "the informality of the two blackboards that announce dinner, the first two courses described in the lounge, and desserts (or cheese) in the dining room". He went on to praise "the sensationally good seafood risotto, full of scallops, scampi and langoustines, followed by halibut in filo pastry, with broccoli, carrots, gratinée potatoes and a good salad, and the chocolate and Tia Maria iced soufflé." Writers also praise the "delightful staff" including Ranald Duff, the young manager. *The Factor's House* falls somewhere between hotel and restaurant-with-rooms, with the special attraction of being at the foot of Ben Nevis in some of Scotland's best walking country. (*Margaret and Michael Firth, HR; also April Young, JM Mackay*)

Open Mid-Jan–mid-Dec.
Rooms 7 double – all with bath and/or shower, telephone and TV. 1 on ground floor.
Facilities 2 lounges, dining room. Small garden but guests have access to *Inverlochy*'s 450-acre grounds and tennis courts. Sailing, fishing.
Location 3 m NE of Fort William on A82, just after turn-off to *Inverlochy Castle.*
Restrictions No children under 6 in dining room for dinner. No dogs.
Credit cards Access. Visa.
Terms (No service charge) B&B: single occupancy £46–£63.25, double £69. Set lunch (residents only) £10, dinner £20. Reduced rates and special meals for children.
Service/tipping: "We do not expect tips but if given they are gratefully received and given equally to each member of staff. We do not leave the bottom of the credit card voucher blank."

Inverlochy Castle [GFG]
Torlundy, Fort William
Inverness-shire PH33 6SN

Tel Fort William (0397) 2177
Fax (0397) 2953
Telex 776229

This is Grete Hobbs's 21st year as châtelaine of her spectacular Scottish baronial hotel, formerly her husband's family home, which stands in 50 acres of grounds, rich in rhododendrons, on the lower slopes of Ben Nevis in the heart of the West Highlands. It has been in a class of its own as a country-house hotel for many years now; it won a César, in our first year of those awards, for "incomparable grandeur". Commenting on our lack of feedback last year, a visitor writes, "Your readers have become blasé. I consider it the finest hotel I have ever stayed in. I was quite unknown to them, but Grete Hobbs and Graham Newbold, the chef, treated me as old friends. I had a wonderful second-floor room overlooking Ben Nevis. The mature staff aren't the least obtrusive, and my two dinners offered an excellent choice. The wine list is a dream and the prices not exaggerated." Another writes, "*Inverlochy* is in a class of its own, but not so much for its 'incomparable grandeur' as for its exceedingly high standards and the remarkable friendliness of those who run it. The vast inner hall and the drawing room were both warm with blazing fires and had comfortable sofas and armchairs to sit in. Room service and service at dinner were smooth, swift and courteous. The soufflées were mouth-watering. The key to the hotel's success is its manager, Michael Leonard, omni-present, plumping up cushions and feeling the coffee pots to see if they are hot enough. He has been there many years yet his perfectionist eye and his enthusiasm are as keen as ever." (*John Davies, Conrad and Marilyn Dehn, and others*) As always, a few dissenters: "The meal had a slight *ancien regime* feel to it, with some hits, some misses. On balance the price seems hard to justify, though I'm sure the *Castle* has no difficulty in filling its tables." "'Incomparable grandeur' alright, but at a price. You see little of other guests, who are not inclined to speak to each other (like London commuters). We cannot fault the ambience, but thought the dinner disappointing – no comparison with *Altnaharrie* or the *Peat Inn*."

Open 20 Mar–12 Nov approx.
Rooms 1 suite, 14 double, 1 single – all with bath and shower, telephone, radio, and baby-listening; 24-hour room service.
Facilities Great hall, drawing room, 2 dining rooms, billiard room; facilities for small conferences out of season. 50-acre grounds with rhododendron gardens; all-weather tennis court; trout fishing on nearby private loch. Several golf courses within easy driving distance; pony trekking. Chauffeur-driven limousines can be hired.
Location Take turning to NW off A82, 3 m N of Fort William just past golf club. Guests met by arrangement at station or airports.
Restrictions Not suitable for ♿. Children under 12 only accepted if sharing parents' room. No dogs.
Credit cards Access, Visa.
Terms B&B: single £110–£121, double £150–£165, suite £210–£230. Set lunch approx £25, dinner £38.50. Reduced rates for children sharing parents' room; special meals.
Service/tipping: "There is no service charge and tipping is not expected."

GIGHA Strathclyde — Map 5

Gigha Hotel — *Tel* Gigha (058 35) 254
Isle of Gigha, Argyllshire — *Fax* (058 35) 275
PA41 7AD

Gigha, six miles long and nowhere more than 1½ miles wide, is the most southerly of the Inner Hebrides and is known for its flowers and its peace. The *Gigha Hotel*, an old inn rebuilt and enlarged in such a way as to retain the traditional facade, looks out over Ardminish Bay. There are sandy beaches to explore, and birdwatchers will find much of interest. Last year a report extolled the many comforts of the hotel, "Good beds, wardrobe space, easy chairs, big fluffy towels changed daily; exceptional dining-room service by local girls with soft island voices and delightful manners." The hotel is the only one on the island, and one writer commented on how tempting it might be to exploit such a monopoly, "But not a bit of it; the owners, Mr and Mrs Roebuck, cater in the very best traditions of Highland hospitality, attracting a regular clientele of yachtsmen who beat a course through the Sound just for the food." Another visitor, who arrived after a tiring journey with her three-year-old child, was struck by the immediate concern for their comfort, "We were asked when we would like the little boy fed, and what he would like to eat. My son, thrilled by the sight of five seals and two cormorants appearing within yards of where we stood, flung off his clothes and dashed in to join them, enthusing me to do the same. Shivering but happy, we returned to the hotel where there was plenty of hot water for baths and his tea was ready on the dot." (*Stewart Yorston, Lucy Irvine*)
Note: Gigha is pronounced "Gee-ah", with the first G hard. As we go to press, we hear that the island is for sale and the future of the hotel uncertain; in any event, the Roebucks are retiring.

Open All year.
Rooms 9 double – 3 with bath; tea-making facilities on request.

Facilities Bar, lounge, TV room, restaurant. Small garden. Loch fishing, sea angling.
Location Only hotel on island, which is reached by ferry from Tayinloan (cars can be left on the mainland).
Restrictions Not suitable for ♿. No dogs in restaurant.
Credit cards Access, Visa.
Terms (No service charge) B&B from £24; dinner, B&B from £39. Set lunch £6.50, dinner £14. Reduced rates for children under 12 sharing parents' room; special meals.
Service/tipping: "Entirely at customers' discretion. Staff have a tronc which they administer."

GLASGOW Strathclyde — Map 5

Babbity Bowster — *Tel* Glasgow (041) 552 5055
16–18 Blackfriars Street
G1 1PE

Winner of a Civic Trust Award in 1987 for a "refreshingly simple" restoration of a derelict villa in Glasgow's Merchant City, *Babbity Bowster* entered the Guide last year. It is "a café/bar/restaurant/hotel", whose name comes from a Scottish dance called "Bob at the Bolster". "A lively pub with six compact bedrooms, all with shower, and up two floors (there is no lift), simply but attractively designed with modern pine furniture, an original print or lithograph; colours are predominantly grey, with a scarlet chair. It is quietly situated up a cobbled pedestrian street; buses and taxis are easily available. Breakfast is excellent; light snacks are served all day; dinner is available in the moderately priced restaurant, open from noon until midnight. The owner, Fraser Laurie, with golden hair, a beard and a black eye-patch, looks like a charming pirate." In addition to offering board and lodging, *Babbity Bowster* holds exhibitions of local artists and Sunday evening concerts of classical music, jazz and poetry. There is private parking for residents. Endorsed this year, but more reports still welcome.

Open All year.
Rooms 5 double, 1 single – all with shower.
Facilities Café/bar, restaurant, patio.
Location In pedestrian street in Merchant City, on eastern edge of city centre, not far from High Street station. Parking for 7 cars.
Restrictions Not suitable for ♿. Not suitable for small children. No dogs.
Credit cards Access, Amex, Visa.
Terms (Service at guests' discretion) B&B: single £28, double £50. Set lunch £8.25, dinner £10.25 (Mon–Wed), £16 (Thu–Sat).
Service/tipping: "We would like to see the industry move towards a sensible pricing policy which would allow realistic wage payments and career opportunities. Tipping confuses this issue."

One Devonshire Gardens [GFG] — *Tel* Glasgow (041) 339 2001 and 334 9494
1 Devonshire Gardens G12 OUX

A trendy, opulent hotel, "furnished in a taste of magisterial confidence", in the fashionable West End suburb one mile from the city centre, promoted to a full entry this year by many enthusiastic endorsements. A typical report, "We had the most amazing room, huge and in a decadent/Victorian style which managed to remain completely tasteful and unintimidating. Fresh fruit and magazines, numerous pillows on the vast four-poster, a bath in which a six-foot rugby player could lie flat out, and many big towels all combined to make an extremely comfortable nay sensuous place to stay." Another view, "One feels at home on an extremely grand scale". A few niggles: bedroom lights, "while very romantic, do not shine where one could read in bed, in the bath, or anywhere else for that matter"; rooms can be noisy as the hotel is on a busy crossroads; and there are many stairs to the top floor, but no lift. The restaurant, oppressively grand to some, acquired a new chef in October 1988. First reports: "Excellent even for vegetarians", and "Well presented but a little disappointing". (*Julia Kreitman, Mrs SE Atkinson, Shirley and John Mowbray; also Uwe Kitzinger, Angela Lambert, and others*)

Open All year except Christmas and New Year.
Rooms 8 double – 7 with bath and shower, 1 with shower, all with telephone, TV, baby-listening.
Facilities Drawing room/reception, restaurant, study.
Location 1 m from centre at intersection of Great Western Road and Hyndland Road.
Restrictions Not suitable for ♿. Dogs by prior arrangement, not in public rooms.
Credit cards All major cards accepted.
Terms [1989 rates] B&B (continental): single £82–£94, double £105–£120. Scottish breakfast £2 extra. Alc lunch (except Sat) £15, set dinner £24. No charge for children sharing parents' room; special meals by arrangement.
Service/tipping: "No service charge. All tips divided between staff."

The White House *Tel* Glasgow (041) 339 9375
11-13 Cleveden Crescent *Fax* (041) 337 1430
G12 0PA *Telex* 777582

The White House, awarded a César in 1988 for enterprise and innovation in a city hotel, is in the centre of a classical Georgian crescent about a mile from the city centre. It was designed by John Burnet Senior, the architect of Glasgow's imposing Stock Exchange. A set of three adjoining terrace houses comprising 32 suites and rooms, its prices compare favourably with the city's conventional five-star establishments. All rooms have a fully fitted kitchenette; the hotel also offers full room service for all meals, and has a tie-in with three downtown restaurants, *Rogano's*, the *Buttery* and the *Colonial*; guests can charge the bill to their hotel account and a courtesy Mercedes is provided for travel to and from the restaurant. Most rooms are large and high-ceilinged, with a dining table and chairs as well as easy chairs and sofas; the bathrooms have all the essentials for comfort. Recent visitors have praised the "good welcome, very helpful staff, decor and facilities". An American couple wrote, "it seemed sinful to stay at this wonderful hotel for only one night. Our *standard* double room was huge and could have slept a family of six (at no extra charge for kids!) And the service was perfect, friendlier than at many small country hotels." (*Linda Oswald and Brad Tomtishen; also JR Rees*)

Open All year.
Rooms Penthouse suite, 6 mews cottages, 17 double suites, 9 single suites, – all with bath and shower, telephone, radio, TV with in-house video, kitchenette. 3 ground-floor rooms.
Facilities Room service for meals; conference/private dining room. Small garden.

Location ½ m W of Glasgow town centre, off Great Western Road (A82). Private parking. Courtesy car to town centre between 8.15 and 8.30 am Mon–Fri.
Restrictions Not suitable for ♿. Dogs by arrangement only.
Credit cards All major cards accepted.
Terms (No service charge) Rooms: single £57, double £69, cottages £78, penthouse suite £115. Room service meals: breakfast from £4.50; full alc dinner £18.
Service/tipping: Tipping at guests' discretion. All tips shared equally amongst all staff."

GLENCRIPESDALE Highland — Map 5

Glencripesdale House — *Tel* Salen (096 785) 263
Glencripesdale, Loch Sunart
Acharacle, Argyllshire PH36 4JH

César award in 1989: Non-pareil hotel for those who want to get even further away from it all.

Bill and Susan Hemmings' highly sympathetic and civilised guest house is one of the most remote hostelries in Britain, standing, as it does, on the south side of Loch Sunart and at the end of an eight-mile rough track through forest and wildlife sanctuary that takes an hour to drive. (For those not having a car, Bill will collect from Fort William, the railhead.) Deer graze on the front lawn. The beach makes excellent beach-combing: "great varieties of shells from across the Atlantic and the most amazing examples of stones positively riddled with quartz and other bright metals, absolutely dazzling in the sunshine". *Glencripesdale* is a recently modernised 18th-century farmhouse; bedrooms are caringly furnished and comfortable; the book-lined sitting room, known as the library, is equally welcoming. "The terms are ridiculously low for a sojourn that is an unbelievable experience in an environment beautiful beyond compare, remote but not desolate, wild without savagery." "Sue and Bill Hemmings have succeeded in creating a perfect haven of rest for the jaded and exhausted. After a very short time in the atmosphere of *Glencripesdale*, one can feel health beginning to surge back again." "Mrs Hemming's meals are delicious, imaginative, and never repetitive – a miracle here." (*Stephanie Sowerby; W Ian Stewart, Judith M Schofield, HR, and others*) Two readers warn about some drawbacks of the terrain: "Nearly all walking from the house involves at least an hour's hike through dense woods, and when you do get out into the open, the going can be *exceedingly* rough if there has been much rain. The shore of the loch is suitable for walking only at low tides." "Once you get your car parked beside the hotel, it usually stays there until you leave, because to drive onto a good road would take you two hours there and back, so you don't!" *Important note*: Acharacle is only a postal address; it is a two-hour drive from the house. A suggestion from one reader, "When you make a booking, an offer to pick up supplies on the way would be much appreciated by the Hemmings."

Open 14 Feb–31 Oct. 23 Dec–7 Jan.
Rooms 4 double – 2 with bath, 2 with shower. 1 self-catering unit.
Facilities Library/lounge, dining room, children's playroom. 2-acre grounds; nature reserve ¼ m; rock and shingle beaches, fishing, nearby; wind surfer and inflatable boat with outboard motor for hire.

Location *Do not* go to Acharacle. Hotel is on S side of Loch Sunart. Take A861 towards Strontian; fork left on A884. *Glencripesdale* is through Laudale estate. (Hotel will send detailed directions.)
Restrictions Not suitable for ♿. Dogs by arrangement.
Credit cards None accepted.
Terms (No service charge) Dinner, B&B (including packed lunch) £42–£48, depending on length of stay. Reduced rates for children; special meals on request.
Service/tipping: "Tips not sought; any money given goes to Cancer Research Campaign, unless we have the occasional temporary help who might get something directly."

GLENLIVET Grampian — Map 5

Minmore House Hotel — *Tel* Glenlivet (08073) 378
Banffshire AB3 9DB

Veteran readers of the Guide may remember from a decade ago the name of Belinda Luxmoore, as the owner of *Foxdown Manor*, Bideford. Now, after a sojourn in Australia, she is back on the domestic hotel scene with daughter Jessica and son-in-law Nick Holmes, at this newly refurbished Victorian country house in the heart of the whisky country. *Minmore House* was formerly the home of George Smith, founder of Glenlivet, whose distillery is just next door. The house is in four acres of secluded garden above the river Livet on which it has fishing rights, and fishing is also available on the Avon and Spey. The area, beautiful and untouristy, has much to offer non-fishing folk: lots of good walks around. Alerted by an enthusiastic report from an alumna of *Foxdown, Gillian Cave* – "Warmest of welcomes. . .huge bedroom. . .Many charming touches-. . .Vases of flowers, pot-pourri, fresh fruit. . .Quite wonderful five-course dinner. . .Breakfast is help yourself to a splendour of wonderful things-. . .Marvellous value" – we sent along an inspector who, after an unfortunate start in a cold room with lukewarm water, felt the Luxmoore family had redeemed themselves and greatly enjoyed all the hospitality and the care of the owners for guests' welfare. She was accompanied by a friend who is already planning a return visit with her husband and children. The proof of the pudding?

Open Easter–Nov.
Rooms 1 suite, 8 double, 2 single – all with bath, and tea-making facilities.
Facilities Hall, drawing room, bar, dining room. 4½-acre grounds with terraced garden, croquet, tennis, swimming pool. Fishing rights on the Livet, and by arrangement on the Avon and Spey.
Location From Grantown on Spey take A95 to Ballindalloch and turn right onto B9008. Follow signs to Glenlivet.
Restrictions Only restaurant suitable for ♿. No dogs in public rooms.
Credit cards Access, Visa.
Terms (No service charge) B&B £25; Dinner, B&B £39. Weekly rates. 1-night bookings may be refused if made far in advance. No charge for small children sharing parents' room; special meals.
Service/tipping: "If guests offer a tip they are always assured that it is quite unnecessary as our terms are completely inclusive. If a guest is very insistent the tip is distributed evenly between the staff (not *family!*)"

> If you have had recent experience of a good hotel that ought to be in the Guide, please write to us at once. Report forms are to be found at the back. Procrastination is the thief of the next edition.

GREENLAW Borders — Map 5

Purves Hall — *Tel* Leitholm (089 084) 558
Greenlaw, Nr Duns
Berwickshire TD10 6UJ

This small country house, built in 1908, is set in ten acres of wooded parkland. It has lovely views south to the Cheviot Hills and secluded gardens, as well as paddocks and stabling for visiting horses. *Purves Hall* was bought three years ago by Wing Commander Brian Everett and his wife, Sheila, and they have made many improvements. "Achieves that feeling of home", was our inspector's verdict. "Two dogs, two cats. One feels that everything here is to be used. Not at all posh, but not in the least tatty. I liked it very much." Here is another view, "My favourite kind of establishment. Perhaps a tiny bit old-fashioned – our shower cabinet must have been the great-great-grandfather of the one we have at home but it worked better than the 1988 version. Bedrooms very well equipped, and the downstairs rooms have roaring fires, family photographs and large, squashy sofas. But the real reason for visiting *Purves Hall* is the food. Sheila Everett is a talented cook. We ate superb dinners three nights running; the food was inventive and interesting but not outlandish, the quality and freshness remarkable." Vegetarians are catered for. (*Patricia Erskine-Hill; also John Rae*)

Open All year.
Rooms 1 suite, 6 double, 1 single – all with bath and/or shower, telephone, radio, TV, tea-making facilities and baby-listening.
Facilities Lounge bar, restaurant. 11-acre grounds with swimming pool, tennis, croquet and mini-golf; stables for visiting horses. Fishing, shooting.
Location SE of Greenlaw. Signposted off A697.
Restriction No dogs in public rooms.
Credit cards Access, Visa.
Terms [1989 rates] B&B £22–£34. Set lunch £7.50, dinner £14. Reduced rates and special meals for children.

INVERNESS Highland — Map 5

Dunain Park Hotel — *Tel* Inverness (0463) 230512
Inverness
Inverness-shire IV3 6JN

Our post-bag has had plenty of favourable reports on *Dunain Park* this year. It re-entered the Guide two years ago when Ann and Edward Nicoll became owners. An Italianate early-19th-century country house, the hotel has eight bedrooms (six in the main house and two in a garden cottage), all individually decorated "in the most delightful fashion", and all very warm. There are books everywhere, "*good* books" a reader hastens to add, "I found the *Oxford Book of Verse* in my bedroom." The lounges have log fires and there are pleasing views from all the windows; the hotel sits in six acres of gardens and woodlands overlooking the Caledonian Canal. "Like a well-lived-in baronial home. Very friendly and welcoming." "Service excellent but not obsequious." "Reception rooms are lovely. Garden cottage very peaceful, next to huge walled kitchen garden where the hotel's produce is grown." "A gem. Ann Nicoll is a great improviser in the kitchen, doing wonderful things with whatever

This ticket is printed to conform to the Small Lotteries and Amusements Act, 1976, and organised by the Promoter under such conditions.

№ 2121

GREY COURT SCHOOL RUGBY TOUR 1991

GRAND DRAW

1st PRIZE—1 CASE CHAMPAGNE

and other prizes

The draw will take place on Friday, 25th May, 1990 at 4 p.m. at Grey Court School, Ham.

Promoter: Mr. J. Caims, c/o Grey Court School, Ham Street, Ham, Richmond, Surrey.

Tickets 50p. each

Coates Printing Works, 53, South Street, Isleworth, Middlesex

happens to be available locally." Breakfasts are abundant. There is a heated indoor pool and sauna where guests can work off the splendid food. We appreciate a note on *Dunain Park*'s menus: "Guests are asked not to smoke in the dining room. If you wish to withdraw to a lounge please let us know and we will be happy to delay your next course." (*AB Russell, Gillian Fairchild, Dr JR Hamilton, Amanda Garrett, G Maclean, and others*)

Open All year. Restricted meal service during owners' holidays – probably 2 weeks Feb, 2 weeks Nov.
Rooms 2 suites, 6 double – all with bath (2 also have shower), telephone, radio and TV; tea-making facilities by arrangement. Suites, both with kitchenette, in converted coach house, 100 yards from hotel.
Facilities 2 lounges, dining room. Indoor heated swimming pool, sauna. 6-acre grounds with garden, badminton and croquet. Fishing, shooting, golf, tennis nearby.
Location 2½ m S of centre of Inverness, off A82 to Fort William. Turn left shortly after Craig Dunain hospital which is on right.
Restrictions Not suitable for ♿. No smoking in dining room. Not suitable for children. No dogs in public rooms.
Credit cards All major cards accepted.
Terms (Service at guests' discretion) B&B £39–£49. Set lunch £12.50, dinner £21.50. Low season breaks.
Service/tipping: "Any tips received are shared equally among all staff."

IONA Strathclyde — Map 5

Argyll Hotel — *Tel* Iona (068 17) 334
Isle of Iona
Argyllshire PA76 6SJ

Our only entry for the tiny pilgrim island of Iona (three-and-a-half-miles long and one-and-a-half wide), reached by a five-minute ferry journey from the Isle of Mull. Mrs Fiona Menzies' *Argyll Hotel* stands in the village street, facing the sea, with its front lawn running down to the shore. It entered the Guide two years ago with the following report: "I went for one night and stayed four, seduced by the island itself, the drawbridge-up pleasure of seeing the last ferry leave in the evening bearing the day's visitors away, and not least by the particular attraction of the *Argyll Hotel*, right by the sea, whose sound lulls one to sleep at night. The bedrooms are smallish, cottagey, each with an original watercolour or etching of real merit (and, despite the Gulf Stream, an electric blanket). There are two sitting rooms with open fires and no TV, full of local history and bird books, and a built-on sun lounge with creaking wicker chairs. The atmosphere is extraordinarily peaceful." A recent visitor adds, "Wonderful food – they bake their own bread, grow their own vegetables, make their own yoghurt and use local salmon and venison. Dinner ridiculously cheap. A vegetarian alternative main course is always provided though the menus are otherwise 'no choice'. Conversation with other guests after dinner included when we were there a Benedictine monk, a couple from Hawaii cycling 1,700 miles around Britain, an American attorney and her daughter and two German walkers complete with *lederhosen*. A great place for getting away from it all – or most of it anyway." (*Rosemary Davidson, AE Jones*)

Open Easter–mid-Oct.
Rooms 10 double, 9 single – 2 with bath and shower, 7 with bath, all with tea-making facilities; baby-listening available.
Facilities 2 lounges, sun lounge, dining room. ½-acre grounds on seashore with rocks, sand, safe bathing; sea and loch fishing.
Location In the village, near jetty. Iona is reached by direct steamer from Oban in summer or by car or bus across Mull to Fionnphort and then passenger ferry. No cars on Iona. Carparks at Oban and Fionnphort.
Restrictions Not suitable for ♿. No dogs in dining room.
Credit cards Access, Visa.
Terms (No service charge) B&B £18–£25; dinner, B&B £28–£35. Set dinner £10.80; snacks and light lunches from £2. Reductions for children July/Aug.
Service/tipping: "We agree with your policy, but any tips given are distributed equally among all staff."

KENTALLEN Highland — Map 5

Ardsheal House [GFG] — *Tel* Duror (063 174) 227
Kentallen of Appin
Argyllshire PA38 4BX

Ardsheal House, historic home of the Stewarts of Appin, was built in the 1500s, sacked in 1745, and rebuilt in 1760. It featured in Robert Louis Stevenson's *Kidnapped*, and stands in a garden full of superb mature trees, in a commanding position overlooking Loch Linnhe and the Morvern hills. "The setting of this hotel is amazing. Up a long single-track drive and into the woods." It is owned and run by two Americans, Bob Taylor and his wife Jane, with polish and professionalism. They winter in the USA and run the hotel in Scotland in the summer. It is on a circuit for visiting Americans who often form the majority of guests. Many praise the warm welcome of Mrs Taylor, the "friendly staff", and the "outstanding and imaginative dinners". The menu offers a limited choice; dinner, presided over by a kilted Bob Taylor, is at a fixed time; coffee afterwards "can be drunk standing up, American style, which enables you to get away from bores". British as well as American guests have appreciated the conviviality of the house, but there have also been complaints of lack of hot water and disappointment with the furnishings – "a wide bed but not long enough, *minute* bath towels, cheap soap." The Taylors tell us there has been more "sprucing up" of bedrooms and baths this year, and that there's a new conservatory addition to the dining room. (*JR Rees, Philip Tattersall, and others*)

Open Easter–1 Nov.
Rooms 12 double, 1 single – all with bath and/or shower, and baby-listening.
Facilities 3 lounges (1 with TV), snooker room, restaurant. 900-acre grounds with tennis court. Rocky beach behind hotel; fishing, boating, riding nearby.
Location 17 m S of Fort William. From Ballachulish roundabout take A828 towards Oban; hotel is 4 m further on, on right.
Restriction Only dining room suitable for ♿. No smoking in dining room.
Credit cards Access, Amex, Visa.
Terms (No service charge) Dinner, B&B £50–£70. Lunch from £6, set dinner £25. 1-night bookings refused for reservations made more than 3 weeks in advance. Reduced rates for children sharing parents' room; high teas.
Service/tipping: "We do not ask for gratuities. If guests want to contribute something to the staff, money goes into a 'kitty' and is distributed to everyone on a work-done basis twice during the season."

Holly Tree Hotel *Tel* Duror (063 174) 292
Kentallen of Appin
Argyllshire PA38 4BY

Kentallen's former railway station right on the shore of Loch Linnhe, now the *Holly Tree Hotel*, entered the Guide last year with this appreciation, "The old station has been enlarged and extensively renovated but still retains Edwardian features – the Glasgow Art Nouveau ticket office is intact; the Railway Bar was formerly the station's tea room. But the bedrooms are distinctly of the eighties, spacious and delightfully furnished in a combination of traditional (lots of pine) and modish (peach chintz etc), with expensive, specially designed carpets throughout. Wonderful views over the loch, and a mile of private waterside grounds, quiet but not isolated." A reader this year writes this endorsement, "You will not get the grandeur or the superior deference of *Claridge's*, but you will get charming, relaxed, efficient service, and delightful food from extensive five-course menus." (*AB Russell, and others*)

Open Mar–Oct, Christmas and New Year.
Rooms 11 double – 19 with bath and shower, 1 with bath, all with telephone, TV and tea-making facilities. 2 ground-floor rooms.
Facilities Residents' lounge, lounge bar, restaurant. 5-acre grounds with slipway, boats for residents' use, fishing, safe bathing in loch. Riding, windsurfing, skiing nearby.
Location On A82, 3 m S of Ballachulish Bridge.
Restrictions No smoking in dining room. Dogs at management's discretion; not in public rooms.
Credit cards Access, Visa.
Terms B&B: single occupancy £34.50–£37, double £61–£68; dinner, B&B: single £52–£58, double £96–£110. Set dinner £21.50. Autumn/winter breaks; Christmas and New Year packages. Reduced rates for children sharing parents' room; special meals.

KILCHRENAN Strathclyde — Map 5

Ardanaiseig Hotel *Tel* Kilchrenan (086 63) 333
Kilchrenan, by Taynuilt *Fax* (086 63) 222
Argyllshire PA35 1HE

On shore of Loch Awe, handsome, large grey stone Scottish baronial mansion with celebrated woodland garden. Comfortable, prettily decorated drawing room, welcoming library, beautifully appointed dining room offering plain grills (Angus beef, fillet of salmon, West Coast lobster) in addition to five-course set dinner. 14 bedrooms vary in decor, all have private facilities. Open mid-Apr–end Oct. Dinner, B&B £75–£85. Set lunch £7.50–£12, dinner £26. In earlier editions, now newly nominated, as Jonathan Brown, whose family home this has been since 1964, has personally assumed the management. More reports please.

Taychreggan Hotel [GFG] *Tel* Kilchrenan (086 63) 211
Kilchrenan, by Taynuilt
Argyllshire PA35 1HQ

An admirably converted old fishing inn peacefully located on Loch Awe, for long a favourite with Guide readers under the Taylors' regime, has new owners, John and Monika Tyrrell. Our inspector, visiting some weeks after the Tyrrells moved in, found much to her liking: comfortable bedrooms, individually furnished – Laura Ashley in the main; impeccable private bathrooms; a delightful dining room with arched windows looking over the water and two lounges simply decorated but with sympathetic, low, modern chairs. She enjoyed her five-course dinner, too, with reasonable choice of starters, main course and desserts. "Breakfast was delightful – good home-made rhubarb jam and croissants, beautifully cooked poached eggs with chopped herbs, tall wine glasses full of chilled fruit juice, and nice friendly service from local waitresses." But inevitably she encountered some lapses in the welcome and the upkeep. Another reader, arriving even earlier in the season, was miffed to find that his booked four-poster bed had been taken ten minutes earlier by a couple in a Porsche, his telephone did not work, the dining room, bar and bathroom were cold and his red wine was positively chilled. But these were early days – teething troubles are to be expected. *Taychreggan* has an exceptional location and we hope things will soon be as smooth and welcoming as before. More reports welcome.

Open End Mar–end Oct, 4 days over Christmas.
Rooms 2 suites, 14 double, 1 single – 16 with bath and/or shower, all with telephone, radio and baby-listening.
Facilities Lounge/hall, 2 lounges, TV lounge, bar, dining room. 25-acre grounds with 500-yard loch frontage; fishing, boating. Riding, shooting, walking nearby.
Location 18 m from Oban, on N shore of Loch Awe, 7 m S of Taynuilt, off B845.
Restriction Not suitable for ♿.
Credit cards All major cards accepted.
Terms (No service charge) Dinner, B&B: single £54–£60, double £108–£116, suite £122–£130. Bar lunches. Full alc dinner £25.00. Reduced rates and special meals for children.
Service/tipping: "Shared equally among all staff from housekeepers to gardeners."

KILDRUMMY Grampian — Map 5

Kildrummy Castle Hotel
Kildrummy, by Alford
Aberdeenshire AB3 8RA

Tel Kildrummy (097 55) 71288
Telex 94012529

One of those great Scottish baronial houses built around the turn of the century, *Kildrummy Castle* has been a hotel for the past 25 years. It is in the heart of the Donside, about an hour's drive from Aberdeen in 15 acres of fine gardens overlooking the ruins of a 13th-century castle. Its entry was in italics last year for lack of feedback, but it is urged back to a full entry by many appreciative correspondents. The appeal for anglers is its 3½ mile private stretch of the Don for trout and salmon fishing. Further attraction for some is the library, "a fascinating fabric-covered room full of character, with a crackling log fire". Another writer comments on the "stunning views over the hotel's gardens" and his "spacious, well-equipped and exquisitely decorated bedroom". Lunch and dinner menus offer more than a dozen choices including hearty Scottish soups, West Coast scallops, North Sea prawns, and pheasant, as well as lighter dishes such as omelettes, and a good selection for vegetarians – "nothing too extravagant, but good-sized portions and well cooked." Other visitors have praised the service as "correct and friendly" without being obtrusive. Only complaints from guests whose visit was marred, in one case, by another's cigar smoke in the bar, in the dining room and in the lounge afterwards, and in another, by stale cigarette smells in the bedroom. Some restriction on smoking would have been appreciated. (*G Maclean, HM Schottlaender, Holly Howard, and others*)

Open 5 Mar–4 Jan.
Rooms 15 double, 1 single – all with bath and shower, telephone, radio, TV, tea-making facilities.
Facilities Drawing room, library, lounge bar, dining room. On 7,500-acre estate; 3½ m private fishing on river Don. Golf nearby.
Location NE of Ballater on A97 Ballater to Huntley road.
Restrictions Not suitable for ♿.
Credit cards Access, Amex, Visa.
Terms (No service charge.) B&B £38–£43; Dinner, B&B £42–£59.50. Set lunch £11, dinner £18.50; full alc £23. Children free if sharing with 2 adults; special meals.

KILFINAN Strathclyde — Map 5

Kilfinan Hotel [GFG] — *Tel* Kilfinan (070 082) 201
Kilfinan, Nr Tighnabruaich
Argyllshire PA21 2AP

A century-old black-and-white coaching inn in the remote and tiny clachan of Kilfinan which entered the Guide two years ago after an inspector's visit. Particularly noted were the warm welcome from kilted Tony Wignell who runs the hotel with his wife Gina; the bar with a log fire and lots of magazines; the two dining rooms with rich burgundy wall-coverings, immaculate napery and fresh flowers, and the "exceptionally good four-course dinners, with choices at each course except for soup". Visitors' reports during the past year have been unanimous in confirming this praise, "Our fourth visit, and this year's stay as delightful as ever," commented one writer, who especially praised the cooking. "So peaceful we can't wait to return. Spotlessly clean, very friendly atmosphere, warm cosy bar. Well worth the 16 miles of single-track road," wrote another. Bedrooms are described as large and bright, and the bathrooms well stocked with extras, "even indigestion pills and Andrews Liver Salts". The hotel is popular as a base for hunting, shooting and fishing, but has also been recommended as "a most restful place to spend a few days, and ideal for bird-watchers, painters, photographers and walkers". (*KB Dallas, Mrs R Grogan; Mrs Ruth Roberts, DJR Fletcher*)

Rooms 11 double – 10 with bath (1 also has shower), all with telephone, radio, TV and baby-listening.
Facilities Public bar, bar lounge, 2 dining rooms; functions room. 1-acre grounds. Private sandy beach on Loch Fyne 1 m. Fishing on Kilfinan Burn; sea angling, golf, deer stalking, clay-pigeon shooting nearby.
Location In tiny village, next to church. On B8000 9 m NW of Tighnabruaich.
Restrictions Not suitable for ♿. No dogs.
Credit cards Access, Amex, Visa.
Terms (Service at guests' discretion) B&B: single occupancy £38, double £56; dinner, B&B: single £56.50, double £93. Set dinner £18.50; full alc £25. Reduced rates for children sharing parents' room; special meals.

> Please never tell a hotel you intend to send a report to the Guide. Anonymity is essential for objectivity.

KILMORE Strathclyde — Map 5

Glenfeochan House *Tel* Kilmore (063 177) 273
Kilmore, by Oban
Argyllshire PA34 4QR

New to the Guide last year, a turreted, Victorian, former baronial home of the Clan Campbell. It stands at the head of Loch Feochan a few miles south of Oban in a 350-acre estate which includes a six-acre garden, one of the Great Gardens of the Scottish Highlands. It is run as a highly select guest house by Patricia Baber, a former Cordon Bleu teacher, and her son, James Petley. Its nominator waxed lyrical, "It is best to arrive after dark – the soft warm lighting of the entrance hall and the magnificent staircase with its beautifully pargeted canopy tell you at once that you've made the right choice. A most excellent dinner in the elegant dining room, followed by coffee in an equally elegant drawing room. Our hostess not only devised and cooked the superb dinner, she is also responsible for the equally superb decor throughout the house. Next morning you gasp at the splendour of the setting, unsuspected the night before: trees, loch and mountain changing all the time as sun and cloud chase over the landscape. At the right time of year you will be stunned by the colour – great carpets of daffodils and snowdrops so thick you cannot see the grass, mountainous masses of rhododendrons, many species not to be seen elsewhere in Britain." (*RC Browning*) There are only three bedrooms; meals (taken communally) are for residents only – guests are consulted about their meals in the morning; much of the food is produced by the estate. More reports please.

Open 1 Mar–31 Oct.
Rooms 3 double – all with bath, radio, TV and tea-making facilities.
Facilities Drawing room, dining room. 350-acre estate with 6-acre garden. Salmon and sea-trout fishing free to guests, clay-pigeon shooting, loch bathing.
Location 5 m S of Oban on A816 at head of Loch Feochan.
Restrictions Not suitable for ♿. No children under 10. Dogs by arrangement only; not in bedrooms or public rooms.
Credit cards None accepted.
Terms B&B double £85–£100. Packed lunch £5, set dinner £22.
Service/tipping: "Tipping is not encouraged; any money left is distributed among all staff."

KINBUCK Central — Map 5

Cromlix House [GFG] *Tel* Dunblane (0786) 822125
Kinbuck, Dunblane *Fax* (0786) 825450
Perthshire FK15 9JT *Telex* 779959 CLXHSE

It is now seven years since the Hon Ronald Eden, whose family have owned the 5,000 acres of *Cromlix* for four centures, turned his massive Victorian house into a luxury hotel – "One of the few hotels able to cater to international tastes without losing the feel of a Scottish manor house." *Cromlix House* is indeed grand in a formal way: the large entrance hall is panelled, the drawing room has comfortable chintz chairs and a giant log basket beside the elegant fireplace, the dining room is candle-lit at night, with stiffly starched white tablecloths. Much of the fish and game comes from the estate. There is a Victorian conservatory, a good library, a chapel, one fishing loch within strolling distance – others nearby, a grouse moor, and complete peace and quiet with lovely views over wooded grounds where deer, pheasants, wild duck and rabbits abound. There are large bedrooms with even bigger bathrooms. "We had the most outrageous suite – pink all the way through, huge bath and a *commode*. The whole thing was marvellous. The most civilised and relaxing break we've ever spent." The house is perfectly suited to the sort of formal shooting party that Edward VII attended here, and which still takes place today; the staff are "charming, skilled and unobtrusive". The young chef, Mark Salter, is praised for his six-course meals (no choice previously, this year improved by the addition of three choices for each course). Last year a reader criticised her four-poster bed which was not lit for reading. *Cromlix House* replies, "*All* bedrooms have been rewired during 1989; all have dressing-table lamps, and the suites now have reading lamps." (*Dr and Mrs AM Mathewson; D and M Thal, Anthony Lewis, and others*) One dissenter found much to criticise: inefficient, unfriendly service, poor upkeep of grounds, pretentious over-priced food at dinner and a sub-standard breakfast.

Open All year except 2 weeks Feb.
Rooms 8 suites, 6 double – all with bath, shower, telephone, TV, baby-listening; 12 with radio.
Facilities Drawing room, morning room, library, dining room, conservatory; functions facilities. 5,000-acre grounds with croquet, clay-pigeon shooting, fishing, tennis, riding and shooting (advance booking advisable).
Location ¼ m N of Kinbuck, 4 m S of Braco. Take A9 out of Dunblane; turn left on to B8033; go through Kinbuck village, take second left after a small bridge.
Restrictions Only dining room suitable for ♿. Dogs by arrangement; not in public rooms.
Credit cards All major cards accepted.
Terms [1989 rates] (No service charge) B&B: single occupancy £75–£110, double from £110, suite £145–£175. Set lunch £7–£20, dinner £30. Winter breaks. 3-day Christmas and New Year packages. Reduced rates for children sharing parents' room; special meals.
Service/tipping: "Our staff do not expect to be tipped. We don't think a service charge should be added or tipping encouraged."

KINGUSSIE Highland — Map 5

The Osprey Hotel — *Tel* Kingussie (0540) 661510
Kingussie
Inverness-shire PH21 1EN

Readers continue to appreciate the *Osprey* for its reasonable tariff, its welcome and its good cooking. "More a very comfortable guest house than a hotel maybe, but the better for it." "Although tiny and – at a glance – unremarkable as a place to stay, it aspires to country-house atmosphere, and through the efforts of Duncan and Pauline Reeves, achieves that goal." The public rooms are small, and guests may be asked to share tables at dinner, "but the delicacy with which two very different couples were seated together – two academics (us) plus a City couple up to display their dogs at a field trial – was delightful and successful." The food is generous and robust (avocado roulade, grouse soufflé, venison casserole), and vegetarians are happily catered for; there's usually a good cheese board, and the wine list is extensive, with a very modest mark-up. Bedrooms are clean and comfortable, though only one has a private bath, and the hotel's proximity to the road produces some traffic noise at night. *The Osprey* is well placed in the heart of the Spey Valley for all the leisure activities of the region – walking, fishing, golf, riding, skiing. Aviemore is 12 miles off, the Cairngorms 30 minutes by car. (*AR Braunmuller; Amanda Garrett, David and Patricia Hawkins, and others*)

Open 27 Jan–4 Nov; also 28 Dec–7 Jan.
Rooms 7 double, 1 single – 1 with bath and shower, 3 with shower.
Facilities Lounge, TV room, dining room. Small garden. Golf, fishing, gliding, sailing, canoeing, wind surfing nearby; sports facilities at the Aviemore Centre.
Location Near A9, about 12 m SW of Aviemore. 200 yds from village centre; parking for 10 cars.
Restrictions Not suitable for ♿. No dogs in public rooms.
Credit cards All major cards accepted.
Terms (No service charge) Dinner, B&B £32–£46. Set dinner £17. Reduced rates for children.
Service/tipping: "If people wish to tip – and some definitely do – the gratuity is accepted with thanks and given to staff as bonus at Christmas."

KINLOCHBERVIE Highland — Map 5

The Kinlochbervie Hotel — *Tel* Kinlochbervie (097 182) 275
Kinlochbervie, by Lairg — *Fax* (097 182) 438
Sutherland IV27 4RP

The Kinlochbervie Hotel, only 27 miles from Cape Wrath, is the most northerly entry in the Guide for the Scottish mainland. It is in lovely countryside surrounded by innumerable sandy beaches and rocky coves, and looks down over the two harbours of one of Scotland's busiest fishing ports. Rebuilt after a fire, it is a custom-built modern hotel, inside and out. Despite its "non-Scottish" exterior, almost all our reports this year have praised the hotel for its comfort, high standard of amenities in the bedrooms, "bright and cheery" decor, and the helpfulness of the proprietors, David and Geraldine Gregory. High praise, too, for the food: "Dinner was magnificent, with the finest freshest fish we have ever eaten, 40 minutes after it had been delivered from the port." "The cooking, with several choices in each course, is quite elaborate and beautifully presented." "My-six-year-old was given a large choice for her high tea, and our dinner was good – superb fillet of lamb. Breakfasts were excellent, squeezed orange juice and fresh rolls." Readers should be warned that only six rooms have sea views and that the bar can be noisy at weekends, but the Gregorys have redesigned and insulated the bar area to minimise the problem. All in all, a hotel that almost everyone seems to find exceptional so far north in Scotland. One reader sums up, "A truly grand experience heightened by juxtaposition with such a rustic rural landscape". (*RP Wynings; also April Young, Pat and Michael Blanchard, Mrs SR Wood, EM Lawson, Mrs MH Box, and others*)

Open All year but restricted service mid-Nov–early Mar – booking essential.
Rooms 14 double – all with bath (4 also have shower), telephone, radio, TV and tea-making facilities; baby-listening by arrangement.
Facilities Lounge, bar, reading room, dining room. ½-acre grounds. Sea and loch fishing, safe, sandy beaches (but the water is cold), 9-hole golf course.
Location Only hotel in tiny village on B801 on N side of Loch Inchard.
Restrictions Not suitable for ♿. No very young children in dining room for dinner (high tea provided). No dogs in public rooms.
Credit cards All major cards accepted.

Credit cards All major cards accepted.
Terms B&B: single occupancy £36–£77, double £48–£93, reduced rates for 2 or more nights. No charge for children sharing parents' room. Bar lunches; set dinner £23.50.
Service/tipping: "No tips are expected but we do not decline if offered. They are distributed to all members of staff."

KNIPOCH Strathclyde — Map 5

Knipoch Hotel [GFG]
Knipoch, by Oban
Argyllshire PA34 4QT

Tel Kilninver (085 26) 251
Fax (085 26) 249

A smart, formal, well-furnished, fairly pricey country house hotel, run by the Craig family. *Knipoch* is an attractive two-storey white-washed house in a particularly beautiful and tranquil setting beside Loch Feochan, an arm of the sea stretching four miles inland just south of Oban. Inside are welcoming log fires, attractive flower arrangements, lots of highly polished wood surfaces, Persian rugs on stripped pine floors and modern pictures on dark green walls. Most readers continue to be pleased: "The food was excellent, home-made and fresh. The room was very comfortable with deep leather armchairs and lots of reading matter." "The best hotel out of nine we stayed at in Scotland." (*Alistair Seabright, MW Atkinson, Ronald McNeill, and others*) But there have been grumbles: about the food – more vegetables would have been appreciated by one party, helpings too large for another; about furnishings in some of the rooms; and about slow service at meals. (See under Oban in *The Good Food Guide*.)

Open Mid-Feb–mid-Nov and New Year. Lunch by arrangement Nov, Mar, Apr.
Rooms 18 double – all with bath and shower, telephone, radio, TV, and baby-listening. Tea-making facilities on request.
Facilities Reception hall, lounge, bar, 3 dining rooms. 3-acre grounds. On sea loch; fishing, sailing, golf, tennis, hill walking, pony trekking nearby.
Location 6 m S of Oban on A816.
Restrictions Not really suitable for ♿. No dogs.
Credit cards All major cards accepted.
Terms (No service charge) B&B £48; Dinner, B&B £75. Set lunch £12.50, dinner £27. Children under 5 half price; special meals.
Service/tipping: "If tips are offered they are not refused, since to refuse can offend some guests. However, they are never *solicited."*

LANGBANK Strathclyde — Map 5

Gleddoch House Hotel
Langbank, Renfrewshire
PA14 6YE

Tel Langbank (047 554) 711
Fax (047 554) 201
Telex 779801

A mixed bag of reports this year on *Gleddoch House*, a useful alternative to staying in the centre of Glasgow (five miles from the airport and 20 minutes by the M8 from the city centre). It stands in a 250-acre estate and its outlook is wholly rural – there are lovely views across the Clyde to the hills of Loch Lomond. The house was built in the twenties by the shipping magnate, Sir James Lithgow, and converted to a small country hotel in the seventies, owned and run by a consortium led by Christopher Longden, the manager. A plus for golfers is that there is a course within the grounds – also a squash court, a snooker table, riding stables and trout fishing. Furnished in plush style, with many pictures formerly belonging to the Lithgows, *Gleddoch* offers some single bedrooms equipped for the business traveller – they have desks and portable telephones. Readers last year praised the service throughout the hotel, and the improved kitchen under the direction of the "impressive chef, Charles Price". Some readers still sing his praises but others have been severely disappointed. The restaurant staff has also come in for criticism for amateurish service. More reports please.

Open All year except 26/27 Dec and 1/2 Jan.
Rooms 1 suite, 25 double, 7 single – all with bath and/or shower, telephone, radio, TV, tea-making facilities and baby-listening; some with business facilities.
Facilities Lounge, bar, restaurant; conference facilities. 250-acre grounds with Golf and Country Club for squash, snooker, plunge pool, bar and restaurant, of which guests are automatic members, riding school.
Location Leave M8 at B789 Langbank/Houston exit. Follow signs to left and then right; after ½ m driveway signposted on left.
Restrictions Not suitable for ♿. No dogs in public rooms.
Credit cards All major cards accepted.
Terms (No service charge) B&B: single £75–£85, double £108, suite £135. Set lunch £14.50, dinner 27.50, full alc £35. Weekend breaks. Reduced rates for children sharing parents' room; special meals on request.
Service/tipping: "We do not charge for service."

NAIRN Highland — Map 5

Clifton Hotel — *Tel* Nairn (0667) 53119
Viewfield Street, Nairn
Nairnshire IV12 4HW

Not for the first time, Gordon Macintyre, maître chef, impresario and *patron* extraordinary of the *Clifton* has had a mixed press. Winner of a César in 1987 for utterly acceptable mild eccentricity, his old family hotel looking over the Moray Firth and stuffed with paintings, sculptures, bas-reliefs, *objets trouvés,* books galore, "the indifferent nestling happily against the tasteful, the tasteless complementing the outrageous" is just too much for some purists. "We simply loved the divine clutter," writes one enchanted reader; "it has the true touch of a connoisseur which illuminates every public room of this remarkable theatrical hotel/restaurant. It wouldn't be true to itself or its actor/manager if it wasn't a weeny bit over the top and collector camp." (*Dr J Batty*) "The proprietor is the best hotelier I have ever encountered, with time to have an interesting and apparently unhurried little chat with every guest." (*HJ Hough*) But then there are the detractors: "The clutter on every available surface is neither fascinating nor interesting, just plain irritating. The menu, all in French, is needlessly pretentious. Everything is contrived for effect. Nothing is genuine." But this critic did concede that the bedroom was quite adequate "with a double bed that nearly required a ladder to mount", that "the vast supply of luxurious toiletries compensated for the smallness of the bathroom", and the food was "really quite good". But even the food, served in the large sea-facing dining room, which doubles as a concert hall or theatre in the winter, divides the critics. The hotel uses its own hens, ducks and geese, the fish is fresh and the salmon wild, and the bread, oatcakes, muesli, marmalade and jams are all made in the kitchen. Mr Macintyre believes his cooking is better than ever, and some readers enthusiastically agree. But to one reader, a supporter of this "delightful *sui generis* hotel", meals have been "very *beta* and the kitchen lets the show down with a bit of a bump". The *Clifton* experience is never bland: long may Gordon Macintyre play the histrionic host – we wish there were more like him.

Open Easter–end Oct.
Rooms 9 double, 7 single – 15 with bath, 1 with shower; beds have continental quilts, but conventional bedding available on request.
Facilities Drawing room, sitting room, TV room, 2 restaurants. 1-acre grounds. Fishing, shooting, riding, beach, tennis courts, swimming pool, golf nearby.
Location 500 yds from town centre; coming from Inverness turn left at roundabout on A96. Parking for 20 cars.
Restrictions Not suitable for ♿. No dogs in dining room.
Credit cards All major cards accepted.
Terms (No service charge) B&B: single £40–£50, double £70–£85. Set lunch £10–£12, dinner £15–£17.50; full alc £20.
Service/tipping: "Service charges should be abolished. They are quite anachronistic."

NEWTONMORE Highland — Map 5

Ard-Na-Coille Hotel [GFG] *Tel* Newtonmore (054 03) 214
Kingussie Road, Newtonmore
Inverness-shire PH20 1AY

Plenty of encouraging reports on the relatively new owners, Nancy Ferrier and Barry Cottam, at this small Edwardian shooting lodge set high above the road in two acres of pine trees, with magnificent views over Strathspey towards the Cairngorms. A three-year programme of upgrading is now two-thirds complete; central heating has been installed, more *en suite* bathrooms added, and the dining room redecorated. Many readers praise the owners for their welcome and their evident desire to please. Full marks, too, for the housekeeping, with "every amenity for the comfort of the guests". The greatest praise, however, is for the kitchen. "Excellent and quite different dinners", "Wonderful subtleties of flavour", and much more in the same vein. Barry Cottam is a wine enthusiast and has included many rarities from his own cellar in the list, which is "fairly priced". (*Mimi and Edward Younie; Mr and Mrs John F Barclay, AJB and D Laybourne, and others*)

Open 30 Dec–31 Oct.
Rooms 6 double, 3 single – 3 with bath, 4 with shower, 6 with WC, all with radio and baby-listening.
Facilities Lounge, TV lounge, dining room; drying room; terrace. 2-acre grounds. Fishing, golf, pony trekking, sailing, gliding, shooting, walking, bird-watching nearby; skiing at Aviemore 15 m.
Location Leave A9 at Newtonmore/Kingussie signs. Hotel is at northernmost edge of Newtonmore, just outside speed restriction signs.
Restrictions Not suitable for ♿. Dogs in certain bedrooms only, never in public rooms.
Credit cards None accepted.
Terms (No service charge) B&B £15–£28; dinner, B&B £28–£45. Set dinner £17.50. Special breaks. Reduced rates for children sharing parents' room; high teas.
Service/tipping: Service charges should be abolished by law. Tipping is an iniquitous anachronism. We do not expect gratuities from our customers, but if any are left staff receive an equal share and the remainder is used to support a community charity."

OLD MELDRUM Grampian — Map 5

Meldrum House Hotel — *Tel* Old Meldrum (065) 12 2294
Old Meldrum, Aberdeenshire
AB5 OAE

Grey stone mansion, parts dating from the 13th century, set in several hundred acres in rural Aberdeenshire. Lovely grounds, lake, wildlife. Recommended for "friendly greeting from courteous staff; large, clean rooms, good food with imaginative starters; reasonable wine list – but a little top-heavy with expensive wines." Open early Mar–mid-Dec. 11 rooms, all with bath and/or shower. B&B double £67. Set dinner £20 (excluding 10% service charge). New nomination. More reports please.

ONICH Highland — Map 5

Allt-nan-Ros Hotel — *Tel* Onich (085 53) 210
Onich, by Fort William
Inverness-shire PH33 6RY

Allt-nan-Ros, Gaelic for "burn of the roses", is on the north shore of Loch Linnhe and enjoys panoramic views of the surrounding mountains and lochs. It was originally built as a Victorian shooting lodge and has been attractively converted by its owners, James, Fiona and Lachlan MacLeod. All public rooms and bedrooms overlook the gardens, loch and distant hills, and there is a terraced lawn with tables and chairs where one may enjoy the view. On Saturdays there is a Scottish evening with a piper and Highland dancers. "A very warm welcome on arrival by the young kilted James MacLeod, who obviously has his finger on everything. A lovely bedroom with all the little extras. An excellent dinner. A huge breakfast. A very satisfactory night's stop." (*Barbara M Wooldridge; also Mr and Mrs JT Mills*) This year there is a new lounge with stained glass, and two new bedrooms in converted stables.

Open Easter–early Nov.
Rooms 18 double with bath, 3 single with shower, all with telephone, radio, TV, tea-making facilities, baby-listening. 2 in converted stable. 5 ground-floor rooms.
Facilities Hall, lounge bar, sun lounge, dining room, WC for ♿. 4-acre garden with streams and ponds. Fishing from shoreline, shingle beach across the road, boat available.
Location On A82 10 m SW of Fort William.
Restrictions No dogs in public rooms.
Credit cards All major cards accepted.
Terms B&B £30–£35; dinner, B&B £45–£50. Alc lunch £12.50, set dinner £17. 3-, 5- and 7-day breaks. Reduced rates and special meals for children.
Service/tipping: "If people do tip, we distribute it equally amongst all staff."

> Many hotels put up their prices in the spring. Tariffs quoted in the text may be more accurate before April/May 1990 than after.

> Please make a habit of sending in a report as soon as possible after a visit when details are still fresh in your mind.

PEAT INN Fife — Map 5

The Peat Inn [GFG] *Tel* Peat Inn (033 484) 206
Peat Inn, By Cupar
Fifeshire KY15 5LH

César award: Newcomer of the year, restaurant-with-rooms division

The Residence is the much-heralded new annexe to David and Patricia Wilson's highly regarded *Peat Inn.* Set at a country crossroads six miles from St Andrews, the inn offers some of the finest food in Scotland and, since 1987, eight luxurious mini-suites in the new block adjoining the restaurant, sympathetically built to blend with the environment. "The view from the bedroom window is of Fife fields," writes a recent visitor. "Open the window and the smell of peat smoke drifts by." The bedrooms have been individually decorated by Mrs Wilson, a trained designer, and offer every luxury: carefully chosen fabrics, a separate sitting area, marble bathrooms, TV with teletext, a desk, slippers and bathrobes ("changed along with the towels when we went to dinner!"); even Scrabble and playing cards. But the real reason one comes here is the restaurant, one of only three Scottish establishments to win a *Michelin* rosette in 1989. David Wilson's cooking has won him many awards; there is an outstanding wine list. And recent visitors also cite the "enthusiastic and genuine welcome" and the excellent continental breakfast – "even after a *Peat Inn* dinner, it was wonderful: *fresh* citrus segments, *fresh* orange juice, superb coffee and a basket of fresh breads, fruit loaves, brioche and croissant." (*Alan Rodger and Peter Macaulay, Paul Henderson; John and Kath Lodge, Mrs H Langenberg, and others*)

Open *Residence* open all year, except 2 weeks Nov, 2 weeks Jan, Christmas. Restaurant closed Sun and Mon.
Rooms 8 double – all with bath, shower, telephone, radio and TV. 1 adapted for ♿.
Facilities Ramp. 2 lounges (1 in *Residence*), restaurant. ¾-acre grounds.
Location At junction of B940/B941 6 miles south of St Andrews.
Restrictions No smoking in restaurant. No children under 12. No dogs.
Credit cards All major cards accepted.
Terms B&B (continental) £92–£97 per suite. Set lunch £14.50; full alc dinner £30.
Service/tipping: We add nothing to the bill and do not expect anything extra.

PEEBLES Borders — Map 5

Cringletie House Hotel [GFG] *Tel* Eddleston (072 13) 233
Peebles, Peeblesshire EH45 8PL

A pink stone mansion built in the Scottish baronial manner with turrets and dormers, surrounded by garden, woodland and a 28-acre estate. It has a faithful clientele, attracted by the reasonable price, the standard of comfort and pleasant welcome, and the spaciousness of the grounds. Some reports this year: "The setting is magnificent, right out in the country with marvellous views over the surrounding hills, while it is possible to go for quite extensive walks in the park-like estate. The historic house is extremely attractive, not to say impressive, with furnishings and decor appropriate to its architectural style and period."

"We thoroughly enjoyed this hotel – the sort of place where you felt comfortable spending all day just relaxing in the gardens and playing tennis or croquet. After a day out, they are delighted to serve you a wonderful tea in the garden or in the lounge." The two-acre walled garden produces "many of the fine vegetables that ultimately find their way to the table"; dinners are appreciated as much as ever – "I have never had a bad or poor meal yet" writes a faithful returner. Many of the bedrooms have high ceilings; they are prettily furnished, with an absence of fussiness. "Mrs Maguire is wonderfully clever at finding just the right ornaments to give individual touches to rooms. One of the pleasures of our spring visits is to see what changes have been made during the winter." This year, we are told, three single rooms have been made into bathrooms so that every bedroom is now *en suite*. The Maguires, now in their 19th year at *Cringletie*, have been joined by their two elder sons, Paul and Simon. (*John and Joan Wyatt, A Richard; Richard C Fraser, Françoise Walker, and others*)

Open Mid-Mar–Christmas.
Rooms 12 double, 1 single – all bath and/or shower, telephone, TV and baby-listening.
Facilities Bar lounge, 2 lounges (1 non-smoking), dining room. 28-acre grounds with tennis, 9-hole putting green, croquet, children's play area, kitchen garden. Golf, fishing, indoor swimming pool nearby.
Location 2½ m N of Peebles on A703.
Restrictions Not suitable for ♿. Smoking discouraged in dining room. No dogs in public rooms.
Credit cards Access, Visa.
Terms (Service at guests' discretion) B&B £32.50. Lunch from £4.50 (£11.50 on Sun), set dinner £18.50. Off-season rates. Reduced rates for children sharing parents' room.

PITCAPLE Grampian — Map 5

Pittodrie House Hotel — *Tel* Pitcaple (046 76) 444
Pitcaple, Aberdeenshire AB5 9HS — *Fax* (046 76) 648
Telex 739935

Aberdeenshire country house in large estate with tennis, squash, clay-pigeon shooting. Dates back to the 17th century, but mostly Victorian, acquired by the present owner's grandfather in 1900. Family portraits and original library retained; log fires, good antique furniture. Bathrooms – pre-1920 vintage with original fittings – have plenty of hot water. 12 double rooms – all with bath and/or shower. B&B double £80. Set dinner £20.50. In italics because of varied criticisms: geriatric beds, some poor housekeeping and disappointments in the restaurant. More reports please.

PORT APPIN Strathclyde — Map 5

The Airds Hotel [GFG] — *Tel* Appin (063 173) 236
Port Appin, Appin
Argyllshire PA38 4DF

Many readers this year have written again to praise the hospitality and impeccably high standards of hotel-keeping offered by Eric and Betty

Allen at this early 18th-century ferry inn looking across a small road towards Loch Linnhe, the islands of Lismore and the mountains of Morvern. "Our room was superbly appointed, and the staff were friendly and attentive as always. Mr Allen had even remembered that we didn't like duvets. Mrs Allen's cooking was as inspired as ever – marvellous soups, delicate mousses – trout with chive and champagne sauce." "The Allens must have a warehouse for the vast selection of wine on offer, and should the odd abstemious person pass this way he or she will be spoiled for choice in the half-bottle department." "The garden in front of the hotel, charming with lawn and colourful flower beds, has plenty of comfortable chairs; I could sit all day gazing at the breathtaking view across Loch Linnhe. (*John and Moira Cole, Gillian Cave, P Grogan, Lydia Lim, and others*) "Any criticisms of this well-run establishment are nit-picking; it stands head and shoulders above most others", wrote a devotee last year. But at least one reader had a nit to pick, "We succumbed to the garden with the sun shining, bees buzzing, water sparkling in the distance, and liked the sleek and elegant dining room, and the awesome wine list (386 bottles, ranging from £9 for Airds' Claret to £250 for Château Pétrus 1970). But Room 21 was a disappointment: my knees hit wooden shelves under the dressing table skirt, the wardrobe shelves were deep enough only for socks or a shirt, there was only a tiny shelf in the bathroom and we had to keep shaving kit and cosmetics on the floor, and the room was so small one of us couldn't walk around the bed if the other was sitting on a chair. There were hooks in the bathroom, but they hid the mirror when robes were hanging up. Why can't rooms be better designed?"

Open Mar–Nov.
Rooms 1 suite, 12 double, 1 single – all with bath and/or shower, telephone, radio, TV and baby-listening. 2 in garden annexe.
Facilities 2 lounges, small residents' bar, dining room. Small garden; near loch with shingle beach, bathing, fishing, boating; pony-trekking, forest walks.
Location 2 m off A828, 25 m from Fort William and Oban. Parking for 30 cars.
Restrictions Not suitable for ♿. No children under 5. No dogs.
Credit cards None accepted.
Terms (No service charge) Dinner, B&B £80–£90. Set dinner £28. Reductions for children sharing parents' room; special meals.
Service/tipping: "We do not expect tips. When guests insist the money is distributed to all members of staff."

PORTPATRICK Dumfries and Galloway — Map 5

Knockinaam Lodge Hotel [GFG] — *Tel* Portpatrick (077 681) 471
Portpatrick, Wigtownshire
DG9 9AD

Knockinaam Lodge nestles in a wooded glen with steep cliffs which shelter it on three sides; on the fourth it faces the sea, looking towards the coast of Ireland. There are superb cliff walks. It is so secluded that deer sometimes graze among the trees on the slopes beside the hotel. In spring there are carpets of bluebells and primroses in the woods. There is a beach, sandy at low tide, though this is no bucket-and-spade place, but an exclusive small hotel with imaginative, sophisticated cooking. It is run by the young French owner Marcel Frichot and his English wife, Corinna. The five-course menus – described this year as "interesting, often unusual" – change daily; if you find dishes too adventurous something simpler will be served on request. Lots of country-house-type extras in the rooms: sewing kit, pot pourri, bath oil in a bottle, travelling robes and fresh flowers. Beds are turned down during dinner. All our correspondents speak warmly of the creature comforts of the house – comfortable armchairs, good lamps for reading, large bathrooms, firm beds. The grounds, reported unkempt last year, have been much improved. Only one complaint: portions at meals are too *nouvelle* for those with robust appetites.

Open End Mar–beginning Jan.
Rooms 9 double, 1 single – all with bath and shower, telephone, TV.
Facilities Lounge, residents' lounge, bar, restaurant. 30-acre grounds, with garden and croquet. Private beach 100 metres, swimming "for the brave"; sea fishing. Wildlife, walks, golf nearby.
Location 3 m SW of Portpatrick, 8 m SW of Stranraer. Signposted off A77. From Stranraer turn left after Lochans, do not go to Portpatrick.
Restrictions Bedrooms not suitable for ♿. No smoking in restaurant. Dogs by arrangement only; not in public rooms.
Credit cards All major cards accepted.
Terms [1989 rates] Dinner, B&B £57–£77. Set dinner £23; bar lunches £2–£9. High tea and reduced rates for children under 12.
Service/tipping: "Tipping not encouraged; any money left is distributed among all staff."

PORTREE Skye, Highland — Map 5

Viewfield House — *Tel* Portree (0478) 2217
Portree, Isle of Skye
IV51 9EU

A newcomer to the Guide last year, nominated in piquant terms by *Derek Cooper*, "This is one of the few country-house hotels in the Highlands where commercial imperatives do not intrude. It was for many decades the home of Colonel 'Jock' Macdonald and his wife Evelyn, who had spent a large part of their life in India. They ran their family home as an extended house party; passing tourists found themselves swept into a lifestyle almost Victorian in its prodigality. In his day the Colonel would bring out his pipes. Now, mourned by the whole of the West Highlands, he rests in nearby Stromhuirinish cemetery. Mrs Jock has reluctantly handed over the day-to-day running of the house to her grandson Hugh but she remains a powerful voice in the drawing room. Guests are still expected to contribute to the enhancement of life after dinner. Crammed with china and *objets impériaux, Viewfield* is time-capsuled and unique. No country house hotel in Britain rivals its period aura. The food is good too."

Viewfield House stands in large grounds up an avenue just off the main road into Portree, the largest town on Skye. A few bedrooms may have private bathrooms this year; all have hand basins and electric fires. No telephone, no TV. Prices are very reasonable. A typical dinner menu features creamy mushroom pâté, leek and potato soup, fresh Skye salmon, blackcurrant flummery, cheese and biscuits. "All cooking is home cooking, no packets or cardboard gateaux!" says Hugh Macdonald. More reports welcome.

Please make a habit of sending a report if you stay at a Guide hotel.

Open May–mid-Oct.
Rooms 9 double, 5 single – all with H&C and tea-making facilities; baby-listening available. 4 *en suite* bathrooms planned for 1990.
Facilities Drawing room, TV room, dining room. 20-acre grounds with croquet, woodland walks (and midges).
Location On S side of Portree, 10 minutes' walk from centre; driving towards Broadford turn right just after BP petrol station on left.
Restrictions Not suitable for ♿. No dogs in public rooms.
Credit cards None accepted.
Terms [1989 rates] (No service charge) B&B £16–£18. Packed lunch £2.50, set dinner £12. Reduced rates for children; special meals, given advance notice.
Service/tipping: "Tips should only be left by those who feel they have received outstanding service."

RAASAY Skye, Highland — Map 5

Isle of Raasay Hotel
Isle of Raasay
by Kyle of Lochalsh, Skye
Inverness-shire IV40 8PB

Tel Raasay (047 862) 226; and 222 (winter only)

"A remote and beautiful spot and a good hotel. An unusual combination which we can recommend," writes a correspondent this year on the *Isle of Raasay*, a small hotel on a tiny island (four miles by 15) reached by a 15-minute ferry journey from Skye. The hotel sits 300 yards from the water; it is run by Mrs Nicholson, whose husband is the ferry master, "with a very effective 'hands-on' technique, assisted by able local staff, always available for advice or just a chat. The food is first class with fresh ingredients and imaginative soups and desserts. The residents' lounge and dining rooms have magnificent views, though the lounge could do with more comfortable chairs. The bar is open to the public most evenings, and some 15 or 20 locals drop in, providing alternative company if one fancies a change." Raasay itself is "one of the Inner Hebrides' most enchanting islands – a world apart from the increasingly crowded roads of Skye, with breathtaking views of the Cuillin Hills on Skye and the Torridon Hills on the Scottish mainland". Visitors are advised to weatherproof shoes or boots for straying anywhere off the (very few) stretches of road, also to fill up their tanks and get other requirements before leaving Skye since there is no petrol on the island and the village shop is sparsely stocked. (*Mr and Mrs Roger Bland, and others*)

Open Mid-Apr–end Sept.
Rooms 11 double, 1 single – all with bath, radio, TV and tea-making facilities. 6 ground-floor rooms, 1 specifically designed for ♿.
Facilities Lounge, TV lounge, lounge bar, dining room. 1-acre grounds. Good walking and bird-watching country; trout fishing in lochs; 5 mins from sea.
Location Travel to Kyle from Inverness or to Mallaig from Glasgow; take the ferry to Kyleakin or Armadale respectively. Proceed to Sconser village on Loch Sligachan; there are three ferries daily (except Sun) to Raasay, taking about 15 mins. Hotel is signposted from ferry terminal.
Restriction No dogs in public rooms.
Credit cards None accepted.
Terms (No service charge) B&B from £25; dinner, B&B from £39. Bar and packed lunches available. Set dinner from £14. 50% reduction for children under 10; special meals.
Service/tipping: "Tips are at guests' discretion and shared by all members of staff."

ROTHES Grampian — Map 5

Rothes Glen Hotel *Tel* Rothes (034 03) 254
Rothes, Morayshire IV33 7AH

Baronial country hotel at head of Glen of Rothes designed by architect of Balmoral, retaining period features and antique furniture but comfortably modernised. "Superbly run, varied five-course dinners and comprehensive breakfasts, cheerful staff." Comfortable and spacious bedrooms. Quietly situated in 40-acre grounds with burn, paddocks, small herd of Highland cattle. Good selection of malt whiskies. Closed Jan. 16 rooms, 13 with bath. B&B double £76.45. Set dinner £19.25. 10% service charge added. Recent nomination, and a new chef since last year. More reports please.

ST OLA Orkney — Map 5

Foveran Hotel *Tel* Kirkwall (0856) 2389
St Ola, Nr Kirkwall
Orkney KW15 1SF

Small modern hotel owned and run – "informally but professionally" – by Norma Gerrard; Scandinavian in design, in 18-acre grounds overlooking Scapa Flow. Bedrooms small and simple, but all have private facilities. Restaurant makes good use of fresh local products and offers separate menus for vegetarians and children. Good walks, fishing, bird reserves, archaeological sites and golf nearby, but a car is needed. Open Apr–Oct. 8 rooms, all with private facilities. B&B double £41. Full alc from £14.50. Few recent reports. More would be welcome.

SCARISTA Western Isles — Map 5

Scarista House Hotel [GFG] *Tel* Scarista (085 985) 238
Scarista, Isle of Harris PA85 3HX

This Georgian manse, one of the few listed buildings in the Western Isles, overlooks a magnificent three-mile stretch of Atlantic beach on the western, gentler part of Harris. It has had enthusiastic entries in the Guide for many years, not least from visitors who shared Alison and Andrew Johnson's interest in cooking only with ingredients raised or produced without cruelty. "No TV, no radio," we said, "but an individual and highly innovative standard of cooking, a first-rate library, specially strong in the wildlife and nature studies section, and a passion for excellence in every aspect of hotelmanship." Last year we reported that the Johnsons were planning to run the hotel more as a cooperative venture with two long-time colleagues, Lena Macklennan and Morag Macleod; although the Johnsons wouldn't be around all the time, Alison Johnson assured us that guests would hardly notice the difference – the food would be simpler but the general style would stay much the same. First reports on the new set-up suggest that the restaurant has become less central to the *Scarista* experience. More reports please.

Open End Apr–end Sept. Possibly 1 weekend end July. Restaurant closed to non-residents on Sun.
Rooms 7 double – all with bath (5 also have shower), telephone and tea-making facilities. 4 in annexe.
Facilities Drawing room, library, 2 dining rooms. 2-acre grounds. Access to miles of sandy beach; sea fishing.
Location 15 m SW of Tarbert on A859. Regular ferries from Ullapool to Stornoway and from Uig to Tarbert; daily flights to Stornoway from Glasgow and Inverness. Hotel will arrange car hire.
Restrictions Children by arrangement, not under 5. "Well trained" dogs only, not in public rooms.
Credit cards None accepted.
Terms (No service charge) B&B: single £45–£47, double £62–£68. Set dinner £17.50.

STEWARTON Strathclyde — Map 5

Chapeltoun House Hotel [GFG]
Off Irvine Road (B769), Stewarton
Nr Glasgow, Ayrshire KA3 3ED

Tel Stewarton (0560) 82696
Fax (0560) 85100

A substantial Edwardian house 20 miles south of Glasgow, *Chapeltoun* was built by a wealthy industrialist as a private residence; it has oak-panelled public rooms with log fires, well-equipped, individually decorated bedrooms, and large grounds with mature gardens. It is conveniently situated for visits to Culzean Castle and Glasgow, there is excellent golfing in the area, and Prestwick Airport is nearby. Owned by Colin and Graeme McKenzie, it is "comfortable in every way". A report this year, "We were given a very large room with a king-size bed and a round bay window that overlooked fields. There was a bowl of fresh fruit and two glasses of sherry waiting for us. The bathroom had brass fixtures, plenty of towels and extra shampoo and soap. A wonderful tea followed in one of the three sitting rooms. There was a roaring fire in the large lounge. It seemed as though we had found our own castle. There is a large menu with daily specials that feature the freshest game and produce. The dessert table is divine!" From another recent visitor, "The hotel is surrounded by fields and woodland with a kitchen garden full of herbs and vegetables. There were good things on the menu like lentil broth, local salmon with crayfish sauce, ballotine of duckling, steak and kidney pie and Cullen skink. Most of the food is bought daily from the market and is cooked with restraint. Bedrooms and public rooms have a period feel – it is all very relaxed and peaceful." (*Deborah Hogan Ross; also John K Burton*)

Open All year except 1–5 Jan.
Rooms 8 double – 6 with bath, 2 with shower, all with telephone, radio and TV.
Facilities 2 lounge areas, bar, 2 dining rooms. 25-acre grounds with river and mature gardens. Golf, fishing, riding nearby. Sea 6 m.
Location 2 m SW of Stewarton. At crossroads in Stewarton turn left onto A735, straight on at mini-roundabout, then second on right after viaduct onto B769. 2 m to hotel.
Restrictions Only restaurant suitable for ♿. No smoking in dining room. No children under 12. No dogs.
Credit cards Access, Amex, Visa.
Terms (No service charge) B&B: single occupancy £60–£74, double £89–£115. Set lunch £16, dinner £23. Reduced rates for children sharing parents' room.

Service/tipping: "Tips entirely at customers' discretion; they are added to a tronc and distributed to all members of staff."

STRATHTUMMEL Tayside — Map 5

Port-An-Eilean Hotel — *Tel* Tummel Bridge (088 24) 233
Strathtummel, by Pitlochry
Perthshire PH16 5RU

An 1865 sporting lodge beside Loch Tummel with glorious Highland scenery all around. Spectacular sweep through 21 acres of rhododendrons and silver birches to the loch shore. Mr and Mrs Gordon Hallewell are "welcoming but unobtrusive" hosts. Public rooms have lofty ceilings and a collection of works by modern Scottish artists on the walls: prints, oils, tapestries, collages. Bedrooms vary greatly in size; most overlook the loch. Open late Apr–mid-Oct. 9 rooms, all with bath. B&B double £48. Set dinner £12. In italics because of criticisms of decor, furnishings and pokiness of some rooms, and of the cooking. More reports please.

STRONTIAN Highland — Map 5

Kilcamb Lodge Hotel — *Tel* Strontian (0967) 2257
Strontian, Argyllshire
PH36 4HY

Small and hospitable hotel or guest house in 30-acre grounds on Loch Sunart, with half-a-mile private shoreline. Recommended for its "glorious position, helpful and friendly owners, John and Suzanne Bradbury, and simple but well-cooked food". Comfortable bedrooms, "prettily furnished". Open Easter–15 Oct. 9 rooms, all with private facilities. Dinner, B&B £42 [1989]. New to the Guide last year. More reports please.

TANGUSDALE BEACH Barra, Outer Hebrides — Map 5

Isle of Barra Hotel — *Tel* Castlebay (087 14) 383
Tangusdale Beach, South Uist — *Fax* (087 14) 385
Isle of Barra PA80 5XW

New hotel on smallest of the inhabited Western Isles, overlooking a white sandy beach with Atlantic rollers. Beachcombing, bird-watching and hill walking available. Recommended for good food, especially fish dishes, and comfortable twin-bedded rooms with picture-window views of the sea. "The journey alone is worthwhile, either by sea or by air, landing a on cockle-shell beach." Open mid-May–end Sept. 35 double rooms, all with bath, shower, TV. *Dinner, B&B £24.50–£30. New nomination. More reports please.*

> Our italicised entries indicate hotels which are worth considering, but which, for various reasons – inadequate information, lack of feedback, ambivalent reports – do not at the moment warrant a full entry. We should particularly welcome comments on these hotels.

TIMSGARRY Lewis, Outer Hebrides **Map 5**

Baile-na-Cille *Tel* Timsgarry (085 175) 242
Timsgarry, Uig
Isle of Lewis PA86 9JD

César award: Shangri-La of the Outer Hebrides

A spray of compliments this year for Richard and Joanna Gollin's converted 18th century manse, magnificently situated on the edge of a sandy bay looking across to mountains and islands, on the wild west coast of Lewis, The village is 34 miles from Stornoway; the hotel is "at the end of a 15 mile single-track road across the soggy landscape of peat interspersed with tiny lochs. When you reach Timsgarry, however, the scenery changes to soft, springy turf, hazy blue hills, and long white sands." "'Where the Rainbow Ends', I nicknamed it." "Why is this our favourite place? It could be the miles of deserted sandy beaches, the marvellous collection of tapes, records and books (for rainy days!), the comfortable furnishings, but more important than all this is the 'atmosphere'. The owners always have time for a chat, they *genuinely* enjoy having guests. We arrived at 1 o'clock *a.m.* in a bad storm; Richard and Joanna were waiting for us with sandwiches, cake and whisky. She is a lovely cook: our favourite meal was the special lobster evening. Happy memories, too, of collecting mussels – Richard, four guests, three children and a dog in Richard's car down to a beach. From rock to bucket to dinner table within an hour or so. They were the best I've ever tasted." *Baile-na-Cille* has now been fully modernised (central heating and double glazing). Most rooms have sea views; one reader mentions cupboard and drawer space as "limited but adequate"; some bedrooms are a little small. Many praise Joanna Gollin's "varied and exciting cooking. Eating is communal, and service can be slow when the house is full. Richard Gollin travels almost daily to Stornaway to collect supplies, and guests without transport can take advantage of these regular trips to be deposited at various points for walking and climbing. It is a wonderful area for naturalists. "This remote area would not suit people looking for sophisticated five-star treatment, but for anyone wanting to get away from it all it is an ideal hideaway." (*Mr and Mrs C Freeman, C and M Dehn, Tim Brierly, and others*)

Open 15 Jan–15 Oct, possibly longer (phone for details).
Rooms 2 family suites, 8 double, 2 single – 6 with bath, all with tea-making facilities. 9 in 3 converted stable blocks by main entrance. Some ground-floor rooms.
Facilities 3 lounges (1 with TV, 1 with music), dining room. 3-acre grounds with walled garden, children's play area, direct access to beach (dinghy, windsurfer and fishing rods available). Near 7 sandy beaches with safe bathing; fishing, sailing.
Location 34 m W of Stornoway. Take A858 from Stornoway or Tarbert to Garynahine, B8011 towards Uig; at Timsgarry shop turn right down to shore.
Restriction Not really suitable for ♿. No smoking in dining room. Dogs by arrangement.
Credit cards None accepted.
Terms B&B £15–£22.50; dinner, B&B £29–£37.50. Set dinner £14–£15 (lobster dinner £24); packed lunches about £3.50. Weekly packages for walkers, bird watchers, fishermen. Reduced rates and special meals for children.
Service/tipping: "Service included. We are 100% against tipping, but if people insist, the money goes straight to the girls. Note: *We have a lot fewer problems and embarrassment*

with tipping than with smokers! We say 'no smoking' in the dining room but some still try to 'just light up' between courses. Mrs. G. goes in with the fire extinguisher – that's when the story really starts. . ."

TIRORAN Mull, Strathclyde — Map 5

Tiroran House [GFG] *Tel* Tiroran (068 15) 232
Tiroran, Isle of Mull
Argyllshire PA69 6ES

Mull has rugged mountains, leafy glades, many waterfalls, charming small ports, and a ferry to historic Iona. Many consider *Tiroran House* the ideal base for a visit. Robin and Sue Blockey's well-bred modernised shooting lodge above Loch Scridain, with 15 acres of gardens and woodlands sweeping down to the loch, is very much their own elegant home which they open as a hotel for six months of the year. "No TV, room phones, muzak, or even newspapers" we wrote two years ago, but this has changed – *The Times* is now delivered daily, and rooms do have small radios. "The remarkable thing about the place is the high standard it achieves in such a remote spot. The bedrooms are filled with antiques and the tables covered with so many small *objets d'art* that it is difficult to find space for the contents of your own pockets. But the 'Tovey touches' of *Miller Howe* are all there down to the binoculars on the window sill! All very smooth, very discreet and extremely enjoyable – so that at the end the bill, enclosed in an envelope and left on the hall table, is paid with a smile and a firm intention to return when the money has been saved up for the next visit." Other readers this year cite the tea trays with three kinds of tea, the huge bath towels and pretty embroidered hand towels that are changed twice daily, and the "spectacular packed lunches: pretty wicker baskets, different sandwiches every day, jugs of hot soup and hot water and cold milk, fresh fruit, delicious cakes, half bottles of wine and openers!" Breakfasts, served with damask napkins and lovely silver, include smoked haddock and kippers. Dinners feature a choice of three starters, a single main course (e.g. poached Mull salmon, roast gigot of Tiroran lamb), Scottish cheeses, and three puddings, one of which is always hot (e.g. steamed maple syrup pudding with whisky sauce). Vegetarians are willingly catered for. (*W Ian Stewart, R and M Bourne, Benjamin Holme, V Joel, and others*)

Open May–Oct. Restaurant open only to residents at lunchtime.
Rooms 8 double, 1 single – all with bath and shower, radio and tea-making facilities. 3 in cottage 30 yards from hotel.
Facilities 2 drawing rooms, dining room, games room. 60-acre grounds with woodlands, field, croquet; on sea loch safe for bathing, sailing, canoeing.
Location Oban–Craignure ferry (45 mins) bookable with Caledonian McBrayne, The Pier, Gourock PA19 1QP. (Lochaline–Fishnish ferry, not bookable, but much cheaper, necessitates a longish but superb drive through Morvern.) From Craignure take A849 to Fionnphort. At head of Loch Scridain (17 m) turn right onto B8035; after 5 m turn left to Tiroran (1 m). Entrance through stone gate marked "Tiroran" and "Bungalow".
Restrictions Not suitable for ♿. No children under 10. Dogs by arrangement, not in public rooms.
Credit cards None accepted.
Terms Dinner, B&B from £70. Set lunch £9.50, dinner £21.50. Reductions for stays of 3 nights or more; 5- and 7-day holidays include car ferry reimbursement. *Service/tipping: "There is no service charge and no gratuities are expected."*

ULLAPOOL Highland — Map 5

Altnaharrie Inn [GFG] — *Tel* Dundonnell (085 483) 230
Ullapool, Wester Ross IV26 2SS

"It is the food that makes this place a mecca for sybarites", writes a reader this year. Owned by Fred Brown and his Norwegian wife Gunn Eriksen (she is the cook), *Altnaharrie* has been delighting readers of the Guide for years, and has developed an international reputation for inventive food in an unlikely setting. In 1989 it received a *Michelin* rosette, one of only three for the whole of Scotland. "Superb", "delicious", "pure bliss" are other comments on the five-course no-choice menus which include medallions of Sika deer with morels and girolles, ravioli of seafood with scallops, lobster, prawns and crab, selections of cheese from France and Norway as well as Ireland, Scotland and England – and three desserts every night ("You must try them all, or Gunn will be upset!"). (You are asked to give advance warning about allergies, etc.) An old drover's inn, *Altnaharrie* lies across the waters of Loch Broom; guests are fetched by ferry from Ullapool harbour for the ten-minute ride. Because of its small size (seven bedrooms), it helps if you enjoy your fellow guests; conversation between adjoining tables is the norm, says Fred Brown, "though not obligatory". Last year bedrooms and lounge areas were expanded; the original house has been enlarged by building into the hillside, creating a larger kitchen and wine cellar, and a new lounge and extra bedroom above. The decor is cosy, and there are books for days when the weather might tempt one to stay inside. "The shy but warm hospitality of Fred Brown and Gunn Eriksen combined to make *Altnaharrie* the most memorable part of our stay in Scotland" wrote one reader this year; "We have stayed here for the last five years", wrote another, "it is our favourite of all time". (*Norman W Turner, D and M Thal, Dr WA Henderson, John and Kath Lodge, and others*) *Altnaharrie* is a non-smoking hotel.

Open Easter–late Oct. Closed occasionally for a few days.
Rooms 7 double – all with bath and/or shower. 2 in separate buildings.
Facilities Hall, 2 lounges, dining room. 15-acre grounds with gardens, on loch; pebbled beach, safe (but cold) bathing; deep-sea fishing free, trout and salmon fishing by arrangement; hill walking.
Location On shore of Loch Broom. Access by launch from Ullapool harbour (normal afternoon collection times 2.45, 4.45, 6 pm). Private parking in Ullapool. Guests requested to telephone on arrival in Ullapool.
Restrictions Not suitable for ♿. No smoking. Children "only if old enough to enjoy our dinner which lasts over 2 hours usually". Dogs by arrangement, not in public rooms.
Credit cards None accepted.
Terms (No service charge) Dinner, B&B £79–£95. Set dinner £35. Reduced rates for children sharing parents' room.
Service/tipping: "We try to discourage tipping. The staff are told not to expect tips and to try to refuse politely any that are offered."

Before making a long detour to a small hotel, do check that it is open. Some are known to close on impulse.

Don't let old favourites down. Entries are dropped when there is no endorsement.

The Ceilidh Place *Tel* Ullapool (0854) 2103
14 West Argyle Street
Ullapool, Wester Ross IV26 2TY

We haven't had many reports on *Ceilidh Place* lately, though one correspondent took against the *Place* comprehensively. Is this far-off, far-out hotel/clubhouse/restaurant/coffee shop/bookshop complex near the centre of Ullapool still enchanting readers? Jean and Robert Urquhart (he a TV actor when not a hotelier) run this new world establishment with genuine verve, offering low-price accommodation, food and myriad activities (sea angling, water skiing, loch fishing, pony trekking) – as well as more leisurely pursuits such as music listening, book browsing, etc. A writer a few years ago said, "The ageing hippy atmosphere of peace, love and lots of brotherhood in a place very successful at separating tourist from money grates. They are very busy at times. However without grudge one has to support their entry in the book. There is plenty of enthusiasm, charming staff and hostess, very interesting if somewhat trendy food and a good atmosphere among guests. The place is well designed and a pleasant environment, even if the annexe bedrooms are a mixed lot." More reports please.

Open All year except 2 weeks mid-Jan (limited restaurant service Nov–Feb).
Rooms 12 double, 3 single – 8 with bath. 11 extra rooms (simpler, with bunk beds, etc.) in Clubhouse annexe.
Facilities Lounge, Clubhouse bar with live music, coffee shop, games room, dining room; ceilidhs, jazz, classical and folk music evenings at least once a week in summer. Rocky beach.
Location First right after pier at W end of Main Street. Large car park.
Restrictions Not suitable for ♿. No dogs in public rooms.
Credit cards All major cards accepted.
Terms (No service charge) B&B £22–£38 (less in Clubhouse). Packed lunches available. Coffee shop buffet service from £3.50. Set dinner £14.50. Special rates for 6 days or more; occasional courses; activity holidays. Reduced rates and special meals for children.
Service/tipping: "We do not look for tips. Wages should be paid to allow people to live on them and prices charged must cover this. However, some people do still leave tips and they are shared equally by everyone."

WEST LINTON Borders — Map 5

Medwyn House *Tel* (0968) 60542
Medwyn Road
Peebleshire EH46 7HB

Former coaching inn, 18 miles south of Edinburgh, converted to country house in 1864, now a hotel. Panelled hall with open fire, luxuriously appointed bedrooms, peaceful surroundings, 30-acre grounds with stabling and grazing for visiting horses. Recommended for "civilised and friendly welcome, fine food, warm hospitality, five-star treatment with no formality". Large drawing room, elegant dining room, "likes and dislikes" ascertained on arrival to assure that dinner pleases. No licence – bring your own drink (no corkage). 18-hole golf course next door (50% reduction on greens fees). 3 rooms, all with bath, Separate cottage sometimes available. B&B £23.50–£33.50. Set dinner £14.50. Attractive new nomination. More reports please.

WHITEBRIDGE Highland — Map 5

Knockie Lodge [GFG] *Tel* Gorthleck (045 63) 276
Whitebridge
Inverness-shire IV1 2UP

"Fulfils my expectations of what a country house hotel should be. Perfect setting, perfect decor, and that most essential ingredient, perfect hostmanship." (*RP Wynings*) A typically generous report on Ian and Brenda Milward's 200-year-old hotel, formerly a hunting lodge for the Chief of Clan Fraser, which enjoys a beautiful wild position in unspoilt countryside, in the high, lightly wooded area of hidden valleys and small lochs on the eastern side of Loch Ness. It has a comfortable sitting room, with books and magazines, and a billiard room with a full-size table. The dining room – entirely refurbished this year – is inviting, with silver and candle-light; the menus (no choice until dessert) are "better than ever", and there is a "wide-ranging wine list"; dinner is at 8 pm. Bedrooms are unfussy and snug, with fitted carpets, good hanging space, fresh flowers, and immaculate modern bathrooms – although one writer this year warns that at least two have baths so small that "one needs to be a contortionist". The absence of telephone, radio and TV add to the country house atmosphere, and another visitor has commented on the pleasing contrast between daytime and evening pursuits, "The breakfast and dinners are delicious and elegant – and since one is rather 'outdoorsy' during the day, it is pleasant to dress for dinner, and spend a delightful evening with the hosts and fellow guests. The *Lodge* is ideally situated for fishing and deer-stalking but is also an excellent place to "get away from it all in sybaritic comfort". (*JT Simon; also R Berry, RCJ Gordon, Diana Gates, and others*)

Open End Apr–end Oct.
Rooms 8 double, 2 single – all with bath (4 also have shower); tea-making facilities on request.
Facilities Drawing room with self-service bar, sitting room, dining room, billiard room. 10-acre grounds. 2 lochs with free trout fishing for guests; deer stalking, pony trekking, golf nearby.
Location 2 m down single-track private road W off B862, 8 m N of Fort Augustus.
Restrictions Not suitable for ♿. No smoking in dining room. No children under 10. Dogs by prior arrangement; not in public rooms.
Credit cards All major cards accepted.
Terms B&B £50–£69. Bar lunch from £6, set dinner £18. Reduced rates out of season.
Service/tipping: "No service charge, but if guests particularly want to leave something it is given in its entirety to staff."

Channel Islands

LONGUEVILLE MANOR HOTEL
ST SAVIOUR

HERM **Map 1**

White House Hotel *Tel* Guernsey (0481) 22159
Herm, via Guernsey

Good hotels on tiny islands are to be cherished; Herm is one-and-a-half miles long and one mile wide, with a native population of 36 including children (though it has to meet an invasion of 1,000 or more day-visitors from Guernsey in August). It is also a unique fief, run by the Tenants of Herm, Peter and Jenny Wood. It has one hotel, one pub, one church. An earlier visitor called it the most perfect island he had ever clapped eyes on, a paradise. The official brochure dubs it "heaven on earth". Readers repeatedly return, describing the White House as "a good welcoming country house, comfortable, clean and friendly." They like the setting, and the isolation. "We were given one of the new rooms, with a glorious view over the sea to Guernsey in the distance and a balcony overlooking the swimming pool. All the staff were kindness itself. Yes, there are boats full of trippers but most go to Shell Bay, the shop and pub; it is easy to find solitude." (Non-resident visitors *do* come to the hotel, drawn to its

Ship Inn restaurant, but there are problems with numbers only during the high season.) Swimmers will be pleased to learn that solar-heating panels have been installed in the pool this year. We'd welcome more reports.

Open Easter–early Oct.
Rooms 30 double, 2 single – all with bath and shower, radio, tea-making facilities and baby-listening. 22 in 3 cottages in grounds. 7 ground-floor rooms.
Facilities 2 lounges, 3 bars, 2 restaurants. 3-acre garden with swimming pool, tennis court. Sandy beaches with safe bathing; private harbour and mooring facilities; fishing.
Location Travel via Guernsey (hourly ferry service from St Peter Port taking 15–20 minutes). Hotel meets guests at airport or ferry. (No cars on Herm.)
Restrictions Herm not really suitable for ♿ (those wishing to visit must land at high tide). No smoking in restaurant. No dogs.
Credit cards Access, Visa.
Terms (No service charge) Dinner, B&B £30–£45; full board £35–£50. Set lunch £7 (£8 on Sun), dinner £11.25–£12.50. Reduced rates for children, special meals.
Service/tipping: "Gratuities are not expected. When given they are shared out on a monthly basis to all the hotel staff."

ROZEL BAY Jersey — Map 1

Château La Chaire — *Tel* Jersey (0534) 63354
St Martins — *Fax* (0534) 65137

Small luxury hotel in a valley on north-eastern tip of Jersey, built in 1843, surrounded by a terraced garden and 7-acre grounds; sandy beach with safe swimming two-minutes' walk. Handsome oak-panelled public rooms. Restaurant specialises in local seafood. 13 double rooms, all with bath and shower. B&B double from £65. Set dinner £12 [1989]. 10% service charge added. New nomination. More reports welcome.

ST PETER PORT Guernsey — Map 1

La Collinette Hotel — *Tel* Guernsey (0481) 710331
St Jacques — *Fax* (0481) 713516

Unpretentious friendly family hotel in Georgian-style mansion on outskirts of town. 1-acre sheltered garden with heated swimming pool and children's play area. Well-equipped bedrooms and bathrooms; varied menu and generous portions of food. Possibly closed Christmas, New Year. 30 rooms, all with private facilities, also 7 self-catering units. B&B £19.50–£29.50. Set dinner £7, full alc £15. Little feedback. More reports badly needed.

La Frégate Hotel — *Tel* Guernsey (0481) 24624
Les Cotils — *Fax* (0481) 20443

Once an 18th-century manor house, though you would hardly guess that from its present appearance, *La Frégate* has a fine location in its own terraced garden high on a hill above St Peter Port harbour, about five minutes' walk from the town. Some rooms have double-glazed patio windows leading onto a private balcony, most enjoy splendid views; they are spacious, and well furnished in a functional but comfortable style. A bonus is *La Frégate*'s esteemed restaurant, fairly formal – ties and jackets *de rigueur*; it has a busy non-residential trade attracted by the ambitious and comprehensive menu (French with a good selection of seafood). The table d'hôte menu (for residents only) is served between 7 and 7.30 pm, full à la carte from 7 to 9.30 – an arrangement not to everyone's liking. More reports please.

Open All year.
Rooms 9 double, 4 single – all with bath and shower, telephone and tea-making facilities; 6 with private balcony; TV on request.
Facilities Residents' lounge, lounge bar, restaurant. 2-acre grounds with terraced gardens. 5 mins' walk to harbour with fishing, 10 mins to indoor leisure centre; beaches nearby.
Location Near Candie Gardens. 5 mins' walk from town centre. Difficult to find: telephone for directions on arrival on the island. Private carpark.
Restrictions Not suitable for ♿. No children under 14 in hotel, under 9 in restaurant. No dogs.
Credit cards All major cards accepted.
Terms (Service at guests' discretion) B&B: single £45–£50, double £75–£98. Set lunch £9.50, dinner (residents only) £14.50; full alc £23. 1-night bookings refused Apr–Oct.

Midhurst House *Tel* Guernsey (0481) 24391
Candie Road

We continue to receive warm comments on this "modest but immaculate hotel with truly caring owners" in an elegant Regency town house quietly located ten minutes' walk up from the harbour. Prices are very reasonable. "*Midhurst House* amply fulfilled the expectations raised by the Guide report. Brian and Jan Goodenough were friendly and helpful in every way, and our rooms comfortable and spotlessly clean. Brian's cooking made us forget any good resolutions we might ever have had." "For people who want a modest, friendly and quiet hotel, this is first rate." A drawback for some is the early dinner-time of 6.45 pm. Jan Goodenough writes, "The style of cooking and our low prices preclude us from having flexible timings if food is to be served at its best. The present time suits the majority of our guests because our over-50s do not like to eat late; they take a gentle stroll after dinner while it is still light and most guests attend concerts, theatres, etc. starting at 8; this way they are not rushed." (*Dr RJ Sandry; RF Mayers, Georgina Woolley, FM Rothwell, and others*) Guests must be on half or full board in high season.

Open 12 April–14 Oct.
Rooms 8 double – 2 with bath, 6 with shower, all with TV and tea-making facilities. 3 in cottage annexe. 4 ground-floor rooms.
Facilities Lounge, dining room. Small garden. Sea 5 mins' walk.
Location 5 mins' walk from town centre, near Candie Museum and Cambridge Park. Free public parking nearby.
Restrictions Not suitable for ♿. No children under 8. No dogs.
Credit cards None accepted.
Terms (No service charge) B&B (low season only) £18–£23; dinner, B&B £24–£28.50; full board £30–£34.50. Set lunch/dinner £6. 50% reductions for children aged 8-10 if sharing with 2 adults.
Service/tipping: "Tipping is not expected. If guests insist tips are distributed between all employees in proportion to hours worked."

> There is no VAT in the Channel Islands.

ST SAVIOUR Guernsey — Map 1

La Hougue Fouque Farm Hotel — *Tel* Guernsey (0481) 64181
Bas Courtils

Comfortable converted farm house in centre of Guernsey. 4-acre grounds with mature gardens, solar-heated swimming pool, tubs of flowers, poolside tables with umbrellas. Outside barbecues, weather permitting. Very reasonable prices, particularly out of season. Friendly staff, good though not outstanding food. 17 comfortable bedrooms, all with bath and access to balcony. B&B £18–£28, Dinner, B&B £23–£34 [1989]. Nominated last year. More reports please.

ST SAVIOUR Jersey — Map 1

Longueville Manor Hotel [GFG] — *Tel* Jersey (0534) 25501
Fax (0534) 31613
Telex 4192306 LMH

Without much competition – though perhaps *Château La Chaire* at Rozel Bay (q.v.) may now give it a run for its money – *Longueville Manor* has long been the *prima donna assoluta* of sophisticated country house hotels in the Channel Islands. It stands in large grounds at the foot of its own private wooded valley, one-and-a-half miles inland from Jersey's capital, St Helier, well away from the tourist hubbub, and – a plus for golfers – only two-and-a-half miles from the Royal Jersey Golf Club. The manor has comfortable sitting-around places including a small, well-chosen library; outside there is a large heated swimming pool where lunch may be taken in fine weather. Bedrooms, individually decorated, have been comprehensively upgraded. The hotel has been run by the Lewis and Dufty families for the past forty years. Its restaurant used to be its Achilles' heel but recently Barry Forster, previously at London's *Ritz* and still in his twenties, became *chef de cuisine* to general acclaim. Much of the produce is grown in the manor gardens. Wine waiters are praised for being "exceptionally helpful without the snobbery so many seem to affect", and "women dining without an escort – often made to feel uncomfortable – are not so here."

Open All year.
Rooms 2 suites, 30 double, 1 single – all with bath (7 also have shower), telephone, radio, TV. 8 ground-floor rooms.
Facilities Lift. Bar/lounge, sitting room, library, dining room; conference facilities. 16-acre grounds with swimming pool (heated in season) and putting green. Golf, bowls, squash, tennis within easy reach. 1½ m from sea with sandy beaches.
Location 1½ m E of St Helier; bus stops near main hotel gates. From airport, take main road to St Helier; near harbour follow sign A17 to Georgetown. Take A3 for 1 m; hotel is on left.
Restrictions No children under 7. No dogs in public rooms.
Credit cards All major cards accepted.
Terms B&B: single £60–£71, double £93–£146, suite £182–£203; dinner, B&B £18 per person added. Set lunch £13.50, dinner £21; full alc £31. Winter weekend breaks; Christmas/New Year package. Reductions for children sharing parents' room.
Service/tipping: "Service now included in in bills."

All inspections are carried out anonymously.

SARK — Map 1

Hotel Petit Champ — *Tel* Sark (048 183) 2046
Sark, via Guernsey

Sark, only three-and-a-half miles long but with nearly 40 miles of coastline, is the smallest of the four main Channel Islands. There are no cars, but all parts of the coast are easily reached on foot or by bicycle. The *Petit Champ* is a pleasant late 19th-century granite building in a secluded part of the island, well away from the day-trippers' tracks. Most of its rooms ("comfortable without being luxurious") have views of the sea and neighbouring islands. All are now centrally heated. No radio or television. The hotel has three sun lounges, a library and bar, a well-tended, sheltered garden and a solar-heated swimming pool built into a disused quarry – a fine sun-trap out of the wind. It will take you ten minutes to walk down to a secluded bay with sand at low tide – but allow half an hour for the climb back. It's a fairly formal sort of place: "Please bring something smart to wear in the evenings," reads the brochure, "as befits dinner by candle-light." Recommended last year for "friendly and efficient service under the civilised ownership of Mr and Mrs Terry Scott". We would welcome more reports.

Open Mid-Apr–early Oct.
Rooms 2 family suites (doubles with adjoining singles), 11 double, 3 single – 15 with bath and/or shower. Some ground-floor rooms.
Facilities 3 sun lounges, lounge (no-smoking), TV lounge, bar, 3 dining rooms. 1-acre garden with heated swimming pool. Steep walk to sandy beach, safe bathing.
Location 10 mins' walk from centre. Head for Beau Regard and turn right along the field path just before the duck pond.
Restrictions Sark not suitable for seriously ♿. Children must be old enough to sit with parents at dinner. No dogs.
Credit cards All major cards accepted.
Terms Dinner, B&B £31–£35. Set lunch from £8.50 (or snacks), dinner from £13; full alc £16. One-third reduction for children sharing parents' room, special meals on request.
Service/tipping: "We abandoned a service charge several years ago but some guests still insist on leaving gratuities. When it is impossible to refuse tips without causing offence, they are pooled and shared out at the end of the season (with interest added) by agreement of all the staff."

La Sablonnerie — *Tel* Sark (048 183) 2061
Sark, via Guernsey

"From the welcome at the boat from Guernsey by Philip Perrée, to the first friendly cup of tea on arrival after the ride to the hotel by horse and carriage, the mood was set for the next fortnight at this comfortable, spotless hotel." So opened a report last year on this off-the-beaten-track hotel in Little Sark, the southern peninsula of the island. "Our room was tiny but beds were made during breakfast, sheets turned back during dinner, towels changed regularly. Everyone, without exception, was extremely friendly. The hotel is run like clockwork by Philip's daughter Elizabeth. Mealtimes are fixed fairly rigidly, but this was no hardship as the food was well worth sitting down for." Drink is reasonably priced and since there is nothing much to do in the evening in Sark one does rather a lot of drinking. The lounge and dining room are small so one gets to know people very quickly. Single people and couples may be asked to share a table." The rooms – "simple and charming" – are sprinkled about the tiny hamlet. The hotel is surrounded by its own working farm, interesting walks and striking scenery. A few drawbacks: not many rooms have private facilities; the bar/lounge gets overcrowded in the evening; some might find the situation rather cut off owing to the absence of cars on Sark.

Open Easter–Oct.
Rooms 1 suite, 14 double, 6 single – 6 with bath and shower, 6 with shower only. Many in cottages in courtyard and garden.
Facilities 2 lounges, 2 bars, sun lounge, conservatory, 2 restaurants. 5-acre grounds with gardens and croquet lawn, surrounded by hotel's 100-acre farmland. Small coves and pebble beaches suitable for bathing nearby; sandy bay 15 mins' walk. Hotel boat for trips round island; fishing.
Location At southern tip of island. Guests are met by tractor or horse and carriage.
Restrictions Sark not suitable for severely ♿. No children under 8. No dogs.
Credit cards Access, Amex, Visa.
Terms (Excluding 10% service charge) B&B £18.50; dinner, B&B £30.50–£40; full board £32.50–£42; £2.50 per person supplement for private bathroom. Set lunch £11, dinner £15. Reduced rates and high tea for children.
Service/tipping: "10% added; distributed between all the staff."

Stocks Hotel *Tel* Sark (048 183) 2001
Sark, via Guernsey

From a reader this year, "It's quite amazing how Sark's best hotel/restaurants keep up their standards year after year. Every year one of them comes slightly ahead of the others, and this time *Stocks* wins. The Armorgie family run an efficient ship and Paul Armorgie lends a distinct tone to the restaurant – he's so obviously enthusiastic about every detail of his menus." Other correspondents, too, appreciate the virtues of this old-established characteristically granite Sark hotel in the Dixcart Valley, even if their raptures fall short of this earlier encomium, "Not only worthy of the Guide, but in the paradise category. The old-fashioned air of the rooms is in keeping with Sark, but *Stocks* is exceptional (1) in its position: you walk to it through meadows of wild flowers; as it is in the middle of the small island it is ideally placed for exploring in any direction; (2) in the friendly skill of the young staff; (3) in the exceptionally good food." There is an outdoor swimming pool surrounded by a sun terrace; a buffet menu is served at lunch. The emphasis is on informality, though after 6 o'clock tee-shirts and jeans are discouraged, and ties expected in the restaurant. (*F Cowly, and others*) The hotel advises guests to use its accommodation/travel package which is financially advantageous.

Open 12 Apr–8 Oct.
Rooms 2 family, 18 double, 4 single – 14 with bath and/or shower. 8 in Dower House annexe.
Facilities Lounge, library/games room with TV, residents' bar, restaurant, buffet/bar with terrace. 5-acre grounds with unheated swimming pool and badminton. Beach 10 mins' walk; fishing, cycling.
Location 5 mins' walk from centre. Take the only road to a finger post pointing down the valley.
Restrictions Sark not suitable for seriously ♿. No dogs.
Credit cards None accepted.
Terms Dinner, B&B £27–£36. Buffet lunch/dinner from £8.50, restaurant lunch £10.50, dinner £14.00. Reduced rates and special meals for children.
Service/tipping: "Service is optional – related to guests' opinion of service and quality. Tronc *split equally regardless of position – Armorgie family excluded!"*

Northern Ireland

BLACKHEATH HOUSE

COLERAINE

ANNALONG Co Down **Map 6**

Glassdrumman House and Lodge
85 Mill Road
Annalong BT34 4RH

Tel Annalong (039 67) 68451
Telex 747717

Our repeated prayers for recommendable hotels in Northern Ireland were answered last year when two Ulster hotels made their debut in these pages. *Glassdrumman House*, now warmly endorsed, is owned by Graeme and Joan Hall, who moved out of Belfast in the early eighties. From a self-sufficiency manual the Halls learned baking, cooking, farming and butchery; the surrounding fields in which their Aberdeen Angus cattle roam present a peacefully pastoral scene. A surplus of produce led eventually to three restaurants: one for quick lunches and afternoon tea, the Kitchen Garden for more up-market lunches and dinner, and the Memories restaurant which, except by special arrangement, is open only on Saturday night and serves a formidable seven-course meal – "medieval in quantity", according to one reader – for £25 [1989]. Recently the Halls converted a farmhouse a mile-and-a-half away into a rather plain eight-bedroomed guest house, *Glassdrumman Lodge*. It nestles in the shadow of Slieve Binian, one of the most spectacular peaks in the Mountains of Mourne – magnificent walking terrain. Bedrooms vary in size, but they are all immaculately clean and comfortable and attractively decorated. All have views of the mountains or the sea about a mile away. "There are new books and magazines in every bedroom and in the library. No muzak. All the fires are *real* fires. A set dinner is served at the Lodge from Monday to Friday; transport is provided if you want to dine at *Glassdrumman House* a short distance away. At Memories, James, the butler, greets you and you feel as if you are in a very elegant private home. The wine list is excellent." "Breakfast is taken communally at a baronial table – a magnificent meal including fresh orange juice, excellent fresh bread, a vast array of marmalades and preserves, and ducks' eggs, liver, kidneys, etc for those who feel strong enough." (*Mrs HL Dawson, and others*)

Open All year. Memories Restaurant open Sat evening; other days by arrangement.
Rooms 8 double – all with bath and shower, telephone and TV; 24-hour room service, nanny available.
Facilities Lounge, drawing room, library, breakfast room; 3 restaurants in separate building 1½ m away. Conference and office facilities. 8-acre gardens, 35-acre farm, tennis, fishing. Use of health club and swimming pool in nearby hotel; tennis, fishing. Sea 1 m.
Location Off A2, 6 m from Newcastle, 1 m N of Annalong.
Restrictions Not suitable for ♿. Preferably no children under 12. Dogs in barns only.
Credit cards All major cards accepted.
Terms (Service at guests' discretion) B&B £32.50–£45, Dinner, B&B £49–61.50. Set lunch £5–£10, dinner from £17.50; in Memories £25.

COLERAINE Co Londonderry — Map 6

Blackheath House — *Tel* Aghadowey (0265) 868433
112 Killeague Road
Blackhill, Coleraine BT51 4HH

Our other entry for Northern Ireland also started life as a restaurant, *MacDuff's*, run by Joe and Margaret Erwin for over ten years in the basement of their restored rectory in the beautiful Aghadowey countryside in the north of the province. The Causeway Coast is just ten miles away (beaches and cliff walks), and there are eight 18-hole and two 9-hole golf courses within twenty minutes' drive. A few years ago the Erwins converted the rectory, *Blackheath House*, into a small hotel. It relies on business trade, but also gives pleasure to a private visitor: "Quietly situated in the midst of prosperous farming terrain, the brown-painted structure stands four-square and solid with no pretensions to grace or beauty, but it is in a large mature garden with lots of trees and a very pretty lily pond. The interior is comfortably cluttered with old furniture, including a considerable number of keyboard instruments; some of the modern furniture in the bedrooms is not altogether in keeping but the general ambience is one of restfulness and old-world gentility. Rooms are well equipped, with fresh fruit, books and magazines but have no telephone. Dinner is à la carte with a range of about six starters and six main courses. Our meal was good, the selection of vegetables was varied, colourful and cooked to perfection, and we considered it excellent value for money. Breakfast is a hearty affair; those not worried about cholesterol can indulge in an 'Ulster Fry' consisting of eggs, bacon, kidney, black pudding, sausage, mushrooms and fried bread, served from 7.30 am." More reports would be welcome.

Open All year. Restaurant closed Sun.
Rooms 6 double – 2 with bath and shower, 4 with shower, all with radio, TV, and tea-making facilities.
Facilities Residents' lounge, residents' dining room, restaurant with lounge. Indoor swimming pool (heated May–Sep). 2-acre garden. Fishing, shooting, riding, golf nearby; sea 11 m.
Location 4 m N of Garuagh on A29 Killeague road, signposted to left.
Restrictions Not suitable for ♿. No children under 12. No dogs.
Credit cards None accepted.
Terms B&B: single occupancy £25–£30, double £45–£50. Full alc dinner £17.
Service/tipping: "We believe tips should not be expected; it is left entirely to the discretion of the customer. If anyone shows satisfaction by tipping the money is divided between those who have contributed to the service of that customer."

Traveller's tale *This "country house" hotel refuses its guests breakfast at 9.40 am on Sunday morning, and then charges for the breakfast on the basis that the guests "should have known that breakfast was off at 9.30 because it was posted up in the bedroom". I told them that there was no such notice in our room. There was a shrug and an "Oh well, it's in all the other rooms".*

Republic of Ireland

ADARE Co Limerick **Map 6**

Dunraven Arms Hotel
Main Street

Tel Limerick (061) 86209
Fax (061) 86209
Telex 70202

On main west coast route, 10 miles from Limerick, picturesque old inn, with new wing and good rooms, in a picture-postcard village. Recommended for "real professionalism", and for its "admirable restaurant – half the price of others, and twice the fun. Excellent fish and rare roast beef, perfect rack of lamb, beautiful bombe surprise". Bar very popular (and noisy) at weekends. Closed Good Friday. 45 rooms, all with bath and shower. B&B single IR£40–IR£45, double IR£65–IR£90. Set lunch IR£6.95, dinner IR£16.50. 12½% service charge added. New nomination. More reports please.

Italicised entries are for hotels on which we need more feedback – either because we are short of reports or because we have had mixed or inadequate reports.

BALLINA Co Mayo — Map 6

Mount Falcon Castle
Ballina

Tel Ballina (096) 21172
Fax (096) 21172
Telex 40899

A grey stone mansion dating from 1876, *Mount Falcon Castle* lies just south of Ballina, in the beautiful wild countryside of County Mayo. It is set in a 100-acre estate with mature woods and parkland leading down to the banks of the river Moy, on which the hotel has eight miles of fishing. Deserted beaches and rugged coast line are nearby. The castle was bought in 1932 by Constance Aldridge and her husband, Major Robert, to entertain their fishing friends and has been run ever since then as a country-house hotel, grand yet informal. The castle has ten large and comfortable bedrooms, most with a large bathroom *en suite*, and is furnished throughout with period furniture. Log fires and fresh flowers greet you in the reception rooms and the gothic hall. In country-house style, dinner is served at a fixed time, all the guests being seated at the long mahogany table with the hostess, now in her late seventies, at its head. Menus make use of the best local produce, beautifully and straightforwardly cooked; there's plenty of local salmon (*Mount Falcon* produces its own excellent gravad lax), local meat and game and vegetables grown on the estate farm. Little feedback this year, more reports welcome.

Open End Mar–31 Jan. Closed 22–26 Dec.
Rooms 8 double, 2 single – 8 with bath and shower.
Facilities Drawing room, TV room, games room, dining room. 100-acre grounds with tennis court, woodland, pasture, river frontage with fishing; shooting in winter. Riding nearby; golf 10 m.
Location 4 m S of Ballina on Foxford road.
Restriction Not suitable for ♿.
Credit cards All major cards accepted.
Terms (Excluding 10% service charge) B&B IR£37.50; half board IR£50; full board IR£57.50. Set lunch IR£7.50 (by arrangement), dinner IR£15. Weekly rates; special rates for family holidays. 1-night bookings sometimes refused at height of fishing season. Reduced rates for children; special meals.

BALLINDERRY Co Tipperary — Map 6

Gurthalougha House
Ballinderry, Nenagh

Tel Borrisokane (067) 22080

"Pigeons and wafts of woodsmoke greet you as you approach this rambling house through the arched gateway. There are books and magazines and conversation, and no telly. I had a splendid stay here, discussing the German postwar economic miracle with the only other guest, a formidable former German Minister of Economics. The Wilkinsons tiptoed compassionately in now and again to revive me with trays of this and that at appropriate intervals. It's a lovely place, and fits very well in the Guide; interesting, stylish, and unpretentious. Good solid antiques and sure-footed but not ostentatious taste. The food was excellent too. A lovely lakeside setting, deafeningly silent while I was there, but duck-shooters sometimes shatter the peace." (*LH*) Others report in a similar vein on the early 19th-century country house run by Michael and Bessie Wilkinson (he the cook, she front of house) in 150 acres of forest on the shores of Lough Derg, the largest lake on the Shannon: "It is truly something from a bygone age. We were welcomed with tea (home-made preserves of course) by a roaring fire in the huge lounge. This was followed by a dinner remarkable both for the food (which was good) and for the fact that we ate entirely by candle-light in a room furnished in the simple elegance of the early 19th century. Our room was the sort Lord Peter Wimsey might easily have occupied and the bathroom (and bath) easily the largest we've seen anywhere." Considerable repainting and recarpeting has taken place in the last year. Children will enjoy the donkey, geese and horses. (*Lesley Le-Tan, and others*)

Open All year except New Year and 2 weeks in June. Restaurant closed for lunch; snacks by arrangement.
Rooms 8 double – 6 with bath, 2 with shower.
Facilities Sitting room, library, dining room. 150-acre grounds with forest walks, gardens, ½ m lake shore with private quay, safe bathing, boats, ghillie available; windsurfing, pony trekking.
Location On shores of Lough Derg, W of Ballinderry village, which is 16 m N of Nenagh. (Signposted from Borrisokane.)'
Restrictions Not suitable for ♿. No small children or dogs in dining room.
Credit cards Access, Amex, Visa.
Terms B&B IR£27. Set dinner IR£18. Weekend breaks. 33% reduction for children under 10.
Service/tipping: "Tipping at guests' discretion; the money is equally divided."

BALLYLICKEY Co Cork — Map 6

Sea View House Hotel *Tel* Bantry (027) 50073 and 50462
Ballylickey, Bantry

Kathleen O'Sullivan's unpretentiously comfortable, friendly establishment continues to receive praise from readers. Set in five-acre grounds three miles north of Bantry, it has good views over Bantry Bay and distant mountains. Bedrooms all have *en suite* facilities; they are individually decorated, "bright and cheerful, comfortable and spotless", and while you are having dinner your room is tidied and the beds folded down. "A good centre for exploring unspoiled areas of coastal and mountain scenery like the Beara Peninsula. Its greatest asset is its owner who runs what was once the family home with an unbeatable combination of integrity, thoughtfulness for her guests, good housekeeping and a real talent for cooking. And it is splendid value for money." (*John and Helen Wright*) "Initial impressions were disappointing: Ballylickey is a rather characterless place, albeit pretty, and we were accommodated in the little lodge (reasonably enough, since we had a dog). But things thereafter went from strength to strength. The welcome and service were delightful; the food was consistently very good, and the breakfasts outstanding. The atmosphere of the place was simply great fun." "The whole range of seafood (scallops, seafood crêpes, prawns, the 'bouquet of seafood', superb pink river-trout, fish mousses) was particularly worthy of note. Lamb is cooked exactly as requested. Good sound wine list, reasonably priced. Wide variety of Irish dishes." Packed lunches are available, and tea and cakes in the afternoon. (*Richard Parish, AG Mursell; Mr and Mrs G Buckland, and others*) Mrs O'Sullivan has applied for planning permission to build a new wing with eight large bedrooms during the winter of 1989.

Open Mid-Mar–31 Oct.
Rooms 12 double, 1 single – all with bath and shower, and telephone. 3 in cottage in garden.
Facilities 2 lounges, TV room, cocktail bar, 2 dining rooms. 5-acre grounds. Game fishing, sea fishing, pony trekking, boating, beaches and golf nearby.
Location 3 m N of Bantry towards Glengarriff, 70 yds off main road.
Restrictions Cottage suitable for ♿. No dogs in public rooms.
Credit cards Access, Amex, Visa.
Terms B&B: single IR£25–IR£30, double IR£50–IR£70. Set lunch IR£9, dinner IR£17.50; full alc IR£20. Midweek and weekend breaks. Reduced rates and special meals for children.
Service/tipping: "10% service charge added in lieu of gratuities; shared equally among all staff; owner does not *receive any portion."*

BALLYVAUGHAN Co Clare — Map 6

Gregans Castle Hotel

Tel Ennis (065) 77005
Fax (065) 77111

Gregans Castle is the only hotel in the heart of the Burren, that weird 100 square miles of lunar landscape roughly halfway between Galway and Shannon airport. It is an area full of rare flowers and plants (alpine and arctic), and is a paradise for botanists and ornithologists. It is also rich in historic and prehistoric remains; Yeats-lovers will be attracted to Thoor Ballylee, the town where he lived for a few years near Lady Gregory. Most readers are enthusiastic about the hotel, quite apart from the uniqueness of its position. "We had a large, tastefully furnished room with a beautiful view overlooking Galway Bay. The staff were very helpful in our exploration of the Burren." "For us the Burren and *Gregans Castle* have been an irresistible combination for seven consecutive years. Peter and Moira Haden, the owners, work hard and have invested much thought and money into improving both the interior and the gardens. The beds are firm, the bathrooms spotless, and the bar, library and lounges – all recently renovated – are ideal for relaxation. The meals are consistently good and the set menu well balanced." (*John and Helen Wright*) A detractor last year, complaining of small, thin towels, had the bad luck to visit early in the season just before all the towels were replaced. This year an ambivalent visitor comments, "The main problem was in the dining room where the food was only fair. Even worse was the lack of generosity. If we were to do it over again, we might still stay here, but eat in the busy seafood restaurant in Ballyvaughan."

Open Easter–late Oct.
Rooms 6 suites, 9 double, 1 single – all with bath and shower. 3 on ground floor.
Facilities Hall, lounge with TV, library, bar, dining room. 12-acre grounds with parkland, award-winning gardens and croquet. Safe, sandy beach 4½ m; harbour with swimming and boating 3½ m.
Location On N67 between Ballyvaughan and Lisdoonvarna, 3½ m SW of village, at foot of "Corkscrew Hill".
Restriction No dogs.
Credit card Visa.
Terms B&B: single IR£47–IR£59, double IR£70–IR£130. Set dinner IR£20; alc lunch available. Half board rates for 3 or more nights. Reduced rates for children; special meals.
Service/tipping: "Guests are not expected to tip for usual services. Many like to leave 'a little something' for some member of staff who has done something special; this is given immediately to the person concerned."

CASHEL BAY Co Galway — Map 6

Cashel House Hotel — *Tel* Clifden (095) 31001
Fax (095) 31077
Telex 50812

Kay and Dermot McEvilly's civilised former manor house, an oasis in the rugged wilderness of Connemara, continues to attract warm praise. "One of the most delightful hotels we've ever stayed in. Lovely peaceful setting and well-kept gardens, staff all friendly and helpful and the food absolutely delicious." "Very civilised, even sumptuous. Lots of intimate little spaces where you can sit and read or talk without meeting every other guest in the place." *Cashel House* stands at the head of Cashel Bay in a 50-acre estate with a prize-winning garden and woodland walks, a hard tennis court and tiny private beach. Now pony/horse trekking has been added – an arena, 11 stables, and 18 horses. Public rooms include a comfortable lounge with antiques and fresh flowers, a library and a spacious modern bar. This year the dining room has been extended without increasing the number of covers, easing the work of the staff and enabling the restaurant to offer more complicated dishes. "We feel," Mrs. McEvilly writes, "that the hotel is the ideal place for rest and relaxation: no music, no noise, no functions. A place for people who don't follow the crowd." (*LH, Mrs M Shenton, HR Lamb*) There have, however, been criticisms this year. About the decor: "frankly over the top – carpets, curtains, and seat furnishings all heavily patterned", "dreadful wallpaper – please warn people". Others have found the food disappointing: "boring green salad each night and the ubiquitous boiled potato, usually tough"; "breakfasts disappointing"; and staff unskilled. We would welcome more reports.

Open Feb–Nov.
Rooms 13 suites, 16 double, 3 single – all with bath (whirlpool bath in 4 garden suites) and telephone. 6 ground-floor rooms.
Facilities 2 lounges, TV room, library, dining room with conservatory. 50-acre estate with 20-acre gardens, tennis, stables – pony/horse trekking, small private sandy beach. Golf, fishing, bird watching, nearby.
Location 42 m NW of Galway. Take N59 from Galway. Turn left to village 1 m after Recess.
Restrictions No children under 5. No dogs in public rooms.
Credit cards All major cards accepted.
Terms (Excluding 12½% service charge) B&B IR£41–IR£55. Set dinner IR£21.50. Snack and alc lunches. Reduced rates for children sharing parents' room; high teas.
Service/tipping: "Service charge made to counteract 'Good tippers get good table or service' syndrome instead of good service being rewarded by tip. No need for further tips, though graciously accepted by staff."

CASTLEBALDWIN Co Sligo — Map 6

Cromleach Lodge Country House — *Tel* Sligo (071) 65155
Castlebaldwin, Nr Boyle

A new nomination: "Superb open setting on a hillside above lovely Lough Arrow, with spreading vistas and hardly a house in sight – rural Ireland at its best. Here an ambitious local couple, Christy and Moira

Tighe, have recently enlarged their own home into a very superior guest house. Apart from the setting, the biggest plus is the food: Moira Tighe, self-taught, must have real flair, for the results are sophisticated and professional: smoked salmon roulade, champagne sorbet, turbot in a creamy sauce, desserts such as rum and brandy soufflé. Unfortunately, the decor in the bar/lounge and the bedrooms was over-ornate. And the insistent piped music was irritating; but the log fire was nice, on a chill March night. Our bedroom was small, with a shower only, but cheap at IR£16 per person, including a superb breakfast (lovely home-made wheaten bread) served on unusual Rosenthal china. (*JA and KA*)

Open All year except 22–31 Dec. Restaurant closed for lunch and on Sun.
Rooms 7 suites, 3 double, 2 single – all with bath and/or shower, and telephone.
Facilities Lounge, 2 dining rooms. 1-acre garden in 30-acre farm.
Private access to Lough Arrow; boating, surfing. Hotel can arrange fishing, walking, hill climbing and archaeology trips.
Location 10 m N of Boyle, signposted off N4 Dublin-Sligo road. Turn E at Castlebaldwin.
Restrictions Not suitable for ♿.
Credit cards Access, Amex, Visa.
Terms (Excluding 10% service charge) B&B single IR£18, double IR£36, suite IR£43. Set dinner IR£16–IR£19. 30% reduction for children sharing parents' room; special meals (before 7 pm).

CASTLEHILL Co Mayo — Map 6

Enniscoe House — *Tel* Crossmolina (096) 31112
Castlehill — *Telex* 40855
Nr Crossmolina, Ballina

Fine Georgian country house on shores of Lough Conn in 150-acre grounds with gardens, woodland and working farm. Plain exterior, antiques, family portraits, open fires inside. "Sympathetic traditional hospitality." Private landing stage, boats and ghillies available for fishing. Open 1 Apr–14 Oct. 7 double rooms, all with private facilities. B&B double IR£35–IR£37. Recent nomination. More reports please.

CORK Co Cork — Map 6

Arbutus Lodge Hotel — *Tel* Cork (021) 501237
Montenotte — *Fax* (021) 502893
Telex 75079 ARBU

"The nicest place we found to stay in Cork. The food is the thing – and the restaurant and its menu are suitably grand." "We have never eaten in a better restaurant – anywhere. We were sorry we could stay only one night." Two reports this year on *Arbutus Lodge*, once the home of the Lord Mayor of Cork, and now a hotel run by the Ryan family, father, mother, two sons and their wives. It is named for the arbutus tree in its prize-winning garden, which has many rare trees and shrubs. The house is in the posh suburb of Montenotte, fifteen minutes' walk or five minutes' drive from the centre of town. It was built *c.* 1802, a master cooper's house, and some rooms still reflect the solid virtues of its origins. Others, in the modern extension grafted on either side of the main building, are "more functional than beautiful", though some have good views over the river Lee to the city beyond; it's worth asking for one when booking. One reader writes: "our room was fairly small, but well equipped with a six-foot bed, television and fridge containing many drinks – and the very small bathroom was kept well stocked with Jean Patou soap, bath oil and shampoo." Another was less satisfied, commenting on a displeasing decor and "plush-disguised shabbiness". The restaurant is spacious, with a large bay window, starched white tablecloths, good china and glass, flowers, and candles. Michael Ryan serves fine Irish meat and seafood, and offers a "tasting menu" (six courses *plus* sorbet and coffee) as well. There is a splendid wine list, reflecting Declan Ryan's zeal in tracing uncommonly good wine at uncommonly low prices. The same personal flair is shown in the public rooms, filled with the work of contemporary Irish artists. (*LH, HR Lamb, and others*)

Open All year, except 1 week at Christmas. Restaurant closed Sun (bar meals available).
Rooms 12 double, 8 single – all with bath and/or shower, telephone, radio, TV and baby-listening.
Facilities Lounge, bar, 2 dining rooms. 1-acre garden with patio and croquet.
Location 1½ m up hill from town centre. Parking.
Restrictions Not suitable for ♿. No dogs.
Credit cards All major cards accepted.
Terms [1989 rates] (No service charge) B&B: single IR£36.50–IR£75, double IR£66–IR£98. Set lunch IR£15.25, dinner IR£18.95; full alc IR£26.50. Weekend rates; gourmet weekends.
Service/tipping: "Guests should tip only if they receive exceptional service."

DUBLIN — Map 6

Raglan Lodge — *Tel* Dublin (01) 606697
10 Raglan Road, Ballsbridge — *Fax* (01) 606781
Dublin 4

B&B in large Victorian residence with small garden, recently restored, in fashionable suburb half-a-mile from centre. Charmingly furnished breakfast /sitting room. "Executive accommodation" emphasised. Recommended for "extremely friendly and helpful owners and good breakfast with freshly-squeezed orange juice." 10 well-equipped bedrooms all with bath and/or shower, 3 in coach house. B&B double IR£75–IR£100 [1989]. New nomination. More reports please.

DUNLAVIN Co Wicklow — Map 6

Rathsallagh House — *Tel* Naas (045) 53112
Fax (045) 53343

A country house in huge grounds 35 miles from Dublin in County Wicklow is enthusiastically nominated, "How does one describe perfection without sounding soppy? Perhaps best by saying that *Rathsallagh House*, which the owners deliberately and rightly say is Not A Hotel, is the lovely country home we would all like to have. A long block of

> When telephoning the Republic of Ireland from abroad, omit the 0 at the beginning of the dialling code.

converted Queen Anne stable buildings surrounded by untold acres of lawns, croquet, golf, a gurgling brook somewhere nearby, and sheep and horses everywhere, close enough to see, far enough not to disturb. The owners are Kay and Joe O'Flynn; she cooks, wonderfully, he runs the large farm and co-hosts at night. There are eight guest rooms, each in different colours, each with a generous bathroom with a huge tub and bath sheets rather than towels; cupboards galore, tea trays, bookshelves – with the right books. Dinner, after pour-yourself drinks in the drawing room, was four courses of delicate joy. At night the beds were made ready and, as we seemed in need of coddling, hot-water bottles inserted to help us sleep. In the morning, after a dip in the indoor solar-heated swimming pool an Irish breakfast awaits – freshly-baked breads, rolls, toast, home-made jams, eggs, black pudding, sausages and perfect bacon. Prices are ridiculously but wonderfully reasonable." "We spent a tranquil evening there and enjoyed the food, the surroundings and the very welcoming atmosphere. But reports suggest that things can be different on the nights of the local hunt meeting!" (*Rathsallagh* is a good base for hunting with some of Ireland's leading packs, and horses may be hired.) (*Gitta Sereny, Neil O'Kennedy*)

Open All year except 18 Dec–2 Jan.
Rooms 8 double, all with bath and shower, telephone and tea-making facilities. 2 in courtyard.
Facilities Drawing room, dining room; billiard room, indoor heated swimming pool. 500-acre grounds with tennis, croquet, golf academy, pheasant shooting, hunting.
Location 2 m SW of Dunlavin.
Restriction No dogs.
Credit cards Access, Diners, Visa.
Terms (Excluding 10% service charge) B&B IR£40–IR£45; dinner, B&B IR£60–IR£65. Set lunch IR£18, dinner IR£20.
Service/tipping: "If guests feel service is especially helpful tipping is acceptable. Otherwise service charge is sufficient."

GOREY Co Wexford — Map 6

Marlfield House

Tel Gorey (055) 21124
Fax (055) 21572
Telex 80757

"One of the outstanding hotels in Ireland. The decor and furnishings, although sometimes over the top, have real style. The dining room is unsurpassed, in my experience, in any hotel. Our bedroom and bathroom were immaculate, The staff, and of course Mrs Bowe, were very welcoming and highly competent. The gardens are greatly improved, and a delight to walk round. Breakfasts are excellent." The former dower house of the Courtown estate, a noble three-storey Regency house, is now Mary Bowe's sophisticated country house hotel. It has won many awards over the years – for the breakfasts, for its garden, for cheese and, repeatedly, for the excellence of the restaurant. And it is in a choice position – a mile from the sea with sandy beaches – close to a golf course, and with plenty of the beauty spots of Co Wicklow at hand. "The house is full of pictures and lovely furniture, nearly all antiques; it has a slightly old-fashioned air apart from the dining conservatory which is pure fantasy, full of greenery and mirrors, lattice and enormous hanging baskets of geraniums. The bedrooms are luxurious in a private house way. Bathrooms very well lit, with jacuzzi and everything you could possibly want including an enormous bath sheet." (*Richard Creed, Patricia Roberts*) A new wing with six sumptuous new suites, and a "very grand reception with marble floor and 18th-century marble mantelpiece" have been added. A few niggles from a regular visitor, "No change of menu for three nights running, and sauces a bit old-fashioned; quality of meat less good than on previous visits, and a few housekeeping negligences." More reports please.

Open All year except 3 days at Christmas, 8–31 Jan.
Rooms 7 suites, 12 double, 1 single – all with bath and shower, telephone and TV; tea-making facilities, baby-listening on request. Some ground-floor rooms.
Facilities Reception, drawing room, library, lounge bar, restaurant, conservatory. 36-acre grounds with tennis court and croquet. Sea with sandy beaches and safe bathing 1 m.
Location 1 m from Gorey on the Courtown road.
Restriction No dogs in bedrooms or public rooms.
Credit cards All major cards accepted.
Terms (Excluding 10% service charge) B&B: single IR£65–IR£120, double IR£110–IR£120, suite IR£150–IR£350. Set lunch IR£17, dinner IR£24.50. Weekend and midweek reductions in off season. High teas for children on request.
Service/tipping: "10% added; tipping discouraged."

KANTURK Co Cork — Map 6

Assolas Country House and Restaurant — *Tel* Kanturk (029) 50015 *Fax* (029) 50795

An elegant and serene 17th-century manor house, set in beautiful grounds beside a river, the home of the Bourke family for the past 70 years. "One of the most beautiful settings we have ever seen; grounds calm and peaceful." "Everything denotes care and good housekeeping – the gravel *outside* the gate is raked, and the grass verges and hedges are neat and trimmed along the driveway. The house, with white paint and green creeper, is beautifully proportioned and excellently maintained and decorated throughout. The lawns and tennis court slope away down to the river which comes complete with wooden bridge, weir, small boat and swans. It is utterly quiet. Our bedroom was in soft gold colours: spotless, bright and comfortable. The public rooms are equally attractive: wonderfully polished furniture, lovely ornaments, lots of books and candles, flowers, sparkling glass and damask napkins in the dining room. Service was quiet, efficient and friendly." Earlier criticism of a limited dinner menu appears to have been taken to heart: a recent visitor describes the food as "superb". (*T Meyer, and others*) Our only criticism this year concerned a room in the Garden Court which "had a beautiful *en suite* bathroom, but storage facilities for clothes were minimal and sitting facilities poor".

Open Mid-Mar–mid-Nov.
Rooms 9 double – all with bath and shower (3 have whirlpool), telephone. 3 in courtyard building.
Facilities 2 lounges, restaurant; private dining room. 7-acre grounds with gardens, tennis, croquet, river with boating and trout fishing. Salmon fishing and golf nearby.
Location 3½ m NE of Kanturk; turn off road towards Buttevant.
Restrictions Not suitable for ♿. No babies. No dogs.

Credit cards All major cards accepted.
Terms B&B: single occupancy IR£46–IR£55, double IR£75–IR£115. Set dinner IR£20. 1-night bookings refused if for more than 1 month ahead. Reduced rates for children sharing parents' room.
Service/tipping: "Our prices are fully inclusive. Tipping is actively discouraged; if guests still tip in appreciation the money is pooled and shared by all staff."

KENMARE Co Kerry — Map 6

Hawthorn House — *Tel* Killarney (064) 41035
Shelbourne Street

More a small guest house than a hotel, with an ambitious dining room offering imaginative cooking. In town, but quietly located; well situated for touring. Small garden. Recommended for friendly welcome, "swish" decor, and attractive restaurant with sparkling crystal, white china and pink tablecloths. Open all year except 2 weeks mid-winter. 6 double rooms, 1 single, 2 with bath, 5 with shower. B&B (full Irish) £IR14–£IR17. Set dinner £IR14.50. New nomination. More reports please.

Park Hotel Kenmare — *Tel* Killarney (064) 41200
Fax (064) 41402
Telex 73905

"A superbly professional enterprise which manages to combine Irish friendliness with efficiency" is once again the consensus view of the *Park Hotel*, a substantial mansion built at the turn of the century as a railway hotel and set in a large, splendidly maintained park with beautiful views of the Kenmare estuary and the mountains of west Cork. It has a magnificent oak staircase; antiques and good paintings abound in the public rooms; bedrooms are spacious and comfortable. The restaurant, under Mathew Darcy, French in style with Irish ingredients, is one of only three establishments in the Republic to earn a *Michelin* rosette. "The *Park Hotel* demonstrates that one can have superb food and lodging in a luxury setting without stuffiness and pretentiousness." "We had a meal to remember on the terrace overlooking the valley." (*HR Lamb, and others*)

Open Easter–New Year
Rooms 6 suites, 32 double, 12 single – 42 with bath and shower, 8 with shower, all with telephone, radio and baby-listening; TV in suites. 7 ground-floor rooms; 1 suite adapted for ♿.
Facilities Lift. Drawing room, cocktail lounge, TV/games room, restaurant. 11-acre grounds, with all-weather tennis court, 9-hole golf course and croquet. Sea and river fishing locally.
Location 60 m west of Cork, adjacent to village. Signposted.
Restriction No dogs.
Credit cards All major cards accepted.
Terms [1989 rates] Dinner, B&B IR£90–IR£165. Set lunch IR£15, dinner IR£30; full alc IR£35. Christmas, New Year programme. Off-season gourmet weekends; murder mystery weekends. Reduced rates for children sharing parents' room; special meals on request.
Service/tipping: "Service included. Tips at guests' discretion.

> Sterling and dollar equivalents of foreign currencies at the date of going to press will be found at the back of the Guide.

LETTERFRACK Co Galway — Map 6

Rosleague Manor Hotel — *Tel* (095) 41101
Letterfrack, Connemara — *Fax* (095) 41102

Regency house in 30-acre grounds seven miles north of Clifden, overlooking sheltered bay surrounded by mountains and forests. Well situated for walks in Connemara National Park; beautiful beaches and harbour of Cleggan nearby. Recommended for the view – "I could see 11 mountains from my bedroom without craning my neck"; the food – "scrumptious. Really fresh fish, delicious soups and puddings"; and the warmth of welcome of owners, Patrick and Anne Foyle, brother and sister. Open Easter–Nov. 4 suites, 11 double – all with bath and/or shower. B&B £IR25–£IR45. Set dinner £IR20. New nomination. More reports please.

MALLOW Co Cork — Map 6

Longueville House and Presidents' Restaurant — *Tel* Mallow (022) 47156
Fax (022) 47459

Noble mansion, owned and run by the O'Callaghan family, in 500-acre wooded grounds overlooking Blackwater river, with game fishing. Georgian in origin with later additions including fine lounge and library and magnificent Victorian conservatory. Bedrooms recently refurbished and William O'Callaghan, after a year with Raymond Blanc, is cooking "wonderful food", using fresh produce from the estate. Open 1 Mar–20 Dec. 17 rooms, all with bath and/or shower. B&B double IR£68–IR£98. Set lunch IR£15, dinner IR£26 [1989]. *Was in earlier editions; now re-nominated. More reports please.*

MOUNTRATH Co Laois — Map 6

Roundwood House — *Tel* Portlaoise (0502) 32120

César award: Outstanding Irish hospitality

"An exercise in pure nostalgia for those of us who have known and loved Ireland since long before the EC. The house is beautiful, the setting very peaceful, and the extremely uneven steps up to the front door mean that one can expect a complete lack of sashcords so that windows open with terrifying rapidity." A characteristically enthusiastic report on this Georgian country house near the centre of the Republic. "Breakfast and dinner traditional and hearty, but the most pleasing aspect of our stay was the informality of the proprietors and friendly talking around the massive fireplaces – traditional Irish hospitality." *Roundwood House* lies in large grounds in the shadow of the unspoilt and beautiful Slieve Bloom Mountains. The owner, Frank Kennan, writes, "This is a truly purist Palladian house, built in 1742. Everything here dates from then or earlier." Some years ago an inspector's report described the purism of this "architectural gem" of a house. Her room had authentic 18th-century furniture and Georgian colours. No curtains on the window, only shutters. The carpet was quite threadbare, but accurately chosen, she felt, for the old-world look. Her bed was extremely comfortable, and there was central heating and plenty of hot water. The sitting room was beautifully furnished, with many books on Irish architecture, and had a fine crackling fire. Dinner was a decent no-choice affair – "a careful amateur meal". There was freshly-baked soda bread for breakfast. The service was faultless, prices very reasonable. Another comment: "*Roundwood House* bowled me over. A great sense of effortless hospitality overwhelms you as soon as you set foot in it." (*Richard Creed, LH, and others*)

Open All year except Christmas Day.
Rooms 6 double – all with bath; baby-listening arranged.
Facilities Drawing room, library, dining room. 18-acre grounds with croquet, swings, stables. Golf nearby.
Location 3 m NW of main Dublin–Limerick road. From Mountrath take Kinnity road to Slieve Bloom mountains.
Restrictions Not suitable for ♿. No dogs in bedrooms or public rooms.
Credit cards Access, Amex, Visa.
Terms B&B: single occupancy IR£28, double IR£44. Set Sun lunch IR£10, dinner IR£16. Reduced rates for children sharing parents' room; special meals.
Service/tipping: (No service charge) "We are at present organising a kind of profit sharing system which will mean that we, the owners, will get all tips – but the staff will earn a lot more than they ever would from tips by receiving from us a set amount for every single booking, i.e., a kind of invisible service charge."

MOYARD Co Galway — Map 6

Crocnaraw Country House — *Tel* Clifden (095) 41068
Moyard, Connemara

A Georgian country house on the shores of Ballinakill Bay, set in 20 acres of prize-winning gardens and fields, with fine views. For years it was run by the late Joanne Fretwell and it had an entry in earlier editions of the Guide. Her daughter Lucy has now taken over, and last year we were urged to readmit it, "We were touring Connemara and just happened to pass the gates of *Crocnaraw*. It looked so idyllic that we decided to call in, and subsequently spent the night. Lucy Fretwell looked after us beautifully. We had a lovely bedroom looking out over the stunning gardens and mountains. Inside, the house was charmingly decorated, warm and comfortable, with interesting paintings, log fires and comfy chairs, and Lucy and her cousin cooked us a delicious dinner – much of it locally grown or home-made, including fresh hot rolls. Our labrador was made most welcome too. We highly recommend this hotel; it was just like staying with an old friend." This year a reader adds to the praise, "We loved *Crocnaraw* when it used to be in the Guide, and were delighted to find it completely unaltered, the garden looking even nicer." (*Richard Creed*) Seafood is a speciality of the restaurant when the weather allows. Good fishing, golf and beaches nearby.

Open 1 May–31 Oct.
Rooms 7 double, 2 single – all with bath (2 also have shower). 1 ground-floor room.
Facilities Drawing room, sitting room, dining room. 20-acre gardens and woodland; croquet, donkeys and ponies. Golf, fishing, sandy beaches nearby.
Location 6 m N of Clifden.
Restriction No dogs in public rooms. No children under 10.

Credit cards Amex, Diners, Visa.
Terms (Excluding 10% service charge) B&B: single IR£30–IR£35, double IR£56–IR£65; dinner, B&B: single IR£46–IR£51, double IR£88–IR£95. Full alc lunch IR£12, dinner IR£18.50. 25% reduction for children; special meals if required.

NEWPORT Co Mayo — Map 6

Newport House Hotel

Tel Newport (098) 41222
Fax (098) 41613
Telex 53740

"*Newport House* has everything in the material sense that a thoroughly good hotel ought to have. I shall not waste space listing its practical impeccable assets – others will. Rather I should like to speak of the welcome, spontaneous and sincere, with which it greets all its guests, making them feel – tired after a long journey – at once not just at home, but as though they had *come* home. Everyone from the proprietor to the gardeners goes out of the way to make your stay happy and comfortable. You are surrounded by their kindness at every turn. When you depart, you leave a bit of yourself behind, but in compensation you carry away the memory of smiling Irish faces and a charm entirely unassumed. With all my heart I salute *Newport House*. There surely must be a leprechaun abroad here!" And a more restrained reader comments, "First-class example of a good old-fashioned fishing hotel; the most relaxing place we stayed at in Ireland." Kieran and Thelma Thompson's Georgian country house, with many attractive architectural features and plenty of good antiques, stands in 20 acres of grounds along the Derrydeevagh river where it flows into Clew Bay. Its extensive private salmon and sea-trout fishing brings many visitors, and sea angling can be arranged nearby. The Thompsons have extensively redecorated and renovated – "it is immaculately smart in its decor, without losing the country-house atmosphere." "Mr and Mrs Thompson believe in delegating and are therefore much in evidence and in a relaxed and friendly frame of mind. The food, based on well-presented local ingredients, is remarkably good." There is a well-stocked cellar (the owner is a wine enthusiast). A non-fishing reader tells us that it is perfectly possible not to feel excluded ("so long as one has something to tell of one's day"), as the area is equally good for mountain walking and visiting monastic remains. (*Betty Ogilvie, Norman Turner, and others*)

Open 19 Mar–30 Sept.
Rooms 2 suites, 16 double, 2 single – 18 with bath, 2 with shower, all with telephone. 3 ground-floor rooms in courtyard, 25 yds from main building.
Facilities Bar, drawing room, sitting room, dining room. 20-acre grounds, walled garden. Extensive private river and lake fishing; golf, shooting, riding nearby; sandy beach 5 km.
Location Just outside Newport; clearly visible from Westport–Achill road. Parking.
Restriction No dogs in bedrooms or public rooms.
Credit cards All major cards accepted.
Terms B&B IR£33–IR£52; dinner, B&B IR£54–IR£74. Set lunch IR£14, dinner IR£26. Reduced rates for children under 10; special meals.
Service/tipping: "Guests are told that tipping is not necessary. If they insist, the money is held in a staff fund and divided among them at end of season."

OUGHTERARD Co Galway — Map 6

Currarevagh House — *Tel* Galway (091) 82312 and 82313
Telex 50982

A mid-Victorian country house on the banks of Lough Corrib, set in 150 acres of its own grounds and offering some of the best scenery and fishing in Ireland. Unashamedly old-fashioned and set in its ways, it has "marvellously capacious beds, splendid bathroom fittings, lots of Edwardian furniture and good home cooking". *Currarevagh* has been in the Hodgson family for five generations; it is now run by Harry Hodgson and his wife, June. A reader this year reports, "I was taken in without the batting of an eyelid when I arrived unannounced two minutes before dinner was served, and given a generous if not outstanding meal. The style is Anglo-Irish rather than Irish, with the kind of self-conscious shyness English hoteliers often suffer from. But it's much nicer than any other places nearby."

Open Easter to Oct. By arrangement other times for parties of 8 or more (except Christmas and New Year).
Rooms 13 double, 2 single – 13 with bath, 2 with shower. 3 ground-floor rooms in mews.
Facilities Drawing room, sitting room, TV room, dining room. 150-acre grounds with lakeshore fishing (ghillie available), boating, swimming, tennis, croquet. Golf, riding nearby.
Location 4 m NW of Oughterard on "Lakeshore" road.
Restrictions Not ideal for ♿. Children tolerated but not encouraged. Dogs by arrangement, only on lead in public rooms.
Credit cards None accepted.
Terms (Excluding 10% service charge) B&B: single IR£30–IR£43, double IR£60–IR£66; dinner, B&B (min 3 days): single IR£43–IR£55, double IR£86–IR£90. Set lunch IR£7.35, dinner IR£14.70. Weekly rates. 1-night bookings sometimes refused for high season if booked too far ahead. Reduced rates for children sharing parents' room.
Service/tipping: "10% is added for service; it is divided among all staff. Our problem used to be that front staff received tips (some quite large) and the kitchen staff received nothing. Guests are asked not to tip individual members of staff."

PROSPEROUS Co Kildare — Map 6

Curryhills House Hotel — *Tel* Naas (045) 68150
Prosperous, Nr Naas

A 'find' by inspectors this year: "On the dull plain west of Dublin, between the Kildare horse-breeding country (hence the horsey chatter of some guests) and the black peat-bogs (hence the fuel for the fire in the big salon/bar). Not a promising setting – but it's a pleasant Georgian farmhouse with modern additions, amid a garden newly landscaped by owners Billy and Bridie Travers, both great characters and both much in evidence. An unpretentious country hotel with a wayward charm, its public rooms typically Irish-shabby, its bedrooms large, modern and comfortable. The basement dining room, a bit enclosed, has vaguely Tudor decor and serves goodish unsophisticated country food: the garlicky mushrooms come from a giant mushroom factory down the road. There's Irish traditional music and singalongs on Fridays and Saturdays in the bar, always filled with chatty locals. The Travers also rear turkeys, and in summer do the catering for the Victorian musical banquets at the nearby *Old Canal Hotel* at Robertstown. And why the name 'Prosperous'? – in the 18th century this village was a wealthy textile-making centre." More reports welcome.

Open All year except 23–31 Dec.
Rooms 10 double or single; all with bath and shower, telephone and tea-making facilities. Radio, TV and baby-listening on request. Ground floor rooms.
Facilities Ramps. Lounge/bar, TV room, restaurant. Award-winning gardens. Horse riding and racing, fishing, golfing nearby.
Location 30 km W of Dublin, 11 km NW of Naas.
Credit cards All major cards accepted.
Terms (Excluding 10% service charge) B&B single: IR£30, double IR£46. Set dinner IR£12.50; alc (excluding wine IR£18). Children sharing parents' room charged for meals only.

RATHMULLAN Co Donegal — Map 6

Rathmullan House Hotel — *Tel* Letterkenny (074) 58188
Rathmullan, Letterkenny — *Fax* (074) 58200

Early 19th-century country house in dramatic setting by Lough Swilly. 10-acre grounds with sandy beach, tennis court; covered swimming pool scheduled for late 1989. Quiet bedrooms with period furnishings. Elegant, well-furnished reception rooms, fresh flowers, well-stocked library, attractive cellar bar, tented dining room created by series of hexagonal-shaped extensions into garden, staffed by pleasant local women. Acceptable wine list. Some criticisms of table appointments (packaged butter, paper napkins), but breakfast "excellent". Open 16 Mar–31 Dec. 18 rooms, most with bath and/or shower. B&B IR£30–IR£38; set dinner: 3 courses IR£15, 5 courses IR£18. 10% service charge added. Was in earlier editions; now readmitted. More reports please.

RATHNEW Co Wicklow — Map 6

Tinakilly House Hotel — *Tel* Wicklow (0404) 69274
Fax (0404) 67806

"When Captain Robert Halpin retired from laying transoceanic cables in the 1870s, a grateful British Government rewarded him with enough money to build *Tinakilly House,* 30 miles south of Dublin. Having once commanded Brunel's *Great Eastern,* the great navigator had a highly developed sense of stylish grandiosity. His retirement home, in seven acres of bosky pleasure gardens, overlooking the Irish Sea (you can just see it) near Wicklow town, is a grey stone mansion of Victorian monumental splendour. The rooms, including the 14 bedrooms, which are outnumbered by the staff, are large and high ceilinged with tall windows. Six of them have four-poster beds of imperial dimensions. The general impression is of old-fashioned opulence – golden chandeliers and sconces, polished dark wood, rococo fireplaces, softly upholstered, formal sofas and chairs, red carpets, potted plants, and a magpie miscellany of glittering bric-à-brac. Meals are served in three dining rooms, each with only a few discreetly separated tables." This earlier inspector's report has been warmly endorsed this year: "A comfortable and stylish place. William Power, the owner, really knows how to run a country hotel and is well assisted by a French manager and a partly French staff. This may help account for the high quality of the food (though the head chef is Irish). Good 'country-house' dishes such as roast lamb, and real French ones such as ris de veau sauce madère (but the tarte tatin was surprisingly poor, also the coffee). For breakfast you can have raw eggs with brandy – but we didn't." Another writer adds, "Your entry is factually accurate but hardly does justice to the *sheer pleasure* of staying here. Dinner was absolutely delicious. Breakfast was a gourmet meal in itself – freshly-squeezed orange juice, porridge, a full cooked breakfast with locally made black *and* white pudding, and Mrs Power's excellent brown bread. The hospitality was generous and warm." (*JA and KA, REK McKeith; Mrs W Munro, and others*)

Open All year.
Rooms 1 suite, 13 double – 13 with bath and shower (4 also have whirlpool bath), 1 with bath, all with telephone, TV, tea-making facilities.
Facilities Hall, bar, residents' lounge, 3 dining rooms; conference facilities. 7-acre grounds, tennis court. Golf nearby.
Location Coming from Dublin on N11, go through Rathnew village on R750. House is signposted on left after about ¼ m.
Restrictions Not suitable for ♿. No children under 8. No dogs.
Credit cards All major cards accepted.
Terms (10% service charge added) B&B: single IR£55–IR£65, double IR£66–IR£110, suite IR£99–IR£110. Set lunch IR£13.20, dinner IR£22. Discounts for stays of 3 nights or more.
Service/tipping: "We include a mandatory 10% service charge which is part of staff remuneration. This saves clients embarrassment."

RIVERSTOWN Co Sligo — Map 6

Coopershill

Tel Sligo (071) 65108
Fax (071) 65466

"A perfect place to stay: our dream of a hotel in every way, providing one is adaptable and sociable. The bedrooms are soothing and pretty to look at, the service perfect, the food of the best country house kind." (*Brigadier Laurence and Fran Fowler*) Just one of this year's collection of panegyrics for *Coopershill*. The house, in the heart of Yeats country, has a spectacular position, with the Bricklieve mountains and vast peat bogs to the south, and the town of Sligo and the sea to the north. Its special qualities won it a *César* in 1987 for outstanding Irish country hospitality. Many readers have endorsed this earlier report: "One of the grand houses built by the landed Anglo-Irish families in the 18th century. It is situated in a huge estate and in complete silence. The atmosphere is that of a country house of 50 years ago. The rooms are tall and gracious and the furniture old-fashioned (five bedrooms have four-poster or canopied beds). Do not expect a smart hotel – this is the home of an old Irish family in which you are a welcome guest." Mrs O'Hara, who ran the place for many years, has retired; her son Brian and his wife Lindy have taken over the day-to-day running of the house. This year, they tell us, they have redecorated two more bedrooms, constructed two new bathrooms, and installed an efficient woodburning stove in the outer hall, and new heaters in the drawing room, dining room and all bedrooms. (*HR Lamb, David Clarke, and others*)

Open Mid-Mar–31 Oct. Out of season house-parties by arrangement.
Rooms 6 double – all with bath and/or shower, and tea-making facilities.

Facilities Halls, drawing room with TV and piano, dining room; table tennis room. 500 acres woods and farmland with wildlife, large garden, river with coarse fishing; trout fishing, sandy beach, championship golf course nearby.
Location At Drumfin crossroads, 11 m from Sligo–Dublin road (N4), turn to Riverstown. *Coopershill* signposted from Drumfin.
Restrictions Not suitable for ♿. Dogs allowed, but not in house.
Credit cards Access, Amex, Visa.
Terms [1989 rates] B&B IR£30–IR£38. Light lunch IR£5; packed lunches on request; set dinner IR£16. Reductions for stays of 3 nights or more. 50%-75% reduction for children under 12 sharing parents' room; special meals on request.
Service/tipping: "Guests not expected to tip. But if they wish to money is distributed entirely among the staff."

ROSSNOWLAGH Co Donegal — Map 6

The Sand House Hotel

Tel Newport (072) 51777
Telex 40460

A large modern family hotel, welcoming to children, so close to the sea that the waves seem almost to be in your room. "The amphitheatre of Donegal Bay lies before you, stretching from the Mullaghmore peninsula on the left to Slieve League and the mountains of Donegal on the right." Guests come to *Sand House* to enjoy the two-mile stretch of safe sandy beach, the comfortable lounges with log fires, and the attractively decorated bedrooms, many of which have views of the sea. The hotel has been run for many years by Mary and Vin Britton and their son Conor; this year their youngest son David has joined them. A recent visitor praises the "delightful staff and feeling of a caring family ownership, the colourful and cheery furnishings, and the faultless service in the dining room". Another appreciated "the touch of luxury in having the bedspread turned down, the night-clothes laid out, and a hot water bottle in the bed". Fish is a speciality (the hotel farms its own Donegal Bay oysters and fresh mussels), and the cooking gets high marks, "mushroom soup was the real thing – with pieces of fresh tomato; cold Donegal ham was succulent; fillets of grilled trout were substantial, fresh, buttery brown, and very good. Desserts of the old-fashioned pudding variety, like Queen of Puddings." There is piped music in the dining room. Lovers of the outdoors will find lots to do, from tennis, golf and fishing to surfing and riding; Glenveagh National Park is nearby. (*F Jeffery, Eithne Scallan*)

Open 1 May–mid-Oct.
Rooms 2 suites, 32 double, 6 single – all with bath and/or shower, telephone and baby-listening.
Facilities 3 residents' lounges, TV lounge, lounge bar, residents' cocktail bar, restaurant, games room. Folk music Fri and Sat in high season. 2-acre grounds with tennis, miniature golf, croquet and paddock; on 2-mile safe sandy beach with swimming, canoeing, windsurfing (boards and canoes available at hotel). Fishing, golf, riding nearby.
Location On Donegal Bay; N of Ballyshannon on coast road; follow signs to beach and hotel.
Restrictions Not suitable for ♿. Dogs by arrangement, not in public rooms.
Credit cards All major cards accepted.
Terms B&B IR£27.50–IR£37.50; dinner, B&B (3 days min) IR£40–IR50. Set lunch IR£9–IR£9.50, dinner IR£16.50–IR17.50. Special breaks; golf and fishing holidays. Reduced rates for children sharing parents' room; children's dinner 6–7 pm.
Service/tipping: "10% added to room rates which is distributed to all staff on a 3-monthly basis on a point system. No service charge in restaurant; gratuities optional."

SCOTSHOUSE Co Monaghan — Map 6

Hilton Park — *Tel* Monaghan (047) 56007
Scotshouse, Clones — *Fax* (047) 56033

This mansion, in 600 acres of parkland including a golf course, three lakes, and many lovely views, has been the family home of eight generations of the Madden family. It is now, under John and Lucy Madden, a "most sympathetic and desirable place to stay". "The owners are lovely, the house splendidly idiosyncratic; rooms are unselfconsciously palatial and it is a bit dilapidated in places but pleasantly so, worn rather than neglected. The food is excellent, and they felt so much like personal friends after one night that I forgot to pay! It didn't seem to occur to them to remind me either; they were surprised to see me when I contritely rushed back across three counties several hours later. It is supremely hospitable, but it isn't and doesn't pretend to be a hotel, and allowances have to be made for that." The Maddens cultivate a house-party atmosphere, with the emphasis on conversation and music; they serve traditional Irish cooking with bread, biscuits, cheeses and ice-cream all made in-house. During the past year a large bedroom with four-poster bed has had an *en suite* bathroom added – giving a "superb view from the bath". (*LH, MA*) More reports welcome.

Open After Easter–end Sept. Other times by special arrangement (minimum 3 couples for 2 nights). Dining room closed for lunch.
Rooms 5 double (1 with dressing room which can accommodate 1 person) – 3 with bath.
Facilities 3 drawing rooms, TV room, dining room; table tennis room. 600-acre grounds with trout lake, 9-hole golf course, pike lake, boating and swimming.
Location On road L46 towards Clones; green gates on left.
Restrictions Not suitable for ♿. Children under 12 not encouraged. No dogs. Guests accepted only by prior reservation.
Credit card Amex.
Terms (Excluding 10% service charge for 1-night stays only) B&B IR£30–IR£40; dinner, B&B IR£44.50–IR£57.50. Set dinner IR£17.50. Weekend breaks; winter shooting parties.
Service/tipping: "Service charge of 10% added for stays of only 1 night and shared among staff. Tips not expected."

SHANAGARRY Co Cork — Map 6

Ballymaloe House — *Tel* Cork (021) 652531
Shanagarry, Nr Midleton — *Fax* (021) 652021
Telex 75208 BHI

"An enchanting establishment, almost magical." "The perfect family hotel. Something for everybody. Amazing meals. Lots of fun for the children. Gorgeous countryside." "One of my favourite hotels of all times and all places," Three unreserved panegyrics (among many similar tributes) for Myrtle and Ivan Allen's famous hotel, 20 miles east of Cork. It is a gracious rambling house, more Georgian than anything else though somehow ageless, with a Norman keep built into the fabric on one side, and relatively modern pink-washed cottages on the other. Decor is restrained and unfrilly, but the walls are full of Ivan Allen's exciting and varied picture collection. The bedrooms vary considerably in size; most are quite large. "My room was more a suite than a bedroom: hall, large bathroom well equipped and with fresh large warm towels each day; six-foot bed large enough for three and supplied in expectation with six pillows; large sofa; ample drawer and cupboard space." Close to the house lies a 400-acre farm; and beyond that, at three miles distance, is the charming little fishing port of Ballycotton. Virtually everything you eat, apart from the wonderful fish, is home-grown or raised on the Allens' farm. "The grounds are delightful, complete with small lake and canoe, and flower-bordered stream with bridges crossing it which are perfect for playing 'Pooh sticks'. Children of all ages seem to pop up everywhere from nowhere." *Ballymaloe* is an exceptionally convivial house, with nearly all the extended Allen family contributing to the special quality of its hospitality. (*Jennifer Kingsley, Lesley Le-Tan, Geoffrey Rowntree; S and E Scallan, and others*) One long-standing complaint – inadequate seating when the hotel is full – should be eased this year with a major extension to the public rooms. One *cri de cœur*: "Could not one of the dining rooms, be reserved for those who do not want cigar smoke with their *breakfast?*"

Open All year except 23–25 Dec.
Rooms 28 double, 2 single – all with bath and/or shower, telephone and baby-listening. 12 in courtyard, 4 on ground floor suitable for ♿.
Facilities 3 sitting rooms, 4 inter-connecting dining rooms. 400-acre farm and grounds with tennis court, heated swimming pool, 5-hole golf course, croquet, children's play area; craft shop. Sea 3 m, with safe sand and rock beaches; fishing, riding by arrangement.
Location 20 m E of Cork; 2 m E of Cloyne on Ballycotton road, L35.
Restriction No dogs in bedrooms or public rooms.
Credit cards All major cards accepted.
Terms (Excluding 10% service charge) B&B (continental): single IR£33–IR£53, double IR£57–IR£70. Cooked breakfast £4 extra. Set lunch IR£12, dinner IR£23. Winter bargain breaks. Special meal rates for children.
Service/tipping: "10% mandatory charge used for annual bonuses and weekly extras in pay packets. Customers and staff seem to like this arrangement as it is quite clear."

WICKLOW Co Wicklow — Map 6

The Old Rectory Country House and Restaurant

Tel Wicklow (0404) 67048

Victorian house in 1-acre garden in beautiful Wicklow countryside, 32 miles south of Dublin. Recommended for care and kindness of its owners, Paul and Linda Saunders, and excellent food; vegetarian and other special diets catered for with advance notice. 5 rooms, all with private facilities. B&B IR£34–IR£44. Set dinner IR£20. Caveats about decor and atmosphere, though some redecoration and refurnishing has taken place since inspector's visit. Recent nomination. More reports please.

Traveller's tale *A man travelling in Ireland stopped at a village where there were only two hotels,* Murphy's *and* Finn's. *He asked a policeman which was the better. The policeman answered: "Well, it's somewhat hard for me to say, seeing they are both good friends of mine. But I can tell you, Sir, that whichever hotel you choose, you will be sure to wish that you had chosen the other." Anon* bathroom well equipped and with fresh large warm towels each day; six-foot bed large enough for three and supplied in expectation with six pillows; large sofa; ample drawer and cupboard space.' Close to the house lies a 400-acre farm and beyond that, at three miles distance, is the [illegible] little fishing [illegible]. Virtually everything you eat, [illegible] fish, is home-grown or raised on the Aleme [illegible]. The [illegible] small lake and canoe [illegible] which are perfect for [illegible]. Children of all [illegible] everywhere [illegible] except [illegible] house, with [illegible] family [illegible] the special quality of [illegible] and [illegible]. Some long-standing complaints – inadequate seating when the hotel is full – should be solved this year with a major extension to the public rooms. One [illegible] should not one of the dining rooms be reserved for those who do not want cigar smoke with their breakfast?"

Open All year except [illegible].

Rooms 28 double, [illegible] all with bath and/or shower, telephone and baby-listening. [illegible] ground floor suitable for [illegible].

Facilities [illegible] connecting dining rooms. 400-acre farm and grounds [illegible] tennis court, [illegible] pool, 9-hole golf course, croquet, [illegible] and rock beaches, fishing, riding [illegible].

Location [illegible]

Restrictions No dogs [illegible]

Credit cards All major [illegible] accepted.

Terms [illegible] dinner IR£2[illegible]. [illegible] Special meals [illegible]

[illegible]

[illegible] Map 6

[illegible] Wicklow (0404) 67048

[illegible]

Part two

Austria
Belgium
Denmark
France
Germany
Greece
Italy
Luxembourg
Malta
including Gozo
Morocco
The Netherlands
Norway
Portugal
including the Azores and Madeira
Spain
including Andorra, the Balearics, the Canaries and Gibraltar
Sweden
Switzerland
including Liechtenstein
Turkey
Yugoslavia

Austria

ALPBACH 6236 Tyrol	Map 15

Hotel Alpbacherhof

Tel (05336) 5237
Fax (05336) 5016

The skiing is good and the air superbly clear at this very pretty village, venue of the European Forum since the end of World War II. The *Alpbacherhof* has an indoor pool, a terrace and a garden, and it serves dinners by candle-light. Most rooms have balconies with views, but the smaller and darker ones on the north side do not. "Very friendly, with spacious rooms and good dinners", is a report this year. "You are constantly waited on hand and foot – I have never known anything like it. Beaming, helpful servants, charming receptionist." "Service is superb – they will even look after an aged parent for you." One reader this year found the food disappointing. (*Jill Haslett, CA Bratherton*)

Open 16 Dec–25 Mar, 13 May–30 Sept.
Rooms 2 suites, 48 double, 5 single – 50 with bath, 5 with shower, all with telephone, radio and mini-bar; some with TV.

Facilities Lift. Bar, lounge, TV room, 2 restaurants; conference facilities; indoor heated swimming pool; terrace (where meals are served in fine weather). Garden.
Location Alpbach is in a valley S of Innsbruck–Kufstein main road. Hotel is central. Parking.
Restriction Not suitable for ♿.
Credit card Visa.
Terms [1989 rates] B&B 500–1,000 Sch. Dinner, B&B 600–1,200 Sch. Set lunch 200 Sch, dinner 250 Sch; full alc 500 Sch. Reduced rates for children sharing parents' room; special meals on request.

Hotel Böglerhof — *Tel* (05336) 5227, *Telex* 051160

A smart and attractive old inn, built in 1470 to house workers at the nearby silver and copper mines. Large lounge, 3 dining rooms, excellent food served by dignified waitresses. Nice bedrooms; splendid views from their balconies. Open Dec–Mar, mid-May–Sept. 48 rooms, all with bath or shower. B&B 550–1,100 Sch; half board 650–1,100 Sch [1989]. Endorsed briefly, but fuller reports welcome.

ANIF 5081 Salzburg — Map 15

Hotel Friesacher — *Tel* (06246) 2075, *Telex* 632943

Anif is an attractive village and all-season resort just south of Salzburg, amid woods and mountains. The *Friesacher*, again approved this year both for cooking and comfort, is a sizeable modern chalet-style hotel with large neo-rustic bedrooms and scenic balconies overlooking meadows and hills. "Good value and very peaceful. Waitresses in pretty national costume serve good basic food either in the rather airless restaurant or in the garden." "Friendly service, warm and cosy room with large bathroom." Besides the hotel restaurant, the Friesacher family own two cheaper ones next door which serve buffet-style meals. A recent visitor enjoyed eating outdoors listening to accordion music at one of these. Less attractive noises were complained of this year by one reader: traffic from the nearby main road, aircraft buzz from the airport. The hotel has just added a sauna, solarium and fitness-centre, as well 15 new bedrooms.

Open All year except 23 Dec – 15 Jan.
Rooms 3 suites, 44 double, 7 single – 49 with bath, 5 with shower, all with telephone, radio and TV; many with balcony. 18 in annexe. Some ground-floor rooms.
Facilities Lift. Lounge, bar, dining room; conference facilities. Sauna, solarium and fitness-room. Garden with children's play area and café.
Location 4 km S of Salzburg. Leave *Autobahn* at Salzburg, turn right at Anif (1 km) and turn ½ km on road to Hellbrunn. Parking.
Restriction Not suitable for ♿.
Credit cards Access, Diners, Visa.
Terms [1989 rates] B&B: single 580–780 Sch, double 880–1,060 Sch, suite 1,160 Sch. Set lunch 120 Sch, dinner 200 Sch; full alc 280 Sch. Reduced rates for children.

> When hotels have failed to return their questionnaire, we have quoted 1989 prices, with a note to that effect.

BERWANG 6622 Tyrol — Map 15

Singer Sporthotel

Tel (05674) 8181
Fax (05674) 8181-83
Telex 55544

Berwang is a busy summer and skiing resort a few miles west of the towering Zugspitze, just off the Innsbruck–Stuttgart main road; here the Singer family's chalet-hotel, sizeable and fairly smart, stands on a pine-studded hillside. Readers this year have again written approvingly of the owners' personal attention, of the efficient and courteous staff, the good food and the spacious rooms with balconies. "The facilities of bathing, sauna, massage, jacuzzi did not impinge on those looking merely to enjoy strolling in the countryside", said an earlier visitor. One reader, this year, visiting out of season, was dismayed to find an old people's bingo session in progress. But another, also a summer visitor, found it one of the best hotels of its kind he had ever stayed in – "hard to manufacture even the smallest complaint". (*RS McNeill*)

Open 17 Dec–10 Apr, 18 May–1 Oct.
Rooms 25 suites, 35 double, 10 single – 58 with bath and/or shower, telephone, radio; many with balcony; TV in suites.
Facilities Lift. Lounge, *Stube*, 2 bars, 2 restaurants; dancing, Tyrolean evenings; fitness/sports centre with whirlpool, sauna and massage. Small garden with terraces. **Location** 80 km NW of Innsbruck. Garages and open parking.
Credit cards Diners, Visa.
Terms [1989 rates] B&B: single 380–950 Sch, double 820–1,600 Sch, suite 1,000–2,100 Sch. Dinner, B&B double 980–1,800 Sch. Set lunch 95–220 Sch, dinner 130–350 Sch; full alc 210–450 Sch. Reduced rates and special meals for children.

BEZAU 6870 Vorarlberg — Map 15

Gasthof Gams

Tel (05514) 2220
Fax (05514 2220-24)
Telex 59144 VVWALD-GAMS

A quiet little town on the edge of the Bregenz forest. The road on one side winds down to the busy resorts of Lake Constance; on the other, it loops over the mountains to the ski-stations of Lech and St-Anton. *Gasthof Gams* is a sizeable 17th-century coaching inn, with modern additions such as jacuzzi (in the basement), heated outdoor swimming pool, and under-floor heating in the rooms. Public rooms are furnished in traditional Austrian style. A report this year: "The succession of small dining rooms adds to the charm, service is quick and friendly, the Austrian cooking is superb." Others have enjoyed the quiet and comfort in this genuinely personal family hotel. But rooms do vary in size. The hotel bus takes guests to and from the ski-slopes in season. (*Mr and Mrs RW Beacroft, Stephen Ruell, BJ Walter*)

Open All year except 1–18 Dec.
Rooms 6 suites, 24 double, 10 single – 15 with bath, 25 with shower, all with telephone; TV on request; some with balcony. Some ground-floor rooms.
Facilities Lift. Lounge, bar, dining rooms; conference/functions rooms; games room, sauna, solarium, hot whirlpool; terraces. Large garden with swimming pool (heated May–Oct) and 3 tennis courts.
Location 30 km SE of Bregenz, 37 km NW of Lech. Central. Parking.
Credit cards Access, Visa.

Terms B&B: single 390–540 Sch, double 740–1,080 Sch; dinner, B&B: single 550–700 Sch, double 1,060–1,400 Sch. Set lunch/dinner 160–350 Sch; full alc 320 Sch. Reduced rates and special meals for children.

DÜRNSTEIN 3601 Lower Austria — Map 15

Hotel Schloss Dürnstein

Tel (02711) 212
Fax (02711) 351
Telex 71147

"One of the world's most beautiful hotels"; "Herr Thiery runs the best hotel in Austria"; "excellent food on a spacious terrace overlooking the Danube" – three new tributes to this always-admired *Schloss*, which stands inside a lovely old village (Richard Cœur de Lion was imprisioned here in 1192). It is perched above the Danube, with spectacular views of the winding river from most bedrooms. Built in 1630, it was owned by the Princes Starhemberg for centuries, and was used as a refuge by the Emperor Leopold I when he was fleeing from the Turks. Some 50 years ago, it was reincarnated by the Thiery family, who still own and run it. Rather a formal place, it has beautiful antique furniture both in the public rooms and in the bedrooms. "Each year Herr Thiery improves his cuisine", says a reader this year; "breakfast on the terrace in the early dawn with the Danube, and the birds singing, is sheer perfection. Our comfortable room was both homely and grand." "Our room the size of a tennis court was filled with antiques. You live with the family as in a stately home, with no choice for dinner." "Breakfast arrived on two huge trays and was placed on a genuine 16th-century table in our room. Go there just for the history and romance." (*M and D Chambers, Ruth H and Robert D Todd, Peter Brown*)

Open 1 Apr–8 Nov.
Rooms 2 suites, 31 double, 4 single – all with bath and/or shower, telephone, radio and TV; baby-listening on request. Some ground-floor rooms.
Facilities Lift. Lounge, TV room, bar, restaurant, grill room with dance floor; private dining room. Courtyard with heated swimming pool. Terrace overlooking Danube; fishing and boating.
Location At end of main street in village. Parking.
Credit cards All major cards accepted.
Terms [1989 rates] Dinner, B&B 875–1,500 Sch. 10% reduction in low season. No charge for children under 6 sharing parents' room; special meals on request.

FILZMOOS 5532 Salzburg — Map 15

Hotel Hanneshof

Tel (06453) 275
Telex 67728

In a skiing and summer resort at the foot of the Dachstein, about an hour by road from Salzburg, the Mayr family run this very friendly and efficient chalet-style hotel, spruce and modern, next to their butcher's shop. Indoor swimming pool, good Austrian cooking, children welcomed. Closed November. 45 rooms, most with private facilities. B&B 350–450 Sch. Half board 500–750 Sch [1989]. *New nomination. More reports welcome.*

Please write and confirm an entry when it is deserved. If you think that a hotel is not as good as we say, write and tell us.

FREISTADT 4240 Upper Austria — Map 15

Gasthof Deim zum Goldenen Hirschen — *Tel* (07942) 2258 and 2111
Böhmergasse 8

Set on a wild granite plateau between Linz and the Czech frontier, Freistadt is a handsome old town with towers, gateways and traces of ramparts. Within these walls is the *Deim*, a genuine old inn with a pretty garden. "Beautiful and charming, with flowers everywhere and the best goulash in Austria or Hungary." "It is still very good – from the individual character of the bedrooms to the excellence of the food (dining rooms get crowded at weekends). All the modern conveniences and luxuries combined with old-world charm." These are last year's tributes. Could we have some more recent travellers' tales please?

Open All year except 2 weeks in Jan.
Rooms 17 double, 6 single – 17 with bath, 2 with shower, all with telephone and radio; 4 with TV.
Facilities Lounge, TV room, 3 restaurants. Garden (meals can be taken outside).
Restriction Not suitable for ♿.
Location Central. Parking. Town is 40 km NE of Linz.
Credit card Diners.
Terms B&B: single 300 Sch, double 520 Sch; dinner, B&B: single 380 Sch, double 680 Sch. Set lunch/dinner 100–120 Sch; full alc 200 Sch. Reduced rates and special meals/portions for children.

FUSCHL-AM-SEE 5330 Salzburg — Map 15

Pension Rupertihof — *Tel* (06226) 447
Fuschl-am-See 106

A clean modern chalet-style *pension* with flower-decked balconies by the shore of the nearest of the Salzburg lakes to Salzburg. It is just outside the village, an easy walk to several hotels for dinner. Recent verdicts: "Excellent value, friendly family owners"; "Comfortable beds, many rooms with balcony; excellent varied breakfasts (muesli, eggs, cheese)." Fuller reports welcome.

Open All year.
Rooms 12 double – 3 with bath, 9 with shower; some with balcony.
Facilities Breakfast room, lounge with TV. Small garden. Lake Fuschl 50 metres (beach and safe bathing, sailing, etc). Walks arranged.
Location 22 km E of Salzburg on road to Bad Ischl. Hotel is first on right at entrance of village. Parking.
Restriction Not suitable for ♿.
Credit cards None accepted.
Terms B&B 170–210 Sch. Reduced rates for children. (No restaurant.)

GARGELLEN 6787 Vorarlberg — Map 15

Hotel Madrisa — *Tel* (05557) 6331
Montafon — *Fax* (05557) 6331-82
Telex 52269 MADRIS

"A great place for children" is a frequent comment on this friendly family-run ski hotel, traditional in style but well modernised, which stands next to nursery slopes in the lovely Montafon valley. "Simply wonderful", runs one report this year: "we had a large airy room in the new wing, with a balcony facing the village church and mountains beyond. The food was scrumptious, and the service very friendly, with the Rhomberg family, the owners, much involved." Earlier views: "The breakfasts were a wonderful array, and the evening meals were imaginative." "As well as for winter holidays, it's splendidly situated for spring and summer." "The Rhomberg family carried our bags and gave us extra bedding. The hotel exuded warmth, and mountains of food appeared regularly. The value for money makes me blink when I think of other ski resorts." The rooms in the older part have been called "ample, warm and rustic", but unlike the newer ones they do not have balconies. (*I Fishman, Ian and Anne Steel*) One reader regretted the limited choice on the half-board dinner, and felt that the hotel's popularity and increase in size was harming its personal touch.

Open 16 Dec–22 Apr, 22 Jun–26 Sept.
Rooms 5 suites, 48 double, 12 single – most with bath and/or shower, telephone and radio; TV on request.
Facilities Lift. Hall, lounge, reading room, games room, *Stüberl*, dining room; children's playroom (with children's films); disco; indoor swimming pool, sauna. Large grounds with terrace, lawn, ski lift.
Location 28 km S of Bludenz. In centre of Gargellen. Parking.
Credit cards Access, Amex, Diners (for extras only).
Terms Dinner, B&B 770–1,275 Sch in winter, 540–840 Sch in summer. Set meals 260 Sch; full alc 330 Sch. In skiing season bookings are normally for 1 week (Sat–Sat). Weekly and Christmas packages. Reductions for children sharing parents' room; special meals on request.

GRAZ 8010 Styria — Map 15

Schlossberg Hotel — *Tel* (0316) 8070
Kaiser-Franz-Joseph-Kai — *Fax* (0316) 8070-160
Telex 312672

A newly renovated 400-year-old inn, in a quiet but central side-street of Austria's second city. Beamed ceilings and rambling corridors but modern lift; large rooms with antiques. Roof garden with swimming pool. Private parking. Good breakfasts: no restaurant, but lots nearby. Open all year. 54 rooms, all with bath or shower. B&B double 1,400–1,700 Sch [1989]. *Re-nominated this year. More reports welcome.*

HALLSTATT 4830 Upper Austria — Map 15

Seehotel Grüner Baum — *Tel* (06134) 263

Hallstatt is a well-known picturesque village on a clear lake south-east of Salzburg, backed by steep wooded hills, with snowy mountains above. The *Seehotel* dates from 1670 and has been in the hands of the Lissbauer family for six generations. It has a terrace by the lake where meals and drinks can be taken; many bedrooms also face the lake and have balconies with geraniums, others overlook the pretty market square. "The quaint village has a lovely atmosphere. Our comfortable rooms in this homely hotel were furnished in typical Austrian style, and from our balcony we enjoyed the view of the lake and mountains. The food was good, though not memorable, and the staff were all helpful and amicable."

Open May–Sept.
Rooms 24 double, 8 single – 13 with bath, 12 with shower, 16 with telephone; TV on request. Some with balcony.
Facilities Lounge, TV room, bar, restaurant; conference facilities. Garden on lake.
Location 50 km SE of Salzburg. Parking in market square.
Credit card Amex.
Terms B&B 230–420 Sch; half board 380–580 Sch; full board 450–670 Sch. Reduced rates and special meals for children.

HEILIGENBLUT 9844 Carinthia — Map 15

Hotel Haus Senger — *Tel* (04824) 2215
Grossglockner

Heiligenblut is a village just below the Grossglockner, in high, wild mountainous country, good for walking or skiing. "Friendly and personal staff, rooms beautifully kept, food delicious, varied and copious, including the world's best apfelstrudel." So runs a recent letter on this "very *gemütlich*" family-run hotel, a typical old mountain chalet with a new extension. It has comfort and the kind of personal attention that makes everyone feel relaxed and good-humoured. Most rooms have a balcony. "The cook bakes Sachertorte and apfelstrudel almost every day and there is always the temptation to try them warm from the oven after a day out on the mountains." More reports welcome.

Open Christmas–Easter, mid-Jun–mid-Oct.
Rooms 8 suites, 6 double, 3 single – all with bath or shower, telephone, radio, TV and tea-making facilities.
Facilities Lift. Lounge with TV, restaurant with bar; games room, fitness room, sauna and turkish bath. Garden and terraces. Winter sports.
Location On the edge of Heiligenblut, which is on route 107, 40 km N of Lienz. Parking.
Credit cards All major cards accepted.
Terms B&B 390–560 Sch; half board 510–690 Sch. Set lunch/dinner 170–230 Sch; full alc 180–250 Sch. Special meals for children.

HOF BEI SALZBURG 5322 Salzburg — Map 15

Hotel Schloss Fuschl — *Tel* (06229) 22530
Telex 633454

The former hunting lodge of the prince-archbishops of Salzburg is today a most elegant and luxurious hotel – still distinctly regal, but now wholly secular. It overlooks Lake Fuschl with the mountains as backdrop, 20 kilometres from Salzburg: you can lunch or dine overlooking the lake, where the sunsets can be spectacular. Two reports this year: "A most sumptuous hotel, with very good food"; "A dream! Sparkling lake and lilac-lined gardens. Very good food, but tiny portions." Earlier accounts: "It retains much of its castle/hunting lodge atmosphere, despite addition of marble swimming pool and jacuzzi. *Nouvelle cuisine* very, very good, but also happy to serve us a lunch of pumpkin soup and smoked ham" (the food has also been described as 'Austrian international'). "Beautifully situated, with an elegant and interesting interior. The staff were outstandingly welcoming and helpful." Rooms facing the roadway can be a bit noisy, owing to the influx of visitors: best are those facing the lake, or the chalets in the garden. Swimming both in an indoor pool and in the lake. (*Marie and Hans Haenlein, and others*)

Open All year.
Rooms 23 suites, 56 double, 5 single – all with bath and/or shower, telephone, radio and TV. 60 in buildings in the garden. Some ground-floor rooms.
Facilities Salons, bar, 2 restaurants, conservatory; conference facilities; beauty farm; indoor heated swimming pool. Large park with terrace for outdoor meals; private beach and swimming area on lake, fishing, boating, refreshments, tennis, 9-hole golf course.
Location 20 km E of Salzburg; take road 158 to St Gilden; turn left 1 m after village of Hof.
Restriction Not suitable for ♿.
Credit cards All major cards accepted.
Terms [1989 rates] B&B: single 1,200–1,800 Sch, double 1,900–3,200 Sch, suite 2,400–5,500 Sch. Set lunch 420 Sch, dinner 500 Sch; full alc 600 Sch. Children under 12 sharing parents' room free; special meals on request.

IGLS 6080 Tyrol — Map 15

Hotel Astoria — *Tel* (05222) 77481
Badhausstrasse 1 — *Fax* (05222) 77481-44
Telex 534121

On the edge of a village above Innsbruck that featured in the 1964 Winter Olympics, a sizeable modern chalet-style hotel, family-run; rather heavily furnished, but with courteous staff and spacious rooms. Flowery balconies, indoor swimming pool, buffet breakfast. 42 rooms, all with bathroom. Half board 480–750 Sch. New nomination. More reports needed.

INNSBRUCK 6020 Tyrol — Map 15

Weinhaus Happ — *Tel* (05222) 582980
Herzog-Friedrich Strasse 14 — *Telex* 533511

"Right in the centre of the action", a small *Weinhaus*-cum-hotel in an old street flanked with arcades, that leads directly to the 15th-century Goldenes Dächl (golden roof). Reports this year: "Not quaint or charming but clean and comfortable." "A narrow winding staircase leads up to the reception where Madame's welcome was warm; another two floors up, our large, rather bare room had a small balcony overlooking the street." Some rooms are larger and better furnished than others; the food has been found "very good and copious" by some (notably the game in autumn), only adequate by others, who suggest the *Weisses Kreuz* down the street as an alternative. (*Angela and David Stewart, A Smith and others*)

Open All year. Restaurant closed Sun.
Rooms 10 double, 5 single – 3 with bath, 5 with shower, all with telephone and radio; TV on request.
Facilities Lift. 3 restaurants; conference facilities. Garden.
Location Central, in pedestrian zone. Hotel garage 3 mins' walk.
Credit cards All major cards accepted.

Terms B&B 390–500 Sch; dinner, B&B 510–620 Sch. Reduced rates and special meals for children.

Gasthof Weisses Rössl *Tel* (0512) 583057
Kiebachgasse 8

An attractive, unassuming little hotel in the old part of town, owned and run by the enterprising Plank family; commended for comfort, charm, good breakfasts and dinners (Tyrolean dishes), fair prices. 14 rooms all with bath and/or shower. B&B single 550–740 Sch, double 880-1020 Sch. Set menus 70–155 Sch. [1989 rates] New nomination. More reports please.

KITZBÜHEL 6370 Tyrol **Map 15**

Hotel Erika *Tel* (05356) 4885
Fax (05356) 467413
Telex 51264

"The hiking and adventure-hotel *Erika*" (as its brochure calls it), where there's never a dull moment and you all join in the fun, might not seem quite our sort of place. It's a large red mansion with a modern annexe, beside a busy road junction at the edge of Kitzbühel. Last year a reader who had just completed her *forty-fifth* holiday there told us, "Uschi and Benedikt Schorer work hard to please. One wet and cold day they produced paints and sheets of glass and we were all put to painting on glass. On other days, Mrs Schorer would take us up the mountains, or inflict an adventurous bicycle ride on us, or Mr Schorer would take guests for a day on the golf course. At the start of each walk or other fiendish activity, we would all join hands in a circle, announce our name, profession, where we came from. Drinks are served in the large garden, and light classical concerts are held in the swimming pool area. Food is ample and enjoyable." An informative orange leaflet, with the programme for the day, is handed out at breakfast – e.g. "Good morning, dear *Erika*-guest! This afternoon at 5 pm we will do some ARCHERY! Tomorrow we will organise a funny ERIKA–BICYCLE–TOUR!"

This year two visitors, admittedly Club Med freaks, also, to their surprise, succumbed to *Erika*'s charms: "The deft professionalism, and the expert exploitation of Austrian charm, simply disarm criticism. The Schorers (their family have owned and run the *Erika* since 1920) are totally dedicated and delightful. The hotel may be no beauty outside, but inside it's been modernised most sprucely with charming trelliswork decor ('we've tried to avoid the usual Tyrolean clichés'); bedrooms, most with balcony, are all comfy and homely. In summer, 80 per cent of guests are English. Rucksacks, Elastoplast and yellow *Erika*-umbrellas are provided free of charge. We were awestruck by the overall good humour and its incredible value." (*JA and KA*)

Open All year except Nov, 15 Apr–15 May.
Rooms 36 double – all with bath, shower, telephone, radio; TV on request.
Facilities Hall, sitting rooms, bar. Indoor swimming pool, sauna, solarium and steam-bath. Garden with children's playground.
Location 3 mins' walk from town centre. Parking.
Restriction Not suitable for ♿.

Credit cards Amex, Diners, Visa.
Terms Dinner, B&B: 530–600 Sch in summer, 750–990 Sch in winter. Reduced rates and special meals for children.

Hahnenhof *Tel* (05356) 2582

A converted 17th-century farmhouse, ten minutes' walk up from the town, set in its own informal garden amid fields: it is a genuine Tyrolean hotel in local style, decorated with knick-knacks and antiques, and run with warmth by the Sauritz family. Substantial, if uninspired, cooking. Closed Apr, May, Oct, Nov. 15 rooms, all with private facilities. B&B 330–650 Sch; half board 420–740 Sch [1989]. Recent nomination. More reports welcome.

LANS 6072 Tyrol — Map 15

Gasthof Zur Traube *Tel* (05222) 77261 and 77406
Lans, Nr Innsbruck

In a pretty village above Innsbruck, with fine mountain views, Zur Traube *is a typical Tyrolean inn with flowered balconies, run by the friendly Raitmayr family for 15 generations. The welcome, comfort and cooking are all admired. Closed 20 Oct–10 Nov. 24 rooms, all with bath and/or shower. B&B double 740–800 Sch. Set menus 130–180 Sch. No recent reports. More welcome.*

LECH AM ARLBERG 6764 Vorarlberg — Map 15

Hotel Alexandra *Tel* (05583) 2848
Telex 52550 ALEXA

Slightly cheaper than our other Lech entries, a very friendly family-run chalet-hotel beside fields and hills, furnished in local style, with excellent food (notably the weekly buffet of roast sucking-pig). Owner is also a ski-instructor. Closed May, Oct, Nov. 19 rooms, all with bath and/or shower. Half board 350–1,050 Sch [1989]. New nomination. More reports welcome.

Hotel Post *Tel* (05583) 22060
Fax (05583) 220623
Telex 52677 PHOT

Here in one of Europe's finest ski resorts is a sophisticated hotel for summer or winter, run by three generations of the Moosbrugger family. Recent visitors loved it: "Lots of atmosphere, friendly reception, antiques and fresh flowers everywhere, food very tasty and nicely presented, charming bedrooms with a small sitting room in each." Others have agreed: "We have been coming here for 25 years. Nowhere else in the world have we met this mixture of perfection and the casual charm of a *pension de famille*. It would be worth staying here for the hotel itself, but it is also in the middle of the most delightful village and the centre of wonderful mountain walking." "Combines efficiency with the friendliness of a family operation. First-class food." (*Berneil Odell, Tim Hart*) More reports welcome.

Open 1 Dec–24 Apr, 24 June–1 Oct.
Rooms 12 suites, 21 double, 8 single – 35 with bath, 6 with shower, all with telephone, radio and TV; baby-listening on request. 2 suites in a chalet opposite.
Facilities Lift. Hall, bar, TV room, dining room, restaurant; conference facilities; children's playroom; indoor heated swimming pool, sauna, massage. Large grounds with landscaped gardens, meadows, café.
Location Central. Garage and parking.
Credit cards Amex, Visa (but only in restaurant).
Terms B&B double 1,150–2,300 Sch; dinner B&B 1,520–2,670 Sch. Set meals 220–420 Sch. In winter only reservations for 1 week or more accepted; Christmas and touring packages. Reduced rates for children; special meals on request.

Hotel-Gasthof Salome — *Tel* (05583) 23060
Oberlech — *Fax* (05583) 230640
Telex 52588 SALHO

A 600-year-old farmhouse, renovated in Alpine style with wooden ceilings and carved beams, now a fairly expensive ski hotel, quite stylish in its cosy Tyrolean way. It is perched on the mountainside at Oberlech with fine views all round and a nursery slope in front (in winter it is probably best approached in daytime, as you have to drive up a narrow winding snow-covered road). A recent verdict, "Constant courtesy and cosiness, style and immense comfort. Our room had a veranda with breathtaking views. Food is out of this world." Others have written: "Seven of us, including three children, had a happy and comfortable week, with delicious food and a welcoming atmosphere"; "The pine cupboards, coloured rugs, ornaments and books made the hotel feel lived in. We got the nicest room we have ever had in a ski hotel." Guests also have a large and comfortable sitting room, a sun terrace, sauna, solarium and whirlpool. Some of the larger bedrooms are divided into sleeping and sitting areas and have a balcony. More reports welcome.

Open 2 Dec–22 Apr, 24 June–10 Sept approx.
Rooms 11 suites, 4 double, 1 single – all with bath, and/or shower, telephone, radio and TV.
Facilities Lift. Lounge, bar, residents' dining room; sun terrace. Garden with children's playground. Sauna, solarium, whirlpool, massage. Evening entertainments.
Location On the mountain above Lech; take road to Oberlech. Parking.
Credit cards None accepted.
Terms [1989 rates] Half board: winter 530–1,670 Sch; summer 530–740 Sch. Set lunch 180–290 Sch, dinner 280–490 Sch. Ski packages. Reduced rates for children sharing parents' room; special meals.

MAYRHOFEN 6290 Tyrol — Map 15

Hotel Elisabeth — *Tel* (05285) 2929
Einfahrt Mitte 432 — *Telex* 534145

High-class *Gemütlichkeit* infuses this stylish holiday hotel in a skiing and climbing resort up the Zillertal valley, some way east of Innsbruck. "We spent Christmas here", says a reader this year, "and Elizabeth Thaler-Moigg made a special effort to create a family atmosphere, while her husband in my view is one of Austria's best chefs. A hotel of highest excellence in every respect – food, service, bedrooms, leisure facilities and fellow clientele." An earlier view: "A wonderful hotel, quite pricey but worth every penny. There's a night-club in the basement, and a fitness centre and indoor pool all beautifully maintained. The 'standard' bedrooms are as luxurious as the suites, while the open-plan public rooms are spacious." British package tours pour into Mayrhofen, but it's also a centre for Innsbruck University's international holiday courses, which engender much animation and folklore activity. (*David Ball*)

Open All year except 1 month in autumn and 1 month in spring.
Rooms 2 suites, 24 double, 10 single – all with bath and/or shower, telephone, radio, TV, mini-bar.
Facilities Lift. Hall, bar, 4 restaurants; conference room; indoor swimming pool, sauna, hot whirlpool, beauty farm. Dancing. Garden with terrace, children's playground.
Location In centre of village, 68 km E of Innsbruck.
Credit cards Diners, Visa.
Terms B&B: 1,050–1,295 Sch, suite 3,450–3,885 Sch; dinner, B&B: 1,150–1,395 Sch, suite 3,750–4,185 Sch. 50% reduction for children in parents' room; special meals.

MÖSERN BEI SEEFELD 6100 Tyrol — Map 15

Hotel Lärchenhof — *Tel* (05212) 8167

The anglophone Holzer family's quiet little chalet-style hotel, four miles south-west of the big resort of Seefeld, has panoramic views of the Inn valley and makes a good centre alike for skiing and summer walking. Recently modernised, it has a welcoming ambience; log fire in the lounge, chaises-longues on the terrace. Good breakfasts; good overall value. Light evening meals available. 24 rooms, all with bath or shower. B&B 210–340 Sch. Recent nomination. More reports please.

MUTTERS 6162 Tyrol — Map 15

Hotel Restaurant Muttererhof — *Tel* (05222) 587491

Nattererstrasse 20
Mutters, bei Innsbruck

Run by twin sisters, the neat flower-girt *Muttererhof* stands on the edge of a picturesque mountain village just south of Innsbruck, facing a "most breathtaking" landscape. It was liked again this year. "Excellent Tyrolean fare, with generous breakfasts (bacon and egg)", runs a recent report; "staff and management, especially Frau Stark-Egger, all very helpful and welcoming. Rooms are not luxurious: some are attractive, some a bit basic." "The hotel's best feature is the large well-heated swimming pool, with solarium and sauna. Decor and furniture of bedrooms is uninspiring, though ours had a balcony (many of them do not, and they face north, getting no sun). Beds were comfortable. The dining room was absolutely beautiful, panelled in dark wood with ecclesiastical-style carvings. Our appetite was well satisfied by the meal, and the *carte* contained Austrian specialities."

Report forms (Freepost in UK) will be found at the end of the Guide.

Open 23 Dec–15 Apr, 10 May–20 Oct.
Rooms 1 suite, 18 double, 1 single – all with bath and/or shower and telephone; many with balcony.
Facilities Hall, bar, *Stube*, restaurant; functions room. Indoor swimming pool, sauna and solarium. Garden.
Location 6 km SSW of Innsbruck, S of Natters, E of Gotzens.
Restriction Not suitable for ♿.
Credit cards Access, Amex, Visa.
Terms B&B 300–450 Sch; half board 380–580 Sch; full board 500–640 Sch. Full alc 200–220 Sch. Reduced rates and special meals for children.

PÖRTSCHACH 9210 Carinthia — Map 15

Hotel Pörtschacherhof — *Tel* (04272) 2335

This is our only entry for the beautiful and famous Wörthersee, in Carinthia, and for the large, lively and prosperous resort of Pörtschach on its north shore, much frequented by Germans. Owned and run by the Koroschetz family, it is a big white traditional villa with modern annexes: "There is a large attractive garden with a small heated swimming pool, and a pleasant lounge. We had a room with bathroom and balcony, adequately furnished. The food is good and varied, the breakfast buffet generous, the waitress service quick and friendly. When we left a pair of slippers and a nightdress behind, they were promptly posted to our home address without our asking." Modern dining room rather dull, but there's an outdoor shaded terrace by the garden.

Open May–Oct.
Rooms 53 – 24 with bath, 22 with shower; most with telephone and balcony.
Facilities Lounge, salon, TV room, restaurant; terrace. Garden with swimming pool.
Location Close to lake; Pörtschach is 13 km W of Klagenfurt.
Credit cards None accepted.
Terms [1989 rates] B&B 440–650 Sch; dinner, B&B 500–710 Sch.

SALZBURG — Map 15

Hotel Elefant — *Tel* (0662) 843397
Sigmund-Haffnergasse 4, — *Telex* 632725 ELHOT
Salzburg 5020

This typical Salzburg town house, tall, narrow and medieval, has been an inn for 400 years. It stands conveniently in the city's historic heart, on a quiet street five minutes' walk from the opera house. The area is pedestrian: you can drive your car up to load or unload, but the police may ask questions. The hotel has recently been renovated, and this year and last readers have been mainly satisfied. Most bedrooms are said to be pleasant and comfortable, though some may be rather dull and functional. The renovated restaurant has been judged attractive, and its cooking reasonable if unremarkable. "We had a top-floor double room, quiet and pretty, not at all small, with a fine view of the cathedral. Helpful front desk, and delicious buffet breakfasts." "A delightful hotel and an interesting meal." One reader this year found the staff very helpful, apart from the lack of room service, but was less happy with his room and the main meals. (*Patrick Barclay, RAL Ogston, Liz and Tom Piatt*)

Open All year.
Rooms 1 suite, 26 double, 10 single – all with bath and/or shower, telephone, radio and TV. Ground-floor rooms.
Facilities Lift. Lounge, bar, TV room, breakfast room, dining room; conference facilities.
Location Central. Municipal parking 5 mins' walk away.
Credit cards All major cards accepted.
Terms [1989 rates] B&B 425–550 Sch; dinner, B&B 580–705 Sch. Reduced rates and special meals for children.

Pension Nonntal
Pfadfinderweg 6–8
Salzburg 5020

Tel (0662) 841427 and 846700
Fax (0662) 8467006

Otto and Anna Huemer run a small and homely *pension* with a pretty garden in quiet residential south-east Salzburg, with a spectacular view of the Hohensalzburg fortress, and only ten minutes' walk from the centre. Readers recently have written of the Huemers' kindness to their guests, of the "warm family atmosphere", and of comfortable rooms with antiques; and this year again most reports have been positive. "Our room was quiet and romantic, overlooking floral gardens, and Herr Otto was an outstanding host", write Americans. "A modest but excellent pension, with imaginative menus." "A warm welcome, and home-cooked Austrian dishes in a cosy restaurant." (*Kathy and Tony Gillett, Diane and Joel Morris, Miss L Hall*) But there have also been reports of instant coffee, of tinned fruit for dessert, and of some rooms shabby or with sloping beds. Rooms in the main building are judged better than those in the annexe. More reports please.

Open All year. Restaurant closed to non-residents.
Rooms 4 suites, 10 double, 4 single – all with bath and shower and telephone. 10 with TV. 8 rooms in annexe. 2 ground-floor rooms.
Facilities Salon/breakfast room, restaurant with bar; functions room. Garden with terrace and lawns. Bicycles available.
Location In SE suburbs. Leave *Autobahn* at Salzburg-Süd, take Friedensstrasse, Hellbrunnerstrasse, Hofhaymer-Allee, Nonntaler Hauptstrasse. Frequent buses to city centre. Free transport by hotel's bus from station or airport.
Credit cards Access, Amex, Visa.
Terms [1989 rates] B&B: single 580–700 Sch, double 850–1,100 Sch, suite 1,100–1,200 Sch. Dinner, B&B double 1,200–1,400 Sch. Set dinner 185–245 Sch; full alc 345 Sch. 3 day packages in winter; ski packages. Reduced rates and special meals for children.

Hotel Schloss Mönchstein
Mönchsberg Park 26
Salzburg 5020

Tel (0662) 848555
Fax (0662) 848559
Telex 632080 MOEHO

Once the guest-house of an archbishop, now an expensive hotel, this dun-coloured creeper-covered *Schloss* stands high on the Mönchsberg just above central Salzburg, but is easy of access: a lift service, running till 2 am, whisks you up in 30 seconds from the tourist hurly-burly below. A large and pleasant garden, antiques in the halls and dining room, spacious rooms, and breakfast on a flowery terrace, are among the assets – but oddly there is no lounge. One reader this year renewed former praise for the friendly service and the tranquillity. (*PC Walker*) Another called it "the star of the journey and worth every schilling". (*C and M*

Hedoin) But yet another thought the high prices excessive, and was very critical of the service in an "unwelcoming, spartan room". We'd be glad of further reports.

Open All year.
Rooms 9 suites, 8 double – all with bath and/or shower, telephone, radio, TV and mini-bar; baby-listening on request; 24-hour room service. Some ground-floor rooms.
Facilities Lift. Hall, bar, café, restaurant; chapel for weddings; terrace with café; weekly concerts. Large garden with tennis court.
Location Above Salzburg on Mönchsberg – hotel is signposted. 3 mins by car from city centre, 7 mins by the Mönchsberg lift. Parking and garages.
Credit cards All major cards accepted.
Terms B&B: single 1,400–1,800 Sch, double 2,200–4,600 Sch, suite 4,100–5,900 Sch. Dinner, B&B 500 Sch added per person. Set lunch 300–700 Sch, dinner 500–1,000 Sch; full alc 550 Sch. Reduced rates and special meals for children.

Hotel Zistelalm *Tel* (0662) 20104
Auf dem Gaisberg, *from Mar 1990* (0662) 641067
Salzburg 5026

Situated 1,000 metres up on the Gaisberg just east of the city, this gemütlich *little chalet-style mountain* Gasthaus, *owned by the Hauser family, caters for skiers in winter, walkers in summer. Good food and beer, swimming pool in a meadow, rustic decor. Closed 21 Oct–21 Dec. 30 rooms, most with bath or shower. B&B double 730–970 Sch. Full alc 285 Sch. New nomination. More reports please.*

SCHLOSS ROSENAU 3924 Lower Austria — Map 15

Museumsverein Schloss Rosenau *Tel* (02822) 8221

The village of Schloss Rosenau, not far from the Czech border, lies amid quiet rolling countryside, good for walking and cross-country skiing. The yellow-fronted Schloss from which it gets its name is now partly a remarkable 18th-century Masonic museum and partly a hotel – outwardly grand-looking but offering fairly simple accommodation. Readers paying a return winter visit liked it as much as ever, "Rooms simply furnished but nicely heated, restaurant first-rate, best in the region, with very good wines. Host most attentive, carried luggage to room himself. Heated pool, delightful walks, lots of cross-country skiing." "Owners very accommodating. Best calf's liver I have ever eaten." The extensive dinner menu offers food that is tasty, plentiful, fairly imaginative and good value. *Note*: the *Schloss* has close links with the *Pension Weissenhofer* next door, and guests who book may find themselves sleeping at the *Pension*, unless they specify. (*Prof. HC Robbins Landon, Mary Clark*)

Open All year except 22 Jan – 28 Feb.
Rooms 18 double – all with shower. Guests also accommodated in Pension Weissenhofer nearby.
Facilities Lift. TV room, dining room, 2 *Stüberl;* conference and banqueting rooms; sun terrace. Masonic museum and baroque church. Park with covered heated swimming pool, sauna, 2 tennis courts and miniature golf. Riding and fishing available.

Location 8 km SW of Zwettl.
Credit cards All major cards accepted.
Terms B&B: single 380–500 Sch, double 560–800 Sch; half board: single 470–590 Sch, double 740–980 Sch. Set lunch/dinner 90–140 Sch; full alc 300–400 Sch. Reduced rates and special meals for children.

SCHRUNS 6780 Vorarlberg — Map 15

Hotel Krone — *Tel* (05556) 2255

Close to the centre of Schruns, a pleasant little market town in the Montafon valley, is this small hotel, all wood panelling, chintzy curtains and cosy *Gemütlichkeit* – "a gem", says a visitor in 1989. The Mayer family have run it for four generations, and readers continue to respond to their hospitality. "Excellent room, food and service, nice furniture." "The Mayers maintain a keen interest in the running of their hotel and the behaviour of the staff reflects their simple kindness. Our meals were beautifully planned, delightfully cooked and served with great charm." *(BJ Walter)*

Open 20 Dec–16 Apr, end May–end Oct. Restaurant closed Thur.
Rooms 8 double, 1 single – all with bath and shower, telephone and radio; TV for hire.
Facilities Lounge, bar, 2 restaurants. Garden terrace; river frontage with trout fishing.
Location 12 km SE of Bludenz. Central, near the Kronen bridge. Parking.
Restriction Not suitable for ♿.
Credit cards None accepted.
Terms B&B 300–450 Sch; dinner, B&B 430–530 Sch. Set lunch 150 Sch, dinner 165 Sch. Reduced rates and special meals for children.

SEEHAM 5164 Salzburg — Map 15

Hotel Walkner — *Tel* (06217) 550

A friendly modern family-run hotel in a rural setting near a lake, amid fairly flat but attractive scenery only 20 kilometres due north of Salzburg, near Mattsee. Lovely gardens with pool, wide stone-flagged terrace with views, where meals are served when fine. Goodish Austrian food, with help-yourself salads. Airy bedrooms. Open 15 May–30 Sept. 20 rooms, most with private facilities. B&B 270–380 Sch; half board 350–460 Sch [1989]. *Recent nomination, endorsed this year. More reports welcome.*

STRASSEN 9920 East Tyrol — Map 15

Strasserwirt — *Tel* (04846) 63540
Telex 46643

This big chalet is a lively and attractive holiday hotel in a hamlet in an East Tyrolean mountain valley between Lienz and the Italian border. Friendly family owners, the Bürglers. Good traditional cooking, plenty of Gemütlichkeit *and local character such as four-poster beds (modern), plus sauna, solarium and fitness room. Parties and excursions organised (horse-trekking, river rafting), with the accent on fun and local folklore. Closed Nov–10 Dec. 30 rooms, all with bath or shower. B&B double 640–920 Sch [1989 rates]. Meals from 200 Sch. Recent nomination. More reports welcome.*

VIENNA **Map 15**

Hotel Amadeus *Tel* (0222) 638738
Wildpretmarkt 5, Vienna 1010 *Telex* 111102

Praise enough to make any Salieri jealous is heaped by readers on this *Amadeus*, a modern hotel in a small street near St Stephan's. "Charming and comfortable, with very helpful service"; "Flowers everywhere, fine prints on the walls, staff all very pleasant. The bedrooms and public rooms are decorated in red and white like the Austrian flag, the hotel is fully carpeted with rich red rugs; crystal chandeliers are scattered throughout." (*H and L Mathé-Dumaine*) An earlier visitor found the atmosphere "pure Maria Theresa and delightful". Another voiced delight about breakfast – "ambrosial coffee and a basket of newly baked rolls". But a visitor this year thought the coffee far from ambrosial.

Open All year except 23–27 Dec.
Rooms 18 double, 12 single – all with bath and/or shower, telephone and radio; 22 with TV.
Facilities Breakfast room.
Location Central, down a small turning off Tuchlauben.
Restriction Not suitable for ♿.
Credit cards All major cards accepted.
Terms B&B: single 890–1,370 Sch, double 1,540–1,760 Sch. Extra bed for child 170 Sch. (No restaurant.)

Hotel Kaiserin Elisabeth *Tel* (0222) 515260
Weihburggasse 3 *Fax* (0222) 515267
Vienna 1010 *Telex* 112422 ELIHO

Franz Liszt, Richard Wagner and others once stayed at this demure traditional hotel in an historic building down a side-street near St Stephan's cathedral. Rooms are quiet, clean and well furnished, and a second lift has just been installed. Readers remain pleased this year: "Friendly staff and wonderful breakfast, including porridge"; "Charming, efficient staff and a delightful room with wooden beds." (*Paul Palmer, and others*) No restaurant, but *Zum Drei Hussaren* just opposite is commended.

Open All year.
Rooms 3 suites, 50 double, 12 single – all with bath and/or shower, telephone, radio, TV and mini-bar.
Facilities 2 lifts. Lobby with bar, lounge.
Location Central, in pedestrian zone near cathedral. Parking arrangement with nearby garage.
Credit cards All major cards accepted.
Terms [1989 rates] B&B: single 800–1,150 Sch, double 1,050–1,700 Sch, suite 1,950 Sch. Extra bed 260 Sch. (No restaurant.)

We asked hotels to estimate their 1990 tariffs. About a quarter of the hotels on the Continent failed to reply, so the prices we quote should not be relied upon.

König von Ungarn *Tel* (0222) 5265200
1 Schulerstrasse 10, Vienna 1010 *Telex* 116240

Kadar may be toppled from his throne, as his country lurches towards democracy: but this "King of Hungary" has continued in 1989 to rule potently over the affections of most of our reporters: "We enjoyed the glass-domed courtyard and our dinner was excellent"; "We had a lovely room and a nice meal." "A very romantic art-nouveau-decorated hotel in the heart of old Vienna. Excellent courteous service." *Und so weiter*. It's a finely restored 16th-century building close to St Stephan's Cathedral, its inner courtyard now an attractive lounge "where an inspired variety of cocktails is served". Everyone praises the "warm and helpful" staff, also the buffet breakfasts and the rooms (those at the back are quietest). "When you go through the fine bevelled-glass doors you have the feeling of entering an exclusive club." The elegant and fashionable restaurant, under separate ownership, has been judged excellent by some, but it is very expensive. One pleasant touch is that the hotel provides its guests with daily reports, in three languages, on places to visit and other suggestions for the day. (*Ruth H and Robert D Todd, Julia and Nigel Rhodes*)

Open All year.
Rooms 70 beds – 28 rooms with bath, 4 with shower, all with telephone.
Facilities Lift. Lounge, bar, TV room, children's room, restaurant (under separate ownership).
Location Central, near St Stephan's Cathedral. Parking.
Terms [1989 rates] B&B 825 Sch; half board 925 Sch.

Pension Nossek *Tel* (0222) 5337041
Graben 17, Vienna 1010 *Telex* 113113

Established by his grandmother 80 years ago, Dr Renato Cremona's high-ceilinged old-world *pension* is very centrally situated in one of Vienna's most fashionable streets, now a pedestrian precinct – five minutes from the Opera, the Hofburg and the Riding School – and it occupies the top floors of a stately office building. "It charmed us because it successfully mixes the ancient and modern", was one of several favourable reports this year. Another was this, from a returning regular, "Atmosphere friendly with Herr Doktor very much in evidence; service and reception worked well; constant boiling-hot water; generous breakfasts." Others have praised the large, clean and airy bedrooms, efficient staff and good value for money. Renovation now seems to have reached nearly all rooms. But there was one complaint this year about lack of ventilation, and slow service at breakfast. (*Claudia Wood, Uli Lloyd Pack, Tom & Gillian Wadden*)

Open All year.
Rooms 3 suites, 21 double, 4 single – 17 with bath, 4 with shower, all with telephone.
Facilities Lift. Reading room, breakfast room.
Location Central, but quiet. Underground carpark 1 min's walk.
Restriction Not suitable for ♿.
Credit cards None accepted.
Terms B&B: single 300–770 Sch, double 850–900 Sch, suite 1,100 Sch. (No restaurant.)

We are particularly keen to have reports on italicised entries.

Hotel Römischer Kaiser
Annagasse 16, Vienna 1010

Tel (0222) 5127751
Fax (0222) 512775113
Telex 113696

Very central but in a traffic-free road, just off the Kärntnerstrasse, and built in 1684 as the private palace of the Imperial Chancellor: today it is a small, very personal and fairly luxurious hotel, with period furnishings and plenty of chandeliers. Some disturbances at night from disco revellers, and the bells of the Annakirche ring from 6.15 am. 24 rooms, 23 with bath. B&B double 1,700–2,100 Sch. No restaurant, lots nearby. Recent nomination. More reports welcome.

Hotel Sacher
Philharmonikerstrasse 4
Vienna 1015

Tel (0222) 51456
Fax (0222) 51457-810
Telex 112520 SAHOT

Heaven knows what Hapsburg ghosts are hiding behind the red velvet drapes of this famous old Viennese institution, founded in 1876. Nowadays it has slipped out of the limelight, and it fell out of the Guide four years ago for want of feedback. But we've had two favourable reports this year – one from a reader who has made over 20 visits in as many years: "Family owned and run, its Grand Hotel atmosphere is mitigated by quite a personal touch. Maybe it trades too much on its role in past Viennese history, but it has now been modernised, i.e. the hall has air-conditioning in summer. The restaurant is a bit too self-consciously Viennese, but it is good – though the much-hyped Sachertorte is actually better in other pastry shops. Decor is traditional Austrian with many original paintings. One upstairs bit of the restaurant has zither music at times, played perhaps by a distinguished professional musician on his day off. The place is expensive, but one is not rooked. And the few single rooms that still exist without bathrooms, presumably former servants' rooms, are good value. I prefer the *Sacher* to the *Inter-Continentals* of this world." "Luxury, courtesy and a romantic atmosphere. We had dinner in the Red Salon, so evocative that I expected Crown Prince Rudolph to walk in at any moment." (*FM Steiner, M and D Chambers*)

Open All year.
Rooms 7 suites, 81 double, 37 single – 122 with bath and shower, all with telephone and TV; 3 with radio.
Facilities Lift. 2 bars, 2 restaurants, 2 cafés.
Location Central, near the Opera. Garage opposite.
Credit cards All major cards accepted.
Terms B&B: single 1,400–1,750 Sch, double 2,500–2,850 Sch, suite 8,100–8,600 Sch. Set lunch 550 Sch, dinner 650 Sch; full alc 590 Sch. Children under 6 free of charge.

Pension Suzanne
Walfischgasse 4,
Vienna 1010

Tel (0222) 5132507

This *pension* close to the Opera House has an entrance next to a sex-shop, but is admired for its pleasant Viennese furnishings (handsome beds and tables, fine mirrors, decent pictures). A recent report, "What a treat! You walk up a long flight of wide marble stairs and come to a tiny office. The staff are scatter-brained and disorganised, but sweet and helpful: typical North Americans, we shocked them with our request for ice, but they let us make our own in their kitchen. The rooms are clean: ours overlooked the street but was quiet (double-glazed). Excellent coffee for breakfast in a small crowded room." One couple this year told us that their bed had collapsed: but others have reported nothing but comfort and helpfulness. (*Jeanette King, Mrs Ann Dowson*)

Open All year.
Rooms 34 beds – 16 rooms with bath, 3 with shower, all with telephone.
Facilities Lift. Breakfast room.
Location Central, near Opera House.
Restriction Not suitable for ♿.
Credit cards None accepted.
Terms [1989 rates] B&B 365–430 Sch. (No restaurant.)

VILLACH 9500 Carinthia — Map 15

Romantik Hotel Post — *Tel* (042 22) 26101
Hauptplatz 26 — *Telex* 45723

In a town on the old Vienna-Venice road, a former 16th-century palace which has been a hotel for 250 years (Empress Marie Thérèse stayed here). Bedrooms combine character with modern comforts; good breakfast buffet and meals, which you can eat in the garden. Friendly service. 77 rooms, all with bath and/or shower. B&B double 780–1,330 Sch. Set lunch 140 Sch; full alc 220 Sch. Re-nominated this year. More reports please.

WAGRAIN 5602 Salzburg — Map 15

Hotel-Gasthof Moawirt — *Tel* (06413) 8818
Schwaighof 123

Backed by forested hills, this spruce modern flower-bedecked chalet stands just outside Wagrain, an all-year resort south of Salzburg, just off the *Autobahn* to Villach. "Quiet, comfortable and spacious. We were the only guests and did not arrive till 8.15 pm, but they opened up the kitchen for us: splendid trout and wines." That report this year follows earlier ones: "Charming owners, the Maurers; a large spotless room with balcony, and good dinners and breakfasts." The attractive countryside is perfect for summer walking and winter skiing (a chair lift is opposite the hotel). (*ECM Begg*) Traffic can be audible from front rooms.

Open All year.
Rooms 23 double, 4 single – most with bath or shower, all with telephone, radio, TV and baby-listening; many with balcony.
Facilities Lift. Lounge/bar, TV room, breakfast room, dining room; folk music once a week. Sun terrace and garden. Bathing in private lake.
Location About 75 km S of Salzburg, just off Salzburg–Villach *Autobahn*.
Credit cards Access, Amex, Diners.
Terms [1989 rates] B&B 230–450 Sch; dinner, B&B 340–610 Sch. Reduced rates and special meals for children.

All inspections are carried out anonymously.

Belgium

DIE SWAENE, BRUGES

BRUGES

Map 9

Hotel Adornes
St Annarei 26
Bruges 8000

Tel (050) 34.13.36
Fax (050) 34.20.85

Warm praise again this year for this small B&B hotel, run by a pleasant young couple, in a 17th-century house close to the *Markt*. Some rooms overlook a canal: those facing the busy street are less quiet. "Despite the modern style, the hotel has retained some of its old character, with polished wood floors and exposed beams. Our comfortable room was bright and airy. Breakfast in an attractive flower-filled room." "Quite the best small hotel we have been to abroad. Breakfast was a welter of goodies of the utmost diversity, with a log fire burning on a hearthstone." (*A Sargent, Oliver Snow, and others*)

Open All year except 2 Jan–17 Feb.
Rooms 20 double (also let as single) – all with bath, shower, telephone, radio and TV. 2 on ground floor.
Facilities Lift, ramps. 2 lounges, breakfast room.

Location Central. Go from *Markt* to theatre; hotel is signposted. Parking.
Credit cards Access, Amex, Visa.
Terms [1989 rates] B&B: single 1,900–2,700 Bfrs, double 2,100–2,900 Bfrs. Winter package including museum tickets, free bicycle. Reduced rates for children. (No restaurant.)

Hotel Anselmus *Tel* (050) 34.13.74
Riddersstraat 15
Bruges 8000

A small B&B in a quiet street near the central market. It is an attractive old Flemish-style gabled house with a massive wooden door, and takes its name from an eminent humanist of Bruges who lived here and was possibly a contemporary of Erasmus. The interior has been skilfully and beautifully converted into a comfortable little hotel, again appreciated in 1989 for its large, fairly simple but very clean rooms, good breakfasts and friendly and solicitous owners, the Dutoit-Schoores. (*David Rhodes, WR Gouger*)

Open All year.
Rooms 1 suite, 8 double, 1 single – all with bath and shower, telephone, radio and TV. 2 ground-floor rooms.
Facilities Hall, lounges, breakfast room.
Location 5 mins' walk from the market square. 1 garage; street parking.
Credit cards Access, Amex, Visa.
Terms B&B: single 2,000 Bfrs, double 2,300 Bfrs, suite 3,500 Bfrs (for 3 people 3,100 Bfrs, for 4 3,500 Bfrs). 1-night bookings sometimes refused. Reduced rates for children. (No restaurant.)

Hotel Bryghia *Tel* (050) 33.80.59
Oosterlingenplein 4, Bruges 8000 *Fax* (050) 34.14.30

A former 15th-century merchant's house, facing a quiet square and canal. Pleasant family owners, well-furnished rooms, good buffet breakfasts below a beamed ceiling (no restaurant). 18 rooms, all with bath and shower. B&B double 2,600–2,950 Bfrs [1989]. New nomination. More reports welcome.

Hotel de Orangerie *Tel* (050) 34.16.49
Kartuizerinnenstraat 10 *Fax* (050) 33.30.16
Bruges 8000 *Telex* 82443 ORANGE

In the heart of Bruges, beside the Dijver canal, this 16th-century house has recently been converted into an elegant small hotel, described as "excellent" this year. "A calm oasis with simple, spacious bedrooms, spotlessly clean; nice touches like fresh flowers and hair-drier. Smashing breakfasts and quiet lounge; staff pleasant and helpful." A charming bar with open fireplace and period furniture gives the impression of a private drawing room. In the summer breakfast and drinks are served on a terrace by the canal. (*Donald Hartog, Mary Lawson*)

The *Orangerie* now has an annexe, *De Tuilerieën*, opposite, with 25 bedrooms, indoor swimming pool, jacuzzi, sauna and solarium. It is slightly pricier.

Open All year.
Rooms 5 suites, 14 double – all with bath and shower, telephone, radio, TV, mini-bar and baby-listening. Some ground-floor rooms. 25 rooms in annexe, *De Tuilerieën* opposite.
Facilities Lift. Bar, TV room, breakfast room; conference facilities. Garden and canalside terrace. Swimming pool, jacuzzi, sauna, solarium in annexe.
Location Central, near Markt. Private parking 5 mins' walk.
Credit cards All major cards accepted.
Terms B&B: single 3,950 Bfrs, double 4,250–5,250 Bfrs, suite 5,950–6,950 Bfrs. (No restaurant.)

Die Swaene
Steenhouwersdijk 1
Bruges 8000

Tel (050) 34.27.98
Fax (050) 33.66.74
Telex 82446 SWAENE

Still a firm guide favourite, the "quietly elegant" *Swaene* is set in a 15th-century house on a canal, almost opposite the Belfry. As a B&B it has long been liked for its "comfortable family atmosphere", and now it has a restaurant too, specialising in fish. Reports this year and last: "First-class food in an elegant dining room. A pretty garden, comfortable bedroom with balcony, and charming service." "An excellent, friendly hotel. The food is good, but the dining room a bit small and airless. Breakfasts lavish. A splendid lounge, with a piano which guests can play. My only major criticism: the slipperiness of the bath which could be dangerous for the elderly." "The predominance of pink and our rose-decorated good-sized room made me think I was staying with a maiden aunt. The staff installed a baby-alarm from our room, so we did not need a baby-sitter." The lounge, with its open fire and fine painted ceiling, is the restored meeting room of the Guild of Taylors, dating from 1779, free coffee and tea are still served here every afternoon from two till four. (*S and K Murray-Sykes, Sir Patrick Reilly, Alan Rodger and Peter Macaulay, and others*) One reader on a package weekend break was given a distinctly inferior room.

Open All year. Restaurant closed Wed, and Thur midday.
Rooms 2 suites, 19 double, 3 single – all with bath and shower, telephone, radio, TV and baby-listening; 4 ground-floor rooms.
Facilities 2 lifts. Lobby, lounge, bar, breakfast room, restaurant. Terrace and garden.
Location Central (but quiet): signposts from the market square. Garage.
Credit cards All major cards accepted.
Terms B&B: single 3,000 Bfrs, double 3,650 Bfrs, suite 6,800–7,800 Bfrs. Set lunch 900 Bfrs, dinner 1,300 Bfrs; full alc 1,900 Bfrs. Special meals for children.

Traveller's tale *There were five waiters of various sorts, so desperately keen to serve you that I felt hideously conspicuous, and had to sneak my bottle out of the wine bucket in order to fill up my glass when no-one was looking, or I got a look of reproach.*

BRUGES **Map 9**

Hotel Ter Duinen *Tel* (050) 33.04.37

Langerei 52
Bruges 8000

A dedicated and very friendly young couple, the Bossu-Van Den Heuvel, run this inexpensive little canalside hotel, about 800 metres from the centre. Numerous readers have again extolled it in 1988/9 – notably for its lavish breakfasts, warm ambience and pleasant newly renovated rooms. "The owners are young, enthusiastic, very much in love with their hotel, and their love for their guests is enormous. The rooms are beautiful and cosy and the view is breathtaking. The breakfast is royal." "Baskets of flowers hang everywhere. Our attractively furnished room had a balcony with canal view. Best coffee I've tasted." "Beds the most comfortable we have ever slept in." "I took a party of seven very fussy German ladies, all pleasantly surprised." "The rooms are furnished with subtle printed fabrics and period furniture. We enjoyed moonlight over the canals at night from our two big windows." Some have found the rooms facing the canal noisy, others not. (*Chava and Amira Teomi, Mr and Mrs G Dove, E Allfrey-Pizer, Sara A Price, and many others*) A connoisseur from New England adds: "Belgian WCs are the best in Europe."

Open All year.
Rooms 18 – all with bath and/or shower, telephone and TV; baby-listening on request.
Facilities Lift. Lounge/bar with TV.
Location On canal 10–15 mins' walk from centre. Street parking in front of hotel; private garage available (100 Bfrs 1st night, 50 Bfrs thereafter). Windows double-glazed.
Restriction Not suitable for ♿.
Credit cards All major cards accepted.
Terms B&B: single 1,800–2,000 Bfrs, double 2,050–2,900 Bfrs. Reduced rates for children. (No restaurant.)

Hotel Wilgenhof *Tel* (050) 36 27 44

Polderstraat 151
Bruges 8310

For those who would prefer to stay just outside Bruges, here is a pleasantly converted farmhouse in the quiet polder two miles to the north-east. Bright, nicely decorated comfortable rooms with modern bathrooms; good breakfasts, served in the garden when fine. No other meals. 6 rooms, all with bath and shower. B&B: single 2,400 Bfrs, double 2,800–3,200 Bfrs. Recent nomination. More reports please.

BRUSSELS **Map 9**

Hôtel Agenda *Tel* (02) 539.00.31

6–8 rue de Florence *Fax* (02) 539.00.63
Brussels 1050 *Telex* 63947 AGENDA

Useful in an expensive city, a small modern medium-priced hotel just off the Avenue Louise. Bedrooms are spacious, comfortable and quiet. "Its charm lies also in the genuinely warm greeting. Our room had big windows, lots of cupboards, soft chairs, and a kitchenette. Breakfast was delicious, served in a small pretty room." There are no other public rooms, and no restaurant, but *Les Cadets de Gascogne* down the block is recommended. (*Andrew Semple*)

Open All year.
Rooms 2 suites, 23 double, 13 single – all with bath and shower, telephone, TV and kitchenette. 2 ground-floor rooms.
Facilities Lounge, breakfast room. Small garden.
Location Fairly central: in side street off Avenue Louise, 700 metres S of Place Louise. Garage.
Restriction Not suitable for ♿.
Credit cards All major cards accepted.
Terms B&B: single 2,725 Bfrs, double 3,250 Bfrs, suite 3,750 Bfrs. (No restaurant.)

Hôtel Amigo — *Tel* (02) 511.59.10
Rue de l'Amigo 1–3 — *Fax* (02) 513.52.77
Brussels 1000 — *Telex* 21618

"Still the best hotel in central Brussels" (a report this year), and the favourite choice of many visiting diplomats, Eurocrats and tourists, the *Amigo* occupies a prime site close to the Grand-Place. It's a large, spacious place of post-war design, still liked for its very swift service, good breakfasts, and quiet rooms (especially those at the back). But some find it too impersonal to be a true *amigo*, and there has been one complaint about shortage of hot water. Some rooms have a balcony. The restaurant is wholesome rather than enterprising, but there are many exciting eating-spots in the Grand-Place area. (*C and A Daintree, Toni Citroën*)

Open All year.
Rooms 11 suites, 157 double, 26 single – 173 with bath and shower, telephone, radio and TV; baby-listening on request. Some ground-floor rooms.
Facilities Lift, ramps. Salon, TV room, bar, restaurant; conference rooms and banqueting facilities.
Location Central, behind the Grand-Place. Garage.
Credit cards All major cards accepted.
Terms B&B: single 4,750–5,850 Bfrs, double 5,200–6,400 Bfrs, suite 8,400–20,100 Bfrs. Set meals 1,190 Bfrs; full alc 1,900 Bfrs. Children under 12 sharing parents' room free; special meals on request.

COUVIN 6400 Namur — Map 9

Au Petit Chef — *Tel* (060) 34.41.75
6 Dessus la Ville

A modern red-walled white-shuttered restaurant-with-rooms, decorated à la *House and Garden*, with patterned floral wallpaper, and some four-poster beds; the seven bedrooms have names such as Casanova and Romeo et Juliette; the cuisine is *nouvelle*, with dishes like foie gras with raspberry sauce. The hotel is just outside a small town down by the French border west of the Meuse, with an industrial estate on one side but open country on the other. "Our room was very pretty, with white furniture and a large bathroom under the eaves. Good breakfasts. Food enjoyable though not quite of *Michelin* rosette standard." More reports please.

Open All year except 15 Feb–10 Apr.
Rooms 7 double – all with bath and shower, telephone and TV.
Facilities Salon, bar, dining room. Terrace; large grounds.
Restrictions Not suitable for ♿. No children under 12.
Location On edge of town which is 44 km S of Charleroi.
Credit cards All major cards accepted.
Terms B&B: single 3,600 Bfrs, double 4,800 Bfrs. Dinner, B&B: single occupancy 5,500 Bfrs, double 8,500 Bfrs. Full alc 2,250 Bfrs. Reduced rates for children sharing parents' room; special meals.

CRUPET 5332 Namur — Map 9

Hôtel Les Ramiers — *Tel* (083) 69.90.70
1 rue Basse — *Fax* (083) 69.98.68

New to the Guide this year, a delectable little restaurant-with-rooms in a rural setting by a stream, on the edge of an out-of-the-way Ardennes village between Namur and Dinant. "Charming, flower-decked, with an outside terrace for drinks. Bedrooms are in the annexe, a functional building 15 minutes' walk away, but the room was satisfactory. The restaurant, small and elegant, bore accolades on its walls that seemed richly deserved – judging by my warm chicken liver salad with poached quail's egg. Breakfast was above average, too." (*Gault Millau toque* for such dishes as sweetbreads in port.) (*Bettye Chambers*)

Open All year except 2–19 Dec and 16–25 Mar. Closed Mon and Tue.
Rooms 6 double – all with bath and/or shower, radio and TV. Rooms are in annexe 800 metres from restaurant.
Facilities Lounge. 2 restaurants; terrace where lunch is served in fine weather.
Location Crupet is 20 km S of Namur, reached either from N47 or N49.
Restrictions Not suitable for ♿.
Credit cards All major cards accepted.
Terms B&B: single 1,650 Bfrs, double 2,050 Bfrs. Set lunch/dinner 1,700, 2,550 and 2,950 Bfrs (including drinks). Reduced rates and special meals for children.

DURBUY 5480 Luxembourg Belge — Map 9

Hostellerie le Sanglier des Ardennes — *Tel* (086) 21.10.88 and 21.32.62
Rue Comte Théodule d'Ursel — *Fax* (086) 21.24.65
Telex 42240 SANDUR

Set amid lovely forests in the valley of the river Ourthe, Durbuy is a pretty little village, overcrowded in summer. Here three small hotels, the *Sanglier*, the *Cardinal* and the *Vieux Durbuy*, are under the same ownership (Maurice Caerdinael) and are run jointly, with the *Sanglier* serving as the restaurant for all three. Its sophisticated cooking is reputed (two *Gault Millau toques*) and this year a reader who had truite amoureuse and tournedos de biche thought it excellent but expensive. He liked his spacious bedroom, too. Others have liked the frogs' legs and sole poached in vermouth, and have admired the bedrooms in all three hotels, and the views of the river and medieval castle. "Nicely welcomed, we enjoyed our room with its pleasant fabrics; breakfast was a dream – except for the tea." (*Endorsed by Dr A John Robertson*)

Open All year except Jan. Restaurant closed Thur.
Rooms 11 suites, 34 double – all with bath and shower, telephone and TV. Suites have radio and kitchenette. Some ground-floor rooms.
Facilities 2 Lounges, TV room, 4 restaurants; banquet room, conference facilities; terrace. The *Cardinal* has a large garden.
Location 45 km S of Liège. Hotels are central; the *Cardinal* has private parking.
Credit cards All major cards accepted.
Terms Rooms 2,200–2,700 Bfrs, suite 3,500–4,500 Bfrs. Breakfast 275 Bfrs. Set meals 1,200–1,750 Bfrs; full alc 1,600 Bfrs. Reduced rates and special meals for children.

GENT 9000 East Flanders — Map 9

Hotel St Jorishof
Botermarkt 2

Tel (091) 24.24.24
Fax (091) 24.26.40
Telex 12738 SJORIS

Belgium's fourth largest town is quite industrial, but it contains also a famous medieval quarter, where the splendid cathedral of St Bavon holds Van Eyck's masterpiece *The Adoration of the Mystic Lamb*. The *St Jorishof* (or *Cour St-Georges*), in the heart of the old town, dates from the 13th century – Charles V, Napoleon and other great figures stayed there – and it has maintained in fine order many of its original public rooms, including a spacious Gothic hall. Most recent visitors have found the food excellent and impressively served, and the staff competent and friendly: but one thought his dinner expensive and pretentious. The hotel itself is said to be spacious and clean: but some rooms, especially in the new annexe, can be small, simple and noise-afflicted, and one reader this year expressed concern about the state of fire precautions. More reports welcome.

Open All year except 3 weeks in July and 3 weeks over Christmas. Restaurant closed Sun and public holidays.
Rooms 5 suites/family rooms, 26 double, 6 single – all with bath and shower and telephone; 19 with TV. 26 in annexe across road.
Facilities Lift. Bar, 3 restaurants; conference facilities.
Location Central, opposite Town Hall. Garage and carpark.
Credit cards All major cards accepted.
Terms B&B: single 1,825–3,500 Bfrs, double 2,350–3,500 Bfrs, suite 3,500–5,000 Bfrs. Set lunch/dinner 1,050–1,500 Bfrs; full alc 1,800 Bfrs. Weekend breaks. Reduced rates and special meals for children.

HERBEUMONT 6803 Luxembourg Belge — Map 9

Hostellerie du Prieuré de Conques
Route de Florenville 176

Tel (061) 41.14.17

A stylishly converted 18th-century priory, long, low and white, surrounded by neat gardens, and standing by the banks of the river Semois in the heart of the Ardennes forests. Long lawns set with apple trees run down to the curving river. And most correspondents continue to find the hotel equally delectable: "Madame was pleasant and chatty, the owner is fatherly and friendly, and service is carried out by efficient country women. Furniture is either genuine rustic or good repro, and the beamed second floor rooms ooze atmosphere (bedrooms vary in size and style). I enjoyed the food tremendously – fantastic home-smoked salmon, hot lobster salad, sensitively cooked foie de veau, good cheeses. Public rooms are comfortable and smartly furnished with antiques, and a profusion of gorgeous old ornaments and lovely old paintings. We enjoyed our stay." Others likewise have praised the elegance, good cooking, and general professionalism. But we continue to get some criticisms – of poor housekeeping upstairs, or muddles over bookings. (*Ian and Francine Walsh, William A Grant*) The owners have built a new annexe, *La Résidence* with six suites.

Open 1 Mar–1 Jan. Restaurant closed Tue.
Rooms 6 suites with TV in annexe, 8 double, 3 single – all with bath, shower, telephone and radio.
Facilities 2 salons, bar, 2 restaurants. Garden; private fishing.
Location 3 km from Herbeumont, between Florenville and Bouillon.
Restriction Not suitable for ♿.
Credit cards All major cards accepted.
Terms B&B: single 2,700 Bfrs, double 3,200 Bfrs, suite 4,500 Bfrs. Set lunch 1,050 Bfrs, dinner 1,750–2,200 Bfrs; full alc 1,500 Bfrs. Half board rates (min 3 days). Reduced rates and special meals for children.

MAISSIN 6852 Luxembourg Belge — Map 9

Le Roly du Seigneur — *Tel* (061) 65.50.49
Av. du Roly du Seigneur

In an Ardennes village along the main Sedan-Liège road, an extremely friendly modern hotel. Large, clean, well-equipped rooms, some with balconies; excellent food, good breakfasts. Closed Jan, and Wed (except summer). 16 rooms, all with private facilities. Dinner, B&B double 2,800 Bfrs. Set meals 600–1,300 Bfrs. New nomination. More reports welcome.

MALMÉDY 4891 Liège — Map 9

Hostellerie Trôs Marets et Résidence — *Tel* (080) 33.79.17, *Fax* (080) 33.79.10
2 route des Trôs Marets

In lovely rolling wooded country north-east of Malmédy, near the German frontier, this sleek modern hostelry has a neat garden set amid thick trees. Readers this year have again spoken well of the bedrooms, the welcome, the peace and quiet, and the food – especially the "delightful" breakfasts that include Ardennes ham and home-made jam. "It's immaculate, elegant and comfortably welcoming. Well-furnished bedrooms with 16 TV channels – imagine watching *Popeye* in Italian on a Sunday morning, after a swim and walk in the forest. In the beautiful dining room we had very imaginative, light little courses – cubes of warm goose-liver, turbot lasagne, quail with wild mushrooms. The design of the public rooms is of the slightly heavy Belgian country style." One reader this year found the tall trees that surround the main building a bit oppressive: the annexe, *La Résidence* on a hillside close by, has better views and more feeling of space. (*TH Nash, John W Behle*)

Open All year except 15 Nov–23 Dec.
Rooms 4 suites, 7 double – all with bath and/or shower, telephone, radio and TV; baby-sitting. Suites in garden annexe.
Facilities Lounge/bar, restaurant; conference room; indoor swimming pool and solarium. Garden, terrace.
Location At Mont, 5 km NE of Malmédy on N28 to Eupen. Parking.
Restriction Not suitable for ♿.
Credit cards All major cards accepted.
Terms [1989 rates] B&B: single 2,850–3,100 Bfrs, double 4,100–6,200 Bfrs, suite 7,150–15,000 Bfrs. Set lunch/dinner 1,375–2,100 Bfrs; full alc 1,850 Bfrs.

NEERIJSE 3055 LEUVEN — Map 9

Kasteel van Neerijse
Lindenhoflaan 1

Tel (016) 47.28.50
Fax (016) 47.23.80
Telex 20519 CASTLE

Ten kilometres south-west of the university town of Leuven (Louvain), a red-brick 18th-century mansion newly converted into a four-star hotel, set in a lovely park, with a pond and old mill nearby. Extensive conference and function facilities. Golf, riding, tennis nearby. Pleasant staff, pretty bedrooms. 30 rooms, all with bath. B&B: single 3,000 Bfrs, double 3,500–3,800 Bfrs. Set menus 1,000 Bfrs. New nomination. More reports please.

NOIREFONTAINE 6831 Luxembourg Belge — Map 9

Auberge du Moulin Hideux
Route de Dohan 1

Tel (061) 46.70.15
Fax (061) 46.72.81
Telex 41989 HIDEUX

Along with one or two daring notes of criticism, the eulogies have continued to pour in for this famous and luxurious country hotel in the Ardennes, near the French border. "One of the best small hotels in Europe", "a wonderful experience, as usual", "one of our favourite hotels for the past six years", "to have breakfast on the terrace on a beautiful morning is probably the nearest we'll ever get to heaven" – a selection from this and last year's postbag, mostly from returning regulars. It's a big converted millhouse by a pond, secluded in a wooded valley, and is owned and run by Charles and Martine Lahire who are steeped in the traditions of good hotel-keeping. Not only do they provide very distinguished cooking, and bedrooms with superlative modern comforts, but they and their highly trained staff know exactly how to welcome and cosset their guests, and make them feel like well-remembered friends – "When we wrote to book a return visit after two years", says a reader this year, "the Lahires sent us a note to say that the family of owls that had nested outside our bedroom last time had all survived. After a wet and tiring drive, the warmth of welcome was a delight. We had a newly refurbished bedroom with padded armchairs and *en suite* a huge triangular bath of beige marble. The set menu as usual was superb (better value than the very pricey *carte*): the cooking is both visually pleasing and full of strong positive flavours – feathery mousses, salmon in a light creamy sauce, magret with fresh figs, etc. Breakfast, served in our room, is surely one of the best in Europe." (*Padi and John Howard; Marcia and*

Dominic Chambers, K and SM-S, JF Holman and others). However, the wine mark-ups are steep, and we note that while the *Moulin* keeps its two red *Gault Millau toques, Michelin* has this year downgraded it from two rosettes to one. One new visitor, while finding rooms and dinners superb, regretted that the set menu did not change over three nights. Another found the staff snooty; he was made to feel guilty, he told us, because he did not order champagne as an aperitif.

Open Mid-Mar–mid-Nov. Restaurant closed Wed Mar–July.
Rooms 3 suites, 10 double – all with bath (2 also with shower), telephone, radio and TV.
Facilities Sitting room, loggia, restaurant. Garden with tennis court.
Restriction Not suitable for ♿.
Credit cards All major cards accepted.
Terms B&B: single occupancy 4,800 Bfrs, double 5,200–5,500 Bfrs, suite 7,000 Bfrs. Set meals 1,900–2,200 Bfrs. Special meals for children on request.

DE PANNE 8470 West Flanders — Map 9

Hostellerie Le Fox — *Tel* (058) 41.28.55
Walckierstraat 2

In a popular coastal resort near Ostend, a family-run restaurant-with-rooms, reputed for its fish and good regional dishes (Michelin *rosette*). *Good, well-equipped rooms, recently modernised and extended. Closed October, 15–31 Jan, 1 week May, restaurant closed Tue. 15 rooms, all with bath and/or shower. B&B double 1,500–2,500 Bfrs. Meals alc 1,550–2,100 Bfrs* [1989]. *Some noise from main road. Endorsed this year. More reports welcome.*

RENINGE 8981 West Flanders — Map 9

't Convent — *Tel* (057) 40.07.71
Halve Reningestraat 1 — *Fax* (057) 40.11.27

A short drive inland from either Ostend or Dunkerque, this idiosyncratic hotel "really a medieval barn in a field" has bedrooms ranging in style from Louis XVI to Provençal, some with four-poster beds. "Ours was small but beautiful, with wood panelling and velvet drapes", says a reader this year, "we were welcomed warmly, and food and service were brilliant during one of their 'gastronomic weekends' - seafood, foie gras, salmon mousse, pigeon, presented with style." (*Sandra E Garrick*) Others have written: "We had most unusual rooms, outrageously decorated but great fun. Ours looked on to a pasture with cows whose heavy breathing woke me in the night. The loft bar for drinks is charming, and the meal was a delight, served efficiently by shy young girls." "The meal was superb, especially in its visual appeal: our neighbours photographed each course as it arrived." "Some rooms are fairly small, but others are bigger and retain a convent flavour: canopied painted bed, stone floor, icons and other such medieval trinkets, and a bathroom like a private chapel with the basin in an arched alcove."

Open All year except Feb and last week of Aug. Restaurant closed Tue evening and Wed.

Rooms 7 double – all with bath, telephone. All in annexe 50 metres from restaurant. Some ground-floor rooms.
Facilities Bar, restaurant; conference facilities. Terrace.
Location On edge of village, 15 km NW of Ieper (turn off N65 at Oostvleteren).
Credit cards All major cards accepted.
Terms [1989 rates] Rooms: single 1,500 Bfrs, double 2,000–2,500 Bfrs. Breakfast 250 Bfrs. Alc 1,700–2,180 Bfrs (excluding wine).

RONSE 9681 East Flanders — Map 9

Hostellerie Shamrock
Ommegangstraat 148
Maarkedal, Ronse

Tel (055) 21.55.29
Fax (055) 215683
Telex 86165 SHAMRO

Just to the north-east of Ronse, a textile town between Brussels and Lille, amid rolling wooded country, is this smart and stylish restaurant-with-rooms that seems to be of mixed English and French inspiration (let alone its Irish name). Up a long drive in a well-kept garden, it has the air of a private house in mock-Tudor style, but the large and airy bedrooms are furnished à la Louis XV. It dropped out of the last Guide through lack of news, but visitors in 1989 thought it "one of the very best hotel/restaurants in Belgium" (*Michelin* gives it a rosette, and *Gault Millau* two red *toques*, for its modern French cooking). "A comfortable, welcoming and relaxed atmosphere, with expert and charming service. The rooms have recently been refurbished and are now brighter and lighter, with sumptuous bathrooms. The food we found better than ever." The main staircase with carved wooden balcony descends directly into the elegant dining room, giving residents the opportunity for spectacular entry. (*Pat and Jeremy Temple*) Wine prices have been called "fiendishly" high.

Open All year except 15–31 Jul. Closed Sun evening to Tue midday except public holidays.
Rooms 1 suite, 4 double – all with bath and shower, telephone and TV.
Facilities Salon, bar, restaurant; small conference room. Garden.
Location 5 km NE of Ronse, off N62, near Louise-Marie.
Restriction Not suitable for ♿.
Credit cards All major cards accepted.
Terms [1989 rates] B&B: double 4,200 Bfrs, suite 5,200 Bfrs. Set meals 1,500–2,700 Bfrs; full alc 1,700–2,700 Bfrs.

TILFF-SUR-OURTHE 4040 Liège — Map 9

Hôtel du Casino
3 place du Roi Albert

Tel (041) 88.10.15
Fax (041) 88.33.16

In the winding valley of the Ourthe, just south of the Liège industrial conurbation, a restaurant-with-rooms nominated this year, "A charming, small family-run hotel with reasonable prices. The building, a former brasserie dating from 1622, has been lovingly restored by the owners, the Claes. Our good-sized room was tastefully decorated in French country style, with beamed ceiling, silk-covered walls, and windows overlooking the river. Our only complaint: the usual one of inadequate light for reading. The food was delicious – terrine of rabbit, lobster mousse, breast of wild pigeon. Breakfast, too, was excellent, including cheese and baked apples." (*John and Connie Partridge*)

Open All year except 15 Dec–15 Jan. Restaurant closed Mon.
Rooms 6 double – 5 with bath and shower, all with telephone.
Facilities Salon, bar, 2 restaurants.
Location 11 km S of Liège.
Restrictions Not suitable for ♿.
Credit cards None accepted.
Terms [1989 rates] B&B: single 1,400 Bfrs, double 1,900 Bfrs. Set lunch/dinner 1,750 Bfrs; full alc 2,000–2,500 Bfrs. Reduced rates for children; special meals on request.

Traveller's tale *On the night in my arrival in Sydney from Hong Kong, after 20 hours without sleep, I asked the telephone operator not to put through calls – and looked for a Do Not Disturb notice to hang outside my door. There was none. So I rang room service, asked them to be good enough to hang Do Not Disturb on 3404 – and went to sleep. Not long afterwards there was a knock on my door, then another, then more. I staggered out of the bed in which I had slept for barely 50 minutes to find a man wanting to know whether this was the right room for the Do Not Disturb sign.*
Sir Clement Freud (letter in The Times, 27.2.89)

Denmark

STEENSGAARD HERREGÅRDSPENSION, MILLINGE

COPENHAGEN — Map 7

Hotel d'Angleterre
Kongens Nytorv 34, Copenhagen 1050

Tel 33.12.00.95
Fax 33.12.11.18
Telex 15877

"Recommending the *Hotel d'Angleterre* is a bit like urging travellers to discover the *Connaught* in Britain" a reader once wrote. It is the epitome of a grand hotel, and also something of a national institution, having first opened its doors in 1755. It is close to the harbour, the royal palace and the state theatre, and is at one end of the famous street, Strøget. It has a fine restaurant (speciality: canard à la presse), and a brasserie with the longest bar in Copenhagen. A reader this year, re-nominating the *d'Angleterre* (which was in earlier editions) writes, "To book in at 'the white lady of Copenhagen' you sit at an individual desk and are welcomed with that discreet but warm courtesy that is the hallmark of the service here. Imagine a room that has been furnished with a mixture of first class repro and genuine antiques, a large bathroom where all the fittings are luxurious antique reproductions (allied with a telephone) and you have the ultimate in comfort and efficiency. Scandinavian breakfast (do they eat the rest of the day?) arrived on a trolley delivered by a cross between Ursula Andress and Marilyn Monroe, who apologised for waking me up! The brasserie claims 'reasonable prices' but you won't get out for under £20 a head, and more with wine, though the food is good. The prices in the restaurant are astronomical – but compared with London, it is a bargain." (*Braham Murray*)

Open All year.
Rooms 28 suites, 81 double, 21 single – 127 with bath and shower, 3 with shower, all with telephone, radio, TV.
Facilities Lifts. Lobby, bar, 2 restaurants.
Location Central, opposite the Royal Theatre.
Credit cards Probably all major cards accepted.
Terms Room: single 1,600–1,800 Dkr, double 1,800–2,000 Dkr, suite 2,600–10,000 Dkr. Breakfast 90 Dkr.

Hotel Ascot — *Tel* 33.12.60.00
57 Studiestræde — *Fax* 33.14.60.40
Copenhagen 1554 — *Telex* 15730

On quiet pleasant street close to Tivoli, the air terminal, railway station, and Strøget, Copenhagen's famous pedestrian area. 18th-century facade, old-fashioned beautiful red-carpeted winding stairway; contemporary colour schemes in bedrooms, some of which are small, others of which are in suites with kitchenette, terrace, sitting room. Attractive breakfast room, no restaurant. 10 suites, 55 double, 35 single, all with bath or shower. B&B: single 520–690 Dkr, double 690–1090 Dkr. In Guide previously, dropped when house-keeping standards were criticised, re-nominated after recent renovation. More reports please.

---

71 Nyhavn Hotel — *Tel* 33.11.85.85
Nyhavn 71, Copenhagen 1051 — *Fax* 33.93.15.85
Telex 27558 NYHHOT

Hans Christian Andersen lived next door to this converted early 19th-century warehouse on the *Nyhavn* (New Harbour) in the heart of the old city. Readers have enjoyed especially the "lively bustle" (though no traffic noise) and the adjacent canal with its mixture of restaurants and bars. The building was restored about 20 years ago as a smart hotel, with the sea motif much in evidence. Its *Pakhuskælderen* restaurant has an excellent reputation, with its smörgåsbord specially recommended. The cheapest bedrooms are very small (thick walls and low beams have obviously imposed restraints on room space); the dearer ones have a view over the canal. Staff are helpful and welcoming. A visitor this year writes, "A charming conversion with comfortable rooms, friendly service and a good breakfast. My only caveat would be that the double room I occupied at the maximum single person rate was on the small side for *two*, though nice for one. Otherwise highly recommended." (*Anthony Land*)

Open All year. Restaurant closed 24–26 Dec.
Rooms 6 suites, 39 double, 37 single – all with bath and/or shower, telephone, radio and TV; baby-listening on request.
Facilities Lift. Lounge, bar, restaurant; 2 conference/function rooms.

Location In town centre, near Royal Opera and Royal Castle, facing Nyhavn Canal and harbour. Parking for 8 cars.
Restriction Not suitable for ♿.
Credit cards Probably all major cards accepted.
Terms B&B: single 825–1,125 Dkr, double 1,075–1,375 Dkr, suite 1,850–2,250 Dkr. Set lunch 170 Dkr, dinner 300 Dkr. Reduced rates 18 June–13 Aug; weekend reductions 1 Oct–30 Apr. Children under 12 sharing parents' room free; special meals on request.

Hotel Vestersøhus *Tel* 01.11.38.70
Vestersøgade 58 *Telex* 15708
Copenhagen 1601

"First-rate; this is one of our favourite hotels, with modest but well-furnished rooms and extremely pleasant staff." "I had a spacious sixth-floor room with lobby, large bedroom overlooking the canal, and kitchen/dining area with balcony overlooking the other side – well equipped and clean. Good to be able to cook where dinner can be very expensive." The centre of the old town is within ten minutes' walk, and the nearest train station, with frequent trains to the suburbs and about half of Zeeland, is even closer. Breakfasts are praised (buffet style) and joggers will like the nearby paths along the Skt Jørgens Lake. The Vestersøgade has fast traffic during the day; not a problem with double-glazing in the winter, but rooms at the rear probably quieter during the summer (though they lack the view). (*Robert W Phillips, Mary E Hanson*) A room on the sixth floor is said to have low water pressure and irregular hot water.

Open All year.
Rooms 15 apartments, 37 double, 7 single – all with bath or shower, telephone; some with radio and TV; baby-sitting service.
Facilities Lift. Salon, breakfast room; roof garden.
Location 10 mins' walk from centre, on W edge of old town. Parking.
Credit cards All major cards accepted.
Terms [1989 rates] B&B single 750–850 Dkr, double 850–975 Dkr. (No restaurant.)

FALSLED 5642 Funen — Map 7

Falsled Kro *Tel* 62.68.11.11
Telex 50404

Jean-Louis Lieffroy is a great French chef working in Denmark at a charming inn on the south-west coast of the central island of Funen. Readers of the Guide have been enjoying his restaurant and hotel for many years. "Utterly charming," begins a report this year, "the last word in luxury and our meal was superb (which it should have been, at the price)." Meals are taken seriously here: "langoustines in a cream sauce, monkfish au beurre blanc, moist breast of guinea-fowl". Breakfasts have been praised as well: "crème fraîche with honey, freshly squeezed orange juice, quails' eggs served on bacon and endless excellent coffee!" During the 15th century the hotel was a smugglers' inn; it is now a cluster of old thatched buildings round a small cobbled courtyard with a fountain. The "enchanting" bedrooms – some with Spanish floor tiles, and some with four-poster beds – are in outbuildings and cottages across the road. The garden runs down to the sea and the yacht harbour. Expensive, yes, but recommended nonetheless, "given the beauty of the hotel". Criticisms have been few: a small uncurtained window in a bedroom; a smell of stagnant water, possibly from the marina during one visit. More reports please.

Open All year except Jan, Feb, Christmas and New Year. Restaurant closed Mon in low season.
Rooms 3 suites, 9 double, 2 single – 12 with bath, 2 with shower, all with telephone and TV. Suites, with lounge and mini-bar are in *Ryttergården* farmhouse opposite the hotel. Some ground-floor rooms.
Facilities Lounge, salon with TV, bar, café, restaurant. Garden. Sea 100 metres.
Location 10 km NW of Millinge; S of Odense on Fåborg–Assens road.
Restriction Not suitable for ♿.
Credit cards All major cards accepted.
Terms [1989 rates] Rooms: single 630 Dkr, double 1,100 Dkr, suite 1,650 Dkr. Breakfast 105 Dkr. Set lunch 210 Dkr, dinner 250–630 Dkr. Special meals for children on request.

MILLINGE 5642 Funen — Map 7

Steensgaard Herregårdspension — *Tel* 62.61.94.90
Steensgård 4 — *Fax* 62.61.78.61
Millinge, Fåborg

"Would appeal to those in search of the genuine country house atmosphere rather than a grand country house hotel", begins a report this year on the beautiful half-timbered 14th-century manor house on the middle island of Funen (Fyn), north-west of Fåborg. Many people consider the countryside here to be the prettiest in Denmark – an area of hills and fields dotted with long low farmhouses. The hotel is situated in one of three buildings round a cobbled courtyard; on one side is a working farm, on the other a tennis court and an enclosure with deer and wild boar. The rooms are furnished with many antiques – Louis XIV, Italian rococo and English.. There are several spacious lounges, a library lined with leather-bound volumes, and a grand hall decorated with hunting trophies. "A very beautiful place. The feeling of space and privacy abundant. We thought the food was good – wholesome and not too rich. It was nice for a change to have food simply presented." Dinner (three courses) is served in the candle-lit dining room promptly at 7 o'clock. (*JD Monteith; BJ Walter*) *Warning*: the stable clock chimes every half-hour throughout the night – "the wrong number of rings too!"

Open All year except Feb.
Rooms 3 suites, 10 double, 2 single – 13 with bath and/or shower, all with telephone and mini-bar. Some in annexe.
Facilities Hall, 5 salons, library, dining room; billiards, piano, chess. Large park with deer and wild boar; lake (fishing), tennis and riding. Rocky beach 2 km.
Location NW of Millinge, between Assens and Fåborg on the Middlefart road.
Restriction Not suitable for ♿.
Credit cards All major cards accepted.
Terms [1989 rates] Rooms: single 310–520 Dkr, double 510–950 Dkr. Breakfast 60 Dkr. Set lunch 135 Dkr, dinner 240 Dkr. Reduced rates for 3 or more nights; reduced rates for children.

> We asked hotels to estimate their 1990 tariffs some time before publication so the rates given are often arbitrary. Please always check terms with hotels when making bookings.

NYBORG 5800 Funen **Map 7**

Hotel Hesselet
Christianslundsvej 119

Tel 65.31.30.29
Fax 65.31.29.58
Telex 9297122

Low-built modern hotel thirty kilometres from Odense, with views of the sea to the east. "The architect has been strongly influenced by Japanese tradition, and it looked somewhat forbidding from outside. Inside, however, everything was lovely – helpful staff, good food, beautiful swimming pool, free bicycle hire – in fact everything 'laid on'." International/French cuisine. Hotel does substantial conference business. Closed 2 weeks Christmas/New Year. 46 rooms, all with bath and shower. Dinner, B&B 800–1,130 Dkr. New nomination. More reports please.

RIBE 6760 Jutland **Map 7**

Hotel Dagmar
Torvet 1

Tel 75.42.00.33
Fax 75.42.36.52

Ribe, with its 800-year old cathedral, nesting storks and narrow cobbled streets, is an old town of great charm lying on the flat windy west coast of Jutland. The *Dagmar*, a hotel of great character, built in 1581, looks across the main square to the cathedral. The ground floor rooms are hung with splendid paintings, and filled with antique and repro furniture. Front bedrooms have tiny windows overlooking the church. Several readers have had rooms without a view, but have not minded: most have lovely paintings and are quiet. A visitor this year praised the "attentive staff" and "elegant food: we chose to eat in the more casual cellar restaurant and were surprised by the quality and quantity. Breakfast was 'serve yourself' and there was no way that you could go away hungry." Other readers have enjoyed the candle-lit restaurant and, in summer, the arrival of the night watchman "dressed in black, carrying a lantern and singing his watchman's song". Guests are invited to join him on his traditional nightly rounds. Mr. Petersen, the former owner, has sold the hotel this year but remains as manager. "No changes", we are assured. (*K and J Beal, and others*)

Open All year, except Christmas and New Year.
Rooms 50 double – all with bath and/or shower, telephone, radio, TV, and mini-bar.
Facilities Lounge, bar, 3 restaurants; conference facilities; music and dancing on Fri and Sat in July. Fishing 3 km.
Location Central; Ribe is 34 km SE of Esbjerg.
Restriction Not suitable for ♿.
Credit cards All major credit cards accepted.
Terms [1989 rates] B&B: single 450–550 Dkr, double 650–750 Dkr. Set menu 95 Dkr, full alc dinner 300 Dkr. Reduced rates and special meals for children.

Hotel Restaurant Weis Stue
Torvet

Tel 75.42.07.00

A tiny inn, also in the medieval town centre, and exuberantly nominated last year as a much cheaper alternative to the *Dagmar*: "Denmark is the best-kept holiday secret of Europe, Ribe of Denmark, and the *Weis Stue* of Ribe – the sort of place to enthral many Guide readers. As the *Blue Guide* states, it is perhaps the finest of Ribe's old buildings, and its early 18th-century interior contains some notable furniture. Our room, the Panel Room, is the showpiece, its two longer walls covered in magnificent medieval panelling; the windows, with tiny ancient panes, looked out onto the cathedral. The twin beds were comfortable. We managed to get into this room by bending low and almost crawling, with our heads bowed beneath innumerable beams (if you were Falstaff, they would hoist you in through the window). There is no lounge, but three dining rooms each stuffed with antiques, plus a courtyard and banqueting hall. The food was superb, our best meal in Denmark, though breakfast was modest by Danish standards. Service was efficient, but a little impersonal." (*Rev. Michael Bourdeaux*) The manager tells us that personal service can now be guaranteed, as the owners themselves take part in the serving of guests.

Open All year except 24/25 Dec.
Rooms 4 double, 1 single.
Facilities Restaurant, banqueting hall; small courtyard. 200 metres from river.
Location Central, in old town.
Restriction Not suitable for ♿.
Credit cards None accepted.
Terms Rooms: single 150 Dkr, double 300 Dkr. Full alc 180–200 Dkr. Extra bed for child 75 Dkr; special meals.

SØNDERHO 6720 Fanø — Map 7

Sønderho Kro — *Tel* 75.16.40.09
Kropladsen 11

"Certainly the most exciting thing on the island of Fanø, which is really only a long sand dune", writes a reader this year. The inn is at one end, in the picturesque old fishing village of Sønderho; it is one of the oldest inns in Denmark, dating from 1772. It has been owned by the same family for three generations (Olga and Erik Jensen until recently, now their daughter and son-in-law Birgit and Niels Steen Sørensen). Modern comforts have not been overlooked – there is a new extension where the bedrooms are large and very comfortable. The entrance hall has an open fireplace with a roaring fire in cold weather; antiques and modern paintings abound. "My husband was most taken with the waitresses, all blond bombshells, very helpful and friendly, and spoke good English. The food was delicious and the service fast and efficient. The puddings were decorated imaginatively with all manner of exotic fruits, most of which I couldn't name. Breakfasts, too, were superb, with an excellent selection of home-made jam." The innkeepers have written to us this year to say: "Our cooking is 100% *ecological* (without poison). It is Danish, natural, with French influence, and local produce if possible." (*JD Monteith*)

Open All year except 8 Jan–10 Feb. Possibly closed Christmas.
Rooms 7 double – all with bath and/or shower. 5 ground-floor rooms.
Facilities Hall, salons, restaurant. Garden. By sea with sandy beach and safe bathing; golf and tennis nearby.
Location 20 mins by ferry from Esbjerg. In SE part of Sønderho, on left by church.
Credit cards Access, Diners, Visa.
Terms B&B: single 450–570 Dkr, double 610–850 Dkr. Set lunch 125 Dkr, dinner 270 Dkr, full alc 338 Dkr. Half- or full-board only certain times of year. Reduced rates for children; special meals.

France

HÔTEL-RESTAURANT
GEORGES BLANC, VONNAS

AIRE-SUR-LA-LYS 62120 Pas-de-Calais **Map 9**

Hostellerie des Trois Mousquetaires *Tel* 21.39.01.11
Château du Fort de la Redoute *Fax* 21.39.50.10

The Venet family run a very popular *hostellerie* where you need to book. It's a small late 19th-century château in a garden beside a pond, 40 miles from Calais and with easy access to the motorway. And therefore it gets *very* full of the British – to the detriment of its French ambience, some readers feel. This, and the often slow service, have been the main criticisms this year, but otherwise there's been little but praise, especially for the rooms in the new wing. "Very charming atmosphere, the family are most welcoming", say returning regulars in 1989; "breakfast was good, the large lounge bar is attractively furnished, and the new wing has been built with great taste" (one of the rooms is "furnished in the Japanese style with maize-coloured grass wallpaper and antiques"). Another new report, "Service before dinner was a bit chaotic, but we then enjoyed our truite aux baies sauvages, jugged pork and the farandole of desserts". A reader who stayed on till lunch the next day found that all his fellow-countrymen had gone – "We were now surrounded by French families enjoying a relaxed Sunday lunch. It was one of the best meals we've ever had in France, complemented by charming waitresses." (*NA and JM Rhodes, Philippa Herbert, Kay and Neville Varley*)

Open 20 Jan–20 Dec. Closed Sun evening, and Mon.
Rooms 1 suite, 26 double – all with bath and/or shower and telephone; 24 with TV. 3 in pavilion in park.
Facilities 2 salons, bar, TV room, garden room in summer, 2 restaurants. 1-acre grounds.
Location On N43 between St-Omer and Lillers, 2 km from centre of Aire on Arras side. Private parking.
Restriction Not suitable for ♿.
Credit cards All major cards accepted.
Terms [1989 rates] Rooms 200–400 frs. Breakfast 35 frs. Set lunch/dinner 79, 122, 184 and 264 frs; full alc 280 frs. Reduced rates and special meals for children.

AIX-EN-PROVENCE 13100 Bouches-du-Rhône — Map 11

Hôtel "Le Mozart" — *Tel* 42.21.62.86
49 cours Gambetta

A modern and cleverly designed hotel, inexpensive, spacious and quiet, on a boulevard less than a kilometre from the city centre. Comfortable bedrooms – most have a balcony with views; dull breakfast room. Garage. 48 rooms, all with bath and/or shower. B&B double 264–284 frs. No restaurant, but lots nearby. Recent nomination. More reports welcome.

AJACCIO 20000 Corsica — Map 11

Eden Roc — *Tel* 95.52.01.47
Route des Sanguinaires — *Telex* 460486

This fairly smart family-run hotel above the sea, beside the coast road west of Ajaccio, has been much admired again this year: "A delightful choice for our two weeks' holiday. The hotel is set into the hillside, and from our balcony (all rooms face seaward) there's a magnificent view of the varying shades of blue of the bay. Meals (food was excellent) are taken on a beautiful terrace above a lovely garden in which is a swimming pool. Staff were all most courteous and helpful, the ambience is totally relaxed, and breakfast included marvellous coffee. Rooms are air-conditioned. Just across the quiet road is a small sandy rock-girt cove from which one can swim in the clear, clean blue water." (*Diane and Keith Moss*) A fitness centre has just been completed.

Open May–Sept.
Rooms 40 – most with bath and/or shower, telephone and TV; many with balcony.
Facilities Lift. Lounge, restaurant, terrace. Garden with swimming pool.
Location 8 km W of Ajaccio. Parking.
Credit cards All major cards accepted.
Terms [1989 rates] Rooms 720–920 frs. Breakfast 60 frs. Half board 620–750 frs per person. Set meals 200–480 frs. Special meals for children.

ALBERTVILLE 73200 Savoie — Map 10

Hôtel Million — *Tel* 79.32.25.15
8 place de la Liberté — *Telex* 306022 HOTMILLION

This dullish sub-alpine town will be hosting the 1992 Winter Olympics. Just off its main street is this sophisticated hostelry, where Philippe Million's "original cooking in the modern style" (e.g. lake fish with snails) is rated among the finest in Savoy (two *Michelin* rosettes, two red *Gault Millau toques*). Our latest reports consider the bedrooms adequate if unexciting, the waiters friendly, and the fixed price meals "magnificent and extremely good value". An earlier view, "Traditional atmosphere with modern comforts. Rooms not very large but pleasantly decorated: most are in a modern extension behind the building. There is a comfortable lounge and bar. Plentiful breakfasts, and a good wine list with delicious local Savoy wines at low prices." The savoury pastries, sweets and chocolates are especially praised. In summer you can dine in elegance on a flowery terrace facing the small and pretty garden. Around the hotel, alas, are new apartment blocks, obscuring the outlook. But 20 minutes' walk up the hill is the medieval walled hill-village of Conflans, where the views are superb." (*Dave Watts*)

Open All year except 24 Apr–8 May, 18 Sept–2 Oct. Restaurant closed Sun evening and Mon.
Rooms 26 double, 2 single – 27 with bath and/or shower, all with telephone and 26 with TV.
Facilities Lift. 3 lounges, bar, breakfast room, dining room. Small garden, terrace for dining.
Location Central. Parking. Albertville is 45 km SE of Annecy.
Credit cards All major cards accepted.
Terms Rooms: single 200–350 frs, double 280–550 frs. Breakfast 50 frs. Set lunch/dinner 150, 250 and 450 frs. Special meals for children.

ALBI 81000 Tarn — Map 10

Hostellerie Saint-Antoine — *Tel* 63.54.04.04
17 rue St-Antoine — *Telex* 520850

A former monastery in the town centre where the Rieux family have run an inn since 1734. An inspector this year "liked the feel of the place" and enjoyed the food. Other recent views: "Not long ago the fine 18th-century building was pulled down and a characterless new one put up. But much old furniture remains, and spaciousness; also a garden at the back with big trees; and total silence, despite its being a stone's throw from the centre. Good food indeed." "A little impersonal, but it provides elegance and comfort. In the pleasant dining room, food expensive but adequate" (*Gault Millau* red *toque* however for its "modern regional cooking"). Bedrooms have been found "charmingly pretty". It is advisable to ask for garden-facing rooms.

Open All year. Restaurant closed Sun Nov–Mar.
Rooms 6 suites, 34 double, 10 single – all with bath and shower, telephone, TV and tea-making facilities. 4 in annexe.
Facilities Lift. 3 lounges, bar with TV, restaurant. Garden. Guests have access to swimming pool and tennis court at *La Réserve* (under same management) 3 km away.
Location Central. Parking.
Credit cards All major cards accepted.

Terms B&B: single 350–500 frs, double 490–750 frs, suite 850–950 frs. Set lunch/dinner 140–200 frs; full alc 220 frs. Reduced rates and special meals for children.

St-Clair *Tel* 63.54.25.66
Rue St-Clair *Telex* 521605

In the pedestrian quarter of the old town, near the cathedral, here is a cheaper but still comfortable alternative to our other Albi entry. Most rooms face a courtyard and are quiet. No bar or lounge, but adequate breakfasts, including some fresh fruit. Open Easter–Oct. 12 rooms, all with bath and shower. B&B double 240–290 frs. No restaurant, lots nearby.

LES ANDELYS 27700 Eure — Map 9

Hôtel de la Chaine d'Or *Tel* 32.54.00.31
27 rue Grande

This 18th-century *auberge* had an entry in earlier editions, now, after a change of ownership it is welcomed back. It enjoys a spectacular position on a loop of the Seine above Rouen; most of the bedrooms, the dining room and the breakfast room overlook the shimmering river and the island opposite. At night it is quiet save for passing barges but they don't operate very late. Bedrooms are large; most are freshly decorated and well furnished; bathrooms are not their strongest point and an inspector reports a dowdy and poorly lit back room and a casual reception "but dinner was a very different matter: a beautiful beamed dining room, tables well spaced with fresh flowers and candle, exemplary service, not slow, not rushed, not standoffish, not fulsome, and the 200 franc menu [1989], with exciting new tastes, could not be faulted." The old part of Les Andelys is a pictureque village, dominated by the ruins of Richard Coeur de Lion's Château Gaillard; it is only 15 minutes by car from Giverny, with Monet's lovely garden. (*Gillian Seel, PA Catling, and others*)

Open 2 Feb–31 Dec. Closed Sun evening and Mon.
Rooms 11 double, 1 single – 5 with bath, 2 with shower, all with telephone.
Facilities Dining room, breakfast room, functions room. Courtyard.
Location In Petit Andelys, on the river. Parking. (Village is 39 km SE of Rouen).
Restriction Not suitable for ♿.
Credit card Visa.
Terms [1989 rates] Rooms: single 240 frs, double 390 frs. Breakfast 45 frs. Set meals 130, 200 and 320 frs.

ANTIBES 06600 Alpes-Maritimes — Map 11

Mas Djoliba *Tel* 93.34.02.48
29 avenue de Provence *Telex* 461686

In a quiet street in the southern suburbs, near the beach, a villa hotel in a lovely garden, with a little of the air of a private house, but not smart. Simple, pretty bedrooms. Meals served in a vine-arbour when fine. Swimming pool. 15 rooms, 14 with bath and/or shower. Dinner, B&B double 510–630 frs. New owners this year, "friendly and charming". More reports welcome.

ARDRES 62610 Pas-de-Calais — Map 9

Grand Hôtel Clément — *Tel* 21.82.25.25
91 esplanade du Maréchal Leclerc — *Telex* 130886 RES CLEMENT

On the edge of a small town near Calais, a family-run hotel much frequented by the British. Garden with swings, log fire in bar in winter. Beautiful well-known restaurant, with nouvelle-*ish cooking* (Gault Millau *red* toque) *done by the son of the house, François Coolen. Some bedrooms are attractive, but many others tend to be sub-standard: small, dingy, fusty, unkempt. Closed 15 Jan–15 Feb and Mon. 17 rooms, 16 with bath and/or shower. B&B double 244–344 frs. Set meals 100–300 frs. Continued 1988/9 criticism of bedrooms, but restaurant again admired by readers. Back rooms are quietest.*

ARLES 13200 Bouches-du-Rhône — Map 11

Hôtel d'Arlatan — *Tel* 90.93.56.66
26 rue du Sauvage — *Telex* 441203 ARLATAN

Located down a quiet street in the heart of old Arles, this lovely 15th-century building (with later additions) was the ancestral home of the Counts of Arlatan, and its pleasant little garden is enclosed on one side by the high wall of the palace of Constantine. "The best place to stay in Arles", says one recent visitor. "It has a Proustian discretion to it, as rooms open out of each other into shady courtyards." "You enter through a fine courtyard with palm trees and an interesting stone fountain. The public areas and bedrooms carry out the theme of old Provence, with antiques, colourful print fabrics and art objects." This ever-popular hotel is owned by the "warm and helpful" M. Desjardin, "quite a character", and run by his family. Its vaunted charms may have pitched expectations too high, for again in 1988/9 reports have varied. Most readers have stressed the friendly staff, good breakfasts and pleasant rooms, but one thought breakfast too basic and the staff impersonal, while some others have found their rooms a little too small and basic. (*PJ Borrett, Shelley B Andrews, JA*) No restaurant, but try the *Vaccarès* or excellent *L'Olivier*, both upper-medium-priced.

Open All year.
Rooms 7 suites, 32 double, 5 single – all with bath and/or shower and telephone; 36 with mini-bar, suites with TV.
Facilities Lift. Bar, reading room, salons; conference room. Garden with patio for outdoor refreshments.
Location Central, near place du Forum, but quiet (rooms overlook garden and patio). Garage parking (with a charge).
Restriction Not suitable for ♿.
Credit cards All major cards accepted.
Terms Rooms: single 298–385 frs, double 385–598 frs, suite 850 frs. Breakfast 40 frs. (No restaurant.)

Hôtel Le Calendal — *Tel* 90.96.11.89
22 place Pomme

Mistral's epic poem about fishermen has given its name to this modest but pleasant little B&B hotel near the Roman theatre and arena. Rooms simply but well furnished; lovely shady garden where drinks and breakfast are served. Closed 15 Nov–31 Jan. 27 rooms, all with bath and shower. Rooms 150–270 frs. Breakfast 26 frs. Hostellerie des Arènes *and* Le Grillon *are good inexpensive restaurants nearby. Recent nomination endorsed this year. More reports please.*

ARNAY-LE-DUC 21230 Côte-d'Or — Map 10

Chez Camille — *Tel* 80.90.01.38
1 place Edouard-Herriot

Fondue of snails with Brussels sprouts, and cream of frogs' legs with Japanese pearls (but these dishes do sound more convincing in French) are just two of the delights that have won owner-chef Armand Poinsot a *Michelin* rosette and two *Gault Millau toques*. His converted 16th-century posthouse in a small Burgundy town, now a *soigné* little hotel, was commended again in 1989 for its comfortable rooms, good food and charming Madame, thus endorsing last year's report, "Our room was furnished with antiques and it was rather like staying in a friend's house. The restaurant is pretty, in a glassed courtyard, where one has full view of the kitchen – almost a distraction from the food, which was excellent light Burgundian. Madame presides over a fleet of well-trained young waitresses." Outdoor summer dining under parasols or by torchlight. Vegetarians well catered for. (*Tony and Harriet Jones, Stanley Burnton*)

Open All year except Christmas Eve.
Rooms 3 suites, 11 double – all with bath, telephone, TV and baby-listening. 3 doubles in house 6 km away.
Facilities 2 lounges, dining-room; sauna.
Location Central. Town is on N6, 28 km SE of Saulieu.
Restriction Not suitable for ♿.
Credit cards All major cards accepted.
Terms [1989 rates] Rooms: double 385 frs, suite 550–750 frs. Breakfast 45 frs. Dinner, B&B 470 frs per person. Set lunch/dinner 160 frs. Special meals for children.

ARPAILLARGUES 30700 Gard — Map 11

Hôtel d'Agoult, Château d'Arpaillargues — *Tel* 66.22.14.48, *Telex* 490415
Arpaillargues, Uzès

Three miles west of fascinating Uzès (q.v.), on the edge of the village of Arpaillargues, stands this 18th-century château, formerly the home of the d'Agoult family (Marie d'Agoult was a mistress of Liszt). It is now a stylish country hotel, beautifully modernised and maintained, with a library, park, and views over the rolling hills. "Luxurious and restful", runs a report this year; "the pool and tennis facilities were excellent, the dining in the garden delightful and the service friendly." Another visitor enjoyed breakfast in the privacy of his balcony, and the lunchtime restaurant by the pool, but thought the cooking "too adventurous for the chef's abilities" (the French guides do not rave either). "A finely furnished room, more like a suite, and a perfect dinner that included terrine de rascasse and magret de canard." (*Anna Steiger, Dave Watts, Denis Tate*)

Open 15 Mar–2 Nov. Restaurant closed Wed in low season.
Rooms 25 – all with bath or shower and telephone.
Facilities Salon, library, restaurant; conference facilities; courtyard. Large grounds with tennis courts and swimming pool.
Location 4.5 km W of Uzès.
Credit cards All major cards accepted.
Terms [1989 rates] Rooms 420–690 frs. Breakfast 45 frs. Half board 415–680 frs per person. Set lunch/dinner 185 frs. Special meals for children.

ARRAS 62000 Pas-de-Calais — Map 9

Hôtel Univers — *Tel* 21.71.34.01

3 place Croix-Rouge

A finely restored 18th-century monastery, down a cobbled road off a main shopping-street. All rooms, newly refurbished (some have four-posters), look onto the central cloister. Walls are thin, but food and service are excellent. 36 rooms, all with bath or shower, 285–335 frs. Breakfast 32 frs. Set menus 88–205 frs [1989]. Re-nominated. More reports please.

AUVILLERS-LES-FORGES 08260 Ardennes — Map 9

Hostellerie Lenoir — *Tel 24.54.30.11*

Jean Lenoir's comfortable restaurant-with-rooms, in a village near the Belgian frontier, is reputed to be one of the best in the Ardennes, but expensive (*Michelin* rosette, two *Gault Millau toques*, for such dishes as mousse of pigeon with foie gras). It used to be a modest café run by M. Lenoir's parents, in the pre-war days when he was born in a room above the bar. Now it has some pretensions – as our nominator reports, "Each course is accompanied by a different bunch of flowers, varying with the colour of your car: ours was a red Mercedes, so we were welcomed by red roses, served on a silver tray. It's a charming little hotel, with attentive service, nice decor, and a fountain next door. The elegant and cosy dining room is lined with diplomas" (M. Lenoir is a member of the Order of the Dynasty of Hong Kong, *inter multa alia*). Another visitor this year found it "quiet and exquisitely furnished", and the food "expensive but very good". (*Dr Christine Herxheimer and Gabriele Berneck, EM Jacob*)

Open 1 Mar–1 Jan. Closed 24 Dec evening, and Fri except public holidays.
Rooms 21 – 12 with bath, 6 with shower, all with telephone, 18 with radio, 3 with TV; baby-listening on request. All rooms in building across terrace from restaurant; some on ground-floor.
Facilities Lift. 2 Lounges, bar, 2 dining rooms; functions room. Terrace, garden.
Location 14 km SW of Rocroi, on D 877 to Laon.
Credit cards All major cards accepted.
Terms [1989 rates] B&B: single 173 frs, double 201–325 frs, suite 421 frs; dinner, B&B 265–400 frs per person. Set lunch/dinner 150–390 frs. Reduced rates and special meals for children on request.

> In all continental European and Scandinavian countries except Denmark, France, Hungary, Malta, Spain and Turkey, the dialling codes begin with a 0. Omit this when dialling from outside the country in question. Spanish codes begin with a 9, which should also be omitted.

AUXERRE 89000 Yonne — Map 10

Le Parc des Maréchaux — *Tel* 86.51.43.77
6 avenue Foch — *Telex* 800997

"An attractive little place, staffed by people who seem to enjoy working in a hotel", runs a 1989 report on what an inspector has called "this idiosyncratic little bed-and-breakfast hotel", in a quiet street of a dignified cathedral city. "It is run in an appealing and very personal way by its *patronne*, Espérance Hervé, a doctor's wife. The genteel 1856 mansion is set in its own big garden amid lovely and unusual trees. This was formerly known as the Parc des Maréchaux, so the comfortable bedrooms are now all named after French marshals such as Lyautey (but not Pétain). The American bar, all plush red velvet, is called L'Araucaria, after the 100-year-old Chilean monkey-puzzle tree in the garden. These may be gimmicks, but there is nothing forced about the private house atmosphere, especially in the comfortable sitting room where under chandeliers I took a pleasant breakfast to the strains of Chopin. Breakfasts and drinks are served on the lawn in summer." Visitors in 1989, arriving late, were offered a cold supper in their room – pretty good, for a B&B hotel. (*MR Freeman*)

Open All year.
Rooms 4 triple, 20 double, 1 single – all with bath and shower, telephone, TV and baby-listening. 3 ground-floor rooms.
Facilities Lift, ramps. Lounge, bar, breakfast room, tea room; conference room. Garden.
Location 500 metres W of town centre. Private parking.
Credit cards Access, Amex, Visa.
Terms B&B: single 234–239 frs, double 319–364 frs, suite 379–404 frs. No charge for children under 7. (No restaurant.)

Hôtel de Seignelay — *Tel* 86.52.03.48
2 rue du Pont

Suitable for a stop-over, this modest hotel in the town centre consists of a group of old buildings around a tiled patio where drinks and meals can be taken. The restored half-timbered facade adds a picturesque touch. A reader this year had a comfortable modernised room, and enjoyed "large helpings of solid Burgundian food", cheerfully served. (*Jill Thomas*) Front rooms facing a narrow street can be noisy; courtyard rooms are quieter.

Open All year except 4 weeks Jan/Feb. Closed Mon Nov–July.
Rooms 16 double, 5 single – 5 with bath, all with telephone, 14 with TV.
Facilities Lounge with TV, 2 dining rooms. Patio.
Location Central. Garage nearby.
Credit cards Access, Visa.
Terms [1989 rates] Dinner, B&B 191–218.50 frs. Full alc 150 frs.

AVALLON 89200 Yonne — Map 10

Les Capucins — *Tel* 86.34.06.52
6 avenue Paul-Doumer

Little Avallon, a charming and typical old Burgundy town, has far more than its share of good hotels. This recent recruit to our own short-list is a villa in a tree-

lined boulevard, with a friendly staff, and a pleasant garden at the back. Bedrooms newly modernised, but the beamed dining room is rustic style: good food, nouvelle-*ish but with generous portions (menu changes little, so short stay might be best). Closed Wed; Tue evening in low season, 15–20 Oct, 15 Dec–20 Jan. 8 rooms, 7 with bath and shower. Rooms 250 frs. Set menus 110–270 frs* [1989]. *New nomination. More reports welcome.*

Le Relais Fleuri — *Tel* 86.34.02.85
Route de Saulieu — *Telex* 800084

A modern motel-type place on the Saulieu road, providing a useful alternative to our more "picturesque" entries for this much-visited and much-hotelled town. "A cut above other main-road stop-over hotels. Originally an old *auberge*, it has recently been extended. Our large well-equipped room faced fields and was very quiet. The hotel has comfortable seating areas, a bar and a smoke-soaked card room. The large and attractive new restaurant is nicely lit and has a welcoming feel: friendly multilingual waiter, an open fire in October, and a good, reasonably priced meal. Open-air solar-heated swimming pool with pleasant poolside bar." OK, but nothing special, says a reader this year.

Open All year except 24 and 31 Dec.
Rooms 48 double – 45 with bath and shower, 3 with shower, all with telephone, radio and TV. All on ground-floor, 2 specially equipped for ♿.
Facilities 2 lounges, bar, restaurant; 3 conference rooms. Garden with heated swimming pool; 2 tennis courts.
Location 4 km E of Avallon on N6 to Saulieu.
Credit cards All major cards accepted.
Terms Rooms: single 280–310 frs, double 310–380 frs. Breakfast 35 frs. Set lunch/dinner 100–175 frs; full alc 210 frs.

Le Moulin des Templiers — *Tel* 86.34.10.80
Vallée du Cousin

An idyllically situated old watermill, attractively converted into a small bed-and-breakfast hotel beside the quiet-flowing Cousin, in a pastoral valley outside Avallon. Breakfast served on a terrace by the water's edge or in a tiny but pretty salon. Bedrooms, though charming, are very small and washing facilities cramped: best for a night stop, not a long stay. Open 15 Mar–31 Oct. 14 rooms, all with bath and/or shower. Rooms 190-280 frs. Breakfast 27 frs [1989 *rates*]. *More reports please.*

AVIGNON 84000 Vaucluse — Map 11

Hôtel d'Europe — *Tel* 90.82.66.92
12 place Crillon — *Fax* 90.85.43.66
Telex 431965

This former 16th-century aristocrat's house was already an inn when Napoleon stayed here in 1799, and it has far more character than the average modern Avignon hotel. It is in a small square just inside the old city walls, close to the Papal Palace. "Tranquil and cool, elegantly furnished, staff very helpful"; "a lovely hotel: dinner in the charming courtyard was perfectly served" – two reports this year that endorse an earlier view. "The courtyard and public rooms, filled with flowers and antiques, are a feast to the eye and spirit." However, readers warn that a few of the bedrooms are "poky", and that those at the back can suffer from traffic noise. The Provençal cuisine in the hotel's *Vieille Fontaine* restaurant is admired. You can eat in a rather formal dining room or, preferably, under the plane trees beside a fountain in the graceful courtyard – "a magical experience". (*Simon Small, Bettye Chambers, WG Frick*)

Open All year.
Rooms 3 suites, 47 double – all with bath, shower, telephone, radio and TV.
Facilities Lift. 2 salons, bar, TV room, restaurant; conference facilities. Courtyard. 5 mins' walk from Papal Palace.
Location By Porte de l'Oulle on W side of city. Private garage (40 frs).
Restriction Not suitable for ♿.
Credit cards All major cards accepted.
Terms Rooms 420–975 frs, suite 1.500 frs. Breakfast 55 frs. Set lunch 160 frs, dinner 210 frs; full alc from 300 frs. Reduced rates for children; special meals on request.

BARBAZAN 31510 Haute-Garonne — Map 10

Hostellerie de l'Aristou — *Tel* 61.88.30.67 and 61.88.37.55
Route de Sauveterre

Barbazan is a spa village in the central Pyrenean foothills, within striking distance of the big resort of Luchon and of the ancient walled hill-town of St-Bertrand-de-Comminges, first built by the Romans, whose ruins survive (Herod the Tetrarch was exiled here by Caligula). Exile today to the stylish but far from expensive *Aristou* could be most agreeable, according to our reporter, "Without a doubt the nicest of the hotels we have used during the past three years of touring in France. It is on a hill above the village, with good views. Beds are very comfortable. Service was good *and* charming. We were warmly welcomed by the *patron*-chef, M. Geraud, whose food is excellent and plentiful. Breakfast included freshly squeezed orange juice and a basket of apricots, peaches and oranges. Nice furnishing and decoration." This latter is very *soigné* in its Victorian boudoir manner, with chintzy wallpaper and some antiques. The hotel is a low white traditional building, with tables and chairs in an attractive patio. More reports would be welcome.

Open All year.
Rooms 1 suite, 5 double, 1 single – 7 with bath and shower, all with telephone, radio and TV.
Facilities Lounge/bar, 2 restaurants; conference facilities. Terrace, garden.
Location On edge of village, 13 km SW of St-Gaudens.
Restriction Not suitable for ♿.
Credit cards All major cards probably accepted.
Terms B&B: single 290–330 frs, double 330–360 frs; Set lunch/dinner 95–220 frs. Children under 7 free; special meals.

> The 1991 Guide will appear in the autumn of 1990. Reports are particularly useful in the spring, but need to reach us by May 1990 if they are to help the 1991 edition.

BARBIZON 77630 Seine-et-Marne — Map 9

Hôtellerie du Bas-Bréau — *Tel* 60.66.40.05
22 rue Grande — *Telex* 690953 BABRÉAU

A well-known traditional auberge, *very luxurious, frequented by rich Parisians, in a village near Fontainebleau that once had an important artists' colony. Commended this year for its charming peaceful atmosphere, beautiful garden, tennis court, and excellent food* (Michelin *rosette, two* Gault Millau toques). *Closed Jan. 8 suites, 12 double, all with bath and shower. B&B double 1,350 frs. Alc from 260 frs. New nomination. More reports needed.*

LE BARROUX 84330 Vaucluse — Map 11

Hôtel Les Géraniums — *Tel* 90.62.41.08

A new nomination this year: "Le Barroux is an out-of-the-way hill-village, topped by an old castle, amid glorious country up near Mont Ventoux. This old stone building, pleasantly converted but still quite simple, is the kind of authentic local *auberge* that is becoming harder to find in touristy Provence: you need to go right up into the wilder hinterland, as here. The charming young *patronne* supervises the meals, served in a beamed *salle* or out on the terrace, facing the view. Good local cuisine: tripes provençales, fresh apple pie; local wine a bit rough. The best bedrooms, with modern bathrooms, are in the new annexe. As befits the hotel's name, there is plenty of pink in the decor." (*JA*)

Open 10 Feb–5 Jan. Restaurant closed Wed in low season.
Rooms 22 double – 8 with bath, 14 with shower, all with telephone. 9 in nearby annexe
Facilities Salon with TV, bar, restaurant; 2 terraces. Garden. Solarium, table-tennis.
Location Le Barroux is 12 km N of Carpentras. Parking.
Restrictions Not suitable for ♿.
Credit cards All major cards accepted.
Terms Rooms 160–200 frs. Breakfast 25 frs. Dinner, B&B 170–250 frs per person. Set meals 60, 110, 140 and 200 frs; full alc 150 frs. Reduced rates and special meals for children.

BAUDUEN 83630 Var — Map 11

Auberge du Lac — *Tel* 94.70.08.04

In upper Provence, just west of the mighty Gorges du Verdon: three old houses in the village have been joined into one, to form this pleasant unassuming auberge, *directly overlooking the large lake of Ste-Croix (bathing, sailing, fishing). Comfortable rooms with old furniture, good classic cooking, friendly service. Open 15 Mar–15 Nov. 10 rooms, all with bath and shower. B&B double 350–400 frs. Set menus 100–240 frs. New nomination. More reports please.*

> We asked hotels to quote 1990 prices. Not all were able to predict them in the late spring of 1989. Some of our terms will be inaccurate. Do check latest tariffs at the time of booking.

LES BAUX-DE-PROVENCE 13520 Bouches-du-Rhône Map 11

Oustaù de Baumanière

Tel 90.54.33.07
Telex 420203

This ruined hill-village-cum-castle, on a rocky spur of the Alpilles, is one of the show-places of Provence. In the Middle Ages it was the seat of a great feudal family and a leading "court of love" where troubadours played. Then it came under the rule of a sadistic viscount who would kidnap his neighbours and laugh as he forced them to jump to their deaths from the clifftop. In 1632 Richelieu had the castle demolished. Today it is a ghost realm, where coach parties daily pick their way across the jagged rocks of bauxite (named after Les Baux) and through the spooky remains of medieval grandeur. It is best visited by moonlight.

The renowned *Baumanière*, in the valley below the village, is owned by that doyen of great French chefs, Raymond Thuilier, who is aged 92 but last year was still present in the restaurant most evenings in his white hat, mixing with his guests. His grandson runs the place. Their chef Alain Burnel still wins *Michelin*'s top rating of three stars and five red knives and forks, and he is now beginning to innovate with new dishes in a restaurant that had long held out against the *nouvelle* tide. Prices are in the top bracket, and, as you would expect, not everyone is sure that they are worth it: some readers this year found service a shade aloof, and one minded being put without warning in an annexe 800 metres from the main building. But many have been impressed alike by the luxurious bedrooms, the splendid breakfasts, and the very real beauty of the place. "A large garden with peach, fig and olive trees, roses and a plethora of flowers. Breakfast was served in our own garden." "At night, the crescent moon, starlight and floodlit château, the eerie white rocks, the discreetly lit pool . . ." "As near to perfection as one is likely to get in an imperfect world." (*Marie and Dominic Chambers*) More reports welcome on the kitchen's break with classic tradition.

Open All year except 15 Jan–2 Mar. Closed Wed, and Thur afternoon 1 Nov–15 Mar.
Rooms 12 suites, 12 double – all with bath, telephone, TV and air-conditioning. 14 in 3 annexes. 8 ground-floor rooms.
Facilities Salon, arcaded restaurant. Garden, swimming pool, tennis courts, riding stables.
Location 19 km SW of Arles; 86 km NW of Marseilles.
Credit cards All major cards accepted.
Terms Rooms: single 700 frs, double 820 frs, suite 1,120 frs. Breakfast 75 frs. Dinner, B&B double 2.100–2,400 frs. Set lunch/dinner 500–600 frs; alc 600 frs.

La Benvengudo

Tel 90.54.32.54

This creeper-covered farmhouse, in the valley south-west of the village, is far cheaper than the *Baumanière* but quite glamorous in its own way: dinners are served in a cosy room with antiques or on a floodlit patio, and there is a large and lovely swimming pool in a big garden. "The great romantic-looking crags of the Alpilles rise above the garden. I found the food excellent: cooking very fresh and individual, e.g. a delicious combination of moules and escargots. The service was good and prompt, and breakfast first-class. Madame seemed a little sharp at first, but we came to like her, especially when she padded round gardening in bare feet." Others have found it "very comfortable and friendly", "peaceful and civilised". This year, two readers admired the beautiful setting and "lovely rooms"; one had a very good meal, but another thought the food "not above average" – a view we have heard more than once. (*N D'Emden and H Osman, G Evans*)

Open 15 Feb–11 Nov. Restaurant closed lunchtime and Sun evening.
Rooms 3 suites, 17 double – all with bath or shower, and telephone; suites have kitchenette. 10 (with terrace and TV) in annexe. Ground-floor rooms.
Facilities Salon, TV room, restaurant. Garden with terrace, swimming pool and tennis court.
Location 2 km SW of Les Baux, off D78. Parking.
Credit card Visa.
Terms Rooms 370–470 frs, suite 700–750 frs. Breakfast 50 frs. Dinner, B&B double 860 frs. Set dinner 230 frs.

BAYEUX 14400 Calvados — Map 8

Hôtel d'Argouges — *Tel* 31.92.88.86
21 rue St-Patrice — *Telex* 772402

"Exactly as provincial France should be - owners delightful", writes a visitor this year to this 18th-century private town house, now converted into a charming and elegant little family-run B&B hotel, warm and welcoming, with beamed bedrooms, an attractive lounge, and a small garden. It is also quiet, being set back from the street behind a courtyard, opposite the market square, and has private parking. The cathedral and that tapestry are 600 metres away. (*Mr and Mrs George R Staton, Mary Hanson, Peter and Ann Jones, Peter Hill*) *Warning:* "Tall people should beware of the ceilings on the staircase."

Open All year.
Rooms 2 suites, 20 double, 3 single – 20 with bath, 5 with shower, all with telephone, radio and baby-listening; 19 with TV. 12 in building in garden.
Facilities Salon, breakfast room; courtyard. Garden.
Location Central. Parking.
Restriction Not suitable for ♿.
Credit cards All major cards accepted.
Terms B&B: single 188–348 frs, double 208–348 frs, suite 350–518 frs. Reduced rates for children. (No restaurant.)

BEAULIEU 06310 Alpes-Maritimes — Map 11

La Réserve — *Tel* 93.01.00.01
Boulevard Maréchal Leclerc — *Telex* 470301

This famous pink palace beside the rocky shore was one of the most fashionable venues of pre-war Riviera society. Greta Garbo, Virginia Woolf and of course Scottie all stayed or dined here; today regular guests include Robert Maxwell. It dropped out of the Guide in 1987 for lack of feedback (probably few of our readers fancy its prices). But an inspector returned this year: "Still much the same, save that it's just been renovated and has a new chef, Joël Garault, who I think deserves his two *Gault Millau toques*, judging by my poissons crus marinés, carré d'agneau aux aromates and hot lemon soufflé. You can dine on the terrace by the sea, or in an elegant paved patio. Period furniture and a tinkling piano recall the old days. The piscine is heated in winter, or you can bathe from the rocks. Most rooms, suitably luxurious, face the sea." M. Maria, the "charming manager", has retired after 12 years, but we are assured that the team otherwise remains the same and will continue the traditions of *La Réserve*. More reports please.

Open 23 Dec–20 Nov.
Rooms 3 suites, 50 double – all with bath and shower, telephone, radio and TV.
Facilities Lift. Salon, bars, restaurant; terrace. Garden with swimming pool. Sauna, solarium.
Location On seafront. Parking.
Restrictions Not suitable for ♿. No children under 10 in July and Aug.
Credit cards Amex, Diners, Visa.
Terms [1989 rates] Rooms: single 710–1,280 frs, double 960–2,100 frs, suite 2,300–4,350 frs. Breakfast 85 frs. Set lunch/dinner 330–440 frs; full alc 550 frs.

BEAUNE 21200 Côte-d'Or — Map 10

Hôtel le Cep — *Tel* 80.22.35.48
27 rue Maufoux — *Telex* 351256 CEPHOTL

Recently extended and modernised, this beautiful 17th-century house in the centre of Burgundy's wine capital has antique furnishings and continues to be admired. One reader this year enjoyed breakfast in the garden courtyard with its elegant tables and chairs, and thought the staff "exceptionally kind". Last year's view, "A charming little hotel. Dinner was very good, in the lovely restaurant that bears the name of its chef, Bernard Morillon." Each bedroom is named after a *Grand Cru* wine of the Côte d'Or vineyards; the modern ones, though nice, have less character than the old rooms; front rooms could be noisy. (*Deborah F Reese, Joe Van der Sneppen*)

Open All year. Restaurant closed Feb.
Rooms 49 – all with bath and/or shower, telephone and TV. 5 suites in courtyard annexe. 1 room equipped for ♿.
Facilities Lift. Lounge, bar, restaurant; functions facilities; courtyard. Garden.
Location Central, near Hôtel-Dieu. Garage parking.
Credit cards All major cards accepted.
Terms [1989 rates] Rooms: single 450 frs, double 550–800 frs. Breakfast 50 frs. Set lunch/dinner 160–320 frs. Special meals for children.

La Closerie — *Tel* 80.22.15.07
61 route de Pommard — *Fax* 80.24.16.22
Telex 351213

A modern purpose-built hotel in the quiet southern outskirts, just off the N74 to Chalon. Spacious foyer, modern bedrooms, and plenty of creature comforts, including large garden, pleasant swimming pool and lido. Closed 25 Dec–14 Jan. 32 rooms, all with bath or shower. B&B double 400–424 frs. No restaurant. Recent nomination. More reports please.

> Our italicised entries indicate hotels which are worth considering, but which, for various reasons – inadequate information, lack of feedback, ambivalent reports – do not at the moment warrant a full entry. We should particularly welcome comments on these hotels.

BEAUREPAIRE 38270 Isère — Map 10

Hôtel Restaurant Fiard — *Tel* 74.84.62.02
Avenue des Terreaux

In a small town south-east of Vienne, off the Rhône valley, a quite smart, newly refurbished restaurant-with-rooms: gracious hostess, attractive modern furniture, excellent classic cooking and Côte-du-Rhône wines. Closed 1 Jan–14 Feb. 15 rooms, all with bath and shower. B&B double 320–370 frs. Set menus 110–380 frs. New nomination. More reports please.

LE BEC-HELLOUIN 27800 Eure — Map 8

Auberge de l'Abbaye — *Tel* 32.44.86.02

Peacefully situated on a village green, this old half-timbered Norman *auberge* has simple but clean rooms at modest prices, and a dining room with low-beamed ceilings, providing good food. Our readers remain content: one had a room "furnished with lovely antiques" and a fine breakfast, while others have admired the cooking, though one this year found it expensive. Le Bec-Hellouin was the home of one of Europe's great Benedictine monasteries, and no fewer than three archbishops of Canterbury came from here in medieval times. The monastery, formerly a ruin, has now been substantially restored and once again houses a religious community. The Gregorian chant in the abbey is worth hearing: but its resonant bells do start ringing early. (*Lynne and David Allen, and others*) The hotel asks you to take one meal in the hotel for each night you stay and strongly recommends that you use its courtyard parking.

Open 23 Feb–8 Jan. Closed Mon night and Tue out of season.
Rooms 1 suite, 7 double – all with bath and shower, and telephone.
Facilities TV lounge, 3 dining rooms; courtyard.
Location 5 km from Brionne; SW of Rouen, W of N138. Parking.
Restriction Not suitable for ♿.
Credit cards Access, Diners, Visa.
Terms Rooms 300–500 frs. Breakfast 30 frs. Dinner, B&B: double 560 frs, suite 760 frs. Set lunch/dinner 100, 175 and 250 frs; full alc 195 frs.

BELLEGARDE-SUR-VALSÉRINE 01200 Ain — Map 10

Hôtel Le Fartoret — *Tel* 50.48.07.18
Éloise

Set amid fine scenery on a hillside near the Swiss frontier, this old country auberge *has expanded considerably and become grander, losing some of its former simple charm. Still run jovially by the Gassilloud family, it has small but pretty and comfortable rooms with nice views, a sheltered swimming pool, Savoyard furnishings and cuisine. 40 rooms, all with bath and/or shower. Rooms 190–350 frs. Breakfast 35 frs. Set menus 95–250 frs [1989]. Food, service and ambience criticised this year: more reports please.*

> We don't lack *Michelin*-rosetted hotels in France but would be glad of more nominations at the more modest end of the price scale.

BÉNODET 29118 Finistère — Map 8

Hôtel Menez-Frost — *Tel* 98.57.03.09
4 rue J Charcot

Bénodet is an attractive resort in south-west Brittany, at the mouth of the quiet river Odet studded with pleasure-boats. It is busy with French families in August, but the season ends in early September when many amenities close, even if the hotels stay open longer. This one has been commended again this year as perfect for a family holiday. A devotee explains, "it has so many facilities – heated outdoor swimming pool, tennis, ping pong – and is near very good beaches. Our bedroom had dull decor but a balcony overlooking the pool; in our building the rooms were grouped in pairs, useful for a family. Breakfast was very good, apart from the packaged butter and jams. The manager was wonderful, keeping an eye on everything in a charming fashion." Many rooms face the pool, but are not noisy. No restaurant, which some families might find a handicap, but there are plenty of good eating-places near by.

Open Easter–Oct.
Rooms 7 suites, 30 double, 23 single – all with bath and shower, telephone and baby-listening; some with balcony. 12 ground-floor rooms. 5 self-catering apartments.
Facilities Salon, bar, TV room, reading room; conference facilities; billiards and table tennis. Garden with heated swimming pool (lessons available), solarium and sauna; tennis.
Location Central, near post office, port and ferry. Parking.
Credit card Access, Visa.
Terms Rooms: single 260–390 frs, double 280–450 frs, suite 460–700 frs. Breakfast 30 frs. (No restaurant.)

BEUZEVILLE 27210 Eure — Map 8

Auberge du Cochon d'Or and **Le Petit Castel** — *Tel* 32.57.76.08 and 32.57.70.46
Place du Général-de-Gaulle

This old Norman *auberge* and adjacent modern hotel, in a small town near Honfleur, are both owned and run by the Folleau family. Most guests sleep at the *Castel*, a *Logis de France*, recently renovated and as well liked as ever: visitors this year had a pleasant room facing the quiet walled garden (those at the front, by the main road, might be noisier). The welcome is friendly. As for the *Cochon d'Or*, where you eat, again this year readers felt that it well deserves its *Michelin* red "R" for good value (one couple enjoyed truite farcie and tripes au calvados). Earlier views: "Normandy cooking at its best"; "an enjoyable meal in a relaxing atmosphere – guinea-fowl in a grapefruit and orange sauce." One reader who liked the food thought the hotel itself a bit ordinary. (*Jack B Ainslie, Peter and Ann Jones*) It is recommended that you book in advance.

Open 15 Jan–15 Dec. Restaurant closed Mon.
Rooms 21 double – 17 with bath, 4 with shower; 16 with telephone; 7 with TV. 16 at *Le Castel*.
Facilities 2 lounges (1 at *Le Castel*), TV room, restaurant; 2 conference rooms. Garden.
Location In centre. Quietest rooms in *Petit Castel*. Beuzeville is 15 km SE of Honfleur, just N of Paris–Caen motorway. Parking.

Credit cards Access, Visa.
Terms B&B: single occupancy 195 frs, double 305 frs. Set meals 90, 140 and 190 frs; full alc 200 frs.

BEYNAC 24220 Dordogne — Map 10

Hôtel Bonnet — *Tel* 53.29.50.01

We are grateful to the readers this year who responded – all favourably – to our appeal for new reports on this charming and unpretentious little hotel with its flowery creeper-covered terrace, in a village above a curve in the Dordogne where four medieval castles are in view. "A superb hotel with wonderful food". "Madame Bonnet is always cheerful. The rooms in the annexe are particularly nice, being quieter and away from the main road" (this road is the hotel's main drawback, making some front rooms noisy). (*Josephine Barratt, J Alan Thornton, Mary Connolly and Fred Sweet, LH*)

Open 14 Apr–15 Oct.
Rooms 21 double, 1 single – all with bath and/or shower and telephone. Some rooms in annexe.
Facilities Lounge, restaurant, terrace. Garden.
Location 10 km W of Sarlat.
Credit cards Access, Visa.
Terms Rooms: single 120–160 frs, double 185–240 frs. Breakfast 26 frs. Half board: single 250–279 frs, double 520–550 frs. Set lunch/dinner 110–200 frs. Special meals for children.

BIOT 06410 Alpes-Maritimes — Map 11

Hôtel-Galerie des Arcades — *Tel* 93.65.01.04
16 place des Arcades

An idiosyncratic 15th-century inn/café/bistro/art gallery in the arcaded main square of a picturesque hill-village behind Antibes. Engagingly Bohemian *patron*, André Brothier, has lined the dining room with Braques and Miros, and he attracts a lively clientele of local fellow-Bohemians. Bedrooms are olde worlde, but the plumbing is not. The inn's hyper-relaxed atmosphere may not suit all tastes: pop music may resound from the café while you eat your aïoli or sardines farcies. Restored to the Guide this year after a period of no news: "Typically and rustically French. The rooms were perfectly acceptable, but as we all know the French see food as more important. On our visit, my charcuterie and soup could have fed the whole restaurant, and standards were superb. Madame was charming." (*David Lees, JA*)

Open All year. Restaurant closed 15 Nov–8 Dec.
Rooms 12 double – all with bath (7 also have shower) and telephone; 7 with TV.
Facilities Bar, TV room, 2 restaurants. Patio.
Location Central, some garages. Biot is 8 km NW of Antibes.
Restriction Not suitable for ♿.
Credit cards None accepted.
Terms [1989 rates] Rooms 180–350 frs. Breakfast 30 frs. Set lunch/dinner 140 frs; full alc 170 frs. Reduced rates for children.

We depend on detailed fresh reports to keep our entries up-to-date.

BLOIS 41000 Loir-et-Cher — Map 8

Anne de Bretagne — *Tel* 54.78.05.38
31 avenue Jean-Laigret

Useful for a night's stop in the Loire valley: a clean and comfortable little hotel in the upper town, near the castle, well above the river. Madame is friendly. Pleasant bar, and patio for drinks and breakfast. Closed 19 Feb–12 Mar. 29 rooms, most with bath and/or shower. Double rooms 195–330 frs [1989]. Breakfast 22 frs [1989]. No restaurant: plenty in town. Recent nomination. More reports please.

BONNEVAUX-LE-PRIEURÉ 25620 Doubs — Map 10

Le Moulin du Prieuré — *Tel* 81.59.21.47

Another French charmer new to our pages this year. It's secluded in the glorious Brême valley, a green winding cleft in the Jura, near picturesque Ornans where Courbet was born and painted (museum). "The scenery is grandiose and the silence complete," says our 1989 nominator; "the hotel is a converted water-mill, and parts of its mechanism can still be seen; the bedrooms are in separate modern chalets. Guests prepare their own breakfasts in their rooms, a system developed with fishermen and walkers in mind, who want to start at crack of dawn. Monsieur deals mostly with the fishing (season begins in May), while Madame looks after the restaurant in regal manner. Innovative dishes of high quality, with menus changing seasonally." *Gault Millau toque*. Public rooms are gracefully furnished in local style. (*AF Thomas*)

Open 15 Mar–20 Dec. Closed Sun evening and Mon, 15 Mar–1 May and 1 Oct–20 Dec.
Rooms 8 double – all with bath/shower, telephone and TV.
Facilities Lounge, restaurant. Garden. Fishing.
Location 8 km NE of Ornans by D67 and D280.
Credit cards All major cards accepted.
Terms [1989 rates] Rooms 300–325 frs. Breakfast 25 frs. Alc meals 180–330 frs (excluding wine). Special meals for children.

BONNIEUX 84480 Vaucluse — Map 11

Hôtel L'Aiguebrun — *Tel* 90.74.04.14

In a narrow upland valley of the lovely and curious Luberon hills, north of Aix (the church at Bonnieux village, four miles from the hotel, has remarkable 15th-century German paintings). Here Roger Chastel, a gentle Parisian, artist and former couturier, has taken over a small 19th-century manor beside a stream, which he runs more like a private home than a hotel. "Lovely, lovely place. The countryside is wild, with nothing to be heard but birdsong and the waterfall. The lounge was so inviting, with its country antiques, fresh flowers, original oil paintings (some by M. Chastel) and a fire crackling in the great stone fireplace. Comfortable bedrooms, also with country antiques, plus modern tiled bathrooms. You can breakfast on a terrace above the river. Food was delicious." "We arrived to find the air full of garlic and oil paints, and a Mozart concerto playing. The pigtailed M. Chastel runs the hotel very professionally and the food is superlative." This year, however, a reader was disappointed – poor upkeep, and food overpriced, he felt.

Open 19 Mar–1 Nov. Restaurant closed for lunch on Mon.
Rooms 7 double, 1 single – all with bath and telephone.
Facilities Salon, restaurant. Riverside garden where meals are served in summer.
Location Just off D943, 6 km SE of Bonnieux which is 48 km N of Aix.
Credit cards None accepted.
Terms [1989 rates] Rooms 380–420 frs. Breakfast 35 frs. Set meals 190 frs.

BOURBON-L'ARCHAMBAULT 03160 Allier — Map 10

Hôtel des Thermes — *Tel* 70.67.00.15
Avenue Charles Louis Philippe

"The rooms are most comfortable, and an exquisite dinner was served in an atmosphere of old-fashioned courtesy and cherishing: the brothers Barichard deserve highest praise for civility of the grave kind", writes a Brigadier this year. Indeed the brothers have already won First Prize for Welcome and Friendliness in the Allier *département*, in their sedate and spruce little hotel: it is set in a spa town of northern Auvergne where Talleyrand used to take a cure for rheumatism. An earlier report: "M. Barichard gave us a memorable dinner of omelette, sole meunière and steak in a special sauce" – he wins a *Michelin* rosette for the kind of orthodox dishes that *curistes* probably prefer. The hotel has a garden-terrace facing the cure centre and a private lake for fishing. One visitor had a spotless room with a large tiled bathroom, overlooking a flowery patio. But another found front rooms noisy, for they face a main road: rear ones are quieter. (*Brig. Laurence and Fran Fowler, ME Chamberlain*)

Open 24 Mar–31 Oct.
Rooms 1 suite, 17 double, 4 single – 10 with bath, 6 with shower, all with telephone. 4 in annexe.
Facilities Salon with TV, dining room. Large grounds with terrace, garden and private lake; fishing.
Location 100 metres from town centre. Town is 23 km W of Moulins. Garage.
Restriction Not suitable for ♿.
Credit cards All major cards accepted.
Terms B&B: single 145 frs, double 280 frs, suite 306 frs; full board 270–320 frs per person. Set lunch/dinner 82, 142 and 189 frs. Special meals for children on request.

LE BOURGET-DU-LAC 73370 Savoie — Map 10

Hôtel Ombremont — *Tel* 79.25.00.23
Fax 79.25.25.77
Telex 980832 CHAMBERY

The large Lac du Bourget is Lamartine's *Le Lac* where he mourned his lost love – and one reader, maybe caught by the poet's volatile moods, found it "pleasant only when the sun shines, otherwise black, vast and unfriendly". But the *Ombremont* shares none of these three epithets – a handsome gabled country house, run sympathetically by its young owners, and secluded in its big garden by the lake, just outside the smart resort of Le Bourget. One report this year criticises food and room upkeep, but others have again been quite lyrical: "Elegantly furnished bedrooms, superb views from the dining room's open balcony, food of good quality. The owner was actively involved in serving every table." "The menu at 320 frs [1989] was innovative and exquisite – roquefort terrine, and coconut mousse in dark chocolate with mango" (*Michelin* rosette, two red *Gault Millau toques* for such dishes as ravioli of frogs legs with fresh herbs). But the stairs are numerous and the swimming pool not easy of access. (*David Grant, FW Hulton, and others*)

Open All year except 2 Jan–5 Feb. Restaurant closed Sat midday except Jul and Aug.
Rooms 4 suites, 16 double – all with bath and shower, telephone, radio and baby-listening; some with TV. 2 in chalet in park.
Facilities 2 salons, billiard room, restaurant; conference facilities; terrace. Garden, with swimming pool, leading down to lake; rocky beach with lifeguard; fishing.
Location 2 km N of Le Bourget, on N504.
Restriction Not suitable for ♿.
Credit cards Access, Visa.
Terms [1989 rates] Rooms 425–750 frs. Breakfast 46 frs. Set lunch 175 frs, dinner 420 frs. Reduced rates and special meals for children.

BRANTÔME 24310 Dordogne — Map 10

Le Châtenet — *Tel* 53.05.81.08

Brantôme, on the river Dronne north of Périgueux, is a beautiful but trippery little town. Just outside it, away from the crowds and by the river, stands this delightful little 17th-century ranch-like manor, all mellow brown stone, with creepers and outdoor galleries. It was converted by its English-speaking owners, the Laxtons, and has again won a torrent of praise this year. "This lovely comfortable hotel feels like a home, and Mrs Laxton is a charming lady. Bedrooms are spacious: most overlook the garden." "A perfect hotel, with beautiful swimming pool, extensive grounds with a bar in the club-house. Bedrooms were elegant: ours even had an electric mosquito-killer. Delicious breakfast, including eggs, served on Limoges china." Bed-and-breakfast only: but there are no fewer than three *Michelin*-rosetted restaurants nearby (see Champagnac-de-Belair), while the Laxtons will recommend good cheaper places too. (*Eileen Broadbent, Judy Smith, Patricia and Christopher Bevan, and others*) There is a new garden room specially equipped for the disabled.

Open All year, except possibly a short while in low season (1 Nov–1 Apr).
Rooms 2 suites, 8 double – all with bath and shower, and telephone; TV and baby-listening on request. 1 ground-floor room equipped for ♿ with electrically manned bed and special fittings (20% reduced rate for ♿). 2 rooms in cottage with lounge and kitchenette.
Facilities Ramps. Lounge; club house with bar, billiards; terrace. 10-acre grounds with swimming pool heated 20 Apr–15 Oct, tennis court, children's playground, areas for bowls and cricket, river frontage, fishing.
Location 1/2 m W of Brantôme, off D78.
Credit cards Access, Visa.
Terms Rooms 300–430 frs, suite 500–620 frs. Breakfast 45 frs. Extra bed 50 frs. (No restaurant.)

> Deadlines: nominations for the 1991 edition should reach us not later than 1 May 1990. Latest date for comments on existing entries: 1 June 1990.

BRESSON 38320 Isère — Map 10

Chavant — *Tel* 76.25.15.14

"Within 20 minutes' drive of the centre of Grenoble, yet in the unspoilt setting of a quiet village, this delightful old auberge is today smart and sophisticated, but is still run with unaffected personal warmth by the Chavant family who have owned it for three generations: Émile Chavant was in the 1930s a disciple of the then aged Escoffier, and Jean-Pierre Chavant still provides the best food in the Grenoble area (*Michelin* rosette). Each of the seven bedrooms is pretty and cosy, with period furnishings. Ours had blue-and-pink matching fabrics and a large carpeted balcony/sun-terrace with views of the Vercors massif; we awoke to birdsong. The old building has beamed ceilings and Louis XIII decor; meals in winter are served in a spacious panelled room before a log fire. Our visit was in June and we lunched under the chestnut trees in the idyllic flower-filled garden. A large lunch-party of the local *haute bourgeoisie* was in progress (*Chavant* is Grenoble's most chic venue for such events) but this did not affect the service. The cooking is rich and classic rather than *nouvelle*: especially superb were the escalope de foie gras de canard with nuts, and the coquilles St-Jacques aux girolles in a cream-and-wine sauce – vive Escoffier! Much play is made of the local noix de Grenoble (walnuts): they even get into the pain aux noix, delicious. A splendid range of old armagnacs, too."

Open All year except 25–31 Dec. Restaurant closed Sat lunch and Wed.
Rooms 7 – all with bath and shower, telephone and TV.
Facilities Lift. Salon, restaurant; conference room. Garden. Swimming pool.
Location 8 km S of Grenoble: go to Eybens and turn right (signposted).
Credit cards All major cards accepted.
Terms [1989 rates] Rooms 380–720 frs. Breakfast 45 frs. Set meals 158 frs.

BRIGNOGAN-PLAGES 29238 Finistère — Map 8

Hostellerie Castel-Regis — *Tel* 98.83.40.22
Telex 940941

In a beautiful rocky setting on the North Brittany coast, only 36 km west of Roscoff and its ferries, a spruce and quite elegant little hotel where you can drink or dine by the water's edge, with fine views. Most rooms are in bungalow style; pleasant service, and very good local fish dishes (Gault Millau toque). *Heated sea-water swimming pool. Open 8 Apr–30 Sept. 21 rooms, all with bath and shower. B&B double 275–380 frs. Set menus 110-175 frs. New nomination. More reports please.*

BRIOUDE 43100 Haute Loire — Map 10

Hôtel Le Brivas — *Tel* 71.50.10.49
Avenue du Velay — *Telex* 392589

Midway between Le Puy and Clermont-Ferrand, Brioude is a good centre for touring the Massif Central – a market town with narrow medieval streets and a fine 12th-century romanesque basilica. Here on the broader main road to Le Puy, on the town's edge, is one reader's "find of the year". He goes on: "It is modern and very much a concrete slab, for all that the owners are trying to soften its harshness with ivy and creepers. The garden terrace in front blocks out all traffic noise from the road. Bedrooms are large, comfortable and well furnished in the modern idiom. The large and airy restaurant has fine views of the mountains. The chef, son of the owners, is obviously working on his reputation, with his own specialities: he appears at the end of dinner and is willing to debate with you the mysteries of his trade." "Service friendly, food ample and well cooked." There is now an outdoor heated swimming pool.

Open All year except 17 Nov–27 Dec, Fri evening 27 Dec–7 Apr and 5 Oct–Dec; restaurant closed Sat midday in low season.
Rooms 30 – all with bath or shower, telephone, and TV.
Facilities Lift. Salon, bar, restaurant; conference facilities. Garden with swimming pool.
Location Outskirts, on N 102 to Le Puy. Brioude is 69 km S of Clermont-Ferrand.
Credit cards All major cards accepted.
Terms [1989 rates] B&B double 310 frs; dinner, B&B 235–315 frs per person. Set lunch/dinner 80, 110 and 140 frs; full alc 155 frs. Reductions for long stays. Children under 7 free in parents' room; special meals.

Hôtel de la Poste et Champanne *Tel* 71.50.14.62
1 boulevard Docteur Devins

On the main street, a down-to-earth and very traditional hotel, run "with tremendous verve and atmosphere" by the octogenarian Albertine Barge and her family. Recently enlarged and modernised, it has lost some of its rough-and-ready simplicity and Madame Barge's grandchildren provide "considerable panache", even if not fine frills. But again this year several readers have been content, "A smiling welcome, a decent modern bedroom and balcony, a good dinner and breakfast"; "M. Barge is a wonderful character. Good plain peasant-style cooking, in contrast to the mouthwatering and beautifully presented sweets"; "the menu of regional dishes was a delight". *Michelin* and *Gault Millau* concur, by awarding their "good value" red print for the cheaper set menus (local dishes such as potée de lentilles and tripoux d'Auvergne) which are preferred to the dearer ones. Rooms in the new annexe are best. (*RA Mayor, Sara Price, William A Grant, BW Ribbons*)

Open All year except 1–15 Jan and Sun evening Oct–May.
Rooms 20 double – 10 with bath and shower, 4 with shower, all with telephone. 14, with balcony, in nearby annexe.
Facilities 2 lounges (1 with TV), bar with terrace, 4 dining rooms. Small garden.
Location Central; annexe has parking.
Credit cards None accepted.
Terms Rooms 100–200 frs. Breakfast 20 frs. Half board 170 frs per person; full board 220 frs. Set lunch/dinner 60, 85 and 140 frs. Reduced rates for children.

BUSSIÈRES 71960 Saône-et-Loire — Map 10

Relais Lamartine *Tel* 85.36.64.71

Modern hotel on edge of quiet village west of Mâcon, where Lamartine lived. Large terrace with views of vineyards, sparklingly clean but "with old-fashioned values". Warm praise for five-course dinners, and breakfasts with home-made apricot and blackberry jams. Open 15 Jan–1 Dec; restaurant closed

Sun evening and Mon in low season. 8 rooms, all with bath and shower, 210–310 frs. Set meals 95–250 frs. Sadly Madame Gacon died at the end of 1988 but her husband plans to continue the business as before. More reports please.

CABASSON 83230 Var — Map 11

Hôtel Les Palmiers — *Tel* 94.64.81.94

West of Le Lavandou, secluded in woodland yet near to sandy beaches – not an easy combination on this crowded coast. A cheerful well-modernised hotel in local style, fairly smart yet not pretentious, run with style by the Guinets (he reserved, she charming). Bedrooms and cooking both approved. 21 rooms, some with shower, 460–700 frs. Set menus 120–220 frs [1989]. Was in very early editions of the Guide. Now re-nominated. More reports welcome.

CABOURG 14390 Calvados — Map 8

Pullman Grand Hôtel — *Tel* 31.91.01.79
Promenade Marcel Proust — *Telex* 171364

"As my teeth bit lovingly into the madeleine that all guests here are served at breakfast, and as my gaze wandered out through the picture windows of the huge *belle époque* dining room that Proust called 'the aquarium', to the broad sandy beach where his hero first glimpsed Albertine with her brilliant, laughing eyes and her black polo-cap, I fell to musing what this great white wedding-cake of a seaside hotel in a once-so-fashionable Normandy resort (today the *Grand* mostly hosts business seminars) must have been like in the 1880s when Proust came on the first of his many long visits, listening to the same surging of the waves that lulled me to sleep last night, mesmerised by the same shifting colours of the sunlight on the sea that he described so poetically in his novel, which transmuted Cabourg into Balbec, for though much today is taken, much abides, including the same marble pillars and chandeliers in the vast foyer, and though no one knows exactly which was Proust's bedroom (in fact he had several, and today the hotel has been totally remodelled inside, and has only 70 rooms, against 200 in his day), still you can if you wish, ask for the '*chambre* Marcel Proust' which has *belle époque* furnishings including a big brass bedstead and old-fashioned taps on the bath (but, oddly, a modern telephone), and you can enjoy as I did a rather good gigotin de turbot and panachée de quatre viandes in the intimate winter restaurant that of course is called *Le Balbec*, while reflecting that Pullman have done quite a good job of restoration, to provide nostalgic Proustians with an experience that can only be called (to use an overworked word) "Proustian", even though one disappointed visitor this year felt the hotel was "living on its past", but then we might ask what is more Proustian than to live on the past, while at the same time requesting further insights from correspondents, please. (*JA with more than a nod to MP*)

Open All year.
Rooms 70 – all with bath, shower, telephone, radio and TV; baby-listening on request.

Facilities Lift. Salon, bar, restaurant; conference rooms. Casino.
Location Central, by the beach. Free parking. Cabourg is 24 km NE of Caen.
Restriction Not suitable for ♿.
Credit cards All major cards accepted.
Terms Rooms 440–1,010 frs, suite 1,270–1,690 frs. Breakfast 62 frs. Half board 645–860 frs per person. Set lunch/dinner 170–230 frs. Reduced rates and special meals for children.

CABRERETS 46330 Lot — Map 10

La Pescalerie — *Tel* 65.31.22.55

This 18th-century Quercy country house, restored and decorated in exquisite taste (many bedrooms have antiques), stands alone at the foot of a rocky hill, just outside the village . A large semi-formal garden stretches away to the wooded banks of the Célé where you can swim if you wish and where jays call and kingfishers arrow through the shadows. "The atmosphere", suggests a reader, "is rather like that of an English country house hotel with French overtones. We were all made very welcome by Hélène Combette and her surgeon husband. Our room was small but the cream marble bathroom was palatial. Food good and different, and the ambience in the dining room one of total enjoyment." "Breakfast on the terrace, attended by a friendly cat, was a joy – fresh orange juice, honey in the comb." "The luxury of the bedrooms was almost sinful, the elegance of breakfast on the terrace under a huge magnolia tree, with oleanders in bloom, was unforgettable." This year, one reader found dinner "delicious", but another thought it only average, and the welcome judged to be a bit too nonchalant. (*Lynne and David Allen, Minda Alexander*)

Open 1 Apr–1 Nov.
Rooms 10 double – all with bath and shower, and telephone; TV on request.
Facilities Lounge with TV, bar, dining room; breakfast terrace. Garden leading to river with swimming, fishing, boating.
Location At La Fontaine de la Pescalerie, 2.5 km NE of Cabrerets on D41 to Figeac.
Restriction Not suitable for ♿.
Credit cards All major cards accepted.
Terms [1989 rates] Rooms 600 frs. Breakfast 50 frs. Dinner, B&B 685 frs per person. Set lunch/dinner 195–230 frs.

LA CADIÈRE-D'AZUR 83740 Var — Map 11

Hostellerie Bérard — *Tel* 94.90.11.43 and 94.90.14.98

Rue Gabriel Péri — *Telex* 400509

Though only five miles from the busy coast at Bandol, La Cadière is a fairly unspoilt hill-village. In its narrow main street, above the valley, stands this 19th-century *auberge*, today much modernised and smartened up but still sympathetic. An inspector this year found it unchanged, endorsing his 1988 report, "A family venture by René and Danièle Bérard – he, rather shy, does the cooking, while she is the exuberant front-of-house. The Bérards have ambitiously turned their *auberge* into quite a sophisticated place, catering for business seminars out of season, and the homely touch has possibly been muted in the process. But prices are still reasonable, and all is attractively done – new beamed ceilings and tiled floors, a spacious and cosy lounge/bar, and a bright dining room with wide views of hills and valley. The menu du terroir (135 francs, 1988) offers Provençal specialities such as pieds-et-paquets; other dishes, more expensive, lean towards the *nouvelle*, such as loup en croûte à la sauce champagne. We thought the results very good and the service charming. But the breakfast coffee was poor. Bedrooms, comfortable and well equipped, are mostly in a nearby annexe: ours was in a converted monastery, above the pool and sun-terrace." "Enjoyable." Some rooms can be noisy. Many guests are British. (*JA and KA; Janet and Dennis Allom*)

Open All year except 5 Jan–18 Feb.
Rooms 3 suites, 37 double – all with bath and/or shower, telephone and TV; baby-listening on request. All in 3 different buildings. Some ground-floor rooms.
Facilities 2 salons, bar, TV room, games room, dining room; conference room. Terrace, small garden with heated swimming pool. Sandy/rocky beaches 7 km.
Location 9 km N of Bandol: if coming from Marseilles, leave *autoroute* at Les Lecques, go through St-Cyr village. Garage parking.
Restriction Not suitable for ♿.
Credit cards Access, Amex, Visa.
Terms Rooms: single 355–405 frs, double 405–484 frs, suite 525–580 frs. Breakfast 42 frs. Set lunch/dinner 140, 190 and 290 frs. Reduced rates and special meals for children.

CAEN 14000 Calvados — Map 8

Le Dauphin — *Tel* 31.86.22.26
29 rue Gémare — *Telex* 171707

Two Bath hoteliers returned this year to their "magic find" in the centre of Caen near the castle and liked it as much as the year before, "Listed in *Michelin* as a three-*couverts* restaurant 'avec chambres' (always the best value in *Michelin*, we feel), it forms part of an ancient priory in a quarter which miraculously escaped the 1944 devastations. Owner-chef Robert Chabredier offers numerous fish specialities, including an excellent barbue à l'oseille, and St-Jacques in a light Calvados sauce. We have lasting memories, too, of a really gamey game terrine, a fine classic poulet vallée d'Auge and a tender young partridge in a cider sauce. The cheeseboard (including Livarot) vies with Normandy's best, while the apple and pear tarts come with that delicious ivory-coloured Normandy cream. House claret superb and ridiculously inexpensive. The dining room, with a log fire, is full of atmosphere, whilst the bar has a full array of farmhouse Calvados. Breakfast, with home-made breads, stewed and fresh fruit, Norman cream cheese, is the best we have found in France. The bedrooms, which vary in size, are less exciting, but they are now being renovated, and our new one had fine beds." (*Malcolm and Jean Seymour*)

Open All year except 17 Jul–8 Aug and Christmas Eve. Restaurant closed Sat.
Rooms 21 double – all with bath and/or shower, telephone and TV. 7 in annexe next door.
Facilities Lift in annexe. Bar, restaurant.
Location Central; signposted from château. Rooms in main building are quiet, the others are sound-proofed. Private parking; garage nearby.
Restriction Not suitable for ♿.
Credit cards All major cards accepted.
Terms [1989 rates] Rooms 170–320 frs. Breakfast 30 frs. Set meals 80, 140, 195 and 280 frs; full alc 260 frs. Special meals for children on request.

CALVI 20260 Corsica — Map 11

Hôtel Résidence "Les Aloës" — *Tel* 95.65.01.46
Quartier Donatéo

The old fortified port of Calvi, now a popular summer resort, has one of Corsica's most spectacular settings – a big sandy bay, guarded by an old Venetian citadel, with a back-drop of high snow-capped mountains. An ideal spot for viewing all this is the peace and cool of the *Aloës*, an unpretentious modern (1965) B&B hotel above the town and away from the noise. "Rooms are small, but all are quiet and some have a superb view of the bay", says a reader this year; "we took breakfast on our own small terrace" (rooms at the back facing the maquis are especially quiet). Others have referred to the "helpful management", but one visitor thought the plumbing "bizarre". A good choice of restaurants down by the port. (*Christian Draz*)

Open May–Oct.
Rooms 26 – all with bath and/or shower, and telephone. 5 with terrace in annexe.
Facilities Salon, bar, TV room, library. Terrace and garden. Beach 1 km.
Location 1 km SW of town centre: take route d'Ajaccio or route de l'Usine Électrique. Parking.
Credit cards All major cards accepted.
Terms Rooms: single 170 frs, double 240–400 frs. Breakfast 26 frs. 1-night bookings sometimes refused in high season. (No restaurant.)

CAMBRAI 59400 Nord — Map 9

Hôtel Beatus — *Tel* 27.81.45.70
718 avenue de Paris — *Telex* 820597

A low white building set back from the road, a mile out of town on the N44 to St-Quentin. Very friendly and helpful owners; quiet and comfortable rooms furnished in Louis XV/XVI styles; elegant little bar; good breakfast; private parking. No restaurant, but there are several in town. 26 rooms, all with bath or shower. B&B double from 340 frs. Re-nominated in 1989, but we'd welcome fuller reports.

CARCASSONNE Aude — Map 10

Domaine d'Auriac — *Tel* 68.25.72.22
Route St-Hilaire, 11009 — *Telex* 500385

An imposing creeper-covered 19th-century mansion, lying peacefully amid its own woodlands two miles outside Carcassonne, and just across the motorway (out of earshot) from the medieval hilltop fortress. An elegant dining room with a blazing fire in winter; terrace for alfresco meals in summer; dishes such as cassoulet approved. Most bedrooms pleasant and spacious. Closed Sun evening and Mon midday. 23 rooms, all with bath and shower. Rooms 450–950 frs. Set menus 160–300 frs [1989]. Some criticism of food and service this year. More reports please.

Hôtel du Donjon *Tel* 68.71.08.80
2 rue du Comte-Roger, La Cité, 11000 *Telex* 505012

Of our two new 1990 entries within the walled medieval fortress, this Logis de France *is the smarter – a beautifully converted ancient building with red tiled floors, rough stone walls (but all mod cons) and a charming rear garden where you can escape from the tourist mob, and eat out in summer. Affable welcome, good local dishes such as cassoulet. Restaurant closed Sun night. 36 rooms, all with bath and/or shower, 260–380 frs. Set menu (dinner only) 100 frs. New nomination. More reports please.*

Hôtel des Remparts *Tel* 68.71.27.72
3 place du Grand Puits, La Cité, 11000

In a relatively secluded part of the much-visited medieval Cité, *an old house with friendly owners and a fine 14th-century spiral staircase; but the bedrooms are modern. 18 rooms, all with bath and shower. B&B double 290 frs. New nomination. No restaurant, but try the* Donjon *(above).*

CARSAC-AILLAC 24200 Dordogne — Map 10

Le Relais du Touron *Tel* 53.28.16.70

Plenty of unaffected Dordogne rural charm is to be found at this 19th-century gentilhommière, *on the outskirts of a small village 9 km east of Sarlat, tastefully converted and recently opened as a hotel by its charming Belgian owner, Claudine Carlier. Food good value (lots of regional specialities), staff friendly, swimming pool a joy. Open 15 Mar–15 Nov. 12 rooms, all with bath or shower. B&B: double 234-350 frs. Set menus 60-180 frs [1989]. New nomination. More reports welcome.*

CASTELPERS 12170 Aveyron — Map 10

Château de Castelpers *Tel* 65.69.22.61

In deep countryside far from anywhere, off the main N88 from Rodez to Albi, an old stone mansion turned into a small unpretentious hotel/restaurant by the family who have owned it for generations. "We spent two enjoyable days," say recent visitors. "The château is at the bottom of a heavily forested ravine, beside a river, in a lovely park with friendly sheep and stunning conifers. The interior is still furnished like the family home it was, with portraits on the stairs. There is a magnificent lounge with baronial open fireplace; our bedroom had two four-poster beds and windows rimmed with red stained glass, giving a cosy feel. We were welcomed by an enthusiastic collie and Madame, who had put an electric radiator on 'in case the baby might be cold'. We had dinner in front of a blazing fire: the menu was not very exciting, but service was friendly. There were swings in the grounds, and a children's menu. The place has all the makings of a classic Guide entry: they just need to throw away the long menu and make a couple of simple dishes each day and it would be fine." Your views, please, on this idyll.

Open 1 Apr–1 Oct. Restaurant closed Tue to non-residents.
Rooms 2 suites, 7 double – all with bath and/or shower, and telephone; 8 with TV. 1 equipped for ♿.
Facilities Salon with TV; 2 dining rooms. Garden bordered by 2 rivers with fishing.
Location 12.5 km SE of Naucelle by D10, down road to Requista.
Credit cards Access, Visa.
Terms B&B double 260–400 frs. Dinner, B&B 185–260 frs per person. Set lunch/dinner 90–195 frs; full alc 206 frs. Reduced rates and special meals for children.

CÉRET 66400 Pyrénées-Orientales — Map 10

La Terrasse au Soleil — *Tel* 68.87.01.94
Route de Fontfrède

Splendidly situated in the Pyrenean foothills south of Perpignan, this small modern hotel built in local Catalan style has fine views of the mountains and distant sea. Bedrooms are large, modern and comfortable, notably those in the new annexe. "The ladies of the house were friendly, and we had a fine view from our balcony", says one reader this year, "but the food was nothing special and service was slow." Another visitor thought the hotel "wonderful", with *nouvelle*-ish food generously served; a third judged the food "adequate rather than brilliant", and found the tables too close-packed. (*Sara Price, Mrs JE Lyes, Dave Watts*)

Open 10 Mar–10 Jan.
Rooms 1 suite, 25 double – all with bath, telephone and TV. 14 in 2 annexes. Ground-floor rooms.
Facilities 3 salons, bar, 2 restaurants; terrace. Garden with swimming pool, golf practice and ping-pong.
Location Céret is 31 km SW of Perpignan.
Credit cards Access, Visa.
Terms Rooms 380–410 frs. Breakfast 45 frs. Dinner B&B 565–820 frs. Full alc 250 frs. .pa

---

CHABLIS 89800 Yonne — Map 9

Hostellerie des Clos — *Tel* 86.42.10.63
Rue Jules Rathier — *Telex* 351752 HOSCLOS

Patron-chef Michel Vignaud's elegant and select hotel/restaurant, a converted almshouse in a well-known wine town, is now firmly established as one of the best in North Burgundy, winning a *Michelin* rosette and two red *Gault Millau toques* for such regionally inspired dishes as pike cooked in Chablis, and kidneys and grapes also cooked in Chablis. Our earlier nomination, from a connoisseur, "It's a restaurant that is totally professional, serving light creative cookery perfectly complementing the great wines of Chablis. The rooms are carefully decorated and furnished in the modern style." This year, others have largely agreed: "Modern, comfortable and friendly, with beautiful food"; "Excellent food, and breakfast included anything from poached pears to home-made fruit loaf. Our spacious room had a view over the flower-filled courtyard." The only complaint (from a Britisher): "Too many British guests." (*C Carter, Simon Small, Peter and Ann Jones*)

Open All year except 10 Dec–10 Jan. Closed Wed, Thur midday except 1 May–30 Sep.
Rooms 26 double – all with bath, telephone, radio, and TV. 2 specially adapted for ♿.
Facilities Lift. Salon, bar, restaurant; conference room; garden.
Location Central, parking. Chablis is 19 km E of Auxerre.
Credit cards All major cards accepted.
Terms Rooms: single occupancy 180–240 frs, double 215–470 frs. Breakfast 42 frs. Dinner, B&B 420–470 frs per person. Set lunch/dinner 140, 238 and 340 frs; full alc 320 frs. Extra bed for child 50 frs; special menus.

CHAGNY 71150 Saône-et-Loire — Map 10

Château de Bellecroix — *Tel* 85.87.13.86

Two kilometres south of Chagny, a turreted castle of medieval origin, set in its own park, with a heated swimming pool and tables under the trees for drinks. Large and charmingly-furnished bedrooms; excellent classic cooking in the panelled dining room; friendly staff. Closed 1 Jan–1 Feb, and Wed. 19 rooms, all with bath and/or shower. Rooms 400–650 frs. Set menus 95–280 frs. [1989] Recent nomination warmly endorsed this year.

Hôtel Lameloise — *Tel* 85.87.08.85
36 place d'Armes — *Telex* 801086

Jacques Lameloise's elegantly converted 15th-century mansion is renowned for its cuisine, arguably the best in Burgundy (three *Michelin* rosettes and three *Gault Millau* red *toques*). It stands in the main street of a dullish little town amid woods and vineyards. "There's not much to say about it because it's all perfect", says one of this year's visitors and others are equally laconic, "As good as ever: cuisine superb, staff splendid, bedrooms luxurious". . .and so on. Terrine de foie gras aux artichaux and a warm apple tart with sharp sorbet have been singled out. Recently returning visitors found a smart new lift to all floors, and renovations in the bedrooms which have superb bathrooms. Others have spoken of "the best cuisine we've had in France", "elegant rooms, with antiques, beamed ceilings and fireplaces", "a quietly luxurious atmosphere, attentive and courteous service", and "the top *sommelier* of France, Georges Pertuiset, is a charming and modest man". (*Rosamund Hebdon, Alan F Thomas, Aaron Esman, Jeff and Karen Nebel*)

Open All year, except 20 Dec–19 Jan and 1 May. Closed Wed, and Thur midday.
Rooms 21 double – all with bath and shower, telephone, radio and TV.
Facilities Lift. Salon, bar, restaurant.
Location Central. Garage parking.
Credit cards Access, Visa.
Terms Rooms 280–980 frs. Breakfast 60 frs. Alc meals (excluding wine) 290–450 frs.

> Set dinner refers to a fixed price meal (which may have ample, limited or no choice on the menu). Full alc is the hotel's own estimated price per person of a three-course meal taken à la carte, with a half-bottle of house wine.

CHÂLONS-SUR-MARNE 51000 Marne — Map 9

Hôtel d'Angleterre et Restaurant Jacky Michel

Tel 26.68.21.51
Telex 842078

19 place Monseigneur Tissier

This traditional hotel in the town centre, small but very *soigné*, and newly modernised, is praised above all for owner Jacky Michel's innovative cooking (*Michelin* rosette, *Gault Millau toque*). Dropped from last year's Guide for lack of feedback, it has been liked by several visitors this year. "It's been recently renovated and we found it delightful – exceptional value for very high quality. The welcome was smiling and friendly, the furnishings and decor are attractive, and the bathrooms super. The cooking is superb, especially the 155-franc set menu available on weekdays, and the food is beautifully presented in modern style. The wine list includes 12 pages of champagnes alone." You can take drinks on a pretty terrace. (*Pat and Jeremy Temple; ML Dodd*)

Open 8 Jan–30 Jun and 23 Jul–20 Dec. Closed Sun; restaurant also closed Sat lunch.
Rooms 18 double – all with bath and/or shower, telephone and TV.
Facilities Lounge with TV, bar, restaurant. Small terrace where meals are served in summer.
Location Central; near Notre Dame en Vaux. Parking.
Credit cards All major cards accepted.
Terms Rooms 300–520 frs. Breakfast 38 frs. Dinner, B&B: single 490–690 frs, double 700–900 frs. Set meals 155, 225 and 350 frs; full alc 350 frs. Special meals for children.

CHALON-SUR-SAÔNE 71100 Saône-et-Loire — Map 10

Hôtel St-Georges

Tel 85.48.27.05
Telex 800330

32 avenue Jean-Jaurès

The idea of a commercial hotel next to the station in a biggish town would not make mouths water in Britain or the US: but this is France, and readers in 1988/9 have again warmed to young Yves Choux's "non-eccentric *nouvelle* cooking" (e.g. vinaigrette de rougets, pot-au-feu de la mer) which wins a *Michelin* rosette and *Gault Millau* black *toque*. "Ideal for a stopover. Plain rooms with excellent modern bathrooms, and fine cuisine." "A civilised hotel with tremendously friendly welcome, *un*patronising waiters, best dinner of our whole holiday." (*Mary Hanson*)

Open All year except Christmas Eve.
Rooms 3 triple, 45 double – 17 with bath, 31 with shower, all with telephone, radio, TV, mini-bar and air-conditioning.
Facilities Lift. Bar with TV, restaurant; conference facilities.
Location Central, near railway station. Garage.
Credit cards All major cards accepted.
Terms Rooms: single 230–290 frs, double 280–330 frs. Breakfast 36 frs. Set lunch/dinner 105, 170, 195 and 380 frs; full alc 320 frs. Reduced rates for children sharing parents' room; special meals.

> Always let a hotel know if you have to cancel a booking, whether you have paid a deposit or not. Hotels lose thousands of pounds and dollars from "no-shows".

CHAMONIX 74400 Haute Savoie — Map 10

Hôtel Albert Premier *Tel* 50.53.05.09
119 impasse du Montenvers *Telex* 380779

Long popular with readers, this sizeable chalet-type ski-hotel stands in its own big garden near the middle of the resort. Latest reports: "Incredible value. We had a lovely room with a view of Mont Blanc. Fantastic breakfasts and dinners." "Our room was impeccably clean with lovely furnishings and a balcony with view. The dining room with fresh flowers and beautiful china was the perfect setting for the superb meal – salmon with basil butter." Others have praised the ambience and professionalism and have enjoyed using the pool, jacuzzi and sauna. "A roomy and comfortable hotel, full of well-heeled skiers enjoying their *après-ski*. Log fire and piano in the salon." In the large sophisticated dining room, the interesting and ambitious cooking by the son of the *patron*, Pierre Carrier (*Michelin* rosette, two red *Gault Millau toques*), is mostly much admired. When fine, it's well worth taking the *téléphérique* (the world's highest, they claim) to a point just below the summit of Mont Blanc.

Open All year except 2–22 May, 22 Oct–5 Dec. Restaurant closed Wed midday in low season.
Rooms 5 suites, 24 double, 3 single – all with bath and shower, telephone, TV and mini-bar.
Facilities Lift. Bar, lounge, 3 dining rooms, table-tennis room; sauna, whirlpool, solarium. Large garden with tennis court, swimming pool (heated in summer), children's play area. Winter sports, walking.
Location In side road, 150 metres from station; 500 metres from town centre. Parking and garages.
Credit cards All major cards accepted.
Terms B&B: single 450–530 frs, double 560–820 frs; dinner, B&B 390–630 frs per person; full board 460–700 frs. Set meals 150–380 frs; full alc 380 frs. Reduced rates and special meals for children.

CHAMPAGNAC-DE-BELAIR 24530 Dordogne — Map 10

Moulin du Roc *Tel* 53.54.80.36
Telex 571555

Solange Gardillou, wife of the *Moulin*'s owner, is the most highly reputed woman chef in France (two *Michelin* rosettes). She and her husband run a very trendy operation in a gracefully converted 17th-century walnut mill, set quietly beside a stream in a Périgord village near Brantôme. An earlier account paints the picture: "Tiny hotel, small rooms, flowers everywhere, *objets*, old walnut-mill equipment. Our room with four-poster bed. Silver-tray breakfast: strawberries, home-made jams. View from our window of maids rinsing a bin in the millstream." Mme Gardillou's forte is variations on local dishes, e.g. foie gras poêlé à la ciboulette. This, and the idyllic setting, has led the *Moulin* to be much publicised in the glossy press and the rich international tourists are still flocking in. But most of our readers remain contented. A report this year, "Every year more flowers, and now the addition of a swimming pool reached by a 'celestial bridge'. M. Gardillou in yet another new jacket, and a well-drilled corps (slightly lacking in humour) serving to perfection." However, another visitor, who thought the set 190 fr menu [1989] "the best value in France", found it unchanged the next night and felt that the *Moulin* might be resting on its glossy laurels. (*DAC Cartwright, I and N Pressnell*) And *Mrs C Smith*, who otherwise liked the place a lot, reports a muddle over her room booking because "three couples all called Smith" were arriving on the same day. . .

Open All year except 15 Nov–15 Dec and 15 Jan–15 Feb. Restaurant closed Tue, and Wed midday.
Rooms 4 suites, 10 double – all with bath, telephone, radio and TV.
Facilities Salons, restaurant. Small garden. Swimming pool and tennis court
Location 6 km NE of Brantôme by D78 and D83. Parking.
Restriction No smoking in dining room.
Credit cards All major cards accepted.
Terms [1989 rates] Rooms 380–550 frs, suites 620 frs. Breakfast 50 frs. Set lunch/dinner 190–350 frs. Reduced rates and special meals for children.

LA CHARTRE-SUR-LE-LOIR 72340 Sarthe — Map 8

Hôtel de France — *Tel* 43.44.40.16
20 place de la République

A pleasant little market town between Tours and Le Mans, just west of the Ronsard country where the poet lived and loved; also near the strange hill village of Trôo where some English writers and others live in cunningly modernised caves in the tufa cliffside. The *France* is an unpretentious hostelry on the main square, breezily described to us: "Madame is dead brisk but v. amiable and proved happy to stay up after all the waiters had gone home. The hotel is obsessed with motor-racing – toy cars and photos of heroes in the public areas. Our long meal was OK, good solid stuff, jolly attempts at presentation (the caneton had a bandage, the escalopes came with sort-of horseshoe rosettes). The place was full of Brits, which does tend to slow down service. You need to be able to bark out your order very fast, as in New York delis. Nice room, comfy, quite pretty. Very short fat bath, just about fitted me after three weeks pigging French food." Rooms in the annexe are said to be less good than those in the main building. More reports please.

Open All year except 15 Nov–15 Dec.
Rooms 26 double, 2 single – 22 with bath, 4 with shower, all with telephone; 22 with TV. 12 in annexe.
Facilities 2 salons, bar, restaurant; conference facilities. Garden on river Loir.
Location In main square; parking. Town is 40 km N of Tours.
Restriction Not suitable for ♿.
Credit cards Probably Access, Visa.
Terms Rooms: single 110 frs, double 170–210 frs. Breakfast 22 frs. Set lunch/dinner 62, 95, 170 and 220 frs.

CHÂTEAU-ARNOUX 04160 Alpes-de-Haute-Provence — Map 11

La Bonne Étape — *Tel* 92.64.00.09
Chemin du Lac — *Fax* 92.64.37.36
Telex 430605 BONETAP

Some of the best cooking in Provence (two *Michelin* rosettes, three red *Gault Millau toques*) is provided by the anglophile Gleize family (father created the restaurant at the *Capital* in London, son worked at the *Connaught*) at their elegantly converted and fairly expensive 17th-century coaching-inn. The setting is a bit cramped, on the main Grenoble-Marseilles highway, in a small town in a dull part of the Durance valley: but there are open fields at the back, and some rooms have a balcony facing these, over the swimming pool. Front rooms can be noisier. "A wonderful place, with charming rooms", say visitors this year; "in the beautiful dining room we enjoyed roast pigeon, wild boar with raisins and pignon nuts, and stuffed courgette flowers." Try also the local herb-fed lamb. (*Lynne and David Allen*)

Open 15 Feb–26 Nov, 4 Dec–5 Jan. Closed Sun evening and Mon out of season. Restaurant closed 24 Dec.
Rooms 7 suites, 11 double – all with bath and shower, telephone, radio and TV.
Facilities Salon, bar, 2 dining rooms; small conference room. Garden with heated swimming pool and patio. Lake 200 metres.
Location Near town centre, which is 14 km S of Sisteron. Parking.
Restriction Not suitable for ♿.
Credit cards All major cards accepted.
Terms Rooms: single 400 frs, double 600 frs, suite 850 frs. Breakfast 70 frs. Dinner, B&B 725–850 frs per person. Set lunch/dinner 190, 320, 370 and 390 frs; full alc 300 frs. Special meals for children on request.

CHÂTEAUNEUF 21320 Côte d'Or — Map 10

Hostellerie du Château — *Tel* 80.49.22.00

This well-modernised little rural hotel has a dramatic hilltop location in a medieval fortified hill-village west of Dijon. Reports last year: "A charming hostelry, carefully converted, with lots of rough stonework, exposed beams, and a small terrace for drinks. Dinner excellent." "A pretty garden, and an excellent meal in the unpretentious restaurant." "Comfortable, well run and well equipped". The suite and the larger bedrooms are in the annexe, *La Résidence*, a 16th-century house 50 metres from the hotel. This year, some readers found the setting delightful and the food good (*Janet and Dennis Allom, and others*): but another, while admiring the cooking, severely criticised the "patronising" Madame and slow, unsmiling, unhelpful service, so we'd welcome further reports.

Open 15 Mar–12 Nov. Closed Mon evening and Tue 1 Oct–15 Jun.
Rooms 1 suite, 16 double, 2 single – all with bath and/or shower, 11 with WC, all with telephone; 3 with radio. Suite, 5 doubles in annexe.
Facilities Salon, bar, 2 restaurants; banqueting room. Small garden with swings for children.
Location 10 km SE of Pouilly-en-Auxois. Take Pouilly exit from A6 motorway, take Arnay-le-Duc turning (N494), turn left down Beaune road (D977 bis), left again via Vandenesse to Châteauneuf.
Restriction Not suitable for ♿.
Credit cards Access, Amex, Visa.
Terms [1989 rates] Rooms: single 135–155 frs, double 450–500 frs, suite 500 frs. Breakfast 30 frs. Set lunch/dinner 125–260 frs. Special meals for children.

CHÂTILLON-SUR-SEINE 21400 Côte-d'Or — Map 9

Hotel de la Côte d'Or — *Tel* 80.91.13.29
Rue Charles Ronot

Châtillon is a small town on the upper Seine between Troyes and Dijon, noted for its museum of antiquities which include gold and silver Grecian artefacts of the 6th century BC, found in 1953 at nearby Vix, in the tomb of a Gallic princess. Not quite in that class of distinction, but very pretty and charming, is the ivy-covered *Côte d'Or*, new to the Guide this year, "A favourite stop-over point for me. Dinner – ah, dinner! – is served out in the courtyard (when fine), under vast rustling chestnut and sycamore trees, filled with cooing doves. A fountain plays gently, lights in the trees come on as the afterglow fades from the skies, the service is friendly and prompt but not hurried. The *menu régional* at 115 frs [1989] was excellent value: the vast array of cheeses went well with the delicious walnuted brown bread. My little room had a comfortable bed, two elegant chairs, a tiny antique desk, fresh flowers – but a gigantic spider leapt out of the folds when I drew the curtains." (*Hilary Swenson*) More reports welcome on this only slightly tarnished idyll.

Open All year except 18 Dec–23 Jan. Closed Sun evening and Mon except Jul and Aug.
Rooms 10 – 9 with bath and/or shower. all with telephone and TV.
Facilities Salon, bar, restaurant. Garden.
Location Central, near river. Parking. Town is 64 km SE of Troyes.
Restriction Not suitable for ♿.
Credit cards All major cards accepted.
Terms Rooms: single 170 frs, double 255–460 frs. Breakfast 35 frs. Dinner, B&B 80 frs added per person. Set meals 80–220 frs; full alc 180 frs.

CHÂTEAUNEUF-DU-PAPE 84230 Vaucluse — Map 11

Hostellerie Château des Fines Roches — *Tel* 90.83.70.23, *Fax* 90.83.78.42

This creeper-covered neo-Gothic pile with crenellated towers, former home of the Marquis de Baroncelli, stands isolated amid its own vineyards on a low hill above the plain north of Avignon. Readers have admired it (with reservations) for some years, and our inspector reports, "From the outside it looks massively mock-feudal, but inside the public rooms are small and intimate, though still 'baronial'. Soothed by piped classical music and seated on leather chairs, we took drinks in a salon lined with antique books; of the two tiny, elegant dining rooms, one is in modern style, but the other has a log fire and baronial emblems. Service we found deft but impersonal, otherwise all was as sleek and *soigné* as you'd expect in a small superior high-priced château hotel. Our cosy bedroom was well furnished and equipped, with antique bed-lamps, matching fabrics, hair-drier, tiled bathroom, even a trouser-press. The main set menu has limited choice and the cooking was uneven: but it is served with style and just about merits its *Michelin* rosette and *Gault Millau toque*. The wine list is mainly local C-du-P, including some from the hotel's own vineyards. Breakfast, including iced fresh orange juice, was excellent, though marred by piped pop music which had replaced the classical. In summer it is served more peacefully out on the panoramic terrace." A reader this year found the owners unfriendly – as did our inspector.

Open All year except Christmas–end-Feb, hotel closed Sun evening and Mon in low season. Restaurant closed Mon.
Rooms 7 double – 5 with bath, 2 with shower, all with telephone and TV.
Facilities 2 lounges, bar, 2 dining rooms.

Location 3 km S of Châteauneuf (by D17) which is 18 km N of Avignon, 13 km S of Orange.
Restriction Not suitable for ♿.
Credit card Access, Visa.
Terms [1989 rates] Rooms 520–720 frs. Breakfast 60 frs. Set lunch/dinner 195 frs.

CHAVOIRES 74290 Haute-Savoie — Map 10

Pavillon de l'Ermitage — *Tel* 50.60.11.09

The Tuccinardi family's white villa beside the lovely lake of Annecy is a formally elegant restaurant whose Bressane cooking (e.g. fish soufflé) is judged to be well deserving of its *Michelin* rosette and *Gault Millau toque*. "Yes, the cuisine is indeed distinguished, with portions dauntingly large," runs one report this year; "but the bedrooms with their faded decor are serviceable rather than attractive." Others tend to agree, though one recent visitor did have "a lovely room with a view over the lake, and a palatial pink marble bathroom." Back rooms with balconies facing the lake are best: front ones face the main road. "Everyone was cheerful and welcoming and the food excellent." In summer you can dine by the water's edge on a smart terrace under the trees. (*Alex Liddell, PJ Forrest, Peter and Ann Jones*)

Open Mar–end Oct.
Rooms 2 suites, 8 double – all with bath and telephone.
Facilities Lounge, bar, restaurant. Terrace and lakeside garden.
Location 3 km E of Annecy on Lake Annecy, near *téléphérique.*
Restriction Not suitable for ♿.
Credit cards All major cards accepted.
Terms Rooms: double 280–450 frs, suite 500–550 frs. Breakfast 40 frs. Dinner, B&B 350–520 frs per person. Set lunch/dinner 190, 250 and 380 frs; alc 350 frs (excluding wine).

CHEFFES 49125 Maine-et-Loire — Map 10

Château de Teildras — *Tel* 41.42.61.08, *Telex* 722268 TEILDRA

A visitor this year had a "wonderful" stay at this elegant little 16th-century château on the edge of a quiet village beside a pretty stretch of the river Sarthe, north of Angers. It is the family home of the Comte de Bernard du Breil, who some years ago decided that the best way to preserve his estate was to turn it into a hotel. This he has done, meticulously, and is helped by his wife and two daughters, one of them married to an American writer. You can ride, fish or go for walks in the large park. "We sipped tea in the rose garden and enjoyed an elegant room with high beamed ceiling and royal blue floral wallpaper. It had a view across the fields. Dinner was expensive but well prepared." That report this year echoes earlier enthusiasm: "Magnificent atmosphere, delicious food." "The public rooms are beautifully decorated with tapestries, paintings and plants, and the lighting is subdued. Our bedrooms had antiques, and its windows looked on to the park with its lovely trees and three cows munching in the sunlight." However, one visitor this year thought the grounds poorly maintained and the local wines of poor quality. (*Nancy P Barker, TD Baxendale*)

Open Hotel: 1 Feb–31 Dec. Restaurant 1 Apr–2 Nov. Both closed Tue, Wed morning.
Rooms 11 double – all with bath and shower, telephone and TV.
Facilities 2 salons, bar, 2 dining rooms. Wooded park. Golf, tennis, swimming nearby.
Location 19 km N of Angers. Turn out of Cheffes towards Juvardeil; château is signposted.
Credit cards All major cards accepted.
Terms B&B: single 470–774 frs, double 670–999 frs. Dinner, B&B single 730–880 frs, double 1,280 frs. Full alc 250 frs. Children under 12 sharing parents' room free; special meals.

CHÊNEHUTTE-LES-TUFFEAUX 49350 Maine-et-Loire — Map 10

Hostellerie du Prieuré — *Tel* 41.67.90.14
Telex 720379 PRIEURE

A priory dating from the 12th century is now a smart and well-known hostelry, set in a splendid position on a bluff above the Loire, amid 60 acres of private wooded park. "Lovely location, friendly and attentive staff, attractive pool, large room with usual French flock wallpaper, but comfortable." "The multiple terraces and flower gardens are wonderful. Not all bedrooms overlook the Loire, but ours did and the view was superb. The room itself was delightfully furnished with matching materials, and well equipped. The dining room and lounge also look over the river. Here the food was just a little 'over the top' and *too* highly priced: delicious, but fussily garnished". Another visitor has agreed – and we note that *Michelin* has now withdrawn its rosette, though the two red *Gault Millau toques* remain. One reader this year enjoyed the food and lovely setting, but thought that the hotel did not quite merit such prices. (*ATW Liddell, Edwin Prince*) The rooms facing the river are subject to some noise disturbances: express trains and gravel dredgers. One reader recommends the bungalows in the oak and pine woods, slightly less luxurious, but cheaper. It is worth visiting the nearby caves in the tufa rocks. Some are used for growing mushrooms (300 tons per day!), some have ancient sculptures recently discovered, and some are still occupied as troglodyte dwellings (open to tourists).

Open All year except early Jan–3 Mar.
Rooms 2 suites, 33 double – 32 with bath, 3 with shower, all with telephone; 21 with TV. 15 in pavilion in park.
Facilities Lounge, bar with TV, restaurant. Large grounds with mini-golf, tennis court, heated swimming pool; fishing in the Loire.
Location 7 km NW of Saumur off D751.
Restriction Not suitable for ♿.
Credit cards Access, Diners, Visa.
Terms B&B: single 558–708 frs, double 696–1,316 frs, suite 1,116–1,566 frs. Set lunch/dinner 270, 340 and 390 frs; full alc 400 frs. Reduced rates and special meals for children.

> Hotels often book you into their most expensive rooms or suites unless you specify otherwise. Even if all room prices are the same, hotels may give you a less good room in the hope of selling their better rooms to late customers. It always pays to discuss accommodation in detail when making a reservation.

CHINON 37500 Indre-et-Loire — Map 10

Hôtel Diderot — *Tel* 47.93.18.87

4 rue Buffon

This modest B&B, run by a friendly Cypriot, Theodore Kazamias, is in a lovely old town near the Loire, with a famous half-ruined hilltop castle, where Joan of Arc first met the Dauphin. It has long been a Guide favourite. The house is attractive, built of pale stone, much of it covered by a vine, with a wrought-iron balcony on the second floor, reached by a spiral staircase. Inside are exposed beams, and a welcoming salon. Breakfasts, taken communally, are notable for the huge choice of home-made preserves. A great bonus is the courtyard, closed at night, where cars can be safely parked. Some rooms are spacious, others quite small; courtyard-facing ones are the quietest. The hotel went through a slightly rocky patch in 1988, but we are glad to hear from recent readers of immaculate rooms, freshly decorated, and attractive new bathrooms. As before the consensus is that the *Diderot* is "tremendous value for money". (*Jo and Mick Féat, JM Pictet, Nancy P Barker, Peter Nicholls, and others*)

Open All year.
Rooms 24 double – all with bath and/or shower, and telephone; TV on request. 3 in annexe. 4 on ground floor are suitable for ♿.
Facilities Lounge, bar with TV, breakfast room; limited conference facilities. Courtyard.
Location Near place Jeanne d'Arc; hotel is well signposted. Parking in courtyard.
Credit cards All major cards accepted.
Terms B&B: single 185–265 frs, double 250–350 frs. (No restaurant.)

Château de Marçay — *Tel* 47.93.03.47

Fax 47.93.45.33
Telex 751475 MARCAY

Set in open country south of Chinon, here's a familiar Loire valley species – a 15th-century stone château approached by an impressive chestnut-tree-lined gravel drive, with neat pepper-pot towers and formal garden, converted into a smart and stylish hotel, and consecrated by *Michelin* with its full panoply of rosette, red gables and red rocking-chair. "Very seductive", "Large rooms furnished with antiques, and restaurant beautifully appointed", are among this year's comments. Other reports: "Quite a friendly reception. We had a pleasant room in the pavilion annexe. Rather snooty dining room, with so many staff; food very good, but rather a lot of noisy banging of kitchen doors." "Our vast room occupied an entire floor in one of the towers, beds were turned down at night and luxury chocolates left on the bedside tables. Dinner on the terrace was near perfect – the food leans towards *nouvelle* with very few vegetables. Both the maître d' and the sommelier were young ladies, smart and charming. Prompt yet unhurried waitress service. Breakfast just about adequate though 25 frs extra for orange juice seemed extortionate." (*ATW Liddell, Victoria P Turner, Minda Alexander, Ian and Francine Walsh*) Rooms in the annexe are considerably cheaper than those in the château.

Open Mid-Mar–mid-Jan.
Rooms 3 suites, 35 double – all with bath and/or shower, and telephone; 12 with radio and TV. 11 in pavilion annexe.

Facilities Lift. 2 salons, TV room, bar, restaurant; conference/functions facilities; 2 terraces. Gardens with tennis court, heated swimming pool and children's playground.
Location 7 km S of Chinon by D116.
Credit cards All major cards accepted.
Terms Rooms: château 780–1,350 frs, pavilion 495–850 frs. Breakfast 54 frs. Dinner, B&B 610–1,010 frs per person. Set lunch/dinner 200 and 320 frs; alc (excluding wine) 350–400 frs. Reduced rates and special meals for children.

CHONAS L'AMBALLAN 38121 Isère — Map 10

Domaine de Clairefontaine

Tel 74.58.81.52
Fax 74.58.84.18
Telex 308132 CLAIRGI

A cheaper alternative to the *Marais St-Jean* (see below), but equally pleasant: a big stone 18th-century mansion on the edge of the village, in a lovely rural setting, converted into "the nicest kind of French country hotel, family-run, very unpretentious, slightly down-at-heel, reasonably priced", as an inspector relates. "We had breakfast on the terrace amid birdsong, facing vistas of meadows and rolling hills. A big garden and lovely lawn, a pond, a farm-like feeling – idyllic. The house, which once belonged to the bishops of nearby Vienne, is now run by charming petite Madame Girardon and her two sons, who trained chez Outhier at La Napoule. Their cooking is not in that class, but good (poulet à l'ail, truite au fenouil); menus have limited choice and change little, so a short stay might be best. Friendly service by local girls in a high-ceilinged too-brightly-lit dining room. Some rooms in main building, others in converted outhouse, simple but fairly comfortable." Endorsed this year: "Food was delicious"; "Full of kindness: we arrived when the restaurant was closed, but the son of the house made us a scratch meal which was perfection." (*Peter Dingley, Paul Van Broekhoven*) However, a reader who had one of the simpler rooms found it decidedly uncomfortable, and thought the service a bit chaotic, too.

Open All year except Dec and Jan. Closed Mon midday and Sun evening out of season.
Rooms 18 double – 12 with bath and/or shower; 16 with telephone. 6 in annexe next to main building. 4 ground-floor rooms.
Facilities Salon, 2 dining rooms; terrace. Garden, tennis court.
Location Off N7, 9 km S of Vienne; turn off A7 motorway at Vienne Sud. Parking.
Credit card Visa.
Terms Rooms 90–330 frs. Breakfast 28 frs. Set lunch/dinner 95, 130, 160 and 220 frs. Special meals for children.

Hostellerie Le Marais St-Jean

Tel 74.58.83.28

Christian and Suzette Heugas own and run a very stylish modern hotel, in a big pink converted farmhouse set amid pretty country near the Rhône, south of Vienne. "This was the jewel in the crown – what a treat!" runs one recent report; "attractive pieces of old France everywhere, beautiful flowers and lovely antiques. The bedrooms were spacious and comfortable, the view from our room was like a postcard. Dinner was the best meal I have ever had in France, beautifully presented, and breakfast was special too, with bowls of home-made jams. The Heugas are that lovely combination of a dedicated, enthusiastic and modest couple." Others, too, have much enjoyed the food (*Gault Millau toques*) – e.g. duck in a sharp fruit sauce and "real country soups" – as well as the beamed ceiling and tiled floor of the cool and sober dining room, and the luxurious bedrooms. "Our teenage children had great fun with the owners' dogs." One visitor this year thought the rooms nice but the food overpriced; another, who suffered a flight delay, was put out to find that her room had not been kept despite a written confirmation.

Open All year except 1–10 Nov, Feb, Tue evening and Wed.
Rooms 10 double – all with bath, shower and telephone. 1 ground-floor room with easy access.
Facilities 2 salons, bar, restaurant; conference room. Garden with terrace for alfresco meals.
Location Turn off A7 motorway at Vienne Sud; village, well-signposted, lies to W of N7, 9 km S of Vienne.
Credit cards All major cards accepted.
Terms B&B: single 505 frs, double 550 frs. Set lunch/dinner 150, 240 and 290 frs; full alc 250 frs. Reduced rates and special meals for children.

CLUNY 71250 Saône-et-Loire — Map 10

Hôtel de Bourgogne — *Tel* 85.59.00.58
Place de l'Abbaye

A rambling but dignified old hotel in the main square of this picturesque medieval town, facing what remains of the mighty Romanesque abbey that in the Middle Ages was one of Europe's leading religious, artistic and intellectual centres. The well-kept *Bourgogne* has been an inn since the 18th century (Lamartine often stayed here and guests can still sleep in his bed). Most of its bedrooms "ours was the size of a small flat" look out on to green hills or to the towers of the abbey. One reader this year had "an ambitious dinner served by charming novices" and found the Gosse family owners "most cordial". Others agree: the "delicious food" merits its *Michelin* rosette, though one visitor thought the *nouvelle cuisine* preparation rather affected. (*William A Grant*)

Open 10 Feb–15 Nov. Closed Tue except high season; restaurant also closed Wed midday.
Rooms 2 suites, 14 double – 9 with bath, 4 with shower, all with telephone; 2 with TV.
Facilities Ramps. Salon, bar, restaurant. Small courtyard where drinks and breakfasts are served in fine weather. Films, concerts.
Location On N79, 25 km NW of Mâcon. Hotel is opposite the abbey (back rooms quietest). Garage parking.
Credit cards All major cards accepted.
Terms Rooms: double 328 frs, suite 720 frs. Breakfast 40 frs. Set lunch/dinner 110–350 frs; full alc 200–300 frs. Reduced rates and special meals for children.

COLLIOURE 66190 Pyrénées-Orientales — Map 10

Hôtel Madeloc — *Tel* 68.82.07.56
Rue Romain-Rolland

Ten minutes' walk up a steepish hill from the quayside of the picturesque and popular fishing-port-cum-trendy-resort, south-east of Perpignan, is this modern B&B hotel in local Catalan style, cool and welcoming, set in its own garden;

many rooms have balcony or terrace; upper ones have views over the hills. Pleasant decor, efficient bathrooms. Open Easter–15 Oct. 21 rooms, all with bath or shower and balcony. B&B: single 240 frs, double 302–380 frs. No recent feedback. More reports welcome.

COLLONGES-LA-ROUGE 19500 Corrèze — Map 10

Relais de St-Jacques de Compostelle — *Tel* 55.25.41.02, *Telex* 283155

Many fine buildings including a 12th-century church grace this beautiful 16th-century village, built of local purple-red stone, carefully restored and set in lush green valleys a few miles north of the Dordogne. The ruined château of the Vicomte de Turenne, former lord of the region, stands just to the west. The *Relais*, more popular than ever this year, offers inexpensive bedrooms that, although very clean, may be too basic for some tastes: but it also has "delightfully friendly" owners, the Castéras, whose cooking earns a *Michelin* red "R" for good value. "A most delectable place", runs one report this year; "the bedrooms may be simple, but the restaurant's ambience is one of rural sophistication, with expert service (uniformed waiters hover). The food is amongst the best we have had anywhere - tremendous platters of hors d'oeuvre, massive helpings of stuffed lamb, superb goats' cheeses. Breakfast similarly civilised." "Madame slightly disorganised but very welcoming, bedrooms spotless and rather sweet, a very cosy salon and a marvellous dinner." "M. Castéra loves to chat with his guests after dinner, even if their French is poor." Be warned, however, that the bedrooms are small, the shower-rooms can be minuscule, and lavatories are not numerous. (*Melanie Worrall, Minda Alexander, Dr P Blackwell-Smyth*)

Open 1 Feb–30 Nov. Closed Tue evening and Wed in low season.
Rooms 11 double, 1 single – 5 with bath, 2 with shower, all with telephone. 5 in annexe.
Facilities Salon, bar, 2 dining rooms, dining terrace.
Location 21 km SE of Brive; follow signs to Meyssac. Hotel is central. Parking.
Restriction Not suitable for ♿.
Credit cards Access, Diners, Visa.
Terms [1989 rates] Rooms 100–240 frs. Dinner, B&B 160–230 frs per person. Set lunch/dinner 90–220 frs; full alc 250 frs. Reduced rates and special meals for children.

COLY 24120 Dordogne — Map 10

Manoir d'Hautegente — *Tel* 53.51.68.03 and 53.51.60.18

Set amid deep country near Terrasson, some 20 kilometres north of Sarlat, this fine creeper-covered mansion has been owned by the Hamelin family for 300 years and they have now converted it into a small hotel. It makes an appealing Guide debut this year: "The house is beautiful, amid water-gardens, streams, fields and woods, and the interior has been furnished and decorated with imagination. The bedrooms (more are about to be built in the granaries) are all different and all lovely, with antiques and big, comfortable beds. In the salon, a log fire blazes when the evenings get cool. Dinner, a five-course set meal, is cooked by

Madame Hamelin, using her own foie gras, confit de canard, cèpes – and it is excellent. It has a strong regional bias, but there are some lighter, more innovative dishes too. Breakfasts are a delight. A peaceful place and the family are charming, though never intrusive." (*Jennifer Harte*)

Open 1 Apr–31 Oct. Dining room closed for lunch.
Rooms 10 double – all with bath and telephone. 1 ground-floor room.
Facilities Lounge, dining room. Garden. River with private fishing.
Location 19 km N of Sarlat. Parking.
Credit cards Access, Visa.
Terms Dinner, B&B 420–600 frs. Set dinner 200 frs; full alc 280 frs. Reduced rates and special meals for children.

COMBEAUFONTAINE 70120 Haute-Saône — Map 9

Le Balcon — *Tel* 84.92.11.13

In a village on the Langres-Vesoul road, north-east of Dijon, a friendly family-run Logis de France *with rustic decor and excellent food* (Gault Millau toque). *Rooms at back are quietest. 20 rooms, all with bath and/or shower. Rooms 110–350 frs. Breakfast 28 frs. Set meals 130–280 frs* [1989]. *New nomination. More reports welcome.*

COMBLOUX 74920 Haute-Savoie — Map 10

Aux Ducs de Savoie — *Tel* 50.58.61.43
Le Bouchet — *Telex* 319244 AUXDUCS

This big modern chalet, where most rooms have a balcony facing Mont Blanc, is the leading hotel of a sizeable skiing and summer resort near Megève. Warm, friendly and well run, with large bedrooms; food good, but choice limited. Open-air pool, heated in summer. Open 10 Jun–25 Sep, 18 Dec–25 Apr. 50 rooms, all with bath. B&B double 406–496 frs. Set menus 130–190 frs. New nomination. More reports please.

COMBREUX 45530 Loiret — Map 9

L'Auberge — *Tel* 38.59.47.63

On the edge of a village in flat but pleasant woodland country east of Orléans, this creeper-covered *auberge* dates from 1847 and has been liked by several readers. An inspector reports, "Quite unsmart, it is run in a friendly, casual way by its civilised bourgeois owners, Madame Gangloff and her niece. There is a cosy pub-like lounge with log fire, a beamed dining room, and a small rather unkempt garden at the back, with swings and ping-pong; tennis-court and swimming pool are across the road, next to open fields and a bedroom annexe. Rooms are simple but comfortable, good value. All in all, a sympathetic place – save that the classic home cooking (tête de veau, râble de lièvre, tarte tatin) is somewhat overpriced for its only average quality. Nice service by local girls, and good breakfasts." "Good food (e.g. salmon in sorrel sauce), and superior bathrooms."

Open All year except 20 Dec–20 Jan.
Rooms 21 – all with bath and/or shower, and telephone. Some in annexe.
Facilities Lounge, bar, restaurant; conference room. Garden with swimming pool and tennis court.
Location 35 km E of Orléans, 13 km N of Châteauneuf-sur-Loire. Parking.
Credit cards Access, Visa.
Terms [1989 rates] Rooms 250–300 frs. Breakfast 30 frs. Half board 270–330 frs per person. Set lunch/dinner 90–200 frs. Special meals for children.

COMPIÈGNE 60200 Oise — Map 9

Hostellerie du Royal-Lieu — *Tel* 44.20.10.24
9 rue de Senlis

Joan the Maid was captured and sold to the English in this historic town with its huge royal palace; then the Germans in 1918, and later the French in 1940, signed ignominious armistices in a clearing in the nearby forest. In today's happier age, British, French and German tourists rub shoulders in this "excellent hotel" just outside the town. It is not cheap, but offers quality. Apart from one reader this year who liked the bedrooms but had a poor meal, all new reports have been favourable. "It makes a great first night in France because it reminds you of all the things the French do better than us in hotels – delicious food, making their guests feel looked after in an unservile way, an unfussed view of children in public places. We had a superb meal. The rooms are small and cluttered with heavy repro furniture, but all look out onto greenery and a little flock of doves." "An efficient and warm welcome, and superb cooking." "Comfortable, but bed-lighting poor." The main road in front is ugly, but at the back all is calm and green. (*Jeremy Raymond, Carolyn and Gary Smith, Mrs RB Richards*)

Open All year.
Rooms 3 suites, 15 double, 2 single – all with bath and/or shower, telephone and TV. 1 ground-floor room, suitable for ♿.
Facilities Salon, bar, restaurant; terrace for meals in fine weather. Garden.
Location 3 km SW of town, on Senlis road (D932A).
Credit cards Access, Diners, Visa.
Terms Rooms 300–420 frs. Breakfast 30 frs. Set lunch/dinner 180 and 280 frs. Special meals for children.

CONDRIEU 69420 Rhône — Map 10

Hôtellerie Beau Rivage — *Tel* 74.59.52.24
Telex 308946

An old creeper-covered hotel beside the *beau rivage* of the Rhône, in Côte du Rhône vineyard country. In summer you can take drinks under white parasols on the "wonderful" terrace right by the river, or dine out on the stone-flagged patio. The hotel was dropped from the 1989 Guide during a period of ownership reshuffle, but the Humann family are now firmly at the helm, and many readers have spoken well of them this year, and of the *Michelin*-rosetted food. "We had a splendid room with fabric-covered walls and fine furniture. The public areas are spacious and the gardens lovely. The service had a flourish, and the dinners were amongst the best of our holiday." "We were delighted at the standards of cuisine, welcome and service – we found the porter polishing all the guests' cars' windscreens, quite unasked." "A typically French hotel with slightly higgledy-piggledy room arrangements." "The meal was a gastronomic masterpiece." There's a petro-chemical works half a mile away, whose low throbbing can be heard at night. (*Mrs JB Priestley, Stephan and Kate Murray-Sykes, Sarah Curtis, John RL Cook, Carolyn and Gary Smith, and others*)

Open 15 Feb–15 Jan.
Rooms 2 suites, 22 double – all with bath and shower, telephone, radio, TV and baby-listening.
Facilities Salon, bar, 2 restaurants. Terrace restaurant overlooking the Rhône. Garden, fishing.
Location 40 km S of Lyon, on N86. Leave A7 at Condrieu exit (coming from N), or Chanas exit (coming from S).
Restrictions Not suitable for ♿.
Credit cards All major cards accepted.
Terms B&B: single 557 frs, double 614–834 frs, suite 904 frs.
Set meals 250–370 frs.

CONQUES 12320 Aveyron — Map 10

Hôtel Sainte-Foy — *Tel* 65.69.84.03

This famous old village between Figeac and Rodez was a leading staging-post on the pilgrimage to Santiago. It straggles along a steep wooded hillside above a gorge, and its slate-roofed houses and cobbled streets surround a massive and awesome abbey church, renowned for the Romanesque stone carving on the west doorway and for its rich gold and silver treasure. The *Sainte-Foy* is called after the martyred girl whose weird gold relic is still to be seen in the abbey museum. It's a fine medieval house facing the abbey, with handsome old furniture in the public rooms; and in 1988/9 readers have again enjoyed its comforts, food and service, especially "dining in the leafy courtyard, gently floodlit". The food is traditional and regional, very well cooked ("delicious tripoux"). The staff, all female, are helpful and charming, and the atmosphere is restful. Readers warn that some upper rooms are small and thin-walled (but well fitted, apart from one account of a sagging bed) and that plumbing and church clocks can be noisy at night. (*D and L Allen, Dr RL Holmes and Dr MW Atkinson*)

Open Easter–1 Nov.
Rooms 1 suite, 18 double, 2 single – 11 with bath, 10 with shower, all with telephone.
Facilities Reading room, TV room, bar, dining room; conference facilities; interior patio.
Location Off D601 and not far from N662 between Figeac (54 km) and Rodez (37 km). Hotel is central, opposite cathedral. Garage and car park.
Restriction Not suitable for ♿.
Credit cards Access, Visa.
Terms [1989 rates] Rooms 180–380 frs, Breakfast 34 frs. Dinner, B&B 310–370 frs per person. Set lunch/dinner 108–175 frs. Special meals for children.

LES CONTAMINES-MONTJOIE Haute-Savoie 74170 — Map 10

Hôtel Gai Soleil — *Tel* 50.47.02.94

An old farmhouse, modernised into a spruce and friendly little holiday hotel, set on the edge of a ski and summer resort at the foot of Mont-Blanc, south of St-

Gervais. Small but comfortable rooms with good lighting and bathrooms. A leafy garden with deck-chairs, where you can take drinks. Home cooking, simple and without choice, but good; generous breakfasts. Guests almost all French. Open 16 June–18 Sept, 18 Dec–16 Apr. 19 rooms, some with bath and shower. Dinner, B&B 215–260 frs. Set menus 80–150 frs. Recent nomination. More reports please.

CORDES 81170 Tarn — Map 10

Hôtel Le Grand Écuyer — *Tel* 63.56.01.03
Rue Voltaire

This "lovely hotel", a former hunting-lodge of the Counts of Toulouse, is a select little place with fine antiques and spacious rooms. It stands inside a famous old ramparted hilltop village, whose streets today are lined with boutiques and craft shops. It was built by the Counts in the 13th century as a defence against Simon de Montfort and his cruel anti-Cathar crusaders. "A wonderful way to bid farewell to the Cathars," writes one north-bound visitor this year; "a bedroom with a comfortable four-poster, pleasant carpets, a high timbered ceiling, and the best-appointed bathroom I've met outside Paris. A good, relaxed meal, capped by the virtuoso dessert production" (*Michelin* rosette and two red *Gault Millau toques*). Other correspondents were even more ecstatic: "When I die, dear Lord, please send me to *Le Grand Écuyer*. The staff were the best of any hotel in France. The food was wonderful, the desserts fabulous. I have such a poignant memory of rising in the morning and opening the shutters to find myself floating on a sea of mist sunk in the valley while the sun sparkles on the green hills above. There is a knock on the door and the breakfast tray full of breads and croissants, fresh juice and aromatic tea and coffee is set before us on a table by the window. Surely this must be heaven." (*TH Nash, Lynne and David Allen*)

Open 17 Mar–31 Oct. Restaurant closed Mon except July and Aug.
Rooms 1 suite, 12 double – all with bath, telephone, radio and TV.
Facilities 2 lounges, bar, 3 dining rooms. Terrace.
Location In centre of village which is 25 km NW of Albi. Public parking down the hill, crowded in high season.
Restriction Not suitable for ♿.
Credit cards All major cards accepted.
Terms Rooms 500–750 frs, suite 1,200 frs. Breakfast 50 frs. Dinner, B&B 520–620 frs per person. Set lunch/dinner 180–360 frs. Special meals for children on request.

Hostellerie du Vieux Cordes — *Tel* 63.56.00.12
Rue St-Michel — *Telex* 530955

Warmly nominated this year as a cheaper alternative to the *Grand Écuyer*, this newly redecorated and very stylish *Logis de France* stands next to a medieval church: you can dine on the terrace, or in a delightful courtyard under a huge ancient wistaria. "The best hotel of our week's touring, a friendly welcome, and a lovely view of the valley from our room. Much of the old building remains, though the bedroom decor disguises this with a fabric wall cover. The menus range in price and style from traditional to modern: ours was in the middle of both, and was excellent and charmingly served. Breakfast too was the best of our trip." (*CR; John and Rita Newnham*)

Open All year except Jan.
Rooms 21 double – all with bath and/or shower, and telephone; 10 with TV.
Facilities Lounge, bar, TV room, restaurant. Small garden, courtyard.
Location Central; parking nearby.
Restriction Not suitable for ♿.
Credit cards All major cards accepted.
Terms B&B: single 295–405 frs, double 360–465 frs; dinner, B&B: single 350 frs, double 520 frs. Set meals 70–240 frs; full alc 180 frs. Reduced rates and special meals for children.

CORDON 74700 Haute-Savoie — Map 10

Hôtel des Roches Fleuries — *Tel* 50.58.06.71

In a small ski-resort west of Chamonix, this pleasant, spacious and informal chalet-style hotel faces across the valley to Mont Blanc, with spectacular views; many bedrooms have their own balcony. The new owners, the Picot family, continue to please most of our readers, who praise the well-furnished, comfortable rooms and warmth of hospitality. Most of them like the food, too, though one couple thought the medium-price set menu rather poor. The smaller of the two dining rooms is the more attractive. A heated swimming pool has now been installed.

Open 20 Dec–15 Apr, 1 June–25 Sep.
Rooms 27 double, 1 single – all with bath and shower, telephone and TV. 2 in annexe.
Facilities 2 lounges, bar, restaurant. Garden, heated swimming pool.
Location 4 km SW of Sallanches on D113. Parking.
Restriction Not suitable for ♿.
Credit cards Access, Amex, Visa.
Terms B&B double 305–345 frs; dinner, B&B 260–340 frs per person. Set lunch/dinner 120–240 frs; full alc 250 frs. 1-night bookings probably refused in high season. Reduced rates and special meals for children.

CORPS-LA-SALETTE 38970 Isère — Map 10

Hôtel de la Poste — *Tel* 76.30.00.03
Place de la Mairie

At this scenic village along the Route Napoléon, high up on the winding Grenoble to Gap highway (N85) in the Dauphiné Alps, Bonaparte rested on his journey from Elba to Paris and Waterloo. Many tourists today pass this way too, en route to or from Provence, and the highly traditional *Poste* is again much liked by several readers this year: "A busy and bustling hotel with superb food and always full – justifiably so. No *nouvelle cuisine* here – vast helpings (*Michelin* red "R"), a very pleasant dining room, and the best breakfast we had in France. Our room was Victorian (apart from the bathroom) but comfortable." Another 1989 visitor, on a return trip, also found the food enjoyable and copious, but noted a shortage of hot water and a mistaken over-charging for two beers; she felt that the owner's attitude to his guests was a little offhand, maybe due to over-popularity. Of the two annexes across the road, one is "rather basic", the other has smartly decorated rooms giving onto a private courtyard with tables and chairs. One reader had a room with walls "covered in gold silk damask and the shower room was all new in lilac pink with gold taps". (*Philippa and Peter Herbert, Lt. Col. BAS Barnes; also EP Bazalgette*)

Open All year except 31 Nov–1 Feb.
Rooms 19 double, 1 single – all with bath/shower and telephone; 15 with TV. 4 in annexe opposite. 2 ground-floor rooms.
Facilities Salon, TV room, bar, restaurant; terrace. Lake with sailing and fishing 500 metres.
Location In centre of village. Garage parking.
Credit cards Access, Visa.
Terms B&B: single 185–195 frs, double 250–270 frs; dinner, B&B 205–273 frs per person. Set meals 80–200 frs; full alc 200 frs. Reduced rates and special meals for children.

COTIGNAC 83850 Var — Map 11

Hostellerie Lou Calen — *Tel* 94.04.60.40
1 cours Gambetta — *Telex* 400287

This much-visited village in the hilly Var hinterland is oddly situated at the foot of a brown cliff holed with caves, some of them once inhabited. The *Lou Calen* (Provençal for "the place of the oil-lamp"), a small family-run place, "friendly and amateurish but nice", has again been enjoyed this year, by readers who liked dining on the terrace with its wide view, and thought the food well cooked and generously served. Rooms are furnished in local country style, but have modern plumbing. Previous visitors have found the Provençal cooking always reliable and sometimes excellent: one has enthused over the "fantastic array of help-yourself hors d'œuvre with delicious dressings", another over the "pieds et paquets and sinful great hunks of tarte aux fraises" on the cheaper menu. The large swimming pool, not always perfectly tended and sometimes crowded, is reached through a small garden. Only drawback: some traffic noise at night, heard in front rooms. Much of interest to visit in the area: the majestic Gorges du Verdon, the lovely Cistercian abbey of Thoronet and, less well known, the château at Entrecasteaux, housing a most original museum (and which is now a B&B with an entry in the Guide this year). (*Philippa Herbert, Dave Watts, Kay and Neville Varley, and others*)

Open 8 Apr–1 Jan. Restaurant closed Wed in low season.
Rooms 8 suites, 8 double – all with bath and shower, telephone , TV and tea-making facilities. 2 suites in garden annexe.
Facilities Salon with TV, bar, 2 restaurants; conference facilities. Garden with terrace and swimming pool.
Location On Route des Gorges du Verdon. For Cotignac take exit Brignoles or Le Luc-Toulon off N7. Central (3 rooms might have traffic noise). Parking.
Restriction Not suitable for ♿.
Credit cards All major cards accepted.
Terms Rooms 230–410 frs. Breakfast 39 frs. Set lunch/dinner 105, 183 and 238 frs; full alc 300 frs. Special meals for children.

> If you are nominating a hotel, please do make sure that you tell us enough to convey its character and quality. We can't make good bricks without plenty of straw.

COULANDON 03000 Allier — Map 10

Le Chalet — *Tel* 70.44.50.08

"An oasis of rural calm, with charm, comfort and good, simple food." "A spacious, elegant bedroom in the annexe, efficient staff, and a blissful dinner overlooking the park." So run reports this year and last on this former hunting lodge set peacefully (it is a *Relais du Silence*) in its own spacious park with a pond full of fish. Offering rural tranquillity at modest prices, it stands half-way between the market town of Moulins and the village of Souvigny with its fine priory church. "Good value in the old style; a lush pastoral setting with nightingales." Some rooms have exposed beams, and there's even a comfortable library – what a rarity in a modest French hotel. The cheaper menus are "plain but adequate". "The amazing Gallic chinoiserie wallpapers are all Sandersons." (*RHW Bullock, Mr and Mrs RM Booth, JP Berryman*) One reader was disturbed by traffic noise from the main road and recommends the annexe rooms as quieter; another was disappointed by the food.

Open 1 Feb–31 Oct. Restaurant closed midday.
Rooms 25 double – all with bath and/or shower and telephone; 15 with TV. Some in annexe.
Facilities Lounge, dining room with terrace, library. Large park with pond.
Location 6 km W of Moulins, down side-road just off D945 towards Souvigny.
Restriction Not suitable for ♿.
Credit cards All major cards accepted.
Terms B&B: single 200–280 frs, double 270–390 frs; dinner, B&B 185–345 frs per person. Set lunch/dinner 70 and 110 frs; full alc 160 frs. Special meals for children.

COULON 79510 Deux-Sèvres — Map 10

Le Central — *Tel* 49.35.90.20
4 rue d'Autremont

In the 'Venise Verte' of the Marais Poitevin with its many canals, here's a white-walled geranium-bedecked small restaurant-with-rooms whose cooking wins a Michelin *red "R" for good value, and is served with skill. Lively and congenial atmosphere, happy staff. Clean, efficient bedrooms. Closed 15 Jan–4 Feb, 24 Sept–14 Oct, Sun night and Mon. 7 bedrooms, all with bath or shower. Rooms 160–180 frs. Breakfast 20 frs. Set menus 75–162 frs. Recent nomination. More reports please.*

CRÈCHES-SUR-SAÔNE 71680 Saône-et-Loire — Map 10

Hostellerie du Château de la Barge — *Tel* 85.37.12.04

"A handsome creeper-covered 17th-century manor in south Burgundy has been tactfully converted into a pleasant country hotel, graceful but informal, slightly old-fashioned, and exuding Burgundian well-being. The two salons have comfortable period furnishings; some bedrooms are large, also in period style, others are smaller but good value. In the large lovely dining room, with its pink table linen, a log fire burns in winter and big windows look on to the garden; drinks, breakfast and lunch can be served out on its terrace in summer. The cooking, mainly Burgundian but with some inventive touches, we thought excellent: e.g. terrine de brochet in a rich tarragon sauce, and saumon frais aux deux beurres. Admirable desserts and cheeses. We took those tiny hard chèvres which are known as 'boutons de culottes' (fly-buttons) – "Well, we *are* in the Clochemerle country here," said the motherly but very expert and knowledgeable head waitress. Coffee at breakfast was poor; and the hotel's setting is unpromising, on the edge of a dull village south of Mâcon. But it would make a good base for touring south Burgundy and the Beaujolais – including the village of Vaux that was the original for Chevalier's *Clochemerle* and today exploits this full-tilt with tourist-geared oh-là-là ribaldry. It has even built a new *pissotière*. A surly receptionist was encountered this year.

Open All year except 25 Oct–3 Nov, 19 Dec–5 Jan. Restaurant closed Sat, Sun in low season.
Rooms 2 suites, 21 double – 16 with bath, 5 with shower, all with telephone. 2 ground-floor rooms.
Facilities Lift. Salon, TV room, restaurant. Garden with children's playground.
Location In village (follow signposts for Gare TGV) which is on N7 8 km S of Mâcon.
Credit cards All major cards accepted.
Terms [1989 rates] Rooms: single 206 frs, double 226 frs. Breakfast 21 frs. Dinner, B&B 226 frs per person. Set lunch/dinner 72, 123 and 160 frs; full alc 135 frs. Reduced rates and special meals for children.

CREST 26400 Drôme — Map 10

Grand Hôtel — *Tel* 75.25.08.17
60 rue de l'Hôtel de Ville

In a little town south-east of Valence on the road to Nice, with a ruined hilltop fortress above the river Drôme, this Logis de France *has a touch of faded grandeur, with marble pillars and a ramshackle garden. But prices are pleasantly lacking in grandeur, while the large bedrooms are comfortable and the staff friendly, and food is inexpensive, varied and excellent* (Michelin *red "R" for good value). Closed 23 Dec–23 Jan. 22 rooms, 14 with bath and/or shower. B&B double 350 frs. Set menus 70–200 frs. New nomination. More reports welcome.*

DIJON 21000 Côte-d'Or — Map 10

Hôtel La Cloche — *Tel* 80.30.12.32
Restaurant Jean-Pierre Billoux — *Telex* 350498
14 place Darcy

A large, imposing hotel, traditional but well modernised, and centrally located on a big square. "Rooms are all double-glazed, so there is no noise. There is a garage, a quiet garden, a cosy bar, and a lounge which has changing art exhibitions. Our split-level room was large, with good views; lighting could have been better, but the bathroom was huge. The main attraction is the magnificent restaurant in the old cellars (two *Michelin* rosettes, three red *Gault Millau toques*) which Jean-Pierre Billoux, one of Burgundy's best young chefs, rents from the hotel: cooking is traditional Burgundian with modern overtones and wines are of course superb. Lunch is also served in a small conservatory. Very good service." (*Pat and Jeremy Temple*)

Open All year. Restaurant closed Feb.
Rooms 4 suites, 76 double – all with bath, telephone, radio and TV.
Facilities Lifts. Lounge, bar, restaurant; conference facilities; conservatory. Garden.
Location Central (rooms are double-glazed). Garage.
Credit cards All major cards accepted.
Terms [1989 rates] Rooms: single 460 frs, double 540 frs, suite 1100 frs. Breakfast 45 frs. Reduced rates for children. Set menus 230–400 frs.

DIVONNE-LES-BAINS 01220 Ain — Map 10

Château de Divonne
Route de Gex

Tel 50.20.00.32
Fax 50.20.03.73
Telex 309033

The casino at this fashionable spa resort has a bigger turnover than any other in France (Monaco is another country), being much frequented by wealthy international punters from Geneva, only 12 miles away. Many of them make also for the luxurious *Château*, a handsome white building amid parkland, admired by one of our most discriminating correspondents, "This excellent 19th-century reproduction of a Loire Valley château sits on a hill above the charming little town, down a winding drive through trees, with its own helipad by the gate. The marble hall, breathtaking, harbours magnificent modern sculptures; public rooms are smartly furnished in period style.

"On a summer evening, dinner on the terrace was pure ecstasy, the pale-yellow-stone facade floodlit, tables lit by oil-lamps and Mont-Blanc 50 miles away glowing pink in the sunset. The cooking well deserves its *Michelin* rosette and two red *Gault Millau toques* for its beautiful presentation and subtle flavours – chaud-froid de homard et foie gras, two sorts of contrasting lake fish, and fantastic chocolate puddings. Superb wine-list, not over-priced. Breakfast on the sunlit terrace was also splendid, and included delicious goats' cheese. The hotel's young and enthusiastic owners have the knack of choosing caring, charming and very hard-working staff, and the ambience is warm and individual; nor is the place over-expensive – by Geneva standards. Bedrooms are spacious and characterful, with genuine antiques; ours had the same superb view as from the terrace. If you leave your room very untidy, as we did, it is cleared up swiftly and totally." Warmly endorsed this year by *Neil and Jacqueline Britton*.

Open Early-Mar–early Jan. Restaurant closed Tue, and Wed midday in low season.
Rooms 5 suites, 15 double, 7 single – 26 with bath, 1 with shower, all with telephone and TV. 3 ground-floor rooms.
Facilities Lift, ramps. Salon, bar, 2 restaurants; conference facilities. Park with terrace, tennis, table-tennis and helipad.
Location On road to Gex, on W side of Divonne, which is 19 km N of Geneva (leave Lausanne motorway at Divonne-Coppet).
Credit card Visa.

Terms Rooms: single 380–475 frs, double 595–970 frs, suite 970–1,580 frs. Breakfast 60 frs. Set lunch/dinner 215, 305 and 405 frs; full alc 380 frs. Reduced rates and special meals for children.

DOMME 24250 Dordogne — Map 10

Hôtel de l'Esplanade — *Tel* 53.28.31.41

This well-known showpiece village on a cliff above the Dordogne has been tastefully restored in the tradition of Viollet-le-Duc, and is full of expensive antique shops and foie gras. In the daytime in summer it is horribly crowded, but then it quietens when the trippers have gone – "On a midsummer evening, when you stroll along the clifftop path, magic is in the air". The *Esplanade*, a medium-priced *Logis de France*, is worthy of this setting, and is run with style by *patron*-chef René Gillard and his friendly wife. A visitor this year enjoyed her "blue-rose-covered attic room" and her 105-franc dinner. Bedrooms are individually decorated in a variety of floral wallpapers. "Our room had an enchanting small balcony overlooking the wonderful valley. Superb food (try the salmon stuffed with mousseline of trout)." One visitor, while praising the view and the decor, thought the owners and staff cool and churlish. (*Caroline Currie, Mr and Mrs R Porter, P Talbot Smith, and others*)

Open 15 Feb–15 Nov. Closed Sun evening and Mon Feb–Apr.
Rooms 19 double – 15 with bath, 4 with shower, all with telephone; some with balcony. 4 in annexes.
Facilities Salon with TV, bar, restaurant; terraces.
Location 13 km S of Sarlat.
Restriction Not suitable for ♿.
Credit cards Access, Amex, Visa.
Terms [1989 rates] Dinner, B&B 265–370 frs; full board 365–470 frs. Full alc 310 frs.

DONZENAC 19270 Corrèze — Map 10

Relais du Bas Limousin — *Tel* 55.84.52.06 and 55.84.54.62

Usefully placed by the main N20 Limoges–Toulouse highway (at Sadroc, 6 km north of Donzenac), but quiet, here is a cheerful and efficient family-run auberge, *just right for a night's stop. All very clean and well kept, with good bedrooms at low prices and first-rate traditional country cooking. 24 rooms, most with bath or shower. B&B double 146–266 frs. Set menu 60–200 frs. Recent nomination. More reports please.*

DUCEY 50220 Manche — Map 8

Auberge de la Sélune — *Tel* 33.48.53.62

2 rue St-Germain

A neat little hotel with garden and terrace above the river, in a dullish Norman village not far from Mont-St-Michel. Bedrooms are said to be clean and pretty: the best are those at the back, facing garden and river. Some readers this year, but not all, have again been full of good words: "Lovely welcome from Mme Girres, an attractive dining room, and very good food, notably the truite duceyne." "Wonderful food, charming garden." (*Minda Alexander, C Head, Martin Davis, Mr and Mrs G Buckland*) However, some have found the welcome less than warm and the service far less than perfect, with preferential treatment for regulars. More reports, please.

Open All year except mid-Jan–mid-Feb. Closed Mon Oct–Mar.
Rooms 18 double, 1 single – 19 with bath and shower, all with telephone and TV. 3 in garden pavilion.
Facilities Lounge, bar, 3 restaurants; 2 seminar rooms. Garden with terrace.
Location On N176, 11 km SE of Avranches (garden rooms quietest). Carpark.
Restriction Not suitable for ♿.
Credit cards Access, Diners, Visa.
Terms Rooms 203–230 frs. Breakfast 25 frs. Set lunch/dinner 63, 90, 120 and 145 frs.

DURAVEL 46700 Lot — Map 10

Auberge du Baran — *Tel* 65.24.60.34

In the lovely Lot valley west of Cahors, Roger and Letitia Washbourne, from Bath, run a simple village inn (*Logis de France*) which, says our nominator this year, "has become a meeting place for locals to drink. They seem to have set up a very 'French' place here, gaining acceptance from both natives and tourists" – a plus for Euro-integration and the ideals of 1992. "From the road it doesn't look especially inviting, but inside and at the back all is changed. Our ground-floor room had french windows opening onto a little terrace and a pretty 'wild' garden with beautiful views of the fine Romanesque village church. The room was cool and comfortable, furnished in pale blue and cream. The summer dining room is a delightful terrace covered in wistaria and tobacco plants, with a glorious view. Food and service were both excellent: omelette au fromage frais, chicken in garlic sauce, delectable cassis sorbet. Breakfast is taken in the bar." (*David and Melanie Worrall*)

Open All year. Restaurant closed mid-Jan–mid-Mar.
Rooms 7 double – all with bath and shower, and telephone.
Facilities Bar, TV room, restaurant; 2 terraces. Garden.
Location In village, on D911 12 km E of Fumel.
Restrictions Not suitable for ♿.
Credit cards Access, Visa.
Terms B&B 125 frs; dinner, B&B 210 frs; full board 270 frs. Set meals 60, 85, 130 and 195 frs; alc 120 frs. Reduced rates and special meals for children.

ELINCOURT-STE-MARGUERITE 60157 Oise — Map 9

Château de Bellinglise — *Tel* 44.76.04.76 / *Fax* 44.76.54.75 / *Telex* 155048

North of Compiègne, an imposing rose-coloured château, part 16th-century, set beside a big lake in its 600-acre grounds. Its new owners, a Belgian hotel group, run it partly as a rather grand conference centre: it won't appeal to all our readers' tastes, but might suit those seeking a touch of formal grandeur on their way from Calais to Paris. For example, a reader this year thought both the cooking and the bedrooms "excellent" and enjoyed the views, while others wrote last year: "Architecturally it's a gem. My room in the courtyard, one of the cheaper ones, was finely furnished (modern) and well equipped. In the beautiful and spacious dining room, with its panelling and chandeliers, I had the best dinner of my trip." "We found the decor in the public areas rather opulent, if florid: the spacious halls and staircase have walls of yellow marble and gold silk damask. The formal dining room was attractive, and the menu good value, but service was slow." The new chef is a pupil of the great Robuchon, but he has not yet won laurels from the French guides.

Open All year.
Rooms 47 – all with bath and/or shower, telephone and TV.
Facilities Lift. Lounge, TV room, bar, restaurant; 6 conference rooms. Large grounds with tennis court, riding, golf.
Location 15 km N of Compiègne, on D142 to Lassigny. Parking.
Credit cards All major cards accepted.
Terms [1989 rates] Rooms 400–1,000 frs. Breakfast 50 frs. Dinner, B&B 565–740 frs per person. Set lunch/dinner 175–260 frs. Special meals for children.

ENTRECASTEAUX 83570 Var — Map 11

Château d'Entrecasteaux — *Tel* 94.04.43.95

This unusual bed-and-breakfast venture, new to the Guide, occupies part of a Provençal château with a very odd history. It's an austere 17th-century hulk, on the edge of an unspoilt village in a valley west of Draguignan and not far from the lovely Cistercian abbey of Le Thoronet. The château belonged to local lords, one of whom in the 18th century killed his young wife and then vanished into a Portuguese jail. This brought the family into such disgrace that gradually their château fell into ruin – till in 1974 it was bought and carefully restored by the amazing Ian McGarvie-Munn, avant-garde painter, Scottish nationalist, soldier and adventurer, ex-commander-in-chief of the Guatemalan navy and married to the grand-daughter of a former president of that country. He died in 1981; the building is now run by his son Lachlan as a delightfully informal and varied museum (Scottish bagpipes, pre-Columbian ceramics, Murano goblets, Provençal kitchenware, etc) which you enter via the family kitchen. There are many temporary exhibitions, and classical concerts on the lovely terrace in summer: but it's a pity that Lachlan has hidden away his father's surreal pornographic paintings, judged too shocking for local taste. He now lets out three rooms: one has a vast colonnaded Roman-style bathroom, designed by his father. "One room is divinely large with parquet floor and huge antique Provençal bed. Breakfast was a treat, and the owner very friendly and kind." (*Clare Enders, JA*)

Open All year except 5 days in early Aug, Christmas Eve.
Rooms 1 suite, 2 double – all with bath (1 also has shower) and telephone; 2 with tea-making facilities.
Facilities Museum. Terrace. Garden (designed by Le Nôtre) with swimming pool.
Location 8 km S of Salernes.
Restrictions Not suitable for ♿.
Credit card Amex.
Terms B&B: double 600–900 frs, suite 1,200 frs. (No restaurant.)

Please make a habit of sending a report if you stay at a Guide hotel.

L'ÉPINE 51460 Marne — Map 9

Aux Armes de Champagne — *Tel* 26.66.96.79, *Telex* 830998

An old coaching-inn, restored and modernised, in the square of a village east of Châlons-sur-Marne. The dining room and most bedrooms face the huge, floodlit basilica of Notre Dame, a place of pilgrimage in the Middle Ages. Above all it's the food that matters here, not cheap, but awarded a rosette by *Michelin* and a *toque* by *Gault Millau* (for e.g. salad of courgettes and truffles with foie gras). One reader in 1989 thought the cuisine uninspired, especially the vegetables and sweets, but another has written of "refined French cooking at its best", and praised also the "friendly greeting, flowers everywhere and well-groomed little garden". Noisy lorries sometimes pass the dining room, but bedrooms are quiet, especially those at the back and in the new annexe. "The picturesque garden at the back, with a small stream, is an ideal spot for an aperitif." "Clean and comfortable, without the firework-night-in-Hawaii wallpaper which usually tells you that you are in a French hotel." The proprietor has his own champagne vineyard, and the long wine list is devoted mainly to bubbly. (*Dr Peter Woodford, Mrs S Groves, and others*)

Open All year except 7 Jan–12 Feb.
Rooms 39 double – 27 with bath, 12 with shower, all with telephone; 13 with TV. 16 in 2 annexes 150 metres from main building. Some ground-floor rooms.
Facilities Bar, TV room, 2 restaurants; functions facilities; concerts in summer. Small garden with mini-golf.
Location Central; village is 8.5 km E of Châlons, on N3. Parking.
Credit cards Access, Amex, Visa.
Terms [1989 rates] Rooms 400–460 frs. Breakfast 36 frs. Set lunch/dinner 90, 165, 235 and 320 frs; full alc 320 frs. Reduced rates and special meals for children.

ÉTOILE-SUR-RHÔNE 26800 Drôme — Map 10

Château de Clavel — *Tel* 75.60.61.93

The stately Napoleon III château in the Rhône valley south of Valence, has been restored by its new owner, Xavier Wernert, and now opened as a fairly smart hotel. "Peacefully located in a large park amid green countryside, it has an elegant staircase and square-well with chandelier. Our split-level bedroom was *gigantic*, furnished finely with antique-looking bureaux and chairs. M. Wernert is a delightful man, rather vague and seemingly eccentric, but all in all the hotel functions well. The staff were cheerful and the food excellent, including the breakfasts. The lake has many frogs and a swan which M. Wernert told us was a priest, i.e. celibate. He fed it every day. We enjoyed the horses. . ." (*Kenneth E Smith*) More reports please.

Open 1 Apr–31 Dec.
Rooms 6 suites, 17 double – all with bath and shower, telephone and TV. 7 in annexe.
Facilities Lounge with TV. Garden with swimming pool and tennis court. Lake, river, golf, riding nearby.
Location Turn E off N7, 12 km S of Valence.
Restriction Not suitable for ♿.
Credit cards Access, Amex, Visa.

Terms [1989 rates] Rooms 300–350 frs, suites 450–500 frs. Breakfast 32 frs. Set lunch/dinner 120–280 frs; full alc 170–180 frs. Reduced rates and special meals for children.

EUGÉNIE-LES-BAINS 40320 Landes — Map 10

Les Prés d'Eugénie et le Couvent des Herbes — *Tel* 58.51.19.01, *Telex* 540470

Michel Guérard's very superior establishment, in a Second Empire mansion north of Pau, is world-famous as the home of *cuisine minceur.* But robust appetites are catered for too. In the main restaurant the cuisine is *gourmande* rather than *minceur*, quite different from the diets devised by this three-star chef for his health farm next door. Alas, no reader has reported to us this year, though from a food writer we've heard news of a dish of pasta and wild mushrooms, in a redolent sauce, that "encapsulated mushroomness". One recently visiting connoisseur has had mixed feelings: "The food prepared for the wealthy gourmets is totally exquisite, and its accent is on subtlety of taste, not calorie control. Presentation is impeccable, and service is on oiled castors by waiters clearly proud of the masterpieces coming from the kitchen. This said, the place seems to have serious flaws as a hotel. The bedrooms are comfortable and spacious, but they are not serviced properly and have lacunae that seem odd amid so much expensive luxury. Breakfast is idiosyncratic and expensive. Staff are cheerful and relaxed, but reception was somewhat casual." Top ratings in the French guides, needless to say. More reports badly needed, both on the existing hotel and on the new six-room annexe, a renovated 18th-century convent, *Le Couvent des Herbes,* opening in 1990.

Open 13 Feb–10 Dec.
Rooms 7 suites, 28 double – all with bath, telephone and TV.
Facilities Lift. Salon, billiard room, TV room, gallery, bar, dining rooms, restaurant. Beauty salon, thermal baths, sauna. 2 tennis courts, *boules,* unheated swimming pool. Garden and river. 6 more rooms in annexe opening in 1990.
Location Off D944 St-Sever–Aubagnan, 53 km N of Pau.
Credit cards Amex, Diners, Visa.
Terms [1989 rates] Rooms 1,173 frs, suite 1,357–1,403 frs. Breakfast 80 frs. *Menu minceur* (residents only) 230–330 frs. Set lunch/dinner 370–470 frs. Reduced rates and special meals for children.

ÉVIAN-LES-BAINS 74500 Haute-Savoie — Map 10

La Verniaz et ses Chalets — *Tel* 50.75.04.90
Route de l'Abondance — *Telex* 385715

Our first-ever entry for France's leading lakeside spa is quite small but luxurious, with four red *Michelin* gables and a rosette, plus more red print for its chalet-suites secluded amid greenery. Its Californian nominator is enthusiastic, "A perfect mix of charming informal service and elegance. I have been to plenty of hotels whose pool attendants acted like head waiters and vice versa, but here is a balance to be envied. The hotel is up a steep and tortuous drive from Évian, but the reward for that is the view of Lac Léman, Lausanne, the Swiss Alps and Mont Blanc. The peace and quiet is broken only by the faint plonk of tennis balls. The gardens are a riot of colour, the rooms spacious and homey, with balconies that afford both privacy and a fine lake view. The restaurant is the crowning glory – grilled rack of lamb with basil, fresh fish from the lake, game-fowl in local style and superb soufflés. Wines are fairly priced, but I wish they wouldn't chill the port. On fine days you can dine outdoors. The front desk staff are helpful. The Verdier family owners have been hoteliers for generations and can point proudly to some old sepia-toned pictures that document their past. Those ancestors must also be looking down proudly from the walls on the current establishment." (*H Richard Foss*)

Open All year except end Nov–early Feb.
Rooms 5 chalet-suites, 35 double – all with bath/shower and telephone; TV on request; many with balcony.
Facilities Lift. Salons, bar, restaurant; conference facilities; terrace. Garden with swimming pool and tennis court.
Location 2 km SE of centre of Évian. Parking.
Credit cards Access, Amex, Visa.
Terms [1989 rates] Rooms: single 350–550 frs, double 500–950 frs, suites 1,500–2,500 frs. Breakfast 45 frs. Half board 450–885 frs per person. Set lunch/dinner 220–240 frs. Special meals for children on request.

EYNE 66800 Pyrénées-Orientales — Map 10

Auberge d'Eyne — *Tel* 68.04.71.12

Eyne is an unspoilt village up on the glorious Cerdagne plateau near Saillagouse (q.v.): here this beautiful old rural *auberge*, newly restored, with bedrooms in period style, makes its Guide debut. "The ski resorts are rather an eyesore in the Cerdagne but can be avoided. The *auberge* could be called 'up-market rustic'. Quiet and comfortable, run by an ambitious young patron, it has a good lounge with log fire, and friendly staff. Pension dinners were excellent. Very good value." (*John Mainwaring*)

Open All year except Nov. Restaurant closed Mon.
Rooms 11 double – all with bath/shower and telephone. Ground-floor rooms.
Facilities Lounge, bar, reading room, 3 dining rooms. Garden.
Location 6 km E of Saillagouse, 85 km W of Perpignan.
Credit cards Access, Diners, Visa.
Terms Rooms 375 frs. Breakfast 40 frs. Set lunch/dinner 99–150 frs; full alc 185 frs. Reduced rates and special meals for children.

LES EYZIES-DE-TAYAC 24620 Dordogne — Map 10

Hôtel Cro-Magnon — *Tel* 53.06.97.06 *Telex* 570637

Les Eyzies, France's leading "centre of prehistory", is dominated by steep cliffs riddled with palaeolithic caves. It is bedlam at the height of the tourist season, though it quietens down in the evening. In its outskirts is this handsome creeper-covered old hotel – "a traditional family-run place with plenty of atmosphere, good value", runs one report this year. Its chief drawback is proximity to the railway and main road, causing some noise even at night: quietest rooms are those in the pleasant annexe, set in a large garden with a swimming pool on the other side of the railway. The *demi-pension* meals are described this year as "good but not inspirational" (the inspiration is maybe reserved for *à la carte* dishes such as salade périgourdine which earn the *Michelin* rosette). This earlier description remains valid: "The entrance hall has an English coaching inn feel, with wood-panelled walls, pretty flowers, brasses polished daily; there is a delightful and quiet residents' lounge upstairs. Our room was a fair size, spotless, furnished and wallpapered in rustic style; plumbing noises were the only snag. The hotel's family owners, Jacques and Christiane Leyssales, chat warmly with their guests. The ambience is friendly and personal." (*Willis G Frick, N and I Pressnell, and others*) The hotel prefers its residents to dine at the hotel.

Open End-Apr–mid-Oct. Restaurant closed Wed for lunch.
Rooms 4 suites, 20 double – all with bath and shower, and telephone; 4 with TV. 8 in annexe by swimming pool.
Facilities 2 lounges, 2 dining rooms. Garden restaurant. 5 acres of parkland with heated swimming pool and river.
Location 600 metres W of town centre. Parking.
Restriction Not suitable for ♿.
Credit cards All major cards accepted.
Terms B&B: double 380–480 frs, suite 630–780 frs; dinner, B&B 300–400 frs per person. Set lunch/dinner 110–300 frs; full alc 200–300 frs.

Les Glycines *Tel* 53.06.97.07

The creeper-covered *Glycines*, by a river about ten minutes' walk from the village, is regarded by some readers as a better bet than the *Cro-Magnon* above, partly because it is further from the noisy railway. It has won a stint of praise again this year: "The garden is an informal heaven – chairs and loungers under a willow or by the pool, or on lush grass, with farmland beyond. Chic, blonde Madame smiles, the staff are most helpful. Meals were very good – small and delicious helpings, with all vegetables crisp (*à point*) and fresh. The baby deer was pink and juicy – a shame when we'd seen them in the woods that day." "Superb comfortable rooms with lovely views, outstanding cuisine, and a large new swimming pool. The Mercats look after their guests very well." "There is a vine-shaded terrace for drinks or lunch. Our room in the new annexe was quiet but small, with doors opening onto our own table and chairs in the sunny courtyard; rooms in the main building may be a little dark and cramped." (*Mr and Mrs Wilmot-Allistone, Mr and Mrs R Porter*)

Open Mid-Apr–1 Nov.
Rooms 25 – all with bath and telephone. 2 rooms accommodating 4 in separate building in garden. 5 ground-floor rooms.
Facilities 2 salons, bar, restaurant; terrace for alfresco meals. Large garden with swimming pool.
Location On road to Périgueux, by the river. Parking.
Credit cards Access, Amex, Visa.
Terms Rooms 285–318 frs. Breakfast 38 frs. Dinner, B&B 314–344 frs per person; full board 387–417 frs. Set lunch/dinner 105–300 frs; full alc 230 frs. Reduced rates for children under 5; special meals on request.

Le Moulin de la Beune *Tel* 53.06.94.33

"Just the kind of hotel that should be in the Guide" is one 1989 verdict on this big converted mill, tastefully restored: it stands next to the National Museum of Prehistory and beside the river Beune which flows through its garden. "Owners friendly, breakfast good, bedrooms attractive with good modern plumbing." "There is a large old fireplace in the lounge/reception which is attractively furnished as are the bedrooms. Inviting breakfast room, with glass doors leading out to tables by the river. Breakfast exceptional, with home-made jams, hot croissants, coffee *ad lib.* Smart chairs in the garden. Warm welcome from the owners, the Dudicourts." No restaurant, but readers speak highly of the one in the millwheel building (*Au Vieux Moulin*), under separate management. (*DG Randall, and others*)

Open End Mar–early Nov.
Rooms 20 double – 14 with bath, 6 with shower, all with telephone. 4 ground-floor rooms with separate entrance.
Facilities Salon, bar, TV room, breakfast room. Garden. River (fishing), swimming pool and tennis nearby.
Location Central, near the National Museum of Prehistory. Parking.
Credit cards All major cards accepted.
Terms [1989 rates] Rooms: single 190 frs, double 265 frs. Breakfast 30 frs. (No restaurant.)

ÈZE 06360 Alpes-Maritimes — Map 11

Château de la Chèvre d'Or — *Tel* 93.41.12.12
Rue du Barri — *Fax* 93.41.06.72
Telex 970839 CHEVDOR

The best-known and most touristy of all the Côte d'Azur's hill-villages stands in a spectacular site beside the Middle Corniche, on a rocky outcrop almost sheer above the sea (Èze-Bord-de-Mer, see next entry, is just below). It has been scrupulously restored, and its many souvenir shops are not too vulgar; when the trippers have departed, it can be hauntingly quiet at night. There is no motor traffic, but a short walk along its main alley leads to the celebrated *Chèvre d'Or* ("a jewel," writes a recent American visitor), a medieval château artistically converted into a small luxury hotel run with suave efficiency. Soft music plays as you sip your champagne cocktails by the pool, gazing at Cap Ferrat far below; even the telephones in the lavishly furnished bedrooms are Edwardian museum-pieces. If some bedrooms are cramped, blame the 11th-century architect, though the 20th-century redesigners have done their ingenious best. Rooms near the kitchens may be noisy. The panoramic restaurant, frequented by famous and beautiful people, wins a well-deserved *Michelin* rosette and two *Gault Millau toques* for such dishes as hot oysters in champagne. But we'd be glad of up-to-date reports, please.

Open 1 Mar–30 Nov. Restaurant closed Wed in Mar.
Rooms 3 suites, 11 double – all with bath and shower, telephone and TV. All in different buildings 4–10 metres from main building.
Facilities Bar/salon, restaurant, grill room. Garden with terrace and 2 swimming pools; alfresco meals in summer. 10 mins' drive to sea.
Location 10 km E of Nice on "Moyen Corniche" road.
Restriction Not suitable for ♿.
Credit cards All major cards accepted.
Terms [1989 rates] Rooms 1,160 frs–1,950 frs, suite 2,050 frs. Breakfast 75 frs. Alc meals (excluding wine) 340–480 frs. Reduced rates for children; special meals on request.

If you have kept brochures and tariffs for Continental hotels, do please enclose them with your reports.

ÈZE-BORD-DE-MER 06360 Alpes-Maritimes — Map 11

Le Cap Estel

Tel 93.01.50.44
Fax 93.01.55.20
Telex 470305

For years only *Tom and Rosemary Rose* reported to us on this Italianate villa, now an elegant family-run luxury hotel, on a promontory between Beaulieu and Monaco. They visited it annually, reported each year that it was just as good as ever, and praised the excellent bedrooms, all with terrace or loggia and air-conditioning, the comfortable public lounge and poolside bar, the excellent buffet lunches, and the dinners. Last year another reader endorsed the entry with even greater enthusiasm: "If hotel perfection ye seek, here it be. A magnificent position, excellent food and brilliant service by a young highly trained team who would do credit to the Brigade of Guards. Room service arrived in a flash, the lad looking after the open-air swimming pool had a mattress and towels spread out on your poolside bed when he saw you coming. A lovely building in a lovely setting." A 1989 visitor is more cautious in his praise: "Yes, it *is* excellent – but of course not perfect. They allow smoking in the dining room, decoration sometimes borders on kitsch, we had one or two maintenance problems. But it's pretty good!" Half board is obligatory.

Open 1 Mar–31 Oct.
Rooms 8 suites, 40 double – all with bath and shower, telephone, terrace or loggia and air-conditioning.
Facilities Lift. Bar/salon, restaurant, grill room. Garden with terrace; alfresco meals in summer. Indoor and outdoor swimming pool.
Location 10 km E of Nice on "Moyen Corniche" road.
Credit cards Access, Visa.
Terms [1989 rates] Dinner, B&B 1,700–2,550 frs. Full board 250 frs added.

LA FAVÈDE 30110 Gard — Map 10

À l'Auberge Cévenole

Tel 66.34.12.13

A hamlet just off the N106, in the attractive southern foothills of the Cévennes (but be warned that the approach up the industrial valley from Alès, to the south, is not so attractive). Here the *Auberge Cévenole* is a neat, white-walled red-roofed building in local style, sprucely and prettily decorated. It wins *Michelin*'s red rocking chair and two red gables for secluded tranquillity and pleasant charm, and from one reader the comment: "Charming and peaceful, with a lovely and very clean pool. The staff were attentive, the setting elegant and traditional, but the food on the set menu did not quite live up to its promise." Others this year have again approved the well-kept garden and well-furnished rooms, and have enjoyed the food: but charges for extras are said to be very high. Not a hotel, incidentally, for those who want to escape from fellow-Brits on holiday. (*GE Samson, Peter L Aston*)

Open 15 Mar–30 Nov. Possibly Christmas and New Year.
Rooms 2 suites with mini-bar, 18 double – all with bath or shower, telephone; 4 with TV. 8 in bungalows with ground-floor rooms.
Facilities Salon, TV room, dining room. Terrace where meals are served. Garden with swimming pool, mini-tennis.
Location 3 km W of La Grand-Combe, on D283.

Credit cards Access, Visa.
Terms [1989 rates] Rooms 250–350 frs. Breakfast 45 frs. Dinner, B&B 300–550 frs per person. Set lunch 150–250 frs. Special meals for children.

FAYENCE 83440 Var — Map 11

Moulin de la Camandoule — *Tel* 94.76.00.84
Chemin de Notre-Dame des Cyprès

Beautifully restored old olive-mill in delightful Provençal setting amid meadows below hill-village of Fayence; garden, pretty stream, big swimming pool (barbecues in summer). Owned since 1986 by former film-director and novelist Wolf Rilla and his wife Shirley, from London. Rooms recently renovated in traditional Provençal style. Recent reports, while appreciating ambience, find fault with details of room upkeep and general management. Shirley Rilla has now taken over control in the kitchen. 11 rooms, all with bath and/or shower, 175–485 frs. Breakfast 35 frs. Set dinner 155 – 250 frs. More reports please.

FÈRE-EN-TARDENOIS 02130 Aisne — Map 9

Hostellerie du Château — *Tel* 23.82.21.13
Fax 23.82.37.81
Telex 145526

A luxurious manor house, part Renaissance, part 19th-century, that stands in its own sizeable park within a forest, 45 km west of Reims, owned, run and cooked for by the Blot family. Rooms vary greatly: older ones in the main house have more personality, but attic ones are very small; newer ones in the modern annexe are plainer but larger, with superior bathrooms (some suites have a jacuzzi). "Very peaceful and relaxing," say visitors this year; "we had a warm welcome and were shown to a large, attractive room. Dinner was excellent" (serious *nouvelle cuisine*, awarded *Michelin* rosette and two red *Gault Millau toques*). (*Pat and Jeremy Temple*)

Open All year.
Rooms 9 suites, 14 double – all with bath and shower, telephone and TV. Ground-floor rooms. 1 specially adapted for ♿.
Facilities Salon, bar, 3 restaurants; conference facilities. Large grounds with golf and tennis.
Location 3 km N of Fère-en-Tardenois, on road to Fismes.
Credit cards All major cards accepted.
Terms Dinner, B&B: single 1,300 frs, double 1,900 frs, suite 3,300 frs. Set meals 2900–430 frs.

FLAGY 77940 Seine-et-Marne — Map 9

Hostellerie au Moulin — *Tel* (1) 60.96.67.89
2 rue du Moulin

A 13th-century millhouse, beautifully converted into a rustic-style restaurant-with-rooms, in a pretty village south-east of Fontainebleau. There's a pleasant lounge with some of the old mill-wheels and pulleys, and in summer you can eat out under weeping willows beside a stream, with the murmur of rushing water close by. This idyllic and peaceful setting has again been much admired this year, as have the little beamed bedrooms (with modern bathrooms), the staff, and the Scheideckers who own the place: "The owner is a most urbane and courteous man, and his taste must account for the meticulous attention to detail in the pretty little bedrooms and romantic dining room by the river." (*Sharon Gutman, Deborah Reese, Lorraine Carlson, RHW Bullock, and others*) Several visitors this year have been critical of the cooking – we'd welcome more reports on this.

Open All year, except 9–21 Sept, 20 Dec–22 Jan, Sun evening and Mon (Mon evening and Tue at Easter and Whitsun).
Rooms 3 triple, 7 double – all with bath and shower, and telephone; 3 with TV.
Facilities Lounge, bar, restaurant. Garden beside river; fishing (permit obtainable in village).
Location 23 km S of Fontainebleau by N6 (18 km); turn right onto D403, and immediately left onto D120.
Restriction Not suitable for ♿.
Credit cards All major cards accepted.
Terms Rooms: single 170–190 frs, double 210–370 frs. Breakfast 32 frs. Dinner, B&B 251–324 frs. Set lunch/dinner 130 frs; full alc 220 frs. Reduced rates and special meals for children.

FLORIMONT-GAUMIERS 24250 Dordogne — Map 10

La Daille — *Tel* 53.28.40.71

Florimont-Gaumiers, Domme

Several eulogies have reached us this year for this secluded farmhouse south of Domme that Derek and Barbara Brown now run as a tiny four-bedroom hotel-restaurant – a stirring example of the British love-affair with the Dordogne. Set in the hills above the Céou valley, the house is built in local stone with an external stone staircase and pigeon tower, but internally it has been sensitively modernised, with new bathrooms. "The Browns strike just the right balance of friendliness and professionalism and the food was excellent; the rooms enjoy a splendid view across the valley"; "the whole atmosphere was peaceful and relaxed". No lunches are served, but you can buy your own delicatessen and wines and enjoy them under the walnut trees in the pretty garden. (*Dr and Mrs James Stewart, EA and BM Prower, and others*)

Open 1 May–15 Oct. Restaurant closed for lunch.
Rooms 3 double, 1 single – 3 bath, 1 with shower. Single room in annexe.
Facilities Restaurant. Garden, terrace.
Location La Daille is signposted from Gaumiers village, which is just W of the D46, 13 km S of Domme and 5 km NW of Salviac.
Restrictions Not suitable for ♿. No children under 7.
Credit cards None accepted.
Terms Dinner, B&B (min 3 days) 288–325 frs. Set dinner (by reservation only) 120 frs.

FONTAINEBLEAU 77300 Seine-et-Marne — Map 9

Hôtel Aigle Noir — *Tel* (1) 64.22.32.65
27 place Napoléon — *Fax* (1) 64.22.17.33
Telex 694080

Fontainebleau's grandest hotel, in the centre, facing the gardens of Napoleon's favourite palace. Classic Louis XVI and Empire decor plus mod cons. Some bedrooms are lavishly Victorian in style, others plainer; service is good, but room upkeep can be faulty. Food mostly admired: Michelin *rosette and* Gault Millau toque *for such dishes as caneton rouennais aux groseilles. 6 suites, 51 rooms, all with bath or shower. B&B double 940–1,090 frs. Set menus 200–280 frs [1989]. Endorsed this year, but some recent criticisms. Further reports welcome.*

FONTGOMBAULT 36220 Indre — Map 10

Auberge de l'Abbaye — *Tel* 54.37.10.82

Exuding authentic rural Frenchness, this Guide newcomer stands in a village of the Creuse valley between Poitiers and Châteauroux: "An enchanting place: five 16th-century cottages grouped round a shady courtyard (where you take breakfast) have been sympathetically converted into a small comfortable hotel. The *patron* is a man of talents who even mends cameras. The food was delicious, served in the stone-flagged entrance hall. The monastery up the road does a nice Gregorian chant. Front bedrooms suffer from early traffic noise." Madame writes to us: "C'est moi qui fait la cuisine, plûtot du type traditionnel, et nous fabriquons nous-mêmes charcuterie, sauces, pâtisseries. Nous aimons les clients qui aiment la maison et qui apprécient les petits coins tranquilles de campagne. L'été, nous servons le repas le plus souvent sur la terrasse, à l'ombre d'un gros tilleul. À 50 mètres coule une belle rivière. Nous pouvons louer des bicyclettes pour visiter la région." (*Ann Mary Bishop*) Des avis supplémentaires, SVP.

Open All year.
Rooms 4 double, 1 single – 3 with shower (2 have wc).
Facilities Bar, dining room; terrace where meals are served. River 50 metres.
Location 8 km NW of Le Blanc towards Chattelerault.
Restriction Not suitable for ♿.
Credit card Visa.
Terms [1989 rates] Rooms 90–175 frs. Breakfast 20 frs. Set meals 60 and 85 frs. Reduced rates for children sharing parents' room.

FONTVIEILLE 13990 Bouches-du-Rhône — Map 11

Auberge La Régalido — *Tel* 90.54.60.22
Rue Frédéric Mistral — *Telex* 150451

Daudet's windmill (not the real one actually, but that's another story) stands on a hill outside this tiny town in the foothills of the Alpilles, near Arles. Admired as much as ever this year, *La Régalido* is a former oil-mill in a side street, now converted into a most welcoming little *auberge*, luxurious yet unpretentious. It is run by the Michel family: Madame's hand is evident in the flowers which grace all the rooms, and Monsieur's in the cooking (*Michelin* rosette), which our readers continue to find excellent (try the gratin de moules aux épinards or gigot d'agneau en casserole). Latest reports: "A friendly, welcoming hotel, with enthusiastic owner. Wines of particular interest." "A superb lunch with perfect service." "A wonderful place with *really* charming staff. Mme Michel a powerhouse of efficiency and strikingly beautiful; Monsieur a delight, amiable, the perfect host. Not cheap, neither *should* it be." A visitor in October found "a fire blazing in the sitting-room". Bedrooms have individual charm, and there is a flowery garden. (*Mrs JB Priestley, PH Wainman, Ellen & John Buchanan*)

Open All year except Dec and Jan.
Rooms 14 double – all with bath and/or shower, telephone, radio and TV, most air-conditioned. 1 on ground-floor.
Facilities Lounge, TV room, bar, restaurant; function room. Garden, terrace.
Location 5 km NE of Arles. Leave *autoroute* A7 at Cavaillon, direction St-Rémy-de-Provence, or at Nîmes, direction Arles. Parking.
Credit cards All major cards accepted.
Terms Rooms: single 390–500 frs, double 800–1,150 frs. Breakfast 65 frs. Dinner, B&B: single 710–820 frs, double 1,450–1,800 frs. Set lunch/dinner 250, 290 and 380 frs; full alc 300 frs. Special meals for children on request.

FROENINGEN 68720 Haut-Rhin — Map 9

Auberge de Froeningen — *Tel* 89.25.48.48
2 route d'Illfurth

In a village 9 km southwest of Mulhouse, an elegant restaurant-with-rooms (oriental carpets in the red-walled dining room), in a spruce modern house built in local style with flower-decked balconies. Cosy bedrooms, convivial ambience, excellent food. Large grounds. 7 rooms, all with bath and shower. Rooms 260–320 frs. Breakfast 30 frs. Set menus 100–295 frs. New nomination. More reports please.

FUTEAU 55120 Meuse — Map 9

L'Orée du Bois — *Tel* 29.88.28.41

This most seductive hotel, a low white building, stands on a wooded hillside in the pretty Argonne countryside where Lorraine meets Champagne. "We were again delighted", say returning visitors whose nomination last year ran: "The charming and helpful young owners, Paul and Roselyne Aguesse, have been there about four years and obviously enjoy running their little hotel. Its bedrooms are in a new annexe: ours was very clean, freshly decorated, with pretty pink-and-apricot bed-spreads, and was good value. The cosy rustic-style bar had a beamed ceiling and roaring log fire; so indeed did the spacious dining room whose long windows afforded glorious views over the countryside. On each table, fresh flowers and lit candles. The food was not cheap, but really excellent (*Gault Millau toque*). The meal takes time, as all is cooked to order. Breakfast was good too, served by a motherly soul in a room where a fire was already crackling. As we left, M. Aguesse was sweeping the drive. I have never seen an owner-chef take such an active part in keeping his hotel spick and span – long may the enthusiasm last." (*Padi and John Howard*) This year, eating from the *carte*, the Howards especially enjoyed the foie gras chaud, salade de homard, and "the best pigeon dish I've ever eaten. I enthused so much about it that M. Aguesse came out of the kitchen to talk to me about cooking game."

Open All year except Jan. Restaurant closed Tue.
Rooms 7 – all with bath, telephone, TV and tea-making facilities.
Facilities Lounge, bar, TV room, restaurant. Terrace, garden.
Location 1 km S of Futeau, which is 13 km E of Ste-Ménehould (turn S off N3 at Les Islettes).
Credit cards Access, Visa.
Terms Rooms: single 220 frs, double 240 frs. Breakfast 35 frs. Half board 300–360 frs per person. Set lunch/dinner 100, 150 and 280 frs; full alc 320 frs. Reduced rates for children sharing parents' room; special meals.

GÉMENOS 13420 Bouches-du-Rhône — Map 11

Relais de la Magdeleine — *Tel* 42.82.20.05

"Mozart tends to pervade this well-lit hotel in the evening. There is open-air chess and dining by candle-light under the trees. The proprietor is charming and has a superb collection of paintings and tapestries" – an enticing recent report on the sophisticated and much admired *Relais de la Magdeleine*, described also as "a charming 17th-century *bastide*, set in a large walled garden with lovely bathing pool – a peaceful and luxurious oasis on the outskirts of the small town of Gémenos" (which is within easy reach of the coast at Cassis or Marseilles, and the wild and strange *massif* of La Sainte-Baume). "The owners, the Marignanes, made us feel like welcome guests in their own home. The service was faultless, by charming young girls, and the food was delicious, with good breakfasts too." "The public rooms and large bedrooms were attractively furnished with antiques; the beds were high quality. The dining rooms were cool and spacious, with some walls covered with silk or damask. But in spite of this luxury there was nothing pretentious or formal about the atmosphere, which was friendly and happy. There was an aura of peace, especially on the terrace in the early evening when drinks were served under floodlit plane trees. Provençal cooking, plus a large selection of pâtisseries and wonderful cheese. At breakfast, freshly made hot brioches." Two strong endorsements this year, but a third reader was slightly disappointed. The hotel welcomes children. (*Peter L Aston, Sarah Curtis*)

Open 15 Mar–1 Nov.
Rooms 3 suites, 17 double – 18 with bath, 2 with shower, all with telephone and TV.
Facilities 2 salons, 2 restaurants. Garden with swimming pool.
Location On outskirts of Gémenos, which is 23 km E of Marseilles. Exit Pont de l'Étoile from Aix–Toulon motorway.
Restriction Not suitable for ♿.
Credit cards Access, Visa.
Terms B&B: single 415–480 frs, double 435–640 frs, suite 840 frs. Dinner, B&B 415–650 frs per person. Set lunch/dinner 150–180 frs; full alc 220–240 frs. Reduced rates and special meals for children.

We depend on detailed fresh reports to keep our entries up-to-date.

GÉRARDMER 88400 Vosges — Map 9

Grand Hôtel Bragard — *Tel* 29.63.06.31
Place du Tilleul — *Telex* 960964

Within 500 metres of the lovely lake in this big, popular Vosges resort, a sizeable old-fashioned hotel renovated and given a fresh lease of life by its new owners. Pleasant service and bedrooms, comfortable lounge, and excellent food (Gault Millau toque). *Large garden with small swimming pool. 61 rooms, all with bath and shower. B&B double 370–570 frs. Set menus 90–250 frs. New nomination. More reports please.*

LES GETS 74260 Haute-Savoie — Map 10

Hôtel Mont Chéry — *Tel* 50.79.74.55

In a pretty skiing village devoid of modern concrete buildings, 25 miles south of Lake Geneva, here close to the ski-lifts and ski-school is a friendly chalet-style ski hotel, family-run and ideal for families. Very good food. Garden for summer. Open 15 Dec–20 Apr, 1 July–31 Aug. 26 rooms, all with bath. B&B double 280–490 frs. Set menus 78–240 frs [1989]. *Recent nomination. More reports please.*

GIEN 45500 Loiret — Map 10

Hôtel du Rivage — *Tel* 38.67.20.53
1 quai de Nice — *Telex* 375974 BOX RIVAGE

"A splendid old Loire-side town with floodlit castle and church. A friendly welcome, open fire, dining room well filled with locals, food superb and service delightful. Beds comfortable but bath rather small." "The best chicken liver pâté I've ever eaten, champagne sorbet, a wonderful tuna steak in a cream sauce, delicious desserts – all for 135 francs" [1989]. So run two of the four endorsements this year for this very spruce modern hotel just off the main road, close to the river. *Michelin* awards the food a rosette, and *Gault Millau* a *toque*. Everyone praises the service and comfort: one reader had "a charming room overlooking the Loire". There were earlier reports of noisy front rooms, but the owners this year write that all now have double-glazing, and all have been modernised. (*Capt. JS Stewart, SHD Johnson; also Dr John Cliffe and Annie Stott*)

Open All year. Restaurant closed 5 Feb–8 Mar.
Rooms 5 suites, 15 double, 2 single – all with bath, shower, telephone and TV.
Facilities Salon, piano-bar, dining room. Terrace.
Location On road to Nevers, on banks of the Loire (double-glazing). Parking.
Restriction Not suitable for ♿.
Credit cards All major cards accepted.
Terms Rooms: single occupancy 245 frs, double 300 frs, suite 600 frs. Breakfast 35 frs. Set lunch/dinner 140, 175 and 280 frs; full alc 350 frs. Reduced rates and special meals for children.

We are particularly keen to have reports on italicised entries.

GIGONDAS 84190 Vaucluse — Map 11

Les Florets — *Tel* 90.65.85.01
Route des Dentelles

An attractive small country hotel outside Gigondas, near to some of the best Côtes du Rhône vineyards and just below the spectacular Dentelles de Montmirail. "It consists", says a recent visitor, "of a smallish main house and an annexe on the hill behind, all gravel yard, blossom and sunshine. The service is pleasant, the food a bit boring, but the glory of the place is the deliciously tree-dappled, fountain-rilled, Pernod-supplied, chaise-longued terrace, which looks over vineyards and mountains, and is absolutely silent except for the clinking of ice in glasses." Others this year have endorsed that report, save that one visitor thought the management less than friendly. And the reference to boring food has been indignantly refuted by a regular patron of the *Florets'* restaurant for the past 20 years, "The food is always a delight, and the menu is regularly changed too."(*Peter L Aston, AG Catchpole*) The owners write to say that they also possess a Gigondas vineyard.

Open All year except Jan and Feb. Closed Wed; also Tue evening Nov–Mar.
Rooms 13 double, 2 single – 13 with bath and/or shower, all with telephone. 4 bungalows 50 m from hotel.
Facilities Salon/bar, restaurant, TV room; terrace. Garden.
Location 1.5 km E of Gigondas, which is 18 km E of Orange.
Restriction Not suitable for ♿.
Credit cards All major cards accepted.
Terms [1989 rates] Rooms 225–260 frs. Breakfast 32 frs. Dinner, B&B 230–260 frs per person. Set meals 110–170 frs. Reduced rates and special meals for children.

GIVRY 71640 Saône-et-Loire — Map 10

Hôtel de la Halle — *Tel* 85.44.32.45
Place de la Halle

The charming Renard family run a modest but friendly little hotel, well suited for an overnight stop, in a pleasant Burgundy village west of Chalon; it is a venerable building with a fine spiral staircase, facing the former market hall. Reports this year and last have again pointed to its qualities and its faults: front rooms a bit noisy, some rooms rather small and basic, but: "Splendid value", "excellent old-fashioned Burgundian food", and: "Bedrooms though simple are spotlessly clean, and have an interesting conflict of different textile patterns. We had a warm reception from the Renards. It was a pleasure to sit in their good restaurant watching the locals come and go, most of them close friends of the family, judging by all the kissing going on." There are local wine tastings just opposite. (*PA Catling, GC Brown*)

Open All year except 21–28 Aug, 13–27 Nov, 1–7 Jan, Sun evening and Mon.
Rooms 10 double – 2 with bath, 3 with shower, all with telephone.
Facilities Lounge, restaurant. Garden.
Location Givry is 9 km W of Chalon-sur-Saône on D69. Hotel is central (front rooms may be noisy). Parking.
Restriction Not suitable for ♿.
Credit cards All major cards accepted.
Terms [1989 rates] Rooms 100–165 frs. Breakfast 22 frs. Set lunch 55, dinner 165 frs.

GORDES 84220 Vaucluse — Map 11

La Mayanelle — *Tel* 90.72.00.28

Near the centre of the much-visited hill-village of Gordes (a summer resort for the Parisian intelligentsia), M. Bayard's friendly little hotel is perched on a cliff and has fine views over hills and valley from many bedrooms and from the broad stone dining-terrace. Bar with antique decor. Rooms vary in size and some lack a view. Good traditional Provençal cooking. Closed 4 Jan–28 Feb. 10 rooms, all with bath or shower, 200–300 frs. Breakfast 38 frs. Full alc 130–190 frs [1989]. Few recent reports. More welcome.

GOSNAY 62199 Pas-de-Calais — Map 9

La Chartreuse du Val St-Esprit — *Tel* 21.62.80.00
1 rue de Fouquières — *Telex* 134418

This useful stop-over hotel on the way to Calais has an unusual history – it's a former monastery where Princess Isabel of Portugal died in 1471, later rebuilt in classic château style and recently turned into a rather elegant hotel. It lies slap amid the now defunct Pas-de-Calais coal-mines – not the most lyrical of settings, but the Béthune motorway exit is conveniently close. More reports this year: "Comfortable and friendly, with food of a high standard"; "reasonably good value for money, a staff that tries hard to please, but the place has too 'new' a feel and lacks atmosphere." "Great pleasure to walk up the attractive staircase in classic château style. Our room was of imposing elegance, but service was a bit hectic and breakfast disappointing." "A perfect weekend; the food was brilliant." The restaurant is doing well locally, and a swimming pool is planned. (*P Gill, Dr FP Adler, RP Wynings, GB and Dr CH*)

Open All year.
Rooms 23 – all with bath and shower, telephone, TV and mini-bar. Some ground-floor rooms; special bathroom for ♿.
Facilities Ramps. Lounges, restaurant; conference and functions rooms. Garden with tennis court.
Location 5 km SW of Béthune. Leave A26 motorway at Béthune exit and make for Bruay-en-Artois.
Credit cards Access, Amex, Visa.
Terms [1989 rates] Rooms: single occupancy 290 frs, double 420 frs. Breakfast 38 frs. Set meals 110–320 frs. Reduced rates and special meals for children.

GOUMOIS 25470 Doubs — Map 10

Hôtel Taillard — *Tel* 81.44.20.75

"A typical French country hotel, looking a little seedy from outside but with a large terrace which must be lovely in mid-summer. The food is French country cooking at its best with very ample portions – we remember especially the poached salmon." So runs one recent report on the Taillard family's spacious and gracious chalet, much reputed for its cooking (*Michelin* rosette); it is secluded on the slopes of a wooded valley, close to the Swiss border between Belfort and Neuchâtel. Many rooms have a balcony, fine views and "not a sound all night save the gurgling of the little stream in the gardens". This year, one reader thought the rooms nice and the food good, but another found it patchy. And one affectionate regular visitor, on her umpteenth return visit, found the hotel's charms beginning to wane, "Madame Taillard, who has run the hotel with a firm hand since we started going there, has sadly retired, and her nephew and his wife are now in charge. Some of their new additions seemed out of place to us: notably the modern seating area that's replaced the old rustic bar. Some rooms are lovely, but some at the back are small and cramped. The dinner was enjoyable as ever, e.g. warm foie gras and the truite belle goumoise, but the main dishes had rich cloying sauces. Breakfast was exceptionally good." (*Stephen Ruell, Padi and John Howard*) Some other recent reports have been critical, and we'd welcome more, please.

Open Early Mar–mid-Nov. Closed on Wed Mar, Oct and Nov.
Rooms 4 suites, 13 double – 10 with bath, 5 with shower, all with telephone and TV.
Facilities TV room, bar, 2 dining rooms; terrace. Garden with swimming pool. River nearby with trout fishing and canoeing.
Location 50 km SE of Montbéliard, 18 km E of Maiche on D437A and D437B. Leave *autoroute* A36 at Montbéliard Sud exit. The hotel is near the church. Parking.
Restriction Not suitable for ♿.
Credit cards All major cards accepted.
Terms Rooms 150–230 frs, suite 290–310 frs. Breakfast 32 frs. Dinner, B&B 250–295 frs per person, full board 300–345 frs. Full alc 250 frs. Reduced rates and special meals for children.

GRENOBLE 38000 Isère — Map 10

Park Hôtel
10 place Paul-Mistral

Tel 76.87.29.11
Fax 76.46.49.88
Telex 320767

A connoisseur of Grenoble writes, "This large, booming and industrial/university city has remarkably few good hotels, and the *Park* is its most stylish and comfortable. It faces onto the big central park, and some rooms have views of the surrounding mountains. The dark oak panelling and deep easy chairs in the foyer set the pampered tone, for the bedrooms are panelled too (we were less enamoured of the purple velvet linings to the corridor walls). Some rooms have minitels, the videotex computers that are France's favourite new gimmick. Service is deft and friendly, and a good breakfast was served us in the hotel's *Taverne de Ripaille*." More reports please.

Open All year except 29 Jul–21 Aug, 24 Dec–2 Jan. Restaurant closed Sun midday.
Rooms 4 suites, 56 double or single – all with bath and/or shower, telephone, TV and air-conditioning.
Facilities Lift. Lounge, bar, restaurant; conference facilities.
Location Central. Free public parking beside hotel.
Credit cards All major cards accepted.
Terms [1989 rates] Rooms 610–910 frs. Breakfast 40 frs. Alc meals 120–200 frs (excluding wine).

We need feedback on all entries. Often people fail to report on the best-known hotels, assuming that "someone else is sure to".

GRIMAUD 83310 Var — Map 11

Hostellerie du Coteau Fleuri — *Tel* 94.43.20.17
Place des Pénitents

Grimaud is a fashionable hill-village behind St-Tropez, its ancient stone houses neatly converted into summer homes for the Parisian intelligentsia. The *Coteau Fleuri*, on the outskirts, is an old building modernised as a neo-Provençal auberge with tiled floors, and it is as flower-decked as its name implies. New owners, the Minards, took over in 1988, and three recent reports are so complimentary that we restore the hotel as a full entry (after previous criticisms): "A very friendly atmosphere and delicious cooking, e.g. gigot de lotte aux lentilles", writes a Swiss reader. "Meals on the terrace, with a marvellous view, are of high quality – exquisite langoustines. The maids are efficient, the bedrooms small but comfortable." A piano for guests to use, a log fire for chilly days, a spacious lounge and rambling garden slope, plus superb views over the wooded Maures hills. But some bedrooms are *very* small. (*Jean-Michel and Monique Pictet; also M Neale, John and Rita Newnham*) *Note*: it is essential to reserve a table for dinner even if you are resident.

Open All year except Jan. Restaurant closed 2 weeks in Dec and Tue except Jul and Aug.
Rooms 14 double – all with bath/shower and telephone.
Facilities Salon, bar, restaurant. Terrace.
Location 10 km from St-Tropez. On edge of village. Parking.
Restriction Not suitable for ♿.
Credit cards All major cards accepted.
Terms [1989 rates] Rooms 300–450 frs. Breakfast 45 frs. Set lunch 130 frs, dinner 180 frs; full alc 250–300 frs.

GUÉTHARY 64210 Pyrénées-Atlantiques — Map 10

Hôtel Pereria — *Tel* 59.26.51.68
Rue de l'Église

This old Basque house in a big, slightly unkempt garden has been liked again this year: "An uncomplicated holiday hotel catering mainly for French families – a plus point, in our book. Tasty meals, outstanding value." It is "run by youngish, good-looking and friendly owners, with an attractive and demure staff". The annexe, across a busy road, is possibly more comfortable than the hotel itself, and bedrooms in both are large. Recent visitors have enjoyed the friendly efficiency and the good meals (e.g. ttoro, a Basque fish soup) served out on the terrace. You can view the hills and the distant sea, and can watch the sunset from the outdoor dining terrace. (*Helen and Charles Priday; JAG Stonehouse*)

Open 1 Mar–1 Nov.
Rooms 28 double, 2 single – 26 with bath, all with telephone. 11 in annexe across road.
Facilities Salon, 2 restaurants; terrace where meals are served. Garden with *boules* and swings. Beach nearby with swimming, wind-surfing, sailing and fishing.
Location On the coast between Biarritz and St-Jean-de-Luz.
Restriction Not suitable for ♿.
Credit cards Access, Visa.
Terms B&B: single 70–150 frs, double 245–250 frs. Set lunch/dinner 70, 105 and 150 frs; full alc 100 frs. Reduced rates and special meals for children.

HAUT-DE-CAGNES 06800 Alpes-Maritimes — Map 11

Le Cagnard — *Tel* 93.20.73.21
Rue du Pontis-Long — *Telex* 462223

The sizeable town of Cagnes-sur-Mer is divided, like Caesar's Gaul, into three parts: the ugly sprawling resort of Cros-de-Cagnes; just inland, Cagnes-Ville, unremarkable save for the inspiring Renoir museum on its outskirts; and, higher up, Haut-de-Cagnes, one of the region's most sophisticated hill villages (fascinating museum in the château). Here *Le Cagnard*, a well-known and very smart little hotel – "delightful and distinguished", "very romantic", say readers – has been artfully converted out of some 13th-century houses by the ramparts and virtually clings to the side of a cliff. Devotees returning this year admired the newly extended terrace restaurant with its superb hand-painted ceiling. Here there are fine views; you can also eat in a graceful candle-lit room, former guardroom of the château, where sometimes there is guitar music. The food, say readers, is "delicious": it wins a *Michelin* rosette and two *Gault Millau toques* for inventive adaptation of local dishes. Despite these *nouvelle* influences, portions are large. The set menu is expensive, but they do not mind if you take a light snack from the *carte*.

"Our room was the whole floor of a medieval house, with superb antique furniture and a picture window." Rooms, however, vary considerably in size and comfort: for example, Nos 18 and 19 are said to be far nicer than No 22, just above the hotel entrance and a bit noisy. It is worth asking for a room with a view of the coast (but these may be the costlier ones). Parking is a nightmare; it is best to park in the new carpark just below the village, or else leave parking to the hotel. (*Pat and Jeremy Temple, Dr John Cliffe*)

Open All year. Restaurant closed 1 Nov–20 Dec, and Thur midday.
Rooms 10 suites, 8 double, 2 single – all with bath and/or shower, telephone; 16 with TV. Suites in annexe.
Facilities Lift. Salon, bar, 2 restaurants. Small garden and terrace. Sandy beach 6 km.
Location On the ramparts, 2 minutes from château. Parking.
Restriction Not suitable for ♿.
Credit cards All major cards accepted.
Terms Rooms: single occupancy 300–410 frs, double 350–600 frs, suite 730–1,000 frs. Breakfast 50 frs. Set lunch/dinner 340 and 430 frs; full alc 420 frs. Extra bed 120 frs. Special meals for children on request.

HESDIN-L'ABBÉ 62360 Pas-de-Calais — Map 9

Hôtel Cléry — *Tel* 21.83.19.83
Telex 135349

This newly opened country-house hotel just south of Boulogne is already proving popular with British visitors; it's a *Relais du Silence*, and is brought to the Guide by an inspector this year, "Set in five acres of parkland and approached by a tree-lined avenue, this 18th-century château has a splendid facade, and the entrance hall is appealing with a lovely curving Louis XV wrought-iron staircase. The Osselands, who bought the house recently, are helpful and friendly. Our room had prettily painted modern furniture, and decor in soft pastel shades. Reception rooms are well furnished and homely. In the smallish, prettily decorated dining room, service was a trifle erratic but the food good, very professionally cooked in the *nouvelle* manner – salmon with fennel sauce, duck slightly pink, superb marquise au chocolat, etc – and good breakfast too. A pleasant hotel, well suited to a short break." More reports welcome.

Open All year except 15 Dec–15 Jan.
Rooms 19 – all with bath and/or shower, telephone and TV.
Facilities Lounges, bar, restaurant; conference room. Park with tennis court.
Location 9 km SE of Boulogne, off N1.
Credit cards Access, Amex, Visa.
Terms [1989 rates] Rooms 270–480 frs. Breakfast 55 frs. Dinner, B&B 295–510 frs per person. Set lunch/dinner 140–240 frs.

HONFLEUR 14600 Calvados — Map 8

Ferme de la Grande Cour — *Tel* 31.89.04.69
Côte de Grace

An offbeat idyll for those who love rural Normandy – a farmhouse restaurant-with-rooms, set amid apple orchards just west of picturesque but trippery Honfleur. Courteous young staff, simple but comfortable bedrooms, quite good food served in a beamed dining room or on the lawn. Open 1 Feb–31 Dec. 14 rooms, all with bath and/or shower. B&B double 182–352 frs. Set meals 100–195 frs [1989]. More reports welcome.

IGÉ 71960 Saône-et-Loire — Map 10

Château d'Igé — *Tel* 85.33.33.99
Fax 85.33.41.41
Telex 351915

Igé is a small Burgundy village away from the main roads, amid pleasant country lanes. Here the former hunting lodge of the Dukes of Mâcon, "a beautiful little medieval castle", is now a luxurious hotel set beside a stream on the edge of the Mâcon hills: "A proper castle with rounded turrets, grey ivy-covered walls and stone-flagged floors and staircases." One visitor this year enjoyed breakfast on the terrace "with families of ducks to watch", and found the service friendly but slow; another relished the sense of *noblesse*, enhanced by Vivaldi; a third liked her turret room. Other recent visitors have had a suite of rooms full of antiques, or have praised the home farm's goat's cheese and enjoyed being able to select their own trout from a holding pond. Food, not cheap, is straightforward rather than fancy modern. (*Prof. AS Douglas, Peter and Ann Jones, Jeff and Karen Nebel*)

Open 1 Mar–15 Nov.
Rooms 6 suites, 6 double – all with bath and shower, telephone, TV.
Location 6.5 km N of N79; 14 km NW of Mâcon, 11 km SE of Cluny.
Restriction Not suitable for ♿.
Credit cards All major cards accepted.
Terms [1989 rates] Rooms 360–550 frs, suite 650–900 frs. Breakfast 50 frs. Set lunch/dinner 180–330 frs. Special meals for children.

> Hotels are dropped if we lack positive feedback. If you can endorse an entry, please do so.

ILLHAEUSERN 68150 Haut-Rhin — Map 9

Hôtel La Clairière — *Tel* 89.71.80.80
Route de Guémar

The Haeberlin family's celebrated *Auberge de l'Ill* (three *Michelin* rosettes) does not qualify for the Guide, as it has no bedrooms; the *Clairière*, in the same Alsatian village north-west of Colmar, has no restaurant. So they complement each other conveniently: you can eat at one, stay at the other, as our nominator suggests this year: "A fairly new modern building, just outside the village amid fields and woods. We had a warm welcome, joined by four assorted dogs. The hotel is smartly furnished and well kept, with some antiques, lovely pictures, an attractive small lounge. Our enormous bedroom had hessian wallpaper, pretty bedlights, dark oak furniture, beds with heavy wooden frames and pinky-red Paisley-design drapes: the beds, though lumpy and creaky, were comfortable. A huge bathroom with greeny-brown tiles. Breakfast nicely served in the bedroom. Staff friendly." (*John and Padi Howard*)

Open 1 Mar–1 Jan.
Rooms 4 suites, 24 double – all with bath (4 also with shower), telephone, TV and baby-listening. Ground-floor rooms.
Facilities Lift. Lounge with TV.
Location Village is 17 km NW of Colmar. Parking.
Credit cards Access, Visa.
Terms Rooms: single 390 frs, double 430 frs, suite 800–1,000 frs. Breakfast 45 frs.

JOIGNY 89300 Yonne — Map 9

À la Côte Saint-Jacques — *Tel* 86.62.09.70
14 faubourg de Paris — *Fax* 86.91.49.70
Telex 801458 SAINJAC

We continue to receive breathlessly ecstatic accounts of this old coaching inn beside the river Yonne, where *patron*/chef Michel Lorain and his son Jean-Michel win the top ratings of four red *Michelin* gables and three rosettes, and four red *Gault Millau toques*, for their fine cooking in luxury surroundings with bedrooms and prices to match. They have recently created some opulent rooms from old houses facing the river, across the noisy N6, and to provide access they have made a paved tunnel under this road, decorated with Roman remains from the excavation. Readers have stayed there in 1989:

"This is a very sexy place, as only the French can do it. The luxurious new bedrooms are sexy, and the whole set-up slightly outrageous. The dining rooms have gaudy flower arrangements, paintings of scantily dressed girls, candle-light, and very sensuous food. It all works, because it is totally professional – and fun. The entire Lorain family greeted us for dinner, and absurd smiles of ecstasy were on our faces as we ate terrine of marinated sardines and tapenade, quail egg in truffle juice, exquisitely delicate skate in a lemon sauce, grilled lobster in a Sauternes sauce, and more. Our only complaint: in one room the tables are set too closely – nasty if your neighbours smoke. Our bedroom had a combination of antique and contemporary furnishings, with dark beams, Berber carpets over plank floors, a huge marble bathroom. In this new building one is totally unaware of the N6; you overlook the lovely Yonne. I have never been so conscious of being surrounded by beauty, peace and comfort." This was no Xanadu-like dream that flees on waking, for others this year have echoed the praise in more down-to-earth terms: "Delicious light cooking, very good breakfast, faultless service, fittings of the highest quality." "An enjoyable atmosphere. The bedrooms are probably among the finest in France." (*Sharon Gutman; Rosamund Hebdon*)

Open All year except 2 Jan–2 Feb. Restaurant closed for lunch at weekend.
Rooms 3 suites, 11 double – all with bath, shower, telephone and TV; baby sitting on request. All in annexe linked to main building by tunnel.
Facilities Lift. Salon, bar, breakfast room, 3 restaurants; conference room; indoor heated swimming pool, sauna. Garden.
Location 27 km NW of Auxerre on N6; leave at Sens exit.
Restriction Not suitable for ♿.
Credit cards All major cards accepted.
Terms Rooms: 980–1,550 frs, suite 1,550–2,450 frs, triple 1,920–2,800 frs. Breakfast 80 frs. Set lunch 240 frs (not served on weekends); dinner 520 frs. Special meals for children.

JOUÉ-LÈS-TOURS 37300 Indre-et-Loire — Map 8

Hôtel du Château de Beaulieu — *Tel* 47.53.20.26
1 rue de l'Épend

A modernised 18th-century manor on the south-west outskirts of Tours. "Sadly", says an admirer, "they have sold their land to the local council, and the *jardins à la française* are now municipal tennis courts. But it remains an impressive building, inside and out, with huge stone staircase and panelled restaurant. The latter draws a smart and demanding clientele from miles around and was full on our visit. We greatly enjoyed our meal. Our mansarded first-floor bedroom was vast and a bit stark, despite flowery wallpaper, but was comfortable, clean and spacious. We spied more attractive rooms in the annexe. Prices were reasonable, service efficient, breakfast copious and promptly served." Other recent visitors, too, have enjoyed the "excellent" food (mussel soup with puff pastry, duckling served as two courses), as well as the river views (but Tours skyscrapers are also in view). Guests are expected to dine in the hotel between April and the end of October.

Open All year except Christmas Eve.
Rooms 19 double – 18 with bath, 1 with shower, all with telephone, TV and mini-bar. 10 in pavilion.
Facilities Salon, TV room, 2 restaurants; conference room. Large garden.
Location 4 km SW of Tours, by D86 and D207.
Restriction Not suitable for ♿.
Credit cards Access, Diners, Visa.
Terms Double room 350–600 frs. Breakfast 40 frs. Dinner, B&B double 700–930 frs; full board 930–1,210 frs. Set lunch/dinner 165–380 frs. Reduced rates Nov–Mar.

LA JOUVENTE 35730, Ile-et-Vilaine — Map 8

Manoir de la Rance — *Tel* 99.88.53.76

Beautifully set above the boat-filled Rance estuary, 7 km south-east of Dinard, a converted manor with clean rooms, excellent breakfasts, obliging owners, and decor and furnishings in a mixture of styles, some more sympathetic than others.

Closed Jan, Feb. 7 rooms, most with bath and/or shower. B&B double 330–550 frs [1989]. No restaurant. New nomination. More reports please.

KAYSERSBERG 68240 Haut-Rhin — Map 9

Hôtel Résidence Chambard
13 rue de Général de Gaulle

Tel 89.47.10.17
Fax 89.47.35.03
Telex 880272

Albert Schweitzer was born in this picturesque Alsatian wine village, and in its main street is a small museum devoted to him. Down the road is *patron*/chef Pierre Irrmann's smartish restaurant-with-rooms (*Michelin* rosette, two red *Gault Millau toques*), converted from two old buildings with pretty facades. It was dropped from the 1989 Guide for want of feedback, but is restored by a reader this year, "Dinner was costly but excellent; room was comfortable with good view of vineyards." The food is *nouvelle*-ish but not too much so, and such dishes as marinated raw salmon and garlicky ragout of lamb have been admired. The Alsatian wines are reasonably priced. But an inspector thought that the bedroom annexe lacks the personality of a hotel. It might be worth paying extra to secure the special room with a big canopied bed and a quaint round salon in a 15th-century tower. (*LC Foreman*)

Open All year except 1–21 Mar and 21 Dec–4 Jan. Restaurant closed Mon and Tue midday.
Rooms 2 suites, 20 double, 9 single – 20 with bath and shower, all with telephone, radio and TV. Ground-floor rooms.
Facilities Lift. Lounge, bar, restaurant; cellar for conference/functions.
Location 11 km NW of Colmar. Central, but quiet. Parking.
Credit cards All major cards accepted.
Terms: Rooms 400–550 frs. Breakfast 50 frs. Set lunch/dinner 200–340 frs; full alc 400 frs.

LACAVE 46200 Dordogne — Map 10

Le Pont de l'Ouysse — *Tel* 65.37.87.04

Not far from Rocamadour, a restaurant-with-rooms in a fine situation by a river, with a château looming above and a tree-shaded dining terrace for fine weather. "It's charming, and the rooms are delightful with a light, elegant garden look", says a reader this year, backing up last year's view: "A gem. Quiet, friendly and beautifully furnished, with tasteful bedrooms and bathrooms. The service is helpful and the food 'exquisite' but rather too rich for a long stay." Another visitor has spelt this out, "Family run, but by a family of chic urbanites – rooms utterly chic. Food very urban and *nouvelle*-ish, not cheap and portions not large" (*Gault Millau* bestows a red *toque* for variations on regional dishes, such as sautéed foie gras with capers). The dog, Sacha, likes to go on walks with guests – "he came with us to Rocamadour and back and seemed to know the ropes – I should think he does this every day in season."

Open 1 Mar–11 Nov. Closed Mon in low season.
Rooms 1 suite, 12 double – all with bath, telephone, radio and TV. 5 in annexe.
Facilities Lounge, dining room. Terrace, garden with swimming pool. River, fishing nearby.

Location 10 km NW of Rocamadour.
Restriction Not suitable for ♿.
Credit cards All major cards accepted.
Terms Rooms double 400 frs. Breakfast 35 frs. Dinner, B&B 400 frs per person. Set lunch/dinner 150, 250 and 300 frs; full alc 280 frs. Reduced rates and special meals for children.

LAMASTRE 07270 Ardèche — Map 10

Hôtel du Midi/Restaurant Barattéro — *Tel* 75.06.41.50
Place Seignobos

Steady praise again this year for owner-chef Bernard Perrier's serious, well-run hotel/restaurant – "a gem" – in the market square of a pleasant little town west of Valence, on the edge of the Rhône valley: "An excellent family-run place, with Madame Perrier very much in evidence. The food is very good, fully justifying its *Michelin* rosette and two red *Gault Millau toques*, and the menus are a splendid mixture of old and new – including old favourites such as poularde de Bresse en vessie. Despite the *nouvelle* influences, portions are more than adequate. The wine list is good on local Rhône wines, weak if you want to look further afield. The hotel is in two parts, its beautifully cared-for garden and most bedrooms being 30 metres away from the restaurant. Our rooms at the back were pleasant and clean." Another visitor wrote of this annexe (where the rooms are also said to be the quietest), "It looks from outside like a house of correction, very austere, but is beautiful inside: our room was large, with a sumptuous bathroom. Our friends were in the main building, beautiful outside, not as nice as ours within, but OK. Restaurant splendid, with chestnuts featuring in quite a few dishes. All the staff were charming." (*Roger Bennett; also Mr & Mrs RM Booth*) One warning: "The wine list is fairly short and concentrates on high quality, but rather expensive, bottles; not really for 'quaffers'."

Open 1 Mar–15 Dec. Closed Sun evening and Mon except July, Aug, and public holidays.
Rooms 18 – 15 with bath and/or shower, all with telephone; 5 with TV. 1 ground-floor room. Some rooms in annexe.
Facilities 2 salons, 3 restaurants. Garden.
Location Central. Parking.
Credit cards All major cards accepted.
Terms Rooms: single 150–250 frs, double 200–300 frs. Breakfast 40 frs. Set lunch/dinner 140–320 frs; full alc 300 frs. Reduced rates and special meals for children.

Château d'Urbilhac — *Tel* 75.06.42.11
Route de Vernoux

Totally different from the *Midi* (above), here is a finely converted 19th-century château in Renaissance style, complete with pepperpot tower, set high on a hillside in its own 150-acre wooded park just outside the town. Three reports this year have used the words "delightful" and "magnificent", notably this one: "After our fourth visit, this has become one of two top favourite hotels in France. The food used to be dull, but Madame now has a new chef and it's lovely, though the wine list is disappointing.

Breakfasts are copious. Rooms, some with antique furniture, are all comfortable. And the pool is the best you'll find anywhere, superbly situated amid classic scenery, with modern sun-loungers." "A charming châtelaine". (*PA Catling, Brenda Gape, FM and CN Grist*) Best for a short stay as the menu seldom changes.

Open 1 May–10 Oct.
Rooms 11 double, 3 single – all with bath or shower and telephone. 2 in pavilion. 1 ground-floor room.
Facilities Bar, salon, 2 dining rooms; terrace. Garden, heated swimming pool, tennis.
Location 2 km S of Lamastre on D2 to Vernoux.
Credit cards All major cards accepted.
Terms Rooms: single 350 frs, double 500 frs. Breakfast 50 frs. Dinner, B&B 450–500 frs per person. Set lunch/dinner 160, 195 and 250 frs; full alc 200 frs.

LANGEAIS 37130 Indre-et-Loire — Map 8

Hôtel Hosten et Restaurant "Le Langeais" — *Tel* 47.96.82.12
2 rue Gambetta

In a small Loireside town west of Tours with a fine 15th-century château, *patron*-chef Jean-Jacques Hosten's attractive creeper-covered hostelry is introduced to the Guide this year by two reports: "The food richly deserves its *Michelin* rosette (and *Gault Millau toque*) and service is obliging. Our bedroom, though overlooking the main road, was comfortable." "The best hotel we found during three weeks in France. Restaurant outstanding, especially fish dishes. Breakfast hard to beat, with six different types of brioche, croissant, etc." We are told that the salon is being rebuilt after a lorry ran into it. (*Janet and Dennis Allom, and others*)

Open All year except 10 Jan–10 Feb, and 20 Jun–10 Jul.
Rooms 1 suite, 9 double – all with bath and TV.
Facilities Bar, 2 dining-rooms.
Location Central, parking. Langeais is 25 km W of Tours.
Restriction Not suitable for ♿.
Credit cards All major cards accepted.
Terms Rooms: single 230 frs, double 310 frs, suite 520 frs. Breakfast 35 frs. Full alc 180–280 frs.

LANGRES 52200 Haute-Marne — Map 9

Grand Hôtel de l'Europe — *Tel* 25.87.10.88
23-25 rue Diderot

Langres, an interesting old town on a high ridge with a cathedral and ancient ramparts, makes a useful stop on the way to Switzerland. Near its centre is this traditional stone-fronted hostelry, down-to-earth and inexpensive, liked again this year for its simple comforts and good fare. Rooms vary in size and amenities: front ones are best, but all are quiet. One new account, "The restaurant was busy, more like a *relais routier* than an elegant place: many of the diners were enormous, as were the portions. Parking one's car in the tight space provided was an entertainment in itself, as enthralled onlookers watched the harassed drivers trying to obey the arm-waving instructions of the receptionist." (*Joan Powell, Stephen Ruell*)

Open All year except 23 Apr–8 May and 8–31 Oct. Closed Sun evening. Restaurant closed Mon midday in season, all day Mon in low season.
Rooms 2 suites, 25 double, 1 single – some with bath and/or shower, all with telephone; 17 with TV. 8 in annexe.
Facilities Salon, bar, 2 restaurants.
Location Between Chaumont (35 km) and Dijon (66 km). Hotel is central (rooms overlooking garden are quietest). Garage facilities for 20 cars.
Restriction Not suitable for ♿.
Credit cards All major cards accepted.
Terms Rooms 100–190 frs. Breakfast 24 frs. Set lunch/dinner 58, 80, 85 and 145 frs; full alc 210 frs.

LANSLEVILLARD 73480 Savoie — Map 10

Les Prais — *Tel* 79.05.93.53
Telex 309983

In a high ski-resort just below Mont Cenis, a typical little chalet-style ski-hotel amid meadows beside the ski-lifts, liked for its good and plentiful food and friendly staff. Most rooms have mountain views, some have balconies. Swimming pool. Piano bar for après-ski. *Open 18 Jun–15 Sep, 23 Dec–23 Apr. 25 rooms, most with bath or shower. Also annexe with apartments. Dinner, B&B 220–320 frs. Set menus 72–145 frs. New nomination. More reports welcome.*

LAPALISSE 03120 Allier — Map 10

Hôtel Galland — *Tel* 70.99.07.21
20 place de la République

In a small town in the Bourbonnais, near Vichy, quietly located beside a park and a pond just off the N7 Lyon–Paris highway, here is a very spruce little hotel whose attractive restaurant wins a Michelin *red "R" for good value. Bedrooms are simple and clean, Madame is pleasant and efficient. 8 rooms, 6 with bath and/or shower. B&B double 282 frs. Set menus 65–230 frs. Recent nomination. More reports welcome.*

LAPOUTROIE 68650 Haut-Rhin — Map 9

Hôtel-Restaurant Les Alisiers — *Tel* 89.47.52.82

Unlike our other Alsatian entries, mostly smart, this Logis de France *is rustic and modestly priced: an old farmhouse with beamed ceilings, secluded up in the Vosges, but only 19 km from Colmar. Friendly* patron, *simple cooking served in a new panoramic dining room; buffet breakfast. Comfortable rooms, some small, others bigger with glorious mountain views. Open 1 Jan–15 Mar, 22 Mar–22 Jun, 29 Jun–30 Nov, 24–31 Dec. 15 rooms, 13 with bath or shower. B&B double 310 frs. Set meals 100–148 frs. Some criticisms this year, of food and lack of hot water: more reports please.*

LESTELLE-BÉTHARRAM 64800 Pyrénées-Atlantiques Map 10

Le Vieux Logis *Tel* 59.71.94.87
Route des Grottes

Near to Lourdes and not far from Pau and the high Pyrenees, this simple flower-girt country *auberge* could make a useful excursion centre. A visitor this year was delighted, "Monsieur et Madame Gaye have created a charming place, with a park where you can sit under the trees listening to the tinkle of cowbells. A huge courtyard where peacocks strut and two creaky old Pyrenean dogs bound up to welcome you. A sunny terrace with parasols for drinks, but no salon. The cuisine is exceptional (*Michelin* red 'R'), endorsed by the many locals who come to eat here – very good trout from the river, and the lightest crêpe I've ever eaten. The five attractive wooden chalets were full, so we had a huge room in the house, with Pyrenean blue-and-white blankets." (*Eileen Broadbent; JAG Stonehouse*)

Open 1 Mar–15 Nov. Restaurant open 1 Mar–10 Jan. Only restaurant open Christmas and New Year.
Rooms 15 double – all with bath, shower, telephone and TV. 5 chalets in the park.
Facilities Restaurant; 4 functions rooms. Garden; terrace.
Location 12 km W of Lourdes and 3 km E of Lestelle-Bétharram, on N637.
Restriction Not suitable for ♿.
Credit cards Access, Amex, Visa.
Terms B&B: single 185 frs, double 210–250 frs; dinner, B&B: single 255 frs, double 350–390 frs. Set lunch/dinner 80–170 frs; full alc 245 frs.

LEZOUX 63190 Puy-de-Dôme Map 10

Château de Codignat *Tel* 73.68.43.03
Bort-l'Étang

The small town of Lezoux, east of Clermont-Ferrand, was an important ceramics centre in Roman and Gallo-Roman days, as the local museum bears witness. At Bort-l'Étang, eight kilometres to the south-east, on a wooded hill above a valley, stands this handsome 15th-century château, rather fancifully converted (suits of armour, four-poster beds, etc). Bedrooms are in the towers and turrets, reached by winding stairways. A recent account, "It is delightfully run by a middle-aged lady and her personable young son. Our bedroom was nicely furnished with either genuine antiques or excellent replicas. There is a good swimming pool with jacuzzi and large gardens. We had an excellent five-course set dinner." An earlier visitor was equally captivated, "A riot – the castle belonged to the Obolenskys, was bought in a state of collapse by the present owners who did it up in rather camp baroque: even the walls are carpeted. But it's also a gem, absolutely peaceful and very clean and comfortable, with real chic. Service admirable. Found proprietors scrubbing out the lavatories – always a sign that standards are high." More reports welcome.

Open 19 Mar–2 Nov. Restaurant closed Tue and Thur midday except holidays.
Rooms 3 suites, 11 double – all with bath and/or shower (suites also have jacuzzi), telephone and TV. 1 ground-floor room.

Facilities Salon, 3 restaurants; banqueting room. Large grounds with swimming pool, health and beauty centre, putting-green.
Location At Bort-l'Étang, 8 km SE of Lezoux which is 27 km E of Clermont-Ferrand.
Credit cards All major cards accepted.
Terms [1989 rates] Rooms 650–980 frs, suite 1,500 frs. Breakfast 55 frs. Dinner, B&B 605–890 frs per person. Set lunch/dinner 245–305 frs. Reduced rates and special meals for children.

LYON — Map 10

La Cour des Loges *Tel* 78.42.75.75
6 rue du Boeuf *Telex* 330831
Lyon 69005

France's second city is as short on really attractive hotels as it is rich in excellent restaurants. But a high-class hostelry of unusual character recently opened: it is down a narrow street in the St-Jean quarter of Vieux-Lyon, across the Saône from the town centre and behind the Palais de Justice where the Barbie trials were held. An inspector reports: "It has been formed by restoring four adjacent Renaissance mansions. The main one is built round a galleried four-storey courtyard that forms the hotel's lofty foyer, hung with drapes of Lyon silk, cleverly lit and much festooned with foliage: the overall effect is breathtaking. The owners and architect, all local, have done a tasteful job, though I wish they had been less lavish with their modern gimmicks. But it's all great fun – even the top hat in the lift. The small heated swimming pool is really a large jacuzzi. In the cellar is a wine club with church pews. No restaurant, but there are lots of good ones close by (notably *La Tour Rose*, run by a pupil of Bocuse), and the hotel has its own *tapas* bar with a stream of water running down a trough on the counter. This part of Vieux-Lyon is now a sort of St-Germain-des-Prés, bursting with a youthful night-time animation that belies the city's staid image." "A major new asset to Lyon. The contemporary decor works well with the simple lines of this old building." "Service exemplary. One of the best hotels I've ever stayed in." However, a reader this year found the high-tech gadgetry "nightmarish" and inefficient (the air-conditioning did not work), "When we protested, the manager nodded and told us they were suing the architects!" For unloading luggage, you can just about drive your car down the alley to the front door, where the porter will arrange for its garaging and retrieval. (*Jeremy Round*)

Open All year.
Rooms 10 suites, 53 double – all with bath and/or shower, telephone TV and mini-bar. Some ground-floor rooms.
Facilities Lift. Lounge, bar, *tapas* bar, wine club; conference rooms. Terraced gardens. Small indoor pool, sauna, jacuzzi and fitness room.
Location: 1 km from main station. Garaging.
Credit cards All major cards accepted.
Terms [1989 rates] Room 950–1,300 frs. Breakfast 80 frs. Snacks in *tapas* bar 160 frs.

> We get less feedback from smaller and more remote hotels. But we need feedback on all hotels: big and small, far and near, famous and first-timers.

MAILLY-LE-CHÂTEAU 89660 Yonne — Map 10

Le Castel — *Tel* 86.40.43.06
Place de l'Église

This *Relais du Silence* between Auxerre and Avallon, "a rather run-down 19th-century house in a very quiet village", has again been recommended for a short visit: "Good, rich food, and a comfortable, pleasantly old-fashioned room." "We enjoyed Madame's efficient running of the attractive dining room. The countryside is lovely." Others have praised such dishes as snails in garlic butter with chopped hazel-nuts, and calves' liver in a cream sauce. Decor is attractive, but bedrooms vary greatly in size (some are said to be suitable for elves) and the service can be slow. (*Dr RL Holmes, MW Atkinson, Sarah Curtis*)

Open 15 Mar–15 Nov. Closed Wed in low season.
Rooms 2 suites, 10 double – most with bath and/or shower, all with telephone. 2 ground-floor rooms.
Facilities Lounge, restaurant; functions facilities. Garden with terrace.
Location 30 km S of Auxerre, 30 km NW of Avallon. Turn off N6 at either of these towns or at Nitry. Hotel is in centre of quiet village. Parking.
Credit cards Access, Visa.
Terms Rooms: single 140–280 frs, double 180–290 frs, suite 330–345 frs. Breakfast 28 frs. Set lunch 72 frs, dinner 145 frs; full alc 210–230 frs. Reduced rates and special meals for children.

LA MALÈNE 48210 Lozère — Map 10

Manoir de Montesquiou — *Tel* 66.48.51.12

Once a residence of the aristocratic Montesquiou family, this 15th-century stone manor house at the foot of a cliff in the Tarn gorge has been most gracefully preserved and converted. Old-world charm includes four-poster beds and spiral stairways, but comforts are modern. Good regional food and courteous staff. Garden. Open Apr–end Oct. 12 rooms, all with bath or shower, 255–450 frs. Breakfast 30 frs. Half board 295–395 frs per person [1989]. Recent nomination. More reports welcome.

MARSEILLE Bouches-du-Rhône — Map 11

Le Petit Nice and Restaurant Passédat — *Tel* 91.52.14.39, *Fax* 91.59.28.08, *Telex* 401565 PASSEDA
Anse de Maldormé
Corniche JF Kennedy
Marseille 13007

Small, stylish and hugely expensive hotel, owned and run since 1917 by lordly Passédat family. Though right inside the city, it is secluded on a rocky headland below the coastal corniche road, with fine views across bay. Restaurant, in richly decorated Hellenic-style villa with lovely garden, serves just about the finest food in Marseille (two Michelin *rosettes); elegant classical-style bedrooms including two new suites in adjoining building. Very superior clientele. Closed Jan. 18 rooms, all with bath and shower. Rooms 800–1,000 frs. Breakfast 70 frs. Set menus 290–550 frs [1989]. Few recent reports. More please.*

Hôtel Pullman Beauvau *Tel* 91.54.91.00
4 rue Beauvau, Marseille 13001 *Telex* 401778

The recent opening or refurbishment of middle-sized hotels of true individual character, in large provincial cities hitherto bereft of them, has been an encouraging new development in France (see our entries for the *Cour des Loges*, Lyon, and the *Opéra*, Toulouse). The *Beauvau*, a famous old hostelry long moribund, falls into this class and has been recently nominated: "Chopin and George Sand (together), and Cocteau and Mistinguette (separately), are among the past habitués of this 18th-century *relais de poste* which is right in the heart of things beside the Vieux Port, at the foot of La Canebière. Newly restored by its Pullman Group owners after a long decline, it is a hotel of genuine warmth and elegance, still patronised by celebrities such as the singers who perform at the nearby Opéra. The restoration has been finely done and our bedroom was cosy and inviting, in period style (double glazing keeps out the noise and air-conditioning the Midi heat). Service was good. The dark-panelled 'English style' bar was a little claustrophobic for our taste, but the buffet breakfast was excellent and you can get light meals served in the bar or your room till 1 am."

Open All year.
Rooms 71 – all with bath and/or shower, telephone, radio, TV, mini-bar and air-conditioning.
Facilities Lift. Lounge, breakfast room; 3 conference rooms.
Location Central. Garage 800 metres.
Restriction Not suitable for ♿.
Credit cards All major cards accepted.
Terms Rooms 550–700 frs. Breakfast 50 frs. (No restaurant.)

MARTIN-ÉGLISE 76370 Seine-Maritime Map 9

Auberge du Clos Normand *Tel* 35.82.71.01 and 35.82.71.31
22 rue Henri IV

Just inland from Dieppe, on the edge of a forest, this former 16th-century *relais de poste*, now a restaurant-with-rooms, is as redolent of Normandy as its name implies. The bedrooms are in a separate vine-covered building, once stables or a hayloft, with a romantic garden which has a pavilion for eating out in summer, and a stream; it's very quiet except for farmyard noises. The accommodation used to be defiantly unmodernised, and we got reports of sagging beds, gouty chairs, even flooding toilets and rotten balconies. But all that seems to have changed, for the bedrooms have been renovated: this year, it's true, one uncomfortable bed has been slept in, but other visitors in 1988/9 have been happy: "The newly modernised rooms are very attractive"; "Ours was lovely, with pink bedspreads, clean and well appointed"; "The refurnishing has been done with taste and style."

Dinner has long been admired – generous helpings of Norman cooking (e.g. duck terrine and sole meunière) with lashings of cream, butter and Calvados. "Food was delicious", says one 1989 visitor, "and we liked Madame's leisurely personal service", though some have found her shy and reserved. Above all, the setting delights – "We woke to look out on a charming lush garden and stream", "farmhouse sounds and smells", and "a selection of cats, a stick-retrieving dog and the river abounding in young frogs". (*Susan E Rayner, J Guest*)

Open All year except 15 Dec–31 Jan. Closed Mon evening and Tue.
Rooms 1 family, 8 double – all with bath and/or shower and telephone. All in separate building in garden.
Facilities Lounge with mono TV, restaurant; functions room/ballroom. Garden with large lawn and stream; pavilion for outdoor summer meals.
Location 5 km from Dieppe; off D1 to Neufchatel.
Restriction Not suitable for ♿.
Credit cards All major cards accepted.
Terms [1989 rates] Rooms 200–310 frs. Breakfast 25 frs. Alc 180 frs (excluding wine). Guests are expected to dine in the restaurant.

MAUSSANE-LES-ALPILLES 13520 Bouches-du-Rhône — Map 11

Hostellerie l'Oustaloun — *Tel* 90.97.32.19
Place de l'Église

A new nomination, "Unusual and charming: it's a converted 16th-century chapel, in the small main square of an untouristy Provençal village just south of ultra-touristy Les Baux. Owned and run by an affable Bolognese, Robert Bartoli, and his shy French artist wife, Emma, whose pictures adorn the main rooms. The ambience is personal, intimate, cosy, but quite sophisticated – and the clientele likewise. Yet prices are most reasonable. Small, pretty bedrooms with period furniture. Three small, attractive dining rooms with unusual decor, and a short *carte* of mostly regional dishes, quite good. The help-yourself buffet that opens the 130-franc [1990] set menu includes the best tapenade and anchoiade I've ever tasted. Hurry, for the Bartolis might retire before long." (*JA*)

Open All year.
Rooms 9 – all with bath or with shower.
Facilities 3 dining rooms.
Location Central, parking. Maussane is 19 km E of Arles.
Restriction Not suitable for ♿.
Credit cards All major cards accepted.
Terms [1990 rates] B&B double from 275 frs. Set lunch/dinner 130 frs; full alc 120 frs. Special meals for children.

MERCUREY 71640 Saône-et-Loire — Map 10

Hôtellerie du Val d'Or — *Tel* 85.45.13.70
Grande Rue — *Telex* 800660

Renewed praise in 1988/9 for this tidy traditional hostelry in a village producing one of Burgundy's great wines (there are several *caveaux de dégustation* close by). The "courteous and efficient" Cogny family provides locals as well as tourists with generous helpings of mainly traditional local cuisine (*Michelin* rosette, *Gault Millau toque*, for such dishes as fillet of rabbit and parsleyed ham). One recent visitor especially enjoyed the middle-priced menu and had a small but pretty room with a balcony over the garden. Others, too, have found the rooms comfortable and charmingly decorated, if a little cramped. Light and colour in the garden, armchairs in the salon, and sociable chatter in the attractive restaurant with its stone-tiled floor, flowers and lamps, and log-fire in winter. "Splendid" Mercurey wines – but expensive. The hotel is on a busy main street. (*Peter and Ann Jones, and others*)

Open All year except late Aug–early Sep and 17 Dec–17 Jan; closed Mon and Tue midday.
Rooms 10 double, 1 single – 5 with bath, 6 with shower, all with telephone and TV.
Facilities Reception, salon, bar, 2 restaurants. Garden, swings.
Location 13 km from Chalon-sur-Saône. Leave *autoroute* at Chalon Nord and take D978 Autun–Nevers road, then turn right to Mercurey. Parking.
Restriction Not suitable for ♿.
Credit card Access.
Terms [1989 rates] Rooms: single occupancy 130 frs, double 350 frs. Breakfast 35 frs. Set lunch/dinner 140, 200 and 320 frs; full alc 300 frs. Reduced rates and special meals for children.

MEYRUEIS 48150 Lozère — Map 10

Château d'Ayres — *Tel* 66.45.60.10

An old creeper-covered château, originally a 12th-century monastery, now much rebuilt, standing alone in open country outside Meyrueis on the edge of the limestone *causses* and the Cévennes National Park, close to the Jonte and Tarn gorges. Large bedrooms overlook a park of giant sequoias, chestnuts and cedars. A devotee returning this year sets the tone, "The owners, the Comte and Comtesse de Montjou, make you feel that you are not so much hotel guests as family friends staying in their home. The staff, too, are all smiles and courtesy. Huge, comfortable rooms, beautiful breakfasts, more than adequate cuisine, and an air of peace and elegance." That was from *Colin Pilkington*, who last year wrote, "It is in the evening that the hotel's charm best manifests itself: small tables and chairs are set under the sequoias in the park, with candles on each table, and subtle floodlighting tints the château's facade and the trees beneath the hillside, creating perfect reflections in the ornamental pool." We'd be glad of more details, please, about this "more than adequate cuisine".

Open 1 Apr–15 Oct.
Rooms 3 suites, 20 double, 1 single – 22 with bath, 2 with shower, all with telephone and TV; baby-listening on request.
Facilities 2 salons, TV room, 2 dining rooms. Garden with tennis.
Location 1.5 km SE of Meyrueis.
Restriction Not suitable for ♿.
Credit cards All major cards accepted.
Terms Rooms double 270–330 frs, suite 550 frs. Breakfast 40 frs. Dinner, B&B double 550–830 frs. Set lunch/dinner 116–230 frs; full alc 260 frs. Low season rates. Reduced rates and special meals for children.

MIMIZAN 40200 Landes — Map 10

Au Bon Coin du Lac — *Tel* 58.09.01.55
34 avenue du Lac

The long flat Atlantic coast south-west of Bordeaux has splendid sandy beaches, lined by a number of dullish resorts. Just inland are freshwater lakes amid the Landes forests, also with resort facilities, and here is *Au Bon Coin du Lac*. Its main emphasis is on cuisine (*Michelin* rosette, two red *Gault Millau toques*), and readers again this year thought the food "excellent", endorsing last year's verdicts: "One of the most arresting places we have ever stayed at. It is edged by well-kept public gardens, with woods and beaches beyond, and it has rowing-boats for hire (free to residents). Our bedroom above the restaurant was most luxurious, with repro antique furniture, lace bedspread, huge bathroom. Dinner was a delightful affair, served with panache and humour by efficient young waiters; even the cheapest menu was delicious, and supreme value for money. Gorgeous china, impeccable napery, silver candlesticks. Blissful peace at night in the flowery lakeside gardens, and then a good breakfast." "The atmosphere is excellent, with a smiling Madame Caule leading a friendly team. The only sound to disturb us at night was a cat-fight." Rooms in the annexe are equally luxurious. (*Ian and Francine Walsh, EH, PW Arnold*)

Open All year except Feb. Restaurant closed Sun evening and Mon in low season.
Rooms 3 suites, 5 double – all with bath (5 also have shower, telephone, TV and mini-bar. Suites, with kitchenette, in annexe 100 metres from hotel. Some ground-floor rooms.
Facilities Lounges, bar, dining room; functions rooms; terrace. Garden. Lake with fishing, rowing boats. Sea 4 km.
Location 1 km N of Mimizan, which is 111 km SW of Bordeaux.
Credit card Visa.
Terms [1989 rates] Rooms double 480–560 frs. Breakfast 55 frs. Dinner, B&B 400–520 frs per person. Set lunch/dinner 130-350 frs; full alc 350 frs. Reduced rates and special meals for children.

MIONNAY 01390 Ain — Map 10

Alain Chapel

Tel 78.91.82.02
Telex 305605

Alain Chapel is sometimes regarded as the greatest of all the great modern French chefs, and his elegant restaurant-with-rooms, on the edge of a village north of Lyon, wins *Gault Millau*'s highest rating of 19.5 out of 20, as well as the expected three *Michelin* rosettes. He is a serious, rather austere man, not at all a flamboyant showman like his rival Paul Bocuse down the road; a perfectionist and tireless innovator, he changes his menu with the season and the market, creating superb new tastes from simple high-quality products, in the light modern manner. Of course his prices are high (and one reader has judged them excessive): but this year two expert travellers have endorsed ("better than ever") this 1988 inspector's report: "It's an old rural *auberge*, much extended and now very grand and spacious, with stone-flagged halls and patios and a floodlit garden. Chapel tries to keep the rural touch, but he does cheat: one dining annexe with ancient beams looks like a medieval barn but was built in 1987! You eat in a series of small discreet flower-filled rooms, where tables are well spaced and the ambience is quiet and dignified (save for the tourists taking snapshots of their meal). We especially liked the écrevisses in a spicy dark-green coriander sauce, the pigeon à la presse and the very ripe cheeses. Oddly poor bread, but truly friendly service. Quaint loos (the ladies' has a piano). The few bedrooms are not large but pretty and cosy." "Our room was bright and cheerful, with fresh flowers (some road noise at 7 am). Excellent food, notably the strawberry soufflé. Monsieur Chapel was very formal but not unfriendly." (*Pat and Jeremy*

Temple) Only one criticism: a seriously sub-standard breakfast, served badly and slowly. Seven new rooms are planned for 1990.

Open All year except Jan and Mon. Restaurant closed Tue midday except public holidays.
Rooms 13 double – all with bath, telephone and TV.
Facilities 3 lounges, bar, restaurant. Small garden where meals are served in fine weather.
Location 17 km N of Lyons, on N83. Coming from Paris on A6, take first exit after Villefranche, then D51 to Neuville, then Montanay. Parking.
Credit cards All major cards accepted.
Terms Rooms 600–750 frs. Breakfast 75 frs. Set lunch/dinner 460, 600 and 750 frs; full alc 500 frs. Reduced rates and special meals for children.

MOLINES-EN-QUEYRAS 05350 Hautes-Alpes — Map 10

Hôtel l'Équipe — *Tel* 92.45.83.20
Route de St-Véran

"Fantastic value for money", "delightful and charming" – two examples of the enthusiasm engendered by this unpretentious little chalet-hotel in a beautiful Alpine setting. It stands in a broad high valley south-east of Briançon, with ski-slopes and wooded hills all round. Nearby is the 13th-century fortress of Château-Queyras, and the isolated village of St-Véran, which at 2,040 metres claims to be the highest in Europe. "The hotel is simple but well furnished and equipped, and managed with charm and discretion by the Catalins. Our dinner was original, well produced and, unusually for France, served at speed." "The owners were warm and helpful, the meal delicious, the view spectacular." "We had a comfortable bedroom with a balcony giving magnificent views." "There's no night life around here, but interesting 'happenings' in season, such as folk-singing, and firework displays on the hills. Monsieur leads excursions into the mountains." Sometimes the Catalins throw the guests together for a fondue party. (*Endorsed this year by Pat and Brian Lloyd*)

Open 20 Dec–16 Apr, 3 June–18 Sept.
Rooms 22 – all with bath (3 also with shower) and telephone. 11 with 2–4 beds in annexe.
Facilities Salon, TV room, bar, restaurant. Terrace; garden on river. Winter sports (ski lifts 50 metres).
Location 1 km from Molines on road to St-Véran.
Restriction Not suitable for ♿.
Credit cards All major cards accepted.
Terms [1989 rates] B&B double 244 frs; dinner, B&B 215 frs per person; full board 265 frs. Set lunch/dinner 55, 84, 113 frs; full alc 130 frs. Reduced rates and special meals for children.

MOLITG-LES-BAINS 66500 Pyrénées-Orientales — Map 10

Château de Riell — *Tel* 68.05.04.40
Fax 68.05.02.91
Telex 500705

Specialising in skin and lung diseases, the imposing spa buildings of Molitg-les-Bains stand beside a small lake in a hollow of the Pyrenean foothills, west of Perpignan and close to Prades where the Spanish cellist Pablo Casals spent his exile (there is still an annual music festival in his honour). Set on a hillside above the spa, the very smart *Château de Riell* is owned and run by Biche Barthélemy, sister-in-law of Michel Guérard (*see* Eugénie-les-Bains), and its quirky sophistication is clearly in his tradition – as our nominator quirkily reports, "A sudden tower in a more or less vertical wood in the mountains. The architecture (early Gothic revival, 1829) owes more to Sir Walter Scott, we suspect, than to certain medieval buildings in the valley below. The interior, quite new, is devilish stylish: the tiger-skin bar, the carpet-lined lift *and* lift-shaft, strange plastic linings to the dining room which speak of Gaudi, the cushions piled here and there on the floor in your bedroom and – believe it or not – in the public rooms while you are having dinner. The luxury is absolute, the service unconditional, the basins and the bath furniture copper, and the price, though very high, no more than commensurate. A double bed is vast. As to the cooking (*Michelin* rosette, two red *Gault Millau toques*), it is dramatic, careful, perhaps a bit over-complicated: lots of unexpected bits not on the menu turn up to keep you going between courses." The hotel's elegant brochure, written in the quaintest of purple English prose, gives glimpses also of a pretty tiled courtyard for drinks, and lounges by a swimming pool under the trees. The chef, Marc Baudry, was trained by Guérard, and adds his own Catalan flourishes. Thermal and beauty cures are available, but there does not appear to be the same accent on dieting as at Eugénie. More reports please.

Open 1 Apr–5 Nov.
Rooms 3 suites, 18 double – all with bath, shower, telephone, radio, TV. 7 in 3 houses (with kitchenette) in castle grounds.
Facilities 2 lifts. Lounge, salon with TV, bar, dining room; private club; conference centre; terrace. Park with 2 swimming pools, 2 tennis courts. Fitness centre with sauna and beauty cures. Access to lake with beach, fishing.
Location On edge of spa, which is 7 km NW of Prades. Garage.
Credit cards Access, Amex, Visa.
Terms Rooms: single 875 frs, double 1,030 frs, suite 1,355 frs. Breakfast 74 frs. Set lunch 270 frs, dinner 400 frs; full alc 380 frs. Reduced rates and special meals for children.

MONTFORT-EN-CHALOSSE 40380 Landes — Map 10

"Aux Touzins" — *Tel* 58.98.60.22

A mile outside the village of Montfort on the southern fringe of the Landes forest, amid pleasant rolling Gascony countryside, is this unpretentious white-walled auberge. *Comfortable modern bedrooms, nicely decorated, some with balconies and views; smiling staff; good regional cooking, popular with locals. All excellent value. Closed 15 Jan–15 Feb. 20 rooms, 13 with bath or shower. Dinner, B&B double 250–320 frs. Set menu from 90 frs* [*1989 rates*]. *New nomination. More reports welcome.*

MONTPELLIER 34000 Hérault — Map 10

Hôtel Le Guilhem — *Tel* 67.52.90.90
18 rue J-J Rousseau

An inspector reports this year, "Montpellier used to be a sleepy place, but it's now the fastest-growing boom-town in France, an upstart rival to

Toulouse and Grenoble, with some monumental new architecture by Ricardo Bofill. None of this has spoilt the charm of the *vieille ville*, to my mind as lovely as Aix or Arles; and here in a narrow street is this brand-new little B&B hotel, converted from an old building by a former Parisian accountant and his wife, the Charpentiers, both friendly. Rooms are inevitably small, but very well equipped (hair-drier, good reading lights); breakfast comes copiously with flowers, eggs, newspaper, etc. A lovely terrace for summer, amid greenery. Parking is hard." For restaurants, see under *Noailles*, below.

Open All year.
Rooms 22 double, 2 single – all with bath and/or shower, telephone and TV; baby-sitting.
Facilities Lift. Breakfast room, salon. Terrace.
Location Central, in pedestrian zone; follow signs for "centre historique". Public parking 600 metres away.
Restriction Not suitable for ♿.
Credit cards All major cards accepted.
Terms Rooms 200–400 frs. Breakfast 35 frs. (No restaurant.)

Hôtel de Noailles *Tel* 67.60.49.80
2 rue des Écoles-Centrales

"Lovely comfortable hotel on a quiet street"; "charming, with good breakfasts" – two recent verdicts on this 17th-century mansion, graceful in a cool classical style. It is not easy of access by car (without a good street map, at least), for it lies in the heart of the network of quiet alleys, some closed to traffic, that forms the kernel of this beautiful southern city. Readers have found the staff caring and the contrast with modernism quite blissful. But there are warnings that front rooms can be noisy, especially from the bell tower next door. No restaurant, but you can eat well nearby at the *Louvre* (medium price) or cheaply at many places in the charming and lively little squares of the old town. More reports please.

Open 15 Jan–21 Dec.
Rooms 20 double with bath, 10 single with shower, all with telephone and TV.
Facilities Reception, salon/TV room where breakfast is served.
Location Central, near church of Notre Dame de Tables. Look for signs: "centre historique". Nearby parking not easy; use underground carpark in Place de la Comédie, entrance opposite Monoprix (300 metres S).
Restriction Not suitable for ♿.
Credit cards All major cards accepted.
Terms Rooms: single 300 frs, double 350–380 frs. Breakfast 30 frs. (No restaurant.)

MONTPINCHON 50210 Manche — Map 8

Château de la Salle *Tel* 33.46.95.19

Within an hour's drive of Cherbourg, between St-Lô with its national stud and Coutances with its sublime cathedral, a handsome 18th-century stone mansion is now a most elegant country hotel. It is new to the Guide this year: "Peaceful surroundings, lovely bedroom beautifully furnished, and superb food" (a mixture, it seems, of *nouvelle* and *ancienne*: traditionalist *Michelin* awards a rosette for ris de veau braisé *à l'ancienne*, modernist *Gault Millau* picks out lobster in truffle vinaigrette, when bestowing its red *toque*). A huge roaring fire, elegant furniture, some four-poster beds, and a lovely garden where you can take breakfast. (*Mrs D Goodey*) More reports welcome.

Open 16 Mar–5 Nov.
Rooms 1 suite, 9 double, 1 single – 10 with bath, 1 with shower, all with telephone and TV.
Facilities Lounge, 3 dining rooms. Garden.
Location Montpinchon is 12 km E of Coutances, by D7 and D73.
Restrictions Not suitable for ♿.
Credit cards Access, Diners, Visa.
Terms B&B: single 528 frs, double 676–726 frs, suite 856 frs; dinner, B&B: single 758 frs, double 1,136–1,186 frs, suite 1,316 frs. Set lunch/dinner 155–230 frs. Reduced rates and special meals for children by arrangement.

MONTREUIL 62170 Pas-de-Calais — Map 9

Château de Montreuil — *Tel* 21.81.53.04
4 chaussée des Capucins — *Telex* 135205 HOTEUIL

Large old house in lovely walled garden, near ruined citadel in quiet part of medieval hilltop town; stylish and ambitious. Many guests, like the patronne, *are British. Rooms vary greatly in size and style; some have been severely criticised for decor and upkeep in 1988/9, as has the food – despite its* Michelin *rosette, and the service. But recent reports are more favourable – "beautiful, newly refitted garden room, food superb"; could we have more feedback please? Closed 10 Dec–early Feb, Thurs midday except July/Aug. 14 rooms, all with bath or shower, 380–580 frs. Breakfast 45 frs. Alc meals (excluding wine) 250–350 frs [1989].*

MONT-ST-MICHEL 50116 Manche — Map 8

Hôtel La Mère Poulard — *Tel* 33.60.14.01
Telex 170197

No other site in France outside Paris attracts more tourists than Mont-St-Michel, linked to the coast by a causeway at low tide and capped by its towering Benedictine monastery. An overnight stay is well worth it, for then you can appreciate the aura of the place when the day trippers have left, and visit the abbey early the next morning before they arrive. *La Mère Poulard*, just inside the rampart gates, has character and tradition and is much frequented by Americans. Its restaurant has been famous for its omelettes for exactly 101 years, and under a new chef is continuing to provide good classic Norman and Breton cooking (*Gault Millau toque*). A report since that change, "Worth the high prices, and deserves to get back its *Michelin* rosette – we enjoyed salmon, magret de canard in a rich sauce, and more cheese than Brussels could subsidise. A pianist tinkles. The *patron* is charming, the service slick and the rooms comfortable." An earlier view, "The experience of staying Easter Saturday and visiting the Abbey at midnight for the service was perfectly complemented by the hotel. Service was excellent." The hotel has just been renovated, but it's still not a place for the elderly as the stairways to the rooms are steep and narrow. (*Paul Palmer, Victoria Turner*) The late Rita Hayworth and Emperor Hirohito were among past guests, while in December 1988

President Mitterrand entertained Mrs Thatcher here, to scallops, lamb, and dessert omelette flambée.

Open All year.
Rooms 1 suite, 26 double – 24 with bath, 3 with shower, all with telephone and TV. 14 rooms in nearby annexe.
Facilities Lounge, TV room, games room, restaurant, omelette room. Fishing and bathing nearby.
Location Just inside walls of Mont St-Michel. Large car park across causeway.
Restrictions Not suitable for ♿. No babies in restaurant.
Credit cards All major cards accepted.
Terms [1989 rates] Rooms 450–750 frs. Breakfast 50 frs. Set lunch/dinner 120–300 frs. Special meals for children.

MORLAIX 29210 Finistère — Map 8

Hôtel de l'Europe — *Tel* 98.62.11.99
1 rue d'Aiguillon — *Telex* 941676

In the centre of this North Breton market town, a classic and dignified hostelry with fairly simple, modestly priced rooms, many of them spacious and overlooking a quiet courtyard. Excellent, innovative cooking in a Second Empire style brasserie (there is also a restaurant under separate management). 70 rooms, most with bath and shower. B&B double 304–344 frs. Set menus in brasserie 60 and 70 frs. New nomination. More reports welcome.

MUZILLAC 56190 Morbihan — Map 8

Domaine du Château de Rochevilaine — *Tel* 97.41.69.27
Pointe de Pen Lan — *Telex* 950570

Two of the Guide's ace reporters recount their poetic discovery on the south coast of Brittany this year: "This old manor stands on a rocky headland just above the sea. Its many outbuildings, ranging from the medieval to the modern, are scattered in well-tended gardens dotted with ancient Breton sculptures and crosses; these pavilions, each with a private lounge, can be taken by a whole family. Our room was palatial, and all the hotel's furniture is ancient Breton and superb: the huge chest, creaky carved wardrobe and writing desk in our room were of the kind one drools over in antique shops. Bedroom service is impeccable and the breakfast copious. Dinner in the cavernous dining room under its ancient beams can be somewhat noisy, but the view of the sun setting on the sea takes your breath away. Cooking is *soigné*, exploiting the catch of the day, and the table d'hôte offers good value (two red *Gault Millau toques* for e.g. palourdes in truffle vinaigrette). You can take lunch in the modern courtyard. There's a small outdoor swimming pool above the rocks for those who do not fancy the nearby rocky or sandy beaches; and the hotel is about to build a thalassotherapy centre. At high tide, the sea rose right up to our bedroom on the rocks: here, leaving windows and curtains open, we woke bathed in the beams of the rising sun at dawn, to the purr of fishing vessels sailing out. At night, the magical darkness, dotted with distant lights, was undisturbed save for the gentle swish of the waves below. It was the most striking memory of our trip – that amazing room at the edge of the world, with nothing beyond but the sea and the stars." (*Francine and Ian Walsh*)

Open All year except Jan and Feb. Closed Sun evening and Mon midday in low season.
Rooms 27 – all with bath and/or shower and telephone; some with TV. Rooms in pavilions in garden.
Facilities Lounge, restaurant; conference facilities. Courtyard where meals are served; garden, swimming pool. Tennis, riding, golf nearby.
Location At Pointe de Pen Lan, 4.5 km S of Muzillac which is 25 km SE of Vannes.
Credit cards All major cards accepted.
Terms [1989 rates] Rooms 380–920 frs. Breakfast 48 frs. Dinner, B&B 460–730 frs per person. Set lunch/dinner 180–330 frs.

NAJAC 12270 Aveyron — Map 10

Hôtel Miquel: l'Oustal del Barry — *Tel* 65.29.74.32
Place du Bourg

In this remote but scenic part of the Massif Central, Najac is a beautiful medieval village above the Aveyron gorges, with an old castle high on a hill above the river. The *Miquel* is on the village square, yet also has a private garden for sunbathing, with a children's playground. Some rooms have a balcony, and there are wonderful views. An inspector this year had an "amazingly generous" lunch with "really good provincial cooking, not *nouvelle*-ish, served very professionally but with enthusiasm". And another visitor found Madame Miquel "friendly, caring and attentive". Rooms vary in size and quality as the hotel has been converted from several different old houses. (*HR, John Gray*)

Open Apr–end Oct. Closed Mon Apr and Oct except holidays.
Rooms 4 suites, 13 double, 4 single – all with bath and/or shower, telephone and TV. 7 in annexe. Some ground-floor rooms.
Facilities Lift. Salon, TV room, bar, 2 restaurants; 2 terraces. Large garden with play area for children.
Location Coming from Villefranche de Rouergue or Cordes on D122 hotel is on right at entrance of village. Parking.
Credit cards Amex, Visa.
Terms Rooms: single 165 frs, double 195–220 frs, suite 240 frs; dinner, B&B 220–250 frs per person. Set lunch/dinner 100, 180 and 250 frs; full alc 250–280 frs. Reduced rates and special meals for children.

NARBONNE 11100 Aude — Map 10

Hôtel la Résidence — *Tel* 68.32.19.41
6 rue du Premier Mai — *Telex* 500441 SOMARES

In a quiet street in the shadow of Narbonne's great fortified cathedral, here's an unusual but sympathetic small hotel in Victorian boudoir style: Louis XV furniture, gilt mirrors, silk flowers in vases. "Run by very friendly local people, really quite jovial; it is slightly quaint and theatrical, with decor verging on the kitschy. In the corridors, old chests, velvet drapes, red candles on silver sticks. Some of the rooms are in this style too, but ours had plainer decor. It was comfortable and cosy. Adequate breakfast, taken in one of three spruce and elegant little salons." "Breakfast served on pretty china, with an accompanying rose-bud that opened and lasted 11 days." No restaurant, but some good ones close by. (*Endorsed in 1989 by Mrs VA Preston.*)

Open All year except 3 Jan–3 Feb.
Rooms 1 suite, 23 double, 2 single – all with bath/shower, telephone and TV. 4 ground-floor rooms.
Facilities 2 salons, TV room.
Location Central, near cathedral and canal. Parking.
Restriction Not suitable for ♿.
Credit cards Access, Visa.
Terms Rooms: single occupancy 265–290 frs, double 300–390 frs. Breakfast 32 frs. (No restaurant.)

NICE 06300 Alpes-Maritimes — Map 11

Hôtel La Pérouse

11 quai Rauba-Capeu — *Tel* 93.62.34.63
Fax 93.67.59.41
Telex 461411

Of Nice's 350 hotels, nearly all of them dull, the upper-medium-priced *La Pérouse* is possibly the most attractive (apart, of course, from the super-luxury *Negresco*). Its setting is its star feature, for it is perched half-way up the castle rock at the east end of the promenade, with "breathtaking" views of the bay. "More super than ever," say inspectors returning recently; "we enjoyed our lunch on the terrace under the lemon trees: food is just basic grills, but plentiful and nicely served. Idyllic swimming pool under high rocks. The hotel has white marble corridors, bedrooms with cool white decor and marble bathrooms (rooms vary in price, but even the cheaper ones without sea views are well furnished and comfortable). A really lovely bar with comfy chairs and a log fire in winter. The civilised young manager, Roland Muntzer, runs one of the pleasantest city hotels in France. No restaurant, but there are scores of candle-lit bistros close by in the Vieille Ville." Readers this year have been pleased, though one of them thought the beds too short and found the staff less than helpful when sorting out a muddle over booking. (*M and L Piper, ML and MM Gravelle*)

Open All year.
Rooms 2 suites, 60 double, 3 single – all with bath and shower, telephone, radio and TV.
Facilities Lifts. Bar/lounge, terrace, conference facilities. Sauna. Garden with patio; 2 swimming pools. Beach across road.
Location At E end of Promenade des Anglais, by château. Paid parking nearby.
Credit cards All major cards accepted.
Terms Rooms 295–1,020 frs, suite 1,030–1,700 frs. Breakfast 40–45 frs. Reduced rates for children. (No restaurant but light snacks and room service.)

NIEUIL 16270 Charente — Map 10

Le Château de Nieuil

Tel 45.71.36.38
Telex 791230

Originally used as a hunting-lodge by François I, this moated Renaissance château stands in its own huge wooded park north-east of Angoulême. It has fine antiques and an imposing marble staircase – and of course it is not cheap. Visitors continue to appreciate its beauty and comfort, as well as the kindliness of M. Bodinaud, the owner, but again this year they are not entirely sure whether the cooking, though good, quite merits its *Michelin* rosette and two red *Gault Millau toques*. This earlier report remains entirely valid, "The gardens are lovely, and the château bears the stamp of several generations of French nobility. Yet the atmosphere is not pretentious. It is both friendly and sophisticated. Dinner in the panelled dining-room was a mixture of trad and modern, with generous helpings, imaginative salads, and a choice of 15 different fruit tarts. Each course was decorated with fresh flowers. We were somewhat embarrassed, however, by M. Bodinaud's gimmick of putting the flag of the appropriate nation on each guest's table. M. Bodinaud is also an art buff, and in the former stables he exhibits and sells expensive prints, modern paintings and sculptures." (*DG Randall, FW*)

Open End Apr–early Nov.
Rooms 3 suites, 12 double – 11 with bath, 2 with shower, all with telephone; TV and baby-listening on request; many with minibar. 1 in tower 40 metres from main building. 2 ground-floor rooms suitable for ♿.
Facilities Salon/bar with TV, restaurant; conference facilities. 350-acre wooded park with swimming pool, tennis court, fishing in pond, archery and art gallery.
Location Off D739, between Nieuil and Fontagie; 42 km NE of Angoulême.
Credit cards All major cards accepted.
Terms [1989 rates] Dinner B&B: single 675–925 frs, double 1,010–1330 frs. Set meals 190–245 frs. Reduced rates and special meals for children on request.

NÎMES 30000 Gard — Map 10

Hôtel Imperator Concorde — *Tel* 66.21.90.30
Quai de la Fontaine — *Telex* 490635

An imperially classic turn-of-the-century hotel, newly renovated, in a good position between the Maison Carrée and Jardin de la Fontaine. Courteous service, pleasant walled garden, most bedrooms modernised; nouvelle cuisine *not quite up to its pretensions. 62 rooms, all with private facilities. B&B double 460–760 frs. Set menus 165–350 frs. New nomination. More reports welcome.*

NONTRON 24300 Dordogne — Map 10

Grand Hôtel Pélisson — *Tel* 53.56.11.22
3 place Alfred Agard

Between Angoulême and Périgueux, in the so-called "Périgord Vert", an old walled hilltop town where this former coaching-inn, quite modest and unsmart, stands on the main square. Very good simple country cooking, copiously served. Friendly, helpful people. Rooms comfortable, but they vary in size and furnishings are sombre. Parking in large rear courtyard. 26 rooms, most with bath or shower. B&B double 200–270 frs. Set menus 60–220 frs. More reports please.

There are many expensive hotels in the Guide. We are keen to increase our coverage at the other end of the scale. If you know of a simple place giving simple satisfaction, please write and tell us.

NOVES 13550 Bouches-du-Rhône — Map 11

Auberge de Noves

Tel 90.94.19.21
Fax 90.94.47.76
Telex 431312

A 19th-century manor amid pleasant open country south-east of Avignon, owned and run by André Lalleman as a stylish and luxurious hotel, well known for its cuisine (*Michelin* rosette, two red *Gault Millau toques*). An inspector returning this year found it as superb as ever, "Glorious floodlit patio, some new bedrooms of stunning luxury, with lovely decor; some have balconies with pastoral views," and others have concurred, "Breakfast delicious, food consistently good and generous. To listen to M. Lalleman discuss in French, English or German the ordering of the meal is an education and entertainment in itself." Earlier views: "A friendly and helpful atmosphere. M. Lalleman proved an amusing, intelligent and multilingual host. Excellent antiques in the bedroom, elegant pink-marble bathroom – but we could have done with a mini-bar in the heat!" "We can recommend the duck en papillote. M. Lalleman personally advised us on our choice of dishes. The waitresses treat you like honoured guests. The hotel even has its own well, with refreshing spring water; but the pool and gardens were untidy and the public rooms have too much flowery wallpaper." One gripe this year about food and service. And not all rooms are air-conditioned. (*Endorsed by Joy and Raymond Goldman*)

Open All year except Jan, Feb, Wed midday.
Rooms 4 suites, 18 double – all with bath and shower, telephone, and TV; some with balcony; baby-listening on request. Ground-floor rooms.
Facilities Lift. Salon, dining room; conference facilities. Garden with swimming pool and tennis court.
Location Off D 28, 2 km NW of Noves, which is 13 km SE of Avignon.
Credit cards Probably all major cards accepted.
Terms [1989 rates] Rooms 900–1,150 frs. Breakfast 70 frs. Dinner, B&B 880–1,005 frs per person. Set lunch/dinner 300–400 frs. Reduced rates and special meals for children.

PARIS — Map 9

Hôtel de l'Abbaye St-Germain — *Tel* (1) 45.44.38.11
10 rue Cassette, 75006

This *Relais du Silence* is on a busy little street near St-Sulpice, but even front rooms are quiet. It is a former monastery, nicely restored with simple elegance: bedrooms are well furnished, and windows open onto a little flagged courtyard with palms, pot-plants and flowers, where breakfast or refreshments can be taken. For these qualities, the *Abbaye* continues to be admired – "beautiful" and "excellent" are among this year's epithets. (*Phillip Gill, FM and CN Grist*) However, some rooms are very small, and more than one recent visitor complains of imperfect housekeeping and maintenance.

Open All year.
Rooms 4 suites, 44 double – all with bath and telephone, suites with terrace.
Facilities Lift. 2 salons, TV room, bar. Interior courtyard/garden.
Location Central, near St-Sulpice church. (Métro St-Sulpice.)

Restriction Not suitable for ♿.
Credit cards None accepted.
Terms B&B: double room 650–850 frs, suite 1,500–1,800 frs. (No restaurant.)

Hôtel de l'Angleterre *Tel* 42.60.34.72
44 rue Jacob *Fax* 42.60.16.93
Paris, 75006

Once upon a time the British Embassy (hence its name), this spruce and popular little hotel near St-Germain-des-Prés has some elegance (antiques and deep sofas in the foyer). Hemingway once lived in Room 14. Comfortable rooms, some with old beams: the quietest face the inner patio. 29 rooms, all but 1 with bath and shower. Rooms 650–900 frs. Breakfast 30 frs [1989]. No restaurant. Endorsed this year, but further reports welcome.

Hôtel de Banville *Tel* 42.67.70.16
166 boulevard Berthier, 75017 *Telex* 643025 H BANVIL

"The *Banville* calls itself 'the cheapest three-star hotel in Paris', which at under 500 frs a night may well be so. It is also one of the nicest in its class, family-run by very pleasant people, with a friendly staff and warm inviting atmosphere – not always so common in Paris. It fills up with regular clients, mostly French provincials, so needs to be booked well in advance. Bedrooms are comfortable and cosy, exceptional value, and the big foyer is cosy too, as well as elegant, with lots of flowers and pretty fabrics. One snag is the location, on a broad boulevard in the unglamorous *17e*, with few good restaurants nearby. The Métro is quite close, however." (JA) It is also handy for the air terminal. More reports please.

Open All year.
Rooms 40 double – 33 with bath and shower, 7 with shower, all with telephone, radio, TV. Baby-sitting.
Facilities Lift. 2 lounges, breakfast room.
Location 2 minutes' walk from Porte de Champerret, 10 minutes from Étoile. Underground parking nearby. (Métro Porte de Champerret and Pereire.)
Restriction Not suitable for ♿.
Credit cards Access, Amex, Visa.
Terms Rooms 470–490 frs. Breakfast 30 frs. (No restaurant.)

Hôtel Châtillon *Tel* (1) 45.42.31.17
11 square de Châtillon, 75014 *Fax* 45.42.72.09

This cheap and mildly eccentric little hotel is about four kilometres south of central Paris, in the totally untouristy Alésia district, and useful for access to the motorways. A devotee returning this year found the place mercifully unchanged under new owners, as "delightful" as the previous ones, and endorses his previous encomium: "The whole place reeks of Frenchness. The rooms are spacious with wonderful views of the neighbours – we cannot believe what people wear to go to bed. I far prefer it to *EastEnders*. A charming and quiet place where we awoke to birdsong in the trees. The floorboards creak, the furniture is nothing special, but the staff are delightful, the beds comfy, and breakfast deliciously fresh." Others, too, have approved the bedrooms and modern bathrooms. (*Paul Palmer*)

Open All year.
Rooms 2 for 4, 29 double – 30 with bath and/or shower, telephone and TV. 1 ground-floor room.
Facilities Lift, salon, bar, breakfast room.
Location Near Porte de Châtillon and Porte d'Orléans. Underground parking nearby. (Métro Alésia.)
Credit card Visa.
Terms Rooms 230–350 frs. Breakfast 22 frs. (No restaurant.)

Hôtel Duc de Saint-Simon — *Tel* 45.48.35.66
14 rue de Saint-Simon — *Fax* 45.48.68.25
Telex 203277

The sophisticated little *Duc de Saint-Simon* (formerly just the *Saint-Simon*) could be bracketed with the *Abbaye St-Germain* and the *Résidence du Bois* (q.v.) as being perhaps the most stylish of the city's small hotels. Centrally but quietly located down a side-street just off the boulevard St-Germain, it is usually booked up months ahead. Here is an inspector's recent view, "The tiny cobbled forecourt, with its shrubs and trellis-work, gives it a somewhat rural air. Converted from a 17th-century mansion, it is now owned and run by a civilised Swedish couple who have filled it with the antiques they love collecting. Tiled walls, old beams and rough stone walls add to the effect, and there's a small and pretty rear garden for breakfast and drinks in summer. My room was small and unremarkable, but many others are larger and better. The former cellars are now a network of little bars and salons, elegant certainly but a trifle claustrophobic; nor did I like the mindless piped music, not even classical. Clients tend to be reasonably well-off travellers who prefer Left Bank old-world charm to a luxury palace. I can see why they like this place, but I found it slightly snobbish and lacking in warmth, though certainly the staff are efficient." Others have judged it "utterly charming", "very beautiful".

Open All year.
Rooms 5 suites, 29 double – all with bath and/or shower, and telephone; TV on request. 5 in annexe.
Facilities Lift. 2 lounges, bar.
Location Central. (Métro Rue du Bac.)
Restriction Not suitable for ♿.
Credit cards None accepted.
Terms [1989 rates] Rooms 800–1100 frs, suites 1,250–1,500 frs. Breakfast 45 frs. (No restaurant.)

Hôtel des Grands Hommes — *Tel* (1) 46.34.19.60
17 place du Panthéon, 75005 — *Telex* 200185 PANTEON

André Breton and other Surrealist painters and writers are "great men" who used to stay at this little hotel of character, though the hotel is named for the even greater men (Voltaire, Victor Hugo, Rousseau et al) entombed in the Panthéon across the street. Its claim to be the place where Surrealism was created has just been formally recognised by the city with a marble plaque. The hotel was commended again this year, by Americans, for its cleanliness and friendly staff – save for one unwelcoming woman serving breakfast, (which you take in an 18th-century vaulted cellar). Rooms are furnished in period style. "Ours had a stylish canopy bed, and its view of the lighted dome of the Panthéon was the most beautiful nightlight we've ever had." (*Georgene Smith, E and L Marder*)

Open All year.
Rooms 32 double (also let as singles) – all with bath, telephone and radio. 1 ground-floor room.
Facilities Lounge with bar, breakfast room. Small garden.
Location Opposite Panthéon. Underground paying car park 100 metres. (Métro Luxembourg.)
Restriction Not suitable for ♿.
Credit cards All major cards accepted.
Terms [1989 rates] Rooms: single 400–530 frs, double 500–600 frs. Breakfast 30 frs. Reduced rates in low season. (No restaurant.)

Hôtel La Louisiane *Tel* (1) 43.29.59.30
60 rue de Seine, 75006

This simple little Left Bank hotel must be just about the most famous cheap hotel in Europe, for it is hallowed in literary and artistic history. Hemingway, Connolly and others used to stay here (it's mentioned in *The Unquiet Grave*); Sartre here wrote *L'Être et le Néant* during the war, when Simone de Beauvoir was staying here too (in a separate bedroom). Today the plumbing may be better and the geniuses, alas, far fewer: but basically it's unchanged, and it continues to appeal to readers in search of blissful Rive Gaucherie at low cost. Americans write: "The ambience was wonderful – sort of artistic, bohemian and decidedly friendly. We met good people at breakfast and we all shared a love of this little hotel. It has its drawbacks – if you're finicky, then a hotel that has the sounds of the street market waking you up at 6 am, offers glimpses down narrow and often dirty (but secretly so romantic) alleys, may not be for you. But I felt I really was in Paris, far more than I would in some luxury hotel." "This is not a place for those seeking chic, and you may be put off by the cramped foyer and tiny lift: but the young staff are affable and the bedrooms and bathrooms, though *very* plain, are modernised, of a good size, for Paris, and have proper baths. Front rooms look straight on to the colourful Buci street market; but there's double glazing, and upper or back rooms are very quiet." The multinational clientele are always amusing: "A group of precocious child fashion-models were demanding croissants" – this was because the help-yourself breakfast (in a *very* drab room) features not croissants but a kind of brown soda-bread. (*Endorsed this year by Rev. M Bourdeaux, PW Brereton, and by our Continental Editors JA and KA whose regular Paris pad this is*)

Open All year.
Rooms 79 – all with bath and/or shower, and telephone.
Facilities Lift. Breakfast room.
Location Near St-Germain-des-Prés. Underground parking nearby. (Métro St-Germain-des-Prés, Odéon.)
Credit cards Access, Diners, Visa.
Terms B&B: single 300 frs, double 450--600 frs. (No restaurant.)

> If you are nominating a hotel, please err on the side of saying too much. Many suggestions have to be rejected only because they are too brief.

Hôtel des Marronniers *Tel* (1) 43.25.30.60
21 rue Jacob, 75006

Near the heart of hectic St-Germain-des-Prés, but quiet, for it lies at the back of a courtyard: most rooms, well modernised, face this or the tiny garden where you can breakfast on fine days. Some period furniture; staff friendly. But bathrooms are small and walls can be thin. 37 rooms, all with bath, 460–575 frs [1989]. Re-nominated this year. More reports welcome.

Pavillon de la Reine *Tel* (1) 42.77.96.40
28 place des Vosges, 75003 *Telex* 216160

An elegant old building on one of Paris's most beautiful squares, sympathetically converted into a charming little luxury hotel, with white marble bathrooms. The quietest rooms overlook a flower-filled patio. 23 suites, 30 other rooms, all with bath and shower. Double room 900–2,200 frs. No restaurant. New nomination. More reports please.

La Résidence du Bois *Tel* (1) 45.00.50.59
16 rue Chalgrin, 75116

An 1860s mansion in a quiet residential street off the stately avenue Foch, near the Étoile. It is very expensive, but arguably the most delightful of all Paris's smaller hotels – de luxe and exclusive, its salons and bedrooms tastefully furnished with period pieces, silks and satins. Readers this year were again entranced: "We could hardly believe we were in the heart of Paris when we heard the doves cooing and saw the lovely little garden. Madame is so kind – it really is like staying with good friends in an elegant house." "Our wonderful large room looked on to the garden, the staff were pleasant and the breakfasts nice." A couple arriving with a baby found the owner and staff charming, but report that the room walls are thin and the plumbing lively. Light meals served on request. (*M and D Chambers, N and V Elton*)

Open All year.
Rooms 3 triple, 15 double, 2 single – 18 with bath, 2 with shower, all with telephone and TV; baby-listening on request. 1 room in annexe.
Facilities Salon, bar. Garden.
Location Central (near Arc de Triomphe). Parking nearby. (Métro Argentine.)
Restriction Not suitable for ♿.
Credit cards None accepted.
Terms [1989 rates] B&B: 1,040–1,530 frs, suite 2,375 frs. (No restaurant.)

Hôtel des Saints-Pères *Tel* 45.44.50.00
65 rue des Saints-Pères, 75006 *Fax* 45.44.90.83
Telex 205424

A pleasant upper-middle-price Left Bank hotel, centrally situated, with chic modern decor and a charming inner courtyard where you can take breakfast. Rooms are not large. Front desk helpful. 37 rooms, all with bath and/or shower. Rooms 400–1,100 frs. Breakfast 40 frs [1989]. No restaurant. Recent nomination. More reports welcome.

Hôtel de Suède *Tel* (1) 47.05.00.08
31 rue Vaneau, 75007 *Telex* 200596 HT SUEDE

Again approved in 1988/9 for its "courteous and helpful staff", as well as for its quiet, comfort and good value (for Paris), this small medium-priced hotel lies in the heart of the old Faubourg St-Germain, aristocratic in Proust's day, governmental in ours (rooms at the back overlook the gardens of the Hôtel Matignon, the Prime Minister's residence and office, and other ministries close by). "Stylish in a somewhat formal way, and with a discreet, private feel to it. An adequate breakfast is served in the big salon, furnished in Directoire style with yellow-green upholstery. Here you can also get 'mini-snacks' such as omelettes. Clientele of young men in modish dress." (*JA*) "An interior courtyard where they serve breakfast and drinks in summer. The armed police in the street may not exactly create a holiday atmosphere, but they do make this a very safe part of Paris at night." (*Endorsed by William Bentsen, M and L Piper, AE Eldon-Edington*)

Open All year.
Rooms 1 suite, 33 double, 7 single – 36 with bath and/or shower, all with telephone; TV, baby-sitter on request. 7 in pavilion in courtyard.
Facilities Lift. Lounge where drinks and snacks are served 6.30 am–10 pm. Small garden.
Location 10 mins' walk from Seine and St-Germain-des-Prés. (Métro Varenne.)
Credit cards Access, Amex, Visa.
Terms [1989 rates] B&B: single 445 frs, double 490 frs, suite 860 frs. (No restaurant.)

Hôtel de l'Université *Tel* (1) 42.61.09.39
22 rue Université, 75007 *Telex* 260717 OREM 310

This converted 17th-century town house near the Seine, intimate and stylish, continues to be one of the most popular of our Paris hotels. Reports this year: "A delight, and great value for money"; "Small, refined and quiet, with an electronic safe in each room for storing valuables"; "Our room was spacious enough, restfully decorated in a soft silvery green". The public rooms are decorated with antiques and tapestries, and breakfast is taken at small marble tables looking out onto a charming tiny courtyard. Back rooms are quietest, and one reader this year found the decor "slightly gloomy". (*Willis G Frick, Mrs RB Richards, and others*)

Open All year.
Rooms 1 suite, 17 double, 10 single – 20 with bath, 8 with shower, all with telephone and TV; baby-sitters available.
Facilities Lift. Lounge, bar.
Location 5 mins from St-Germain-des-Prés. Underground parking nearby. (Métro Rue du Bac.)
Restriction Not suitable for ♿.
Credit cards None accepted.
Terms [1989 rates] Rooms: single 400 frs, double 780 frs. Breakfast 40 frs. 1-night bookings refused in high season. Reduced rates for children sharing parents' room. (No restaurant, but snacks served in bar.)

> If you have had recent experience of a good hotel that ought to be in the Guide, please write to us at once. Report forms are to be found at the back. Procrastination is the thief of the next edition.

Hôtel de Varenne *Tel* 45.51.45.55
44 rue de Bourgogne, 75007 *Telex* 205329

"Highly recommended" again this year, a converted mansion with a pretty courtyard, near the Invalides. Earlier praise: "Peaceful, with a friendly and efficient staff. Nice comfortable rooms. Breakfast on patio or in lounge area." "Lovely to hear early morning birdsong, but beware the occasional late-night disco party nearby." (*Seymour Sachs*) One reader this year was critical of *accueil* and bedroom furnishings.

Open All year.
Rooms 20 double, 4 single – all with bath, shower, telephone and TV.
Facilities Lift. Lounge, patio.
Location Within walking distance of the Champs-Élysées and St-Germain-des-Prés. Parking in quiet street, 5 mins' walk away. (Métro Varenne.)
Credit cards Amex, Visa.
Terms Rooms: single 320 frs, double 470 frs. Breakfast 30 frs. (No restaurant.)

PASSENANS 39230 Jura Map 10

Auberge du Rostaing *Tel* 84.85.23.70

No fewer than six reports, all favourable, have arrived this year for this modest but charming rural *auberge* that is fast becoming a Guide favourite. All stress the excellent value for money, the good, straightforward cooking, (though the microwave is kept busy) and the friendly helpfulness of the Franco-Swiss owners, the Eckerts (she cooks, he hosts). The hotel is tucked away in unspoilt countryside, on the outskirts of a sleepy village between the Jura hills to the east and the rich farmlands of Bresse to the west: yet it is not hard to reach, for major tourist routes are near by. "It's good walking country – and walking is what many of the guests do. Then they come drifting in to sit in the courtyard under a tree or parasol, sipping a drink. The white 18th-century main building contains a spacious dining room with open fireplace, large peasant cupboards and modern art, and a 'parlour' upstairs with a piano, records, books and games. Some of the rooms are in an attractive vine-balustraded building with an outside staircase and open walkway balcony. Rooms are simple but pleasant; excellent showers and even an electric hair-drier." That earlier report remains valid. One reader this year thought the food "delicious", with good salads and cheeses, and home-made jams for breakfast. Swiss dishes such as fondue and raclette are sometimes offered – "and the Swissness of the place shows up with the long list of admonitions to guests. We liked the one urging visitors to take their showers on sunny days in view of the solar heating." (*E Newall, Mrs Lucy Slater, Group Capt and Mrs HB Verity, and others*)

Open 1 Feb–30 Nov. Closed Tue except school holidays.
Rooms 10 double – 6 with bath and/or shower, 3 with WC; baby-listening.
Facilities Salon with library, 2 dining rooms. Courtyard, garden. Bicycles for hire.
Location Off N83, 11 km S of Poligny, which is where the Dijon–Geneva road crosses the Lyon–Besançon road.
Restriction Not suitable for ♿.
Credit cards Access, Diners, Visa.
Terms Rooms: single 75–139 frs, double 83–152 frs. Breakfast 18 frs. Dinner, B&B: single 126–196 frs, double 189–268 frs. Set lunch/dinner 52–132 frs. 1-night bookings sometimes refused. Reduced rates and special meals for children.

PEILLON 06440 Alpes-Maritimes — Map 11

Auberge de la Madone — *Tel* 93.79.91.17

Only 19 kilometres from Nice, yet remote in the silent hills, this attractive family-run *auberge* stands on the edge of one of the most striking *villages perchés* of the area. Reports this year: "Our room had a balcony overlooking the village and valley, where breakfast came with hot toast. A glorious garden, and a beautiful terrace for meals and drinks. The food was delicious and the service friendly, but dinner was a bit rushed so as to finish by 9.30 pm." "A bedroom with tiled floor and typical French country furniture. The terrace was idyllic but the food was uninspired." Others have commented on the warm ambience created by the Millo family, and the good regionally based dishes such as daube de boeuf à l'orange et aux cèpes. (*Caroline Thomson and Roger Liddle, Philippa Herbert*)

Open 20 Dec–15 Oct. Closed Wed.
Rooms 3 suites, 16 double – 15 with bath and shower, all with telephone; 3 with TV.
Facilities Salon with TV, dining room; conference facilities. Large garden.
Location 18 km NE of Nice on D21.
Restriction Not suitable for ♿.
Credit cards None accepted.
Terms Dinner, B&B: double 360–480 frs, suite 520 frs. Set lunch/dinner 130, 190 and 260 frs; full alc 300 frs. Reduced rates and special meals for children.

LA PEINIÈRE-ST-DIDIER 35220 Ille-et-Vilaine — Map 8

Hôtel Pen'Roc — *Tel* 99.00.33.02 — *Telex* 741457

Renewed praise this year for the "marvellous hospitality" and "delicious fish dishes" at the attractive modern *Pen'Roc*: built in local Breton style, it lies quietly amid meadows, beside a little romanesque church, just off the main road from Rennes to Vitré. "The staff showed warmth and kindness." "The cuisine is refined and imaginative (notably the fishermen's choucroute), the setting is beautiful and the staff charming. Pity about the bedroom decor – someone clearly has a penchant for mauve, purple and brown." An earlier impression, "It's used during the day for business gatherings, but in the evening we found it delightful and peaceful. Family-run by the Frocs. Madame is tall and (even at 8 am) as elegant as the dishes her husband produces." Bedrooms are "large and comfortable". Another Froc speciality is "méli-mélo de la mer à la badiane". (*Robyn Morton, Jack B Ainslie, G Buckland*)

Open All year except 2 weeks Feb. Restaurant closed Sun evening.
Rooms 1 suite, 23 double, 2 single – 11 with bath, 10 with shower, all with telephone, radio and TV. 1 ground-floor room.
Facilities Lift. Lounge, bar, 3 dining rooms; conference facilities. Garden with children's play area.
Location 6 km E of Châteaubourg. Turn off D857 at St-Jean-sur-Vilaine, towards St-Didier, then right to La Peinière.
Credit cards All major cards accepted.
Terms B&B: single 237 frs, double 283 frs, suite 500 frs; half board 237–326 frs per person. Full alc 240 frs. Reduced rates and special meals for children.

PÉROUGES 01800 Ain — Map 10

Ostellerie du Vieux Pérouges

Tel 74.61.00.88
Telex 306898

This medieval hilltop village north-east of Lyon, with its ramparts, cobbles and half-timbered houses, is so well preserved that historical feature films (e.g. *The Return of Martin Guerre*) are often shot here. The hotel, converted from 13th-century buildings, is part of the decor, forming one side of the village square. Its studied folksiness is not to all tastes, but many readers continue to like it. One of them "felt transported back into the Middle Ages," and goes on, "The rooms are period-perfect, and the dining room – with its costumed waitresses – is also a delight with a wood-fire burning. We had an enormous ground-floor suite with medieval furnishings and paintings" (but bathrooms are modern). Others have enjoyed "climbing to our room by way of a winding stone tower" and "breakfast in a private garden". Another visitor was more sceptical, "Rather gimmicky, e.g. the large rolls of parchment on which menus are presented." But most people like the cuisine, e.g. écrevisses pérougienne, duck with green pepper, and the celebrated local griddle cake with raspberries. More reports please.

Open All year except Wed in low season.
Rooms 3 suites, 25 double – all with bath, telephone and TV. 1 ground-floor room.
Facilities Lounges, bar, restaurant; conference facilities. Gardens.
Location In town square. Parking. Pérouges is 39 km NE of Lyon.
Restriction Not suitable for ♿.
Credit cards Visa.
Terms [1989 rates] Rooms 450–750 frs, suite 850 frs. Breakfast 60 frs. Set lunch/dinner 150–320 frs; full alc 300 frs.

PERPIGNAN 66000 Pyrénées Orientales — Map 10

Park Hotel et Restaurant Le Chapon Fin

18 bvd Jean-Bourrat

Tel 68.35.14.14
Telex 506161
Fax 68.35.48.18

Downtown Perpignan's premier hotel: smart and modern, it faces gardens on the inner ring boulevard, but is quiet (double glazing). Period Catalan furniture, polite service, very good food (Michelin *rosette, two* Gault Millau toques). *67 rooms, some suitable for ♿, all with bath and/or shower. B&B double 316–476 frs. Set menus 170–350 frs. New nomination. More reports please.*

LA PETITE PIERRE 67290 Bas-Rhin — Map 9

Hôtel aux Trois Roses

Tel 88.70.45.02
Telex 871150

A fine 18th-century *auberge*, white-walled, flower-bedecked, all cosy inside, and admired again in 1989. It is in the main street of an ancient hilltop Alsatian village (front rooms can be noisy), with remains of ramparts, and hilly forests all around; the dining room has a fine view of the castle, romantic on summer evenings when it is floodlit. Run hectically by the Geyer family and a whole bevy of other Alsatians, it is a sympathetically informal and lively place, very much a local social centre, less in the French than in the Central European tradition – several comfy salons, and a big *Stübe* where snacks and cakes are served all day.

Some bedrooms in the old building are a bit cramped and shabby, but a modern wing has been built down the hillside, and this is preferred by readers (*Michelin*, too, gives it three gables, while the rest of the hotel gets two). The dining room has also been extended, and there is a new outdoor patio. "We had a suite with pleasant views from the balcony", says one reader this year, while another much enjoyed the food (e.g. help-yourself hors d'oeuvre and trout in riesling). Breakfast, formerly criticised, has now improved and is a German-style buffet. (*K and S Murray-Sykes, K and N Varley*)

Open 6 Feb–6 Jan. Restaurant closed Sun evening and Mon.
Rooms 16 suites, 21 double, 9 single – all with bath and shower, telephone and TV; 16 with radio. Some in annexe.
Facilities 2 lifts. 3 lounges (2 with TV), bar, 5 dining rooms; indoor swimming pool. Garden with terrace, children's play area, tennis.
Location 60 km NW of Strasbourg; hotel is central. Parking.
Credit cards Access, Visa.
Terms Rooms: single 80–350 frs, double 160–435 frs, suite 350–435 frs. Breakfast 52 frs. Dinner B&B 185–350 frs per person. Set lunch/dinner 85–198 frs; full alc 230 frs. Reductions for children under 8; special meals on request.

PLÉHÉDEL 22290 Côtes-du-Nord — Map 8

Château Hôtel de Coatguélen

Tel 96.22.31.24
Telex 741300

Seven kilometres from the sea and quite near to good North Brittany beaches, this elegant little 19th-century château stands in its own 170-acre park of woods, lakes and meadows – not to mention a nine-hole golf-course. Dropped from the 1989 Guide for lack of news, it is now reinstated by a reader who found it "superb", with "marvellous" food, and by another more restrained report, "We were quite pleased. It's still owned by the Marquis de Boisgelin, but run by the friendly Le Roys: Louis has written books on modern cookery (his own cuisine gets a deserved two red *toques* in *Gault Millau*), and his wife Nicole, front-of-house, is not only charming, stylish and vivacious but arranges remarkable art exhibitions. Bedrooms have been attractively decorated (ours overlooked the golf-course) and there's much old furniture: the drawing room contains lovely antiques, a gorgeous grand piano and spectacular pictures. The dining room has windows overlooking the lake and the food is interesting – baked oysters, lobster steamed in seaweed en vessie, excellent sauces. The service was very willing, but sometimes erratic and inexperienced. There was a down-at-heel character in reception every evening. Was he a gardener or odd-job-man? My guess is that it was the Marquis in mufti, keeping an eye on the place." (*Francine and Ian Walsh; Helmut Schoen*)

Open 15 Mar–15 Nov, 15–31 Jan.
Rooms 2 suites, 14 double – all with bath and/or shower and telephone.
Facilities Salon with TV, bar, restaurant; conference rooms; children's playroom. Large park with unheated swimming pool, tennis, children's play area, horses, ponies, trout fishing, 9-hole golf course. Beach 7 km.

Location 11 km S of Paimpol, on D7 to Lanvollon. Parking.
Credit cards All major cards accepted.
Terms [1989 rates] Rooms 415–1,300 frs. Breakfast 55 frs. Dinner, B&B 565–790 frs per person. Set meals 200–300 frs.

LE POËT-LAVAL 26160 Drôme — Map 10

Les Hospitaliers — *Tel* 75.46.22.32

A variety of ecstatic admiration in 1988/9 for "this secret paradise", "this divine hotel", "our favourite in France". It stands on a hilltop in a medieval village, above fine wooded countryside where the foothills of the Alps descend to the Rhône valley, on the borders of Dauphiné and Provence. Here the owner Yvon Morin has sensitively restored an old building, with a ruined 12th-century chapel towering above, and a swimming pool facing the glorious panorama. "We dined on an enchanting terrace with tables around a magnificent tree and a superb view over the valley. The owners were most friendly and dinner extremely good" (*Michelin* rosette, two red *Gault Millau toques*). "We had a huge room with balcony overlooking the ruined chapel. The lounge is magnificent – vaulted, beamed, a roaring fire (in March), interesting paintings and M. Morin's personal collection of sculptures. Food was excellent." "M. Morin is a marvellous host, hard working and courteous. Delightful pantomime of tasting each bottle of wine." "The best service I have seen anywhere." "The pool is a delight." The foie gras, carré d'agneau, potage of wild mushrooms and the grilled goats' cheese are much praised. Only quibbles: an unchanging set menu, and pool furniture a bit worn. (*Lynne and David Allen, Tom and Rosemary Rose, PA Catling, Mr and Mrs RM Booth, and others*)

Open 1 Mar–15 Nov.
Rooms 1 suite, 21 double – 21 with bath and shower, 1 with shower, all with telephone. 3 annexes adjacent to main building.
Facilities Salon, TV room, bar, 2 restaurants; conference facilities. Garden with terraces and heated swimming pool.
Location On D540, E of La Bégude-de-Mazenc; Montélimar 25 km.
Restriction Not suitable for ♿.
Credit cards All major cards accepted.
Terms Rooms: double 440 frs, suite 750 frs. Breakfast 65 frs. Set lunch/dinner 200–390 frs; full alc 500 frs. Special meals for children.

POLIGNY 39800 Jura — Map 10

Hostellerie des Monts de Vaux — *Tel* 84.37.12.50
Monts de Vaux — *Telex* 361493

On the N5 from Dijon to Geneva, in a hamlet just south-east of Poligny, here's a rather smart coaching inn, dating from 1793 but with modern extensions. The site, on the edge of a cliff above Poligny, is lovely. Charming family owners, comfortable rooms, excellent food, sophisticated ambience. Garden with tennis court. Closed end Oct to end Dec and Tue, Wed evening in low season. 10 rooms, all with bath and shower. Dinner B&B: single 640 frs, double 900–1,400 frs. Alc (excluding wine) 180–300 frs [1989]. *New nomination. More reports much desired.*

PONS 17800 Charente-Maritime Map 10

Auberge Pontoise *Tel* 46.94.00.99
23 avenue Gambetta

This medieval town above the river Seugne, near the *autoroute* down to Bordeaux, has a castle with a vast keep and a hospice once used by pilgrims Compostela-bound. Our own voyagers mostly – but not all – approve the *Pontoise*, which returns to the Guide this year with these reports: "Modest, clean and comfortable, with a helpful front desk and superbly executed cuisine – a model of what a *Michelin* one-rosette restaurant should be." "Lovely cream stone courtyard, entrance hall beautiful with Persian rugs on stone floors, much well-polished brass. Chic petite Madame smiles a welcome. Bedroom gently old-fashioned. Dining room full of locals, with black-and-white tiled floor, gleaming glasses and silver. Dinner was magic – home-cured smoked salmon, delicious fish soup, langoustines with pasta." (*WG Frick, Minda Alexander*) However, another visitor this year, while finding the room comfortable, strongly criticised the decor, "pretentious" food, and glum service. More reports needed.

Open 30 Jan–21 Dec. Closed Sun evening and Mon 15 Sept–1 Jul.
Rooms 1 suite, 21 double – all with bath and/or shower, telephone and TV. 1 ground-floor room.
Facilities Lounge, bar, 2 dining-rooms.
Location Central. Parking. Pons is 96 km N of Bordeaux.
Restrictions Not suitable for ♿.
Credit cards Access, Visa.
Terms Rooms 200–280 frs, suite 550 frs. Breakfast 40 frs. Set lunch/dinner 160–250 frs; full alc 300–350 frs.

PONT-AUDEMER 27500 Eure Map 8

Auberge du Vieux Puits *Tel* 32.41.01.48
6 rue Notre-Dame du Pré

Three 17th-century timbered houses around a courtyard make up this very picturesque restaurant-with-rooms, which remains popular with many readers, though it comes in for criticism, too. "Beautiful buildings, delicious cooking, friendly service, a very small but comfortable room"; "The warmest of welcomes. The menu doesn't change, ever: but if I can eat truite Bovary and canard aux griottes there once a year, I don't complain." Thus two reports this year, following on last year's, "We were warmly welcomed by Madame Foltz and shown to a pretty and comfortable room in the new wing. The inn is beautifully maintained with fresh flowers in the rooms, and the courtyard has a pretty garden where people gather for aperitifs on fine evenings." The eight original bedrooms by the courtyard are pretty but small, and one visitor this year found their plumbing noisy. The six newer rooms have more comfort: but one recent report called them "soulless and motel-like". (*Mrs RB Richards, E Newall, PF*) One reader this year regretted that the menus do not change – and we note that *Michelin* has now withdrawn its rosette.

Open 18 Jan–2 Jul, 11 Jul–16 Dec. Closed Mon evening and Tue.
Rooms 12 double – 6 with bath and shower, 5 with shower, 9 with WC, all with telephone; 6 with TV. 2 ground-floor rooms, accessible for ♿.
Facilities 2 small salons, 2 restaurants. Small garden.
Location 300 metres from town centre (hotel is signposted), but quiet. Parking.
Credit cards Access, Visa.
Terms Rooms 150–350 frs. Breakfast 32 frs. Set lunch 150 frs, dinner 250 frs; full alc 230–290 frs. Guests expected to dine at the hotel.

PONT-DE-BRIQUES 62360 Pas-de-Calais — Map 9

Hostellerie de la Rivière — *Tel* 21.32.22.81
17 rue de la Gare

We are always glad of new nominations near the Channel ports, and owner/chef Jean Martin's country-style restaurant-with-rooms just south of Boulogne, close to the N1 to Paris, sounds promising: "The expensive menus are excellent value. For 260 francs I had pâté de foie gras, an astonishing (but only semi-successful) shrimps folded into a cabbage leaf bathed in a raspberry (!) sauce, carré d'agneau and a magnificent selection of cheeses. Nice little garden. Quiet – only the river speaks. Our room charge, 110 francs [1988], was less than an eighth of the final bill. But M. Martin says they will be 'rebuilding' the hotel." *Michelin* rosette. *Gault Millau*'s *toque* is in black for 'traditional' cuisine, rather than red for 'inventive' - despite the *Rev. M Bourdeaux*'s raspberry sauce. More reports welcome.

Open All year except 16 Aug–10 Sept and 10 days in Feb. Closed Sun evening and Mon, and Christmas night.
Rooms 7 double, 1 single – 3 with bath and shower, all with telephone; 2 with TV.
Facilities Bar, restaurant.
Location 5 km S of Boulogne, close to N1.
Credit cards Access, Visa.
Terms Rooms: single 250 frs, double 270–330 frs. Breakfast 30 frs. Set lunch/dinner 130, 195 and 260 frs; full alc 300–350 frs.

PONT-DE-VAUX 01190 Ain — Map 10

Le Raisin — *Tel* 85.30.30.97
2 place Michel-Poisat

A pleasant little town just east of the Saône, between Tournus and Mâcon; here Gilles Chazot's warmly decorated restaurant-with-rooms offers excellent traditional Bressane cooking at very fair prices (Michelin *rosette*, Gault Millau toque). *Above-average breakfasts, and simple but comfortable rooms. Closed Jan, Sun evening and Mon. 7 rooms, all with bath or shower. B&B double 210 frs. Set menus 72–230 frs* [1989]. *New nomination. More reports please.*

> In all continental European and Scandinavian countries except Denmark, France, Hungary, Malta, Spain and Turkey, the dialling codes begin with a 0. Omit this when dialling from outside the country in question. Spanish codes begin with a 9, which should also be omitted.

PORQUEROLLES 83540 Var — Map 11

Mas du Langoustier — *Tel* 94.58.30.09

A most seductive Guide newcomer, secluded in its own 75-acre pine-wooded park beside the sea, at the eastern and virtually uninhabited end of a very lovely island, which is mostly a national park (no cars, no smoking outside the village, bike trails with virtually no tarmac, sandy beaches, wooded cliffs). It's a handsome old yellow-walled manor, converted and modernised with some sophistication, and warmly recommended by retired hoteliers: "An outstanding hotel, three-star, but more like four-star. Meals are served on a large terrace: the food is of the highest quality (two red *Gault Millau toques*), the service excellent and the bedrooms well appointed. A new wing of 21 bedrooms blends superbly into the old style of this lovely building. There are new tennis courts, and two sandy beaches three minutes' walk away. Free buses go to the village and port of Porquerolles every hour. Eighty per cent of the clients are French, and the hotel is almost unknown to the British" – quite a rarity in France today. Full board terms only. (*Sally and Curtis Wilmot-Allistone*) More reports welcome.

Open 15 Mar–15 Nov.
Rooms 3 suites, 62 double – all with bath and/or shower, telephone and TV. Ground-floor rooms.
Facilities 2 lounges, bar, restaurant; conference facilities; terrace. Park with tennis, boules, sandy beach, sailing, windsurfing.
Location 3.5 km E of port of Porquerolles which is 15 mins by boat from La Tour Fondue (frequent services). No cars allowed on island. Free bus service from port to hotel.
Credit cards All major cards accepted.
Terms [1989 rates] Full board 762–1,162 frs. Set lunch/dinner 200–440 frs. Special meals for children.

Relais de la Poste — *Tel* 94.58.30.26
Île de Porquerolles

M. and Mme Ghiglion's modern and spotless B&B hotel is in the only village of this beautiful island. Eccentric library, sturdy bikes for hire. No restaurant, but salad lunches available. The church clocks chime all night. Auberge Arche de Noé *recommended for best food on the island. 30 rooms, all with bath or shower. B&B 250–450 frs. Recent nomination. More reports please.*

LE PORT BOULET 37140 Indre et Loire — Map 10

Château des Réaux — *Tel* 47.95.14.40
Le Port Boulet, Bourgueil

Small 15th-century castle on an island, peaceful apart from the occasional passing train, belonging to Château Accueil group. Elegant salon and dining room, small but attractively furnished bedrooms, bathrooms functional; annexe rooms, not on the island, and nearer the railway are simpler and cheaper. "Individual and civilised; excellent food, welcoming hosts." 4 suites, 600–900 frs, 12 double rooms, 300–600 frs. Breakfast 40 frs [1989]. *New nomination. More reports please.*

PORTICCIO 20166 Corsica — Map 11

Le Maquis

Tel 95.25.05.55
Fax 95.25.11.70
Telex 460597

A beautiful and sophisticated hotel with more than a touch of glamour, right by the sea across the bay from Ajaccio. Family-run (Madame Salini is usually dressed in leather), it has been described as "small, very French and absolutely marvellous". It has a smart swimming pool and its own private beach, overlooked by some bedrooms; white walls, black beams and red-tiled floors lend style to the interior decor. "If you have a ground-floor room, your balcony literally meets the sand. The food is good, especially the huge help-yourself hors d'oeuvre table. One of our happiest memories will be eating lunch on the terrace – pink tablecloths, umbrellas, silver, fine china and glass and the bright blue sky and sea below, wonderful fresh seafood and delicious Corsican wines." However, a reader this year found the ambience somewhat mercenary and questions value for money.

Open All year. Restaurant closed Feb.
Rooms 7 suites, 22 double, 1 single – all with bath and/or shower, telephone, TV and video, mini-bar and air-conditioning. Some ground-floor rooms.
Facilities Lift, lounge, bar, dining room; terrace for alfresco meals. Indoor swimming pool. Garden with tennis court, heated swimming pool, and children's play area. On private beach with safe bathing.
Location On the coast 15 km SE of Ajaccio, on the D55. 12 km from airport.
Credit cards All major cards accepted.
Terms [1989 rates] Dinner, B&B: single 980--1,500 frs, double 1,300–2,200 frs, suite 1,870–3,330 frs. Set meals from 200 frs. Reduced rates and special meals for children.

PORTICCIOLO 20228 Corsica — Map 11

Hôtel Le Caribou

Tel 95.35.02.33

The Catoni family's "delightful" hotel, with its "house-party atmosphere" and "cornucopia of food", lies on the road north from Bastia to Cap Corse, in a colourful garden of flowers and trees. Those few readers who report to us on this Eden are always ecstatic. "The welcome from the Catonis – he grizzled, she statuesque – is exceedingly warm. The place glows with atmosphere and we made many friends, fellow guests and staff alike. Guests are an interesting mixture of old regulars and young families with children who mingle with the Catonis' grandchildren, giving the place an ambience of informality. The rooms are old-fashioned and plainly furnished, but comfortable, with good plumbing. And the food is outstanding. For the main dish, you choose from Monsieur's oral selection, but first you have to resist plate after plate of hors d'oeuvre, pâtés, melon and water melon, local smoked ham, langoustines, mussels, home-made pasta. . ." Another view: "As you go up the steep drive, you find a swimming pool set into the garden. Splendid old trees have been interlaced with vines to make a cool shady place for aperitifs or coffee. Our suite across the road, overlooking the sea, was one of several *pavillons* built into the rocks just above the water's edge, each with a small sun-terrace. Fresh flowers had been put in our room when we retired for a siesta."

Open 25 June–25 Sept.
Rooms 1 suite, 29 double – all with bath (6 also have shower), and telephone; some with balcony. Also 13 bungalows, with kitchen, for 3–8 people, let by the week.
Facilities Lounge, bar, TV room, restaurant; terraces. Sauna, fitness room. Swimming pool, 2 tennis courts. Private harbour, fine sandy beach with bathing, water skiing, windsurfing, sailing, fishing, skin diving and volley-ball.
Location On east coast, off N198.
Credit cards All major cards accepted.
Terms Rooms 400–700 frs. Dinner, B&B: single 600–700 frs, double 1,200–1,500 frs. Set meals 280 frs; full alc 300 frs. Reduced rates and special meals for children.

PORT-MANECH 29139 Finistère — Map 8

Hôtel Restaurant du Port — *Tel* 98.06.82.17
30 rue de l'Aven

Superb fish dishes (but not much meat) are on offer at this unpretentious and inexpensive modern inn by the harbour, in a south Brittany fishing-village. Kindly owners, good breakfasts. Simple rooms, some with fine coastal views; the annexe, which is cheaper and has been criticised as "basic", has been upgraded. Open Easter–end Sept. Restaurant closed Mon lunchtime. 35 rooms, 6 with bath, 25 with shower. Dinner, B&B 230–250 frs. Set meals 80–170 frs. Endorsed this year, but past criticisms of room upkeep. More reports welcome.

QUESTEMBERT 56230 Morbihan — Map 8

Le Bretagne — *Tel* 97.26.11.12
Rue St-Michel — *Telex* 951801

Located in a small town east of Vannes, here is Brittany's most distinguished restaurant (*patron*-chef Georges Paineau wins two *Michelin* rosettes, three red *Gault Millau toques*), but maybe because it has only six bedrooms it's not been reported to us before. Now it's described with awe and wonder by two of our keenest sleuths: "The ivy-clad exterior is pretty standard, but within the archway surprise followed surprise – not least the spacious garden with lovingly chosen shrubs, populated by a large number of lean oriental cats adding to the exotic feel. Bedrooms are not palatial but smart and very comfortable. Ours had a huge double bed: it was vaguely exotic, because of the palmed net curtains, imitation bamboo tables, adorable wooden Japanese dolls. The bathroom was amazing, giving the feel of a hot South Sea island, in vivid rainbow hues, with cotton kimonos provided.

"This wild exuberance is reflected throughout the hotel. The Paineaus have travelled widely, buying what took their fancy, and installing these objects side-by-side with Breton antiques regardless of the dictums of so-called 'good taste'. And it works, this colourfully varied tour-de-force. Of the two dining rooms, one is a beautifully panelled expanse of golden wood lit by antique lamps, the other a large glass conservatory straight out of the *1001 Nights*, with a colourful screen painted in 'naïve' style by the *patron* himself. The sitting room is dark and dramatic. And the same bravura is evident in Georges Paineau's forceful style of cooking: sauces are deceptively simple but a delight, presentation is superb, with each dish appearing on an appropriate plate of rare porcelain. We enjoyed hot oysters in cream, melting terrine de foie gras, fantastic pigeon cooked in a shell of rock salt. Service is swift and impeccable. Breakfast included hot brioche slices with apple, and superlative coffee. M Paineau is a fine figure of a man with a splendidly bushy moustache, adept at charming compliments; his wife Michèle is also flamboyant, like an explosive orchid." (*Ian and Francine Walsh*) Prices are remarkably reasonable. If you, too, visit this Xanadu, please don't fail to tell us.

Open All year. Closed Christmas, Sun evening and Mon except Jul, Aug and bank holidays.
Rooms 6 double – all with bath and shower, telephone, radio and TV.
Facilities 2 lounges, restaurant. Garden. Swimming pool 300 metres.
Location 27 km E of Vannes. Central, parking.
Restriction Not suitable for ♿.
Credit cards Amex, Visa.
Terms B&B: single 420–520 frs, double 520–630 frs. Dinner, B&B 780–880 frs per person. Set lunch/dinner 150–420 frs; full alc 380 frs. Reduced rates and special meals for children.

RABASTENS 81800 Tarn — Map 10

Hostellerie du Pré Vert — *Tel* 63.33.70.51
54 promenade des Lices

In the centre of a small town between Toulouse and Albi, a handsome old creeper-covered 18th-century house with a big shady garden, now making its Guide debut: "Rabastens is a sleepy old town, time-warped, unspoilt by tourism (don't miss the 12th-century church of Notre-Dame-du-Bourg), and the hotel is likewise – not at all smart, but welcoming, and the local girls are friendly in a non-professional way. Meals are served in an old-fashioned drawing-room with a cosy ambience: here our meal was thoroughly satisfactory and amazing value at 95 francs [1989]. Bedrooms too are good value." "Helpful owners; large rooms furnished in a solid, old-fashioned way." (*HR, Diana Holmes*)

Open All year except Dec. Restaurant closed Sun evening; also Mon midday in low season.
Rooms 12 double, 1 single – 4 with bath and shower, 8 with shower, all with telephone.
Facilities Bar, TV room, 2 dining rooms. Terrace where meals are served. Garden.
Location Central, parking. Rabastens is 37 km NE of Toulouse.
Restrictions Not suitable for ♿.
Credit cards Access, Visa.
Terms Rooms: single 150 frs, double 160–240 frs. Breakfast 23 frs. Set lunch/dinner 57–150 frs; full alc 185 frs. Reduced rates and special meals for children.

RAGUENÈS-PLAGE 29139 Finistère — Map 8

Hôtel Chez Pierre — *Tel* 98.06.81.06

This old Guide favourite, a most sympathetic family hotel, stands right next to good sandy beaches and is within easy reach of Concarneau and

Pont-Aven (where Gauguin painted). Old Madame Guillou has recently died, but her family are keeping up the standards – and readers remain pleased, with the caveats that rooms in the modern annexe are better than the older ones, and that standards may drop a bit in August when the crush is on. Xavier Guillou's cooking (*Michelin* red "R" for good value) has again been much admired this year, "Very good classical fish dishes with often quite rich sauces. The five-course half-board menu is outstanding value. And if you want to splurge one night, the lobster with tarragon is delicious. As M. Guillou does all the fish dishes and sauces himself, some long waits are inevitable." "A spacious room in the annexe and a cordial reception. Madame Guillou Jr was charm itself, making sure our needs were met." "Garden a bit run-down, in a pleasant informal way." Attractive courtyard, bar and lounge. Service sometimes erratic: the reception desk is not always manned. And this is not a place for those who want to avoid their fellow-Britons on holiday. (*John and Helen Wright, and others*)

Open 24 Mar–12 Apr, 29 Apr–26 Sept. Restaurant closed Wed 21 Jun–6 Sept.
Rooms 29 – 21 with bath and shower, all with telephone. 8 in annexe. 1 ground-floor room.
Facilities Salon, bar, TV room, 2 dining rooms. Garden.
Location 12 km SW of Pont-Aven. Parking.
Credit cards Access, Visa.
Terms [1989 rates] Rooms: single 158 frs, double 310 frs. Breakfast 22 frs. Dinner, B&B 182–265 frs per person. Set meals 80–200 frs. Reduced rates and special meals for children.

RAMATUELLE 83350 Var — Map 11

Hostellerie Le Baou — *Tel* 94.79.20.48
Avenue Georges Clémenceau — *Telex* 462152

The charming hill-village of Ramatuelle stands close to the best St-Tropez beaches; the noble elm in its main square was planted in 1598, and Gérard Philipe lies buried in its cemetery. Plenty of film stars and other trendy people visit this fabled peninsula, and many of them make for *Le Baou*, a very smart hotel on a hillside, with fine views over woods and vineyards to the sea. It has been revived by new owners, the Sarraquignes, who "treat their guests with care", and whose young chef Claude Taffarello worked with Roger Vergé at Mougins and wins two red *toques* from *Gault Millau*. "The food was exquisite, the flavours fresh and unusual", comments one recent visitor. Most rooms have a balcony, and from these and the dining terrace there are lovely views. Grills are served during the day by the pleasant swimming pool. More reports welcome.

Open 6 Apr–14 Oct.
Rooms 2 suites, 39 double – all with bath and shower, telephone, radio and TV; some with private garden.
Facilities Lift. 2 lounges, 2 bars, 2 restaurants; conference facilities; indoor garden. Garden with terrace, grill, swimming pool, jacuzzi, solarium. Sea 3 km.
Location At entrance of village. Garage and parking.
Restriction Not suitable for ♿.
Credit cards All major cards accepted.
Terms B&B: single occupancy 610–860 frs, double 660–1,190 frs, suite 1,450–1,750 frs. Set lunch/dinner 180, 250 and 380 frs; full alc 380 frs. 360 frs; full alc 350 frs. Reduced rates and special meals for children.

RASTEAU 84110 Vaucluse — Map 11

Hôtel Bellerive — *Tel* 90.46.10.20

An ultra-modern *Relais du Silence* with a bright interior and friendly vibes. It lies amid Côtes-du-Rhône vineyards, in open country beside the river Ouvèze, with fine view of the hills; Orange and Vaison-la-Romaine are both quite near. Recent verdicts: "Superb food and local wine, an excellent swimming pool, and a comfortable room with a balcony and fine view." "Good comfortable rooms and a relaxed atmosphere. The dining room is attractive and the food has been improving. The pool gets crowded on Sundays." (*Endorsed this year by JA*)

Open All year except 2 Jan–18 Mar.
Rooms 20 double – all with bath, telephone and balcony; TV on request; some with kitchenette. Some ground-floor rooms.
Facilities Salon with TV, restaurant. Large garden with swimming pool; river bathing and fishing nearby.
Location Leave A7 motorway at Orange, take N575 towards Vaison, then turn right on D69, then left for hotel. Parking.
Credit cards None accepted.
Terms [1989 rates] Rooms 290–320 frs. Breakfast 35 frs. Dinner, B&B 280–300 frs per person. Set lunch/dinner 105–260 frs. Special meals for children.

RECQUES-SUR-HEM 62890 Pas-de-Calais — Map 9

Château de Cocove — *Tel* 21.82.68.29, *Telex* 810985

Usefully located near the autoroute *south-east of Calais, a grey-fronted 18th-century château in a large park, newly opened as a fairly smart hotel. "Bedrooms light and airy, simply but comfortably furnished." The stone-walled restaurant serves food which some guests (but not all) have called "impeccable". Closed Christmas. 24 rooms, all with private facilities. Rooms 295–550 frs. Breakfast 35 frs. Set meals 99, 150, 190 and 250 frs. New nomination. More reports please.*

REIMS Marne — Map 9

L'Assiette Champenoise

40 avenue Paul Vaillant-Couturier — *Tel* 26.04.15.56
Tinqueux, Reims 51430 — *Fax* 26.04.15.69
Telex 830267

Jean-Pierre and Colette Lallement previously owned a much-laureated restaurant of this same name in a village near Reims: in 1988 they moved to this larger 1920s mansion in the western suburb of Tinqueux – and with them come their *Michelin* rosette and two red *Gault Millau toques*. As they now have bedrooms, they qualify for our Guide, too, and this year's nominators find them worthy of it: "It's an unprepossessing area, but the large park-like grounds mean that you hardly notice. Despite the relative grandeur of the main building and the 'interior designed' look of the public rooms, there's a homely family feel – Madame was working as receptionist, and her young son carried our suitcases. Our room was prettily decorated and furnished, with white wood and pastel finishings.

Breakfast was above average, and dinner was of a high standard, with a strong emphasis on fish. Service was good, with a human touch." (*Kate and Stephan Murray-Sykes*) More reports please.

Open All year.
Rooms 2 suites, 28 double – all with bath and shower, telephone and TV; baby-listening on request. 1 ground-floor room.
Facilities Lounge with TV, bar, restaurant; conference facilities. Garden; terrace.
Location 3 km W of centre of Reims; well signposted. Parking.
Credit cards All major cards accepted.
Terms Rooms 450 frs, suite 950 frs. Breakfast 42 frs. Set lunch/dinner 250–380 frs. Special meals for children.

Boyer "Les Crayères"
64 boulevard Henri-Vasnier
Reims 51100

Tel 26.82.80.80
Fax 26.82.65.52
Telex 830959

Gérard Boyer's awesomely superior little hotel is much patronised by the magnates of the leading Reims champagne houses, who use it to wine, dine and lodge their more important guests and clients. It is thus aiming at the very highest standards, with prices to match, and our readers tend to judge it accordingly. And no-one questions that the *cadre* is supremely elegant, in its own manner. *Les Crayères* is a beautiful cream-coloured château in the south-east suburbs, approached through massive wrought-iron gates, its proportions blending with the mature trees and sweeping lawns of its park; the imposing foyer and staircase are in pale beige marble, and hung with huge tapestries. Readers have enjoyed the airy and "palatial" bedrooms with their huge windows facing the park. Most of them also admire the luxurious cooking, which continues to dazzle the French pundits (three *Michelin* rosettes, and four red *Gault Millau toques*)

Last year one reader criticised his bathroom – "had all the character of an aeroplane first-class section. A beautiful and luxurious hotel, but a little too cool and detached." Another wrote, "There is an unstated sense of aristocracy, but allied to very strong, modern, pragmatic, vulgar touches – *Relais et Châteaux* brochures everywhere. The identity of the hotel gets a bit lost, and you start to think you are in the home of Monsieur Relais and Madame Château, the one concession to tourism being the room temperature raised to Bermudan heights." This year most readers have praised both the bed and the board, though one lamented the absence of a salon in which to mingle with fellow-guests before and after dinner. There is a small dark green bar which gets crowded when the restaurant is busy; some tables can be reserved in advance. Another, commenting on the absence of set menus, tells us that you can order half-portions at half prices and so compose your own *menu gastronomique*. (*Rosamund Hebdon, Stefan and Yvette Wiener, Rosemary Smith and David Lawrence, Elaine Cole-Shear, Kate and Steve Murray-Sykes*)

Open All year except 21 Dec–16 Jan. Restaurant closed Mon, and Tue midday.
Rooms 3 suites, 16 double – 11 with bath (8 also have shower), telephone, radio, TV and baby-listening. 3 in annexe.
Facilities Lift. Hall, bar, restaurant; private dining room. Park with gardens, tennis, helipad.
Location Leave motorway at St-Rémy exit. Travel towards Luxembourg for ½ km, then towards Châlons-sur-Marne on N44. Hotel is 3 km from town centre. Parking.
Credit cards All major cards accepted.

Terms Rooms 980 frs, suite 1,590 frs. Breakfast (served only in bedrooms) 70 frs. Full alc 600–650 frs. Special meals for children.

REPLONGES 01750 Ain — Map 10

La Huchette — *Tel* 85.31.03.55
Telex 800787

A quite sophisticated old *auberge* outside a village east of Mâcon, ornately decorated in warm colours and admired for its friendly welcome, regional cuisine and pretty dining room. It has broad lawns with tall trees and a large swimming pool with mattress loungers. And we are grateful to readers who brought us up-to-date views on it this year, enabling us to restore a full entry: "The rooms and bathrooms are spacious, airy and spotless, the service quietly efficient, the à la carte excellent, the wines good but expensive." "A large bedroom beautifully decorated, overlooking the pool." Some traffic noise during the day. A disabled reader was especially pleased: "Not a single step of even an inch to inhibit my chair." (*Denis O'Mulloy, Mr and Mrs AL Fraser*)

Open All year except 10–22 Jan.
Rooms 1 suite, 11 double, 1 single – all with bath and shower, telephone, TV. Ground-floor rooms.
Facilities 2 lounges, dining room. Garden with swimming pool. Golf 500 metres.
Location 4 km E of Mâcon off N79. On edge of village. Parking.
Credit cards All major cards accepted.
Terms Rooms: single 350 frs, double 450–550 frs, suite 750 frs. Breakfast 50 frs. Set dinner 160 frs; full alc 200 frs. Reduced rates and special meals for children.

RIBEAUVILLÉ 68150 Haut-Rhin — Map 9

Le Clos Saint-Vincent — *Tel* 89.73.67.65
Route de Bergheim

The "delicious" breakfast and fine views have been singled out for praise by *Bettye Chambers* this year for this sophisticated chalet-style restaurant-with-rooms, superbly set among Riesling vineyards, and backed by three ruined castles. Earlier comments: "Expensive, but an idyllic place to stay, with management and staff constantly attentive." "Wonderful rooms, superb meals, though the wines are very dear and the menus stay unchanged too long." The hotel's interior is spacious and elegant, with decor in soft muted golds and browns. "Our room was large and airy, with french windows opening on to a small terrace and attractive gardens, with views of the gently rolling countryside and the lights of Colmar in the distance."

Open 15 Mar–15 Nov. Restaurant closed Tue/Wed.
Rooms 3 suites, 8 double – all with bath and shower, telephone and TV; many with terrace or balcony. Ground-floor suites.
Facilities Lift. Salon, bar, restaurant. Garden.
Location In NE outskirts of town, which is 15 km N of Colmar. Parking.
Credit cards Access, Visa.
Terms [1989 rates] B&B: single 520–612 frs, double 570–865 frs, suite 840–988 frs. Set lunch/dinner 200–250 frs; full alc 250 frs. Reduced rates and special meals for children.

RIGNY 70100 Haute-Saône Map 10

Château de Rigny

Tel 84.65.25.01
Telex 362926

"Outstanding – like staying in some well-kept Scottish castle with old-style furniture and exotic bedrooms. Remembered six months later for the very good food, the tranquillity and lovely gardens." (*Brian MacArthur*) That 1989 encomium from a Scot is endorsed by *Gault Millau's toque*, and by *Michelin*'s three red gables, for the attractive charm of this select 13th-century château rebuilt in its present form under Louis XIII. Recently renovated, it is set quietly in its own grounds bordering the Saône and has a 12-acre *jardin anglais* and a large baronial salon. Another comment, "Rooms vary in size but all are well furnished (ground-floor ones in the annexe look the best). Jacques and Brigitte Maupin are excellent hosts."

Open All year except 2–31 Jan and Christmas.
Rooms 24 double – all with bath and shower, telephone and TV. 11 in annexe. 4 ground-floor rooms.
Facilities Salon, bar, dining room; conference/function facilities. 12-acre park with tennis court and swimming pool, pond for fishing, access to Saône river.
Location 4 km NE of Gray on Rigny road; Gray is 45 km NE of Dijon. Parking.
Credit cards All major cards accepted.
Terms Rooms: single occupancy 280 frs, double 350–480 frs, suite 600 frs. Breakfast 40 frs. Set meals 180–280 frs.

LA ROCHE-BERNARD 56130 Morbihan Map 8

Auberge des Deux Magots

Tel 99.90.60.75

In a village just off the Nantes–Vannes highway, a charming and very soignée little family-run auberge, *with clean, neat bedrooms, and a pretty panelled dining room where good local dishes (notably fish) are served at moderate prices. Closed Sun evening and Mon out of season. 14 rooms, 9 with shower. B&B double 270–310 frs. Set menus 80–320 frs. New nomination. More reports welcome.*

ROCHEGUDE 26790 Drôme Map 11

Château de Rochegude

Tel 75.04.81.88
Telex 345661 ROCHGUD

A gracefully restored stone château, dating in part from the 12th century, set in its own park on a rocky bluff above the vineyards of the Rhône plain north of Orange. It is now a smart and very expensive hotel, again much liked this year, "Friendly staff, faultless cuisine, lovely grounds for strolling, a spacious room with four-poster and sympathetic lighting – but in September the pool was unheated." Earlier views: "Our room, furnished with antiques, overlooked the vast plain. A large pool at which one could have a light but lingering lunch. Breakfast served out in a small courtyard was delicious. Madame was even weeding the garden while we were having it"; "Service impeccable, like being in a private house. They make their own wine and olive oil, and food was the best I've had in France." (*Michelin* rosette and *Gault Millau toque*). (*Caroline and Gary Smith*)

Open 1 Mar–2 Jan. Restaurant closed Tue and Wed midday.
Rooms 4 suites, 23 double, 2 single – all with bath and shower, and telephone; 25 with TV. Some ground-floor rooms.
Facilities Lift, ramps. Salon, TV lounge, bar, restaurant; conference facilities. Large grounds with heated swimming pool and tennis court.
Location 14 km N of Orange. From N leave A7 motorway at Bollène and go towards Carpentras. From S leave at Orange and go towards Gap on N7.
Credit cards All major cards accepted.
Terms [1989 rates] B&B: single 460 frs, double 600–1,380 frs, suite 1,700–2,000 frs. Dinner, B&B: single 760 frs, double 1,200–1,980 frs, suite 2,300–2,600 frs. Set lunch 170 frs, dinner 300 frs.

LA ROCHE-L'ABEILLE 87800 Haute-Vienne — Map 10

Moulin de la Gorce — *Tel* 55.00.70.66
La Roche-l'Abeille, St-Yrieix-la-Perche

"Ah, this is a lovely place. A sweet small lake with ducks in it, kind and skilful staff, delectable food (especially the desserts), delightful French people dining out and mercifully few English." That's one among many recent plaudits for Jean Bertranet's enchanting millhouse in a hamlet in pleasant hilly Limousin country between the two porcelain centres of Limoges (large and ugly) and St-Yrieix-la-Perche (small and lovely). The *Moulin*, also small and lovely, is the kind of place that warmly appeals to lovers of French rural simplicity plus high gastronomic complexity (two *Michelin* rosettes and two red *Gault Millau toques*). Very quiet and off the beaten track, it consists of two old buildings; six of the nine bedrooms are in the old mill, beside a small lake with waterfall. The bedrooms have antiques; in one is a fine four-poster bed.

"An enchanting setting, especially if you can watch the sun rise over the lake. Our small room was comfortable and the bathroom luxurious. Breakfast was expensive but wonderful – home-made jam, croissants and rolls straight from the kitchen. Food magnificent." "Dinner was delicious, service impressive. Expensive, but value for money." But you will need a degree in engineering to master the modern high-tech system of mixer taps in the bathrooms. (*Endorsed this year by ME Ricca and BH Jenkinson*)

Open All year except Feb. Closed Sun night and Mon Oct–Apr.
Rooms 9 double – all with bath and shower, telephone and TV. 6 in annexe. 2 ground-floor rooms
Facilities Salon, dining room. Garden with stream; fishing.
Location 12 km NE of St-Yrieix, off the D704. 2 km S of La Roche off D17. Parking.
Restriction Not suitable for ♿.
Credit cards All major cards accepted.
Terms B&B: single 325 frs, double 510 frs; dinner, B&B: single 800 frs, double 1,200 frs. Set lunch/dinner 250 and 320 frs; full alc 355 frs. Special meals for children.

LA ROCHELLE 17000 Charente-Maritime — Map 10

Hôtel les Brises — *Tel* 46.43.89.37
Chemin Digue Richelieu — *Telex* 790821

An efficient and stylish modern hotel, upper-medium price, in a prime position right by the sea, just outside the harbour: it overlooks the islands and estuary, and is a ten-minute walk from the heart of La Rochelle, one of the loveliest old towns in France ("a kind of maritime Bruges", an inspector has called it). "Comfort and quiet; polite and very helpful staff; best breakfast I've had in France for years." So runs one 1989 report. Other recent ones: "Stunning views over the bay, friendly people, firm bed"; "a vast terrace on which one can sun oneself over a drink, and two luxurious lounges." It is essential to ask for a room with a sea view. A reader this year warns that a nearby foghorn and revolving foglight make sleep difficult on foggy nights. No restaurant: you can eat very well, but expensively, at *Richard Coutanceau*, and there are goodish cheaper places along the quayside. (*Elizabeth Nines, Victoria P Turner, AF Thomas, and others*)

Open All year.
Rooms 46 – all with bath and/or shower, telephone, TV and baby-listening.
Facilities Lift. TV lounge, reading room, bar; terrace with direct access to sea and rocky beach.
Location On sea front 1½ km from town centre. Underground garage and carpark.
Restriction Not suitable for ♿.
Credit cards Access, Visa.
Terms [1989 rates] Rooms 340–480 frs. Breakfast 35 frs. Reductions for children. (No restaurant.)

---

33 rue Thiers — *Tel* 46.41.62.23
33 rue Thiers — *Fax* 46.41.64.87
Telex 790821

This remarkable "find" in 1989 is an 18th-century town house in the heart of a lovely old city: "Maybelle Iribe and her *33 rue Thiers* are WONDERFUL. She is welcoming, eternally helpful (she even lent us her and her son's bikes). And she has created a sensational bed-and-breakfast out of this old mansion: six huge guest rooms all with wonderful bathrooms, all decorated differently. Ours, overlooking the tiny interior garden, was decorated with Maybelle's collection of Mexican folk art. The rooms are furnished with pieces from the local auction house. Everywhere you look there is style, character, whimsy and love. Breakfast included delicious scrambled eggs with hot herbs (Maybelle has written several cookbooks)." Cocktails and canapés are served in the garden or the library, and picnic baskets are on offer in summer." (*Lynne and David Allen*) More reports eagerly awaited.

Open All year except 15 Jan–15 Mar.
Rooms 6 double – all with bath and/or shower, 2 with radio.
Facilities Lounge, TV room. Courtyard garden.
Location Central. Parking.
Credit cards None accepted.
Terms B&B: single 300–380 frs, double 380–400 frs, suite 400–450 frs. Dinner, B&B 100 frs added per person. Picnic lunch 60 frs.

LES ROCHES-DE-CONDRIEU 38370 Isère — Map 10

Hôtel Bellevue — *Tel* 74.56.41.42

More approval this year for the good food and "excellent" wines at this pleasant modern creeper-covered hotel, set in a village beside the majestically curving Rhône, south of Lyon; vine-clad hills rise behind.

The restaurant, with its picture windows facing the river, is very popular locally. Bedrooms are modestly comfortable, some on the small side: try to get the one with a big balcony. (*L Sinker, Grania Little*)

Open All year except 1–12 Aug and 6–28 Feb. Closed Mon, Tue midday and Sun evening.
Rooms 18 – 9 with bath, 9 with shower, all with telephone. 3 in annexe. 1 ground-floor room.
Facilities Salon, restaurant; conference facilities.
Location 12 km SW of Vienne.
Credit cards Access, Diners, Visa.
Terms Rooms 180–250 frs. Breakfast 25 frs. Set meals 100–250 frs; full alc 230 frs.

ROLLEBOISE 78270 Yvelines — Map 9

Château de la Corniche — *Tel* 30.93.21.24
5 route de la Corniche — *Telex* 695544 CHAROL

Rolleboise is a village on the Seine between Paris and Rouen, some 12 kilometres from the splendid Monet museum and garden at Giverny. The *Château de la Corniche*, built by Leopold II of Belgium, stands splendidly in its large gardens above a bend in the river (front bedrooms have fine views of countryside and river). Each bedroom is different, and the restaurant, which shares the view, is done in pretty pink napery with bouquets of flowers on each table. The food includes artfully arranged salads and superlative desserts" (*Gault Millau* awards a red *toque* for these and for such dishes as fricassée of winkles). One recent visitor has commended the swimming pool. More reports please.

Open All year except Christmas week. Closed Sun evening and Mon in low season.
Rooms 1 suite, 37 double – all with bath and/or shower, telephone, TV and mini-bar. 17 in 2 separate buildings in grounds.
Facilities Lift. Salons, bar, TV room, 2 restaurants; conference facilities; terrace. 5-acre grounds with swimming pool and tennis court.
Location Just W of Rolleboise, overlooking the Seine. Leave A13 to Rouen at Bonnières exit.
Restriction Not suitable for ♿.
Credit cards All major cards accepted.
Terms [1989 rates] Rooms 260–600 frs, suite 1,200 frs. Set lunch/dinner 200 and 350 frs; full alc 400–500 frs.

ROMANÈCHE-THORINS 71570 Saône-et Loire — Map 10

Les Maritonnes — *Tel* 85.35.51.70
Telex 351060

A fairly sophisticated little hotel at the foot of the vine-clad slopes of the Beaujolais, between Fleurie and the N6 highway. Visitors this year and last have again much enjoyed the parasols and lilos around the swimming pool in its flowery garden, and the Burgundian cuisine in the *Michelin*-rosetted restaurant (e.g. crayfish soufflé and escalope of salmon cooked in Fleurie) as well as the fine local wines. "Delicious food, Guy Fauvin a splendid owner-chef"; "beautifully furnished rooms and a warm welcome from Madame Fauvin". Some rooms are on the small side, and light sleepers may be upset by the nearby railway. (*M and L Piper*)

Open All year except mid-Dec–end Jan, Sun evenings, Mon 15 Oct–15 Apr. Restaurant closed Mon, and Tues midday 16 Apr–14 Oct.
Rooms 20 double – 18 with bath, 2 with shower, all with telephone and TV.
Facilities Lounge, bar, restaurant. Garden with heated swimming pool.
Location Near station. Parking.
Restriction Not suitable for ♿.
Credit cards All major cards accepted.
Terms B&B: single 380–400 frs, double 450–520 frs. Set lunch/dinner 180, 230 and 320 frs.

LES ROSIERS 49350 Maine-et-Loire — Map 10

Auberge Jeanne de Laval — *Tel* 41.51.80.17
Route Nationale

"Dining room very plush. Food excellent, especially the rillettes and delicious local fish" – a recent report on this much reputed restaurant-with-rooms where *patron*-chef Michel Augereau specialises in local beurre blanc fish dishes and wins a *Michelin* rosette and two *Gault Millau toques.* It is a handsome creeper-covered house in a pretty garden, all very *soigné* inside, both the public rooms and bedrooms; simpler, more rustic bedrooms (and at least one uncomfortable bed) are in a nearby annexe, the *Ducs d'Anjou,* a converted manor. "We stayed very pleasantly in the annexe, a short car ride from the hotel: it is a pretty house in a big walled garden, and the rooms were attractively decorated. Breakfast, with good home-made jam, was taken by an open window facing the garden." More reports please.

Open All year except 8 Jan–17 Feb. Closed Mon except public holidays.
Rooms 12 double – some with bath or shower, all with telephone. 8 in annexe, *Ducs d'Anjou,* nearby.
Facilities Restaurant; functions facilities. Garden. Tennis, swimming, riding, golf nearby.
Location 15 km NW of Saumur, on banks of the Loire.
Credit cards All major cards accepted.
Terms [1989 rates] Rooms 330–500 frs. Breakfast 44 frs. Dinner, B&B 450–520 frs per person. Set meals 260–320 frs. Special meals for children.

ROUEN 76000 Seine-Maritime — Map 9

Hôtel de la Cathédrale — *Tel* 35.71.57.95
12 rue St-Romain

A slightly shabby but efficient and friendly hotel of some character, centrally situated on a pedestrian walkway near the cathedral. A reader this year found her room warm and clean, if a bit run down, and thought the building charming. An earlier view, "From the moment you go through the heavy wooden doorway and into the courtyard with its geranium pots, busy lizzies and bits of statuary, you feel the delicious Frenchness of it all. Our room with flowered wallpaper overlooked the courtyard with a view of the cathedral spire; comfortable beds and very quiet at night. Good coffee for breakfast but no croissants. No restaurant, but we had a good fairly priced meal at the popular *Petite Auberge* nearby." (*Georgene Smith, PF*)

Open All year.
Rooms 24 double – 8 with bath, 5 with shower, all with telephone.
Facilities Entrance hall, salon. Courtyard.
Location Central. Public carpark nearby.
Credit cards Access, Visa.
Terms B&B: single 160–254 frs, double 226–318 frs. (No restaurant.)

RUFFIEUX 73310 Savoie — Map 10

Château de Collonges — *Tel* 79.54.27.38

A château hotel an easy drive from Annecy and Aix-les-Bains is warmly nominated: "It glows in the memory, not only for outstanding food but also for heart-warming views across the valley to the mountains beyond. Our stay was memorable for several reasons: the château itself, with circular stone staircase, sumptuously furnished with antiques, spotlessly clean and with great atmosphere. Small but ample swimming pool overlooking the valley below a beautiful garden where chickens strut (and serve as an alarm call in the morning), and where the owner relaxed. He was anxious for silence from the children, and insistent that we should eat on the dot of 7.30, only – as we discovered – so that we could admire the magnificent sunset over the mountains from the terrace where meals are served in summer. In cool weather dinner is served in the comfortably furnished dining room in the cellars." "Virtually perfect. Cool stone interior, atmosphere of calm and charm. Large and beautiful bedroom with comfortable beds; large bathroom. Beds turned down at night. Breakfast with real orange juice and *two* pots of coffee. Food excellent, service impossible to fault. Expensive, but worth every penny." (*Brian MacArthur, Anthony Hinds*)

Open All year except Jan and Feb. Closed Mon in low season; restaurant closed Tue midday.
Rooms 9 – all with bath and shower, telephone and TV.
Facilities Salon, dining room, terrace. Park with swimming pool. Golf, water sports, winter sports nearby.
Location 21 km N of Aix-les-Bains.
Restriction Not suitable for ♿.
Credit cards All major cards accepted.
Terms [1989 rates] Rooms 470–570 frs. Breakfast 45 frs. Set meals 175–400 frs. Half board 450–510 frs per person. Special meals for children.

SABRES 40630 Landes — Map 10

Auberge des Pins — *Tel* 58.07.50.47
Route de la Piscine

This attractive half-timbered chalet, built in local style with a low sloping roof, is in a village in the heart of the vast Landes pine-forests. In the hands of the Lesclauze family it has won first prize for the best flower-decked hotel in Aquitaine. Visitors this year found it friendly and good value, "One end of the ground floor is a plastic-tabled local villagers' bar, the other is a lovely restaurant with good local food. Specialities include woodpigeon cassoulet, and all parts of a duck's anatomy – livers, hearts, whole, etc." Plenty for children – sandpit, swings, ping-pong – and a mini-rail takes you to the local outdoor ecology museum. (*Elizabeth Jones*)

Open All year except 15–30 Nov and 2–15 Jan. Closed Mon in low season.
Rooms 14 double – 4 with bath, 8 with shower, all with telephone; 6 with TV. 4 in annexe.
Facilities Lounge with TV, restaurant; conference facilities. Garden.
Location 35 km NW of Mont-de-Marsan.
Credit card Visa.
Terms Rooms 100–240 frs. Set lunch/dinner 70, 130 and 220 frs; full alc 150 frs. Special meals for children.

SAILLAGOUSE 66800 Pyrénées-Orientales — Map 10

Auberge Atalaya — *Tel* 68.04.70.04
Llo

The Cerdagne, an hour's drive from Andorra and two from Perpignan, is one of the most appealing corners of France – an upland plain of meadows and pine forests, backed by the snowy Pyrenees. It is surprisingly lush and pastoral for such an altitude (1,066 metres) and has France's highest sunshine level. There's much of interest – the fortress of Mont-Louis, the big ski-resort of Font-Romeu, and the strange black Romanesque Madonna at l'Hermitage.

"A charming little *auberge* in a delightful setting, with enjoyable food and tastefully decorated rooms." So runs a recent report on the *Atalaya,* a converted farmhouse in the hamlet of Llo, just outside the resort of Saillagouse, run by Hubert Toussaint, London born and bred. The menu might feature such dishes as fillet of rascasse with fennel. "Very attractive – a stone building with dark wood but light and spacious bedrooms. Ours had a balcony. The Toussaints have a civilised attitude to their guests. A quiet and relaxing place to stay – out of season at least." Just one adverse report, however, last year. More reports welcome.

Open 20 Dec–5 Nov. Restaurant closed Mon, Tue midday in low season.
Rooms 1 suite, 9 double – 7 with bath and shower, 3 with shower, all with telephone, radio, TV and mini-bar.
Facilities Lounge, bar, restaurant. Garden.
Location In Llo, on D33 2 km E of Saillagouse, which is 91 km W of Perpignan.
Restriction Not suitable for ♿.
Credit cards Access, Visa.
Terms Double rooms 390–498 frs. Dinner, B&B 720–830 frs; full board 980–1,090 frs. Breakfast 39 frs. Set lunch 130 frs; full alc 250 frs. Reduced rates and special meals for children.

ST-CHARTIER 36400 Indre — Map 10

Château de la Vallée Bleue — *Tel* 54.31.01.91
Route de Verneuil

Here you are in the heart of the George Sand country. St-Chartier with its high-walled romantic castle is where she set *Les Mâitres sonneurs* and the wedding in *La Mare au Diable,* and just to the south is her family château at Nohant where she lies buried under a yew tree. Her dining-room table is set with place-names for Flaubert, Turgenev, Liszt, etc (people she entertained here). So it is appropriate that the bedrooms in the nearby *Château de la Vallée Bleue* should be likewise named – "Our room was called Flaubert", says our 1989 nominator who "really loved" this family-run *Logis de France*: "Set quietly in a large park, it's a fine 18th-century house, full of light and sunshine, run by the charming Gasquets. Our bedroom had style – two antique chairs, blissfully comfy beds, pale-green watered silk bedheads, marvellous reading lights. Charming lounge where a log fire was lit. Lots of polished wood – obviously first-rate housekeeping. Lots of lovely flowers. The cooking is tilted towards the *nouvelle*, but not over the top – delicious lapin en sauce courte à l'estragon. The house was busy with French guests, including business executives who always know the best places." (*Eileen Broadbent*) More reports welcome.

Open All year except Feb. Closed Sun evening and Mon Oct–mid-Apr.
Rooms 1 suite, 12 double, 1 single – 5 with bath, 8 with shower, all with telephone, radio and TV. 3 ground-floor rooms. 3 rooms in rustic-style annexe.
Facilities Ramps. Lounge, 2 dining rooms; terrace. 10-acre grounds with children's playground.
Location 9 km N of La Châtre on D918, then D69. Parking.
Credit cards Access, Amex, Visa.
Terms B&B: single 215 frs, double 340–475 frs, suite 540 frs. Dinner, B&B 260–370 frs per person. Set lunch/dinner 110, 175 and 265 frs; full alc 250 frs. Reduced rates and special meals for children.

ST-CIRQ-LAPOPIE 46330 Lot — Map 10

Hôtel de la Pélissaria — *Tel* 65.31.25.14

If we held a readers' referendum on their favourite small country hotel in France, this might well win. It is in a famous *village perché*, set dramatically on a cliff high above the river Lot. One of the old houses is now this tiny hotel, lovingly restored by its delightful owners, the Matuchet family; and yet again this year it has evoked rapturous praise from numerous readers – "a perfect place", "all is excellent", "paradise indeed", "this most lovely hotel in idyllic surroundings", and so on. It is on such a steep slope that the entrance is at the top and bedrooms are on the floor below. These, cool and spacious, have tiled floors, white walls, old beams, pine doors, rough-woven white curtains and bedspreads, and they look out onto the old church, the apple orchards and the river Lot beyond. M. Matuchet, "a man of infinite charm", is a musician and singer and will sometimes play the tapes he has made of his own setting of the poems of Ronsard or de Nerval. This music is not obtrusive, and is typical of the hotel's elegance. "The village is spectacular", says one visitor this year, "and the views from the rooms magical. The dining room with its beamed ceiling is intimate and relaxing, like a private dining room. And Madame Matuchet's food is quite, quite delicious." "The Matuchets excelled themselves in making us feel totally at home; rooms very clean and comfortable, with personal touches such as fresh flowers. The cooking was easily the best we have tasted in France" (trout soufflé and brochette of beef in pepper sauce have been singled out). (*Dr Anthony Winterbourne, Mr and Mrs J Alan Thornton, Caroline Currie, Sheila Newman, GE Samson, Eileen Broadbent, and others*) One audacious dissenter writes of unremarkable food and poor value for money.

Open 1 May–15 Nov. Restaurant closed midday.
Rooms 1 suite, 5 double, 2 single – 4 with bath, 4 with shower, all with telephone. Suite, 1 double, with private terrace, in garden.
Facilities Salon, dining room. Music and poetry evenings. Garden.

Location Central. Parking at some distance from hotel. Village 30 km E of Cahors.
Restriction Not suitable for ♿.
Credit cards Access, Visa.
Terms Rooms: single 220 frs, double 290 frs, suite 350 frs. Breakfast 30 frs. Set dinner 120 frs. Special meals for children.

ST-DYÉ-SUR-LOIRE 41500 Loir-et-Cher — Map 10

Manoir Bel Air — *Tel* 54.81.60.10

A low creeper-covered manor house now an unpretentious country hotel, set by the banks of the broad Loire near Blois and Chambord. It is not smart, and one reader this year thought it "scruffy", but others continue to enjoy it for its large, comfortable rooms and good regional cooking. "We had the grandest bedroom, big enough to play cricket in, with a beautiful bathroom and five huge windows. A house martin flew in and out of them. Lovely view of river. Food excellent, served in a beautiful big dining room with pink cloths and lovely plates. Good local wines." "The honest bourgeois food, lots of it, was fabulous value. Served in a delightful dining room, packed with locals at lunchtime, and with wonderful views over the river." Some have found the reception friendly, others less so. Poor housekeeping has also been reported. Charming exterior stone staircase. (*Victoria P Turner, Josephine Barratt, David V Lees, and others*) At certain times of year there are swarms of midges on the river banks making after-dinner strolls uncomfortable.

Open All year except 15 Jan–20 Feb.
Rooms 2 suites, 38 double – all with bath, telephone and TV.
Facilities Salon with bar, TV room, restaurant; conference facilities. Garden.
Location 200 metres from village which is 4 km W of Chambord.
Credit cards Access, Visa.
Terms [1989 rates] Rooms 200–320 frs. Breakfast 25 frs. Half board 280–300 frs per person. Set lunch/dinner 90–180 frs. Reduced rates and special meals for children.

ST-EMILION 33330 Gironde — Map 10

Hostellerie Plaisance — *Tel* 57.24.72.32
Place du Clocher

A former monastery has been converted into a graceful and "delightful" little hostelry, well befitting medieval St-Emilion and its famous wines. The site is most curious, atop a sandstone cliff that contains a troglodytic church dating from the 9th century and a mass of other caves. "The hotel's terrace", says a recent visitor, "juts out to the edge of the cliff, providing a superb view over the town, the castle and the vineyards. The food, and of course the cellar, have been famous in the district for many years, but the new management have recently modernised the bedrooms which are now first-rate." *Gault Millau toque* for such dishes as magret à la vapeur, served in an elegant setting. Very crowded during wine festivals. (*Endorsed this year by Paul A Hoffstein*)

Open All year except 2–31 Jan.
Rooms 11 – all with bath and shower, and telephone.
Facilities Salon, bar, restaurant; conference facilities. Garden.
Location Central, near Syndicat d'Initiative. Open parking.

Restriction Not suitable for ♿.
Credit cards All major cards accepted.
Terms [1989 rates] Rooms 400–600 frs. Breakfast 40 frs. Set lunch 100 frs, dinner 215 frs. No charge for children under 12 sharing parents' room; special meals.

Le Logis des Remparts *Tel* 57.24.70.43
Rue Guadet

An old building in the village, newly renovated and prettily decorated, backing onto vineyards. Garden, private parking. No restaurant, but the nearby Francis Goullée *is admired. Closed 21 Dec–7 Jan. 15 rooms, all with bath and/or shower. B&B double 316–456 frs. New nomination. More reports please.*

ST-ETIENNE-DE-BAIGORRY 64430 Pyrénées-Atlantiques Map 10

Hôtel Arcé *Tel* 59.37.40.14

Only five miles from the Spanish border, this charming and typical Basque village up in the hinterland has a Roman bridge and a fine old church – as well, of course, as a *fronton* for *pelote* and an old smuggling tradition, now on the wane. The riverside *Arcé*, backed by green hills, has been in the hands of the same family for five generations and its fine traditions are by no means waning, as a recent visitor reports, "Its restaurant, *Le Trinquet*, has had a rosette in *Michelin* for over 25 years (pipérade is a speciality). It is a modest hotel of quiet charm: vulgarisation has passed it by, though modern comforts are not lacking. Set beside the fast-flowing river Nive, its firm-bedded rooms have small terraces from which the beauty of the valley can be savoured. The hotel is a bookman's delight, with a multilingual library. There is a heated swimming pool, across the river, and an air of unassuming professionalism at every level." Another visitor appreciated the setting, the pool and the food, but found the reception cool and the service inexperienced.

Open Mid-Mar–mid-Nov.
Rooms 5 suites, 19 double, 1 single – all with bath and/or shower, telephone; TV on request. 3 in annexe by river. 1 ground-floor room.
Facilities Lounge, library, billiard room, 2 restaurants. Gardens and terrace; outdoor swimming pool. River fishing.
Location 11 km W of St-Jean-Pied-de-Port; hotel is near church. Garage and parking.
Credit cards Access, Visa.
Terms [1989 rates] Rooms 300–800 frs. Breakfast 37 frs. Dinner, B&B 270–600 frs per person (3 nights min.). Set meals 90–220 frs; full alc 300 frs. Reduced rates and special meals for children.

Traveller's tale *Someone somewhere – Brussels no doubt – has created the Euro breakfast. Slices of prepackaged shiny ham, slices of processed cheese, salami, bread rolls that the armies of Garibaldi could have used as ammunition, all await your pleasure. Reconstituted orange juice or orange drink and hot coffee-flavoured liquid complete the feast. Blindfolded you could be marched in, and apart from the napkins (paper of course) you could be anywhere.*

ST-FÉLIX-LAURAGAIS 31540 Haute-Garonne Map 10

Auberge du Poids Public *Tel* 61.83.00.20
Telex 532477

An attractive village of timbered houses, perched on a hill in the rolling countryside east of Toulouse. The view from it is magnificent, taking in the snowy Pyrenees to the south and the darker Dordogne hills to the north. The *Poids Public,* admired as ever in 1988/9 ("everything perfect – room, welcome, cuisine"), is a low building much extended from the original village inn where produce was weighed (hence its name) before the proceeds were split between landlord and tenant. "The joy of this place is its complete lack of pretentiousness. Restaurant excellent, even on New Year's night." "Our rooms though small were tastefully furnished, the bathrooms pleasant. We dined on the terrace overlooking the lovely countryside with the smell of lavender in the air." "Interesting pictures everywhere. *Patron*-chef Bernard Augé is a bit of a showman, but produces wonderful food based on local produce (red *Michelin* 'R' and *Gault Millau* laurels for regional cuisine) – our five-course 95-franc [1989] menu included brochet mousseline with walnut sauce and his grand-mère's way of dealing with pig's trotters (interesting!). We sat at our window table watching the setting sun light up houses in Puylaurens 20 kilometres away. The fresh flowers on the table were all wild." "M. Augé is fun in a larger-than-life way and his wife is a poppet." One visitor thought his room "charming but ultra-twee". (*Curtis and Sally Wilmot-Allistone, Mrs VA Preston*)

Open All year except 6 Jan–10 Feb. Closed Sun evening 15 Oct–15 Mar.
Rooms 13 double – all with bath and shower, and telephone.
Facilities Bar, TV lounge, restaurant; terrace. Garden.
Location On N622 43 km E of Toulouse. Back rooms quietest.
Restriction Not suitable for ♿.
Credit cards Access, Amex, Visa.
Terms Rooms 225–260 frs. Breakfast 35 frs. Dinner, B&B 230–265 frs per person, full board 280–315 frs. Set lunch/dinner 95-170 frs; full alc 180–200 frs. Reduced rates for children sharing parents' room; special meals on request.

ST-FLORENTIN 89600 Yonne Map 9

Les Tilleuls *Tel* 86.35.09.09
3 rue Descourtive

A pleasant Logis de France, *making a useful, inexpensive alternative in this small Burgundy town. Warm welcome, charming service, excellent value on the cheaper menus* (Michelin *red "R"). Near centre but not noisy. Small garden. 10 rooms, all with bath or shower. B&B: single 207–242 frs, double 254–319 frs. Set menus 70–220 frs. New nomination. More reports welcome.*

> We don't lack *Michelin*-rosetted hotels in France but would be glad of more nominations at the more modest end of the price scale.

> The length of an entry does not necessarily reflect the merit of a hotel. The more interesting the report or the more unusual or controversial the hotel, the longer the entry.

ST-GERMAIN-EN-LAYE 78100 Yvelines — Map 9

Cazaudehore et La Forestière — *Tel* 34.51.93.80 and 39.73.36.60
1 avenue du Président Kennedy — *Fax* 39.73.73.88
Telex 696055

Within 20 kilometres of Paris, in the heart of the forest of St-Germain, the Cazaudehore family run a fashionable restaurant that bears their name, and next door, in a wooded garden, a stylish little hotel that a reader this year thought "wonderful". It has tasteful modern rooms and suites, elegantly decorated with antiques and prints. Tiled bathrooms, friendly service, and a pleasant outlook on to the oak and beech forest. The restaurant has fresh flowers, gleaming silverware, an interesting menu, and draws a sophisticated clientele – especially at weekends when you need to book, even if you have a room reserved. (*DJ Harden*) *Michelin* is lavish with its red print for style and beauty, but has this year withdrawn its rosette for cuisine. We'd be glad of more reports.

Open All year. Restaurant closed Mon (light meals available for hotel guests).
Rooms 6 suites, 24 double – all with bath and shower, telephone, radio, TV and mini-bar.
Facilities Lift. 2 salons, restaurant; conference facilities. Garden.
Location 1.5 km NW of St-Germain, by N 284 and route des Mares.
Restriction Not suitable for ♿.
Credit cards Access, Visa.
Terms Rooms: single 560 frs, double 650 frs, suite 820 frs. Breakfast 45 frs. Full alc 300–350 frs. Reduced rates for children sharing parents' room; special menu.

ST-GIRONS 09200 Ariège — Map 10

Hôtel Eychenne — *Tel* 61.66.20.55
8 avenue Paul-Laffont — *Telex* 521273

Down a side street in a small town in the Pyrenean foothills south of Toulouse, a very spruce and attractive hostelry, white-walled, blue-shuttered, creeper-festooned, owned and run by the Bordeau family for six generations. Readers this year have again extolled the warm, friendly ambience, solicitous proprietor and excellent regional cooking (*Michelin* rosette, *Gault Millau toque*), nicely served in a large red-walled dining room well patronised by locals. "Fish first class, good local wines, and a pleasant room with balcony overlooking courtyard and garden." Rooms by the courtyard are quieter than those on the street. (*Peter Stattersfield, TH Nash*)

Open All year except 22 Dec–31 Jan.
Rooms 2 suites, 42 double, 4 single – 22 with bath, 20 with shower, all with telephone and TV; some with balcony.
Facilities Lounge, TV room, 2 bars; conference facilities. Garden with heated swimming pool.
Location Central; parking. St-Girons is 99 km S of Toulouse.
Restriction Not suitable for ♿.
Credit cards All major cards accepted.
Terms B&B: single: 273 frs, double 451 frs, suite 461 frs. Dinner, B&B: single 381–473 frs, double 573–662 frs. Set lunch/dinner 103, 160 and 260 frs; full alc 240 frs. Children sharing parents' room free; special meals on request.

ST-JEAN-DU-BRUEL 12230 Aveyron — Map 10

Hôtel du Midi — *Tel* 65.62.26.04

The Papillon family's unpretentious *Logis de France*, in the western Cévennes, vies with the *Pélissaria* at St-Cirq (q.v.) as our most popular rural entry for central France. It is in an old village on the river Dourbie between Millau and Le Vigan, a good centre for walking holidays or for visiting the Gorges du Tarn. Tributes this year: "The Papillons' charm, and the remarkable value they offer, make this the best French hotel of its kind that we know. How do they do it at the price (red 'R' in *Michelin*)? Part of the answer lies in M Papillon's skill with unusual ingredients – tripe, gizzards and sheep's feet, for example: his feuilletée aux gésiers is delicious. The combination of scenery and hotel is irresistible." Service is swift and personal. The no-choice but varied menu for residents is far better than what guests *en pension* normally get given in France – excellent soup ad lib, home-made charcuterie, main courses that may include quail, civet de chevreuil, cassoulet, confit de canard aux lentilles. "Rooms are simple, but food is marvellous, and the whole place is warmed by the Papillon family: Madame never ceases to be utterly kind." "Madame was an elegant bundle of energy." "Our plain but adequate room was in an adjacent building with a fine stone turret stair." Some rooms are modern and pretty; some are a bit cramped and less comfortable. British and German guests are much in evidence. "This is splendid walking country, best in spring when regulars come for the display of wild flowers covering the *causses*. In the evenings, the polyglot conversation between dinner tables is full of botanical Latin." (*JP Berryman, Jack B Ainslie, Jean Seymour, AG Catchpole, BW Ribbons, and others*) Floreat Papillonia.

Open 7 Apr–11 Nov.
Rooms 17 double, 2 single – 15 with bath and/or shower, all with telephone. 2 pairs of communicating rooms in nearby annexe.
Facilities Salon, TV room, bar, restaurant; terrace. On banks of river Dourbie; bathing, fishing.
Location 40 km SE of Millau on D991; 20 km E of N9. Garage and open parking.
Restriction Only restaurant suitable for ♿.
Credit cards Access, Visa.
Terms B&B: single 87 frs, double 122–208 frs; half board: single 163–173 frs, double 274–380 frs; full board: single 191–201 frs, double 330–436 frs. Set lunch/dinner 63–168 frs; full alc 135 frs. Reduced rates for children under 6; special meals.

ST-JEAN-DU-DOIGT 29228 Finistère — Map 8

Le Ty-Pont — *Tel* 98.67.34.06
Plougasnou

A down-to-earth seaside hotel in northern Brittany, offering remarkable value. Readers this year hugely enjoyed the five-course *en pension* meals, especially lunch (the main meal of the day) and the local fish. They had a comfortable room, and loved the "stunningly beautiful" coastline. A family of regular devotees have written lyrically: "The food was staggering: honest cooking and the freshest possible ingredients. Lunch might start with crab-claws and slices of melon, then a fish in a delicate sauce, then a meat course (perhaps guinea-fowl), then cheese, fromage blanc or yoghurt, then ice-cream (home-made) or a good selection of fresh fruit or crème caramel. The scene in the dining room was astonishing – working-class French families, a baby drinking potage out of its bottle, a two-year-old having fromage blanc spooned into it. It was very noisy, but the young waitresses were never flustered. Bedrooms were adequate. There is a garden by a stream, where you can sit in the sun and recover from *la bouffe*. St-Jean is an attractive village amid farmlands, with good views and a pretty church. Lovely beach at Primel-Tregastel nearby." There are good amenities for children, but some adults might find the hotel, though very clean, a bit basic. (*Mrs Lucy Slater*)

Open Easter–31 Oct. Closed Sun evening and Mon, except 1 June–30 Sept.
Rooms 26 double, 6 single – 2 with bath, 18 with shower; 17 with telephone.
Facilities Salon, bar, TV room, 2 restaurants. Garden with children's playground. Sandy beach 700 metres.
Restriction Not suitable for ♿.
Location 17 km NE of Morlaix, 1.5 km E of Plougasnou village.
Credit cards None accepted.
Terms Rooms 90–165 frs. Breakfast 20 frs. Full board 160–193 frs. Set lunch/dinner 48–190 frs. Reduced rates for children.

ST-JEAN-PIED-DE-PORT 64220 Pyrénées-Atlantiques — Map 10

Hôtel des Pyrénées — *Tel* 59.37.01.01
Place du Général de Gaulle — *Telex* 570619

St-Jean, at the foot of the Roncesvalles pass into Spain, is one of the most picturesque of Basque towns (15th-century ramparts, hilltop citadel) and a capital of Basque folklore (summer festival and *pelota* championships). It used to be a major resting-place for Santiago-bound pilgrims about to cross the Pyrenees. And today many of our readers choose to halt there, seeking out this distinguished *auberge* which has been owned and run by the Arrambide family for four generations. One report this year, "Their glorious restaurant fully deserves its two stars in *Michelin* and three red *Gault Millau toques*. My meal started with a magnificent foie gras de canard, then a whole grilled local salmon, most delicious, then stuffed hare, and chocolate desserts. Our first-floor room was more than adequate, but there was some noise from a courtyard below. When the bill came I marvelled at its reasonableness – this place is very good value." Several others recently have extolled the cooking – "It is rumbustious and copious, no *cuisine minceur* here. And we loved the Arrambides, warm friendly people with the simple charm of the working French. Their traditional hostelry has no pretension to elegance, and evokes the *cossu bourgeois* of the 1950s rather than 1980s flair and panache." Rooms have been remodelled this past year; there are some luxury suites with lavish bathrooms on the first floor, and readers have enjoyed them. Back rooms are quietest, but lack a view. (*Roger Bennett; also Willis Frick, Stanley Burnton*)

Open All year except 5 –26 Jan, 20 Nov–20 Dec. Closed Tue except 1 July–15 Sept.
Rooms 2 suites, 18 double – all with bath/shower, telephone and TV.
Facilities Lift. 2 salons, 2 dining rooms; conference rooms; terrace.
Location 54 km SE of Bayonne on D933. Parking.
Credit cards Access, Amex, Visa.

Terms Rooms 460 frs, suite 750–800 frs. Breakfast 40 frs. Dinner, B&B 470 frs per person; full board 670 frs. Set lunch/dinner 165–380 frs. Reduced rates for children sharing parents' room.

ST-LATTIER 38840 Isère — Map 10

Le Lièvre Amoureux

Tel 76.36.50.67
from late 1989 76.64.50.67
Telex 308534 LIEVRE

This "amorous hare" is a pleasant old creeper-covered *auberge* in the Isère valley between Valence and Grenoble, and both *Michelin* and *Gault Millau* give it their red print for attractiveness. The cooking is regional, served outside in summer on a candle-lit terrace under lime-trees, or indoors in a panelled room where a fire blazes in winter. "An excellent hotel with comfortable rooms tastefully furnished and a very good swimming pool," runs a recent report; "Madame Hannelore Breda, the *patronne*, conducted the service of dinner like a stage director and the food and wine were superb and not over-priced." An earlier visitor stayed in the new annexe by the open-air heated pool, "These rooms are quiet and well appointed with sliding 'patio' windows. Though we were staying *en pension*, we were allowed the run of all the menus including the *carte* at no extra cost. The food was excellent, especially the local trout. Breakfasts included optional orange juice, yoghurt and eggs at no extra charge. The staff were competent and friendly, and on our last evening we received a free bottle of champagne over dinner." Rooms in the old building are smaller and simpler but have pretty views through the trees to the Vercors mountains. There is a railway nearby, but trains are few and not too noisy; the plumbing in the newer section is said to be noisy. New reports welcome.

Open All year except 18 Dec–15 Jan. Closed Sun evening and Mon Oct–Apr.
Rooms 14 double – 12 with bath and shower, all with telephone; 5 with radio; 5 with TV. 5 in annexe. 2 on ground floor.
Facilities Salon, bar (in summer), 2 restaurants. Garden with terrace for meals in summer, swimming pool and bar.
Location Halfway between St-Marcellin and Romans on N92.
Credit cards All major cards accepted.
Terms [1989 rates] Rooms 300–400 frs. Breakfast 40 frs. Set meals 195 frs; full alc 225 frs. Reduced rates and special meals for children.

ST-MALO 35400 Ille-et-Vilaine — Map 8

Hôtel Le Valmarin

Tel 99.81.94.76

7 rue Jean XXIII

A clean and friendly hotel, modernised from a beautiful 18th-century house in the suburb of St-Servan, just south of St-Malo harbour. "A bit formal for my taste, but very good"; "warm welcome, helpful staff"; "civilised, with a discreet atmosphere. The proprietor brings you a glass of chilled Muscadet on a silver tray, covered with lace, while you sit in the impressive gardens." One reader had a room beautifully decorated in white, green and gold, but another found his bed too soft and a third reported a lack of comfortable chairs throughout the house. No restaurant, but there are several good cheap fish places in the harbour area. The nearby beach is said to be insalubrious. More reports welcome.

Open 1 Mar–24 Dec.
Rooms 10 double – all with bath, telephone, radio and TV.
Facilities Salon bar. Garden. 300 metres from sandy beach.
Location Centre of St-Servan near Port Solidor; 2 km from old St-Malo. Parking.
Restriction Not suitable for ♿.
Credit cards Access, Amex, Visa.
Terms Rooms 330–510 frs. Breakfast 32 frs. (No restaurant.)

ST-MARTIN-VALMEROUX 15140 Cantal — Map 10

Hostellerie de la Maronne — *Tel* 71.69.20.33
Le Theil

"An immaculate hotel in a lovely setting, with excellent food," says a reader who appreciated the Auvergnat rural charm of this modest hostelry outside the hamlet of Le Theil. It stands in its own informal garden, in the lush upper valley of the Maronne, quite close to the lovely Renaissance hill-village of Salers. "The engaging but slightly eccentric" Alain de Cock and his Malagasy wife provide comfort and a choiceless evening meal (e.g. rêve d'escargots and tripoux flambés au cognac, but some dishes have been judged more "prosaic" than these). "Our room in the cottage annexe small but comfortable", says a reader this year. Others have enjoyed swimming in the pool and have had very good food. *Note:* dinner is not served after 8 pm. (*Diana Holmes, John and Rita Newnham*)

Open 20 Apr–15 Oct. Restaurant closed for lunch.
Rooms 25 – all with bath and shower, telephone and mini-bar. 8 in annexe. Some ground-floor rooms.
Facilities Salon, games room, dining room. Garden with heated swimming pool, tennis.
Location 3 km E of St-Martin-Valmeroux on D37 to Fontanges.
Credit cards Access, Visa.
Terms [1989 rates] Rooms 230–310 frs. Breakfast 30 frs. Half board 230–310 frs per person.

ST-PAUL-DE-VENCE 06570 Alpes-Maritimes — Map 11

La Colombe d'Or — *Tel* 93.32.80.02
Fax 93.32.77.78
Telex 970607

"A beautiful hotel in a marvellous setting. Our balcony overlooking the mountains and valley was wonderful, the room and bathroom were spacious and clean. The food was satisfactory and the atmosphere in the dining room was tops." So runs one of several recent plaudits for this famous little luxury hotel in a show village behind Nice. But some other readers are more critical (the food is generally judged mediocre) and undoubtedly *La Colombe* suffers from its popularity as a tourist attraction in its own right: it houses a private collection of modern art that would be the envy of any museum – Braque and Calder by the swimming pool, César and Miró in the lounge, Matisse, Picasso and Utrillo in the dining room, and much else. Many of these works were given to the former owner, the late Paul Roux, in payment by artists who stayed or ate there.

It's a beautiful old house, with many fine pieces of furniture, and is still owned and run by the Roux family. Some rooms have their original beams, others are all in white stucco with window-seats overlooking gardens; many have a terrace and outside bathroom. There is an idyllic veranda, decorated with a fine Léger mural, where lunch is served; dinner is taken indoors in a large rustic dining room. The swimming pool is surrounded by cypress trees. But not everyone will like the high-class tourist ambience, and the service has sometimes been found erratic or aloof.

Open All year except 10 Nov–15 Dec.
Rooms 10 suites, 15 double – all with bath, telephone, radio and TV; many with terrace. 1 ground-floor room.
Facilities Lift. Salon, bar, restaurant; terrace for lunch or refreshments. Garden with swimming pool. 10 km from sea.
Location 20 km W of Nice; take road to La Colle and Hauts de St-Paul. Parking.
Credit cards All major cards accepted.
Terms [1989 rates] Rooms 850 frs, suite 1,050 frs. Breakfast 40 frs. Dinner, B&B 620 frs per person. Alc (excluding wine) 195–390 frs. Reduced rates and special meals for children.

Le Hameau *Tel* 93.32.80.24
528 route de La Colle

Many of the small idyllic hotels in the Nice/Cannes hinterland have become marred by the overkill of trendy tourism. This one, just outside St-Paul, remains remarkably unspoilt and rural – a white-walled 18th-century farmhouse, imaginatively converted. A recent visitor adored it: "Its low white buildings are on several levels on a hillside, with doors opening on to terraces, some right out of bedrooms. We enjoyed breakfast on the largest terrace, amid flower-beds, trellised arbours and citrus trees, and were invited to pick oranges, tangerines and grapefruit whenever we wished. The main building holds a spacious comfortable lounge with big stone fireplace; there are tables for playing games, and lots of books in both English and French. The white-walled bedrooms are attractively furnished in country style, with many antiques. Rooms vary in size and shape, some being a bit low-ceilinged and dark. Management and staff were all helpful and friendly. Some traffic noise (a main road is nearby), but it did not continue all night." No restaurant, but among the many in St-Paul you could do worse than eat Danish (Lapland reindeer etc) at *La Brouette*.

Open 15 Feb–16 Nov and 25 Dec–8 Jan.
Rooms 2 suites, 13 double, 2 single – 13 with bath, 3 with shower, 16 with telephone and mini-bar.
Facilities Lounge with TV, breakfast room. Terraces and garden.
Location 1 km SW of St-Paul on road to La Colle.
Restriction Not suitable for ♿.
Credit cards Access, Amex, Visa.
Terms [1989 rates] Rooms: single 220–260 frs, double 260–390 frs, suite 490 frs. Breakfast 33 frs. (No restaurant.)

> Our italicised entries indicate hotels which are worth considering, but which, for various reasons – inadequate information, lack of feedback, ambivalent reports – do not at the moment warrant a full entry. We should particularly welcome comments on these hotels.

ST-PÉE-SUR-NIVELLE 64310 Pyrénées-Atlantiques Map 10

Hôtel de la Nivelle *Tel* 59.54.10.27

"A friendly and unassuming little *auberge*, truly Basque", at one end of the main street of a village between Cambo (don't miss Edmond Rostand's flamboyant Villa Arnaga) and St-Jean-de-Luz. "Madame Berrotaran's family have owned the hotel for generations. She and her husband are sweet and welcoming, and his regional cooking we found excellent, at fair prices – pipérade, ttoro (Basque fish soup) and caneton farci on the main menu, and good fish specialities on the *carte*, such as fillet of brill in a subtle wine sauce. A garrulous party of trendies from Biarritz just failed to spoil the ambience in the quaint beamed dining room; breakfast (good coffee) is served in the equally quaint bar, where locals gather. The bedroom area could do with a facelift, and rooms are small and simple. Front ones could suffer from morning traffic noise, so it might be better to opt for the modern annexe, 200 metres away across fields. Nearly all rooms have peaceful views of Basque hills and farmland."

Open All year except Feb.
Rooms 35 double – all with bath and/or shower. 15 in annexe.
Facilities Salon, TV room, bar, 2 restaurants; banqueting facilities. Garden.
Location Village is 13 km E of St-Jean-de-Luz. Parking.
Credit cards Access, Visa.
Terms Rooms 200 frs. Breakfast 25 frs. Dinner, B&B 210 frs per person. Set lunch 90 frs, dinner 130 frs; full alc 100–250 frs. Reduced rates and special meals for children.

ST-PONS-DE-THOMIÈRES 34220 Hérault Map 10

Château de Ponderach *Tel* 67.97.02.57
Route de Narbonne

This splendid 17th-century manor stands in its own 400-acre wooded park, just outside the pleasant old town of St-Pons (fine 12th-century cathedral). It is on the edge of the wild heavily forested hills of the Haut Languedoc nature reserve. For the past 300 years it has been in the aristocratic family hands of the present owner, Madame Counotte. It was dropped from the 1989 Guide purely from lack of news, but a report this year brings it back, "The fact that it's run by a woman shows in many small points – a pot of detergent in our bathroom, flowers in unlikely places. Madame Counotte is an accomplished pianist and her daughter plays professionally: any music in the dining room is always good. The food is decent and plentiful, and the wines reasonably priced. Bedrooms have balconies overlooking the park: some English people staying longer than us were enchanted with the quiet beauty of the hotel. And it's the cheapest of its château-type that I've seen." (*Alan F Thomas*)

Open 1 Apr–early Oct.
Rooms 11 – all with bath and/or shower and telephone.
Facilities Salon with TV, bar, restaurant; conference facilities. Large garden where meals are served in good weather.
Location 1.2 km S of town on Narbonne road.
Credit cards All major cards accepted.
Terms [1989 rates] Rooms 355–405 frs. Breakfast 60 frs. Dinner, B&B 565–570 frs per person. Set lunch/dinner 160–330 frs. Special meals for children.

ST-QUENTIN 02100 Aisne — Map 9

Grand Hôtel et Restaurant Le Président — *Tel* 23.62.69.77
6 rue Dachery — *Fax* 23.62.53.52
Telex 140225

Picardy's second largest town, itself a humdrum place, is worth visiting for the Quentin de la Tour portraits in the Lécuyer museum. And it has other surprises in store – as nominators of the *Grand* found this year: "The town centre and the *Grand* were a revelation – the former for its super reconstructed buildings, the latter for an inspired re-creation. From the outside, despite the floodlighting, it looks like just another turn-of-the century facade in a dull street near the station: but the interior has been gutted and replaced by a central atrium with a glass roof, glassed-in balconies and a glass lift, all very modern and tasteful. In the modern marble foyer, a receptionist sat at a Louis XV repro table. Our large and pleasant bedroom had a marble bathroom *en suite*. To cap it all, *Le Président* restaurant, very popular locally, fully deserves its *Michelin* rosette" (*and* it has three *Gault Millau* red *toques* for its inventive dishes, some of them Picard in inspiration). (*David and Angela Stewart*)

Open All year. Restaurant closed Christmas, New Year and Aug.
Rooms 24 double – all with bath and shower, telephone, radio and TV.
Facilities Lift. Bar, breakfast room, restaurant.
Location Central. Parking.
Credit cards Amex, Diners, Visa.
Terms [1989 rates] Rooms: single 380 frs, double 480 frs, suite 550 frs. Breakfast 50 frs. Set lunch/dinner 185 and 320 frs; alc (excluding wine) 400–500 frs. Reduced rates for children sharing parents' room.

ST-RÉMY-DE-PROVENCE 13210 Bouches-du-Rhône — Map 11

Hôtel Les Antiques — *Tel* 90.92.03.02
15 avenue Pasteur — *Telex* 431146

In the southern suburbs of this typical small Provençal town is the mental home of St-Paul-de-Mausole where Van Gogh spent a year as a patient after cutting off his ear in Arles; nearby are the curious Roman remains of Glanum, known also as Les Antiques. Hence the name of this hotel near the town centre, a gracefully converted 19th-century mansion. You can stay in the main building, or in a *pavillon* with its own terrace. "One of my favourite hotels", says a devotee this year, "a great welcome, grounds and pool attractive, atmosphere delightful". Other regulars, too, have endorsed an earlier view, "Lovely people, charming atmosphere: it was like being guests in a private home. Beautiful gardens, and a grand entrance with marble floors, tapestries, Italian painted ceiling." (*Mrs RB Richards; also Ellen and John Buchanan*) No restaurant, but the *France* and the *Arts* in town are both good value. A September visitor found "carnival noises non-stop, bulls running through the streets and bicycle races, and a fun-fair just opposite" – to her, a nightmare, but maybe to others a good reason for visiting joyous Provence.

Open 7 Apr–15 Oct.
Rooms 26 double, 1 single – all with bath, shower, and telephone. 10 in bungalow in park. 2 ground-floor rooms with ramps.
Facilities 2 salons, TV room. Large grounds with unheated swimming pool.

Location In town centre. Parking.
Credit cards Amex, Diners, Visa.
Terms (Excluding tax) B&B: single 388 frs, double 490 frs. (No restaurant.)

Hôtel Château de Roussan *Tel* 90.92.11.63
Route de Tarascon

"Still one of our favourite places in Europe: we'd probably go here for a second honeymoon" – a recent letter that typifies many readers' feelings about this stately pink 18th-century château, secluded outside St-Rémy in its own big park. It has been the country home of the Roussel family for over a century; today they accept bed-and-breakfast clients to keep it going. Many visitors find it an unusual and civilised experience, more like being the house-guests of cultured friends than staying in a hotel. "Breakfast with the peacocks and doves is a treat under the huge plane trees with the sound of the small fountains." "Our enormous room was full of antiques." "An ideal place for writing. You can set your table and chair in a far corner of the park and be disturbed only by the house dogs who take a well-behaved interest when picnic lunchtime has arrived." Bathrooms are modern, but the rooms are in careful period style, with Louis XV furniture. "Louis Roussel was a courteous host, showing us the 16th-century farmhouse in the grounds where Nostradamus once lived and inviting us to browse in his library." No restaurant, but try the *Café des Arts* or the *France* in town, both quite cheap. (*Endorsed this year by JA – "as delightful as ever"*.)

Open 15 Mar–31 Oct.
Rooms 4 suites, 10 double, 3 single – all with bath and/or shower, telephone and tea-making facilities. 2 ground-floor rooms.
Facilities Lounge, TV room, library. Large park.
Location 2 km W of centre of St-Rémy, off Tarascon road. Parking.
Credit cards Access, Visa.
Terms [1989 rates] Rooms: single 300 frs, double 500 frs. Breakfast 48 frs. (No restaurant.)

Domaine de Valmouriane *Tel* 90.92.44.62
Petite route des Baux *Fax* 90.49.01.79
Telex 431169 DOMVAL

An old stone Provençal *mas* in the rocky foothills of the wild Alpilles, just south of town, which has been exquisitely converted into a small luxury hotel, owned by an Englishwoman, Catherine McHugo, and run by her in association with Jean-Claude Aubertin who was chef at the *Auberge* at Noves (q.v.) and at *Ma Cuisine* in Chelsea. The *Domaine* opened only in 1988 but already has two red *toques* in *Gault Millau* (and four red gables in *Michelin*). Cool white walls, tiled floors, a sense of space and grace, much admired by our nominators this year: "Lovely bedrooms and bathrooms: ours was very stylish. A large sitting room with open fireplace, and a small panelled bar. In the pleasant restaurant with its huge windows, opening onto the terrace, the food was excellent" – and highly inventive in its posh way, e.g. foie gras with peaches and ginger, and fricassée of lamb's foot with truffles. (*Pat and Jeremy Temple*) More reports please.

Open All year.
Rooms 12 – all with bath and/or shower, telephone, TV and mini-bar.

Facilities Lounge, reading room, bar, restaurant; terrace where meals are served. Garden with swimming pool and tennis court.
Location 4.5 km S of St-Rémy, by D27 (petite route des Baux). Parking.
Credit cards Access, Amex, Visa.
Terms [1989 rates] Rooms: single 650–1,000 frs, double 850–1,200 frs. Breakfast 55 frs. Half board 200 frs per person added. Special meals for children.

ST-SERNIN-SUR-RANCE 12380 Aveyron — Map 10

Hotel Carayon — *Tel* 65.99.60.26
Place du Fort — *Telex* 531917 CARAYON

"A real find," says this year's nominator of a country hotel in a thinly populated area well off the main north-south tourist routes: it's in a village on the Albi–Millau road, just south of the lovely valley of the Tarn. "Pierre Carayon, ebullient and enthusiastic, spent some years at the Dorchester and Savoy in London, and is now transforming the family hotel/restaurant into a larger enterprise: fifteen new rooms have just been built into the hillside in a sympathetic way. There's a garden with diversions for children. Our small but neat room in the old part of the hotel had a splendid view across the valley. The food (*Michelin* red 'R') was fantastic value – our 78-franc [1989] dinner included two terrines, a whole trout, quail flamed in brandy and home-made sorbet. Very much a family affair, with *grandpère* and two small boys all in evidence, and elegant Madame supervising the dining room." (*Diana Holmes*) More reports welcome, especially on the new rooms.

Open All year. Closed Sun evening and Mon in low season.
Rooms 5 suites, 40 double – all with bath and/or shower; 40 with telephone, 20 with TV, some with balcony.
Facilities Lift. Lounges, 2 TV rooms, bar, 3 dining rooms. Disco. Terrace. Garden with children's playground and table tennis.
Location St-Sernin is 50 km E of Albi on D999. Hotel is central; parking.
Credit cards All major cards accepted.
Terms [1989 rates] Rooms 99–260 frs. Breakfast 24 frs. Set meals 59–239 frs; full alc 200 frs. Reduced rates and special meals for children.

ST-SYMPHORIEN-LE-CHÂTEAU 28700 Eure-et-Loir — Map 8

Château d'Esclimont — *Tel* 37.31.15.15
St-Symphorien-le-Château — *Telex* 780560 ECLIMON

"C'est mon plaisir", is the motto of La Rochefoucauld on the facade of this stately moated Renaissance château, standing in a 150-acre wooded park between Chartres and Rambouillet. An American visitor this year found the pleasure hers, too, "Fairytale vintage, with its period moats, crenellated towers, stone sculptures. I was charmed by our two-storeyed room, and found the *nouvelle cuisine* good, but expensive; lunch or drinks can be taken on the terrace, overlooking a garden and lovely lake with swans." (*Victoria P Turner*) An earlier view, "Truly glorious, luxuriously appointed. Even on a bitter winter's day, everywhere was deliciously warm. The views are amazing, over park, river and woods; the food is delicious and served in generous portions from an inspired menu (two *Gault Millau toques*). Two recent visitors found the welcome and ambience cool.

Open All year.
Rooms 6 suites, 48 double – all with bath and shower, telephone and TV. 24 in 3 separate buildings.
Facilities Salon, bar, 4 dining rooms; conference facilities. Wooded park with small lake, river, tennis court, heated swimming pool and helipad.
Location 6 km NW of Ablis. Leave A11 or N10 at Ablis; go towards Prunay; turn left on D101.
Restriction Not suitable for ♿.
Credit card Visa.
Terms Rooms: single occupancy 520 frs, double 825–1,210 frs, suite 1,430–2,100 frs. Breakfast 75 frs. Set lunch/dinner 260–430 frs; full alc 450 frs. Special meals for children.

ST-THIBÉRY 34630 Hérault — Map 10

Château de Nadalhan — *Tel* 67.77.87.93
Route de Valros

An Italianate mansion in its own big park, set on the vine-clad Languedoc plain halfway between the lovely Renaissance town of Pézenas, where Molière often performed, and the huge new bathing resort of Agde. "A small pretty château amid vineyards, run as a restaurant *avec cinq chambres* by a pleasant young couple, the Théronds. We had a spacious 18th-century room with a good big bathroom; hand-hemmed linen sheets, two tall arched windows. All spotless. Food well and imaginatively cooked, though the set menu offered limited choice and began to pall after ten days. Piped music during the meal, but we managed to get the cassettes changed to suit our taste. Service cheerful and personal."

Open All year except Jan.
Rooms 1 for 4, 4 double – all with bath; telephone on request.
Facilities Salon, 3 dining rooms. Park. Sea 10 km.
Location On D125 between St-Thibéry and Valros, 7 km SW of Pézenas.
Credit cards Access, Visa.
Terms B&B: single 230–260 frs, double 310–360 frs; dinner, B&B: single 310–340 frs, double 510–560 frs. Set lunch/dinner 105, 150, 180 and 250 frs; full alc 220 frs. Reduced rates and special meals for children.

ST-TROPEZ 83990 Var — Map 11

Le Mas de Chastelas — *Tel* 94.56.09.11
Route de Gassin — *Telex* 462393 CHASTA

Once used for silkworm breeding, this converted 17th-century farmhouse stands secluded in vineyards a little west of St-Tropez and 500 metres from the sea. Guests tend to include French stars of stage, screen and fashion, fleeing the *paparazzi* of the frenzied port area. "A bit of a poseur's paradise" is one view, but for another reader this year it is "a wonderful combination of taste, luxury and informality, very clean and comfortable, with helpful staff and superb *nouvelle cuisine*", while regular visitors concur: "Still pretty, calm and casually elegant, it is a quiet, restful and superior oasis in a crowded area. The *accueil* is warmer, service is unobtrusively good, though occasionally a little amateurish. Dinner was excellent. Our suite in an annexe in the woods was luxurious; flowers were changed daily. Fine breakfast, with cherries and brioches; good food pleasantly served by the pool, but the menus don't change often enough." Others have admired the buffet lunches by the heated pool, the dinners served on a candle-lit terrace, and the pine furnishings. The new chef, Michel Gaudin, wins two red *toques* from *Gault Millau* for some very fancy fish dishes. Some visitors are enthusiastic, but one was critical, particularly of the waiters. (*William G Frick, Stefan and Yvette Wiener*)

Open Easter–early Oct. Restaurant closed to non-residents for lunch.
Rooms 10 suites, 21 double – all with bath and/or shower, telephone; 11 with TV. Suites in separate building with private garden.
Facilities Lounge, TV room, indoor and outdoor restaurant; terrace. Garden with heated swimming pool, jacuzzi, 4 tennis courts. Beaches 10 mins by car.
Location 3 km SW of St-Tropez, just off Gassin road.
Restriction Not suitable for ♿.
Credit cards All major cards accepted.
Terms [1989 rates] Rooms 500–1,100 frs, suite 1,575–1,800 frs. Breakfast 65 frs. Set dinner 350 frs. Special meals for children.

Les Palmiers — *Tel* 94.97.01.61
26 boulevard Vasserot — *Telex* 970941

Much more centrally located than our other St-Tropez entry: five minutes' stroll from the harbour, and facing the place des Lices with its famous trendy-bohemian bar-bistrots, the Café des Arts *and* Bistrot des Lices. *A simple family-run B&B hotel, now getting an overdue face-lift; patio garden, good breakfasts; decent rooms, very good value for a town that Michael Frayn has called 'St-Trop' (the saint of excess). 22 rooms, most with bath and/or shower, 220-330 frs. Breakfast 25 frs* [1989]. *New nomination. More reports welcome.*

ST-VAAST-LA-HOUGUE 50550 Manche — Map 8

Hôtel de France et des Fuchsias — *Tel* 33.54.42.26
18 rue Maréchal Foch

An old oyster-breeding port east of Cherbourg, where Edward III landed his troops before the battle of Crécy. Today troupes of Britons continue to land at this popular family-run hotel, which preserves its exuberant charm even though it is run to something of a formula and has become "a kind of club for the English middle classes". Many readers enjoy the look of the place – very pretty, much festooned indeed with red fuchsias – and admire the garden, cobbled courtyard and thatched canopy, as well as the

---

Traveller's tale *The town of Dreux (Eure et Loire) has no good hotels so the Unwary Traveller, looking for a bed for the night, follows the roadsigns to Môtel St-Georges. The signs are official, not advertisements, so it is clearly an establishment of some importance. Exhaustive search fails to locate it. The U. T. asks a villager who, before replying, fetches his mates out of the café to witness the fun. A verbose explanation in patois then ensues from which one gathers that the Môtel* commence au pont et finit à l'église. *We are therefore right in the middle of it. (Gallery laughter.) After much wordplay it is revealed that there is no motel as such. Môtel St-Georges* est le nom du village. *Howls of mirth all round. They should be sick of the joke by now.*

"superb" meals (the plates and curtains in the dining-room also have fuschia patterns). A recent verdict: "Welcome friendly, rooms unpretentious but well furnished and very comfortable, food superbly cooked and presented, staff charming and efficient." No main lounge, but plenty of sitting space. We should welcome more reports.

Open 1 Mar–2 Jan. Closed Mon except school holidays.
Rooms 3 suites, 26 double, 3 single – 29 with bath and shower, 2 with shower, all with telephone and TV. 12 in annexe.
Facilities Bar, 2 salons, reading room, 2 dining rooms. Garden. Bicycle hire. Sandy beach nearby.
Location Central (some windows double-glazed, quietest rooms overlook garden). Small parking place.
Restriction Not suitable for ♿.
Credit cards All major cards accepted.
Terms Rooms 235–320 frs. Breakfast 30 frs. Dinner, B&B 198–295 frs per person; full board 265–365 frs. Set lunch/dinner 65–180 frs; full alc 190 frs. Children under 8 sharing parents' room half-price; special menu.

STE-ANNE-LA-PALUD 29127 Finistère — Map 8

Hôtel de la Plage — *Tel* 98.92.50.12
Plomodiern — *Telex* 941377

Not far from the lovely old village of Locronan, the beachside chapel of St Anne is the venue of one of the largest and most colourful of Breton *pardons*, held on the last Sunday of August. Near this chapel is the *Plage*, not an ordinary seaside hotel as its *Hulot*-ish name might imply, but stylish and expensive – and strongly admired again in 1989, especially for its cuisine (*Michelin* rosette, two red *Gault Millau toques*): "A lovely place, oozing atmosphere, with its paintings of seascapes and waitresses in Breton costume. The demi-pension menu includes oysters, grilled salmon, and char-grilled lobster which you eat with a special pinny draped tenderly round you by a maternal waitress. A picturesque thatched cottage houses a bar. Bedrooms comfortable and tasteful." Earlier paeans: "A very well-run hotel on a beautiful sandy beach, long and uncrowded. Good and friendly service. At dinner, predominance of fish, always fresh and large portions. Classic puddings, incredibly sweet; cheeses fresh and local; a wonderful platter of fruits de mer at lunch; and delicious croissants, brioches and home-made jams for breakfast." "A good tennis court, and a stunning situation, especially with the light of the setting sun reflected on the wet low-tide sands." Some front rooms can be noisy, and a few may suffer from cess-pit smell in the heat; and one reader points out that though the beach is on the doorstep the sea is often a long way away, owing to the tides, and that the hotel does not have much in the way of facilities for small children. (*Francine and Ian Walsh; Pamela M Zargarani, Philip Carter, BH Jenkinson, and others*)

Open 24 Mar–10 Oct.
Rooms 4 suites, 28 double, 2 single – most with bath and shower, all with telephone; 16 with TV. 2 ground-floor rooms.
Facilities 2 lifts. Salons, bar, TV room, restaurant; conference facilities. Garden with tennis court and swimming pool. Safe, sandy beach.
Location On coast, 16 km NE of Douarnenez.
Credit cards All major cards accepted.
Terms [1989 rates] Rooms 500–700 frs, suite 950 frs. Breakfast 48 frs. Half board 550–680 frs per person. Set lunch 170 frs, dinner 300 frs.

SAINTES 17100 Charente-Maritime — Map 10

Relais du Bois St-Georges — *Tel* 46.93.50.99
Rue de Royan — *Telex* 790488 STGEOR

Saintes, with its ruined Roman amphitheatre and fine Romanesque churches, is one of the most attractive and historic towns of south-west France. The *Bois St-Georges,* well placed in its own big garden near the *autoroute,* in the western outskirts, is by contrast very modern – in an elegantly unusual way, as readers tell us this year. "The indoor heated swimming pool has a grand piano, statuary, and large windows overlooking the lawns." "An excellent hotel with a superb pool. My room was very individual, being on several floors with its own staircase and a good supply of French books. Food and service are excellent. The garden with its lake and fountains is an example of the care and enthusiasm lavished by the owner, very much in evidence and clearly proud of his achievement." "Swimming pool in the dining room" (sic). Bedrooms are said to be tastefully decorated. (*DJ Harden, Peter Aston, AF Thomas, Victoria P Turner*) There is some traffic noise – and a reader warns against taking a chalet room by the lake if it is too near the pool's noisy refiltration plant.

Open All year.
Rooms 3 suites, 27 double – all with bath and shower, telephone, radio, TV and baby-listening. Some with balcony. 6 ground-floor rooms specially adapted for ♿.
Facilities Lounge, 2 bars, TV room, restaurant; indoor swimming pool; terrace where meals are served in season. 14-acre grounds with lake.
Location On W outskirts – 1.5 km from exit 25 of *autoroute* A10. Garage parking.
Credit cards Access, Visa.
Terms Rooms: single occupancy 290–410 frs, double 380–570 frs, suite 740–880 frs. Breakfast 55 frs. Dinner, B&B double 395–459 frs per person. Set lunch/dinner 130 frs; full alc 180–280 frs. Special meals for children.

LES STES-MARIES-DE-LA-MER 13460 Bouches-du-Rhône — Map 10

L'Étrier Camarguais — *Tel* 90.47.81.14
Chemin bas des Launes — *Telex* 403144

On the edge of the Camargue, just north of Les Saintes-Maries, the *Étrier* ("stirrup") is one of several modern ranch-like holiday hotels here that cater mainly for riders: it has its own herd of white Camarguais horses which it hires to guests by the hour (not cheap). It is a spacious, breezy and youthfully informal place, slightly shabby, with log-cabin decor; the simple bedrooms, in chalets in the garden, have patios where you can breakfast in privacy. A family wrote to us this year, "The swimming pool and gardens were attractive, the staff were friendly, and we enjoyed the horse-rides. The dinners were mostly good – on one evening, a magnificent buffet with smoked and fresh salmon, crab, all sorts of shellfish, an array of delicious salads and other delights. Pity that lunch was a full three-course affair, with no chance of just snacks round the pool. Breakfast was adequate." (*JA, and others*) The nearby disco (just out of earshot) is not cheap. Les Saintes-Maries' famous Gypsy festival, every 23–27 May, is well worth seeing.

> Don't let old favourites down. Entries are dropped when there is no endorsement.

Open 1 Apr–15 Nov.
Rooms 27 double – all with bath, telephone and TV. Ground-floor rooms.
Facilities Bar, restaurant, disco; conference facilities. Terrace, garden with swimming pool and tennis court. Sandy beach 2 km.
Location 3 km N of the town, just off N570 to Arles.
Credit cards All major cards accepted.
Terms Dinner, B&B: single 605 frs, double 795 frs; full board: single 755 frs, double 1,095 frs. Set lunch/dinner 150–200 frs.

Hôtel Le Mas de la Fouque *Tel* 90.47.81.02
Fax 90.47.96.84
Telex 403155

The *Mas de la Fouque* is similar in style to the *Étrier* (above) but smaller and much more up-market – a modern whitewashed ranch, very comfortable, set in the Camargue with wildlife all around and a stable full of white horses. "We had a big beautiful room, an amazing bathroom and our own veranda at the edge of a small lake where we saw water-rats, carp, heron and other beautiful birds. The food was mainly straightforward Camargue roasts, and there was no choice for the main course on the daily menu *pension*. Breakfast delicious, but service a bit haphazard." "The pool is lovely, heated but not over-heated, with good beach chairs. The hotel is in superb good taste, and the welcome from owner Jean-Paul Cochat is warm. His wife runs the kitchen, his daughter the bar and dining room (food satisfactory). It is all very informal and relaxed. If one is lucky, one sees flights of white flamingos around sunset taking off from the marsh, and in the morning the white horses will come thundering down the narrow path outside one's bedroom – a wonderful sight."

Open All year except 2 Jan–20 Mar. Restaurant closed Tue.
Rooms 1 for 4, 13 double – all with bath and shower, telephone, TV and mini-bar. Ground-floor rooms.
Facilities Salon, bar, 2 restaurants; terrace with café. Garden with heated swimming pool, tennis, putting. Fishing. Large sandy beach with safe bathing 2 km.
Location 4 km NW of Les Saintes-Maries by D38.
Credit cards All major cards accepted.
Terms Dinner, B&B: double 1,700 frs, suite 2,030 frs. Full board 2,130 frs. Set lunch/dinner 210–320 frs; full alc 245 frs. Reduced rates and special meals for children.

SALON-DE-PROVENCE 13300 Bouches-du-Rhône Map 11

Abbaye de Sainte-Croix *Tel* 90.56.24.55
Route du Val de Cuech *Telex* 401247 STECROI

A venerable 12th-century abbey on a hillside north-east of Salon, sumptuously restored as a luxury hotel. It has a wooded park, and a dining room giving onto a terrace with a fine view across the plain; at night it is cande-lit. "The position is spectacular, and wholly tranquil", writes an inspector this year; "we had their nine-course *menu dégustation* which was perhaps not as *haute* as the view but wholly agreeable. The outdoor pool is well maintained." Bedrooms tend to be small (many are former monks' cells) but some have a balcony. (*HR*)

We are particularly keen to have reports on italicised entries.

Open 1 Mar–31 Oct. Restaurant closed Mon midday.
Rooms 5 suites, 19 double – all with bath and/or shower, and telephone; radio on request.
Facilities Bar, TV room, restaurant; functions facilities. Garden with swimming pool. Tennis 200 metres.
Location 5 km NE of Salon, off D16.
Credit cards Access, Diners, Visa.
Terms B&B: single from 615 frs, double from 680 frs, suite from 1,120 frs. Dinner, B&B: single 905 frs, double 1,140 frs, suite 1,570 frs. Set lunch/dinner 180–420 frs; alc 350 frs. Special meals for children on request.

SARLAT-LA-CANÉDA 24200 Dordogne — Map 10

La Hoirie — *Tel* 53.59.05.62

Just south of Sarlat, this former hunting lodge is now a friendly Relais du Silence, *with swimming pool and garden. Efficient staff, pleasant rooms (those in main house better than annexe); good Périgourdin food, copiously served. Open 15 Mar–14 Nov. 15 rooms, all with bath and/or shower. B&B double 520 frs. Set menus 170–260 frs. New nomination. More reports please.*

Hostellerie de Meysset — *Tel* 53.59.08.29

Route des Eyzies

Périgourdine *douceur de vivre* suffuses this very pleasant rural hotel, built in local style and set on a hill outside the town, in its own park: from its terrace there are wide views over two valleys. Plenty of red print in *Michelin*, and a black *Gault Millau toque* for good regional cooking, back up the report of our nominator who brings it to the Guide this year: "Comfortable, and efficiently run. Madame Brottier is bandbox smart, Monsieur is friendly and likes a joke. Our ground-floor room had french windows opening onto a tiny private lawn. In the well-appointed dining room the atmosphere was relaxing and the five-course *menu pension* was varied: excellent soups." Meals are served on the terrace when fine; the furniture is suitably rustic in style. (*Ann Webber*) More reports welcome.

Open 27 Apr–7 Oct.
Rooms 31 – all with bath or shower and telephone.
Facilities Lounge, restaurant. Large terrace. Garden.
Location 3 km NW of town, off Les Eyzies road (D67). Parking.
Credit cards All major cards accepted.
Terms [1989 rates] Rooms 310–360 frs, suite 565 frs. Breakfast 40 frs. Dinner, B&B 330–355 frs per person. Set lunch 160 frs, dinner 190 frs.

SAULIEU 21210 Côte d'Or — Map 10

Hôtel de La Côte d'Or — *Tel* 80.64.07.66

2 rue d'Argentine — *Telex* 350778

A noble old coaching-inn, on the main street of a dullish little Burgundy town on the old Paris-Lyons highway (N7). It was long famous, for its former owner Alexandre Dumaine was one of the great French chefs of his day (******Michelin***). Then it fell into eclipse, with Dumaine's death and the coming of the *autoroute* which stole most of the through traffic. Today, despite its unpromising location, it is again in form under a new *patron-*

chef, Bernard Loiseau, who has brought it up to the standard where it wins two *Michelin* rosettes and no fewer than four red *Gault Millau toques* – endorsed by one expert reader this year, "I was enthusiastic about the 'cleanness' and intensity of flavour which is characteristic of M. Loiseau's *cuisine à l'eau*; my husband was less so. The inn has been beautifully restored, with masses of fresh flowers and well-polished antique furniture." Others have echoed this: "The cooking, modern and light, is soundly based on old Burgundy dishes. The wine list, mostly expensive, contains some house wines at reasonable prices." Room furnishings are a little heavy, but the lavish new suites are said to be excellent. (*Rosamund V Hebdon; also T and R Rose, Jeff and Karen Nebel, Denis Tate*)

Open All year.
Rooms 10 suites, 13 double – all with bath and/or shower, telephone, tea-making facilities and baby-listening; 10 with radio, 17 with TV. Ground-floor rooms.
Facilities 2 lounges, 3 dining rooms. Garden. Near Morvan National Park with tennis, riding, lakes, fishing and water sports.
Location Central. Garage parking.
Credit cards All major cards accepted.
Terms B&B 330–970 frs per person; suites 1,570–1,870 frs. Set lunch 250 frs, dinner 390 frs; full alc 600–650 frs. Special meals for children.

SAUTERNES 33210 Gironde — Map 10

Château de Commarque — *Tel* 56.63.65.94
Langon

Few names are sweeter than Sauternes – and we are glad to welcome this Guide debutant, a handsome English-owned wine-producing château amid the vineyards, 40 kilometres south-east of Bordeaux. Dr Nigel Reay-Jones and his wife recently bought it to restore the neglected vineyards, and they have now planted eight acres with young vines. They have also converted the outbuildings into self-contained studio apartments, each with an independent entrance opening onto a courtyard, where one reader stayed this year, "An ideal family holiday hotel, excellent value for money. The Reay-Jones were most helpful. They welcome children, and have five well-behaved ones of their own. There's no high luxury, but the basic amenities are there, including a swimming pool. A Basque chef gives a flavour of the south-west with his regional dishes: the 'turbot sur commande' is a must. Dr Reay-Jones, an ex wine-importer, has an unusual, well-chosen wine-list – especially the Sauternes." Meals are served in the former *chai*, probably 17th-century. Local wine tours can be arranged. And the literary-minded might care to know that this is also the Mauriac country: his family home, Malagar, is just across the Garonne at Vergelais, north of Langon, and his boyhood summer home at St-Symphorien, south-west of Sauternes, was the setting for *Thérèse Desqueyroux* and *Le Mystère Frontenac*. (*Stephen and Samantha Pollock-Hill*)

Open All year except Feb. Restaurant closed to non-residents Wed in low season.
Rooms 8 suites with small sitting room, suitable for 4 people (2 grouped together), 1 double – all with shower. 1 ground-floor room.
Facilities Restaurant. 30-acre grounds; garden with swimming pool, vineyard.
Location 40 km SE of Bordeaux. Leave A62 at Langon. Follow road to Sauternes; château is signposted.
Credit cards Access, Visa.

Terms Rooms: double 120–150 frs, suite 180–250 frs. Breakfast 24 frs. Set lunch/dinner 70, 110 and 165 frs; full alc 150 frs. Half board rates (min 4 nights). 50 frs added for use of sofa bed in sitting rooms. Special meals for children.

SAUVETERRE-DE-COMMINGES 31510 Haute-Garonne — Map 10

Hostellerie des Sept Molles — *Tel* 61.88.30.87 and 61.88.31.36
Gesset — *Telex* 530171

This captivating hotel is a large white villa, quite smart and most gracefully furnished, secluded in a verdant wooded valley of the Pyrenean foothills. "*Molle*" is a local word for *moulin*, as the brochure lyrically explains: "On the slopes of the hills overlooking the valley, seven joyous watermills used to cling to the meanderings of the capricious stream flowing from the plateaux. The locals came down on Sundays to fetch sacks full of white flour and drink their fill of mirth. Sadly, times have changed . . . but the seven mills were retrieved by the management and now adorn our gardens." Several readers this year and last have drunk their fill of mirth at the Ferran family's hostelry: "A luxurious hotel run by a young and friendly couple, with innovative high-class food and memorable breakfasts." "We took two of their cheapest rooms, which proved to be comfortable and nicely decorated. The only sound was of cowbells. Service and public rooms were as you'd expect from *Relais et Châteaux*, but informal. A swimming pool and tennis court in the lawned garden; table tennis in the gazebo; and children are entertained by the proprietors' small daughter. Nice touches like poached quails' eggs as appetisers and baskets of fruit in the bedrooms. Menus were imaginative, using local ingredients (rabbit and pigeon) and *nouvelle* in presentation" (*Gault Millau* red *toque*). (*Helen and Charles Priday, Paul A Hoffstein*)

Open Mar–Oct and Dec.
Rooms 2 suites, 17 double – all with bath and shower, telephone and TV; some with balcony.
Facilities Lift. Salon, bar, 2 restaurants. Garden with swimming pool and tennis court.
Location At Gesset, 2 km SE of Sauveterre, 13 km SW of St-Gaudens.
Credit cards All major cards accepted.
Terms Rooms: single 280–450 frs, double 380–520 frs, suite 680–850 frs. Breakfast 40 frs. Set lunch/dinner 140–220 frs; full alc 250 frs. Reduced rates and special meals for children.

SÉGURET 84110 Vaucluse — Map 11

La Table du Comtat — *Tel* 90.46.91.49

This picturesque old village, on a hillside above the Rhône vineyards, is within easy reach of Orange and Roman Vaison, and has fine views of the startling jagged peaks of the Dentelles de Montmirail; it's also a centre of Provençal folk culture, with a Christmas church pageant and craftsmen making *santons*. Here this fine old 15th-century house, now a sophisticated restaurant-with-rooms (*Michelin* rosette and *Gault Millau toque*), is splendidly situated just above the village - "one of our favourite little hotels in France", say readers in 1989. An inspector has been impressed this year too, "The view's the thing, so it's best to eat by daylight, taking advantage of the big windows of the dining room, a bit dull and formal after dark. Service is outstandingly stylish and courteous, and Madame Gomez is friendly though reserved (her husband cooks). The cuisine is superbly done in its more-or-less *nouvelle* way – an *amuse-gueule* of salmon mousse with oyster, superb lamb and lotte au pistou, good cheeses – they are strong on chèvres – and a fine local white Séguret, better than the Gigondas red, also local. Smart international clientele, classical piped music. Rooms comfortable, many with views: mine was well equipped, including even a shoebrush, so new-looking that I used it as a hairbrush, having left mine in my *gîte*. The small piscine, floodlit at night, below its high rock is a stunner – as are the toilets whose unisex basin area is right against the naked rock of the cliff into which the hotel is built." (*Endorsed by David and Lynne Allen*)

Open Mar–21 Nov, 7 Dec–end Jan. Closed Tue evening and Wed except Christmas and Easter.
Rooms 8 double – all with bath, (4 also with shower), and telephone.
Facilities Salon, dining room; terrace. Small garden with unheated swimming pool.
Location 8 km S of Vaison-la-Romaine off the D23; at entrance to Séguret; hotel is signposted. Parking.
Restriction Not suitable for ♿.
Credit cards All major cards accepted.
Terms Rooms: single 380 frs, double 410–560 frs. Breakfast 50 frs. Set lunch/dinner 210, 270 and 400 frs, full alc 350–400 frs. Special children's menu.

SEPT-SAULX 51400 Marne — Map 9

Hôtel Restaurant le Cheval Blanc — *Tel* 26.03.90.27 — *Telex* 830885 CHEBLAN
2 rue du Moulin

A pleasant old creeper-covered coaching inn, run by the Robert family for five generations. It is liked especially for its food (*Michelin* rosette, *Gault Millau toque*), and for its pastoral setting beside a big garden and a stream (it straddles the main road of a village south-east of Reims). "Excellent food, magnificent rooms, and we relaxed in garden hammocks and rocking chairs amid trees and murmuring streams," is a report this year. Earlier ones: "A warm atmosphere, Madame Robert very charming, dinner excellent especially poulet de Bresse in a tarragon sauce." "We were delighted with the food and excellent breakfast. Service competent if not swift – but who wants to rush a good French meal?" The warm attentiveness of the Roberts and their staff is generally praised, though one dissenter this year found the reception cool and thought the food overpriced. Be warned, too, that party walls are thin, making neighbours' night noises audible; and rooms on the road side, where lorries lumber by, hardly justify the hotel's rating as a *Relais du Silence*. (*Prof. AS Douglas, Brian MacArthur, J Masters*)

Open All year except 15 Jan–15 Feb.
Rooms 3 suites, 18 double – all with bath and/or shower, telephone, TV and mini-bar. All on ground floor in building opposite restaurant.
Facilities Hall, salon, restaurant, breakfast room; functions room. Terrace. Large park bordered by river Vesle; tennis, mini-golf, volleyball, fishing.
Location On D37 off N44 in direction of Châlons.
Credit cards All major cards accepted.

Terms Rooms: single 250 frs, double 450 frs. Breakfast 38 frs. Dinner, B&B 490–550 frs per person; full board 610–675 frs. Set lunch/dinner 170, 270 and 370 frs; full alc 300 frs.

SERRES 05700 Hautes-Alpes — Map 10

Hôtel Fifi Moulin — *Tel* 92.67.00.01
Route de Nyons

Somewhat coyly named (who anyway was Fifi?), this in fact is a solid down-to-earth hostelry on the main Grenoble to Provence road. It continues to be popular with readers, especially for its restaurant (*Michelin* red "R" and *Gault Millau toque*) which is strongly patronised by locals. "Delightful, inexpensive meals, dynamic and charming host, excellent rooms with mountain views." "Pleasing fabrics, remodelled bathrooms, pretty dining room, good food especially the cheeses." So run two recent reports. "The hotel is on several levels, with kitchens next to guest bedrooms: for this reason, some rooms may be a little noisy in late evening. Terrace and back bedrooms on upper levels have views over the mountains, with blocks of flats in the foreground." Upper rooms at the back are best.

Open 15 Mar–30 Nov. Closed Wed except in season.
Rooms 25 double – all with bath/shower and telephone. 12 in annexe.
Facilities Bar, restaurant; terrace. Large garden with swimming pool. Near river with bathing and fishing.
Location 107 km S of Grenoble, 64 km from Nyons on N75.
Credit cards All major cards accepted.
Terms Rooms 200 frs. Breakfast 30 frs. Dinner, B&B 220 frs per person. Set lunch/dinner 90 and 150 frs.

SEURRE 21250 Côte d'Or — Map 10

Le Castel — *Tel* 80.20.45.07
20 avenue de la Gare

Set in a small town on the Beaune-Dole road, this attractive Logis de France *has comfortable rooms with modern bathrooms. No lounge but a bar and flowery terrace. Big, bright dining room: excellent local cooking at reasonable prices by the* patron-*chef, who worked for 13 years in England. Closed 2 Jan–5 Feb. 20 rooms, most with bath. Rooms 190–220 frs. Set meals 95–250 frs. Endorsed this year by its original nominators, but another reader warns of train noises.*

SOMMIÈRES 30250 Gard — Map 10

Auberge du Pont Romain — *Tel* 66.80.00.58
2 rue Émile-Jamais

Converted from a 17th-century carpet factory, this somewhat unusual hotel has a riverside setting in a large and attractive Languedoc village. Big bedrooms with tiled floors, shady garden new swimming pool, pleasant staff, but owner a bit domineering. Good if somewhat rich food, including sole Lawrence Durrell, named after Sommières' most famous resident, an habitué. Open 15 Mar–

31 Dec. 18 rooms, all with bath and/or shower. B&B double 260–380 frs. Set menus 140–205 frs [1989]. Some criticisms. More reports welcome.

SOUSCEYRAC 46190 Lot — Map 10

Au Déjeuner de Sousceyrac — *Tel* 65.33.00.56

A rustic *auberge* in a remote village south of the upper Dordogne: under its previous owners, the Espinadel family, it so much delighted one *académicien*, Pierre Benoit, that he wrote a book about it, *Au déjeuner de Sousceyrac*, and the inn then took that name. Some of our own readers in the mid-1980s were equally thrilled: but then Pierre Espinadel retired and it lost its place in the Guide. Now it has been bought by Richard Piganiol, Paris-trained but a local man, and already he's won a *Michelin* red "R" and *Gault Millau* red *toque* for dishes such as paupiette de pigeon au foie gras. Our own re-nomination this year, "I doubt if the bedrooms have changed – ours was cramped but adequate. The dining room decor was freshly done, about right for this simple hotel, and the cuisine is excellent, with more than a touch of the *nouvelle*. Some French fellow-guests were high in its praise and clearly knew what they were talking about." (*Jack B Ainslie*) If you do too, please give us further news.

Open 1 Mar–1 Jan.
Rooms 10 – 3 with bath, 7 with shower.
Facilities Salon, restaurant; terrace.
Location In centre of village, which is between St-Cère and Aurillac, on D673 and D653. Parking.
Credit card Visa.
Terms Rooms: single 110 frs, double 140 frs. Breakfast 30 frs. Dinner, B&B 200–300 frs per person. Full alc 270 frs. Reduced rates and special meals for children.

STRASBOURG 67000 Bas-Rhin — Map 9

Nouvel Hôtel Maison Rouge — *Tel* 88.32.08.60

4 rue des Francs-Bourgeois — *Telex* 880130

Most Strasbourg hotels are expensive, but this medium-priced one is both quiet and very central, 30 metres from the main square, the place Kléber. It has just been renovated in "modern 1930s" style and is again approved by several readers this year, notably for its spacious, comfortable rooms and generous buffet breakfasts ("mouth-watering croissants"). Most reports commend the multilingual staff as efficient and friendly, but some have found them impersonal. The hotel caters heavily for groups but retains its character – even down to the grand piano, for guests' use, on one upper landing. "Our high room at the back was quiet and overlooked the rooftops of old Strasbourg." No restaurant, but you can eat very well all over Strasbourg – for example, expensively at the *Crocodile*, medium-pricewise at *l'Ancien Horloge* and cheaply at *l'Ancienne Douane*. (*Dr FP Woodford, Lynne and David Allen, GB Brook, and others*)

Open All year.
Rooms 1 suite, 131 double, 3 single – 125 with bath, 10 with shower, all with telephone; some with radio and TV.
Facilities 2 lifts. TV room, bar, breakfast room; conference facilities.

Location In town centre (hotel is sound-proofed). Underground parking in place Kléber nearby.
Credit cards All major cards accepted.
Terms [1989 rates] Rooms: single 320 frs, double 460 frs. Breakfast 40 frs. (No restaurant.)

Hôtel des Rohan — *Tel* 88.32.85.11
17 rue Maroquin — *Telex* 870047

"This charmer" (to quote a recent American visitor) is small and family-run, in a discreet traditional style, but is also well modernised. And it lies in the heart of the old quarter, in a cobbled pedestrian area beside the cathedral. Readers this year have again found it friendly, efficient and quiet (apart from some cathedral chimes). Though modern, it has "repro" furniture in the current French taste and is warm and comfortable. They will send a bell-boy to bring your bags from the nearby public parking. The Sunday breakfast with Kugelhopf cakes is commended. (*Prof. Sir Alan and Lady Cook, GB Hart, John Grammer, Kathy and Tony Gillett*)

Open All year.
Rooms 36 – all with bath and/or shower, telephone, radio and TV. Baby-sitter on request.
Facilities Lift. Salon with TV, 2 breakfast rooms.
Location Central, near cathedral. Parking nearby.
Credit cards Access, Visa.
Terms Rooms: single 260–485 frs, double 275–520 frs. Breakfast 35 frs on weekdays, 50 frs on Sun. (No restaurant.)

Hôtel Royal — *Tel* 88.32.28.71
3 rue du Maire Kuss — *Telex* 871 067

This well-modernised B&B hotel on a main street near the station could make a useful alternative to the Rohan *and* Maison Rouge, *both often full. Friendly and helpful staff, excellent breakfasts (continental or buffet), bedrooms and bathrooms well equipped and quiet. Patio garden, health club (sauna, jacuzzi, etc). Open all year. 50 rooms, all with bath and shower. B&B: single 330–380 frs, double 395–500 frs. No restaurant. Recent nomination. More reports please.*

TALLOIRES 74290 Haute-Savoie — Map 10

Hôtel de l'Abbaye — *Tel* 50.60.77.33
Telex 385307 ABBAYE

"A lovely hotel, expensive, yes, but not over-priced", says a visitor this year to this gracefully converted old abbey, idyllically situated beside the Lake of Annecy; it has a fine cloister, vast oak-panelled rooms, and a charming garden and shady dining terrace by the water. Some rooms are small, being former monks' cells, but others are much larger, with sofas and balconies. The food, and the "outstandingly agreeable" owner, are commended. "Ultimate luxury, and a superb setting, peaceful and relaxing. We were delighted by the quality of the food and service, down to the beachboy who looks after the hotel's private jetty. Most water sports are available next to the hotel." Modernised regional cooking: e.g. trout with cabbage, duck with raspberries – and even scrambled eggs with frogs' legs. (*Mrs C Smith, Prof. AS Douglas*)

Open All year except 15 Dec–15 Jan. Restaurant closed Sun evening and Mon midday in low season.
Rooms 2 suites, 28 double, 2 single – all with bath and shower, and telephone; TV on request. 1 ground-floor room.
Facilities Salon, TV room, library, bar, restaurant; conference facilities; concerts and exhibitions in cloisters; medical centre with hydrotherapy, whirlpool, massage, etc. Garden and terrace; private lakeside beach, windsurfing.
Location On E shore of Lake Annecy, 12 km SE of Annecy.
Restriction Not suitable for ♿.
Credit cards Access, Visa.
Terms [1989 rates] Rooms: single 580 frs, double 1,065 frs. Breakfast 50 frs. Dinner, B&B 530–775 frs per person. Set lunch/dinner 200–350 frs. Reduced rates and special meals for children.

Hôtel Beau-Site *Tel* 50.60.71.04

This pleasant and unpretentious hotel offers an alternative to the high prices of the famous *Père Bise* and the *Abbaye*, and is also set serenely by the shores of the glorious lake of Annecy, with lovely views. Two reports this year: "A most enjoyable stay, in a large comfortable room; the food uniformly good and M. Conan an attentive and pleasant host. But the lounge is small." "The five-course 130-franc [1989] menu is marvellous value, apart from disappointing soups, and service is friendly." One reader found rooms in the venerable old annexe a bit austere. And there are hints this year of a slight drop in standards (for example, garden somewhat neglected), maybe because it seems that M. Conan is now running the hotel on his own, and his wife and daughter have moved to the *Prés du Lac* (see below). (*GE Samson, GB Hart*) More reports please.

Open 15 May–Oct.
Rooms 1 suite, 27 double, 1 single – 23 with bath, 6 with shower; 18 with TV. 10 in annexe in garden.
Facilities Lift. 3 salons, dining room; terrace. Garden with private beach on lake; tennis court.
Location Central, on Lake Annecy. Parking.
Credit cards All major cards accepted.
Terms B&B: single 247–300 frs, double 370–590 frs, suite 730–880 frs; dinner, B&B 310–575 frs per person. Set lunch/dinner 130, 170 and 235 frs; full alc 270 frs. Reduced rates and special meals for children.

Hôtel Les Prés du Lac *Tel* 50.60.76.11
Clos Beau-Site *Telex* 309288 PRESLAC

A select and expensive little villa of ultra-modern design, cool and bright, with lawns in front that stretch to its private beach. Pleasant welcome, good views; rooms have patios and terraces, and new annexes are being added. Open 4 Feb–11 Nov. 9 rooms, all with bath and shower. B&B double 616–1,016 frs [1989]. *No restaurant, but meals can be taken at* Beau-Site (*above*), *owned by same family. No recent reports. More welcome.*

> If you think we have over-praised a hotel or done it an injustice, please let us know.

TAMNIÈS 24620 Dordogne — Map 10

Hôtel-Restaurant Laborderie — *Tel* 53.29.68.59

An attractive modern hotel in a truly rural setting, on the edge of a tiny hilltop village between Les Eyzies and Sarlat, facing out over rolling wooded country. The facade is of yellowish stone; inside are beamed ceilings and a log fire in winter. "Excellent hotel with fantastic food and a lovely swimming pool", says a reader this year. Others have referred to the "exceptional value", "pleasant" staff and "good rustic Périgourdin food" served in large helpings, especially on the four-course *demi-pension* menu (but one reader thought there was too much Périgourdin emphasis on duck and goose). Rooms are comfortable: some prefer those in the annexe, but one reader this year thought them a bit small and noisy. "It is a popular eating-place for locals, many of whom were being greeted as old friends." "A warm welcome from the Laborderie family, who are good with children. Bar and lovely terrace." (*Jo and Mick Feat, Diana Holmes, FR Bishop*)

Open 1 Apr–11 Nov.
Rooms 31 double – 24 with bath, 7 with shower, all with telephone. 16 in garden annexe.
Facilities Bar, 2 salons, TV room, 2 dining rooms; functions rooms; terrace. Garden with swimming pool. Lake nearby with swimming, fishing, windsurfing, sandy beach.
Location In centre of Tamniès which is 14 km NE of Les Eyzies. Parking.
Restriction Not suitable for ♿.
Credit cards Access, Visa.
Terms Double room 160–320 frs. Breakfast 25 frs. Half board 200–290 frs per person; full board 250–340 frs. Set lunch/dinner 85, 105, 150 and 240 frs; full alc 110 frs. Reduced rates for children.

TARDETS-SORHOLUS 64470 Pyrénées-Atlantiques — Map 10

Hôtel du Pont d'Abense — *Tel* 59.28.54.60
Abense-de-Haut

The old Basque medieval charades (pastorales *and* mascarades), *with their richly costumed characters, are still sometimes performed at this village south-west of Pau, where this clean, quiet and inexpensive little family-run hotel offers efficiency and friendliness, good food (some local dishes), and real value for money. Attractive small shady garden, where you can eat out in summer. Open 16 Jan–14 Nov, closed Fri out of season. 12 rooms, some with bath and shower, 130–195 frs. Breakfast 20 frs. Set menus 60–170 frs [1989]. Endorsed this year, but further reports welcome.*

THIONVILLE 57100 Moselle — Map 9

L'Horizon — *Tel* 82.88.53.65
50 route du Crève-Coeur — *Telex* 860870

This ivy-covered hostelry, smart and appealing, is an "unlikely find" on the edge of an ugly industrial town amid the decaying Lorraine steel mills, beside the Luxembourg border. But *Michelin* gives it red print for pleasantness, and our readers agree, "It is in a quiet position up on a hillside above the town, with wide views over the countryside as well as industry. We entered through wrought-iron gates, past well-kept gardens ablaze with flowers. The house is very attractive, with an elegant paved terrace at the back where you can have tea or drinks. The light and spacious hall had fresh flowers, plus a ceiling looking like something out of the *Arabian Nights*, but it was very pretty when lit up at night. Our large bedroom had French windows with wide views, and excellent lighting, but some of the fittings were a little worn. The attractive dining room had velvet drapes and a tapestry, fresh flowers and elegant table appointments. The set menu was mostly excellent, including an unusual apple sorbet between meat courses. Though quite expensive, the place has the feeling of a family-run hotel and all the staff were pleasant."

Open All year except early Jan.
Rooms 6 double, 4 single – all with bath and shower, telephone and TV. 3 in annexe
Facilities Salon, bar, TV room, breakfast room, restaurant; conference facilities; terrace. Garden.
Location 2 km NW of Thionville: follow signs to Bel-Air or Crève-Coeur. Garages.
Restriction Not suitable for ♿.
Credit cards All major cards accepted.
Terms Rooms 300–580 frs. Breakfast 45 frs. Set lunch 175 frs, dinner 195 frs.

TOULOUSE 31000 Haute-Garonne — Map 10

Grand Hôtel de l'Opéra — *Tel* 61.21.82.66
1 place du Capitole — *Fax* 61.23.41.04
Telex 521998 ESPI

This is our only downtown entry for France's fourth largest city, capital of the European aviation and aerospace industries. Its medieval rose-pink kernel is the 18th-century place du Capitole, and here stands one of the most beautiful city hotels in the French provinces, with a superb restaurant, too. "Recently converted from a 17th-century convent, it is set back in a leafy courtyard – a haven of peace and grace in this hectic town – and is run with a personal touch by its local owners who have furnished it in period style. Most bedrooms are inviting and cosy – the best is the rococo 'Suite 1260' with its lovely pale murals. The restaurant well deserves its high ratings (two *Michelin* rosettes, two red *Gault Millau toques*): its chef and co-owner, Dominique Toulousy, local boy made good, serves delicious regional-based cuisine that is inventive without being chi-chi (pigeon with crayfish, ravioli with truffles, and an unusual cassoulet). His wife is a charming hostess. On fine days you eat under awnings in the flowery patio, beside an ornamental pool that is also the hotel's tiny swimming pool (bathers are forbidden at meal-times, as they would splash the diners)." "The restaurant has several small rooms, some of whose walls are mirrors: one has all four walls made of mirrors – a narcissist's paradise." Others have concurred: but an inspector this year felt that his room in the 700-franc bracket lacked character; and he disliked the breakfast, even more so the loud musak served with it.

> In your own interest, always check latest tariffs with hotels when you make your bookings.

Open All year. Restaurant closed 2 weeks Aug.
Rooms 15 suites, 39 double, 9 single – 61 with bath and shower, 2 with shower, all with telephone, radio, TV, and air-conditioning; most with 24-hour room service; baby-sitting on request. 4 in annexe.
Facilities Lift. Lobbies, salon, bar, restaurant, brasserie; conference facilities; sports room with sauna and whirlpool. Garden with terrace, restaurant and swimming pool.
Location Central (windows double-glazed). Underground carpark in square.
Credit cards All major cards accepted.
Terms Rooms: single 400–750 frs, double 700–750 frs, suite 980–1,150 frs. Breakfast 60 frs. Set lunch/dinner 280–380 frs (c. 150 frs in brasserie); full alc 400 frs (c. 170 frs in brasserie). Reduced rates for children sharing parents' room.

TOURNUS 71700 Saône-et-Loire — Map 10

Hotel de la Paix — *Tel* 85.51.01.85
9 rue Jean-Jaurès

In the town centre, near the Saône, an unassuming little Swiss-owned hotel, very well run, with comfortable carpeted rooms and good food. Closed 5 Jan–1 Feb, 15–24 Apr, 21–30 Oct, Tue in winter. 23 rooms, many with bath and/or shower. Rooms 205–278 frs. Breakfast 22 frs. Set menus 68–138 frs [1989]. New nomination. More reports welcome.

Le Rempart — *Tel* 85.51.10.56
2 avenue Gambetta — *Telex* 351019

On the main street of a beautiful old town by the Saône, with a fine ancient abbey, here is a modernised hotel with unremarkable decor but bright and comfortable rooms (double-glazing keeps out the noise) and affable service. Pretentious-looking menu, but excellent regional cooking (frogs' legs in garlic, etc.), deserving its rosette and toque. *Open all year. 38 rooms, all with bath. B&B: single 300–330 frs, double 490 frs. Set menus 150–350 frs. Recent nomination. More reports welcome.*

TOURS 37000 Indre-et-Loire — Map 8

Hôtel Colbert — *Tel* 47.66.61.56
78 rue Colbert

A small family-run B&B hotel, in a narrow shopping street near the cathedral and within walking distance of the pleasantly restored Vieux Tours quarter, full of bars and little restaurants. Clean and comfortable, efficient and friendly. 18 rooms, most with bath and/or shower. B&B 208–306 frs. No restaurant. Recent nomination. More reports welcome.

Hôtel Royal — *Tel* 47.64.71.78
65 avenue de Grammont — *Telex* 752006 LE ROYAL

On a main street close to the centre of Tours, but quiet: a useful modernised hotel with Louis XV and XVI 'repro' furnishings, good bathrooms and breakfasts, friendly service, and garage. No restaurant, but lots nearby. 35 rooms, all with bath and shower, 265–312 frs. Breakfast 29 frs. New nomination. More reports welcome.

TOURTOUR 83690 Var — Map 11

La Bastide de Tourtour — *Tel* 94.70.57.30, *Telex* 970827

The medieval hill-village of Tourtour is today a fashionable residential centre and a showpiece: its lovely facades of golden-brown stone have been scoured clean. There are wide vistas on all sides, and the Gorges du Verdon are quite close. *La Bastide,* smart and expensive, was custom-built in the 1960s in mock-château style, and stands in its own wooded garden on the edge of the village. An enthusiastic report this year refers to the "calm, relaxing atmosphere amongst the fragrant pines", as well as to "courteous service and excellent cuisine – the pension menu was different on all eight nights of our stay." Last year, another reader was also pleased, "I had a large and cheery room with cloth-covered walls and matching bed-covers. First-floor balcony rooms face the big swimming pool and are just above the outdoor dining terrace. This makes for some noise and lack of privacy, and I'd rather recommend the second-floor rooms which also have a better view. The food was superb (*Michelin* rosette), especially the ravioli stuffed with goats' cheese and the sweetbreads in a wine sauce. The dining room is intimate and romantic, with doors open to the terrace. Etienne and Francine Laurent, the owners, work hard to give their guests a perfect stay." They also enjoy showing their rare collection of 200 peasant bonnets and hats. (*M and D Chambers, Susan Schmidt*)

Open 15 Mar–31 Oct. Restaurant closed Tue midday, Mon in low season.
Rooms 23 double, 2 single – all with bath and shower, telephone and TV.
Facilities Lift. Lounge, bar, restaurant; exercise room and jacuzzi. Garden with swimming pool and tennis court.
Location 500 m SE of Tourtour on road to Draguignan (20 km). Parking.
Credit cards All major cards accepted.
Terms Rooms: single 350–450 frs, double 400–1,100 frs. Breakfast 60 frs. Set lunch 150 frs (except Sun) 250 and 330 frs; dinner 250 and 330 frs; full alc 350 frs. Reduced rates and special meals for children.

TRÉBEURDEN 22560 Côtes-du-Nord — Map 8

Hôtel Ti al-Lannec — *Tel* 96.23.57.26
Allée de Mézo Guen — *Telex* 740656

Few other seaside hotels in France are more warmly liked by readers than this handsome grey-and-white mansion, set high above the sea in its quiet garden on the edge of a pleasant family bathing resort; it's on an especially delightful stretch of the North Breton coast, where rocks in strange shapes alternate with sandy coves. "A marvellous hotel with excellent food and charming staff; our beautifully furnished room had panoramic views over the bay"; "a superb meal and luxurious lounges". Those two 1988/9 reports echo many earlier ones. The large balconies, immaculate gardens, and attentive owners are all praised. Some rooms have four-poster beds. A big light dining room with sea views; snug,

Don't trust out-of-date Guides. Many hotels are dropped and new ones added every year.

elegant lounge with period decor; white tables and chairs under parasols and trees on the lawn. Rare for a summer seaside hotel, the cooking (seafood especially) wins a red *Gault Millau toque*. (*Mrs JP Holwell, ECM Begg, BH Jenkinson, and others*) Also recommended this year is another very select hotel in Trébeurden, the *Manoir de Lan-Kerellec* (telephone 96.23.50.09), rather more expensive and with possibly even better food (*Michelin* rosette): we'd be glad of reports on that too.

Open 17 Mar–12 Nov. Restaurant closed Mon lunchtime 18 Sept–12 Jun.
Rooms 21 double, 2 single – all with bath and shower, and telephone; TV on request.
Facilities Salon, TV/games room, bar, restaurant; conference facilities. Garden with outdoor chess, table tennis and boules; path leading down to sandy beach, safe bathing and fishing.
Location In centre of village. Signposted from Lannion.
Restriction Not suitable for ♿.
Credit cards Access, Amex, Visa.
Terms [1989 rates] Rooms: single 295 frs, double 540 frs. Breakfast 42 frs. Dinner, B&B 375–455 frs per person. Set lunch/dinner 155–285 frs. Reduced rates for children under 8; special menus.

TRÉGUIER 22220 Côtes-du-Nord — Map 8

Kastell Dinec'h — *Tel* 96.92.49.39

Tréguier is an old grey Breton town with a fine cathedral, not far from the beaches of Perros-Guirec and Trébeurden. Just outside it, liberally daubed in red print by the French guides, is this promising Guide newcomer: "A charming little hotel set quietly down a country lane. It's an old farmhouse in a pretty garden (with small swimming pool); the comfortable rooms, nicely decorated in Laura Ashley-ish prints, are in the main house and a converted stable block. The food deserves its *Michelin* red 'R': we enjoyed salmon with sorrel sauce, a cassolette of lobster tails, chicken with morels, scallops in Pernod sauce. Good breakfasts, too, and friendly service. Not the place to avoid fellow-Brits." (But where is, in northern France these days?) (*Mrs J Thomas*)

Open 15 Mar–12 Oct, 27 Oct–31 Dec. Closed Tue evening and Wed in low season. Restaurant closed for lunch
Rooms 15 – most with bath and/or shower.
Facilities Lounge, restaurant. Garden with small swimming pool.
Location 2 km SW of Tréguier, off the Lannion road.
Credit cards Access, Visa.
Terms Rooms 220–350 frs. Breakfast 35 frs. Dinner, B&B 240–320 frs per person. Set dinner 90–240 frs.

TRÉMOLAT 24510 Dordogne — Map 10

Hôtel Panoramic — *Tel* 53.22.80.42
Route du Cingle de Trémolat

In a superb position overlooking a great loop in the Dordogne river, just outside Trémolat village (where Chabrol set and filmed Le Boucher*), this old stone mansion is now an unpretentious hotel where the welcome is warm, the rooms plain but pleasant, and the food excellent, including breakfast; terrace for drinks and meals, with that fine view. Closed Jan, maybe also Dec. 24 rooms, most with* *private facilities. B&B double 296 frs. Set menus 60–195 frs. Newly nominated for good value. More reports welcome.*

TRIGANCE 83840 Var — Map 11

Château de Trigance *Tel* 94.76.91.18

We've had a mixed bag of reports in 1988/9 for this "most idiosyncratic hotel" – a boldly battlemented medieval pile on a hilltop above the village of Trigance, only about ten kilometres from the dramatic Gorges du Verdon in upper Provence. Access is not easy, by a steep rocky path and stone stair, but you are rewarded by wide views over the encircling rocky hills, where one reader "felt a great sense of pastoral peace" as he watched a flock of sheep being herded. The castle is owned by Jean-Claude Thomas, a Paris ex-businessman, who has turned it into a small hotel. "The physical setting is dramatic and M. Thomas is a superb and entertaining host. I find myself chuckling whenever I recall our stay." "Very imposing from a distance. Warm personal welcome – it's worth staying just to converse with the owner. Rooms are severe and dark, but reasonably priced. Dining room and bar charming; food average. A unique place full of heart." "The only noises to disrupt us were the sheepbells and the cuckoos. But the food was pretentious and disappointing." Some readers have enjoyed the "romantic vaulted restaurant", but one has disliked its "medieval chamber music"; some have warmed to the "lovely canopied beds", but others have found the rooms a bit oppressive. (*David and Lynne Allen, William A Grant, and others*) A new entrance is planned, eliminating the steep steps – "pity, for the access is part of the charm."

Open 18 Mar–11 Nov. Restaurant closed Wed midday in Mar, Apr, Oct, Nov.
Rooms 2 suites, 8 double – all with bath and shower, telephone and TV.
Facilities Salon, dining room, large terrace.
Location 20 km SW of Castellane, 12 km NW of Comps-sur-Artuby.
Restriction Not suitable for ♿.
Credit cards All major cards accepted.
Terms B&B: double 500–660 frs, suite 730 frs. Set lunch/dinner 160, 220 and 300 frs. Reduced rates for children; special meals on request.

UZÈS 30700 Gard — Map 10

Hôtel d'Entraigues *Tel* 66.22.32.68
8 rue de la Calade

In the rolling *garrigue* country north of Nîmes, an enchanting old town of narrow streets and lofty towers: the tallest belongs to the massive turreted ducal castle. Secluded in one of the alleys below is the *Entraigues*, a 16th-century mansion once the home of a general. Its conversion into a select little hotel is supremely aesthetic but not cosy – soft-hued stone and dim-lit low-vaulted ceilings. It is under the same ownership as the *Château* at Arpaillargues (q.v.) and could provide a useful and cheaper alternative. You can eat out on a terrace. "Comfortable and very good value: croissants delicious", is one report this year. Uzès has a classical music festival in July, and quaint country fairs in the main square throughout the year – e.g. pig fair in February, garlic fair in June.

Open All year. Restaurant closed midday on Tue and Wed in season, all day Tue, Wed midday in low season.
Rooms 17 double, 1 single – all with bath, shower, telephone; some with TV. Some in annexe.
Facilities Salons, TV room, bar, restaurant.
Location Central, opposite cathedral, but quietly situated. Uzès is 25 km N of Nîmes. Parking.
Restriction Not suitable for ♿.
Credit cards All major cards accepted.
Terms [1989 rates] Rooms 225–350 frs. Breakfast 25 and 30 frs. Half board 135 frs per person added to room rates. Set lunch/dinner 75 and 130 frs; full alc 210 frs. Extra bed in room 70 frs. Special meals for children on request.

VALENCE 26000 Drôme — Map 10

Restaurant Pic — *Tel* 75.44.15.32
285 avenue Victor-Hugo

In a tree-lined street on the edge of dusty Valence, in the Rhône valley, Jacques Pic and his charming wife run one of France's most renowned restaurants: he earns three *Michelin* rosettes, just as his father did here in the 1930s. As well as a shady garden and just four pretty bedrooms, they offer *nouvelle cuisine* at its least affected, fully worth the high prices. One recent visitor found the meal "elegant" and had a "marvellous" room with oriental rugs and marble bathroom. An American reader adds, "Splendid food, perfect and charming service. We were invited to the kitchen after dinner." "Helpful staff, incredible (but simple) comfort in the bedrooms and total luxury in the dining room. The whole place is so undaunting, the atmosphere is charming and there's no snootiness by anyone, in contrast to what happens at many other prestigious places. Breakfast a dream of warm fresh lemon brioche." (*Ed and Meg Raftis, CM*)

Open All year except Aug and 1 week in Feb. Closed Wed, and Sun evening.
Rooms 2 suites, 2 double – all with bath and shower, telephone and TV.
Facilities Sitting room, dining room. Courtyard and garden.
Location 1 km S of town centre. Take *autoroute* exit for Valence Sud, follow "Victor Hugo" sign. Parking.
Restriction Not suitable for ♿.
Credit cards All major cards accepted.
Terms Rooms: double 400–420 frs, suite 550–700 frs. Breakfast 50 frs. Set lunch 400–500 frs; full alc 500-600 frs. Special meals for children.

VALLIÈRES 37230 Indre et Loire — Map 8

Manoir du Grand Martigny — *Tel* 47.42.29.87

Friendly and inexpensive guest house in 16-acre park, five kilometres west of Tours in 16th-century manor lovingly restored by M. and Mme Desmarais who speak excellent English. "Makes no pretence of being commercially run; atmosphere relaxed and warm; excellent breakfasts. Ideal for Loire sightseeing." Open Mar–Nov, by arrangement in winter. 7 rooms, all with private facilities. B&B double 370–500 frs [1989]. *Evening meals not normally served, but dinner* en famille *by arrangement for minimum of 6, 160 frs with wine. New nomination. More reports please.*

VAL SUZON 21121 Côte d'Or — Map 10

Hostellerie du Val Suzon and **Chalet de la Fontaine aux Geais** — *Tel* 80.35.60.15, *Telex* 351454
Val Suzon Fontaine-lès-Dijon

This hamlet north-west of Dijon is a good base for visiting the city – and here you will find Burgundian rusticity at more moderate prices than in most of our entries for this sophisticated Dijon/Beaune area. It is a double entry – a restaurant-with-rooms and a small chalet-hotel close by, both owned by the same family. A reader suggests, "The best bet is to book a room at the *Chalet*, a two-minute walk up the hill above the *Hostellerie*: its rooms are quieter and more spacious, and have a nice outlook across the gardens to the hills beyond. The grounds are well manicured and contain two aviaries (*geai*=jay). The *Hostellerie* is the restaurant for both buildings; the food is almost one-rosette standard, far better than at many similar country places around, and you can eat outside on fine days or by the fire in winter. The whole place has an air of unpretentious efficiency and relaxed charm." Readers this year have commented on the attractive setting, friendly owners and staff, good value and good cooking (*Gault Millau* gives it two *toques* for such dishes as ravioli of morilles with foie gras). (*ME Chamberland, PJ Robinson, Michel Bourdrez*)

Open 15 Jan–15 Nov. Closed Wed and Thur lunchtime 15 Jan – 30 Apr.
Rooms 16 double, 1 single – 9 with bath and shower, 8 with shower, all with telephone. 10 in the *Chalet*.
Facilities Lounge, bar, 2 dining rooms. Garden.
Location 16 km NW of Dijon, just off N71 to Châtillon.
Restriction Not suitable for ♿.
Credit cards All major cards accepted.
Terms Rooms: single 220 frs, double 340 frs. Breakfast 40 frs. Dinner, B&B: single 440 frs, double 700 frs. Set lunch/dinner 140, 200 and 320 frs; full alc 300 frs. Reduced rates and special meals for children.

VANNES 56000 Morbihan — Map 8

Le Roof — *Tel* 97.63.47.47, *Telex* 951843
Presque'ile de Conleau

In a pleasant waterside setting on the Gulf of Morbihan, just south of Vannes, this spruce white-walled hotel with its odd franglais *name has an outdoor dining terrace facing the bay, and serves good fish. Large bar, smallish bedrooms. Rebuilding and enlarging in progress, 1989. 43 rooms, all with bath and shower. B&B double 360–460 frs. Set menus 70–300 frs. New nomination. More reports welcome.*

VELLERON 84740 Vaucluse — Map 11

Hostellerie de la Grangette — *Tel* 90.20.00.77

A beautifully converted manor house, alone in the open country of the Vaucluse plain, just off the main D938 from L'Isle-sur-Sorgue to Carpentras. Semi-wild grounds with pool and tennis; ornate bedrooms with oak beams, antiques, draped curtains, and views of the Provençal hills. Willing staff, and good sophisticated food (not cheap) in a lovely dining room. 17 rooms, all with bath and or shower. B&B double 500–710 frs. Set menus 139–375 frs. Recent nomination. More reports please.

VENCE 06140 Alpes-Maritimes **Map 11**

Relais Cantemerle *Tel* 93.58.08.18
258 chemin Cantemerle

In a peaceful setting on the southern outskirts of much-visited Vence, this smart little modern hotel in local Provençal style, lyrically attractive, consists of a sequence of self-contained split-level apartments, set around a swimming pool and garden, beautifully landscaped, with lawns well manicured. Breezy modern decor with traditional touches. A report this year, "An enormous room with a lovely antique bureau, very good dinner (perfect noisettes d'agneau), well-groomed staff, maybe a bit too laid-back, a peaceful, friendly ambience and fantastic value for money". (*K Jardine-Young*)

Open 15 Mar–end Oct. Restaurant closed Wed.
Rooms 19 – all with bath, shower, telephone, TV, mini-bar and terrace.
Facilities Lounge, bar, restaurant. Garden with unheated swimming pool; terrace, where meals are served.
Location 1 km S of Vence. Parking.
Restriction Not suitable for ♿.
Credit cards All major cards accepted.
Terms Rooms [1989 rates] 550–790 frs. Breakfast 60 frs. Dinner, B&B 250 frs per person added. Set lunch/dinner 200 frs; full alc 300 frs. Reduced rates and special meals for children.

Hôtel Diana *Tel* 93.58.28.56
Avenue des Poilus

Several returning regulars have again enjoyed this well-run modern hotel near the centre of a busy little Provençal town. Bowls of flowers, helpful staff – just one gripe about inadequate dusting of rooms. Not all rooms are spacious, but they are nicely designed and furnished, with well-equipped *cuisinettes* (washing up is part of the hotel's service). The underground garage is not easy to operate: take advice. Breakfasts are variously described as "generous" or "adequate". The hotel has no restaurant, but it will prepare snacks such as omelettes, while not far away the inexpensive *Farigoule* is again commended. Do not miss Matisse's lovely Chapel of the Rosary in Vence itself (open Tuesdays and Thursdays only), nor the mountain drive to the north, the *circuit des clues*. (*Philippa Herbert, Kay and Neville Varley*)

Open All year.
Rooms 25 double – all with bath and telephone; 15 with kitchenette.
Facilities Lift. 2 salons with TV, bar, library, 2 breakfast rooms. Terrace; solarium.
Location 100 metres from town centre. Garage.
Restriction Not suitable for ♿.
Credit cards All major cards accepted.
Terms Rooms 300 frs. Breakfast 35 frs. (No restaurant.)

VERVINS 02140 Aisne Map 9

La Tour du Roy *Tel* 23.98.00.11
45 rue du Général Leclerc *Telex* 155445

A converted manor house, built on the ramparts of a small town near the Belgian border, in an area of orchards and streams. It is run with warmth and skill by Annie Desvignes, who is also chef – and the food (*Michelin* rosette) and service have again been admired this year. "Annie's robust and enthusiastic presence was obvious, and Monsieur, too, was full of bonhomie, while the staff were cheerful and attentive, especially with children. We have memories of a delicious light monkfish mousseline with prawn sauce, mixed fish with ginger sauce, and a cheese trolley that sent you to bed dreaming." Another reader also liked the food and Annie, but thought her room "fairly basic". Not all are basic, however, as witness this earlier account: "When we asked for a 'nice' room, Madame said, 'We will put you in the Tower', and opening our front door we found ourselves in an enormous circular bathroom with large near-circular bath, and a toilet which was literally a throne, made of decorative porcelain, with chair back and arm rests. We then climbed the spiral staircase to another circular room with a high-domed ceiling, a small decorative sink, and our bed. It was kitschy but comfortable." The hotel is exceptionally kind to children, and it has a pretty garden. (*Diana Cooper*) Front rooms can be noisy.

Open All year except 15 Jan–15 Feb.
Rooms 1 triple, 13 double, 1 single – all with bath and/or shower, telephone, radio, TV, mini-bar and baby-listening. 2 ground-floor rooms in bungalow annexe.
Facilities Salon, bar, TV room, restaurant; functions room.
Location Vervins is off N2, 71 km N of Reims. Hotel is central. Parking.
Credit cards All major cards accepted.
Terms Rooms: single 200–250 frs, double 200–380 frs, suite 450 frs. Breakfast 40 frs. Dinner, B&B: single 390 frs, double 680 frs. Full alc 325 frs. Reduced rates and special meals for children.

VÉZAC 24220 Dordogne Map 10

Rochecourbe *Tel* 53.29.50.79

A small manor house amid lush meadows and gentle wooded hills, in one of the loveliest parts of the Dordogne valley, between Beynac and Domme. "We were delighted with this charming old house", runs a letter this year; "we had a large, comfortable room and liked the beautifully furnished salon – such comfortable antiques are rare in French hotels. Service friendly and attentive." Others have spoken of the charm of the owners, the Rogers. "The old house has been restored with great care. Our spacious room looked out on three castles. Breakfasts are excellent." A spiral staircase in the tower leads from the garden (reclining chairs for drinks) up to the bedrooms. This quiet rural setting is slightly marred by a nearby road and railway, but "they do not intrude unduly". No restaurant, but Madame will serve residents with light meals to order: "Excellent cooking, especially the warm salads of smoked duck breast, crisp skinned trout and luscious puddings." (*Mrs JW Makinson, David Lees*)

Open Probably 1 May–31 Oct.
Rooms 1 suite, 4 double – all with bath and shower, and telephone.

Facilities Salon with TV, breakfast room. Garden.
Location 8 km SW of Sarlat on D57.
Credit cards Access, Visa.
Terms B&B: double 350 frs, suite 450 frs. (No restaurant.)

VÉZELAY 89450 Yonne — Map 10

L'Espérance

St-Père

Tel 86.33.20.45
Fax 86.33.26.15
Telex 800005

Just as the hilltop Romanesque basilica of Vézelay, in northern Burgundy, is one of France's 20 finest buildings, so Marc Meneau's *Espérance* is one of its 20 finest restaurants (three *Michelin* rosettes, four red *Gault Millau toques*). Small and very chic, it lies in a valley just east of the little town, on the Avallon road. Antique furniture, strikingly pretty bedrooms; a garden with a rose arbour and a stream lit up at night. Many bedrooms are in the nearby converted mill. With some caveats, approval this year has again been intense: "Very expensive, but value for money; as near perfect a French hotel/restaurant as I know. Our suite in the mill displayed impeccable taste and luxury, the bathroom being the ultimate for any sybarite (it included a huge cactus). An immense basket of fruit was delivered. Service and reception are very welcoming and friendly, the food needless to say is superb (never has one been so overwhelmed with chocolates at the end of a meal), and breakfast (with scrambled eggs, etc) is the best one has had in France." "An attractive suite in the mill, with expensive if rather heavy rustic-style decor. In the dining room, looking onto the attractive garden, we enjoyed oysters in watercress aspic, brilliant salmon in apple sauce, but the puddings are lack-lustre." The restaurant is in three big glass pavilions full of house plants. Earlier reports: "Sipping drinks on the terrace or in the glass-domed cocktail bar to the sound of a grand piano is a delight. Marc Meneau greets diners with a modest charm. (*Phillip Gill, Helen and Charles Priday, Rosamund Hebdon and others*) One couple begged to differ, feeling that the hotel had become very commercial since their last visit – tour coaches, a gift shop selling purses (!) and staff less friendly than before.

Open All year except early Jan–early Feb. Restaurant closed Tue and Wed midday.
Rooms 4 suites, 17 double – all with bath and shower, telephone, radio and TV; babysitter on request. 8 in annexe.
Facilities Lounge, bar, restaurant. Garden.
Location 3 km E of Vézelay on D957.
Credit cards Amex, Diners, Visa.
Terms [1989 rates] Rooms 600–950 frs. Breakfast 90 frs. Set lunch 280 frs, dinner 520 frs.

Résidence Hôtel Le Pontot

Place de la Mairie

Tel 86.33.24.40

A fine 15th-century stone house, with 18th-century additions, situated near the town centre with superb views over the rooftops and the rolling countryside below. It has long been the home of Charles Thum, an American architect, who has converted it into a select and charming bed-and-breakfast hotel, managed by Christian Abadie. An inspector has written recently: "We were treated with great courtesy, as though we had come to stay in a private house. You enter through an arched doorway into a delightful small walled garden; a stone-flagged spiral stairway leads up to the bedrooms which share a small pleasant lounge. Our suite of two rooms and bathroom was ideal for a couple with children; it was comfortable, furnished with a mixture of antiques and simple modern pieces. Breakfast, beautifully presented with blue and gold Limoges china, can be taken in the garden or in a blue-panelled Louis XV salon; coffee and croissants were excellent. "Superb bedroom and breakfasts. Messieurs Thum and Abadie were attentive and erudite hosts, and the measures of drinks were gigantic, served in attractive glassware."

Open 17 Mar–Nov.
Rooms 3 suites, 7 double – 9 with bath, 1 with shower, all with telephone, radio and coffee-making facilities. 1 suite in separate wing.
Facilities Entrance hall with boutique, lounge, bar, breakfast room. Walled garden with breakfast and bar service in fine weather. Canal trips, hot-air ballooning by prearrangement.
Location Central. "Ignore signs at entrance to town inviting tourists to walk. Drive straight up main street to Place de la Mairie and park."
Restriction Not suitable for ♿.
Credit cards Access, Amex, Visa.
Terms Rooms: double 450–600 frs, suite 550–750 frs. Breakfast 50 frs. Extra bed 100 frs for children sharing parents' room. (No restaurant).

VIEILLE-TOULOUSE 31320 Haute-Garonne — Map 10

Hôtel de la Flânerie — *Tel* 61.73.39.12
Route de Lacroix-Falgarde — *Telex* 531666

An unusual little hotel six miles south of Toulouse along D4, on a hillside with a splendid view over the curving Garonne just below. The cosy bedrooms are got up in kitschy boudoir style, with a nicely naughty flavour. Period furnishings, affable and very helpful owners, sleek lounge (with questionable decor), and a lovely terrace above the river where drinks and the (very good) breakfasts can be served. Central Toulouse is 15 minutes by car, more at rush hour. 12 rooms, all with bath or shower. Rooms 175–290 frs, breakfast 36 frs [1989]. No restaurant (but TV *suppers served). Recent nomination. More reports would be welcome.*

VILLEFRANCHE-SUR-MER 06230 Alpes-Maritimes — Map 11

Hôtel Welcome et Restaurant St-Pierre — *Tel* 93.76.76.93
1 quai Courbet — *Telex* 470281

Villefranche is a lively and colourful old fishing-port on a deep bay – remarkably unspoilt, seeing that Nice and Monte Carlo are both so close. The *Welcome*, a classic and dignified hotel recently modernised, stands on the harbour opposite the tiny fishermen's chapel decorated by Cocteau. In the past its name has sometimes been judged inappropriate, but this year a reader found the staff "charming" – and the food excellent. "Rooms reasonable, with harbourside balconies; the smaller ones at the top, though without bath, are the most quiet and pleasant." "A few faults, such as broken lamp-bulbs, but the food at the delightful ground-floor *St-*

Pierre restaurant was exceptional, especially fish in a variety of ways" (if you want a cheaper and less smart alternative for a meal, try *Ste-Germaine* down the quay, says a reader). Night noises may include some trains, and: "The US Navy was in town and 'Jingle Bells' outside the door at 2 am was not 'Welcome'." (*Peter Wade, Brian MacArthur*)

Open All year except 25 Nov–18 Dec.
Rooms 35 – all with bath and/or shower, telephone, mini-bar and air-conditioning; TV on request.
Facilities Lift, ramps. Breakfast room, bar with TV, restaurant. Terrace. 600 m from beach; windsurfing, scuba diving etc.
Location Central, on quai. Parking nearby.
Credit cards All major cards accepted.
Terms [1989 rates] Rooms 490–770 frs. Breakfast 35 frs. Dinner, B&B 290–525 frs per person. Set lunch/dinner 145–310 frs. Reduced rates and special meals for children.

VILLENEUVE-DE-RIVIÈRE 31800 Haute-Garonne — Map 10

Hostellerie des Cèdres — *Tel* 61.89.36.00

In a village just west of St-Gaudens, near the Pyrenean foothills, a stylishly converted 17th-century manor with cedars and palms in its wide courtyard. Garden with swimming pool. Large, pretty rooms (the lightest have shower, not bath). Good regional cooking (Gault Millau toque). *18 rooms, all with bath and/or shower. B&B double 356–526 frs. Set menus 120–265 frs. Attractive new nomination. More reports welcome.*

VILLENEUVE-LÈS-AVIGNON 30400 Gard — Map 11

Hostellerie le Prieuré
7 place du Chapitre

Tel 90.25.18.20
Fax 90.25.45.39
Telex 431042

The town of Villeneuve contains almost as much of interest as Avignon itself, directly across the Rhône. Relics of the great age when the popes held sway in their palace include the gigantic Chartreuse, the Fort St-André, the municipal museum (superb painting by Enguerrand Charonton) and the church of Notre-Dame with its remarkable carved ivory statuette of the Virgin. Next to this church is the *Prieuré*, a 14th-century priory, well converted and run with panache by the Mille family as an elegant and sophisticated little hotel. It looks out over fields and an ugly school building.

"I judge this to be the nearly perfect hotel", says a returning admirer this year; "it is larger and grander than when I knew it in the old days, but the Milles have managed to keep an air of informality, and service is excellent. The garden is pleasant and the big shady terrace delightful. The food is not of the highest flight but good and reliable." (*Jacquetta Priestley*) Others have written: "A superb place, expensive but not unfairly so. We had lovely rooms in a new block, with balconies facing the pool. Dinner by candle-light on the lawn under the plane trees is most romantic." "A very special place. The public rooms and gardens are delightful, the service faultless. We preferred the rooms in the old building to those in the new extension." "Beautiful, desirable and totally romantic." (*M and D*

Chambers; also SJ) You can choose between a "characterful" bedroom in the old building (antiques, but modern bathrooms) or a larger, more expensive one in a new annexe (wide balcony, big sofas). Noise from a nearby railway has irritated some readers.

Open 10 Mar–8 Nov. Restaurant closed 1 May.
Rooms 10 suites, 19 double, 7 single – all with bath, shower, telephone, radio, TV, double glazing, air-conditioning. 17 rooms in annexe. Some have access for ♿.
Facilities Lift. 2 salons, bridge room, library, bar, breakfast room, dining room and dining patio. Large garden with 2 tennis courts and swimming pool.
Location 3 km N of Avignon. In village centre, behind the church. Carpark.
Credit cards All major cards accepted.
Terms B&B: single 525 frs, double 930–1,130 frs, suite 1,350–1,700 frs; dinner, B&B: single 785 frs, double 1,450–1,650 frs, suite 1,870–2,220 frs. Set lunch/dinner 220–380 frs; full alc 360 frs. Special meals for children on request.

VONNAS 01540 Ain — Map 10

Hôtel-Restaurant Georges Blanc

Tel 74.50.00.10
Fax 74.50.08.80
Telex 380776 GEBLANC

"In our opinion, easily the best of France's three-rosette establishments", is the weighty judgment of two of our most trusty connoisseurs of the French scene, who have again revisited M. Blanc's famous and sophisticated little hotel-restaurant. Half-timbered and pink-bricked, it stands in pretty countryside beside the river Veyle on the edge of a quiet *village fleuri* between Mâcon and Bourg-en-Bresse. "Our dinner was superb, the hotel is always immaculate, the staff welcoming and friendly: when I arrived for lunch with my jacket soaked in a storm, Madame Blanc immediately dried and pressed it." Her husband retains his top-level rating of three rosettes and four red gables in *Michelin*, and four red *toques* in *Gault Millau*, and our readers remain *d'accord* as ever. "They are always happy to serve just one or two light courses, if you are staying for lunch *and* dinner and two full meals are too much." "Better than ever, with new recipes and puddings", is another comment this year; "and the sommelier, who is English, knows his job to perfection". "Georges Blanc *is* Vonnas, with two shops in the village selling his provisions and souvenirs. But there's a refreshing candour about his enterprise. His chefs can be seen at work as you walk through the kitchen to the large elegant dining room with its beamed ceiling, antiques and tapestries." Rooms vary in grandeur, some are small and plain, some huge with marble bathroom. A "winter garden" – a bar/lounge area, which can become a riverside terrace in summer, but with a roaring log fire in winter – has recently been added. (*Pat and Jeremy Temple, M and D Chambers, David Grant*) An 11-room annexe, *La Cour aux fleurs*, was being added in 1989.

Open All year except 2 Jan–9 Feb. Restaurant closed Wed and Thur (except 15 June–15 Sept when open Thur evening).
Rooms 6 suites, 35 double – all with bath and/or shower, telephone, TV, mini-bar and air-conditioning. 11 in annexe.
Facilities Lift. 2 lounges, breakfast room, bar, dining room; conference room; winter garden, terrace on river Veyle. 2½-acre grounds with tennis court, putting-green, swimming pool and helipad.
Location 20 km E of Mâcon. From N leave *autoroute* at Mâcon Nord; from S leave *autoroute* at Villefranche, then direction Châtillon-sur-Chalaronne, Neuville-les-Dames and Vonnas.

Credit cards All major cards accepted.
Terms Rooms: double 450–1,000 frs, suite 1,900 frs. Breakfast 65 frs. Set meals 350 and 540 frs; full alc 540 frs. Special meals for children.

WIERRE-EFFROY 62720 Pas-de-Calais — Map 9

Ferme-Auberge du Vert — *Tel* 21.92.82.10

A number of French farms nowadays have turned themselves into small *auberges* while retaining their farming activities. This one, just off the Boulogne to Calais road, in a truly rural setting, provides visitors with an opportunity to move straight from the hassle of hovercraft and ferries into the bosom of French peasant life – into a real farmyard full of ducks and geese. And a number of readers in 1988/9 have again been enthusiastic. It is not exactly a hotel, and the pine-clad rooms fashioned from converted barns are fairly small and a bit basic, but they are very clean and good value. One reader adored sleeping in a modernised hayloft, another found the early cries of geese an acceptable alarm clock. Everyone likes the charm and skilful management of the Bernard family. They have now handed over the restaurant to separate management, and it gets very crowded with local French at weekends, but the food is still approved by readers as sound and unpretentious, not aiming at high gastronomy. Recent comments: "A delightful place, with total peace"; "M. Bernard is a genial host and his prices absurdly reasonable"; "Breakfast was as substantial as required, with coffee drunk in traditional bowls. A really warm welcome with lots of handshaking." Bicycles are for hire. (*Jo and Mick Feat, BN Turvey, H Schon, PJ Robinson, HR, and others*)

Open All year. Restaurant closed 15 Dec–31 Jan.
Rooms 1 suite, 13 double, 1 single – 2 with bath and shower, 13 with shower, all with telephone; suite has TV. 12 in 2 farm buildings. 4 ground-floor rooms.
Facilities Salon with TV, bar/restaurant, breakfast room.
Location Off N1 between Calais (N) and Boulogne (S); SE of Marquise. Follow signs "Ferme H** Auberge" from Marquise and from Hypermarket Auchan.
Credit card Visa.
Terms B&B: single 250 frs, double 400 frs. Set lunch/dinner 80–150 frs. Reduced rates and special meals for children.

****

Traveller's tale *Through the whole south of France, the inns are cold, damp, dark, dismal and dirty; the landlords equally disobliging and rapacious; the servants awkward, sluttish and slothful; and the postillions lazy, lounging, greedy and impertinent. If you chide them for lingering, they will continue to delay you the longer; if you chastise them with sword, cane, cudgel, or horse-whip, they will either disappear entirely, and leave you without resource; or they will find means to take vengeance by overturning your carriage. The best method I know of travelling with any degree of comfort is to allow yourself to become the dupe of imposition, and stimulate their endeavours by extraordinary gratifications.*
Tobias Smollett (*Travels through France and Italy, 1766*)

****

Germany

BÖTTINGERHAUS AND GÄSTEHAUS STEINMÜHLE, BAMBERG

ALFDORF 7077 Baden-Württemberg **Map 13**

Haghof Hotel-Restaurant *Tel* (07182) 5 45
Telex 7246712

In pleasant Swabian countryside east of Stuttgart, near Schwäbisch Gmünd, a modern purpose-built hotel whose spacious rooms have balconies and local-style wooden furniture; very good Swabian cooking (Michelin *red "Karte" for good value) and buffet breakfast. Swimming pool; golf-course next door. 50 rooms, all with bath. B&B double 125–135 DM. Full alc 33–60 DM* [*1989*]. *New nomination. More reports welcome.*

> In all continental European and Scandinavian countries except Denmark, France, Hungary, Malta, Spain and Turkey, the dialling codes begin with a 0. Omit this when dialling from outside the country in question. Spanish codes begin with a 9, which should also be omitted.

ALT-DUVENSTEDT 2371 Schleswig-Holstein — Map 13

Hotel Töpferhaus — *Tel* (04338) 3 33
Am Bistensee — Restaurant (04338) 2 22

Approved again this year for its "excellent" main meals and breakfasts, and its "kindly proprietor", this stylish rural hotel lies in the pleasantly pastoral Schleswig plain just east of the Hamburg–Flensburg *Autobahn*. Reached down a drive through woods, it is an attractive white-painted building with thatched roof, on a bluff above a lake. Inside, there are Persian rugs on the floor, a very comfortable lounge, and sizeable bedrooms. An inspector's "faultless meal" included labskaus, the traditional sailors' dish of North Germany – a hash of pickled meat, herring and potato with fried eggs, tasting a bit like a pickled shepherd's pie. (*Russell W Field Jnr, TH Monteith*)

Open All year except 2–30 Jan. Restaurant closed Mon.
Rooms 8 double, 4 single – 10 with bath, 2 with shower, all with telephone.
Facilities Hall, lounge, breakfast room, restaurant in annexe. Garden with terrace and lawns. On lake; swimming and sailing; riding and golf nearby.
Location 12 km N of Rendsburg; leave *Autobahn* at Rendsburg-Nord if coming from S, at Owschlag if coming from N. Hotel is at S end of Bistensee. *Note*: do not go towards town of Bistensee on N side of lake.
Credit cards None accepted.
Terms [1989 rates] Rooms: single 60–85 DM, double 130–150 DM. Breakfast 12 DM. Meals 25–50 DM. Reduced rates and special meals for children.

AUERBACH 8572 Bayern — Map 13

Romantik Hotel Goldener Löwe — *Tel* (09643) 17 65
Unterer Markt 9 — *Telex* 631404

"This ordinary little North Bavarian town used to be an iron-mining centre", writes our nominator this year, "and the theme is assertively reflected in the decor of this pleasant traditional inn: an old black mining cart stands in the foyer, and one part of the restaurant has been done up to look like a mine-shaft, with mining lamps hanging from the ceiling, and the back wall actually made of rough iron-ore. A gimmick, if you like, but a true reflection of local tradition. It's claimed that an inn has stood on this spot since 1144, almost since the Iron Age! – but today this Golden Lion is nicely modernised, with comfortable rooms, and heavy furnishings in the Bavarian style. The friendly Ruder family have owned the place only since 1847. Service by local girls is smilingly willing, if not always expert; the local cuisine very good, if hardly sophisticated – smoked trout, Schweinbraten with dumplings, etc. The local Franconian wines, though reputed, are not to my taste, and I opted instead for a sweetish, fizzy Ahr red that looked – and tasted – a bit like Campari soda. But I *like* Campari soda." (*JA*)

Open All year.
Rooms 2 suites, 16 double, 5 single – all with bath and shower, telephone, radio, TV and mini-bar.
Facilities Lift. 3 dining rooms, bar; conference facilities.
Location Central. Parking. Auerbach is 42 km SE of Bayreuth.
Restriction Not suitable for ♿.
Credit cards All major cards accepted.

Terms B&B: single 104 DM, double 158 DM, suite 226 DM; dinner, B&B 30 DM added per person. Set lunch/dinner 38–75 DM; full alc 50 DM. Reduced rates and special meals for children.

AYING 8011 Bayern — Map 13

Brauereigasthof Aying — *Tel* (08095) 7 05
Zornedinger Strasse 2 — *Fax* (08095) 88 50

A big creeper-covered pub, very traditional, right next to a famous brewery in a picturesque flower-decked village south-east of Munich, where commuters and dairy-farmers rub shoulders. Large airy bedrooms with Biedermeier furniture; walloping great breakfasts, served with beer if you wish. Good food served indoors or in the courtyard: some delicate dishes, as well as the usual hefty pork-based Bavarian ones. And beer, beer, beer... Closed mid-Jan–early Feb. 19 rooms, most with bath or shower. B&B double 150–175 DM. Meals 29–68 DM [1989]. New nomination. More reports welcome.

BAD BERGZABERN 6748 Rheinland-Pfalz — Map 13

Hotel-Pension Pfälzer Wald — *Tel* (06343) 10 56
Kurtalstrasse 77

Fine Renaissance buildings and a modern spa centre are features of this neat little town at the southern end of the Pfalz *Weinstrasse*, just east of the strange red crags of the Wasgau (the ruined clifftop castles of Altdahn are not to be missed). The *Pfälzer Wald*, a small traditional family hotel, stands alone beside a lake, with green hills behind, and has been liked again this year: "A good base for a comfortable holiday, and excellent value. Our room was spacious, clean and quiet, the cooking was plain but good, buffet breakfasts were copious." Other visitors have found the welcome warm and the staff helpful, though some rooms are said to be small and not too well equipped. (*Ronald S McNeill; Mary Clark*) *Warning*: the hotel faces a busy main road.

Open All year except Feb.
Rooms 17 double, 10 single – all with shower, telephone and TV.
Facilities Lounge, TV room, wine bar, dining room, restaurant; functions room; terrace. Large garden by lake.
Location About 1 km W of town centre; 38 km NW of Karlsruhe. Parking.
Restriction Not suitable for ♿.
Credit cards Some accepted.
Terms B&B 30–55 DM; half board 47–72 DM. Set lunch/dinner 20–30 DM. Reduced rates and special meals for children.

BAD HERRENALB 7506 Baden-Württemberg — Map 13

Mönchs Posthotel — *Tel* (07083) 74 40
Doblerstrasse 2 — *Telex* 7245123

The first hotel that our Continental Editor and his wife ever visited together remains blissfully unchanged, as they found this year. Nor are they its only admirers. "Expensive but worth the cost, with a superb restaurant"; "Elegant, yet intimate and cosy. And better than ever." So run reports this year and last, on this smart and stylish old half-timbered flower-decked post-hotel, at a crossroads in the centre of a Black Forest spa town. The setting is less urban than this may suggest, for the hotel also has an outdoor swimming pool and large and graceful gardens leading to a river. "Our large bedroom was superbly equipped. The lovely dining room has beamed ceilings, wood panelling and several discreet alcoves. The food, beautifully prepared and presented, tends towards *nouvelle cuisine* and is worthy of its *Michelin* rosette. Service was smooth and affable. The breakfast buffet was the most lavish we have found in Germany – and that's saying something. All in all, a romantic place – despite the prevalence of rich businessmen." But front rooms facing the noisy road should be avoided, and service can be slow. (*William A Grant; JA and KA*)

Open All year.
Rooms 2 suites, 23 double, 14 single – 24 with bath, 15 with shower, all with telephone, most with radio and TV. 14 in adjoining annexe.
Facilities Lift. Salon, TV room, bar, restaurant, breakfast terrace; conference facilities; beauty parlour. Garden with heated swimming pool. Tennis and 9-hole golf course nearby.
Location Central. (Road-facing rooms can be noisy.) Parking.
Restriction Not suitable for ♿.
Credit cards Access, Amex, Diners.
Terms B&B 97–218 DM; half- and full-board rates (3 days min). Set lunch 35–45 DM, dinner 40–70 DM; full alc 50–70 DM. Reduced rates and special meals for children.

BAD HERSFELD 6430 Hessen — Map 13

Romantik Hotel Zum Stern — *Tel* (06621) 7 20 07
Am Markt

This sizeable spa town close to the Kassel-Würzburg *autobahn* contains the ruins of a Benedictine monastery; the *Zum Stern*, now in the spa's pedestrian zone, was once part of that monastery, used to house its secular guests. It returns to the Guide this year: "A hotel of real class, its neat flowery window-boxes overlooking the market square. Our room was in the old building, with antique furniture; the modern extension, leading deep behind, includes the covered swimming pool. Welcome slightly impersonal, but the meals were excellent, especially salmon soup with caviare and côte d'agneau en croûte. A feast of a breakfast served in a warren of tiny rooms." (*Rev. Michael Bourdeaux*)

Open All year. Restaurant closed Fri midday.
Rooms 3 suites, 30 double, 15 single – 49 bath and/or shower, all with telephone, and radio; most with TV. 3 with baby-listening. 1 room suitable for ♿.
Facilities Lift. Lounge with TV, 2 restaurants; conference facilities. Indoor swimming pool.
Location Central, in pedestrian area. Parking. Bad Hersfeld is 69 km S of Kassel.
Credit cards All major cards accepted.
Terms B&B: single 95–100 DM, double 168–192.50 DM. Dinner, B&B: single 125–130 DM, double 228–252.50 DM. Reduced rates and special meals for children.

> We asked hotels to quote 1990 prices. Not all were able to predict them in the late spring of 1989. Some of our terms will be inaccurate. Do check latest tariffs at the time of booking.

BAD MERGENTHEIM 6990 Baden-Württemberg — Map 13

Haus Bundschu — *Tel* (07931) 30 43
Cronbergstrasse 15 — *Fax* (07931) 30 46

Bad Mergentheim is an important spa centre on the "Romantic Road" south-west of Würzburg, in the Tauber valley; it has a 16th-century castle of the Teutonic Order. Our inspector's 1989 nomination, "The delightful *Bundschu* naturally has its share of the *Kurgäste* who go in their millions to popular spa resorts such as this: the Germans are the world's most assiduous spa-cure addicts. But we found this far removed from the usual image of a spa hotel: it's cosy, inviting, informal, run very cheerfully by the kindly Bundschu family, Swabians all, and in summer it gets lots of ordinary tourists too. It's a *Relais du Silence*, set in the outskirts of the town beside fields and woods, a spacious, rambling modern building – no beauty – but the rooms are very comfortable (with unusual brass bedlamps, resembling old gas-lamps), and the big rustic-style dining room is pretty. Good *Maultaschen* soup and other Swabian dishes (a red *'Karte'* in *Michelin* for good value, equivalent of its 'R' in France) and a sumptuous buffet breakfast. The hotel has its own spa facilities, such as fango."

Open 15 Feb–15 Jan. Restaurant closed Mon.
Rooms 5 suites, 20 double, 40 single – all with bath and shower, telephone, radio and TV. Some ground-floor rooms.
Facilities Lift. Bar, restaurant, TV room; functions room. Garden. Spa cure facilities.
Location In outskirts, parking. Town is 53 km SW of Würzburg.
Credit cards All major cards accepted.
Terms B&B 65–80 DM; dinner, B&B 18 DM added. Set dinner 25–50 DM. Reduced rates and special meals for children.

BADEN-BADEN 7570 Baden-Württemberg — Map 13

Hotel "Der Kleine Prinz" — *Tel* (07221) 34 64
Lichtentaler Strasse 36 — *Telex* 781433
(entrance Du-Russel Strasse)

A Victorian building in the town centre, now probably the most elegant and appealing of Baden Baden's many small hotels: it is owned and run by a charming and sophisticated couple, Norbert and Edeltraud Rademacher, who spent 22 years in the US (he was catering director of the *New York Hilton* and *Waldorf Astoria*), and today many guests are cultivated Americans travelling individually. Three satisfied customers this year restore it to full entry: "We adored this lovely hotel, whose owners truly care about their guests. Dinner was outstanding." "Our supper party went superbly, and the pillows were the most comfortable we slept on in Europe". "Intimate and classical, with pleasant modern touches, such as the charming *motif* of the carrot-mopped, blue-cloaked *Kleine Prinz* that appears in every room – but the hotel has *no* connection with St-Exupéry; its name was chosen at random by the Rademachers. Elegant decor in the little salon and restaurant, where food and service are both very stylish. We had a lovely suite, with bathroom in grey marble and the thickest bath-foam I've ever seen, covering us so that we emerged from the bath looking like Alps!" (*JA and KA, and others*) A new tunnel under the town now diverts through-traffic: the hotel is in a pedestrian zone, and quiet.

Open All year.
Rooms 10 suites, 15 double, 6 single – all with bath and/or shower, telephone, radio and TV; some with whirlpool.
Facilities Lift. Lounge, bar, restaurant.
Location Central. Some parking.
Credit cards All major cards accepted.
Terms B&B: single 125–200 DM, double 200–275 DM, suite 300–350 DM. Set lunch 40 DM, dinner 60 DM; full alc 60 DM. Reduced rates and special meals for children.

BAMBERG 8600 Bayern — Map 13

Böttingerhaus and Gästehaus Steinmühle
Judenstrasse 14
Tel (0951) 5 40 74
Telex 662946 BOETT

This jewel lies in the old quarter of Bamberg, one of the loveliest of Bavarian towns, its narrow streets and Baroque palaces unscathed by wartime bombing. The *Böttingerhaus* is itself a Baroque mansion of great beauty (built in 1713 as the home of a rich merchant and diplomat) recently acquired and renovated by a Hamburg architect and now run by his daughter, Maria, and her Parisian husband, Victor Orsenne, as a distinguished restaurant and cultural centre. They have also renovated a lovely old mill house on the river close by, and run it as a guest house annexe, the *Steinmühle*. Our nominator has returned this year, endorsing her previous field dispatch:

"A dream hotel in a dreamy maze of cobbled streets, wonderful churches, enchanting old houses, antique shops and delicious *Konditorei*. When you stay at the *Steinmühle*, you have superb views of the 15th-century Rathaus set on its tiny island; light sleepers who might be disturbed by the roar of the millstream can take rooms facing the street. Our room, though smallish, was charming and elegantly furnished. All meals – including the generous buffet breakfast – are taken amid the splendours of the *Böttingerhaus*. Dishes from the menu were delicious and beautifully served, not at all heavy and over-copious as is often the case in Bavaria. Windows look out on to ancient roofs, or on to the delightful terrace garden where you can take aperitifs; the sound of Mozart drifts gently in the distance." The cuisine includes local Franconian specialities with French influences coming from M. Orsenne; there is also an informal bistro for lighter meals. Live piano music at weekends and classical concerts fill out the scenario, as do official banquets of all kinds. A second, very comfortable bedroom annexe, the *Molitor Haus*, next to the *Steinmühle*, with an integral garage, opened in 1988. (*Eileen Spencer, EW Smallwood*)

Open All year.
Rooms 5 suites, 23 double – all with bath, shower, telephone, radio and TV; kitchenette in suites; babysitter on request. All in 2 houses about 80 yds from main building. 2 ground-floor rooms suitable for ♿.
Facilities Lift. Lounge, restaurant, bar, tea room, wine cellar (piano player nightly); conference facilities. Garden terrace, children's playground.
Location Central. Garages.
Credit cards All major cards accepted.

Terms [1989 rates] B&B: single 95–110 DM, double 160–260 DM, suite 350 DM. Meals: restaurant 48–66 DM, wine cellar 33–51 DM. Reduced rates and special meals for children.

Hotel Sankt Nepomuk *Tel* (0951) 2 51 83
Obere Mühlbrücke 9

Very close to the *Böttingerhaus* (see above), and almost equally delightful, this "most original and magic hotel" stands on stilts on the river Regnitz between the rushing millraces, and was again much liked by inspectors this year. It belongs to an affluent Catholic foundation which has managed the conversion with fastidious taste. Everything is stylishly open-plan, notably the big restaurant on two floors, with handsome fireplace, curving stone stairway, and picture-windows facing the river. This year's report, "We enjoyed fresh tomato soup with mushrooms and gin (sic), roast leg of lamb with herbs, and excellent vegetables. The cooking remains ambitious but not pretentious, with generous helpings, and is delightfully and skilfully served by young people. The staff are exemplary." Try Bamberg's curious 'smoky beer' made from smoked malt. The bedrooms are in light modern Scandinavian style, and vary in size. "The special glass of our bathroom window gave out a dazzling prismatic light effect; glow-worms darted and shone above the river; and we were lulled to sleep by the therapeutic roar of the millrace – to awaken next day to a sumptuous buffet breakfast, served in a lovely room with cheerful modern murals of local scenes." (*JA and KA, Eileen Spencer*)

Open All year except Christmas Eve.
Rooms 10 double, 2 single – all with bath and/or shower, telephone, radio, TV and mini-bar.
Facilities Lift. Bar, café, 2 restaurants; conference facilities.
Location Central. Do *not* try to drive car up to hotel (narrow streets); leave it in public car park in Geyerswörthstrasse just across river.
Credit cards Access, Diners, Visa.
Terms B&B: single occupancy 80–90 DM, double 130–150 DM. Set lunch/dinner 65–70 DM; full alc 55–60 DM. Special meals for children on request.

BARGUM 2255 Schleswig-Holstein — Map 13

Andresen's Gasthof-Friesenstuben *Tel* (04672) 10 98

An inn on the edge of a small village near the flat and windswept west coast of Schleswig, on Route 5 between Husum and Niebüll (Nolde museum). Delicious North German cooking (Michelin *rosette) and good service in the lovely dining room with its beamed ceilings. Comfortable rooms facing a garden and fields. Closed 3 weeks Jan, 2 weeks Sept; restaurant closed all Mon, Tue midday. 5 rooms, all with shower (8 more planned for 1990). B&B double 135 DM. Set menus 90–110 DM. Recent nomination. More reports welcome.*

> Hotels often book you into their most expensive rooms or suites unless you specify otherwise. Even if all room prices are the same, hotels may give you a less good room in the hope of selling their better rooms to late customers. It always pays to discuss accommodation in detail when making a reservation.

BAYRISCHZELL 8163 Bayern — Map 13

Romantik Hotel Die Meindelei — *Tel* (08023) 3 18
Michael-Meindl Strasse 13

Bayrischzell is a pleasant hiking and skiing resort in the Bavarian Alps, at the foot of the rocky Wendelstein peak (go up it by cable-car for roof-of-the-world views). The *Meindelei,* in a quiet location backed by pinewoods, comes new to the Guide: "A fairly typical Romantik Hotel, named after a local writer, Herr Meindl, now dead, and run by his perfectionist, fiercely hardworking daughter and her quieter husband. The heavily kitschy Bavarian decor might not suit all tastes (lots of painted cupboards, china stoves, folk objects; in the dining room, bowls of plastic fruit, even a crucifix), but it's very comfortable, spruce and well run. First-class, sophisticated cooking by the Swabian son-in-law of the owners (paprika soup with cream, delicious mixed salad with pine-nuts, rare roast venison – and an oyster au gratin offered as an *amuse-gueule*), all daintily presented but not too *nouvelle.* Lavish breakfast buffet, including various types of fruit salad. Some rooms are in the main buildings, others in bungalows in the big tree-filled garden. A small heated pool is free to guests, and there's a bigger public one across the road. A very good hotel in its own way." (*JA and KA*)

Open All year except 2 weeks in Mar/Apr and 15 Oct–22 Dec. Restaurant closed for lunch and Tue.
Rooms 17 – all with bath and/or shower and telephone. 5 bungalows in garden.
Facilities Lounge, bar, restaurant. Indoor swimming pool and sauna. Garden; terrace where meals are served.
Location Fairly central; parking. Bayrischzell is 77 km SE of Munich.
Credit cards All major cards accepted.
Terms [1989 rates] B&B: single 85–95 DM, double 135–165 DM. Meals 30–65 DM.

BAYREUTH 8580 Bayern — Map 13

Bayerischer Hof — *Tel* (0921) 2 20 81
Bahnhofstrasse 14 — *Telex* 642737

A post-war building near the station, outwardly dull-looking but probably the best of Bayreuth's hotels, owned by the Seuss family since 1918. Large, quiet, well-furnished rooms; fine heated indoor pool; rooftop bar and restaurant with outdoor terrace, serving local dishes; pleasant staff and good breakfasts. Restaurant closed Sun. 62 rooms, all with bath and shower. B&B double 110-210 DM. Meals 35–63 DM [1989]. Few recent reports. More welcome.

BAYREUTH-SEULBITZ 8580 Bayern — Map 13

Waldhotel Stein — *Tel* (0921) 90 01

Seulbitz is an attractive village just east of Bayreuth (you can see the floodlit *Festspielhaus* from your window). Here Frau Stein's peaceful modern family hotel has again been liked this year, for its "above average" cooking (most of the ingredients are organically produced locally) and spacious rooms – some are bedsitters with balcony, some are in bungalows in the large garden. Swimming pool; very efficient service.

A new bungalow with a luxurious bridal suite has just been built and further expansion is planned. (*Philip A True*)

Open Jan–end Nov.
Rooms 5 suites, 48 double, 6 single – all with bath and/or shower, telephone, radio and TV. 4 with kitchenette. Most rooms in bungalows. Some on ground floor.
Facilities Lounge, breakfast room, 2 restaurants; conference facilities. Indoor heated swimming pool, sauna, solarium, massage. Large grounds. Tennis 3 km.
Location 6 km E of Bayreuth, near Seulbitz village; follow signs for Eremitage. Parking.
Credit cards All major cards accepted.
Terms B&B: single 58–180 DM, double 98–280 DM, suite 200–1,200 DM (prices increase hugely during opera festival period). Set lunch/dinner 25–48 DM; full alc 45 DM. Reduced rates and special meals for children.

BEILSTEIN 5591 Rheinland-Pfalz — Map 13

Hotel Haus Lipmann — *Tel* (02673) 15 73

Metternich was the last overlord of this very picturesque old village in the Mosel valley, and his castle stands on the hill above. To the south is the wooded plateau of the Hunsrück where Edgar Reitz set and filmed his 16-hour masterpiece *Heimat*. "Very characterful and atmospheric", says a visitor this year to the *Lipmann*, a cheap and unpretentious little family-run half-timbered *Gasthof*, in the main square. "Our rooms were quaint, but comfortable, and our window opened on to a wonderful view of the river." Some rooms are in a modern annexe amid trees; others, newly renovated but smaller, are in the charming old *Alte Zollhaus* annexe. Interesting dishes such as smoked Mosel eel with scrambled eggs are served generously in a baronial hall, while opposite is the hotel's lovely old vaulted pub where you can drink wine with locals. (*Mrs AJ Goodwin, JA and KA*)

Open 15 Mar–15 Nov.
Rooms 20 double, 4 single – 1 with bath, 23 with shower. 18 in 2 annexes.
Facilities Restaurant; conference/functions facilities; wine cellar (wine tastings held); terrace on Mosel.
Location Central, near market place. Parking.
Credit cards None accepted.
Terms B&B: single 45–65 DM, double 70–85 DM; dinner B&B (min stay 4 days) 12 DM per person added; full board 20 DM added. Full alc 25–55 DM. Special meals for children on request.

BERCHTESGADEN 8420 Bayern — Map 13

Hotel Krone — *Tel* (08652) 6 20 51
Am Rad 5

Few German resorts are more teemingly popular than Berchtesgaden. Hitler's eyrie has been rased to the ground, and only its ghosts remain; but the mountains and alpine lakes are gorgeous, and a guided tour of the extraordinary salt-mines is not to be missed. The unpretentious *Krone*, attractively white-walled and blue-shuttered, and furnished in local rustic style, stands on a hill just outside the town, aloof from the madding throng. It now makes its Guide debut: "In a town where all other hotels seem large and package-tour orientated, here's just the kind of small, idiosyncratic but wholly delightful place that should appeal to readers. All its good rooms away from the road open onto communal balconies facing the valley and hills. Ours was fairly small, but snug and wood-panelled, and the house is full of Bavarian hand-painted furniture. The Grafe family gave us a warm welcome, and they provide good home cooking. Frau Grafe dresses quite naturally in Bavarian costume as she serves in the dining room." (*Angela and David Stewart*) More reports please.

Open All year except Nov–20 Dec. Restaurant closed for lunch; dinner for residents only.
Rooms 28 – most with bath and/or shower, telephone and TV.
Facilities Lounge, restaurant; terrace.
Location 1 km N of town centre, off Salzburg road. Parking.
Credit cards None accepted.
Terms [1989 rates] B&B: single 65–77 DM, double 120–150 frs. Half board: 12 DM per person added.

BERGISCH GLADBACH 5060 Nordrhein-Westfalen — Map 13

Waldhotel Mangold — *Tel* (02204) 5 40 11
Am Milchbornsberg 32

Set in the midst of rolling hills, next to a forest and running stream, this "woodland hotel" (*Michelin* red print for pleasantness) is in some ways very rural. Yet it is only ten miles from Cologne, just beyond the eastern fringe of its urban sprawl. A long low white building, it has been in the hands of the Mangold family since 1927. "Rooms both in the annexe and in the main building are large, clean, comfortable and well furnished. The large reception area is furnished with antique clocks and pictures. The small restaurant has a terrace for summer: cooking is imaginative, using high-quality fresh ingredients. Good breakfast."

Open All year except 3 weeks in Jun/Jul. Restaurant closed for lunch and on Mon, Sun and public holidays.
Rooms 20 – all with bath and/or shower, telephone and TV; some with balcony.
Facilities Lounge, salon with open fireplace, restaurant; conference facilities. Terrace.
Location 17 km E of Cologne: leave *Autobahn* E40 at Bergisch Gladbach/Bensberg exit, follow sings to Bensberg. Parking.
Credit cards None accepted.
Terms [1989 rates] B&B: single 100–135 DM, double 150–180 DM. Meals 46–72 DM.

BERLIN 1000 — Map 13

Hotel Belvedere — *Tel* (030) 826 10 77
Seebergsteig 4, Grunewald
Berlin 33

Some three miles west of the city centre, the smart residential suburb of Grunewald, aptly named, is next to a forest that leads to the big Havel lake. It's a setting that puts paid to the false image of West Berlin as a claustrophobic city without space or greenery (in fact, it has 80 farms). Here, in a quiet and leafy side-street, this turn-of-the-century villa in its own garden was liked again this year. Reports have praised the buffet breakfasts, the thickness of the feather duvets and the welcome to small children: but while some rooms are large and sunny, basement ones may be dark. One was "adorable but tiny". "Stylish bedrooms with antique cane and wood furniture. Public rooms have the air of a bourgeois private house. Peaceful, relaxed, unpretentious. Breakfast in a funny conservatory-like annexe". (*EW Smallwood, Stephanie and Bryan Lorge*) No restaurant, but there are some nearby such as the lakeside *Chalet Corniche.* Or bus 19, five minutes' walk, will take you to the city centre. Visit the fabulous Dahlem museums, quite near by.

Open All year. Restaurant open to residents only.
Rooms 12 double, 7 single – 10 with bath, 2 with shower, all with telephone, radio and TV.
Facilities Salon with TV, breakfast room. Garden.
Location In Grunewald, 4 km SW of city centre.
Restriction Not suitable for ♿.
Credit cards Access, Diners, Visa.
Terms [1989 rates] Rooms: single 55-100 DM, double 85-140 DM. Breakfast 8 DM. Reduced rates for children.

BONN 5300 Nordrhein-Westfalen — Map 13

Haus Hofgarten — *Tel* (0228) 22 34 82
Fritz-Tillmann Strasse 7

In a residential street close to the university and the traffic-free heart of old Bonn, well away from the modern Regierungsviertel, *here is a tiny, friendly hotel with lots of wood panelling and good pictures, and huge old-fashioned bedrooms, comfortable and well equipped. Breakfast, complete with the day's newspapers, served in a room facing the garden. 15 bedrooms, some with bath and/or shower. B&B double 85–145 DM [1989]. No restaurant, but lots nearby. Restored to Guide. More reports please.*

Schlosshotel Kommende Ramersdorf — *Tel* (0228) 44 07 34
Oberkasseler Strasse 10
Bonn 3-Beuel

Just across the Rhine from Bonn, some three kilometres from the city centre and government area, this massive ancient *Schloss* stands incongruously in the middle of a motorway network (but the traffic is not audible). Parts date from 1220, but most is 19th-century neo-Gothic. Dropped from the 1989 Guide for lack of feedback, it is restored by two reports this year: "A delight. Our large room was furnished with antiques, and a plentiful breakfast was served in a charming room." "We arrived at 10.30 pm but were kindly cosseted with a cold meal. The good service compensated for the worn carpets and other shabbiness. Incredibly cheap by German standards." Part of the *Schloss* is a museum of furniture, paintings, etc, and some items are for sale. (*Claire W Enders, J Thérèse Simon*) Reports on the cooking would be welcome.

Do you know of any good budget hotels in Berlin?

Open All year. Restaurant closed 4 weeks in Jul/Aug and Tue.
Rooms 10 double, 8 single – all with bath and shower, telephone and radio; some with TV.
Facilities Bar, TV room, breakfast room, restaurant; terrace-café. 2 functions/conference rooms. Courtyard and garden.
Location Take A59 motorway in direction of Königswinter, leave it at Niederholtorf exit; turn left, and after 300 metres left again.
Restrictions Not suitable for ♿.
Credit cards All major cards accepted.
Terms [1989 rates] B&B: single 85–120 DM, double 150–170 DM. Meals 46–70 DM.

BOPPARD AM RHEIN 5407 Rheinland-Pfalz — Map 13

Klostergut Jakobsberg — *Tel* (06742) 30 61
Im Tal der Loreley — *Telex* 426 323

Readers this year endorse last year's picture of this large and remarkable Rhineland hotel: "In 1157 Frederic I Barbarossa founded a monastery 'für Mönche und Nonnen' high on the hills above Boppard, overlooking a magnificent stretch of the Rhine. This had a chequered history and even became a school for French émigré children during the Revolution. Finally the owner of the Harribo sweets empire bought it and converted it into a smart hotel, adding a number of new buildings, complete with superb indoor sports centre, pool and tennis. The courtyard at dusk with its fountain and scores of sculptured glass lanterns is impressive. Reception rooms are vast and comfortable, decked out with modern bronze sculptures, antique wooden statues, stained-glass windows. All bedrooms are individual, with genuine paintings, modern wooden furniture. Some have a sun balcony; ours overlooked a rocky wooded escarpment. It was very cosy, and the bathroom had a ceiling-to-floor mosaic. All is beautifully maintained by a charming staff. There are two bars (one in the old wine cellars) and two restaurants, one with views over the trees to the Rhine. Food is interestingly presented (excellent quails, lobster tails, veal in cream) and many ingredients come fresh from the adjacent home farm. Breakfast was superb and lavish, and service quick and pleasant: we saw one waitress taking particular care over single old ladies. At the weekend the hotel was full of families with children; during the week, of businessmen and conference guests. English and Americans prefer the old part for its atmosphere." (*TH Nash, Miss D Tunstall*)

Open All year.
Rooms 110 – all with bath and/or shower, telephone and TV.
Facilities Lift. Lounge, 2 bars, 2 restaurants; conference facilities. Large garden with children's playground. Indoor swimming pool, sauna and solarium. Indoor and outdoor tennis, squash and bowling alley. Rifle range. Chapel for weddings.
Location 12 km N of Boppard: turn off B9 Rhineside main road at Spay, take Rheingoldstrasse turning.
Credit cards Probably all major cards accepted.
Terms [1989 rates] B&B: single 110–180 DM, double 160–280 DM; half board 40 DM added per person, full board 60 DM added.

> When hotels have failed to return their questionnaire, we have quoted 1989 prices, with a note to that effect.

BREITNAU 7821 Baden-Württemberg — Map 13

Hotel Kaiser's Tanne-Wirtshus — *Tel* (07652) 15 51
Am Wirbstein 27 — *Fax* (07652) 15-07

Set in rolling pastoral country a few miles away from the big resort of Hinterzarten, and thus secluded from the main tourist crowds, here is a welcoming chalet-style Black Forest hotel, all gables and flowery balconies outside, all folksy *Gemütlichkeit* within. "Beautifully decorated, very ornate, full of antiques and pictures and homely touches making it one of the most pleasant hotels I have visited in Europe. Very friendly staff. Bedroom and bathroom clean and airy. Excellent duvets. If you arrive in time do not miss the tea downstairs, which is a real treat. Excellent dinner and first class buffet breakfast." Many bedrooms have a balcony with peaceful rural views which include cows to-ing and fro-ing. Indoor swimming pool and attractive garden. (*John Moseley, and others*)

Open All year except mid-Nov–mid-Dec. Restaurant closed Mon.
Rooms 2 suites, 24 double, 5 single – all with bath, shower, telephone, radio and TV.
Facilities Lift. Lounge, bar, 2 restaurants, indoor heated swimming pool and sauna; terrace. Garden, playground for children.
Location Just SW of Breitnau, which is 30 km E of Freiburg, off route 500.
Credit cards None accepted.
Terms B&B 70–100 DM. Dinner, B&B 105–135 DM.Set lunch 25–40 DM, dinner 35–70 DM; full alc 45 DM. Reduced rates and special meals for children.

BÜSINGEN 7701 Baden-Württemberg — Map 13

Alte Rheinmühle — *Tel* (07734) 60 76
Junkerstrasse 93 — *Telex* 793788 HOTEL

The village of Büsingen is a German enclave inside Switzerland near Schaffhausen (either Swiss or German currency can be used). Here this converted 17th-century mill on the Rhine serves some of the best food in Baden-Württemberg (Michelin *rosette). The beamed dining room is large but cosy, and overlooks the river. Bedrooms (some have four-posters and painted wooden wardrobes) are scattered on various levels, in a random but homely fashion. Closed 20 Dec–15 Jan. 16 rooms, all with bath or shower. B&B double 130–180 DM. Meals from 30 DM* [1989]. *Few recent reports. More please.*

CELLE 3100 Niedersachsen — Map 13

Fürstenhof Celle – Restaurant Endtenfang — *Tel* (05141) 20 10
Fax (05141) 20 11 20
Hannoversche Strasse 55 — *Telex* 925293 CEHOG

This pink-fronted mansion, a stylish and rather formal hotel, stands on a main road near the centre of an historic old city where the Guelph princes ruled (imposing baroque *Schloss*, lovely *Altstadt* of ancient timbered houses). "We've tried four different rooms", say devotees this year, "and all have been pleasant, with a balcony overlooking the garden where drinks are served. This separates the older part of the hotel, a 17th-century palace, from the new bedroom wing. Service is impeccable, the breakfast buffet is good, and excellent duck is served in the hotel's *Endtenfang* restaurant (*Michelin* rosette). We haven't tried its cheaper *Kutscherstube*. The comfortable lounge is in baroque style." (*Stephan and Kate Murray-Sykes*)

Open All year. *Kutscherstube* closed midday and Sun.
Rooms 3 suites, 75 double or single – all with bath and shower, telephone, radio, TV and baby-listening.
Facilities Lift. Lounge, bar, beer-cellar, 2 restaurants; conference and function facilities; indoor swimming pool, solarium, sauna. Garden and terrace.
Location Central, near *Schloss*. Parking.
Credit cards Access, Amex, Diners.
Terms [1989 rates] B&B: single 98–190 DM, double 180–380 DM, suite 400 DM. Meals: *Kutscherstube* 33–52 DM; *Endtenfang* 85–125 DM.

COCHEM 5590 Rheinland-Pfalz — Map 13

Hotel "Alte Thorschenke" — *Tel* (02671) 70 59 and 39 31
Brückenstrasse 3 — *Fax* (02671) 42 02

Cochem, with its painted houses and neat gardens along the river, and its high-pinnacled hilltop feudal castle, is the most picturesque town on the Mosel – and this Guide newcomer, in an old gabled house dating from 1332, is worthy of it, "The entrance opens onto an ancient carved circular wooden staircase, leading to rooms in the old building. Behind is a post-war bedroom extension, fitted out with splendid antique pictures and furniture. Here we slept deliciously well in a vast family heirloom of a bed, all massive carved oak. The bathroom was somewhat clinical but adequate. The welcome was warm yet professional, and dinner in a superb baronial dining room included the best game we've ever had." (*Angela and David Stewart*)

Open 15 Mar–5 Jan. Restaurant closed on Wed 15 Nov–5 Jan.
Rooms 38 double, 6 single – 34 with bath and shower and radio; 22 with telephone; TV on request. 4 in nearby annexe.
Facilities Lift. Hall, restaurant, *Weinstube*. Terrace.
Location Central, parking. Cochem is 51 km SW of Koblenz.
Credit cards All major cards accepted.
Terms B&B: single 55–115 DM, double 125–180 DM; half board 28 DM per person added; full board 48 DM added. Full alc 50–60 DM. Reduced rates and special meals for children.

COLOGNE 5000 Nordrhein-Westphalen — Map 13

Hotel Spiegel — *Tel* (02203) 6 10 46
Herman-Löns-Strasse 122, Porz-Grengel

The Guide's search for good hotels in Cologne is rarely successful, so this newcomer is welcome: a small family-run gasthof *in the south-eastern outer suburb of Porz-Grengel, conveniently near the airport, but set peacefully by a forest. Good food, and a personal touch. Closed 3 weeks in summer. 19 rooms, all with bath or shower. B&B double 130–180 DM. Alc 50–65 DM. New nomination. More reports please.*

DAHLEM-KRONENBURG 5377 Nordrhein-Westfalen — Map 13

Eifelhaus
Burgbering 12
Tel (06557) 295

In a hilltop village south-west of Dahlem, in the lovely but little-known Eifel massif, quite near the Belgian border, a white-walled old building has been converted into a modest but appealing little hotel; vaulted dining room, terraced garden, helpful owners, clean, simple rooms and good food. Amazingly low prices. Lake and castle nearby. 19 rooms, all with bath and/or shower. B&B 30–35 DM. Set menus 9.50–25 DM [1989]. New nomination. More reports eagerly requested.

DAUN 5568 Rheinland-Pfalz — Map 13

Schloss-Hotel Kurfürstliches Amtshaus
Auf dem Burgberg
Tel (06592) 30 31
Fax (06592) 49 42
Telex 4729310

Daun is a resort in the lovely rolling volcanic hills of the Eifel, west of Koblenz. On a hill in the village centre, this handsome yellow-walled 18th-century schloss has been converted into a stylish and fairly expensive hotel, admired by several readers this year. Public rooms and most bedrooms have bracing views of the surrounding woods, hills and ski-slopes. The decor and furnishings are somewhat baronial, with heavy oak chests, etc. "Most of the decor is what we call 'pseudo-Germanic semi-kitsch', though others might call it 'altdeutsch'. But the main restaurant is inviting and intimate, and here we had a wonderful meal, with sophisticated haute cuisine (tomato mousse with smoked breast of goose, fried quail with quince sauce, date ice-cream with apple sauce, etc) and excellent service. The high-quality table accessories included fresh roses in December. Our comfortable room had a view of an old chapel and fir trees. Rich buffet breakfast with lots of unusual extras." Another reader thought the meal good but the service slow. Inspectors report, "The heated swimming pool is almost as hot as a sauna, for its water comes from the local volcanic springs; it has red and green alcoves and is chiselled out of the volcanic rock. The garden terrace contains barbecue facilities. Bedrooms are smallish but pleasant. One of the splendid suites, the Fürstensuite, contains a famous bed acquired from the Government's hotel at the Petersberg in Bonn, where it was slept in by Brezhnev, the Shah of Iran, etc. It is now covered in fancy orange drapes and an orange silk canopy, and the bath *en suite* is triangular. All this for only 320 DM [1990]. A snip." (*GB and Dr CH, Mrs CM Hunter*)

Open All year except 3 days early Jan.
Rooms 1 suite, 25 double, 17 single – 8 with bath, 34 with shower, all with telephone, radio, TV and mini-bar; baby-listening on request.
Facilities Lift. Lounge, bar, 2 restaurants, conference facilities. Garden; terrace. Indoor swimming pool, sauna.
Location Central, parking. Daun is 70 km W of Koblenz.
Credit cards All major cards accepted.
Terms B&B: single 95–105 DM, double 160–220 DM, suite 320 DM. Dinner, B&B 38 DM per person added. Set lunch 39–52 DM, dinner 64–94 DM; full alc 75 DM. Reduced rates and special meals for children. 2 nights minimum stay at weekends.

DEIDESHEIM 6705 Rheinland-Pfalz — Map 13

Romantik Hotel Deidesheimer Hof — *Tel* (06326) 18 11
Am Marktplatz — *Telex* 454675

Chancellor Kohl comes from Mainz, the nearby *Land* capital, and his local connections led him to select this stylish and well-known hotel for his summit meeting with – guess who? – on 30th April 1989. They sat at a white table and argued fruitlessly about short-range nuclear missiles, after which Mrs T. drank the local white wine and confided to the TV cameras, "*Very* dry, with just a *touch* of sweetness", (giggles all round). This however is not why we are now restoring the *Hof* to the Guide, from which it was dropped in 1988 purely through lack of feedback. An inspector this year has admired the wood-panelled *Weinstube*, full of Germanic warmth and prettiness, and an American has written: "A real joy! Cheerful, helpful staff, exceptional food. Despite the crowds in the food rooms and front terrace, the back bedrooms are quiet – and beautifully decked out" (rooms do vary). Run by the Hahn family, leading local vinegrowers, the hostelry stands on the busy main street of a picturesque little wine-town on the Pfalz *Weinstrasse* (its balustraded *Rathaus* has a wine museum). (*SR Holman, JA and KA*) More reports please.

Open All year except 4–15 Jan. *Schwarzer Hahn* restaurant closed midday, Sun, and in low season.
Rooms 27 – all with bath and/or shower, telephone and TV.
Facilities 2 restaurants; conference facilities. Terrace.
Location Central, parking. Deidesheim is 23 km SW of Mannheim.
Credit cards All major cards accepted.
Terms [1989 rates] B&B: single 57–118 DM, double 88–179 DM. Meals: *Weinstube* 37–67 DM, *Schwarzer Hahn* 58–87 DM.

DÜSSELDORF 4000 — Map 13

Hotel Schnellenburg — *Tel* (0211) 43 41 33
Rotterdamerstrasse 120 — *Telex* 8581828 BURG
Düsseldorf 30

Recommended again in 1989, especially for its bedrooms and its fine position beside the Rhine, this is a pleasantly unusual place in a big commercial city full of dull hotels. A low white building with iron grilles on the windows, it looks more Spanish than German. "A light room where it was easy to work, and a first-class breakfast, and smiling service." The restaurant, newly renovated with lots of brass and marble, has a good view of the river.

Open All year except Christmas and New Year.
Rooms 3 suites, 35 double, 11 single – all with bath, shower, telephone, radio, TV.
Facilities Lounge, residents' bar, restaurant (under separate management). Small garden.
Restriction Not suitable for ♿.
Location 4 km N of city centre, opposite Nord Park, on the Rhine. Parking.
Credit cards All major cards accepted.
Terms B&B: single 125–190 DM, double 160–260 DM, suite 220–360 DM. Full alc 35 DM. Reduced rates and special meals for children.

Please make a habit of sending a report if you stay at a Guide hotel.

FEUCHTWANGEN 8805 Bayern — Map 13

Greifen-Post
Marktplatz 8

Tel (09852) 20 03
Fax (09852) 48 41
Telex 61137

A solidly down-to-earth coaching inn, spacious and rambling, with parts dating back to 1450 or earlier. It stands in the main square of this pleasant little north Bavarian town (interesting Frankish folk museum) and has been owned by the Lorentz family for three generations. "Friendly greeting, lovely rooms and fine food", runs one recent report. Others have relished the Frankish specialities served in an old beamed dining room, the buffet breakfast, and the owners' personal touch. Wide corridors full of antiques are part of the charm. Most bedrooms are well modernised, though some definitely need attention. Those in the front may be noisy, those in the newer annexe are quieter but have less cachet. The pool, done up in the style of Roman baths, is much commended – "like swimming in a Roman grotto".

Open All year. Restaurant closed 2 Jan–15 Feb.
Rooms 3 suites, 35 double, 6 single – all with bath and shower, telephone, radio and TV; baby-listening on request. 3 in annexe.
Facilities Lift. Bar, breakfast room, 3 restaurants; conference facilities; indoor heated swimming pool, sauna, solarium; garden terrace.
Location Central. Garage parking.
Credit cards All major cards accepted.
Terms B&B: single 85–115 DM, double 125–200 DM, suite 250–380 DM. Set lunch 42 DM, dinner 89 DM. Reduced rates and special meals for children.

FRANKFURT-AM-MAIN 6000 Hessen — Map 13

Westend
Westendstrasse 15, Frankfurt 1

Tel (069) 74 67 02 and 74 50 02

"A very pleasant contrast to the concrete monstrosities I normally have to stay in on business trips," runs one recent report on this small and select hotel of charm and character, most unexpected in downtown Frankfurt. It is in a quiet residential district that has somehow survived the metallic frenzy of post-war rebuilding; yet it is very central, only five minutes' walk from the Fair centre, the *Hauptbahnhof* and the banking district. One reader this year found reception discourteous, but others have enjoyed the serenity and cordial efficiency, confirming this earlier view, "The late 20th century has been carefully excluded from the *Westend*, which is tastefully furnished throughout with antiques and old pictures; gracious old-world service by discreet middle-aged men in black suits who address lady guests as 'Gnädige Frau' ('Esteemed Madame'). Very comfortable rooms; lavish German breakfasts; light evening meals on request; a leafy garden for summer; prices very reasonable for central Frankfurt." A lift has just been installed: and the hotel promises that almost all rooms will have private bath or shower by the end of 1989.

Open All year except Easter holidays, Christmas and New Year.
Rooms 20 – 8 with bath, 2 with shower, all with telephone and mini-bar.
Facilities Lift. 3 lounges (1 with TV). Garden and terrace where light meals and drinks are served.

Location Central; 5 mins' walk from station. By car approach from Westkreuz. Private parking.
Credit cards Access, Amex, Visa.
Terms Rooms: single 75-150 DM, double 150–200 DM, triple 280 DM. Breakfast 14 DM. (No restaurant, but light evening meals served on request.)

FREIBURG IM BREISGAU 7800 Baden-Württemberg — Map 13

Zum Roten Bären — *Tel* (0761) 3 69 13
Oberlinden 12 — *Fax* (0761) 3 69 16
Telex 7721574 BAER

Blue-and-pink diamond-shaped designs adorn the painted facade of this famous and very *gemütlich* old inn, dating back 600 years, and set near the centre of a lovely old university city on the edge of the Black Forest. It has also been comfortably modernised, its newer parts skilfully integrated into the old ones; old prints line the walls, fresh flowers are everywhere. One reader this year found dinner "divine", and an inspector fared well, too: "Good traditional cooking, e.g. Tafelspitze (boiled beef), but the local 'Freiburger Festtagsuppe' was boringly unfestive. Staff wear local Baden *tracht*, including – incongruously – our deft Pakistani waiter. A good but expensive Baden Bürgheimer red. It's a hotel that breathes confident well-being, nicely supervised by its jolly and expansive *Wirtin*, Monika Hansen." Others have approved braised venison and the breakfast buffet. One reader found her bathroom unkempt. Parking is difficult.

Open All year. Restaurant closed 24 Dec.
Rooms 3 suites, 17 double, 5 single – all with bath, shower, telephone, radio and TV.
Facilities Lift. Reception, lounge, TV room, restaurant; conference room. Courtyard and boulevard café.
Location Central; in old part of city. Underground carparks. From Basle highway take exit Freiburg Mitte; follow signs for Stadtmitte, Schwabentor, *Hotel Bären*.
Credit cards All major cards accepted.
Terms B&B: single 125–145 DM, double 170–190 DM, suite 280–300 DM; dinner, B&B 30 DM per person added. Set lunch 26 DM; full alc from 45 DM. Reduced rates and special meals for children.

FREUDENSTADT 7290 Baden-Württemberg — Map 13

Hotel-Restaurant Gut Lauterbad — *Tel* (07441) 74 96
Dietrichstrasse 5, Lauterbad

Freudenstadt, one of the larger Black Forest resorts, lies on a pine-clad plateau astride the old hill-road from Stuttgart to Strasbourg, amid excellent hiking country. After destruction in 1945, it was completely rebuilt in its former 17th-century style: note its curious church, with the aisles set at right-angles. The admired *Gut Lauterbad*, a modern building in local style, lies just outside the town, amid meadows, woods and streams; it has a garden terrace beside a trout pond. "We had an excellent room, spacious and comfortable, and very good food in ample portions on the set menus. Staff friendly." More reports welcome.

Open All year except 15 Nov–15 Dec and 10 Jan–1 Feb. Restaurant closed Wed.
Rooms 1 suite, 16 double, 4 single – all with bath and shower, telephone, radio and TV. 1 suite, 4 double in annexe.

Facilities Lounge, bar, TV room, restaurant; conference room; indoor heated swimming pool. Park with children's playground, small lake and stream; trout-fishing.
Location 3 km SE (B294) of centre; follow directions to Freiburg then to Dietersweiler/Lauterbad. Hotel is at end of road on left. Garage and parking.
Restriction Not suitable for ♿.
Credit cards All major cards accepted.
Terms B&B: single 48–58 DM, double 78–106 DM, suite 150 DM; dinner, B&B 21.50 DM per person added. Set lunch/dinner 21.50–35 DM; full alc 38–50 DM. Children under 2 free; under 12, 50% reduction; special meals.

FRIEDRICHSRUHE 7111 Baden-Württemberg — Map 13

Wald-und Schlosshotel Friedrichsruhe
Öhringerstrasse 11

Tel (07941) 6 08 70
Fax (07941) 6 14 68
Telex 74498 WAFRI

A large white-walled red-roofed mansion in the hilly and wooded Hohenlohe country, built in 1712 by the *Fürsten* of that ilk and still owned today (after conversion in 1953 into a very superior hotel) by the Prinz Kraft zu Hohenlohe-Öhringen. His chef/manager, Lothar Eiermann, runs it in lordly style and provides some of the most ambitious cooking in Germany (a second *Michelin* rosette added in 1989). Rooms are in the old mansion or, along with the restaurant, in a modern and stylish extension. "The best hotel we stayed at in Germany. A lovely room, excellent food", say some readers this year. "Germany's answer to England's *Priory* in Bath (q.v.)." (*Robert and Ruth Todd*) But others were inclined to endorse a more ambivalent view recorded last year. Reception: pleasant but a bit cool. Their room: large and very comfortable but showing signs of wear and tear, and lighting no more than adequate. No complaints about the bathroom, or the service or the breakfast ("delicious"). As for the dinner, it was good – but not *that* good in view of the prices; the wines (the Perrier too!) had in their view an excessive mark-up. More reports welcome, especially on the food.

Open All year. Restaurant closed Mon.
Rooms 13 suites, 26 double, 11 single – all with bath, shower and telephone; radio, TV and baby-listening on request. 22 rooms in hunting lodge.
Facilities Lifts. Lounge/bar, 2 restaurants; functions room. Large grounds with outdoor and covered swimming pools, tennis court, 9-hole golf course, children's playground.
Location 30 km E of Heilbronn; leave the Nürnberg motorway at Öhringen exit, drive through Öhringen till Friedrichsruhe is signposted.
Credit cards All major cards accepted.
Terms B&B: single 170–300 DM, double 260–400 DM, suite 400–800 DM. Set lunch 110 DM; full alc 120 DM. Reduced rates for children; special meals on request.

FULDA 6400 Hessen — Map 13

Hotel "Zum Kurfürsten"
Schlosstrasse 2

Tel (0661) 7 00 01

The old city of Fulda near the East German border, has a cathedral where St Boniface, an 8th-century English missionary to Germany, lies buried, having anointed Pippin the Short as king and then himself been murdered. The life of the Zum Kurfürsten *has also been eventful, for it was built in 1737 as a palace of the Prince Bishop; later Queen Victoria, Bismarck,* et al, *stayed in it. It is now a sleek, well-run hotel in the classic style, with good food. 68 rooms, 40 with bath or shower. B&B: single 49–90 DM, double 90–150 DM. Set menus from 30 DM [1989]. New nomination. More reports please.*

FÜSSEN-WEISSENSEE 8958 Bayern **Map 13**

Seegasthof Weissensee *Tel* (08362) 70 95

In a lakeside village just west of the old town of Füssen, and quite near the Royal Castles, this pleasant little Gasthof *has fine mountain views. Two modern buildings with alpine decor (lots of stripped pine); spacious bedrooms, cordial staff, lavish breakfasts, average main meals (good for fish). Closed 11 Jan–11 Feb, 16 Nov–19 Dec. 22 rooms, all with bath and shower. B&B double 102–138 DM. Set meals 25–45 DM. Endorsed this year, but fuller reports welcome.*

GEISLINGEN AN DER STEIGE 7340 Baden-Württemberg **Map 13**

Burghotel *Tel* (07331) 4 10 51
Burggasse 41
Weiler ob Helfenstein

Down a winding road in the rolling hills of the Schwäbische Alb, north-west of Ulm, an attractive modern building in superior motel style. Pleasant owners, nice rooms with balconies, varied breakfasts, indoor pool plus jacuzzis, and a large garden. No restaurant, but the Burgstüberl *close by has been found excellent. Closed 3 weeks in summer, also Christmas/New Year. 23 rooms, all with bath and shower. Rooms: single 50–100 DM, double 98–145 DM. Breakfast 8–20 DM. No recent reports: more welcome.*

GRAINAU 8104 Bayern **Map 13**

Hotel Alpenhof *Tel* (08821) 80 71
Alpspitzstrasse 22

Grainau, just west of Garmisch, is a popular village-resort at the foot of the high Alps. The *Alpenhof*, down a quiet side-road, is a big modern chalet in typical local style. Many rooms have a flower-decked balcony looking on to the craggy Zugspitze massif. The hotel has a pleasant garden and sun-terrace with yellow parasols, and a good indoor swimming pool. Reports this year have again been enthusiastic: "A delightful hotel in a lovely setting. Good honest German food very well presented; staff friendly and helpful; our room large and comfortable." "The meals were wonderful." Buffet breakfasts include a heated covered dish of bacon, scrambled eggs and sauté potatoes. (*Dr RH Freeman, Diane and Joel Morris*)

Open All year except 3–30 Apr and 10 Nov–17 Dec.
Rooms 29 double, 7 single – all with bath and shower, telephone, radio and TV; some with balcony.

Facilities Lift. Salon with open fireplace, TV room, restaurant; banqueting room. Indoor heated swimming pool and sauna. Garden and terrace.
Location 6 km SW of Garmisch-Partenkirchen. Hotel is central, but quietly situated. Parking.
Credit cards Access, Amex, Diners.
Terms [1989 rates] Dinner, B&B: single 78–120 DM, double 180–240 DM. Reduced rates and special meals for children.

GUTACH IM BREISGAU 7809 Baden-Württemberg — Map 13

Hotel-Restaurant Adler — *Tel* (07681) 70 22
Landstrasse 6

There are two Black Forest villages called Gutach, quite close to each other, and this is the less well known of the two, on the main Freiburg–Elzach road. The *Adler* is a new building in traditional rustic style, with oak-beamed ceilings and tiled floors. The staff are friendly, and the food has again been enjoyed this year, notably the soups and vegetables. An earlier view that still holds good: "Our bedroom was airy and attractive, furnished in repro rococo style with pretty pictures. It was at the back, quiet, looking on to a steep pine-clad hillside with huge rocks. The gardens are well tended: you can eat outside on warm days. One dining room has an open log fire and beautiful Victorian oil-lamps. The other has an original 19th-century mechanical organ with moving military statuettes, playing hum-pah-pah music. We enjoyed the frogs' legs, wild duck, venison with spätzle. Good Bodensee wine. Dogs permitted in restaurant: we were treated to a howling concerto for poodle, dachshund and mongrel."

Open All year except 2 weeks in Jan. Closed Sun, and Mon until 5 pm.
Rooms 1 suite, 10 double, 3 single – 13 with bath, 2 with shower, all with telephone; some with radio and TV.
Facilities Lounge/bar, TV room, 2 restaurants. Garden terrace with outdoor meals and barbecues in summer.
Location 21 km NW of Freiburg, just W of D294 to Elzach.
Credit cards None accepted.
Terms [1989 rates] B&B: single 60–80 DM, double 78–120 DM. Meals 31–70 DM.

HAGNAU 7759 Baden-Württemberg — Map 13

Erbguth's Landhaus — *Tel* (07532) 62 02 and 90 51
Neugartenstrasse 39 — *Telex* 733811 ERBHA

Lake Constance (Bodensee) is a busy holiday area. Wisely, the Germans have put the accent here on smallish hotels of character rather than big lakeside palaces, and this *Landhaus* (country house) is typical – a converted private house, newly renovated, on the edge of a pretty lakeside village. It is a hotel of much personality, run with flair by a young couple, the Erbguths (he cooks, she hostesses). An inspector's recent assessment: "The elegant white marble hall leads to an equally elegant and small restaurant, newly decorated in soothing blue tones. Our comfortable bedroom had a small terrace and solid wooden furniture – more the feeling of a guest house than a luxury hotel. The welcome was warm. We took the 98 DM [1989] 8-course menu and judged it to be borderline *Michelin* rosette standard – excellent salad with sweetbreads.

Good buffet breakfast." An earlier view: "You dine by candle-light, amid flowers and modern 'antiques'. Much of the food was smoked and preserved in their own kitchens – e.g. superb home-smoked caviar. Frau Erbguth has panache and artistry: she dresses smartly, is charming, modern and slick, and the same could be said of her clientele. Not a cheap place, but the quality is superb." A *Jugendstil* villa by the lake, with four bedrooms, has just opened.

Open All year except 4 Jan–1 Mar. Restaurant closed Tue.
Rooms 16 double, 4 single – all with bath and/or shower, telephone, radio and TV. 5 in lake-side annexe 5 mins away. Some ground-floor rooms.
Facilities Lounge, TV room, bar, 2 restaurants; fitness room with sauna and solarium. Gardens and terraces. Private beach on lake.
Location On Lake Constance (Bodensee), just E of Meersburg. Parking.
Credit cards All major cards accepted.
Terms B&B: single 65–150 DM, double 110–320 DM; half board 35 DM per person added; full board 48 DM added. Set lunch/dinner 38–50 DM; full alc 45–50 DM. Reduced rates for children sharing parents' room.

HAMBURG 2000 — Map 13

Hotel Abtei — *Tel* (040) 44 29 05 and 45 75 65

Abteistrasse 14, Hamburg 13 — *Telex* 2165645 ABHA

An elegant little B&B hotel in a quiet residential district two miles north of the centre, near the Alster. Large, attractive rooms with good bathrooms; interesting breakfasts; small garden. Light meals provided on request. 18 rooms, all with bath and/or shower. B&B double 180 DM. No recent reports. More welcome.

Hotel Hanseatic — *Tel* (040) 48 57 72

Sierichstrasse 150
Hamburg 60

The very select *Hanseatic*, a pink-fronted patrician villa in a residential area north of the big Alster lake, is said to be Hamburg's smallest hotel, with just 13 rooms. But lucky are those who, by booking well ahead, are privileged to share in the very personal atmosphere created by owner-manager Wolfgang Schüler. "Herr Schüler's dedication and courtesy make this small hotel a rare jewel", "truly magnificent bedrooms", are two reports this year. Last year's: "He was exceedingly gracious and charming, takes great pride in his intimate hotel and should receive the 'Host of the Year' award. Fresh flowers in our room and a plate of fresh fruit on beautiful old Rosenthal china, plus big white towelling bathrobes. Breakfast was wonderful, served in a beautiful room hung with old oil paintings. The antique sterling coffee service gleamed." "He makes his own breads and marmalades, and serves his superb breakfasts personally in a high style verging on the camp." Some film, theatre and opera people visiting Hamburg prefer to stay here rather than at the larger and more expensive *Vier Jahreszeiten* (q.v.). (*H Langenberg, Jeremy and Anthea Larken*)

Open All year.
Rooms 1 suite, 2 studios, 10 double – all with bath and shower, telephone, radio and TV; baby-sitting on request. Ground-floor rooms

Facilities Lounge/bar, breakfast room; fitness room and sauna. Small garden. Alster lake and city park both 2 blocks away.
Location In Winterhude, 4 km N of city centre. Parking in street, but difficult.
Credit cards Access, Amex, Diners.
Terms Rooms: single occupancy 150–170 DM, double 180–250 DM, suite 250–350 DM. Breakfast 20 DM. Children under 12 sharing parents' room free. (No restaurant.)

Hotel Prem
An der Alster 9
Hamburg 1

Tel (040) 24 54 54
Fax (040) 28 03-851
Telex 2163115 PREM

Facing the Alster on its eastern shore, a mile from the city centre, this smallish and elegant hotel, not cheap, has again been liked in 1988/9. "Service is friendly and efficient," write Americans; "we had a wonderful meal, and took the breakfast buffet in their lovely garden." Others have spoken of "a charming flower-filled hotel with a courteous staff" and "large, airy, colourfully decorated rooms". Rooms however do vary in size: some look over the lake, some over gardens, and those facing the street can be noisy. The hotel's French restaurant, *La Mer*, has a good reputation; its garden restaurant serves German food. (*David and Patricia Hawkins, Russell W Field, JR Welby and others*)

Open All year.
Rooms 40 double, 11 single – all with bath and/or shower, telephone and TV. Some ground-floor rooms.
Facilities Lift. Lounge, TV room, bar, restaurant, *Stüberl*; conference facilities. Garden with restaurant. Garage.
Location On SE shore of Alster lake, 10 mins' walk from city centre and station.
Restriction Not suitable for ♿.
Credit cards All major cards accepted.
Terms B&B: single from 140 DM, double from 220 DM. Set lunch 65 DM, dinner 100 DM; full alc 145 DM. Reduced rates and special meals for children.

Hotel Vier Jahreszeiten
Neuer Jungfernstieg 9-14
Hamburg 36

Tel (040) 3 49 40;
Reservations (040) 3 49 46 93
Fax (040) 3 49 46 02
Telex 211629

We are sorry to have received no reports this year on one of Europe's most famous and gracious luxury hotels, which faces Hamburg's inner lake, the Binnen Alster. Founded in 1897, it has no connection with the other *Vier Jahreszeiten* hotels (e.g. in Munich), it is privately owned and run by the Haerlin family who have carefully amassed its antique furnishings over the years. Despite its splendour it avoids pretentiousness, and although fairly large, with conference facilities, it is neither bustling nor impersonal, but has something of the calm atmosphere of a private club. The elegant rooms have antiques and splendid tapestries. Some, with balcony, look over the lake. "Nice extras included a shoehorn, and a thermometer for checking the bathwater – but you might well expect this at 300 DM a night." "Super-efficient German service dished up with a smile. Huge classy rooms with glittering chandeliers and gilt carved mirrors – all thoroughly plush and decadent. Best venison I've ever eaten – the restaurant (*Michelin* rosette) is one of Hamburg's best." The restaurant is beautiful, in a modern style; so is the *Konditorei Condi* that serves light lunches. Could recent visitors bring us up to date, please?

Open All year.
Rooms 11 suites, 75 double, 86 single – all with bath and shower, telephone, radio and TV.
Facilities Lounge, 2 bars, tea-room, 4 restaurants; conference and functions facilities; night club, barber's shop, wine shop.
Location Central, on W side of Alster lake. Parking.
Restriction Not suitable for ♿.
Credit cards All major cards accepted.
Terms Rooms: single 275–355 DM, double 375–545 DM, suite 650–930 DM. Set lunch/dinner 60-125 DM; full alc 80–100 DM.

Hotel Wedina *Tel* (040) 24 30 11
Gurlittstrasse 23,
Hamburg 1

Very modestly priced for Hamburg but quite central (in a quiet side-street near the southern end of the Alster lake), the useful Wedina *offers pleasant spacious bedrooms and good German breakfasts, plus the bonus of a small garden, with outdoor heated pool and sauna. Street parking. Open 10 Feb–12 Dec. 23 rooms, most with bath or shower. B&B: single 60–90 DM, double 88–120 DM [1989]. No restaurant. Recent nomination, endorsed in 1989, but we'd like more reports please.*

HEIDELBERG 6900 Baden-Württemberg — Map 13

Hotel Alt Heidelberg *Tel* (06221) 91 50
Rohrbacher Strasse 29 *Fax* (06221) 164272
Telex 461897

Ten minutes' walk from the heart of the *alt* part of town (the university library, former students' prison, and Friedrich-Ebert museum are all worth a visit), this Guide debutant is a neat, well-modernised hotel on a main street (but quiet), whose *Graimberg* restaurant serves some of the best food in town – "a French chef doing wonders with German dishes" (e.g. venison with spätzle, warm röte grütze, both enjoyed in 1989). "Charming, cosy and friendly", says a regular. But another visitor found service erratic. Some rooms are spacious and modern; others smaller, with antiques. (*Reginald B Vaughan, Eileen Spencer, JA and KA*) Live jazz on Fridays in the basement bar: but it's more fun to visit one of the uproarious old student pubs in the old town, such as *Scnookeloch*, or *Seppl* where you sit round big tables and beer is drunk communally out of giant glass boots.

Open All year. Restaurant closed Sat till 6 pm.
Rooms 80 – all with bath and shower, telephone, radio and TV.
Facilities Lift. Hall, restaurant, bar; conference facilities. Sauna.
Location Central. Parking.
Credit cards All major cards accepted.
Terms [1989 rates] Rooms: single 95–130 DM, double 125–165 DM, suite 185 DM. Breakfast 15 DM. Alc 35–60 DM. Children under 12 sharing parents' room free.

> If you are nominating a hotel, please err on the side of saying too much. Many suggestions have to be rejected only because they are too brief.

HELLENTHAL 5374 Nordrhein-Westfalen — Map 13

Haus Lichtenhardt — *Tel* (02482) 614

In the northern part of the Eifel massif, not far from the enchanting old town of Monschau and the absorbing open-air museum of rural life at Kommern, this unpretentious modern hotel is in a quiet hilly setting outside the village. Comfortable rooms, friendly and personal service, modest prices. Indoor pool. Closed 17–27 Dec. 19 rooms, most with bath and/or shower. B&B double 65–90 DM. Set menus 13–31 DM [1989]. New nomination. More reports welcome, especially on the food.

HINTERZARTEN 7824 Baden-Württemberg — Map 13

Pension Hotel Sassenhof — *Tel* (07652) 15 15
Adlerweg 17

"This very superior yet friendly *pension* is just what you might expect to find in one of the smartest of Black Forest resorts, popular alike with skiers and walkers. It's a modern gabled building, flower-decked, facing the wide village green, with views of the hills. Elegant public rooms, and a big indoor swimming pool with picture windows facing the lake and woods." "Fabulous!" runs another report this year; "a romantic garret room, delicious and copious breakfast, proprietors charming." (*JA and KA, Bettye Chambers*)

Open All year except 20 Nov–20 Dec.
Rooms 6 suites, 7 double, 10 single – all with bath and/or shower, telephone, radio, TV and tea-making facilities.
Facilities Lift. Hall, lounges, TV room, breakfast room. Indoor swimming pool, sauna, solarium. Terrace; garden.
Location. Central, parking. Hinterzarten is 26 km E of Freiburg.
Restriction No children under 3.
Credit cards All major cards accepted.
Terms B&B: single 50–90 DM, double 60–80 DM per person, suite 70–90 DM. (No restaurant.)

HOFGEISMAR 3520 Hessen — Map 13

Burghotel Dornröschenschloss Sababurg — *Tel* (05678) 10 52, *Fax* (05678) 10 32
Hofgeismar-Sababurg

An inspector's discovery this year, on the rolling wooded plateau west of the Weser valley: "A self-consciously romantic old 14th-century schloss, whose twin green cupolas tower up through the oakwoods. It was long a country home of the princes of Hessen: the brothers Grimm were invited here for hunting parties, and it is said to have been the model for the castle in *Dornröschen* (*The Sleeping Beauty*). Today it capitalises on these fairy-tale associations: statuettes of Puss in Boots and Cinderella stand by

> Please write and confirm an entry when it is deserved. If you think that a hotel is not as good as we say, write and tell us.

the entrance, and the garden shop will sell you some rather grim Grimm Kitsch. Off-putting, maybe: but the hotel itself is delightful, a stylish conversion, very well run by its cultivated owner, Karl Koseck. Lovely rooms in the tower with canopied beds; lovely views, too, from rooms and restaurant; good food, especially the pheasant and venison in season. Sometimes, Grimm tales are read aloud during meals; in summer, there are concerts and fairy-tale plays in the medieval courtyard. It is much liked by Americans and very popular for functions (five wedding parties were in progress on the day of our visit). For further good measure, the 120-hectare zoo on the Sababurg estate is Germany's oldest (1571). It has buffaloes, bears, penguins, even Exmoor ponies – but no Frog Prince."

Open All year except Jan and Feb.
Rooms 17 double, 1 single – 8 with bath, 10 with shower, all with telephone and radio; 8 with TV.
Facilities Salon with TV, dining rooms; conference/functions facilities; museum. Courtyard. Garden. Zoo adjacent.
Location 14 km NE of Hofgeismar, 30 km N of Kassel.
Restrictions Not suitable for ♿.
Credit cards All major cards accepted.
Terms B&B: single 80–150 DM, double 150–240 DM. Set lunch/dinner 55–70 DM; full alc 45–60 DM. 1-night bookings refused at weekends. Special meals for children.

HOLZAPPEL 5409 Rheinland-Pfalz — Map 13

Altes Herrenhaus zum Bären — *Tel* (06439) 70 14
Hauptstrasse 15

This most stylishly decorated restaurant-with-rooms stands in a village square amid pleasant wooded country between Koblenz and Limburg: "The half-timbered 17th-century hotel, small and intimate, is a gem inside, with pleasant furnishings, bowls of flowers, and a cared-for atmosphere. Our room was well equipped, the owners were helpful and informative, and the food was some of the best we have eaten in Germany, making the most of fresh ingredients. Breakfast was a feast, including raspberries and omelettes. Each departing guest gets a packet of fruit." The delightful annexe, the *Goethehaus*, once visited by the poet, houses all the bedrooms (ten are new this year) and has a wine cellar.

Open All year except Jan.
Rooms 10 suites, 10 double, 4 single – all with bath and shower, telephone, radio TV and baby-listening. Ground-floor rooms. All in *Goethehaus*.
Facilities Lift. Restaurant, wine cellar; 2 conference rooms. Terrace. Garden.
Location In village, 16 km W of Limburg, on road to Bad Ems. Parking.
Credit cards All major cards accepted.
Terms [1989 rates] B&B: single 49.50–95 DM, double 98–165 DM, Set meals 30–35 DM; full alc 70 DM. Reduced rates and special meals for children.

HOPFEN AM SEE 8959 Bayern — Map 13

Hotel Alpenblick — *Tel* (08362) 70 18
Uferstrasse 10 — *Telex* 541343 ABLIK

As its name indicates, there are views of the Allgaü Alps (and of the lake) from the front-room balconies of this spruce flower-decked chalet-style hotel, modern but in traditional style, set beside a lake in a pleasant little Bavarian resort north of Füssen. Large airy rooms, friendly staff, better-than-average food. 46 rooms, most with bath and shower. B&B double 126–156 DM. Meals 25–55 DM [1989]. New nomination. More reports welcome.

HÖRSTEL-RIESENBECK 4446 Nordrhein-Westfalen **Map 13**

Schlosshotel Surenberg
Surenberg 13

Tel (05454) 70 92
Telex 94586 SUREN

This appealing Guide newcomer, a *Relais du Silence,* lies in a little-known part of Germany – the opulent farming country of northern Westphalia, flat but pleasantly pastoral, not unlike Norfolk: "The name is misleading, for it's not a converted castle but a modern sporty ranch-hotel on the estate of a moated *Wasserschloss,* the home of the influential president of the German farmers' union. He owns this lovely, spacious hotel, and it is run for him with breezy efficiency by jovial Klaus Trottier, a Huguenot, who also cooks: in his big open-plan restaurant, very popular locally, we enjoyed a good meal, especially the foie gras salad and braised vegetables. Service by local girls was remarkable, even by high German standards, for its smiling stylish courtesy. Our large bedroom was rather bare in decor, but well equipped, with french windows opening onto a flowery balcony and the wide grounds. The hotel is much used for sporty weekends: as well as a fine heated indoor pool, and various games, it has large riding stables where many local people keep their horses. The restaurant's wide panoramic windows give straight onto the main indoor riding hall, so that you can watch the riders and horses while you eat. We've never seen this in a hotel before."

Open All year except 9–22 Jan.
Rooms 23 – all with bath and/or shower, telephone and TV; many with balcony.
Facilities Restaurant; conference facilities. Indoor swimming pool, sauna, fitness centre. Large grounds with stables; children's playground, minigolf; bicycles for hire.
Location 6 km SW of Hörstel which is 44 km N of Münster.
Credit cards Access, Amex.
Terms [1989 rates] B&B: single 83–94 DM, double 139–160 DM. Meals 34–65 DM.

ISMANING 8045 Bayern **Map 13**

Hotel Fischerwirt
Schlosstrasse 17

Tel (089) 96 48 53
Fax (089) 96 35 83

In an attractive commuter town on the northern edge of Munich, set back in a quiet courtyard, this typical modern German inn is clean, friendly and efficient. Nice lounge, small garden; lavish breakfasts; good restaurant. Closed Christmas and New Year. 44 rooms, all with bath or shower. B&B double 78–165 DM. Latest reports vary between "very good" and "overpriced". More welcome.

> If you are nominating a hotel, please do make sure that you tell us enough to convey its character and quality. We can't make good bricks without plenty of straw.

KETTWIG 4300 Nordrhein-Westfalen — Map 13

Hotel Schloss Hugenpoet — *Tel* (02054) 1 20 40
August-Thyssen-Strasse 51 — *Fax* (02054) 1 20 450

The winding valley of the river Ruhr is not an industrial blackspot but quite rural and idyllic (the big mines and steelworks are a few miles to the north); and here on its banks, within the borders of the Essen residential suburb of Kettwig, is this moated 16th-century castle, now a luxurious hotel. Its newly renovated bedrooms and *Michelin*-rosetted cuisine have been again admired this year, endorsing these 1988 views: "The atmosphere is warm and welcoming, with the open fire and stately furnishings. Our room was large, with a curtained-off sleeping area, newly re-covered antique and modern chairs, and a large marble-tiled bathroom." "A fine black-marble staircase with red carpet in the foyer, reception staff very thoughtful, wonderful afternoon tea, and interesting French cooking." The hotel and restaurant cater for functions, but these are not usually obtrusive. (*Derek and Annette Lambert*) The grandiose Krupp family mansion in Kettwig, Villa Hügel, now a museum, is worth visiting; and do not miss the Folkwang museum of local history in Essen. Both provide poignant insights into the splendours and horrors of the Ruhr's mighty past.

Open All year except 24 Dec.
Rooms 1 suite, 13 double, 5 single – all with bath and shower, telephone, radio TV, and mini-bar.
Facilities Lift. Large hall, salon, wine cellar, restaurant; conference facilities; chapel for weddings and christenings; terrace. Large grounds with garden and tennis court.
Location 11 km SW of Essen off A52, near A2 and A3 motorways. Parking.
Credit cards All major cards accepted.
Terms B&B: single 190–255 DM, double 245–365 DM, suite 410 DM. Alc (excluding wine) 100–130 DM. Reduced rates for children sharing parents' room.

KOBLENZ 5400 Rheinland-Pfalz — Map 13

Zum schwarzen Bären — *Tel* (0261) 4 40 74
Koblenzer Strasse 35,
Koblenz-Moselweiss

This city at the confluence of the Rhine and the Mosel has been largely rebuilt since wartime bombing: it contains few buildings of note save the massive Ehrenbreitstein citadel, but it remains a good base for exploring these two rivers. The "Black Bears", a small modern winehouse-with-rooms, which has been in the same family since 1810, is in the suburb of Moselweiss, west of the city centre. "Rooms are comfortable but basically furnished, the bathrooms all have a shower, not a bath. There is a spectacular lack of mirrors – just as well, for the lighting is appalling. But the hotel's real strength lies in the warmth of the welcome provided by the Kölsch family and Peter Kölsch's superlative cuisine – e.g. stuffed breast of chicken poached in white wine, pigeon with truffles in a whisper of pastry, apple pancakes with cinnamon ice cream. He cooks with love, and tells you where you're going wrong when choosing your meal." An endorser this year laments the lack of comfortable chairs. (*Marion Godfrey and Judy Smith; also NR Measey*)

Open All year except 2 weeks in Feb and 2 weeks in Aug. Restaurant closed Sun evening and Mon.
Rooms 10 double, 3 single – 1 with bath, 12 with shower; all with telephone; TV on request. 8 in annexe. Some ground-floor rooms.
Facilities Lounge, *Bierstube*, TV room; conference facilities; terrace.
Location 1.5 km W of Koblenz. Parking.
Credit cards All major cards accepted.
Terms B&B: single 60 DM, double 95 DM. Set lunch 26–48 DM, dinner 45–98 DM; full alc 40 DM. Reduced rates and special meals for children.

KRONBERG IM TAUNUS 6242 Hessen — Map 13

Schlosshotel Kronberg
Hainstrasse 25

Tel (06173) 7 01 01
Fax (06173) 70 12 67
Telex 415424 SHLO

This vast grey towered and gabled *Schloss*, eminently Victorian, was built for Queen Victoria's eldest daughter after the death of her husband, Kaiser Friedrich III. It is now a classy hotel (still sometimes also used privately by visiting royalty) but is no more expensive than the leading hotels in central Frankfurt, 17 kilometres away. This year the management changed, but regulars returning in 1989 felt that standards had improved, if anything, as a result. Guests are now given gift-wrapped ashtrays as a "welcome" present! "For comfort and style, still our favourite hotel in the Frankfurt area," is their view; "our bedroom overlooking the beautiful grounds was lovely. The public rooms are imposing, with wood panelling and huge tapestries. Service can be a little slow, but staff are polite; the dining rooms are attractive and the food good. Lavish breakfasts." Male guests must wear jacket and tie for dinner. (*Stephan and Kate Murray-Sykes*) The grounds contain an 18-hole golf course.

Open All year.
Rooms 7 suites, 24 double, 26 single – all with bath and/or shower, telephone, radio and TV.
Facilities Lift. Lobby, lounge, bar, restaurant; functions facilities. Park with 18-hole golf course.
Location 15 mins' walk from centre of Kronberg. Open parking.
Restriction Not suitable for ♿.
Credit cards All major cards accepted.
Terms Rooms: single 220–325 DM, double 340–530 DM, suite 630–1,400 DM. Breakfast 23 DM. Set lunch 49.50 DM, dinner 125 DM; full alc 116 DM. Special meals for children on request.

LEMGO 4920 Nordrhein-Westfalen — Map 13

Auf dem Brokhof
Zur Behrensburg 19, Lemgo-Lüerdissen

Tel (05261) 44 82

"A delightful surprise", say this year's nominators. "The charming Wittigs, retired farmers in their early 60s, have converted their farmhouse into a very sympathetic guesthouse, set in open rolling country just north of the fine old Hanseatic town of Lemgo, near Bielefeld. Pleasant, unforced touches, such as an old cartwheel for garden decor. Bedrooms in the new annexe are very spacious; the main building has smaller ones.

Furniture is modern utility, but serviceable. The Wittigs provide hearty, wholesome rural fare, such as home-made soups, braised pork, and big breakfasts. Prices are absurdly low. This would be an ideal base for a quiet country holiday in a little-known part of North Germany where there's much to see: Lemgo itself has a superb Altstadt of medieval gabled houses, and a museum of torture inflicted on witches." (*JA and KA*)

Open All year.
Rooms 6 rooms, 3 apartments, all with bath and/or shower.
Facilities Sitting room with piano, 2 dining rooms (one for non-smokers), playroom with ping-pong, swings. Garden.
Location 4 km N of Lemgo, in suburb of Lüerdissen.
Terms B&B 26–30 DM. Dinner 10 DM.

LENZKIRCH 7825 Baden-Württemberg — Map 13

Hotel Ursee — *Tel* (07653) 7 81
Grabenstrasse 18

Set amid rolling wooded country just outside the popular resort of Lenzkirch, in the southern Black Forest near Titisee: a big modern chalet, mixing the smart and cosy in true local style. Spacious rooms (with clashing decor), excellent food including buffet breakfast. Closed early Nov–mid-Dec. Restaurant closed Mon. 49 rooms, most with bath and/or shower. B&B double 98–138 DM. Meals 30–60 DM [1989]. New nomination. More reports please.

LIMBURG AN DER LAHN 6250 Hessen — Map 13

Hotel Zimmermann — *Tel* (06431) 46 11
Blumenröderstrasse 1 — *Fax* (06431) 4 13 14

Dull-looking from outside, but inside richly furnished with antiques, this modern hotel behind the station is only a short walk from Limburg's picturesque old quarter and hilltop Gothic cathedral. Triple glazing ensures quiet. Prices moderate, owner friendly, service very thoughtful; dinner for residents only. 30 rooms, all with bath and/or shower, double 98–220 DM [1989]. Endorsed this year, but further reports welcome.

MARKTHEIDENFELD 8772 Bayern — Map 13

Hotel Anker — *Tel* (09391) 40 41
Obertorstrasse 6–8 — *Telex* 689608 DEPAN

In a small wine-growing town on the Main west of Würzburg, this enticing Guide newcomer is a smart modern white building, stylishly furnished in good taste (red print in *Michelin*), owned by the Deppisch family who also have the elegant *Weinhaus Anker* restaurant just opposite, "A delightful family-run place. Much care and pride has been lavished on the rooms. Herr Deppisch owns extensive vineyards round the hotel, and you can buy his excellent Franconian wines. The *Weinhaus* well deserves its *Michelin* rosette: all food, including butter and cheese, comes from their local farm. The perfect combination of a hotel and restaurant run by people who really care for their guests." (*Judy and Gordon Smith*) Though they are central most rooms are quiet as they overlook a courtyard. More reports welcome.

Open All year. Restaurant closed Mon and Tue midday.
Rooms 3 suites, 22 double, 13 single – 30 with bath, 8 with shower, all with telephone, radio, TV; baby-sitting on request. Ground floor rooms suitable for ♿.
Facilities 2 lifts, ramps. Lounge, TV room, breakfast room, restaurant, cellar (wine tastings); conference facilities. Courtyard where meals are served.
Location Central, next to church. Garage (8 DM). Town is 29 km W or Würzburg on B8.
Credit cards Access, Amex. (Diners in restaurant only).
Terms B&B: single 85–95 DM, double 135–175 DM, suite 250 DM. Set lunch 40 DM, dinner 50 DM; full alc 90 DM. Reduced rates and special meals for children.

MEERSBURG 7758 Baden-Württemberg — Map 13

Hotel-Gasthof zum Bären — *Tel* (07532) 60 44
Marktplatz 11

The prettiest town on Lake Constance has half-timbered houses, a romantic old castle and a newer pink baroque one, all crowded together in the *Altstadt* on a hill above the lake. Here in the lovely market square is the *Hotel-Gasthof zum Bären*, a stunning old building with flower-pots and carvings on its quaint corner-tower, an inn since the 17th century, now owned and run by the charming Gilowsky family. Readers this year have again liked this "unpretentious guesthouse with its creaking wooden floors", and its warm family welcome. "The restaurant is a delight; I was asked if I would mind sharing a table, and this seemed to be the status quo. An excellent meal of baked perch from the lake and fine cheeses." Others have admired the beamed ceilings, Alpine furniture and cheerful rooms: "A spacious, comfortable room facing the square, with a charming sitting-alcove in the quaint old tower." Be warned that the stairs are fairly steep and there is no lift; also the quieter back rooms lack a view. (*Dr FP Woodford*)

Open 20 Mar–15 Nov. Restaurant closed Mon.
Rooms 13 double, 3 single – all with shower. 1 double in annexe.
Facilities 2 restaurants.
Location Central (back rooms quietest). 15 garages.
Restriction Not suitable for ♿.
Credit cards None accepted.
Terms B&B: single 52 DM, double 98–108 DM. Set lunch/dinner 22–32 DM; full alc 37–47 DM. Extra bed for child in parents' room 20 DM; special meals.

MUNICH 8000 Bayern — Map 12

Hotel Biederstein — *Tel* (089) 39 50 72
Keferstrasse 18, Munich 40

A spruce little hotel, modern but with some good classic furniture, in a residential street between the Englischer Garten and the raffish night-club quarter of Schwabing, Munich's Chelsea-cum-Soho: the city centre is two miles to the south. Service mainly efficient, bedrooms clean and comfortable; no restaurant, but light meals on request. Garage. Some redecoration has taken place this year. 31 rooms, all with bath and shower, and balcony. B&B: single 110–125 DM, double 135–165 DM. Restored to Guide after earlier criticisms. More reports still needed.

Gästehaus Englischer Garten *Tel* (089) 39 20 34
Liebergesellstrasse 8
Munich 40

Only 4 km from the city centre, a creeper-covered 18th-century millhouse beside a stream at the edge of the Englischer Garten in Schwabing, popular with artists and writers. Garden, old furniture, helpful staff, family owners. Cosy rooms in main building: those in annexe less attractive. 37 rooms, 20 with bath and shower. B&B double 99–172 DM. No restaurant. Some criticisms. More reports please.

Marienbad Hotel *Tel* (089) 59 55 85
Barerstrasse 11, Munich 2 *Fax* (089) 59 82 38

Centrally and quietly located near the Alte Pinakothek, this little B&B hotel has few frills or graces but is friendly and serviceable and continues to have its fans. A report this year: "Perfectly quiet, and the better rooms at least are quite large and well equipped. More wattage would be appreciated. Breakfast room gloomy: but an ample breakfast will be brought to your room." (*Dr FP Woodford*)

Open All year.
Rooms 16 double, 11 single – 22 with shower, all with telephone.
Facilities Lift. Salon with TV.
Location Central, but very quiet; approach from Karolinenplatz. Parking nearby.
Credit cards None accepted.
Terms B&B: single 65–120 DM, double 160 DM. Reduced rates for children sharing parents' room. (No restaurant.)

Hotel an der Oper *Tel* (089) 22 87 11
Falkenturmstrasse 10 *Telex* 522588
Munich 2

Down a small side-street off the famous and fashionable Maximilianstrasse, this bed-and-breakfast hotel is much frequented by visitors to the nearby Opera – as its name implies. "Very good value," is an inspector's judgement; "the white-walled bedrooms are plain (apart from the ubiquitous chandeliers) but comfortable, with modern bathrooms. The green-leather armchairs and sofas in the lobby were comfortable, and newspapers on wooden handles were available in the best Mitteleuropa tradition. Service was helpful and personal, especially with regard to carrying luggage. Breakfast was adequate. The elegant, intimate and expensive *Bouillabaisse* restaurant is in the same building: its French cooking did not greatly impress us, but there are many cheaper and better places nearby" (e.g. the huge, bustling *Franziskaner*).

Open All year.
Rooms 55 – all with bath and/or shower, telephone and radio.

Facilities Lift. Lounge, TV room, breakfast room.
Location Central, near Opera House.
Restriction Not suitable for ♿.
Credit cards Access, Amex, Diners.
Terms [1989 rates] B&B: single 110–125 DM, double 170–190 DM. (No restaurant.)

Trustee Parkhotel
Parkstrasse 31, Munich 2

Tel (089) 51 99 50
Fax (089) 51 99 54 20
Telex 5218296 TRUP

A new upper-medium-priced hotel, west of the city centre and close to the main station, exhibition centre and Theresien park (where the Oktoberfest is held). "I had an enormous room, beautifully furnished," says a recent visitor. "Cheerful and efficient service, first-class welcome with fresh fruit in the room, good food, and every facility for the business traveller." The hotel is quiet, built around its own courtyard; some rooms have a balcony. (*Endorsed this year by Garry and Janette Collier*)

Open All year except Christmas and New Year.
Rooms 36 – all with bath and shower, telephone, radio and TV. Ground-floor rooms.
Facilities Lift. Lounge, bar, restaurant; conference facilities. Garden.
Location 1 km SW of central station. Parking.
Credit cards All major cards accepted.
Terms Rooms: single 185–250 DM, double 220–290 DM, suite 300–390 DM. Breakfast 18 DM. Set lunch/dinner 35 DM; full alc 50 DM. Children under 12 free of charge; special meals.

MÜNSTER 4400 Nordrhein-Westfalen — Map 13

Hotel Schloss Wilkinhege
Steinfurter Strasse 374

Tel (0251) 21 30 45

The area around Westphalia's historic capital is well known for its numerous *Wasserburgen* – old castles girt by broad moats or even by lakes. These watery surrounds were originally defensive, but are now ornamental. Some of the castles are still lived in by descendants of the original owners in this very aristocratic part of Germany; others are now colleges, or museums. This one in the city's north-west outskirts, dating from the 16th century, is a fairly smart hotel, brought to the Guide by two reports this year: "A lovely peaceful setting with a golf course behind. Ducks, geese, peacocks, etc, strut in the courtyard within the moat. We stayed in a modern room in the annexe, converted from the stables. The food was excellent and the young staff were pleasant." "We got a friendly welcome and a huge family suite. There's an atmospheric *Schlosskeller*, but we dined out on the terrace – a relaxed ambience, thoughtful service and the best food we had in Germany (but not cheap). The very pretty chapel is open to guests." (*Dr Carolyn A Cooper, Mary Hanson*)

Open All year.
Rooms 4 suites, 38 double and single – all with bath and shower, telephone, TV and mini-bar.
Facilities Lounge, 3 restaurants, conference and banqueting facilities; terrace. Park with tennis courts and golf course.
Location 2 km NW of city centre, just off B54. Parking.
Credit cards All major cards accepted.

Terms [1989 rates] B&B: single 115–160 DM, double 165–180 DM, suite 280 DM. Meals 58–79 DM.

NECKARGEMÜND 6903 Baden-Württemberg — Map 13

Hotel zum Ritter — *Tel* (06223) 70 35
Neckarstrasse 40 — *Telex* 461837

In a pretty part of the Neckar valley, just east of Heidelberg, here's an old hunting lodge dating from 1579, well modernised but with folksy touches such as suits of armour. Rooms with riverside views; good breakfasts. 39 rooms, all with bath or shower. B&B double 98–180 DM. Set menus 45–55 DM. New nomination. More reports please, especially on the food.

OBERAMMERGAU 8103 Bayern — Map 13

Gasthof "Zur Rose" — *Tel* (08822) 47 06
Dedlerstrasse 9

Those keen to see the much-contested 32-year-old mother-of-two Virgin Mary in the 1990 *Passion Play* had better book quick for the *Zur Rose*, as for any other hotel in this about-to-be-crowded-out little town. Even outside Passion Play Year (once a decade), it's an unashamedly touristy place, with every other shop a *Holzschnitzerei* selling wood carvings, mostly of a religious or religiose character. But in any year it is also a good centre for hiking or cross-country skiing, and for exploring the Bavarian alps. The *Zur Rose* "is the quintessence of the *gemütlich* – a fine example of a friendly Alpine inn, and has been in the Stückl family for two generations. They speak good English and are warmly hospitable. The rooms, well heated, are simple but not spartan. In the big attractive dining room, meals are substantial meaty affairs; public rooms are full of fine furniture and old paintings (family heirlooms)." Admired again this year for its "excellent food, simple comfort and friendly owners". (*Stephen Ruell*)

Open All year except 1 Nov–15 Dec.
Rooms 24 double, 4 single – 4 with bath, 2 with shower. 10 self-catering units for 2–6 people with shower, kitchenette, telephone and TV.
Facilities Salon, dining room. Garden.
Location In town centre. Parking. Oberammergau is 19 km N of Garmisch.
Credit cards All major cards accepted.
Terms B&B: single 30 DM, double 58 DM. Dinner, B&B 18 DM added per person. Full alc 30 DM. Reduced rates and special meals for children.

OBERWESEL 6532 Rheinland-Pfalz — Map 13

Burghotel-Restaurant Auf Schönburg — *Tel* (06744) 70 27
Telex 42321 BURG

Visitors this year were mightily impressed: "Upstream from Koblenz, towering high above the west bank of the Rhine, the massive medieval stronghold of the Dukes of Schonburg is three fortresses in one, each with its own keep. One is now used as a Catholic holiday and social centre, but the others have been tastefully converted into as delightful a hotel as any that we have visited recently in Germany. It is owned and run by a friendly and civilised young couple, the Hüttls. While the *Burg*'s outward aspect is severe, inside all is intimate and cosy – small beamed courtyards and dining rooms, a handsome library, slightly twee bedrooms with four-posters (best are those with balconies in the old tower). It's the kind of obviously super-romantic place that foreign tourists would adore, yet is no phoney tourist-trap, for it's all done with such taste and unaffected grace. Of course the view over the river is superb. The Hüttls have painted one of the outer walls bright red, because that's how it was in the 16th century, when painted walls were a sign of wealth." "Attractively furnished with antiques; beautiful restaurant with a sense of intimacy, excellent food and service." (*ECM Begg, and others*)

Open 1 Mar–30 Nov. Restaurant closed Mon.
Rooms 1 suite, 17 double, 3 single – 12 with bath, 8 with shower, all with telephone, radio and TV.
Facilities Lift. Small library, 3 dining rooms; courtyard where meals are served in fine weather.
Location 2 km S of Oberwesel, which is 42 km S of Koblenz.
Restriction Not suitable for ♿.
Credit cards Access, Amex, Visa.
Terms B&B: single 85–90 DM, double 130–220 DM, suite 240 DM; dinner, B&B 50 DM per person added. Set lunch/dinner 40–85 DM; full alc from 70 DM. Reduced rates and special meals for children.

OFFENBURG 7600 Baden-Württemberg — Map 13

Hotel Sonne — *Tel* (0781) 7 10 39
Hauptstrasse 94

Commended again in 1989, this old coaching-inn makes a useful stopover. Industrial Offenburg is close to Strasbourg, the Black Forest and the Frankfurt–Basel *Autobahn*. The Schimpf-Schöppner family claims to have been running an inn here since 1350, and though much rebuilt in the 19th century, the hotel still has many earlier antiques. Napoleon stayed here, and you are shown the pewter tureen he used. "Despite this weight of history, the *Sonne* is utterly unpretentious; no foyer, the front door leads straight into the big beamed *Stube*, which today is very much a social centre. At its big round *Stammtisch*, elderly local worthies were tippling and speechifying in true German style, while we enjoyed sound Baden cooking and local wine from the Schimpfs' own vineyards." "Good value, with wholesome, unsophisticated cooking; the rooms in the new part are fairly spartan, but adequate", runs a report this year. Rooms vary, some being old and full of charm, but unmodernised; some newer, but duller.

Open All year. Restaurant closed Sat and Christmas.
Rooms 2 suites, 14 double, 21 single – 7 with bath, 13 with shower, all with telephone; 3 with TV.
Facilities TV room, 2 dining rooms.
Location Central; in pedestrian zone in old part of town. Parking.
Restriction Only restaurant suitable for ♿.
Credit cards Access, Amex, Visa.
Terms B&B: single 46–62 DM, double 65–88 DM; dinner, B&B: 14 DM added. Full alc 18–35 DM. Reduced rates for children.

Report forms (Freepost in UK) will be found at the end of the Guide.

PEGNITZ 8570 Bayern — Map 13

Pflaums Posthotel
Nürnberger Strasse 14

Tel (09241) 72 50
Fax (09241) 404
Telex 642433 PPP

The Pflaum family have run this old post house in a small town between Bayreuth and Nuremberg since 1707. It is now a stylish and fairly expensive hotel. This year a returning regular has renewed her eulogies, "All Pflaums hospitable as ever. They gave us a delicious room full of colour, armchairs, desk, lots of lights, even a CD set-up. The lay-out of breakfast is pure theatre – five round tables laid out with *everything*. The staff used to be in *Tracht* but now look slinky and *moderne* in pretty blouses and skirts." This reader's earlier view, "If you like a country-house-style hotel with an international and musical flavour, this one is very much worth a detour, though during the Bayreuth Festival or the Nuremberg trade fairs it is hard to find a room. One brother Pflaum is the charming manager of house and another is considered one of the best chefs in Germany (*Michelin* rosette). Delicious food in the two restaurants (kid and game are specialities). Drinks by the fire in winter, with pretty little curved sofas to sit on; in summer, coffee out in the sunshine with the fountains playing, or strawberry cake for tea."(*John and Eileen Spencer*) Some rooms are in a modern extension. The Pflaums also offer Bayreuth Wagner operas on a large screen.

Open All year.
Rooms 25 suites, 25 double – all with bath and shower, telephone, radio and TV. 1 ground-floor suite.
Facilities Lift. Lounge, bar, 2 restaurants; conference facilities. Indoor swimming pool and health club, massage, sauna; indoor golf. Garden with terrace for dining.
Location 1 km SW of Pegnitz, 33 km N of Nuremberg.
Credit cards All major cards accepted.
Terms Rooms: single 135–240 DM, double 168–490 DM, suite 290–1,150 DM. Buffet breakfast 18 DM. Set lunch/dinner 32 DM and 140 DM; full alc 110 DM. Reduced rates and special meals for children.

RAVENSBURG 7980 Baden-Württemberg — Map 13

Romantik Hotel Waldhorn
Marienplatz 15

Tel (0751) 1 60 21
Telex 723211 WHORN

In an attractive old Swabian town, a family-run hotel of some character, in an old building with panelled public rooms. Pleasant bedrooms, excellent local dishes (Michelin *rosette*)*, good buffet breakfasts in a cosy room. 40 rooms, all with bath. B&B single 88–125 DM, double 130–180 DM. Set menu 28 DM. New nomination. More reports please.*

REICHENAU (Insel) 7752 Baden-Württemberg — Map 13

Romantik Hotel Seeschau
Schiffslände 8

Tel (07534) 2 57
Fax (07534) 78 84

Reichenau is a pastoral low-lying island in the western part of the Bodensee (Lake of Constance) , linked to the mainland by a causeway. In the Middle Ages it was a major monastic centre, and two glories survive from that time: the late 9th-century Carolingian church of St-George (amazing wall paintings of *c.* AD 1000), and the Romanesque abbey at Mittelzell. Today the island is given over to market gardening and tourism, and its best hotel is the *Seeschau*, a gabled building by the water's edge, run by the Winkelmann-Roser family for 60 years. A report this year, "A charming and friendly little place, quite spruce and smart – panelled walls, old framed prints, uniformed waitresses. Bedrooms a bit small, but most have lake views. Good local fish, prepared by Horst Winkelmann in a somewhat *nouvelle* style, just about deserving its *Michelin* rosette. Lovely setting by the little landing-stage, but very trippery in summer." (*JA and KA*)

Open All year except 6–25 Jan and 15 Oct–20 Dec. Restaurant closed Sun night and Mon.
Rooms 11 double – all with bath or shower, telephone and TV.
Facilities Salon, 2 restaurants; conference facilities. Garden, terrace.
Location 10 km W of Konstanz. Reached by ferry or causeway. Parking.
Restriction Not suitable for ♿.
Credit cards Access, Amex, Diners.
Terms B&B: single 75–100 DM, double 150–180 DM. Set lunch 35 DM, dinner 70 DM; full alc 65 DM. Special meals for children.

RETTENBACH 8449 Bayern — Map 13

Kurhotel Gut Schmelmerhof — *Tel* (09965) 189-0
St-Englmar–Rettenbach

About 15 minutes' drive from the Schwarzach exit of the Regensburg–Passau motorway, Rettenbach is a small village amid the hilly pine-wooded landscapes of eastern Bavaria, between the Danube and the Czech border. On its outskirts, the *Gut Schmelmerhof* is a large chalet-style building owned by the Schmelmer family since 1630; its sporting facilities include indoor and outdoor pools, jacuzzi and sauna. "A beautiful situation and a restful atmosphere. Though family-owned it lacks personal intimacy, but the service is very courteous; the food is good, without the helpings being too overwhelming. A regular and mostly older clientele, but there's a children's playground." The Bavarian room furnishings include wood panelling and hand-made rugs; fillet of wild hare has been commended on the large menu in the restaurant with its low-vaulted ceiling – good buffet breakfast, too.

Open All year.
Rooms 7 suites, 17 double, 10 single – all with bath and/or shower, telephone, radio and TV. 5 holiday apartments 150 metres from main building.
Facilities Lounge, TV room, bar, restaurant; conference facilities. Heated indoor swimming pool, jacuzzi, fitness room and sauna. Garden with swimming pool and children's playground.
Restrictions Not suitable for ♿.
Location 4.5 km SE of St-Englmar, 15 km N of Schwarzach. Parking.
Credit cards None accepted.
Terms [1989 rates] B&B 52–86 DM. Dinner, B&B 22 DM per person added; full alc 43 DM. Reduced rates and special meals for children.

> If you have difficulty in finding hotels because our location details are inadequate, please help us to improve directions next year.

ROTHENBURG OB DER TAUBER 8803 Bayern — Map 13

Hotel-Gasthof Glocke — *Tel* (09861) 30 25
Am Plönlein 1 — *Telex* 61318

Our only surviving entry for this much-visited medieval ramparted town on the Romantiker Strasse. Central, but fairly quiet and off the main tourist circuit; good food, wine and service. Closed 23 Dec–11 Jan. 28 rooms, 22 with bath or shower. B&B double 136–150 DM. Meals 15–45 DM. Few recent reports. More welcome.

RÜDESHEIM-ASSMANNSHAUSEN 6220 Hessen — Map 13

Hotel Krone — *Tel* (06722) 20 36
Rheinuferstrasse 10 — *Fax* (06722) 30 49
Telex 413576 RAST

Hoffmann von Fallersleben composed *Deutschland über Alles* in 1841 at this famous old Rhineside inn which dates from 1541 and has long been a haunt of writers and musicians. It is now a fairly big and grand hotel in two buildings: many bedrooms have a balcony overlooking the gardens and river. Many reports have reached us this year, nearly all favourable. "Even more wonderful than last time. We were given a sumptuous room, close to the secluded, beautiful swimming pool, surrounded by climbing roses. The view of the Rhine from the vine-covered dining terrace is unforgettable, and the food is masterly – start your meal with the local red Sekt and you will be at peace with the world. Whether or not because of the previous Guide entry, I found the head porter's manners greatly improved." Thus spake a devotee this year, who earlier had written, "Don't be put off by the stags' antlers and gloom of the 19th-century furnishings in the main halls. The bedrooms are clean, new and well plumbed. And how lovely to watch the westering sun in peaceful isolation." The rooms in the main annexe are heavily furnished in pompous Victorian style, but comfortable. "We had a room with circular turret and elegant marble bathroom." "Super classical food as always." One reader claims that the foliage on the terrace is not vines but jacaranda. And you should be warned of some night noise from the railway. (*Dr FP Woodford, JA and KA, Ruth and Robert Todd, ND Bain, and others*)

Open 1 Mar–31 Dec.
Rooms 7 suites, 38 double, 12 single – 51 with bath, 6 with shower, all with telephone, radio and TV; many with balcony, 5 with jacuzzi. Most rooms in annexe. Some ground-floor rooms.
Facilities Lift. Salon, TV room, bar, restaurant; riverside terrace/restaurant; conference facilities. Garden with lawn and swimming pool.
Location On the Rhine; parking. Assmannshausen is 5 km W of Rüdesheim, 36 km W of Wiesbaden.
Restriction Not suitable for ♿.
Credit cards Access, Diners, Visa.
Terms Rooms: single 90 DM, double 190 DM, suite 340 DM. Breakfast 18 DM. Set lunch 45 DM, dinner 75–98 DM. Reduced rates and special meals for children.

Give the Guide positive support. Don't just leave feedback to others.

SCHARBEUTZ 2409 Schleswig-Holstein — Map 13

Kurhotel Martensen - Die Barke — *Tel* (04503) 71 17
Strandallee 123 — *Fax* (04503 7 35 40
Telex 261445 KAMA

Just north of elegant Travemünde, the Deauville of the Baltic, where Thomas Mann used to stay and set parts of *Buddenbrooks*, Scharbeutz is a less prestigious but lively family bathing resort; and the *Martensen*, white-walled and red-roofed, is the best of its many holiday hotels along the beach. "We had a spacious room in the old part, with generous balconies facing the smiling Baltic", says a reader this year; "helpful staff, a dinner of good solid bourgeois fare, and a superb covered swimming pool." The buffet breakfast with Holstein specialities has also been commended. (*Rev. Michael Bourdeaux; Eleanor Hope*)

Open 1 Mar–15 Nov.
Rooms 3 suites, 20 double, 15 single – all with bath and shower, telephone, radio and tea-making facilities; many with balcony.
Facilities Lift. Lounge, TV room, restaurants. Indoor swimming pool, sauna, massage. Garden.
Location On seafront. Parking. Scharbeutz is 26 km N of Lübeck.
Restriction Not suitable for ♿.
Credit cards Access, Diners, Visa.
Terms [1989 rates] B&B: single 85–125 DM, double 150–200 DM. Dinner, B&B 22 DM added per person; full board 37 DM added. Set lunch/dinner 25–35 DM; full alc 40–50 DM. Reduced rates and special meals for children.

SCHLESWIG 2380 Schleswig-Holstein — Map 13

Strandhalle — *Tel* (04621) 2 20 21
Strandweg 2 (am Jachthafen) — *Telex* 221327

Northern Germany is still rather sparsely represented in the Guide, so we were glad to hear about this "unusual and attractive" modern hotel in an ancient city that looks on the map as if it is well inland, but in fact is linked to the Baltic by a long inlet, the Schlei. Among its many maritime souvenirs is the remarkable Nydam Boat, an Anglo-Saxon oaken craft of the 4th century displayed in a building beside Gottorf Castle. The *Strandhalle* and its pleasant café terrace face a marina on the Schlei: "I could not decide whether it was a hotel in a museum or a museum in a hotel. It's a sailor's dream, with model boats of every sort, figureheads (including Lord Howe's), framed sailors' knots and a diver's helmet. My small room (cabin?) was comfortable, the food good and the atmosphere friendly."

Open All year.
Rooms 28 – all with bath and/or shower, telephone, radio, TV and mini-bar.
Facilities Salons, restaurant; conference facilities. Café-terrace and garden. Indoor and outdoor swimming pools, sauna.
Location Central; by yacht harbour. Parking.
Credit cards All major cards accepted.
Terms [1989 rates] B&B: single 72 DM, double 120 DM. Meals alc.

> We asked hotels to estimate their 1990 tariffs. About a quarter of the hotels on the Continent failed to reply, so the prices we quote should not be relied upon.

SCHÖNWALD 7741 Baden-Württemberg — Map 13

Hotel Zum Ochsen — *Tel* (07722) 10 45
Ludwig-Uhland Strasse 18 — *Telex* 792606

"Elegant rustic" is how visitors this year describe this typical chalet-style Black Forest hotel, set amid rolling woods and meadows just outside the resort-village of Schönwald, south of Triberg. Owned by the Martin family for generations, it has recently been rebuilt in a style at once smart and folksy, with lots of light new wood and pale carpets. The ambience too is informal yet sophisticated, appealing to "the classier kind of hiker" – you could arrive in an old jersey with a rucksack or dressed by Lagerfeld and feel equally at ease. Good Baden-cum-Alsatian cooking (soupe aux escargots, foie gras maison, etc) served by waitresses in Baden costume, on the patio in summer, by a log fire in winter. Musical evenings and excursions are organised. Pleasant indoor hexagonal pool. "Good food, and Frau Martin a welcoming hostess", says another visitor this year. (*JA and KA, Mr and Mrs RW Beacroft*)

Open All year. Restaurant closed Tue and Wed.
Rooms 4 suites, 30 double, 6 single – 4 with bath, 36 with shower, all with telephone and TV.
Facilities Lounge, 4 restaurants; terrace. Indoor heated swimming pool, sauna and solarium. Large grounds with tennis court and lake with fishing. Bicycles.
Location 8 km S of Triberg. Just outside village. Parking.
Restriction Not suitable for ♿.
Credit cards All major cards accepted.
Terms B&B: single 57–101 DM, double 104–176 DM, suite 96–109 DM; Dinner, B&B 78–135 DM per person. Set lunch/dinner 35–50 DM; full alc 65 DM. Reduced rates for children.

SCHWANGAU 8959 Bayern — Map 13

Schlosshotel Lisl und Jägerhaus — *Tel* (08362) 8 10 06
Neuschwansteinstrasse 1–3 — *Telex* 541332
Hohenschwangau

The Bavarian royal castles in their glorious mountain setting – Mad Ludwig's high-pinnacled fairytale Neuschwanstein, and Hohenschwangau – are both close to this hotel. One recent visitor had an excellent venison dinner, a good spacious room with a view of one of the castles, and found the staff efficient and courteous. Readers have always emphasised the castle theme: "What a romantic spot to spend the night – silent Neuschwanstein bathed in light and all the daytime crowds gone." "We had a comfortable if idiosyncratic room, with lavish use of wood, figured velvet carpet on the floor and half the walls ditto, presided over by an engraving of the impossibly handsome King Ludwig. The dining room's immense windows had Hohenschwangau castle in full, floodlit view."

Open All year except 6 Jan–21 Mar.
Rooms 45 double, 11 single – 26 with bath, 19 with shower, all with telephone and radio; some with TV. 21 in annexe.
Facilities Lift. Lounge, TV room, 5 dining rooms.
Restriction Not suitable for ♿.
Location 6 km SE of Füssen.
Credit cards All major cards accepted.

Terms B&B 40–110 DM. Full alc 45 DM. Reduced rates and special meals for children.

SCHWARZWALD-HOCHSTRASSE 7580 Baden-Württemberg — Map 13

Höhen-Hotel Unterstmatt — *Tel* (07226) 2 04 and 2 09
Bühl 13

The Black Forest High Road winds along the hillcrest south from Baden-Baden, with fine views over the Rhine plain below. This friendly and informal ski-hotel is circled by meadows and deep pine forests, and has the bonus of superb food (*Michelin* rosette). It has been owned and run since 1905 by the Reymanns, and caters for families who come to ski in winter or hike in summer. "Very well run", says a reader this year, "I had a superb meal in the more formal restaurant, clad in collar and tie, but also enjoyed eating in the cosy cellar Stube wearing my walking gear, and I felt at home in both." Returning inspectors this year have also been delighted: "Quite unchanged. The lively Stube has harmonica music and singing, and attracts locals. Superb local smoked ham, served with kirsch and crispy country bread by dirndl'd waitresses. Bedrooms are simple, in rustic style, with bright colours; some have four-posters and Baden painted cupboards. The hotel's own ski-slope (for beginners) rises from its back terrace: this is floodlit for night-skiing and has a snow-machine using up to 100,000 litres of water a day." (*Trevor Lockwood*)

Open All year except 1 Nov–15 Dec and Tue.
Rooms 1 suite, 12 double, 5 single – 16 with bath and shower, all with telephone.
Facilities Hall, bar, 2 restaurants. Music on Fri evening. Garden with terrace, where meals are served
Location 15 km S of Baden-Baden.
Credit cards All major cards accepted.
Terms [1989 rates] B&B 55–90 DM; dinner, B&B 25 DM per person added; full board 45 DM added.

SEEG 8959 Bayern — Map 13

Pension Heim — *Tel* (08364) 2 58
Aufmberg 8

This quiet family-run *pension* is a modern building in white-washed Bavarian style, set on a small hilltop north of Füssen and the royal castles. It has views of the Allgäu Alps to the south and over lakes and forests to the north; south-facing rooms have balconies. A report this year, "A luxurious version of the homely style, with solid carved furniture, both in the room and on the balcony, with its ravishing view of the Alps beyond nearby lush meadows. The single-choice evening meal can be hampering, especially if you don't like pork, but they cooked up a huge omelette on request." (*Dr FP Woodford*) Others, too, have found the cooking a little plain – but you can eat out in the village if you prefer. Apart from this one drawback, several readers have stressed the comfort of the rooms, the "superb" breakfasts, the idyllic rural setting. "Charming host and hostess, sparkling cleanliness." There is a pleasant lounge; some of the carved furniture is Herr Heim's own work.

Open 20 Dec–1 Nov. Restaurant closed for lunch.
Rooms 14 double, 4 single – 3 with bath, 15 with shower, all with telephone; some with balcony; TV on request.
Facilities Salon, restaurant, Allgäuer Stube, TV room; sauna. Terrace.
Location On hilltop outside Seeg, which is 15 km NW of Füssen.
Restrictions Not suitable for ♿.
Credit cards None accepted.
Terms B&B: single 55 DM, double 100 DM. Reduced rates for children.

STUTTGART 7000 Baden-Württemberg — Map 13

Gaststätte zum Muckenstüble

Tel (0711) 86 51 22

Solitudestrasse 25
Stuttgart 31–Weilimdorf

A bare ten kilometres from the city centre, yet on the edge of deep country just below the hilltop Schloss Solitude that an 18th-century Duke of Württemberg built for one of his mistresses. An inspector this year again enjoyed the "excellent Swabian cuisine" (e.g. Stuttgartertopf, and roast sucking-pig with spätzle) which is served at modest prices, on a garden terrace or in the rustic-style *Stüble,* at this unpretentious family-run inn, a modern building in traditional half-timbered style. Bedrooms are plain and fairly small, but newly modernised; there's a garden with kids' playground. "We were so close to the big industrial city, yet seemed to be in the heart of rural Swabia. If you have a car, an ideal alternative to the soulless downtown hotels."

Open All year except Jul. Restaurant closed Tue.
Rooms 25 – all with shower and telephone; many with balcony.
Facilities Lift. TV room, restaurant. Garden with terrace and children's play area.
Location In suburb of Weilimdorf. 10 km W of city centre. Parking.
Credit cards None accepted.
Terms [1989 rates] B&B: single 60 DM, double 100 DM. Meals 24–42 DM.

TIEFENBRONN 7533 Baden-Württemberg — Map 13

Ochsen Post

Tel (07234) 80 30
Telex 783485

Franz-Josef Gall-Strasse 13

Tiefenbronn (its ancient Gothic church deserves a visit) is a big village near Pforzheim, at the heart of a wealthy area devoted to jewellery-making. Here the Jost family's *Ochsen Post* is suitably lavish and ornate – an old 17th-century inn, black-beamed and flower-girt outside, opulently folksy inside in the south German manner, and with modern comforts. Recent visitors enjoyed an excellent lunch in the light and summery conservatory (filet of salmon-trout, venison with spätzle: *Michelin* rosette). Earlier views: "Tables were set for dinner with silver platters edged with gold, silver cutlery and crystal glass. The cosy bedrooms all have wooden beams, chintzy drapes and solid furniture; one has a four-poster honeymoon bed. A new cocktail bar does not fit in with the hotel's character: but on warm evenings you can sit in the courtyard with a cool beer." "Irritatingly pretentious in some ways, but the food *is* first-rate and the welcome genuinely warm." More reports welcome.

We depend on detailed fresh reports to keep our entries up-to-date.

Open All year except Jan. Restaurant closed Mon midday and Sun.
Rooms 12 double, 7 single – 7 with bath, 12 with shower, all with telephone, radio and TV.
Facilities Lounge, bistro/bar, restaurant, winter garden.
Location Leave *Autobahn* A8 (E52) at Heimsheim exit. Continue to Heimsheim and turn right at Tiefenbronn sign. Hotel is central; parking.
Restriction Not suitable for ♿.
Credit cards All major cards accepted.
Terms [1989 rates] B&B: single 69–98 DM, double 98–138 DM. Meals 57–83 DM.

TRIBERG IM SCHWARZWALD 7740 Baden-Württemberg — Map 13

Parkhotel Wehrle — *Tel* (07722) 8 60 20
Gartenstrasse 24 — *Telex* 792609

"For a combination of facilities, service, atmosphere and food this hotel must be hard to beat," writes a devotee of this fairly luxurious and sumptuously furnished old hostelry, owned and run by the Wehrle/Blum family since 1707. It is in the centre of Triberg, a leading Black Forest resort known also for its cuckoo-clock-making and local costumes (the Schwarzwald folk museum is fascinating). Some rooms are in the old building, where party walls are thin; others are in two more modern ones beside a garden. The cooking (*Michelin* rosette) has this year been judged "excellent" by one visitor, though another thought it lacked flair. It is *nouvelle*-ish, but helpings are not stinted; trout is a speciality, prepared in 20 different ways. "Claus Blum is a warm and civilised host and imparts a cultivated atmosphere; service is skilled and stylish. Delightful outdoor and indoor swimming pools. Many rather grand people, such as groups of Arab sheikhs or Stuttgart tycoons, come here for special occasions." "Scrupulously managed in old-fashioned style but with plenty of space-age plumbing facilities." (*Angela and David Stewart, WG Francis*)

Open All year.
Rooms 2 suites, 43 double, 14 single – 58 with bath and shower, all with telephone, radio and TV. 20 in annexe.
Facilities Lounge, TV room, dining rooms, billiard room; conference room. Indoor and outdoor heated swimming pools; sauna, solarium, massage. Large garden.
Location Central, near market place (quietest rooms overlook garden). Parking.
Restriction Only dining rooms suitable for ♿.
Credit cards All major cards accepted.
Terms B&B: single 85–135 DM, double 150–250 DM. Half board 30 DM per person added. Set lunch 36 DM, dinner 52–72 DM; full alc 58 DM. Reduced rates and special meals for children.

TRIER 5500 Rheinland-Pfalz — Map 13

Petrisberg Hotel — *Tel* (0651) 4 11 81
Sickingenstrasse 11-13

Trier is not only the centre of the Mosel wine trade and the town where Karl Marx was born (his house is a museum), but under the Emperor Diocletian it was the capital of Gaul, and this past grandeur is today evoked by the Porta Nigra, finest Roman relic in Germany, and by the Imperial Baths. One great merit of the *Petrisberg*, a modern family-run bed-and-breakfast hotel, is that it stands in a splendid position amid vineyards, high on a hill above the city with a view of those Roman ruins – and rooms facing the city have a balcony. This year once again it has been much admired – for the view, the spacious rooms, the "bountiful" breakfasts (sometimes including bacon and egg), and the personal service by the "gracious" owner, Herr Pantenburg. He has leased his vineyards to the Bishop of Trier who then sells this Riesling wine back to the hotel – "the best Mosel we tasted in the region". (*Dr FP Woodford, E Allfrey-Pizer, Ruth and Robert Todd, and others*)

Open All year.
Rooms 3 suites, 28 double, 1 single – all with bath, shower and telephone; many with balcony. 14 in annexe. 3 ground-floor rooms.
Facilities Salon, TV room, breakfast room, wine bar. Garden and terraces. Forest nearby.
Location 20 mins' walk from town centre (near Roman amphitheatre). Parking area and garages (5 DM).
Restriction Not suitable for ♿.
Credit cards None accepted.
Terms B&B: single 75 DM, double 120 DM, suite 180 DM. Reduced rates for children sharing parents' room. (No restaurant, but light evening meals available.)

Hotel Villa Hügel *Tel* (0651) 3 30 66
Bernhardstrasse 14

An attractive alternative to the Petrisberg: *a white chalet-like Jugendstil villa, on a hillside with good views of the city. Helpful hosts, tasteful furnishings, large rooms, simple but well-prepared food. 23 rooms, all with bath and/or shower. B&B double 95–135 DM. Full alc 25–45 DM. New nomination. More reports please.*

WANGEN IM ALLGÄU 7988 Baden-Württemberg Map 13

Romantik Hotel Alte Post *Tel* (07522) 40 14
Postplatz 2 *Telex* 732774 APOST

After three years absence, this old Swabian coaching-inn – much modernised – is restored to the Guide by an inspector's report. "Wangen, quite near the Bodensee and the Allgäu Alps, is a picturesque old town of painted facades; it also has some quirky modern sculptures in its main streets – we especially liked the scattered bronze piglets in the Marktplatz. The centrally situated *Alte Post*, dating from 1409, is well run by the Veile family; the bedrooms, full of character, are reasonably priced. Ours had a four-poster canopied Himmelbett, sofas, hairdrier, chintzy curtains, and a rafter inscribed '1610'. The dining room is elegant in a restrained way, entirely lacking the heavy kitsch you find across the Bavarian border. We were nicely served by a polite young man in *Tracht* . The à la carte dishes we thought too bland and dull, but the Swabian ones were fine, including beef braised in cider, accompanied by a version of Spätzle known as Buabenspitzle which means literally 'little boys' penises'. That's just what it looks like, too."

Open All year. Restaurant closed Sun evening Nov–Mar.
Rooms 3 suites, 17 double, 8 single – all with bath or shower, telephone, radio and TV. 9 rooms in annexe.
Facilities Lounge, TV room, 2 restaurants. Garden. Golf nearby.
Location Central, parking. Wangen is 20 km NE of Lindau.
Restriction Not suitable for ♿.

Credit cards Access, Diners, Visa.
Terms B&B: single 80–90 DM, double 130–150 DM, suite 180–250 DM. Dinner, B&B double 186–206 DM. Set lunch 25–45 DM, dinner 25–90 DM; full alc 50 DM. Reduced rates and special meals for children.

WEIKERSHEIM 6992 Baden-Württemberg — Map 13

Hotel Laurentius — *Tel* (07934) 70 07
Marktplatz 5

This attractive little town on the Romantic Road, 42 kilometres south of Würzburg, is built round a 17th-century Hohenlohe castle beside the Tauber, worth seeing for its splendid Knights' Hall (it also hosts an international music school). Here the *Laurentius* is a recently opened hotel in an old building where Goethe's ancestors lived; it overlooks the pretty market square. "The rooms are cosy and comfortable, individually decorated; the management is helpful and friendly, and we took dinner on the quiet terrace." "Dinner was perhaps the best of our trip." "Our roomy bedroom overlooked the *Marktplatz*." You eat in an old vaulted cellar, and can take drinks and breakfast on a flowery patio.

Open All year except Feb.
Rooms 10 double, 2 single – all with bath and/or shower, telephone and radio; TV on request.
Facilities Lift. Lounge, restaurant, breakfast room, café; conference room; terrace.
Location Central. Parking.
Credit cards Access, Diners, Visa.
Terms B&B: single 65–75 DM, double 100–120 DM. Set meals 27.50–72 DM; full alc 40 DM. Reduced rates and special meals for children.

WEITENBURG 7245 Baden-Württemberg — Map 13

Hotel-Restaurant Schloss Weitenburg — *Tel* (07457) 80 51

This large 16th-century hilltop castle has "a marvellous rural setting" and "most romantic views" over the Neckar valley between Horb and Tübingen. Owned since 1720 by the Barons of Rassler, it is one of a number of *Schlösser* in this area that have been turned into hotels by their baronial owners as the best way of keeping the family estates together. It is run by a manager, but the baron still lives there and is much in evidence, a charming and cultivated man and a great hunter. He has sensibly kept the hotel in its original style, modernising only those aspects that need it (e.g. bathrooms). Recent visitors have especially enjoyed the indoor swimming pool, the food (with a few reservations) and the large bedrooms furnished with antiques (but some rooms could do with a spot of paint). Chris, the English head waiter, has been found to be very helpful. "A sophisticated hotel, very good value." It is in extensive grounds, with a riding school and sauna as well as the pool. There is a balcony over the valley where you can have drinks and meals. The dining room is massive. More reports welcome.

Open All year except 24–25 Dec.
Rooms 1 suite, 20 double, 18 single – 13 with bath and shower, 18 with shower, all with telephone and radio.

Facilities Lift. Hall, 4 lounges, bar, TV room, dining room; chapel for weddings and christenings; conference facilities; large balcony for drinks and meals. Park with riding school, golf, heated covered swimming pool, sauna and solarium.
Location 7 km N of Starzach; from A81 motorway take Rottenburg exit, drive 5–10 mins in the direction of Ergenzingan then follow signposts to Weitenburg.
Credit cards Access, Diners, Visa.
Terms [1989 rates] B&B: single 60–90 DM, double 110–160 DM. Full board 110–142 DM per person. Meals 36–72 DM. Reduced rates and special meals for children.

WERTHEIM-BETTINGEN 6980 Baden-Württemberg — Map 13

Hotel-Restaurant Schweizer Stuben — *Tel* (09342) 30 70
Geiselbrunnweg 11 — *Fax* (09342) 3 07 55
Telex 689190 CHSTU

"Wonderful! The food, service and surroundings were all first-class and nothing could be faulted", enthuses a 1988 visitor to this modern, spacious and luxurious restaurant-with-rooms, to which *Michelin* awards two rosettes and four red gables. Built in chalet style, it stands beside open fields on the edge of a village by the Main, west of Würzburg, and has pleasant views of the river valley. "Our bedroom in the main building (others are in a villa 200 metres away) was large, elegant and comfortable. The food in the main restaurant, *nouvelle cuisine*-ish in style, deserves its rosettes – but the cost! My God! – 511 DM for two! The more countrified *Schober* restaurant is *much* cheaper, and the food nearly as good, though less elaborate." Visitors this year enjoyed veal marinaded in crushed olives, "exquisitely delicate" lobster mousse and grand marnier crêpes with blood oranges, but thought the wine mark-ups excessive. Others have had a room with painted country furniture, and a breakfast that included quails' eggs with smoked salmon. (*Stephan and Kate Murray-Sykes*) One reader this year thought the welcome poor and the cooking over-ambitious. A new wing, the *Landhaus*, has just opened, with a third fancy restaurant, this time Italian.

Open All year. *Schweizer Stuben* restaurant closed Jan; Mon, Tue for lunch. *Schober* restaurant closed Tue, Wed for lunch.
Rooms 2 suites, 30 double – all with bath and/or shower, telephone, radio and TV. Some in villa in garden. Ground-floor rooms.
Facilities Salon, 3 restaurants; conference facilities. Garden with tennis park (indoor and outdoor court and school); swimming pool, sauna.
Location 6 km E of Wertheim; 3 km from *Autobahn* (exit Wertheim).
Credit cards All major cards accepted.
Terms B&B: single 200–345 DM, double 250–395 DM, suite 450–950 DM. Dinner, B&B 190–540 DM per person.

Greece

HOTEL ALIKI, SIMI

ATHENS — Map 17

Clare's House — *Tel* (01) 9222.288 and 9220.678
24 Sorvolou Street, Mets

This small, friendly, cheap and simple B&B featured in early editions of the Guide when it was in an old mansion in the Plaka. It is readmitted this year, having moved to a modernish house on a hill in a residential area southwest of the Akropolis, near the Temple of Zeus. "To arrive on a hot and dusty afternoon is bliss. The entrance has a cool marble floor with a minimum of good modern furniture. My bedroom was simply but well furnished with nice lamps and varnished wood, pictures on the white walls and an efficient modern bathroom. The balcony overlooked the small garden and had a grape-vine trailing from top to bottom – I was told I was welcome to pick the grapes. The location is very quiet; taxi-drivers find it elusive, but the hotel has printed instructions in Greek to help them. Breakfast is simple but the bread (except on Sunday when it was dry) was some of the best I have found in Greece. The coffee pot was bottomless. I cannot praise enough the helpfulness of the staff when I had problems with a delayed flight. Manos Anglias, the owner, speaks perfect English and employs an English receptionist; he is a mine of information on the Greek islands and has a wonderful collection of up-to-date guides." (*JS Jenkinson*) Some of the rooms have a private shower, some adjoining rooms share a shower and can be let as a family suite. Mr Anglias writes engagingly: "We are a family-run pension where the emphasis is to provide good – no frills – accommodation at reasonable rates. We are clean, quiet, have *hot* water and know people by their names. If the opportunity arises I invite them for a drink in my flat or go out to dinner with them. In the off-season we let rooms on a monthly basis at about 50,000 drs a month and provide basic cooking facilities for long-term guests." More reports please.

Open All year.
Rooms 20 double (also let as single) – most with shower, all with telephone.
Facilities Lift. Lounge with TV, breakfast room.
Location 1 km from Syntagma Square. Garage for 3 cars.
Restriction Not suitable for ♿.
Credit cards None accepted.
Terms B&B: single 3,000–4,000 drs, double 4,500–6,000 drs. Monthly rates Oct–Mar.

Herodion Hotel
Rovertou Galli 4
Makrigiani

Tel (01) 923.6832
Telex 219423 HERO

The cradle-city of Western civilisation hardly distinguishes itself by its hotels (just see how few entries we have). The *Herodion*, an unbeautiful modern cube in a quiet street quite near the Akropolis, is better than most. It has a patio garden where drinks are served beneath the trees, and a roof terrace with views of the Akropolis. And it has been well liked this year: "Cool, comfortable and clean, with quite pleasant rooms and willing and friendly staff. The inclusive breakfast was standard international, but adequate. We didn't try the restaurant since the lively Plaka is so close, and about the best place in Athens for good medium-priced eating, the *Dionysius*, is just up the road." (*Elizabeth Stanton*)

Open All year.
Rooms 4 suites, 77 double, 9 single – all with bath and/or shower, telephone, radio, TV, air-conditioning.
Facilities Lounge, bar, restaurant. Patio, rooftop terrace.
Location Central; near Plaka and Akropolis.
Restriction Not suitable for ♿.
Credit cards All major cards accepted.
Terms B&B: single 7,200–10,500 drs, double 9,400–13,700 drs. Set lunch/dinner 1,900 drs; full alc 4,000 drs.

St George Lykabettus Hotel
Kleomenous 2, Platia Dexamenis

Tel (01) 729.0710
Fax (01) 729.0439
Telex 214253 HEAM

A modern hotel, luxury class but not too expensive by British standards, in the fashionable Kolonaki district, on the foothills of Lykabettus hill and ten minutes on foot from Constitution Square. A regular visitor again liked it a lot this year: "Views from the bedrooms vary from good to sensational. It has recently been refurbished and the air-conditioning now works well. Staff are helpful and efficient. There's a rooftop restaurant, and another pleasant open-air one serving light meals. The hotel is used by some tour groups but not taken over by them." Similar praise last year: "The location is magnificent: from the bedroom balconies you look across to the Parthenon. The rooms are comfortable rather than opulent, but they have good bathrooms. The rooftop swimming pool is a rarity in Athens, and the roof-level restaurant serves excellent food and also has a view of the Akropolis." Some rooms, however, have been judged too small, or imperfect in upkeep, and front ones may suffer from traffic noise. (*Sir William Goodhart*)

Open All year.
Rooms 4 suites, 124 double, 21 single – all with bath, telephone, radio, tea-making facilities and air-conditioning; some with balcony; TV on request. Some ground-floor rooms.
Facilities Lift. Lounge, TV room, bar, restaurant, grill room; roof garden and swimming pool; nightly entertainment in restaurant; dancing on roof.
Location At foot of Lykabettus hill. Large garage.
Credit cards All major cards accepted.
Terms [1989 rates] Rooms: single 7,150–13,500 drs, double 8,600–15,000 drs, suite 18,000–31,500 drs. Breakfast 800 drs. Set lunch/dinner 1,900 drs.

CHANIA Crete — Map 17

Hotel Contessa — *Tel* (0821) 57437
Theofanous 15, Palio Limani

With its mix of Turkish and Venetian architecture, Chania is probably Crete's most attractive town. Here, in a maze of pretty streets by the harbour, an old family house has been carefully converted into a tiny bed-and-breakfast hotel, admired again this year apart from being a bit noisy. "The hospitality and atmosphere were all the Guide promised," ran a report last year, "and breakfast was really good and elegantly served. I'd advise asking for a front room with a view (one has a lovely painted ceiling), for ours at the back was rather airless. Tasteful decor and a courteous owner. It may be hard to persuade taxi-drivers to enter the old town with its narrow streets, but we phoned the hotelier and he helped us solve the problem." (*Col. TCH Macafee*)

Open 1 Apr–end Oct.
Rooms 2 triple, 4 double – all with shower, telephone and radio; baby-listening on request. All in annexe.
Facilities Breakfast room. Swimming pool at *Xenia* hotel nearby. 15 mins' walk to beach.
Location Overlooking old Venetian harbour; 1 km from town centre. Parking 150 metres.
Restriction Not suitable for ♿.
Credit card Diners.
Terms B&B double from 7,200 drs. (No restaurant.)

If you have had recent experience of a good hotel that ought to be in the Guide, please write to us at once. Report forms are to be found at the back. Procrastination is the thief of the next edition.

CHIOS Aegean Islands — Map 17

Villa Argentikon — *Tel* (271) 31599 and 31465
Chios — *Telex* 294135

"Just about the most sophisticated hotel in all Greece," says a recent visitor. It lies on the plain of Campos in the southern part of the island of Chios, just off the Turkish coast. Chios used to play a key maritime role in the Aegean, and its rulers from 1346–1566, the Genoese, have left a legacy of many fine buildings. One of them is the *Villa Argentikon* which the Argenti family from Genoa built in the 16th century and still own today. Together with two adjacent mansions of the same period, all in patterned marble, they have turned it into an elegant hotel whose recent guests have included the Princess of Savoy and the former American president, Jimmy Carter. There are flowered colonnades, beautiful gardens, bedrooms gracefully furnished in period style, with marble bathrooms. You can dine by candle-light in the floodlit gardens, where good food, expensive by Greek standards, is elegantly presented.

Open 28 May–15 Oct.
Rooms 4 suites – all with bath or shower, and terrace or patio.
Facilities Restaurant. Garden. Horse riding and motor sailing can be arranged.
Location About 5 km S of town of Chios.
Terms On application.

DELPHI Central Greece — Map 17

Hotel Pan — *Tel* (0265) 82294
53 Vassileos Pavlou

In a peaceful location at the quieter end of town, but only a short walk from the main shops and restaurants, an unassuming and hospitable little family-run B&B hotel, with glorious views from the balconies of rooms facing the valley. Clean, simple bedrooms; cheerful breakfast room. 30 rooms, all with bath and shower. B&B double 4,800 drs. New nomination. More reports please.

FERMA Crete — Map 17

Coriva Village — *Tel* (0842) 61263
Ierapetra — *Telex* 262508 CORV

Not far from the port of Ierapetra, and just outside the village of Ferma, here is a quiet hotel and not-too-large bungalow complex on the south coast of Crete where new hotels are sprouting fast. Recent visitors have liked it a lot, singling out the restaurant, the large clean swimming pool, the "friendly owners" and the "beautiful tropical garden". Many rooms are in bungalows surrounded by flowering shrubs. The beach is not impressive, but nearby are small secluded coves excellent for swimming.

Open March–Nov.
Rooms 35 double – all with bath and/or shower, telephone and air-conditioning. 11 in main house, 24 in bungalows with terrace.
Facilities Salon with TV, bar, taverna, restaurant. Garden with swimming pool; private beach with water sports; Cretan evenings once a week.
Location 8 km E of Ierapetra; 1 km from Ferma. Parking.

Restriction Not suitable for ♿.
Credit cards None accepted.
Terms [1989 rates] Rooms: single 7,000 drs, double 10,000 drs, suite 15,000 drs. Breakfast 1,000 drs. Set lunch/dinner 2,000 drs.

FIRA Santorini, Cyclades — Map 17

Atlantis Hotel — *Tel* (0286) 22232 and 22111
Fax (0286) 22821
Telex 293113 ATRA

The volcanic island of Santorini is a striking crescent shape. You sail into a wide bay, thought to be the crater of a volcano which erupted in Minoan times, throwing up the spectacular cliffs of pumice and lava that surround the bay. The white-washed town of Fira is perched on the cliffs, 800 steps up from the harbour: you can ride up by mule or take a cable car. Perched above it is the *Atlantis*, whose elegant facade of white arches is visible from afar. It has been admired for its comfortable rooms in one recent report. Other visitors had a large and spacious room, and a big balcony with a fine view of the town, the sea and the island of Nea Kamani, the only live volcano in Greece. The hotel has an airy lounge with the same view, and a helpful staff. More reports welcome.

Open 1 Apr–31 Oct.
Rooms 19 double, 8 single – 6 with bath, 21 with shower, all with telephone and radio; most with balcony.
Facilities Lounge, TV room, bar, breakfast room; meeting room; terrace. Beach 6 km.
Location Central. Parking.
Credit cards All major cards accepted.
Terms [1989 rates] Rooms: single 8,733–10,538 drs, double 12,049–14,486 drs. Breakfast 780 drs. (No restaurant.)

GALAXIDION Central Greece — Map 17

Hotel Ganimede — *Tel* (0265) 41328
Euthumiou Blamis 6

"Quiet, relaxed, informal, all-round idyllic, the sort of place one dreams of finding in Greece but never does", has been one comment on this idiosyncratic Italian-owned *pensione* in a tiny ancient town on the Gulf of Corinth, near Delphi. It is formed by two houses back-to-back, one a 19th-century captain's house, the other a modern facsimile, with a large garden-cum-patio in between – trees, flowers, comfortable chairs. "It's in a quiet part of town, almost suburban, though in itself it is nearly louche. The house has been beautifully kept and furnished, and has a marble tiled hall and fine woodwork. The ambience is somewhat precious. We were warmly welcomed. You can take drinks (listed on a blackboard) in the garden with its central fountain. The two best bedrooms, 1 and 2, are on the first floor front. They have tall panelled doors, coffered ceilings and lovely old wooden furniture. The breakfast room is also pretty, but covered with ikons, pictures, home-made preserves for sale, and postcards from patrons saying how lovely their stay had been. Breakfast is very generous (for Greece), and includes good fig jam, and eggs poached, scrambled and even 'mumbled', whatever that might be." An earlier visitor has written: "If Bruno Perocco, the owner, does not like the look of you, you will not get a room. In winter he runs courses on making ikons. The British and American embassies have found the place, but he is careful to spread the nationalities." Others have considered the rooms "comfortable, dark and cool". No restaurant, but *To Steki* and *To Galaxidi* are good harbourside tavernas. (*DM*)

Open 1 Mar–31 Oct.
Rooms 6 double, 1 single – 2 with shower.
Facilities Lounge. Courtyard. 10 mins' walk to sea.
Location Central; Galaxidion is 33 km SW of Delphi, via Itea and the coast road. Parking.
Restrictions Not suitable for ♿. No children under 10.
Credit cards None accepted.
Terms [1989 rates] Rooms: single 3,070 drs, double 4,995 drs. Breakfast 875 drs.

HERMOUPOLIS Syros, Cyclades — Map 17

Hotel Vourlis — *Tel* (0281) 28440 and 23750
Mavrogordatou 5 — *Telex* 293206 MIT

The capital of the Cycladean island of Syros is a picturesque town of predominantly neo-classical architecture, with houses that rise in tiers on the slopes of two hills. The *Hotel Vourlis* is a 19th-century mansion in this neo-classical style, transformed into a gracious little private hotel, beautifully furnished. It is owned by Alexandra Mavrogordatou Petritzh, a well-known Greek artist, and recent visitors have endorsed this earlier praise: "A real oasis and sheer luxury. We were warmly welcomed and given two very elegant rooms in pink and blue, with lots of space and beautiful pictures. The bathroom was big, and we found chocolates and Metaxa brandy by the bed. Service was excellent and breakfast superb, including fruit salad and scrambled eggs." No restaurant, but snacks available, and plenty of tavernas nearby.

Open All year.
Rooms 1 suite, 5 double, 1 single – all with bath and/or shower, and telephone. 3 ground-floor rooms.
Facilities Hall, lounge/breakfast room, bar. Small front garden and patio. 100 metres from shingle beach with safe bathing and fishing. Windsurfing, water skiing, sailing, tennis and mini-golf nearby.
Location Hermoupolis is capital of Syros, capital of the Cyclades. Daily boat connections from Piraeus and Rafina. Hotel is central. Parking.
Credit cards All major cards accepted.
Terms [1989 rates] Rooms: single 3,500–4,800 drs, double 4,500–7,000 drs.

HYDRA Hydra, Saronic Gulf — Map 17

Hotel Miranda — *Tel* (0298) 52230

Hydra town, on the island of Hydra, has a beautiful harbour where the houses rise in tiers. Up one of these steep narrow streets is this finely converted 18th-century mansion with hand-painted ceilings and parquet floors; now a most select little hotel, it is furnished with genuine local antiques and run in a somewhat lordly way. Its own regular clientele (smart Athenians) keep it often full. No restaurant: good tavernas nearby. Closed Nov–Feb. 14 rooms, all with shower. B&B double 6,500–11,000 drs [1989]. Recent nomination. More reports please.

IOS Cyclades — Map 17

Ios Palace Hotel — *Tel* (0286) 91269 *and* (*in Athens*) (01) 413.7406
Telex 213315

Homer is said to have died on the Cycladean island of Ios, now heavily colonised by students and other youthful back-packers from northern Europe and North America; discos abound. The fairly expensive and sophisticated Ios *stands on the edge of a wide sandy beach, a mile from the island's main village. Rooms in bungalow style; sea-water swimming pool; water sports. Open 1 May–10 Oct. 46 rooms, all with bath and shower. B&B double 5,868–14,000 drs. Set menus 1,000–1,300 drs [1989]. Recent nomination. More reports please, especially on the food.*

LIA Epirus — Map 17

Hotel Lia — *Tel* (0664) 31208
Lia, Nr Filiates

This brand-new hotel in the wilds of Epirus, up near the Albanian border, must be one of the most remote in this book. It has an unusual genesis, too, as its nominator reports, "A marvellous hotel. It was established by Nicholas Gage, the *New York Times* reporter who wrote *Eleni*, the story of his family caught in the Greek civil war in Lia – his mother was executed for helping her children to escape. The book is what led us to Lia in the first place. Each bedroom has a balcony looking over the village and wooded mountains. The manager has worked for years in hotels in Brussels and has returned to his homeland well equipped. His wife cooks and gave us an excellent evening meal. Dozens of local villagers were in the restaurant." (*Patricia Peterson*)

Open 15 May–15 Oct.
Rooms 1 suite, 9 double – 6 with bath, 4 with shower.
Facilities Lounge, bar, TV room, restaurant. Garden with children's playground.
Location 40 km N of Filiates.
Restrictions Not suitable for ♿.
Credit card Access.
Terms [1989 rates] Rooms: double 3,500 drs, suite 4,500 drs. Set lunch/dinner 800 drs; full alc 2,100 drs. Special meals for children on request.

METSOVO Epirus — Map 17

Hotel Egnatia — *Tel* (0656) 41263 and 41485
L. Tossitsa

An appealing new discovery this year, in a small town on the main road over the mountains from Kalambaka (Meteora) to Ioannina: "The drive to Metsovo takes one up the spine of the Pindus range, over what not long ago must have been a road of hair-raising difficulty and which still affords spectacular views. Metsovo is a small, prosperous town hidden in a mountain valley; it is being developed as a ski resort, but still retains its tradition and integrity, and has a rich heritage of handicrafts (needlework, copperwork, wood-carving). Many of the older women still wear the traditional costume on a daily basis, which adds to the local charm. The *Egnatia*, on the main road in the town centre, has a somewhat alpine exterior (flowerpots and balconies), but the interior is traditional Greek. The public rooms have warm wooden panelling, coffered wooden ceilings beautifully carved, and lovely old brass lamps. The lobby is lined in the old style with benches covered with rich red weavings and intricately designed cushions; above the fireplace is a wild boar's head. The bedrooms are simple but comfortable, and their balconies afford delightful views of the town and hills. We met a warm and genuine welcome." (*Dr SL Martin*) We'd be glad of reports on the hotel food. You can also eat at the *Victoria* (see below).

Open All year.
Rooms 2 suites, 24 double, 8 single – all with bath and shower; many with balcony.
Facilities Lounge, TV room, bar, restaurant. Garden. Winter sports 2 km.
Location Central. Metsovo is 50 km E of Ioannina.
Credit cards All major cards accepted.
Terms [1989 rates] B&B: single 3,150–3,983 drs, double 4,100–5 100 drs, suite 6,050–7,883 drs. Set meals 800–1,000 drs.

Hotel Victoria *Tel* (0656) 41771 and 41761

Slightly more expensive, and on the town's outskirts overlooking the deep valley, here's another new entry this year for Metsovo, from a reader who has also been struck by local craft traditions: "The hand-carved ceiling of the spacious dining room, the hand-carved chairs, hand-woven cushions and wall decorations make a stay at this hotel a visit to a living museum. It is family-run, and the multilingual staff are friendly and helpful. The meals included local dishes not normally available in restaurants, such as mountain sausage and a kind of feta soup. Good local red wine. A highly recommended hotel." (*Patricia Peterson*) Metsovo also has a museum of local arts and crafts, and an interesting monastery.

Open All year.
Rooms 34 double, 3 single – all with bath and/or shower and telephone.
Facilities Lounge, bar, restaurant. Nightclub. Winter sports 2 km.
Location On W outskirts. Parking.
Terms [1989 rates] B&B: single 3,650–4,300 drs, double 4,750–5,520 drs; half board: single 4,950–5,600 drs, double 7,350–6,120 drs.

MONEMVASSIA Peloponnesus — Map 17

Hotel Malvasia *Tel* (0732) 61113 and 61435

Several old houses with barrel-vaulted ceilings have been most attractively converted into a hotel of character, with a real sense of history; in wonderful position in an ancient town with a famous 6th-century castle in the south-east of the Peloponnese. Spacious rooms, nicely furnished lounge. Bar and café; plenty of restaurants close by. Very quiet (town is closed to car traffic), but not midge-free. 28 rooms, all with shower. B&B 6,000 drs. Few recent reports; more welcome.

MYRINA Lemnos, Aegean Islands — Map 17

Hotel Akti Myrina
Myrina Beach

Tel (0254) 22681
Telex 297173 MYRI
in winter: Athens
Tel (01) 72191591
Telex 216324

Long admired by readers, the *Myrina* is a large, fairly luxurious and quite original holiday venture, set above a bay just outside Myrina, the tiny capital of the lovely island of Lemnos. Spread over the hillside are 125 bungalows, with everything you could desire – air-conditioning, good lighting and linen, lots of hot water, efficient room service – each hidden by greenery from its neighbours. Most have a little patio/garden with a view, "idyllic for one's breakfast or evening drink". The central services (pool, beach) are all within two minutes' walk. "Must be a strong candidate for the most attractive hotel on the Mediterranean. Set in a garden of flowering shrubs; if you are lucky enough to be in the front row of the bungalows your garden looks straight over roses and grapes down to the sea. You can have delicious Greek yoghurt with honey and wholemeal toast for breakfast as well as the more ordinary continental fare, eggs etc. For dinner you can choose between buffet type restaurants and one serving a more conventional five-course meal. For lunch you can eat in a small taverna or at another restaurant serving a great variety of salads and hot dishes. The sea is shallow for a long way out and the beach is very clean. Service is efficient and courteous." "The hotel is a paradise for young children (you can leave your kids in their cots while you dine)". Others have praised the lunchtime garden buffet, the poolside bars for snacks and drinks, and the beach sports and caïque excursions. "Firm management – everything ran like clockwork". (*Conrad and Marilyn Dehn, and others*)

Open 6 May–15 Oct.
Rooms 15 suites, 110 double – all with bath and/or shower, telephone, refrigerator, baby-listening, air-conditioning, veranda and small garden. All in bungalows.
Facilities Lounge, TV lounge, coffee shop, restaurants, taverna; hairdresser, boutique; disco. 25-acre grounds with 3 tennis courts, swimming pool, children's pool, mini-golf, ping-pong, private sandy beach with restaurant; fishing, bathing, water sports.
Location 2 km (about 15 mins' walk) from Myrina Town. Lemnos is reached by direct flight from Athens, or by boat from Piraeus.
Restriction Not suitable for ♿.
Credit cards All major cards accepted.
Terms Dinner, B&B: single 12,000–25,000 drs, double 19,500–46,000 drs per person, suite 28,000–50,000 drs. Set lunch/dinner 5,000–7,000 drs; full alc 8,000 drs. Reduced rates and special meals for children.

Deadlines: nominations for the 1991 edition should reach us not later than 1 May 1990. Latest date for comments on existing entries: 1 June 1990.

Italicised entries are for hotels on which we need more feedback – either because we are short of reports or because we have had mixed or inadequate reports.

OLYMPIA Peloponnesus Map 17

Hotel Amalia *Tel* (0624) 22190
Telex 215161 AMAL

On the other side of the modern town from the ancient site of Olympia, a large modern luxury-class hotel amid fields, a bit impersonal, but quiet and comfortable. Garden with swimming pool, international cuisine, good lunchtime buffet. 147 rooms, all with bath and shower. B&B: single 8,300 drs, double 11,800 drs. Set menu 1,600 drs [1989]. No recent reports. More welcome.

PALEA EPIDAVROS Peloponnesus Map 17

Paola Beach Hotel *Tel* (0753) 41397

On the edge of a fishing-village 12 km from the classical theatre at Epidaurus, a modern hotel set quietly by a sandy beach; clean and comfortable, with plumbing that actually works. Open 1 Apr–30 Oct. 27 rooms, all with bath, shower and balcony facing sea or farmland. B&B double 4,200 drs [1989]. No restaurant: tavernas in village. Endorsed this year, but fuller reports welcome.

SIMI Dodecanessus Islands Map 17

Hotel Aliki *Tel* (0241) 71665 / 71655

"For ten years it has been my favourite hotel in Greece," says an ardent philhellene, of this neo-classical mansion on the waterfront of the little port of Simi, capital of the small bare island of that name between Rhodes and the Turkish coast. "Simi used to be a prosperous mercantile centre. Then it declined into a ghost town, but today some of its fine old mansions are being restored. This one has been done up most tastefully by its owner, George Kypreos, who runs it as a very sympathetic little hotel. There is a bar and roof garden, with fine views. Some bedrooms, too, have sea views from their balconies, but others face the back; all have a cool, simple elegance. There are tables with parasols, by the water. No beach, but you can walk straight from the *Aliki*'s front door into the warm, crystal-clear sea. No restaurant: tavernas nearby. Simi today has its share of day-trippers from Rhodes: but in the evening it remains a lovely peaceful unspoilt place."

Open Apr–Oct.
Rooms 2 suites, 11 double, 2 single – 4 with bath, 11 with shower, all with telephone and radio.
Facilities Bar, TV room, breakfast room; roof garden.
Location Simi is about 40 km NW of Rhodes; daily boat services.
Credit cards None accepted.
Terms [1989 rates] B&B: single 4,200–5,000 drs, double 5,400–8,000 drs, suite 10,000–11,800 drs. Breakfast 600 drs. (No restaurant.)

We asked hotels to estimate their 1990 tariffs some time before publication so the rates given are often arbitrary. Please always check terms with hotels when making bookings.

SKOPELOS Sporades **Map 17**

Prince Stafylos Hotel *Tel* (0424) 22775
Telex 282229 SKOP

Skopelos is the second largest of the Sporades islands, and just outside its main town, also called Skopelos, is this pleasant modern hotel, a long low white construction with verandas and slate roofs, built in local style by its owner, an architect. Clean, well-kept swimming pool amid lawns and flowers; light, attractive bedrooms. Open 1 May–25 Oct. 49 rooms, most with bath or shower, double 6,000–10,000 drs. Breakfast 600–800 drs. Set menus 1,300–1,800 drs. Recent nomination. More reports please, especially on the food.

SPETSES Spetses, Saronic Gulf **Map 17**

Hotel Possidonion *Tel* (0298) 72208 and 72308

This island off the Argolid coast is where John Fowles set *The Magus*, having taught here in the 1950s at a well-known boarding school, founded as a copy of an English public school. Today the English connection continues, in a different manner, for Spetses is given over to the UK package-tour trade. But it also remains a haunt of wealthy Athenians, who have built summer homes along the coast: so, if you wander off into the pinewoods, you might always – who knows? – stumble into the enchanted clutches of some latter-day Conchis. Failing that, you can certainly be beguiled by the 1920s ghosts that haunt the *Possidonion*, described by a recent visitor as "the only surviving historic hotel in all the Greek isles. It was built in 1914 by Sotiros Anagyros, a Spetsian who emigrated to the US, became a rich tobacco baron, then returned to found the boarding school and the hotel. He built it in the grand European manner, with terrace, esplanade and attendant casino, scene of great society parties in the inter-war years. Today it is somewhat down-at-heel, but it remains characterful, and there are plans to refurbish. It keeps away from the package-tour trade and retains a sophisticated clientele – lots of chic French grumbling about 'les Anglais' down in Spetses town." More reports, please, on mundane matters such as food and bedrooms.

Open Apr–Oct.
Rooms 55 – most with bath and/or shower.
Facilities Lounge, restaurant. Beach 300 m.
Location In Spetses town, 30 mins by boat from the mainland.
Terms [1989 rates] Rooms: single 2,220–4,820 drs, double 3,520–7,230 drs. Breakfast 800–850 drs. Set lunch/dinner 1,800–1,850 drs.

THASSOS 64004 Macedonia **Map 17**

Hotel Amfipolis *Tel* (0593) 23101
Telex 452195 AMF

The sophisticated little town of Thassos, also known as Limenas, is on the island of Thassos in the north Aegean; it has ramparts and an akropolis. The *Amfipolis*, inside the town, is a blue-grey four-storey building, newly nominated: "It was built in the 1920s as a Bulgarian jail and has recently been nicely converted; it is well run by a local family. There is a bar under a tree in the pretty patio, where you can dine outdoors; also a swimming pool (beach about three miles away). Good bedrooms."

Open 20 Apr–30 Oct.
Rooms 6 suites, 31 double, 5 single – 30 with bath, 12 with shower, all with telephone and radio; some with TV and mini-bar. Some ground-floor rooms.
Facilities Lift. Lounge, TV room, bar, restaurant. Garden with swimming pool. Sand/rock beach nearby.
Location Central. Frequent ferries from Keramoti on the mainland (30 mins).
Credit cards All major cards accepted.
Terms B&B: single 6,000–8,000 drs, double 8,000–10,000 drs. Set lunch/dinner 1,500 drs; full alc 3,600 drs. Children under 10 half price in parents' room; special meals.

TOLO Peloponnesus — Map 17

Hotel Minoa
56 Aktis Street

Tel (0752) 59207
Fax (0752) 59707
Telex 298157 MINO

Run by a large family of Cretans, the *Minoa* is one of many modern hotels along the sandy beach of this popular resort, once a simple fishing-village. An inspector in 1989 has summed it up neatly: "Not luxurious or charming in itself, but an OK hotel with pleasant staff in an enchanting *pieds-dans-l'eau* position – you even drive your car onto the sandy beach in front of it, to unload. Apart from the boats putting out for night fishing, it's very peaceful. Essential to ask for a room at the front (moon on sea at night very beautiful): back ones look over a sprawl of houses. Welcome was warm, also brisk and efficient. As in all the hotels we visited in Greece, the bedrooms were no more than basic by British standards, but adequate. The dining-room's marble paved floor and table numbers give a municipal effect – but the full-length windows offer that wonderful view again. The fixed menu has little choice – cheese pie, adequate meat balls, nice oily Greek salad, and just an apple. The waiters had time to be pleasant, everyone speaks English, and there's a pleasant drawing room." Other reports this year vary both about the breakfasts and main meals – "better than average Greek fare", says one, "very poor", says another. Clearly it's the location that you come for, not the food. But there are some good tavernas in town, if you are not staying *en pension*. (*JS Jenkinson, Patricia Peterson*) The hotel has two annexes, the *Kronos* nearby and the *Phaistos*, a short way up the hill, with a swimming pool.

Open 15 Mar–7 Nov.
Rooms 75 double, 7 single – all with bath or shower, telephone and radio. 18 in annexe *Kronos*, 20 in annexe *Phaistos*.
Facilities Lift. Lounge with TV, bar, restaurant. Garden. *Phaistos* has a swimming pool. Sandy beach.
Location Near old port; parking. Tolo is 12 km SE of Nafplion.
Restriction Not suitable for ♿.
Credit cards All major cards accepted.
Terms [1989 rates] Dinner, B&B: single 4.320–5,120 drs, double 6,550–7,460 drs, triple 8,760–9,890 drs. Special meals for children on request.

Many hotels put up their prices in the spring. Tariffs quoted in the text may be more accurate before April/May 1990 than after.

VATHIA Lakonia — Map 17

Kapetanakou Towers *Tel* (0733) 54244

Not a hotel but a "traditional settlement" – state controlled but locally run. In a fascinating medieval village, not far from Areopoli, by the sea near the tip of the wild and gorgeous Mani peninsula in the southern Peloponnese, some of the ancient grey towers have been converted into well-modernised accommodation – tastefully furnished bedrooms, attractive reception, large restaurant, terraces, lovely views, friendly multi-lingual staff. 44 rooms, all with private facilities. B&B: single 6,273 drs, double 8,159 drs. Meals 1,000 drs [1989]. New nomination. More reports please, especially on the food.

Traveller's tale *The* Hôtel Bellevue, *which looks upon the sea and hears always the waves dashing upon the worn and jagged rocks, was overflowed by one of those swarms which are the nuisance of independent travellers, known as a "Cooks Party", excellent people individually no doubt, but monopolising hotels and steamboats, and driving eveybody else into obscurity by reason of their numbers and compact organisation. We passed yesterday one of the places on the coast where Jonah is said to have left the whale; it is suspected – though without any contemporary authority – that he was in a Cooks Party of his day, and left it in disgust for this private conveyance.*
Charles Dudley Warner (In the Levant, 1876)

VATHIA Lakonia Map 17

Kapetanakou Towers Tel (0733) 54244

[illegible]

Italy

HOTEL LOGGIATO DEI SERVITI
FLORENCE

ACQUAVIVA PICENA 63030 Ascoli Piceno **Map 16**

Hotel O'Viv *Tel* (0735) 764649
Via Marziale 43 *Fax* (0735) 83697

In an old hill-village just inland from the Adriatic coast between Pescara and Ancona, this old stone building – once the house of a bishop – is now an oddly named small hotel, delightfully run by its young Anglo-Italian owners. Bedrooms full of character; panoramic terrace; good local cooking. Equestrian centre. 14 rooms, all with shower. B&B double 71,000–80,000 L. Set menus 25,000–28,000 L. New nomination. More reports welcome.

The success of this guide in North America has led to a sister publication on American and Canadian hotels based on the same principles. Readers with recent experience of good hotels in North America are urged to send their nominations to Sandra W Soule, America's Wonderful Little Hotels and Inns, PO Box 150, Riverside Avenue, Riverside, Conn. 06878, USA.

ALPE FAGGETTO 52033 Arezzo — Map 16

Fonte della Galletta — *Tel* (0575) 793925
Caprese Michelangelo

Secluded amid woodlands in the wild Apennines, this idiosyncratic little restaurant-with-rooms has been described as "quite an experience – as unlike any British hotel as one could imagine". Readers have long enjoyed the robust cooking of its jovial and well-named proprietor, Boncompagni Gheldo, who uses local mushrooms and fungi in various fascinating and unusual ways. "He is intensely energetic and kind", ran a recent report. "Once dinner began the whole place roared into tremendous activity, and it was necessary to eat rapidly (and not to allow attention to wander from one's food) in order to keep up with the vigorous service, led by the Signor himself. After dinner the staff not surprisingly appeared to collapse with exhaustion, and all the clearing up was left till morning. There were big parties for local weddings, evidence of the place's popularity. Above the hotel are some interesting walks and the great monastery of La Verna is not far away." Roads wind down to Michelangelo's birthplace amid lovely flowery countryside. There is no menu but guests are asked for their approval of the night's dinner in advance – this could include mushroom soup and various pastas stuffed with mushrooms and truffles. The local wine is "deep purple and delicious". Clearly the place is more of a "typically Italian experience" than a conventionally dependable hotel – no one speaks English, the local guests make cheerful noise, TV may be on in the restaurant, lighting in the lounge is inadequate for reading, the bedrooms can be rather cold, and a visitor this year found the staff slow. But just think of the compensations. More reports welcome.

Open All year. Closed Wed Feb–May.
Rooms 20 – all with bath, shower and telephone. 6 in bungalows nearby.
Facilities Lounge with TV, bar, restaurant; banqueting facilities. Garden.
Location 5 km SW of Caprese Michelangelo; 50 km NE of Arezzo.
Credit card Amex.
Terms B&B: single 35,000 L, double 50,000 L; dinner, B&B 37,000 L per person; full board 45,000 L. Set meals 15,000–30,000 L; full alc 20,000–30,000 L. Reduced rates and special meals for children.

AMALFI 84011 Salerno — Map 16

Hotel Luna Convento — *Tel* (089) 871002 and 871050
Via P. Comite 19 — *Telex* 770161 LUNAHT

A cool white-walled Byzantine monastery half as old as time (St Francis of Assisi is said to have lived here in 1220), on the dramatically beautiful Amalfi coast. Goethe and Ibsen stayed here too. "The *Luna* is a calming place, and its staff have that grave, serious sweetness that charms and reassures. The hotel is beautifully situated at the sea's edge, looking back over Amalfi, with wonderful views, a lift down to the old tower and private bathing rocks and pool, an old cloister, for breakfast outside, and comfortable though simple accommodation. No air-conditioning, but prompt and friendly room service, and good, simple varied meals (excellent fish). There was a large wedding party going on in the hotel, yet we were not neglected but treated as a welcome audience to a fine free spectacle. A friendly, cheerful hotel with personal attention. And one would never tire of sitting on that balcony." Endorsed this year by an inspector who points out that road-traffic is audible from the dining-terrace, and maybe from some bedrooms.

Open All year.
Rooms 5 suites, 40 double – all with bath, shower, telephone.
Facilities Lift. Lounge, bar, 2 restaurants; banqueting facilities; discothèque. Garden with cloisters, terrace, sea-water swimming pool.
Location 300 metres from centre. Garage and private parking.
Credit cards All major cards accepted.
Terms B&B: single 90,000–100,000 L, double 130,000–170,000 L; dinner B&B 110,000–130,000 L per person. Set meals 50,000 L. Reduced rates and special meals for children.

AMEGLIA 19031 La Spezia — Map 16

Paracucchi-Locanda dell'Angelo

Tel (0187) 64391
Fax (0187) 64393

A sophisticated country hotel in a very modern style, set back from the main road just inland from Lerici and La Spezia. Owner-chef Angelo Paracucchi wins a *Michelin* rosette for his cooking, and readers concur: "Excellent, different food in a lovely dining room with informed, courteous service. Breakfast was lovely too." "A large daily menu based on the best local ingredients. The cooking is adventurous and modern, far removed from the usual idea of Italian cooking. The wine list is superb. Rooms are comfortable and adequately furnished in cool style with well-fitted bathrooms. Each has a small balcony with views to the hills or over the plain. There is a comfortable bar and lounge area, and many interesting paintings hang throughout the building." The hotel's "near-suburban location", just off a busy main road, is compensated by the long sandy beach a mile or so away. More reports please.

Open All year. Restaurant closed 10–12 Jan.
Rooms 1 suite, 26 double, 10 single – all with bath and/or shower, telephone, TV, mini-bar; many with balcony. Some ground-floor rooms.
Facilities Lounge, bar, restaurant; conference facilities. Garden.
Location 3 km SE of Ameglia on Sarzana–Marinella road.
Credit cards All major cards accepted.
Terms Rooms: single 62,000 L, double 125,000 L. Breakfast 16,000 L. Full alc 75,000. Reduced rates and special meals for children.

ASOLO 31011 Treviso — Map 16

Hotel Villa Cipriani
Via Canova 298

Tel (0423) 55444
Fax (0423) 52095
Telex 411060 CIPRAS

An old town of arcaded streets and Venetian palaces and villas. One of them is the *Cipriani*, once the home of Robert Browning, and here he wrote the lines, "God's in his heaven, all's right with the world" – sentiments echoed by many of today's visitors to what is now a luxurious hotel, part of the big CIGA chain, but run in personal style. "A magnificent place: we walked straight into paradise," runs one report this year; "the view from our bedroom was breathtaking, the food superb, and all the staff seemed to share the manager's concern for our comfort." A comment last year: "Dinner was delicious (try their grilled vegetables from the garden). Not only did our room look on to the quiet garden and a view of valleys and mountains, but it had a beautiful sitting area with oriental rug, burgundy velvet love-seat, and a marble-topped credenza on which they had placed a basket of fresh fruit and a vase of pink roses." Another visitor found that breakfast on the terrace included wild strawberries and black figs, and called the *Cipriani* "one of those very special hotels that seasoned travellers speak of with nostalgia". "The food and atmosphere are what you dream of when you think of Italy", is a further Browningesque comment. But some rooms are small and some face the street. (*M and D Chambers; Godfrey and Hilary Hodgson, Mary Ann Meanwell*)

Open All year.
Rooms 31 double – all with bath and shower, telephone and TV. 11 in garden annexe.
Facilities Lift. Lounge, bar, TV room, restaurant.Garden.
Location 35 km NW of Treviso. 300 yards from town centre. Parking.
Credit cards All major cards accepted.
Terms [1989 rates] (Excluding taxes) Rooms: single occupancy 190,000–250,000 L, double 210,000–270,000 L. Breakfast 16,500 L. Dinner, B&B 79,500 L added per person; full board 142,500 L added. Alc 90,000 L. Special meals for children.

ASSISI 06081 Perugia — Map 16

Hotel Country House — *Tel* (075) 816363
San Pietro Campagna 178

This Guide newcomer is a *pensione* with a garden, about a mile outside the city walls – "An old house", says its nominator, "with a big chaise-longuey patio, fine views over the valley and pleasant walks around. Italian breakfast is fairly standard. The place doubles up as an antique shop, so if you take a fancy to any of the excellent furniture in your bedroom, you can make an offer for it." This shop is called the "3 Esse" (3 Ss) because "it's kept by three women all of whose names begin with S: I met only one of them, a lady of equal charm and volubility" (probably Silvana Ciammarughi, the owner). (*Jan Morris*)

Open All year.
Rooms 1 apartment with kitchen and private balcony, 10 double, 2 single – all with bath, and/or shower. 2 ground-floor rooms.
Facilities 2 lounges with TV. Garden and terraces.
Location 1½ km from Assisi towards Perugia. Parking.
Credit cards Amex, Visa.
Terms B&B: single 40,000 L, double 75,000 L. Reduced rates for children. (No restaurant.)

Hotel Umbra — *Tel* (075) 812240
Via degli Archi 6

Much renewed praise in 1988/9 for this reasonably priced little family-run hotel down an alley off the main square. It has a touch of Italian elegance about the public rooms, and a pleasant patio at the back where you can eat out under the trees. The food is what counts here, far more than the bedrooms, described as clean but a little basic. "My room was institutional, suitable for earnest young YMCA pilgrims. By contrast, dinner was superb, served in a strikingly beautiful high-ceilinged room: I was given the sweetest prosciutto crudo I've ever tasted, and enough of it to paper my room. The manager insisted on carrying my bags to my car himself." "A delicious veal en croûte with madeira sauce and wild mushrooms. Management friendly." (*PA Bispham, Philippa Herbert, Elizabeth Ring, CLG Worn*)

Open 15 Mar–15 Jan.
Rooms 3 suites, 20 double, 5 single – 17 with bath, 7 with shower, all with telephone; 3 with TV. Some ground-floor rooms.
Facilities 3 lounges, bar with TV, 2 restaurants. Garden with terraces for meals in fine weather.
Location In town centre, near main square.
Credit cards Amex, Diners.
Terms B&B: single 57,000 L, double 90,000 L, suite 120,000 L. Dinner, B&B 75,000–90,000 L per person. Full alc 35,000–45,000 L. Reduced rates for children.

BELLAGIO 22021 Como — Map 16

Grand Hotel Villa Serbelloni
Via Roma 1

Tel (031) 950216
Fax (031) 951529
Telex 380330 SERBOT

"A superb hotel", says a visitor returning recently to this huge ornate villa beside Lake Como. It enjoys the lake vistas that Stendhal once called "sublime" and is backed by a large park famous for its display of magnolias, camellias and pomegranates. Inside, the palatial public rooms are hung with gold chandeliers and decorated with original frescos; the staircase is flanked by gilt *putti* on giant candelabra, and the spacious bedrooms have wonderful views over lake or gardens. There is a heated swimming pool and a private beach. So far, so good: but whereas the staff are generally found efficient and courteous, both management and cuisine have been criticised this year and last by readers who feel that the hotel does not live up to its sublime appearance – and that it overcharges for extras (e.g. 5,000 lire for orange juice). What's more, rooms facing the road can be noisy. (*Roberta Garza de Elizondo*) More reports please.

Open 15 Apr–20 Oct.
Rooms 6 suites, 71 double, 15 single – all with bath and shower, telephone and mini-bar; radio and TV on request. Some ground-floor rooms.
Facilities Lifts. Lounge, TV room, writing room, games room, bar, breakfast room, restaurant; banqueting and conference facilities; hairdressing salon, boutique; terrace (also for meals), evening orchestra with dancing. Gardens with tennis courts, heated swimming pool with snack bar; private beach with boating, wind-surfing, water skiing, boating excursions.
Location Central. Private garage and large parking place.
Credit cards All major cards accepted.
Terms [1989 rates] B&B: single 220,000 L, double 315,000 L, suite 625,000 L; dinner, B&B: single 255,000 L, double 385,000 L, suite 695,000 L. Set lunch/dinner 60,000 L. Reduced rates for children; special meals on request.

The 1991 Guide will appear in the autumn of 1990. Reports are particularly useful in the spring, but need to reach us by May 1990 if they are to help the 1991 edition.

BOLOGNA 40123 — Map 16

Hotel Roma — *Tel* (051) 274400
Via Massimo d'Azeglio 9 — *Telex* 583270
Bologna

"The best medium-priced hotel in Bologna, and we've tried quite a few", is a comment this year by regular visitors to the biggish *Roma*, centrally located in a narrow street just off the magnificent Piazza Maggiore, heart of the historic core of medieval Bologna. It is fairly quiet, save for a few clock chimes, and even has a roof-garden. The air-conditioning is always appreciated; however, one visitor in July found it turned off from 2 to 8.30 am ("a police regulation", she was told), making her room very hot. She also thought the service unhelpful. The food is "acceptable" though expensive: but there are masses of good cheap places all around in the world capital of good pasta. (*W Ian Stewart, Brian MacArthur*)

Open All year. Restaurant closed 1–23 Aug.
Rooms 80 – most with bath or shower, telephone, TV and air-conditioning (10,000 L).
Facilities Lift. Restaurant; roof-garden.
Location Central: by car, go to the back entrance which is not in pedestrian zone. Garage.
Credit cards All major cards accepted.
Terms [1989 rates] Rooms: single: 77,000 L, double 102,000 L. Breakfast 10,000 L. Full board 121,000–147,000 L per person. Set lunch/dinner 30,000 L.

BORDIGHERA 18012 Imperia — Map 16

Hotel Villa Elisa — *Tel* (0184) 261313
Via Romana 70 — *Telex* 272540 ELISA

A handsome white villa with a pretty garden, set quietly on an elegant avenue, ten minutes' walk above the seafront of this busy Riviera resort. Friendly welcome, good service, spotless upkeep, copious meals – "they look boring, but taste good" – in a graceful dining room with outdoor terrace. Many rooms have big balcony facing south; second-floor rooms have sea view. Closed 15 Nov–19 Dec. 32 rooms, all with bath or shower. B&B double 90,000–104,000 L. Set menu 35,000 L. In Aug half or full board only. More reports please.

BRESSANONE 39042 Bolzano — Map 16

Hotel Dominik — *Tel* (0472) 30144
Via Terzo di Sotto 13 — *Telex* 401524 DOMNIK

A bright and breezy modern hotel, all orange and yellow colours, set close to the Rienz river on the edge of this busy resort, a good centre for exploring the Dolomites and Tyrol. "Wonderful and good value", says a 1989 visitor; "staff friendly and professional, food excellent – and the indoor swimming pool is marvellous." But another reader found the place somewhat rigid and aloof. The decor is a bit garish, but the gardens are pretty. (*Martin L Dodd*)

We are particularly keen to have reports on italicised entries.

Open Easter–Nov. Restaurant closed Tue except Jul, Aug, Sept.
Rooms 19 double, 10 single – all with bath and shower, telephone and radio; 15 with TV.
Facilities Lounge, bar, TV room, restaurants. Indoor swimming pool. Garden and terrace.
Location Central, parking. Bressanone is 41 km NE of Bolzano.
Restriction Not suitable for ♿.
Credit cards Access, Amex, Visa.
Terms [1989 rates] B&B 70,000–120,000 L per person. Dinner, B&B (min 3 days) 90,000–140,000 L. Set lunch/dinner 30,000–40,000 L; full alc 30,000 L. Reduced rates for children; special meals on request.

Hotel Elefante — *Tel* (0472) 32750
Via Rio Bianco 4 — *Fax* (0472) 36579

Unlike the modern Dominik, *the* Elefante *is strictly classical – a 16th-century building near the town centre, lavishly furnished with antiques, old paintings and tapestries. Rooms comfortable (some a little dark; back ones quieter and lighter); charming old-fashioned service; food very good. Delightful big garden with curved swimming pool. Open 1 Mar–mid-Nov, 25 Dec–8 Jan, restaurant closed Mon. 44 rooms, all with bath and/or shower. B&B 95,000 L. Full alc 45,000 L. Recent nomination. More reports welcome.*

Hotels are dropped if we lack positive feedback. If you can endorse an entry, please do so.

We asked hotels to quote 1990 prices. Not all were able to predict them in the late spring of 1989. Some of our terms will be inaccurate. Do check latest tariffs at the time of booking.

Hotels often book you into their most expensive rooms or suites unless you specify otherwise. Even if all room prices are the same, hotels may give you a less good room in the hope of selling their better rooms to late customers. It always pays to discuss accommodation in detail when making a reservation.

Traveller's tale *Monlucon, July. I was looking for rooms in a hotel near the railway. As the landlady and I went along a corridor upstairs, I said I hoped the noise of trains could not be heard in the bedrooms. "One hears nothing," she answered positively. She opened the door of a room and a tremendous engine-shriek met us, seeming to drive us both back from the threshold. She shut the door, and tried another one, and we were met instantly by another tremendous engine-shriek. She burst out laughing. I laughed too. If she had not proved her sense of humour, I might have walked straight out of the hotel. But her sense of humour kept a customer with a sense of humour. I got quiet rooms at the back.*
Arnold Bennett (Journals, 1929)

CAPRI 80073 Naples — Map 16

Hotel Luna
Viale Matteotti 3

Tel (081) 8370433
Telex 721247

A beautiful but expensive hotel in a secluded position above the sea, next to the fashionable Augusto gardens on the southern side of Capri town. Large bedrooms with sea views, attractive public rooms, lovely swimming pool and gardens, good food and impeccable service. Open Apr–Oct. 44 rooms, all with bath or shower. 'Rooms 110,000–230,000'L. Breakfast 18,000 L; alc meals (excluding wine) 45,000–55,000 L [1989]. Recent nomination. More reports please.

CASALPUSTERLENGO 20071 Milano — Map 16

Hotel Fiesta
Viale della Stazione

Tel (0377) 84871, 84945 and 84954

A useful stop-over hotel in a small town just off the Autostrada del Sole, *16 kilometres north-west of Piacenza. Outwardly unpromising, down a back street near the station, and no special chic, but clean, comfortable and modern, run by a most affable family. 40 rooms, all with bath. Double rooms 60,000–100,000 L [1989]. Set menus 25,000–35,000 L. Recent nomination. More reports please, especially on the restaurant.*

CASTELLINA IN CHIANTI 53011 Siena — Map 16

Pensione Belvedere di San Leonino

Tel (0577) 740887
Telex 741034

An old stone farmhouse with outbuildings, all recently and tastefully converted into a bed-and-breakfast pensione, *cleverly combining a rustic ambience with modern comforts. Spacious lounge bar in rural style, pleasant patio for drinks etc; snacks served. Swimming pool. 28 rooms, all with bath and shower. B&B double 85,000 L. Set meals 20,000 L. Recent nomination. More reports welcome.*

Pensione Salivolpi
Via Fiorentina

Tel (0577) 740484
Fax (0577) 741034

A converted Tuscan farmhouse with beamed ceilings, set on a hill with broad views towards Siena and Volterra; it consists of three buildings in a pretty garden with a sizeable swimming pool. It fell out of last year's Guide through lack of feedback, but is now restored by four reports calling it friendly, modest and agreeable: "Comfortable and good value, very clean, with lovely typical Tuscan rooms; manageress efficient but a bit aloof. Breakfast boring: better to pop down to the main bar in the village." Others have mentioned elegant bathrooms and a family ambience. No restaurant, and the trattoria in the village is not rated highly: but there are others a bit further afield. (*Simon Small, John RL Cook, Michael and Margaret Crick, Richard Osborne*)

Open All year.
Rooms 18 double, 1 single – all with bath, shower and telephone. 7 rooms in 2 annexes.
Facilities Lounge with bar and TV, breakfast room. Garden with swimming pool.
Location 1 km NW of Castellina towards San Donato.
Restrictions Not suitable for ♿.
Credit cards All major cards accepted.
Terms [1989 rates] Rooms: single 30,000 L, double 60,000 L. Breakfast 7,000 L. (No restaurant.)

Tenuta di Ricavo *Tel* (0577) 740221
Fax (0577) 741014

This much-loved old manor house in rural Tuscany is now back in the hands of the Swiss family Scotoni who originally converted it into a delightfully informal hotel. A report since their return: "It is in 'Chiantishire', the area so beloved of English residents who bought up deserted farm houses. Guests appreciate its classic Quattrocento atmosphere. The central manor contains the dining room, lounges and libraries, plus a few guest rooms; outbuildings around the 'village square' of the old hamlet have been converted into studio rooms and apartments, plus good bathrooms, with Tuscan furniture and Mara Scotoni's luscious flower paintings. The terraces face beautiful views of the hills, with oakwoods, vineyards and distant towns. The food is *alla casalinga*, simple Italian" (one reader felt it lacked variety). "The nice Scotoni family speak all languages; service is excellent, food is good too, and lunch can be taken under trees in the garden, near the two swimming pools. Our room was charming and comfortable." "Beautiful, remote, peaceful and wonderful." Others have enjoyed the Chianti wines from the hotel's own vineyards, and the log fires in winter. Some have found the ambience more international than Italian. Siena, Florence and Volterra are all within easy reach. Guests are expected to dine in the hotel; there is a small à la carte lunch menu.

Open Apr–Nov. Restaurant closed Wed midday.
Rooms 9 suites, 13 double, 2 single – all with bath and shower, and telephone. 3 ground-floor rooms. Some in annexe.
Facilities 3 lounges, TV room, bar, dining room. Garden with 2 swimming pools; table tennis.
Location 22 km NW of Siena, 34 km S of Florence. Leave Siena *superstrada* at San Donato exit.
Restrictions Not suitable for severely ♿. No smoking in dining room.
Credit cards None accepted.
Terms Dinner, B&B 120,000–168,000 L. Alc lunch 40,000 L; set dinner 42,000–45,000 L. 1-night bookings sometimes refused if made too far in advance. Reduced rates for children sharing parents' room; special meals on request.

CASTIGLIONCELLO 57012 Livorno — Map 16

Hotel Villa Godilonda *Tel* (0586) 752032
Via Biagi 12

This pleasant seaside hotel, making its Guide debut, stands on a rocky promontory with small sandy beaches on either side in a family bathing resort south of Livorno. "All rooms have a sea view. Ours, decorated in glass and plastic, Italian style, was very clean and pleasant. The excellent public rooms are very modern, clean, comfortable, expensively done, with marble floors and chromium. Service impeccable, lots of staff; breakfast room charming with excellent breakfasts – good coffee etc. The attractive swimming pool is not crowded, and has plenty of places to sit and sunbathe. No restaurant, and the ones in town are poor: but the *Antico Moro* in Livorno has marvellous fish stew." (*Gerald Campion*)

Open All year.
Rooms 23 – all with shower, telephone, radio, TV, baby-listening.
Facilities 2 lounges, TV room, bar. Indoor and outdoor swimming pools; direct access to private beach.
Location On edge of village 20 km S of Livorno. Parking.
Terms B&B: single 93,500–108,000 L, double 120,000–254,000 L, suite 226,000–340,000 L. (No restaurant.)

CAVALESE 38033 Trento — Map 16

Mas del Saügo — *Tel* (0462) 30788
Masi

A 17th-century farmhouse, secluded in a forest at the western end of the Dolomites, newly converted with exquisite taste into a fine restaurant with just four guest rooms. It was unearthed for us last year by a well-known British hotelier who has been back this year and found it "better than ever" – and his praise has become more exuberant than ever: "This may be our favourite place in the world, and it's perhaps the best value for money in Europe". Rub your eyes in disbelief, and now read his initial report: "Owned and run by a young couple, Lorenzo Bernardini and Donatella Zampoli. He is an architect (as well as artist and oenophile) and has renovated with great style – stripped wood floors and beams, modern pictures (mostly his own work), bright colours in carpets and fabrics. Window frames and fittings are in bright red which sounds ghastly but looks great. In fact everything delights the eye. They use Ginori china embossed with their own logo. There is a small study with family photographs where they serve breakfast. We drank Müller-Thurgau in the garden, listening to cowbells and admiring the view, then spent three-and-a-half hours over the seven-course set menu that Donatella had composed and cooked. Everything close to perfect: carpaccio, white truffles, freshly-gathered porcini, really good gnocchi, fillet of beef in an intense red wine sauce. Lorenzo is a most professional *sommelier*." (*Paul Henderson*) In 1989 an American couple have assured us that Mr Henderson has not been day-dreaming: "We thoroughly agree. Like visiting in a friend's home. Dinner and wines delicious. Even breakfast was way above Italian standard". (*William and Anita Taylor*) PH tells us that Signor Bernardini, amazingly, is vice-president of a cricket club. Now that explains it all.

Open All year. Restaurant closed Thur.
Rooms 1 suite, 2 double, 1 single – all with shower.
Facilities 2 lounges, bar, restaurant. Large grounds.
Location At Masi, 4 km SW of Cavalese which is 42 km SE of Bolzano.
Restriction No children under 8.
Credit card Visa.
Terms B&B 80,000–100,000 L. Set lunch/dinner 80,000–95,000 L.

CAVASAGRA DI VEDELAGO 31050 Treviso — Map 16

Villa Cornèr della Regina Country Hotel — *Tel* (0423) 481.481, *Telex* 433391 CORNER

This dazzling new Guide entry (why have we not heard about it before?) is described as "everyone's idea of a Palladian villa": built in c.1500, then rebuilt in *c.*1700 by one of Palladio's pupils, it stands in its own formal park, amid vineyards that provide it with red, white and sparkling wine. Venice is a bare hour's drive away. Two nominating reports this year: "Never before have I come across a hotel of this quality. It has no lifts: but who wants a lift if one can walk up a lovely staircase lined with old prints, to a bedroom the size of a ballroom, decorated in 18th-century Venetian style, with breathtaking views across the Veneto countryside? Beautifully restored in keeping with its illustrious history, the villa has courteous and attentive staff and an excellent restaurant. On our visit, guests were mainly Italian: the hotel doesn't seem to have been much discovered yet by tourists." And this, written *in situ*: "The interior is elegant, more through clever modern design than the use of antiques, though a few of these are sprinkled around. The huge central hall on the *piano nobile* has been decorated in a tent style with pink and white stripes, irresistibly reminiscent of Leander during Henley regatta. In my suite, the luxurious bathroom is housed in a kind of pagoda. The dining room (in what was once the orangerie and keeps that character) aims high, but does not quite get there: my meal last night was mediocre, but tonight's was delicious. The adjacent farm and stable buildings are now an annexe." Large heated swimming pool; bedrooms all different and superbly elegant. (*Robert Ribeiro, ATW Liddell*)

Open All year.
Rooms 7 suites, 14 double – all with bath and shower and telephone. Most double rooms in annexe.
Facilities Hall, lounge, bar, 2 restaurants. Park with tennis court and swimming pool, sauna. Golf nearby.
Location 18 km W of Treviso, near Albaredo.
Terms [1989 rates] B&B: single 180,000 L, double 240,000 L, suite 300,000 L. Set meals 35,000 L.

CEFALÙ 90015 Sicily — Map 16

Hotel Riva del Sole — *Tel* (0921) 21230
Viale Lungomare 25

A very modern, comfortable hotel on the promenade, in a fascinating ancient town on the north Sicilian coast, set below a great Gibraltar-like rock. Cheerful staff, large rooms with balconies, good menu. 28 rooms, all with bath and shower. Full board double 60,000–80,000 L. Set menu 18,000 L. New nomination. More reports welcome.

> Don't keep your favourite hotel to yourself. The Guide supports: it doesn't spoil.

> In your own interest, always check latest tariffs with hotels when you make your bookings.

CETRARO 87022 Cosenza — Map 16

Grand Hotel San Michele — *Tel* (0982) 91012
Loc. Bosco 8/9 — *Fax* (0982) 91430

Calabria, Italy's toe, has long been a blank space on our map of good hotels, so this one on its upper west coast is especially welcome. It's a big white palace in traditional style, standing alone on a hillside above the broad blue sea, and *Michelin* gives it three red gables. "After a week's tiresome touring of Calabria, this was a find and a pleasure. It is very comfortably furnished, with a huge and splendid lounge. The head waiter speaks good English and the staff are keen to anticipate your wishes: miming to the chambermaid regarding pillows, soft bedding and mosquitoes produced instantly just what we needed. The food is excellent, with a good choice of local Calabrese dishes. There is a good-sized pool and excellent sea bathing, with a cabin for every room. The grounds are large and well kept, with wonderful views of sea and mountains." A lift leads down a cliffside to the hotel's mile-long private beach.

Open All year except Nov.
Rooms 6 suites, 52 double, 7 single – all with bath and/or shower, telephone and TV.
Facilities Lift. Salons, bars, TV room, restaurant; conference facilities. Garden with terrace, swimming pool, tennis court, 9-hole golf course. Lift down to private beach.
Location On coast road 6 km NW of Cetraro, 61 km NW of Cosenza.
Restriction Not suitable for ♿.
Credit cards All major cards accepted.
Terms [1989 rates] Rooms: single 140,000–220,000 L, double 118,000–200,000 L per person, suite 180,000–260,000 L. Breakfast 15,000 L. Set meals 40,000 L. Special meals for children.

CHIAVERANO D'IVREA 10010 Torino — Map 16

Castello San Giuseppe — *Tel* (0125) 424370

Only five miles north-east of industrial Ivrea, where Olivetti produces its computer-age wizardry, here in utter contrast is an ancient hilltop mansion, once a monastery, then turned into a fortress by Bonaparte, and now a charming hotel with large garden and terrace, reached along a narrow winding hill road. Comfortable bedrooms with modern bathrooms and fine views; dining by candle-light, with unpretentious home cooking; warm welcome and friendly service. 16 rooms, all with bath and/or shower. B&B double 110,000–130,000 L. Set menus 35,000–55,000 L. Endorsed this year, but we'd be glad of reports on the bedrooms.

CIOCCARO DI PENANGO 14030 Asti — Map 16

Locanda del Sant'Uffizio — *Tel* (0141) 91271

A graceful old 16th-century monastery, converted into a small, very attractive hotel in a tiny village set amid peaceful hills in the wine area north-east of Asti. "A fantastic place, luxurious and comfortable, with charming rooms", says a reader this year, endorsing last year's nomination: "The owner is also the local estate owner: his family occupy the larger monastery building, and the cloister buildings are now the guest rooms, each with a small terrace overlooking a garden which leads down to a swimming pool. The *Locanda* has views over the village, vineyards and hills. Bicycles are provided for those who wish to explore. Our large room had a small kitchen area with cooker and fridge. Breakfast, taken in the open beside the pool, is a self-service buffet with cheese, meats etc; a buffet lunch is served there too. The food was not cheap, but cooking and ingredients were superb. House wine, served as a matter of course, included a sparkling aperitif, with peach juice and a bottle of their own Barbera. A relaxing, informal, casual place, our only niggle being that housekeeping could have been better." The hotel's restaurant, *Da Beppe* (*Michelin* rosette), serves a nine-course set meal (no menus) that a reader this year found "hedonistic" if expensive, and "totally inappropriate for children". (*Betsy C Maestro*) Half- and full-board rates only.

Open All year except 1–20 Jan, 1–10 Aug. Restaurant closed Tue.
Rooms 3 suites, 26 double, 2 single – all with bath and/or shower, telephone, TV, balcony or terrace. 7 ground-floor rooms.
Facilities 2 salons, bar, restaurant; billiard room, games room. Conference facilities. Small gymnasium. Terrace. Large grounds with unheated swimming pool and tennis court; bicycles available.
Location Village is 20 km NE of Asti, 5 km SE of Moncalvo.
Credit cards All major cards accepted.
Terms Half board 180,000 L, full board 220,000 L. Set meals 90,000 L. Reduced rates and special meals for children.

CISTERNINO 72014 Brindisi — Map 16

Country Club Villa Cenci — *Tel* (080) 718208
Via Ceglie Messapico — *Fax* (080) 718208

Our only entry for Apulia lies right in the heart of the region of the *trulli*, those strange little round white stone houses with domed roofs. Nearby are the great caves of Castellana, rich in stalactites and stalagmites. The *Cenci*, on the Semeraro Farm, is rather unusual too, as a recent visitor reports, "Called a 'country club', it consists of an old farmhouse, a collection of *trulli*, and some new self-catering units which blend in well. You can have rooms in the house or, as we did, in one of the *trulli* – simply furnished, lovely tiled floors, comfortable beds. It is a delightfully peaceful place, with a nice swimming pool, charming grounds." Some of the rooms are small apartments with kitchenette, so this could help solve the food problem. The sea is about 12 kilometres away. More reports please.

Open Apr–Oct.
Rooms 17 suites, 3 double – all with shower; some with kitchenette. Many in *trulli* not far from main building.
Facilities 2 lounges, bar, TV room, restaurant. In large farm with garden and swimming pool. Sea with safe bathing 12 km.
Location 48 km W of Brindisi, 1 km from Cisternino.
Restriction Not suitable for ♿.
Credit cards None accepted.
Terms B&B 35,000–55,000 L. Half board 60,000–86,000 L. Full alc 30,000 L. Reduced rates and special meals for children.

COGNE 11012 Aosta — Map 16

Hôtel Bellevue — *Tel* (0165) 74825
Rue Grand Paradis 20 — *Fax* (0165) 749192

Renewed praise this year for this solid traditional hotel – a big square block of a building – just outside a summer and skiing resort in a mountain valley south of Aosta, facing the Gran Paradiso massif: "The location is superb, with the elegant dining room seeming to float out over the view. Food and comfort are excellent, and the service is warm and welcoming, maybe because the place has been in the same family for 50 years or more, and many of the staff are old-timers. It has the human qualities of a family place." Others have written in similar vein – "good traditional local food". Fine mountain walks, and good swimming facilities. (*Peter Dingley*)

Open 20 Dec–17 Apr; 1 Jun–30 Sept. Restaurant closed Wed.
Rooms 4 chalets, 3 suites, 32 double, 6 single – all with bath and/or shower, telephone and radio. Chalets have TV and cooking facilities.
Facilities Lift. 3 lounges, TV room, pub with video and music, games room, restaurant; gala dinners once a week; conference room. Indoor swimming pool, whirlpool, sauna, solarium and gymnasium. Garden.
Location 27 km S of Aosta. Hotel is central; parking.
Credit cards None accepted.
Terms B&B: single 130,000 L, double 140,000 L. Dinner, B&B 80,000–120,000 L per person. Set lunch/dinner 30,000–35,000 L. Reduced rates and special meals for children.

COURMAYEUR 11013 Aosta — Map 16

Hotel Bouton d'Or — *Tel* (0165) 842380
Strada Statale 26, n.10 — *Fax* (0165) 842152

A medium-sized hotel in this big ski-resort: some rooms face Mont Blanc, others look across the valley to lesser peaks. A recent report: "The greeting was friendly, the room modern, clean and comfortable with good-sized bathroom. Breakfast good too." Most rooms are small but tastefully decorated with hessian-lined walls and stylish bedspreads. No dining room, but the owners also have a restaurant in the village, *Le Vieux Pommier*. More reports please.

Open All year except May, June and Nov.
Rooms 21 double, 3 single – 15 with bath, 9 with shower, all with telephone and TV.
Facilities Lift. Salon, bar, TV room, library, games room; sauna and solarium.
Location 100 metres from town centre. Parking.
Restriction Not suitable for ♿.
Credit cards All major cards accepted.
Terms B&B: single 56,000–62,000 L, double 93,000–103,000 L. Reduced rates for children sharing parents' room. (No restaurant.)

> In all continental European and Scandinavian countries except Denmark, France, Hungary, Malta, Spain and Turkey, the dialling codes begin with a 0. Omit this when dialling from outside the country in question. Spanish codes begin with a 9, which should also be omitted.

ERICE 91016 Sicily — Map 16

Hotel Elimo — *Tel* (0923) 869377
Via Vittorio Emanuele 75 — *Fax* (0923) 869252

An old stone building, fastidiously converted in a whole series of styles, some a bit bizarre, and newly opened as a smart little hotel. Charming owner, helpful staff, nice bedrooms, good pension menu. Roof-terraces. 21 rooms, all with private facilities. B&B double 70,000–88,000 L. Set menus 30,000–35,000 L. New nomination. More reports please.

Hotel Moderno — *Tel* (0923) 869300
Via Vittorio Emanuele 63 — *Fax* (0923) 869139

Beautiful but tourist-filled Erice has been described as "an atmospheric sun-bleached town at the tip of a high pinnacle of rock, with views of the sea. The medieval atmosphere is stronger than virtually anywhere we've seen. The castle and churches are marvellous." The friendly, family-run *Moderno*, modern indeed but furnished with style and originality, has this year drawn oddly conflicting reports: "Modern fittings squeezed into impossible spaces, lots of stairs and odd-shaped corridors, but warm, clean and welcoming. The food is very good (rare in Sicily), and a large family are all involved in reception, cooking, waiting, and eating with the guests." But: "Service was a bit haphazard, as everything seemed to be done by one girl. Dinner was pretty uninspiring. But the hotel is a wonderful oasis of luxury in parched Sicily." A third new report, between these extremes, found the food "acceptable, with portions not over-generous", the girl at the desk "helpful" and the ambience "welcoming". Driving through the narrow one-way streets is difficult, and visitors are advised to park in the square just inside the town gate. (*Angela and David Stewart, PA Bispham, Philippa Herbert*)

Open All year.
Rooms 6 suites, 28 double, 6 single – all with bath and/or shower, telephone and TV. Some ground-floor rooms.
Facilities Lift. Lounge, bar, dining room; terrace.
Location Central. Parking.
Credit cards All major cards accepted.
Terms B&B: single 55,000–60,000 L, double 85,000–90,000 L, suite 90,000–100,000 L; dinner, B&B 75,000–90,000 L per person; Set lunch/dinner 35,000 L; full alc 40,000 L. Reduced rates and special meals for children.

FASANO DEL GARDA Brescia — Map 16

Grand Hotel Fasano — *Tel* (0365) 21051
Corso Zanardelli 160, 25083 — *Fax* (0365) 21054

A fairly smart and sizeable holiday hotel in traditional rather than modern style, with a fine lakeside setting just outside the busy resort of Gardone Riviera, and liked by several recent visitors: "Lots of wood panelling and comfortable armchairs. Our large and well-furnished room offered a lovely view of the lake. Food was excellent." "The pretty swimming pool among the bougainvillea and cypresses was lovely, with plenty of umbrellas and loungers on the spacious lawns beside the lake.

Dinners are excellent with splendid help-yourself salads; breakfast was also self-service, with scrambled eggs and bacon and much else. Elegant Louis XV chairs. There is ping-pong, tennis and water-skiing." While one reader found the service "fast and friendly", another this year thought it less than courteous. More reports please.

Open May–Sept/Oct.
Rooms 5 suites, 50 double, 20 single – 49 with bath, 26 with shower, all with telephone. Some ground-floor rooms.
Facilities Lift. 2 lounges, bar, 2 dining rooms; conference facilities. Large grounds with garden, terrace overlooking the lake; swimming pool, tennis, private beach, water sports. Yacht marina and golf nearby.
Location 1 km NE of Gardone, on lake shore.
Credit cards None accepted.
Terms [1989 rates] (Excluding 9% tax) Half board 75,000–120,000 L. Full board 20,000–25,000 L added per person. Set lunch/dinner 33,000 L. Reduced rates and special meals for children.

Hotel Villa del Sogno *Tel* (0365) 20228
Fasano del Garda, 25080 *Fax* (0365) 21145

A magnificent wide flowery terrace with lovely views of Lake Garda is possibly the best feature of this fairly grand but not-too-daunting hotel, a big yellowish villa built in the 1920s. It is perched high above the lake, amid finely landscaped gardens, just north of Gardone Riviera. Biggish rooms, some with balcony; swimming pool; staff helpful; food copious but unremarkable. Open Easter–Oct. 35 rooms, all with bath or shower. B&B: double 200,000–240,000 L. Set menu from 45,000 L [1989]. Endorsed this year but more reports needed.

FIESOLE 50014 Florence — Map 16

Hotel Villa Bonelli *Tel* (055) 59513 and 598941
Via F. Poeti 1/3

Many visitors to Florence prefer to stay up in the peace and quiet of Fiesole, a lovely old town on a cypress-clad hill five miles north of the busy city. Here the *Villa Bonelli*, a modern unpretentious family-run place, partakes of that famous view down to the spires and palaces, and is served by regular buses to the city. "Helpful owners, cheerful young waitresses, well-cooked meals, comfortable bed", is typical of the kind of report that has again been reaching us in 1988/9. Other views: "We were impressed by the sheer professionalism of the owners, the Boninsegni brothers, and by the variety, quantity and quality of the table d'hôte meals"; "The Tuscan cooking was excellent, and the measures of after-dinner sambuca were most generous." Bedrooms vary in size, some being small, some "huge but sparsely furnished", but all are comfortable; those at the back are subject to some traffic noise . The top-floor restaurant (guests share tables) can become overcrowded and a bit noisy, and there's not much in the way of a lounge. (*Alan F Thomas, Mr and Mrs Bernard Dunstan, Ian and Ann Steel, and others*)

> When hotels have failed to return their questionnaire, we have quoted 1989 prices, with a note to that effect.

Open All year. Restaurant closed for dinner Nov–Mar.
Rooms 1 suite, 16 double, 7 single – 1 with bath and shower, 13 with shower, all with telephone. Some ground-floor rooms.
Facilities Lift. Foyer with TV, restaurant; terrace.
Location Coming from Florence turn right at Piazza Mino da Fiesole; hotel is 300 metres on right. Garage. Regular bus link with Florence.
Restriction Not suitable for ♿.
Credit cards All major cards accepted.
Terms B&B: single 43,000–52,000 L, double 68,000–86,000 L; dinner, B&B: single 74,000–83,000 L, double 130,000–145,000 L. Set lunch/dinner 35,000 L; full alc 40,000 L. Reduced rates and special meals for children.

FLORENCE **Map 16**

Pensione Annalena *Tel* (055) 222402
Via Romana 34
Florence 50125

Originally an aristocratic mansion, then successively a convent, a school for young ladies, a home for the poor, a gambling house, and since 1919 a family pensione, *set on the quieter south side of the Arno. A place of traditional charm and personality, very hospitable, filled with old furniture and paintings (but bathrooms are modern and rooms comfortable). Lounge and cocktail bar. 20 rooms, all with bath and shower. B&B: single 77,000–88,000 L, double 120,000–132,000 L. No restaurant. Recent nomination. More reports please.*

Hotel Calzaiuoli *Tel* (055) 212456
Via Calzaiuoli 6 *Telex* 580589
Florence 50122

Centrally situated on a pedestrian street leading from the Duomo to the Palazzo Vecchio, a clean and well-run little hotel, recently modernised, with air-conditioning and a friendly staff. Back rooms are largest and quietest, front ones may be noisy. Some upper rooms have views of the Duomo. Street parking difficult; garage nearby, but expensive. 37 rooms, all with bath and shower, 73,000–109,000 L [1989]. Breakfast 9,000 L. No restaurant. Endorsed this year, but fuller reports welcome.

Hotel Loggiato dei Serviti *Tel* (055) 219165
Piazza SS. Annunziata 3 *Telex* 575808 LOGSER
Florence 50122

Popular with visiting English art lecturers, this lovely building in the heart of Florence has been described as "probably the city's most elegant small hotel". It was built in 1527 for a religious order, the Serviti, and has been newly and sympathetically restored. "We had a light and spacious two-level room with gorgeous beamed ceiling; breakfast service was prompt and friendly", runs a 1989 report, and others have agreed. "It combines the best of old (Renaissance building, antique furnishings) and new (including the plumbing). The lovely piazza has been mercifully rescued from its undignified role as a parking lot (but the hotel will park your car for you)." Air-conditioning is said to have been just installed – mercifully, for one visitor found the heat stifling. (*Mary Hanson, AF*

Thomas, ML and MM Gravelle) One dissenter this year thought the hotel overrated and criticised staff and beds.

Open All year.
Rooms 4 suites, 19 double, 6 single – all with bath, shower, telephone, radio and TV.
Facilities Lift. Lounges, TV room, bar, breakfast room; air-conditioning. Conferences/functions can be arranged at an adjacent *palazzo*.
Location Central, 200 metres from cathedral in pedestrian zone. Garage service.
Restriction Not suitable for ♿.
Credit cards All major cards accepted.
Terms B&B: single 90,000 L, double 140,000 L, suite 200,000–350,000 L. (No restaurant.)

Hotel Tornabuoni Beacci *Tel* (055) 268377 and 212645
Via Tornabuoni 3
Florence 50123

Centrally situated near the Palazzo Strozzi, this admirable hotel is in a 14th-century palace – and it's on the top floor, so it suffers very little from street noise. "Indeed most pleasant", says a reader this year; "every room is different and all are large and beautifully decorated. The restaurant is nice, the roof-terrace is a lovely oasis after a day in Florence, and the ambience is homey, helped along by the smiling, willing staff and the ever-present whirlwind of Signora Beacci." Others have called the food "satisfactory", and have enjoyed taking breakfast on the roof-garden, amid trees and shrubs, or sitting in the comfortable lounge amid tapestries, plants, bookcases and fine old furniture. (*Roberta Garza de Elizondo*)

Open All year.
Rooms 31 double – all with bath and telephone; TV on request. 5 in annexe.
Facilities Lift. Salon, bar, restaurant; roof-terrace.
Location Central, close to Palazzo Strozzi. Parking.
Credit cards Amex, Diners, Visa.
Terms On application.

Hotel Villa Belvedere *Tel* (055) 222501
Via Benedetto Castelli 3 *Fax* (055) 223163
Florence 50124 *Telex* 575648 VILBEL

Again commended this year, notably for its thoughtful staff and its swimming pool set in a flowery garden, this modern family-run hotel stands peacefully on Poggio Imperiale hill, removed from the hurly-burly. "We had a large well-furnished room with a huge terrace overlooking the garden and the city below." Another account rhapsodised, "I drove down through a tunnel of trees to the delightful villa, where only the cicadas disturbed the silence. Inside were cool, shiny marble floors, and simply but elegantly furnished rooms. Breakfast is served in a glass-walled veranda which looks down on to the Duomo, the roofs of Florence and the hills beyond. At night you can sip coffee or drinks in the garden, the perfume from the roses scenting the air and the lights of Florence twinkling below." There is no restaurant, but the bar serves snacks and simple dishes such as pasta and omelettes. Some rooms are quite small, and it might be worth asking for one of the larger (and more expensive) upper rooms with big terraces. (*PA Bispham*)

Open 1 Mar–30 Nov.
Rooms 2 suites, 22 double, 3 single – all with bath and/or shower, telephone, TV and baby-listening; some with balcony. Some ground-floor rooms.
Facilities Lift. Lounges, TV room, bar. Garden with swimming pool, tennis, children's play area.
Location 2.5 km S of centre; leave Florence by Porta Romana, turn E off Via Senese.
Credit cards All major cards accepted.
Terms B&B: single 120,000–140,000 L, double 190,000–210,000 L, suite 240,000–250,000 L. Reduced rates for children sharing parents' room. (No restaurant, but light meals available.)

FORTE DEI MARMI 55042 Lucca — Map 16

Hotel Alcione

Tel (0584) 89952
Viale Morin 137

Smarter and more expensive than the *Tirreno* (see below), but smaller, this gabled mansion stands in a quiet residential street a mile south of the town centre; the beach is only 150 yards away, but across two main roads. "At the end of September we were virtually the only pebbles on the beach, so abrupt is the end of the Italian holiday season. The hotel is unpretentious, comfortable, clean (our room was adequately furnished); the cuisine is competent, and service pleasant if a bit slow. The owners were friendly." A shady terrace and neat lounge. More reports please.

Open 25 May–end Sept.
Rooms 45 – all with bath and/or shower and telephone.
Facilities Lift. Lounge, bar, restaurant; terrace. Garden with swimming pool.
Location 1.5 km S of resort which is 35 km NW of Pisa.
Credit cards Amex, Diners, Visa.
Terms [1989 rates] Rooms: single 100,000 L, double 130,000 L. Breakfast 12,000 L. Full board 80,000–140,000 L per person. Set lunch/dinner 30,000–45,000 L.

Hotel Tirreno

Tel (0584) 83333
Viale Morin 7

One of the most attractive towns on the coast north of Pisa, and very Italian in atmosphere, Forte dei Marmi is a traditional seaside resort of villas with shady gardens, a wide traffic-free promenade, a pier and a long golden beach. Here the family-run *Tirreno* with its "lovely peaceful garden" has again been liked this year, "Warm and homey; generous rooms with balconies, a staff who work hard to please." Previous accounts: "Excellent room, food, service, garden and situation." "Our room afforded a lovely view of both the sea in front and the mountains behind." Another reader had a marble bathroom "as big as a bedroom in some hotels". Most guests receive a complimentary bottle of Italian champagne with dinner on the night before their departure. (*Diane and Joel Morris*) The beach close by is said to be uncrowded and clean.

Open 12 Apr–1 Oct.
Rooms 49 double, 10 single – all with bath and/or shower, and telephone; 20 have balcony with sea views. 21 in villa in garden.

Facilities Lounge, TV room, games room, bar, dining room; dancing. Garden. 50 metres from fine, safe beach with bathing and boat rental.
Location Central; parking. Town is 35 km NW of Pisa.
Restriction Not suitable for ♿.
Credit cards Amex, Diners, Visa.
Terms [1989 rates] B&B: single 63,400–64,300 L, double 100,600–101.400 L; dinner, B&B 90,000 L per person; full board 98,000–133,000 L. Reduced rates for children sharing parents' room; special meals.

GARDONE RIVIERA 25083 Brescia — Map 16

Villa Fiordaliso — *Tel* (0365) 20158 and 21948
Via Garibaldi 132 — *Telex* 301088 MOLINA

The brochure of this exquisitely beautiful villa on Lake Garda does not balk at reminding its public that this was a favourite residence of Claretta Petacci, Mussolini's consort. But that's past history. And here is an enthusiastic 1989 nomination: "Now a restaurant with seven bedrooms, it's been carefully restored to its former (pre-Petacci) glory – marble and alabaster, tapestries and paintings, blended with modern lighting and high black-lacquer and leather chairs in the dining rooms, to produce a relaxing and attractive atmosphere. The situation is superb – lovely views, its own small pier, waterside gardens and outdoor dining terrace. Our room was lovely, with traditional furniture, and the bathroom was a delight. The excellent cooking is in modern style, but based on traditional and local recipes, with a changing daily menu related to the market; service, a little unsure, was by local girls. Front lake-view rooms are best: back ones could be noisy, for the main road passes there." (*Pat and Jeremy Temple*)

Open Feb–Nov.
Rooms 1 suite, 6 double – 3 with bath, 4 with shower, all with telephone, radio, TV, mini-bar.
Facilities Hall, piano bar, 4 dining rooms. Terrace where meals are served. Garden, private beach. Golf and tennis nearby.
Location 500 metres from centre of Gardone which is 34 km NE of Brescia. Parking.
Restrictions Not suitable for ♿.
Credit cards Amex, Diners, Visa.
Terms Double room: with breakfast 128,000 L, with half board 254,000 L, with full board 380,000 L. Full alc 70,000 L.

GARGONZA 52048 Arezzo — Map 16

Castello di Gargonza — *Tel* (0575) 847021 and 847053
Monte San Savino — *Fax* (0575) 847054
Telex 571466 REDCO

"A delightful place to stay", "I'll sing its praises to the rafters" are among the superlatives for this unusual paradise which is not exactly a hotel. On a hilltop in the Tuscan woodlands above the Chiana valley, it is an intact 13th-century walled village which Count Roberto Guicciardini's family have owned for centuries and which he has converted into a partly self-catering hotel-cum-conference centre and rural community. Below the *Castello* itself with its tall turreted tower are a score of red-roofed cottages that cluster round it for ramparted protection. The count has turned these village homes into bedrooms and suites, which can be hired either for a week or more on a self-catering basis, or else per night as hotel rooms. He and his wife have done the conversion most elegantly, with true Italian flair – clean stone walls, beamed ceilings, pretty rustic decor, neatly cobbled alleys.

A recent description: "You enter the village through its single great portal, surmounted by a plaque commemorating Dante's stay here in 1302 at the start of his exile from Florence. When the count inherited it, Gargonza was falling into ruin and nearly all the villagers had left. His restoration has been a labour of love, aiming at the recreation of a living community (there are concerts, exhibitions, study-groups, etc). The cottages are furnished in individual style, and there are always flowers when you arrive. Inside the village are two small gardens, one shady under pines, the other an enclosed hanging garden embellished with lemon trees and grapevines. At the foot of the old mule-track down from the village is the restaurant, whose pleasures are country ones. Calves' liver, brains, fillet of beef with green peppercorns, spatchcocked bantam and other meats grilled over charcoal are delicious. They have excellent wines, Chianti and others. In winter you eat indoors with a blazing log fire and the wrought-iron candelabra lit; on warm summer evenings you can sit in the open on the long roofed terrace above the wooded valley, with bats flitting through the rafters." Those booking just for a night or two should be warned that hotel service as such hardly exists. And cars can enter the village only for loading or unloading baggage.

Open All year except 8 Jan–2 Feb. Restaurant closed Mon.
Rooms 37 double – all with bath and/or shower, and telephone; TV on request. 30 in 18 cottages with self-catering facilities, 7 in Guest House.
Facilities Lounge, TV room, restaurant; auditorium, meeting halls, conference rooms. Large grounds with garden, children's play area, woods and farm.
Location 8 km W of Monte San Savino on SS73 towards Siena (35 km). From *autostrada* A1, exit 27, Monte San Savino is 10 km.
Restriction Not suitable for ♿.
Credit card Amex.
Terms [1989 rates] B&B 63,000–80,000 L, half board 88,000–105,000 L, full board 113,000–130,000 L. Full alc 28,000–35,000 L. 10% discount for children under 10.

GIARDINI NAXOS 98035 Messina, Sicily — Map 16

Hotel Arathena Rocks — *Tel* (0942) 51348
Via Calcide Eubea 55

In a busy seaside resort just below Taormina, this much-admired family-style traditional hotel has a central but quiet location down a private road – "a lovely peaceful place". There is much antique furniture, and doors painted with local scenes, while fresh flowers from the large garden decorate all the rooms – Signora Arcidiacono has an enthusiasm for gardening. The free-form swimming pool hewn out of lava rocks is an extra luxury, but you can also swim in the clear sea a few metres away. Recent visitors have found the place "spotless, bright and cheerful"; some have enjoyed the food, despite the lack of variety on the menus, though others have been critical. Rooms have just been redecorated: ask for one facing the sea and garden. New reports welcome.

> We should be glad to hear of some good hotels in Sardinia.

Open 1 Apr–31 Oct.
Rooms 2 suites, 40 double, 10 single – all with bath and/or shower and telephone. 3 rooms in annexe.
Facilities Lift. Lounge, TV room, 2 bars, restaurant. Gardens with sea-water swimming pool and tennis court.
Location In Naxos, 5 km S of Taormina. Hotel has minibus to take guests to Taormina.
Credit cards Access, Visa.
Terms Dinner, B&B: single 85,000–90,000 L, double 160,000–170,000 L, suite 200,000–220,000 L. Set lunch/dinner 30,000 L. Reduced rates and special meals for children.

LECCE 73100 — Map 16

Hotel Risorgimento — *Tel* (0832) 42125
Via Imperatore Augusto 19 — *Telex* 860144

The second city of Apulia (Italy's heel) has some glorious Baroque architecture, and one of the fine old buildings in its centre is this old-fashioned, slightly shabby but comfortable three-star albergo. *Rooms air-conditioned, good baths and plumbing, excellent food, anglophone manager. An oasis in a region of few good hotels. 57 rooms, most with bath or shower. B&B double 110,000 L [1989]. Recent nomination. More reports please.*

MANTUA 46100 — Map 16

Albergo San Lorenzo — *Tel* (0376) 220500
Piazza Concordia 14 — *Fax* (0376) 327194

There is a sombre quality to the flat Mantuan countryside, which may explain the melancholy of Virgil, who was born in a village nearby. Mantua itself, however, is a beautiful city, and has a grand and colourful ducal palace. The *San Lorenzo*, one of its two best hotels, is a modern building with elegant period furnishings. Recent visitors have found it comfortable, cool and very friendly: "Our room with its terracotta floor tiles was a bit austere but well decorated. The quality of the cotton sheets is amazing." "Good breakfast with first-rate coffee." Many rooms have a view of the Piazza delle Erbe and the lovely rotunda church of San Lorenzo. The hotel is quiet (if you don't count the ringing of church bells as noise). Upstairs lounge and well-kept roof-terrace. (*Endorsed this year by Mary Ann Meanwell*)

Open All year.
Rooms 3 suites, 25 double, 10 single – all with bath and/or shower, telephone, radio, TV and baby-listening.
Facilities Lift suitable for ♿. Lounges, bar, TV room. Rooftop terrace.
Location Central, in pedestrian precinct. Garage 100 metres.
Credit cards All major cards accepted.
Terms [1989 rates] B&B: single 129,000 L, double 200,000 L, suite 179,000–250,000 L. (No restaurant.)

> Important reminder: terms printed must be regarded as a rough guide only to the size of the bill to be expected at the end of your stay. For latest tariffs, check when booking.

MARINA DI CAMPO 57034 Isola d'Elba — Map 16

Hotel Montecristto

Viale Nomellini 11

Tel (0565) 976861
Fax (0565) 97597
Telex 590220

On the south coast of Elba, a mile outside the fishing port of Marina di Campo, a pleasant and efficient modern seaside hotel with big well-equipped pool and lido, large clean sandy beach, and fine views of sea and hills. Good bedrooms with balconies, superb breakfasts, helpful staff. Open 23 Mar–21 Oct. 43 rooms, all with shower, B&B double 240,000 L [1989]. No restaurant, but plenty in village. Recent nomination. More reports please.

MELE 16010 Genova — Map 16

Hotel Fado 78

Via Fado 82

Tel (010) 631802

Recommended as a congenial stopover, we said last year: a small family-run Anglo-Italian hotel on the road that runs up inland from the Riviera at Voltri, west of Genoa. "Worth a detour," adds a correspondent this year, "to enjoy Italian regional cooking at its best. Excellent dinner, a very warm welcome, comfortable beds, fresh mountain air and pleasant views." (*Peter Saynor*) An earlier report: "A gracious old building, with bedrooms in a modern extension, all have stupendous views across the valley. Mine was high and airy, with a marble floor. The owners, Gianni Canepa and his English wife Christine, gave me a courteous welcome, then a first-class dinner of crêpes and rabbit casserole with garden herbs. Lovely secluded garden. The main road is not busy, and trains are infrequent along the line down in the valley."

Open All year. Restaurant closed first 2 weeks in Sept.
Rooms 5 double, 2 single – all with bath and/or shower and telephone.
Facilities Lounge, bar, 2 dining rooms. Garden, terrace.
Location 7 km N of Voltri on SS456 to Ovada. Leave A26 motorway at Masone or Voltri.
Restrictions Not suitable for ♿.
Credit cards None accepted.
Terms Rooms: single 35,000 L, double 55,000 L. Breakfast 7,000 L. Full alc 25,000 L. Children under 2 free, under 12 half price when sharing parents' room; special meals.

MERANO 39012 Bolzano — Map 16

Hotel Fragsburg (Castel Verruca)

Via Fragsburg 3 (PO Box 210)

Tel (0473) 44071

"A beautiful hotel with delightful owner and friendly staff", says a recent visitor to this small but handsome chalet-style hotel with two names. It stands high on a hill overlooking the spa town of Merano in the Alto Adige, and is surrounded by woods, meadows and mountains, as well as its own orchards. It's only a 20-minute walk to the highest waterfall in the country. Most rooms have a balcony and meals are served on an open-air terrace in summer. The owner Hubert Ortner keeps his own bees and has fresh honey on hand. "Our annexe room was small (the only one left), but the front rooms with balcony looked exquisite. Super open-air heated pool." Others have referred to the good food (interesting à la carte), but one visitor found the local red wine poor. "We were the only non-Germans. Everyone was amicable."

Open 10 Apr–5 Nov.
Rooms 2 suites, 14 double, 2 single – all with bath and/or shower, telephone, radio and TV; many with balcony.
Facilities 2 lounges, bar, TV room, dining room; terrace for summer meals. Park with heated swimming pool, children's play area, ping-pong, chess tables.
Location 5 km NE of Merano. From Merano take road to Bolzano (Bozen), turn left towards Schenna; after 2.5 km turn right at Rametz. Hotel is 5.5 km along this road.
Restriction Not suitable for ♿.
Credit cards None accepted.
Terms B&B 50,000–60,000 L per person; dinner, B&B 60,000–90,000 L, full board 70,000–100,000 L. Set lunch/dinner 18,000–20,000 L. Reduced rates and special meals for children.

Hotel Villa Mozart *Tel* (0473) 30630
Via San Marco 26

Black and white is a dominant theme of Emmy and Andreas Hellrigl's much-admired little hotel: it extends to the china and candles on the tables, the chequered marble floors, even the towels and the brochure. The hotel is about ten minutes' walk from the town centre, approached through big iron gates that open electronically to bona fide guests. A visitor this year praised the "unsurpassed personal attention to detail" of Emmy Hellrigl. Others have written: "I cannot think of a hotel that combines luxury, good service and excellent cuisine in such abundance." "Dinner, served at 8 pm to hotel guests only, with printed dated menu cards, offered no choice (even the wines are chosen for you), but all was exquisite. Breakfast on the terrace was also excellent, the indoor pool was refreshing and the staff pleasant and polite." "The building, outside as well as in, is immaculately designed and furnished in the style of the Viennese Secession. This includes everything – carpets, curtains, door fittings, cutlery, crockery, glasses and even the waitresses' uniforms! For architects and interior designers the hotel is worth a detour." Red print and a rosette from *Michelin*, needless to say. (*Dan and Michlyne Thal*) Andreas Hellrigl, who till last year did the cooking himself, remains co-owner, but the chef is now Raimund Frötscher, whose cuisine this year has been found "light and innovative". Two distinguished British restaurateurs, who had come to Merano specially to experience the *Mozart*'s cooking, were bitterly disappointed to discover that as they were the only guests that night, they had been booked into another restaurant for dinner. We should welcome more reports.

Open Easter–2 Nov.
Rooms 8 double, 2 single – 8 with bath, 2 with shower, all with telephone, radio and TV.
Facilities Lift. Lounges, library, bar, restaurant. Large grounds with sun terrace, covered heated swimming pool, sauna, solarium.
Location Coming on main road from Bolzano, via Rome, take third street on right. Private parking.
Restriction Not suitable for ♿.
Credit card Access.

Terms B&B 147,000 L; dinner, B&B 195,000 L (excluding beverages). Extra bed in room 81,000 L. Set dinner for non-residents, by arrangement only, 110.000 L.

MILAN — Map 16

Hotel Gran Duca di York — *Tel* (02) 874863 and 874943
Via Moneta 1/a
Milan 20123

Not far from the Duomo this *Duke of York* is not oppressively grand, and medium-range in price. "A gem," says a reader this year; "the atmosphere was calm, quiet and elegant, the staff were competent, the quiet lounge had a lovely desk on which to write. My room was very small, but clean and well decorated." Others have had larger rooms and big bathrooms, and have praised the breakfast coffee, though the room where it is served is said to be no beauty. "A suit of armour outside the lift, but poor reading lights." (*GB Brook, Bettye Chambers*) No restaurant, but the fairly cheap *Al Mercanti* (super fresh fish) is five minutes' walk away. *Warning*: parking in the area is tricky, and the one-way system is such that access by car is a nightmare.

Open All year except Aug.
Rooms 33 – some with bath or shower, all with telephone and TV.
Facilities Lift. Lounge, breakfast room.
Location Central; 500 metres W of Duomo. No private parking.
Credit cards None accepted.
Terms [1989 rates] Rooms: single 80,000 L, double 116,000 L. Breakfast 10,000 L. (No restaurant.)

Hotel Manzoni — *Tel* (02) 76005700
Via Santo Spirito 20 — *Fax* (02) 784212
Milan 20121

A modern hotel, well run and fairly cheap by Milan standards, in a small side street near the Via Manzoni which leads to the Piazza della Scala and the cathedral. Difficult to reach by car, and back rooms can be noisy. Accommodation, service and breakfast generally praised. 52 rooms, all with bath and/or shower. Single 90,280 L, double 129,560–178,560 L. Breakfast 12,000 L. No restaurant. Endorsed this year, but further reports welcome.

Hotel Pierre Milano — *Tel* (02) 8056220
Via De Amicis 32 — *Fax* (02) 8052157
Milan 20123

Fairly central, about a kilometre west of the Duomo, a newly opened luxury hotel with striking decor, a mix of ancient and modern. Relaxed ambience, good cooking and buffet breakfasts. Most rooms overlook a quiet street or inner courtyard. 47 rooms, all with bath and shower. B&B double 460,000–720,000 L. Meals 60,000–70,000 L [1989]. New nomination. More reports welcome.

> Please make a habit of sending in a report as soon as possible after a visit when details are still fresh in your mind.

MONTIGNOSO 54038 Massa-Carrara — Map 16

Il Bottaccio

Tel (0585) 340031
Fax (0585) 340103
Telex 500283 PPMS

"Tucked away under a ruined castle", between Carrara and Viareggio, here's another startling new Italian discovery: "A beautiful 18th-century olive-oil mill, converted with Italian style and panache into a charming sophisticated restaurant with just five incredible rooms. The spectacular restaurant is beside a cascading fountain with pools: our ten-course *menu degustazione* was fantastic, fully deserving its *Michelin* rosette. Service was by the owner and his wife. The delicious breakfast was equally impressive. And so was our vast room, containing an original mill wheel and a Roman-style sunken bath. The tiled floor had exotic rugs and on the walls were pictures which looked as if they should have been in a museum. Our large modern black steel-framed four-poster had a silk embroidered bedspread; on an antique Arabian chest stood bottles of cognac, grappa, etc. It was all an amazingly successful blending of ancient and modern. The bathroom, covered with tiny mosaic tiles and hand-painted antique tiles, was also fantastic. There's a Roman pavement in the garden, and a beautiful terrace. It was the most expensive night we have ever had anywhere: but worth it." (*Pat and Jeremy Temple*)

Open All year.
Rooms 5 suites – all with bath and telepone.
Facilities Hall, restaurant. Garden; terrace.
Location Montignoso is 5 km SE of Massa: leave Genova-Livorno Autostrada at exit 12.
Credit cards All major cards accepted.
Terms [1989 rates] Suites: 300,000–450,000 L. Breakfast 20,000 L. Set lunch/dinner 60,000–80,000 L.

ORVIETO 05018 Terni — Map 16

Hotel Virgilio

Tel (0763) 41882
Piazza del Duomo 5/6

Facing the side of the glorious Duomo, this is "the kind of small city hotel one always hopes to find but rarely does", according to an inspector. "On the outside it is an unspoiled and shuttered old building, inside it is designed and furnished in good modern Italian style – gleaming chrome, white and pink marble. In the reception area, a large piece of Roman sculpture is flanked by good contemporary original drawings; a beautiful old tapestry is hung alongside delightful puppets. Our room had a side view of the Duomo's richly decorated front. The bedroom was not large but attractively furnished, with a big bed, and the bathroom was elegant. Breakfast, as in most Italian hotels, was minimal and expensive. This apart, the hotel is marvellous value. Ask for room 15. Parking under trees across the square." No restaurant, but the *Maurizio*, close by, is recommended. (*Elizabeth Ring*)

Open All year except 20 days in Jan.
Rooms 14 double, 2 single – all with bath, 2 also have shower, all with telephone. 2 doubles in annexe 20 metres away. Some ground-floor rooms.
Facilities Lift. Bar, TV room.

Location Central, near *Duomo*. Parking.
Credit cards None accepted.
Terms B&B: single 60,000 L, double 90,000 L. (No restaurant.)

PALESTRINA 00036 Rome — Map 16

Albergo Stella — *Tel* (06) 9558172 and 9558637
Piazzale della Liberazione 3

The 16th-century composer Palestrina was born in this ancient town that bears his name, set in the lovely hills east of Rome: it contains the ruins of a classical Roman temple dedicated to Fortune. A visitor this year returned to the modern and unpretentious *Stella*, found the food as excellent as before ("antipasto a meal in itself, Easter lamb roast to perfection") and confirms his earlier view: "There in the tiny piazza is this delightful hotel, its restaurant very popular with locals. We loved the place. Our room was large and clean, the bathroom modern, and only the church clock disturbed the peace. Ideal as a night stop." (*Paul Palmer*)

Open All year.
Rooms 1 suite, 14 double – all with bath and/or shower, and telephone.
Facilities Lift. Lounges, bar, restaurant. Public park next door.
Location Central. Town is 38 km E of Rome, off S6 to Frosinone. Public parking.
Credit cards Amex, Diners, Visa.
Terms Rooms: single 26,000 L, double 45,000 L, suite 90,000 L. Breakfast 5,000 L. Full board 55,000–65,000 L. Set lunch 18,000–25,000 L, dinner 23,000–30,000 L; full alc 23,000–30,000 L. Reduced rates for children under 7.

PANZANO IN CHIANTI 50020 Florence — Map 16

Villa Le Barone — *Tel* (055) 852215
Via San Leolino 19

A former home of the famous Della Robbia family, this graceful villa stands high on a hilltop between Florence and Siena. It has a swimming pool, and spread out below it is the hilly Tuscan landscape of vineyards, olive groves and cypresses. The Duchessa Visconti is the present owner of what is now a sophisticated *pensione*, retaining the atmosphere of a cared-for private home. Most rooms are elegantly furnished with good antiques, carefully arranged flowers and fine linen sheets. Two reports this year describe the *Villa* as "delightful" and praise the food highly, whereas some earlier visitors have found it too "bland and international" (to suit the mainly Anglo-American and German clientele?). But all agree that the public rooms are charming and the staff discreetly helpful. The "honour system" with the evening drinks is also admired. (*R Andresen, Joan Haslip*)

Open 1 Apr–1 Nov.
Rooms 26 double, 1 single – 21 with bath, 6 with shower; 3 with tea-making facilities. 17 in 3 different garden annexes. Some ground-floor rooms.
Facilities 4 sitting rooms (1 with TV), bar, breakfast room, dining room. 5-acre grounds with swimming pool and table-tennis.
Location Off SS 222 to Siena, 31 km S of Florence. Hotel is SE of Panzano.
Credit card Amex.
Terms On application.

Give the Guide positive support. Don't just leave feedback to others.

Hotel Villa Sangiovese *Tel* (055) 852461
Piazza Bucciarelli 5

Uri and Anna Maria Bleuler, from Switzerland, were till recently managers of the much-admired *Tenuta di Ricavo* in nearby Castellina (q.v.), and now they have opened their own hotel which enters the Guide as our second entry for this little town south of Florence: "The villa lies on the edge of the town, surrounded by the beautiful steep Tuscan hills where cypresses, olives and vines grow. It is an old stone house, remodelled and restored, with terraces offering fine views of countryside which comes right up to the edge of its own grounds. The Bleulers' welcome could not have been kinder, and it is clear that they are aiming to create a homely atmosphere combined with Swiss efficiency. The comfortable public rooms are decorated mainly in soft yellows and fawns to give a cool, cheerful atmosphere. You can dine on the terrace when it's fine. Our bedroom, not large, was simply furnished with meticulous attention to detail – excellent bedside lamps. A Florentine cook produces a limited à la carte menu: the dishes change nightly and all were good. Breakfast with excellent Swiss-style coffee is served in an attractive small room." "Beautiful rooms, food simple and excellent, staff friendly" is another 1989 report. An outdoor unheated pool is planned for 1990. (*Margaret and Charles Baker, Wendy Geiringer*)

Open All year except Feb. Restaurant closed Wed.
Rooms 3 suites, 16 double – all with bath and/or shower, telephone.
Facilities 2 lounges, bar, restaurant; terrace. Garden.
Swimming pool planned for 1990.
Location Parking. Bus to Florence, which is 31 km to N.
Restrictions Not suitable for ♿.
Credit cards None accepted.
Terms [1989 rates] B&B: double: 95,000–160,000 L, suite 160,000–210,000 L. Alc meals 30,000–35,000 L. Reduced rates and special meals for children.

PERUGIA 06100 Map 16

Hotel La Rosetta *Tel* (075) 20841
Piazza Italia 19 *Telex* 563271

A reader this year who spent all August at *La Rosetta* thought the staff friendly and the food excellent, and especially enjoyed eating out in the attractive shady courtyard. Other recent visitors, too, have found it comfortable and efficient and have praised the cooking. "We had a quiet and cool room over the dining courtyard; service was excellent." "The decor is not always alluring – our bathroom in shiny bronze was a bit much – but the bedrooms were large." The hotel enjoys a prime situation at the top of the main street, Corso Vanucci, but this is where Perugia's nightly *passeggiata* takes place – and one reader warns that "this non-stop cocktail party" makes sleep in the front rooms difficult – "bring earplugs, or ask for rooms at the back, which are less attractive". (*David C Craig*)

Open All year.
Rooms 7 suites, 60 double, 32 single – 96 with bath/shower, all with telephone, radio, TV and baby-listening. Some ground-floor rooms.
Facilities Lift. Salons, bar, games room, reading room, restaurant; conference/banqueting facilities. Courtyard where meals are served in fine weather.

Location Central; some traffic noise. Parking and 2 garages (extra charge).
Credit cards Access, Amex, Visa.
Terms [1989 rates] Rooms: single 60,000 L, double 110,000–140,000 L, suite 140,000–190,000 L. Breakfast 8,000 L. Half board 85,000–130,000 L per person. Set meals 33,000–38,000 L; full alc 38,000–40,000 L. Reduced rates and special meals for children.

PETTENASCO 28028 Novara — Map 16

Hotel Giardinetto

Via Provinciale 1, Lago d'Orta

Tel (0323)-89118 and 89219
Fax (0323) 89483
Telex 200206 SIMTUR

A sizeable modern white-walled hotel, family-run, in a superb position on the shore of little Lake Orta, a busy summer resort. "Our room faced the lake, and we sat on its terrace watching the sunset. Meals were exceptional." "Friendly informal service, and a fantastic Thursday dinner buffet." "Excellent breakfast." Those three reports this year back up earlier praise for the seafood buffet, the swimming pool, and the watchfulness of the owners, Oreste and Caterina Primatesta. However, service was sharply criticised by one reader this year. Rooms facing the road are rather dark and noisy, lake-facing ones are quieter and have a better view, notably those in a new wing with balconies. (*Brian MacArthur, Arnold and Joan Wolfe, Barbara Hill*)

Open Easter–end Oct.
Rooms 2 suites, 45 double, 7 single – all with bath and/or shower (2 with jacuzzi), telephone and baby-listening; 2 with tea-making facilities; TV on request.
Facilities Lift, ramps. Lounge, 2 bars, TV room, restaurant, coffee shop; conference room; gala evening with dancing Thur in summer; indoor swimming pool and sauna; terrace on lake.Garden with heated swimming pool, children's playground; table tennis.
Location 4 km S of Orta San Giulio. Hotel is 500 metres from town centre, on lake shore. Private parking.
Credit cards Probably Access, Amex, Visa.
Terms B&B: single 53,000–58,000 L, double 168,000–188,000 L, suite 220,000–240,000 L. Dinner, B&B 44,000–69,000 L per person; full board 54,000–75,000 L. Set lunch 25,000 L, dinner 30,000 L; full alc 45,000 L. Reduced rates and special meals for children.

POMPONESCO 46030 Mantova — Map 16

Trattoria Il Leone

Piazza IV Martiri 2

Tel (0375) 86077

An enthusiastic 1989 nomination for this stylish trattoria-with-rooms beside the river Po, between Parma and Mantua, "In a distinctly uncharming village of the Po valley we found this hotel of idiosyncratic charm, with excellent food. It fronts onto the street, giving no outward clue to its inner delights – antiques and bric-à-brac everywhere, chaotically organised, and at the back a tiled courtyard with swimming pool and white garden furniture. In the ornately decorated dining room (strange blue-tinted frieze of classical scenes just below the beamed ceiling), we were served by members of the family, charmingly concerned that we should enjoy our meal. And we did – delicious fish salad with salmon, trout and octopus; a rich ravioli; wild duck with fruit, marvellously tender; and a tempting sweet trolley. Oddly, there were no prices on the menu (we were told this was their custom); but we found them to be very fair. The weak spot of the place is the bedrooms, a bit basic, but with modern bathrooms, and comfortable enough for a night stop at what is essentially a restaurant." (*Philippa and Peter Herbert*) More reports eagerly awaited.

Open All year except Jan. Restaurant closed Sun evening and Mon.
Rooms 5 double, 3 single – all with bath/shower, telephone and baby-listening.
Facilities Lounges, bar, restaurant, TV room; conference room. Garden with swimming pool.
Location In village, which is 32 km from Parma, 38 km from Mantova, off S 420.
Credit cards All major cards accepted.
Terms [1989 rates] B&B 40,000 L; dinner, B&B 65,000 L. Full alc 40,000 L. Reduced rates for children.

PORTO ERCOLE 58018 Grosseto — Map 16

Hotel Il Pellicano — *Tel* (0564) 833801
Cala dei Santi — *Fax* (0564) 833418
Telex 500131 PELICAN

A stylish and very expensive hotel in a lovely rocky coastal setting, unspoilt by mass tourism. "Impossible to find fault after an idyllic week", writes one devotee this year, while another confirms his earlier lyrical words, "Beautiful rooms, furnishings with lots of glamour, classy bar service, but patchy food. Nadia and Ennio Emili, a young couple, bring an Italian warmth to their very personal style of management. Our room, its vast terrace lined with pots of geraniums, looked out across the gardens and up to the mountain on one side, on the other over tiled roofs to the pool and sea. Breakfast included a glass of delicious red orange juice. The hotel is scrupulously maintained in first-class nick. The gardens are similarly immaculate, and the staff efficient and welcoming. The cooking is honest Tuscan, using first-class fresh produce." The cheaper rooms above the garden are said to be less nice than the sea-facing ones. If you want to bathe in the sea be prepared to walk down ninety steps. (*David Wooff, EE Hunt*) One report this year speaks of "friendly efficiency". But one well-known British hotelier found the staff grossly inefficient when adding up the bill, and thought the prices exorbitant, so we'd welcome more reports.

Open 12 Apr–Oct.
Rooms 4 suites, 30 double – all with bath, shower and telephone; TV and radio on request. 9 in annexe, 7 in cottages.
Facilities Lounge, TV room, bar, restaurant; conference facilities; terrace; dinner-dance Fri July and Aug. Large grounds with restaurant, heated swimming pool with bar and barbecue, tennis, rocky beach with safe bathing, water-skiing.
Location 4.5 km S of Porto Ercole on Monte Argentario coast. Parking.
Restrictions Not suitable for ♿. No children under 12.
Credit cards All major cards accepted.
Terms Double room 180,000–495,000 L, suite 600,000–900,000 L. Breakfast 25,000 L. Dinner, B&B 185,000–545,000 L per person; full board 255.000–615,000 L.

If you have kept brochures and tariffs for Continental hotels, do please enclose them with your reports.

POSITANO 84017 Salerno — Map 16

Hotel Casa Albertina — *Tel* (089) 875143
Via della Tavolozza 3 — *Fax* (089) 811540

"The fabulous view of Positano that you have from every room" is just one of the qualities that draws readers again and again to Michele Cinque's medium-priced hotel in a justly renowned but expensive resort. The lobby and lounges have cool white walls and vaulted ceilings, while the rooms and dining room are decorated in pastels. "We were received with style and warmth, and had one of the best breakfasts ever", is one report this year, while another mentions a very good, simple meal enjoyed on the terrace facing the sea. "Style, intimacy, friendliness, great quality and good value. Grandmother cooks – 'you eat what we eat' – and it is perfect Italian *cuisine paysanne*. Quiet, the rustle of the sea, spotless tiled bedrooms, clean sheets every other day – and cheap, by Positano prices." The best rooms are on the first floor, but the quietest are the smaller top-floor ones. Drinks charges are high, and parking costs 20,000 lire a day extra. (*Tex and Hella Sessoms*)

Open All year.
Rooms 2 suites, 18 double, 1 single – all with bath and/or shower and telephone, 2 with air-conditioning.
Facilities Lift. Sitting room, TV room, bar, dining room, open-air restaurant; terraces. 10 mins' walk to beach.
Location Central, but quietly situated. Parking 300 metres.
Credit cards All major cards accepted.
Terms B&B: single 90,000 L, double 130,000 L, suite 190,000 L; dinner B&B 90,000–125,000 L per person. Reduced rates for children.

PRAIANO 84010 Salerno — Map 16

Hotel Tramonto d'Oro — *Tel* (089) 874008
Via Gennaro Capriglione — *Telex* 720397

In a small resort on the glorious coast between Amalfi and Positano, here's a spruce modern hotel in a splendid setting high above the sea. Most rooms have balconies with sea views. Swimming pool on roof; bus service down to the beach. Friendly staff. 50 rooms, all with bath and shower. B&B single 50,000 L, double 80,000 L. Set menu 20,000 L. New nomination. More reports please.

RANCO 21020 Varese — Map 16

Del Sole — *Tel* (0331) 976507
Piazza Venezia 5 — *Fax* (0331) 976620

In a village at the south-east end of Lake Maggiore, the Brovelli family run a well-known stylish restaurant (two *Michelin* rosettes) that has recently added six smart modern bedrooms, and is brought to the Guide this year by two connoisseurs: "One of North Italy's best restaurants. It is charmingly situated by the lake's edge, with views over the harbour and across to the shore opposite. The restaurant is most attractive, with a huge chandelier and fresh flowers; there's a large terrace, too, for summer eating. The food is superb: a small menu with specialities that change daily (including fish from the lake), and an excellent wine list. Breakfast is also very good, served on the terrace in summer. Service was charming and friendly. The bedrooms are split-level, cleverly designed to obtain maximum space, and with good modern furniture. Highly recommended." (*Pat and Jeremy Temple*)

Open 10 Feb–1 Jan, closed 25 Dec. Restaurant closed Mon evening and Tue except public holidays.
Rooms 7 suites, 1 double, 1 single – 6 with bath, 3 with shower, all with telephone, TV and mini-bar.
Facilities Lounge, bar, restaurant; functions room. Terrace where meals are served, garden.
Location 67 km NW of Milan. Parking.
Restrictions Not suitable for ♿.
Credit cards All major cards accepted.
Terms B&B: double 150,000 L, suite 180,000–200,000 L; dinner, B&B 140,000–160,000 L per person. Set lunch/dinner 75,000–90,000 L; full alc 80,000–100,000 L. Reduced rates for children.

RAVELLO 84010 Salerno — Map 16

Hotel Giordano e Villa Maria

Via Santa Chiara 2 — *Tel* (089) 857170 and 857255 — *Fax* (089) 857071

Two small adjacent hotels, both very attractive, run jointly by the Palumbo family. Villa Maria *is a converted private villa, with large bedrooms, nice terrace.* Giordano *has a swimming pool, and shady garden for summer dining. Elegant furnishings, lovely views. 19 rooms, all with bath and/or shower. B&B double 76,000–90,000 L. Set menus 35,000 L. Recent nomination. More reports welcome.*

Hotel Marmorata

Strada Statale 163 — *Tel* (089) 877777 — *Telex* 720667 HOTMAR

Again this year judged "very beautiful" and "excellent in every way", the *Marmorata*, which was once a paper mill, is four miles from Ravello itself, nestled in the cliff face beneath the coastal road to Amalfi. "Good varied food, helpful staff, excellent bedrooms"; "the cool, restful interiors designed in the style of a ship, the seafront terraces and the friendly, helpful service are simply superb. The food was well cooked and presented. There is a steep slope from the road down to the hotel and about 30 steps down to sea level, so not suitable for the infirm." "My cabin-like room had a simple stylishness which combined superbly with its fine view of the sea." One recent visitor found the staff and the Signora most helpful, but adds, "It's on the English package-tour circuit, which means they play very safe with the food. Nonetheless, a super place to stay, but the parking is horrific." (*PA Bispham, Mrs MP Richards*) It is essential to ask for a room with a sea view: others have no view at all.

Open All year. Restaurant closed 31 Oct–30 Apr.
Rooms 5 suites, 36 double, 3 single – 3 with bath, 36 with shower, all with telephone, radio, TV, mini-bar and air-conditioning.
Facilities Hall, lounge, 2 bars, restaurant. Small grounds with terraces down to sea, sea-water swimming pool, private rocky beach with safe bathing and fishing.

Location 1 km W of Minori, 3 km E of Amalfi, 300 metres off the road to Ravello. Parking.
Restriction Not suitable for ♿.
Credit cards All major cards accepted.
Terms B&B: single 103,000–139,000 L, double 165,000–231,000 L; half board 110,000–171,000 L per person; full board 143,000–193,000 L. Set lunch/dinner 45,000 L; full alc 55,000 L. Reduced rates and special meals for children.

Hotel Palumbo
Via S. Giovanni del Toro 28

Tel (089) 857244
Fax (089) 857347
Telex 770101 VUILLE

Pasquale Vuilleumier's startlingly beautiful hotel, much liked again this year for its "old world charm", has a strange story attached to it. In the mid-19th century his grandfather, from Switzerland, bought a 12th-century episcopal palace up the road and on the advice of Wagner (who was writing bits of *Parsifal* in a nearby villa) turned it into a hotel. Over the years his guests there included Longfellow, Grieg, DH Lawrence (he worked on *Lady Chatterley* in one of the rooms), Garbo, Bogart and the Kennedys. But about seven years ago Signor Vuilleumier transferred the hotel to his own residence, the Palazzo Confalone, also 12th-century. The original *Palumbo* is now deserted save for its illustrious ghosts, but the newer *Palumbo* he has converted with exquisite taste. Its high-ceilinged central foyer is a miracle of cool white arches, plants and flowers, and vistas of the azure sea far below. The canopied dining room terrace and the lemon-tree-shaded lounge terrace have the same miraculous view. "The most romantic place I have ever stayed in. The view from our bedroom balcony was breath-taking, literally between sea and sky, and the bedroom itself was stunning with its blue and white tiles. Signor Vuilleumier, now in his seventies, was very amiable although regretting the grandeur of the past." "The food was above average, the staff very courteous, and the Signor ever present", adds a reader this year. (*Miss EH Nicholls*)

Open All year.
Rooms 3 suites, 17 double – all with bath and shower, telephone, TV and baby-listening. 7 in annexe 50 yards from main building.
Facilities Salons, bar, TV lounge, restaurant; sun terrace. Garden; solarium. Beaches 10–15 mins by car.
Location Above the Amalfi Drive, overlooking Ravello. Parking.
Restriction Not suitable for ♿.
Credit cards Access, Visa.
Terms Dinner, B&B 201,000–319,000 L per person; full board 210,000–350,000 L. Set lunch/dinner 55,000 L; full alc 70,000 L. Reduced rates and special meals for children.

Hotel Parsifal
Via G. d'Anna 5

Tel (089) 857144

This delectable hotel is much cheaper than most of our other Ravello choices: "Not grand, but clean, cool, restful and very beautiful. The hotel is built around parts of a 13th-century Augustinian monastery, and has a cloister and flowery garden, with a pool overflowing with fish. Views from our room, from the garden and restaurant were sensational, and the food was almost as good (but breakfast not so hot). The bed was the most comfortable we found in Italy and the towels the thickest." Pastel shades, and a lovely outdoor terrace above the sea. Guests can use the swimming pool at *Le Terrazze* free of charge.

Open 1 Apr–15 Oct. Closed Tue.
Rooms 19 – all with bath and/or shower, and telephone.
Facilities Salon, restaurant. Cloister. Garden.
Location Fairly central. Parking.
Restriction Not suitable for ♿.
Credit cards All major cards accepted.
Terms [1989 rates] Rooms: single 30,000–37,000 L, double 44,000–56,000 L. Breakfast 7,000 L. Set lunch/dinner 28,000 L; full alc 30,000 L. Reduced rates and special meals for children.

RIVA DI SOLTO 24060 Bergamo — Map 16

Albergo-Ristorante Miranda "da Oreste" — *Tel* (035) 986021
Via Cornello 8

The attractive but little-known Lake Iseo lies amid hills and olive groves to the east of Bergamo, and high up on its western shore is this white modern villa: "A family-run hotel with glorious views above the lake. Bedrooms are clean, well lit, with spacious wardrobes, and many have a balcony. The food is simple but well cooked (*Michelin* red *Pas* for good value), and the menu is discussed with guests. Efficient and friendly service. Picnics are readily provided. Pleasant swimming pool down a steep path in the garden." More reports please.

Open All year except 15 Jan–15 Feb. Restaurant closed to non-residents Tue in winter.
Rooms 3 suites, 11 double, 3 single – 6 with bath and shower.
Facilities Lounge with TV, restaurant. Terrace, garden with swimming pool.
Location In centre of village 40 km E of Bergamo.
Credit cards None accepted.
Terms Rooms: single 22,000 L, double 43,450 L. Breakfast 6,000 L. Half board 38,000 L per person, full board 45,000 L. Set lunch 35,000 L, dinner 40,000 L. Full alc 35,000–40,000 L. Reduced rates for children; special meals on request.

ROME — Map 16

Hotel Cesàri — *Tel* (06) 6792386 and 6790882
Via di Pietra 89a, Rome 00186 — *Telex* 623300

This "tremendous bargain", just off the strident via del Corso, has been a hotel since the early 18th century, and former guests – says its brochure – have included Stendhal, Mazzini and Garibaldi. But, though it was once a palace, today it is a modest and quite low-priced hotel, rating just one gable in *Michelin*. "This is as near as you will get in central Rome to a *Relais du Silence*: we had a pleasant room overlooking the small street, but as it is a cul-de-sac the curse of the Lambretta is relieved. The phones would have been instantly recognisable to Alexander Graham Bell, and the lift reminded me of Fellini's *Giulietta degli Spiriti*, but it did work. The beds were comfortable and the staff charming. Breakfast was typical of Italy – delicious *hot* coffee with UHT milk pulverised to atoms and reconstituted à la milk-shake, fresh rolls like cannon-balls and revolting soggy buns tasting of some chemical." Visitors this year and last have agreed – about the charming staff, good value, *and* the breakfasts. (*Bettye Chambers*)

Open All year.
Rooms 40 double, 10 single – all with bath and/or shower, and telephone.
Facilities Lift. Lounge, TV room, bar.
Location Central, off via del Corso. Free parking in piazza di Pietra.
Credit cards All major cards accepted.
Terms B&B: single 91,000 L, double 133,000 L. 10% reduction for children under 10. (No restaurant.)

Hotel Forum
Via Tor de' Conti 25–30
Rome 00184

Tel (06) 6792446
Fax (06) 6799337
Telex 622549

A solid classic ochre-coloured building, fairly smart and upper-medium in price. As its name implies, it is very close to the Foro Romano, but tucked away down a small street. And it has an attractive rooftop restaurant and bar. "The ideal place to stay in Rome if you want to explore the pagan monuments and leave the Christian ones alone. The lobby, all polished wood, period furniture, and bits of Roman wall and marble column, offers a welcome respite. There is a clubby, aristocratic, but far from stuffy, atmosphere in the public areas that is appealing. Rooms are on the small side, but ours was clean and comfortable: two sets of shutters and two sets of curtains proved an adequate baffle against the noise of Rome. The service is obliging. But prices are fairly steep." Following that earlier report, a visitor this year thought the service poor and food only average, so we'd welcome other verdicts.

Open All year. Restaurant closed Sun.
Rooms 79 – all with bath or shower, telephone, radio, TV and baby-listening.
Facilities Hall, bar, TV room, panoramic restaurant; meeting rooms; roof-garden.
Restriction Not suitable for ♿.
Location Central, just E of Via dei Fori Imperiali and Forum. Garage
Credit cards All major cards accepted.
Terms [1989 rates] Rooms: single 140,000–230,000 L, double 230,000–330,000 L. Breakfast 20,000 L. Alc (excluding wine) from 65,000 L. Winter discounts. 20% reduction for children sharing parents' room; special meals.

Hotel Gregoriana
Via Gregoriana 18
Rome 00187

Tel (06) 6794269

A former convent near the top of the Spanish steps has been turned into a clean and sophisticated little hotel with friendly staff and owners; it has unusual decor – a landing with black satin walls and leopard-skin cushions. Despite its location it is fairly quiet, especially rooms at the back (there is some street noise in front); a few upper rooms look out over roof-gardens and orange and lemon trees. Some readers find bedrooms too small and the lack of lounge a drawback, but generally these earlier views are confirmed: "Our room was generous and comfortable in a mixture of Erté and American Chinese, with a big, sunny bathroom in blues and mauves." "No frills offered, but one gets what one pays for: peace and quiet in a prime locality, combined with unpretentious, professional service." Book well ahead. (*Dr DM Keyzer, I Zetterström*)

Open All year.
Rooms 16 double, 3 single – 12 with bath, 7 with shower, all with telephone; TV on request. 4 ground-floor rooms.
Facilities Lift. Hall.
Location Central, above Spanish Steps. Parking.
Credit cards None accepted.
Terms [1989 rates] B&B: single 110,000 L, double 170,000 L. Reduced rates for children. (No restaurant.)

Hotel La Residenza
Via Emilia 22
Rome 00187

Tel (06) 463271 and 460789
Fax (06) 485721
Telex 410423 GIOTEL attn La Residenza

"A true gem, and excellent value," says an American visitor this year about this small but quite luxurious hotel, nicely located around the corner from the Via Veneto and near the Villa Borghese. Everyone speaks well of the friendly staff, the breakfast buffet, the comfortable rooms and pleasing decor. Some rooms however are quite small, and the hotel faces a night-club which could be noisy; rooms at the back are preferable. No restaurant: but there are good ones in the area, such as the small family-run *Tempio di Bacco*, via Lombardia. (*Arnold H Wolfe, and others*)

Open All year.
Rooms 7 suites, 17 double, 3 single – 24 with bath, 3 with shower, all with telephone, radio, TV and mini-bar.
Facilities 2 lounges, bar, breakfast room; terrace and patio.
Location Central, near the Via Veneto and American Embassy (back rooms quietest). Parking.
Restriction Not suitable for ♿.
Credit cards None accepted.
Terms [1989 rates] B&B: single 95,000 L, double 170,000 L, suite 190,000 L. (No restaurant.)

SAN GIMIGNANO 53037 Siena — Map 16

Bel Soggiorno
Via S. Giovanni 91

Tel (0577) 40375
Fax (0577) 940375

A lovely 13th-century building, just inside the ramparts of this splendid little medieval Tuscan town, famous for its 14 slender towers rising above the rooftops. Apart from one complaint of an indifferent meal, again this year every *soggiorno* reported to us has been *bello*, with service, food and fair prices all commended. The top floor of the hotel is to be avoided if possible: hot, and noisy with plumbing. The remaining rooms, though small, are adequate, some with terraces and most with magnificent views. There is a TV salon but no garden, and if hot water is a priority, you had better think twice; otherwise, "a good find"! On the unchanging but "excellent" menu, readers especially admire "a delicious first course called trittico" and "pollo al diavolo which comes aflame". From the wide windows, the views of the Tuscan hills and olive groves are spectacular." (*Richard Osborne, G Evans, RW Baker*)

Open All year. Restaurant closed Mon.
Rooms 25 double, 2 single – all with bath, shower and telephone.
Facilities Lift. Salon with TV, bar, restaurant. Terrace.
Location 30 km from Siena; cars allowed in for loading and unloading only. Carpark nearby (10,000 L per day).
Restrictions Not suitable for ♿. No children under 8.
Credit cards All major cards accepted.
Terms [1989 rates] B&B: single occupancy 48,000–55,000 L, double 68,000–73,000 L. Full board 90,000–95,000 L per person.

Hotel La Cisterna *Tel* (0577) 940328
Piazza della Cisterna 23 *Telex* 575152 HOTCIS

"We had to share a bathroom, but waking up to look down into the square of San Gimignano was a real treat", runs one of many favourable 1988/9 reports on this 14th-century ivy-clad *palazzo*. It fronts the animated main piazza, and many rooms have balconies facing either this scene or the wide Tuscan landscape. Rooms are quite large, some simple, some more interesting with painted furniture, and service is mostly friendly. There's a splendid church-like lounge, and a beamed restaurant with stunning panoramic views. The food used to be poor: but a new chef has arrived and the cooking is much improved, say several readers this year. (*Gerald Campion, Daniel and Pamela Waley, ATW Liddell, and others*)

Open 10 Mar–10 Nov. Restaurant closed Tue and Wed midday.
Rooms 50 – all with bath and/or shower and telephone. 4 rooms share a balcony overlooking the town. 9 ground-floor rooms.
Facilities Lift. 14th-century salon, salon with TV, bar, 3 dining rooms. Garden.
Location Central. Cars allowed in for loading and unloading only. Paying car park 400 metres.
Credit cards All major cards accepted.
Terms [1989 rates] B&B: single 54,000–58,000 L, double 86,000–93,000 L; dinner, B&B 72,000–84,000 L per person. Set meals 26,000 L; full alc 38,000–50,000 L.

Le Renaie *Tel* (0577) 955044
Pancole

A quiet rural hotel with lovely views over the Tuscan hills, outside the hamlet of Pancole, just north of San Gimignano. "There's nothing grand about it, but nor is it scruffy or second-rate", runs a 1989 report; "the decor is light and gay, our bedroom was spacious and comfortable. We dined out on the terrace by candle-light: the food was good honest Tuscan, very good value, e.g. wild boar casserole and pork tenderloin in herbs and Chianti. Our only quibble is that the owners, a father and son it seems, do not stamp their personality on the place – it lacks a woman's touch." "Breakfast on the terrace was enjoyable." Many rooms have a balcony, and there's a cool lounge in modern design, also a swimming pool. The cooking is preferred to our other San Gimignano entries. (*Philippa Herbert; Betsy C Maestro*)

Open All year except 10 Nov–2 Dec. Restaurant closed Tue.
Rooms 24 double, 2 single – all with bath/shower and telephone; TV on request.
Facilities Lounge with TV, bar, restaurant. Terrace, garden with swimming pool.
Location 5 km N of San Gimignano towards Certaldo. Parking.
Restriction Not suitable for ♿.
Credit cards All major cards accepted.

Terms [1989 rates] Rooms: single 48,000 L, double 68,000–74,000 L. Breakfast 6,500 L. Dinner, B&B 64,000 L per person. Full alc 25,000–30,000 L. Reduced rates and special meals for children.

SAN GREGORIO 06081 Perugia — Map 16

Castel San Gregorio — *Tel* (075) 8038009

"Man enters into this magic place with his soul", proclaims the brochure of this Guide newcomer – and also, we suggest, with his sense of humour and conviviality. It's a creeper-covered crenellated neo-Gothic castle, set amid vines and parkland between Assisi and Perugia, overlooking the plain. "Fairly eccentric, but delightfully so", says its nominator; "it's a peaceful, rambling place with varied, well-furnished bedrooms. The dining room has one big table where you all dine together, chatting to your neighbours: food ranges from the very good to the pedestrian, and is washed down by good local cheap wine. We thought the *Castel* bliss and can't wait to get back." (*W Ian Stewart*) Some rooms have antique beds, others have four-posters with medieval-style linen drapes; the bathrooms in the towers are circular. Beamed ceilings, spiral stairways, fancy atmospheric lighting all add to the ambience. More reports, we beg you.

Open All year except 15–30 Jan.
Rooms 12 – all with bath and/or shower and telephone.
Facilities Reading room, dining room. Small garden.
Location 13 km NW of Assisi.
Restrictions Not suitable for ♿.
Credit cards Access, Amex, Diners.
Terms [1989 rates] Rooms 47,000–66,000 L. Breakfast 6,000 L. Full board 94,000 L per person. Set meals 30,000 L

SAN MAMETE 22010 Como — Map 16

Hotel Stella d'Italia — *Tel* (0344) 68139
Piazza Roma 1 — *Fax* (0344) 68729
(postal address: PO Box 46
San Mamete, Valsolda
6976 Castagnola, Switzerland)

Right on Lake Lugano and close to the Swiss border, this "gem of a place" (a report this year) has a very special quality. Its English-speaking owners, the Ortellis, have been running it for decades, and have won a faithful clientele, many of them English. The bedrooms, each with its own balcony on which you can breakfast, have views across the lake to the green slopes and mountains in the distance. There is a garden leading down to a "lido" for swimming or sun-bathing. In good weather, dinner is served on the pretty trellised terrace, with the water at one's feet, but the indoor dining room also has fine views.

Visitors this year have commented especially on the good cooking and very reasonable prices, though one or two have found the upkeep less than perfect (little things like inadequate clothes-hangers). An earlier view, "The un-Italian aura is more than compensated for by the fat delights of the beautiful veranda restaurant, the attentive service, the tranquil lido by the lake and a library which must have the largest collection of Warwick Deeping in north Italy." Some have found the *en pension* food is a little plain and boring. (*Mary and Harold Larsen, Dorys and Murray Bernbaum, BJ Walters*)

Open Apr–Oct.
Rooms 31 double, 5 single – 23 with bath, 13 with shower, all with telephone and balcony.
Facilities 2 lounges, bar, restaurant. Garden with restaurant. Lake bathing, fishing, surfing, boating.
Location 10 km NE of Lugano on Lake Lugano between Gandria and Menaggio. Garage for 14 cars.
Restriction Not suitable for ♿.
Credit cards All major cards accepted.
Terms B&B: single 57,000 L, double 88,000 L; dinner, B&B 69,000–71,000 L per person; full board 77,000–79,000 L. Set lunch/dinner 27,000 L; full alc 30,000–40,000 L. Reduced rates and special meals for children.

SAN PAOLO 39050 Bolzano — Map 16

Hotel Schloss Korb — *Tel* (0471) 633222
Missiano

West of Bolzano, in a marvellous open setting amid terraced vineyards and fortress-crowned rocky hills, a medieval castle very stylishly converted – beamed ceilings, rough stone walls, strange statuary. Quaint and pretty bedrooms, those in the tower specially recommended. Hearty Tyrolean food. Indoor and outdoor swimming pools, sauna, sun terrace, floodlit tennis courts. Open Apr–5 Nov. 56 rooms, all with bath and shower. B&B 65,000–70,000 L; half board 90,000–95,000 L. Set menu 40,000 L [1989]. Enticing new nomination. More reports eagerly requested.

SANTA MARIA DI CASTELLABATE 84048 Salerno — Map 16

Hotel Sonia — *Tel* (0974) 961172

On the edge of an old fishing-port 45 miles south of Salerno, and only 15 miles from the Greek temples of Paestum, this unpretentious little seaside hotel has been enjoyed by a correspondent who spent a happy beach holiday there with her eight-year-old son: "We went in May, which was lovely as it was not too crowded. The family owners are very kind and Italian in their attitudes to children, and fed my son, who is fussy about food, masses of chips and pasta. The food is very plain, which suited me fine. The rooms, too, are simple but nice, some facing the village square, some the sea. I was able to sit on my balcony and watch my son on the beach. A quiet, civilised place." Deckchairs and umbrellas on the sandy beach, free of charge to guests. More reports please.

Open All year.
Rooms 4 suites, 16 double, 2 single – 20 with bath and/or shower; 2 with telephone. Many with balcony.
Facilities Lounge, TV room, bar, dining room. Hotel is on beach.
Location Castellabate is 71 km S of Salerno.
Credit cards None accepted.
Terms Rooms: single 28,000–30,000 L, double 38,000–45,000 L, suite 74,000–88,000 L. Breakfast 6,000 L. Dinner, B&B 40,000–50,000 L per person. Set meals 18,000 L; alc 22,000 L. Reductions for long stays out of season. Reduced rates for children; special meals on request.

SELVA DI VAL GARDENA 39048 Bolzano — Map 16

Hotel Dorfer — *Tel* (0471) 75204
Via Cir 5

Selva, between Bolzano and Cortina, is a Ladinisch and German-speaking village in the upper Val Gardena, now a popular skiing and summer resort. This is one of its simpler hotels, but homely and comfortable, run with great warmth by Frau Dorfer. An 1989 report, "Selva with its many hotels strikes one as being the Blackpool of the Dolomites, but the *Dorfer* manages to insulate itself from the noise. The view from the front rooms is magnificent, but the back ones are to be avoided. The restaurant manager, a Humphrey Bogart look-alike, is witty and solicitous, breakfast is extensive and the set dinner menu is good." The skiing, too, is good. (*Esler Crawford*)

Open 18 Dec–18 Apr, 16 Jun–30 Sept.
Rooms 21 double, 9 single – all with bath and/or shower and telephone, most with radio and TV; many with balcony.
Facilities Lounge, bar, TV room, restaurant; gym, whirlpool, sauna and solarium. Garden with terrace for alfresco meals and table tennis.
Location 42 km E of Bolzano.
Restriction Not suitable for ♿.
Credit cards None accepted.
Terms [1989 rates] B&B 55,000–95,000 L. Set lunch 18,000 L; full alc 35,000 L. Reduced rates and special meals for children.

SIENA 53100 — Map 16

Hotel Certosa di Maggiano — *Tel* (0577) 288180
Via Certosa 82 — *Telex* 574221 CERMAG

Of the oldest Carthusian monastery in Tuscany (built 1314) just the cloister and tower remain, and these now form part of this luxurious and well-converted little hotel, lying a mile outside the city walls in a bucolic setting. It is an unusual place with a powerful personality which may not suit everyone, and some have judged it overpriced. A returning devotee this year thought the food improved but was critical of breakfast. He had written earlier, "Some might find the intimacy, relentless good taste and attention to detail a little precious, but others, myself included, are enchanted by the beautiful old building, the sumptuous bedrooms, the recorded Mozart in the library, the swimming pool looking over the vineyards to the walls of Siena, and the formal but *nice* service. Food is modern Italian: dishes may sound dull (e.g. veal with herbs) but most of them look and taste superb." "The swimming pool is in a natural garden with peach and apricot trees overlooking the vineyard which supplies the excellent house wine. Our room was large, furnished with antiques, chintz curtains and wall coverings. The bathroom was bright and modern with green and white tiles." "We breakfasted and dined in the central courtyard, but could have eaten in a ravishingly pretty dining room. While we were lounging by the pool, a bowl of freshly picked figs and grapes was put in our room; while we dined, a dish of sweets was placed by the bedside. All in all, the manners and civilised charm of an earlier epoch, bolstered by 20th-century plumbing." Several readers have objected to the high prices charged for extras. And one this year received no apology when a booking was not honoured.

Open All year.
Rooms 9 suites, 5 double – all with bath, shower, telephone, radio and TV. Some on ground floor.
Facilities Salon, library, TV room, games room, bar, dining room. Large garden with heated swimming pool and tennis court.
Location 1 km SE of Siena outside Porta Romana. Parking.
Credit cards All major cards accepted.
Terms B&B: single 250,000–290,000 L, double 280,000–320,000 L, suite 430,000–530,000 L; dinner, B&B 215,000–375,000 L per person; full board 280,000–450,000 L. Full alc 90,000 L. Special meals for children.

Park Hotel *Tel* (0577) 44803
Via di Marciano 18 *Telex* 571005 PARKSI

Michelin awards its full range of red print, including four red gables, to this converted 15th-century villa secluded in the north-west outskirts, now a stylish and sizeable hotel. "The rooms recently had a major renovation. Ours was completely upholstered in a beautiful muted blue-pink cloth. All furnishings were ultra-modern, a pleasing respite from Italy's mostly antique-filled hotel rooms. The bathroom had a proper stand-up shower, while its walls and floor were in beautiful blue marble. Some rooms look over to Siena across a wild, flower-filled garden, others face the attractive swimming pool and vine-covered rolling hills beyond. Staff were cordial and professional." "The food is wonderful and the waiters friendly. This is a CIGA hotel, so has a sort of business atmosphere." More reports please.

Open All year.
Rooms 4 suites, 64 double, 1 single – all with bath and shower, telephone, TV and air-conditioning. Some ground-floor rooms. 4 in garden annexe.
Facilities Lift. 3 bars, TV room, 2 restaurants; conference facilities. Gardens with swimming pool, tennis.
Location 2 km NW of city centre. Minibus service into town. Parking.
Credit cards All major cards accepted.
Terms (excluding 19% tax) Rooms: single 150–188,000 L, double 190–250,000 L, suite 450,000 L. Breakfast 18,000 L. Dinner, B&B: single 228,000–258,000 L, double 346,000–406,000 L, suite 606,000 L. Alc meals 80,000 L. Children under 8 free of charge; special meals on request.

Villa Scacciapensieri *Tel* (0577) 41441
Via di Scacciapensieri 10 *Telex* 573390 VISCA

A Tuscan villa on a hillside, surrounded by vineyards and olive trees (but industrial suburbia is close). Despite some criticisms, it has long been liked for its lovely garden, quiet atmosphere and friendly owners, and is restored to the Guide this year by three positive reports. "We had an excellent large bedroom facing Siena. The service was exemplary, the food first-class, and the grounds are lovely. The weak spots are the bar and lounge." "All very clean. Many dishes quite superb. Service both professional and warm-hearted." (*VN Wright, Mary B Dawson, TCH Macafee*)

We should be glad to hear of some good hotels in Sardinia.

Open Mar–Oct.
Rooms 2 suites, 22 double, 5 single – all with bath and/or shower, telephone and TV. 10 rooms in annexe.
Facilities Lift. Lounge, bar, TV room, restaurant; terrace. Garden with swimming pool and tennis.
Location 3 km N of Siena. Regular bus service.
Credit cards All major cards accepted.
Terms B&B: single 160,000 L, double 250,000 L, suite 325,000 L; dinner, B&B: single 195,000 L, double 329,000 L, suite 395,000 L. Set lunch 35,000 L, dinner 45,000 L; full alc 100,000 L. Reduced rates for children.

SINALUNGA 53048 Siena — Map 16

Locanda dell'Amorosa

Tel (0577) 679497
Fax (0577) 678216
Telex 580047 AMOR

"One of the nicest hotels we have found in Italy" – a cluster of old stone buildings on the edge of the lovely Sienese hills, transformed from a private residence into a select and expensive little country inn, had its first entry last year. Its nominators returned this year and found it unchanged. They had written, "Converted from an old estate, it is still a working farm, producing its own wines, jams and honey. The beautiful old buildings of various shapes and sizes surround a central courtyard with a huge well. The estate chapel has some superb frescoes. Our room was really a suite, its beamed rooms comfortably furnished with antiques; floors were red Tuscan tiles, with rugs. The restaurant, in the old stables, is a fascinating room in very rustic style. The food is excellent, including traditional Tuscan dishes and unusual fish from Lake Trasimeno. Service, by local girls, is quiet and efficient. Breakfast was also excellent, with lovely hot fresh-baked brioches. There is a comfortable lounge, and chairs under giant umbrellas in the courtyard. Siena, Arezzo and Perugia are all within easy reach." (*Pat and Jeremy Temple*) The hotel has this year lost its *Michelin* rosette, and we'd be glad to hear from other readers.

Open All year except 20 Jan–28 Feb. Restaurant closed Mon and Tue midday.
Rooms 7 suites, 8 double – all with bath and/or shower, telephone, TV, fridge.
Facilities Lounge, bar, restaurant. Garden and courtyard.
Location 2 km S of Sinalunga which is 45 km E of Siena. Parking.
Credit cards All major cards accepted.
Terms B&B: double 231,000–276,000 L, suite 356,000–536,000 L. Full alc 60,000–70,000 L.

SIRMIONE 251019 Brescia — Map 16

Hotel Golf et Suisse
Via Condominio

Tel (030) 916176
Fax (030) 916304
Telex 300395

Catullus' "*venusta Sirmio*" is now a delightful medieval walled townlet on a small peninsula at the south end of Lake Garda. Just outside it is this clean, modern family-run hotel, set back from the road. "The owner was charming, and our large rooms had balconies", runs a report this year. There's a small garden with chairs for drinks and a good swimming pool, while the hotel also has a nearby jetty and private beach for lake bathing. No restaurant, but lots in town. (*Wende West*)

Open 1 Mar–31 Oct.
Rooms 14 suites in annexe opposite hotel, 30 double – all with bath and/or shower, telephone and TV; 14 with radio and tea-making facilities. Ground-floor rooms.
Facilities Lounge with TV, bar. Garden with swimming pool. Private beach.
Location 1 km from Sirmione which is 35 km W of Verona.
Credit cards Access, Amex, Visa.
Terms Rooms 65,000–140,000 L. Breakfast 15,000 L. Reduced rates for children. (No restaurant.)

TAORMINA 98039 Messina, Sicily — Map 16

San Domenico Palace Hotel — *Tel* (0942) 23701
Piazza San Domenico 5 — *Fax* (0942) 25506
Telex 980013 DOMHOT

This famous and palatial hotel on its high promontory began life as a monastery. In 1943 Kesselring used it as his headquarters and much of the original 15th-century building, apart from the cloister, was destroyed by Allied bombs. Today it is rebuilt, and in many ways is very beautiful. The view from its balcony, of Etna and the coast, is sensational; below stretch the palm-studded gardens, ablaze with colour. But there have been tales of dull food, and recently a sharp-eyed British hotelier gave this view: "Lovely cloister and courtyards to which has been added an ill-proportioned, gloomy and ill-furnished Edwardian block. We much preferred the old section, though the rooms lack the large balconies of the Edwardian part. Garden beautifully kept – unusual for Sicily. Housekeeping poor. Would be a wonderful place if properly managed. As it is, passable." So we advised readers to go for the historic splendour but not to expect a "good hotel". This year, a sharp retort to this has come from a leading playwright: "All these comments are ridiculously unfair and almost caused us to pass over what turned out to be the most delightful hotel we've ever stayed at anywhere in the world. 'Don't expect a "good hotel"'. Blimey. Don't expect too much of paradise, either." (*Michael Frayn*) Your views, please, as to which of these controversial noises is 'off', and which is on target.

Open All year.
Rooms 10 suites, 80 double, 28 single – all with bath, telephone, radio, TV and air-conditioning.
Facilities Lift. Hall, 4 lounges, bar, TV room, games room, dining room; conference facilities; mandolin group every night in bar; courtyard terrace. Garden with heated swimming pool and snack bar. Private beach (car service).
Location On promontory on W side of town, but close to centre.
Restriction Not suitable for ♿.
Credit cards All major cards accepted.
Terms [1989 rates] B&B: single 250,000 L, double 425,000 L, suite 610,000–665,000 L; full board 300,000–330,000 L per person. Set lunch/dinner 90,000 L. Reduced rates for children sharing parents' room.

Villa Belvedere — *Tel* (0942) 23791
Via Bagnoli Croci 79

"A superbly run hotel in a fine situation overlooking the bay. Beautiful garden and swimming pool with a palm growing up through the middle." "Run by a friendly and cultivated Franco-Italian family. The bar by the pool serves delicious snacks." So run two reports, this year and last, on the bed-and-breakfast *Belvedere*. And here, caveats and all, is a third: "One of the two prettiest places to stay in Taormina. The sea is 800 feet below, palm trees sway and creak, Mount Etna smoulders moodily, the lights of Naxos twinkle in the dark. My room was unique. It was cool and shaded, with a little garden of its own; the bathroom was cramped but functioning, though prone to ant invasions. The garden rambles as much as steep terracing will allow, with little hidden places for a quiet read or writing a report to the Guide. The pool is not for Olympic swimmers, nor for those muscular Germans who tense their pectorals and breasts at each other; it is a pool for a quick cooling dip. Beside it one can have a tolerable and cheapish lunch." Since last year, air-conditioning has been installed in the top-floor rooms (which have balconies) and in the rooms facing the street which can be noisy. (*Christina Bewley*)

Open 15 March–31 Oct.
Rooms 38 double, 3 single – 13 with bath, 28 with shower, all with telephone. Some with air-conditioning. Ground-floor rooms.
Facilities Lift. Lounge, 2 sitting rooms (1 with TV), lounge bar, breakfast room. Garden with terrace, swimming pool and snack bar. Sea 3 km away.
Location Central, near public gardens and tennis court. Parking.
Credit cards Access, Visa.
Terms B&B: single 60,000–65,000 L, double 106,500–116,500 L. Reduced rates for children. (No restaurant.)

Villa Fiorita *Tel* (0942) 24122
Via L. Pirandello 39

A villa that clings to the hillside, amid paved patios filled with flowers and foliage, right next to the cable car station that takes you down to the beach. Honeymooners this year much enjoyed their private terrace and fine views over the coast. Others have written: "It's on the busiest stretch of the approach road to Taormina yet manages to be cool and quiet. Our room was large and comfortable with french windows opening onto a large terrace, where breakfast amid the flowers was the high spot of our stay. But the lounges are somewhat gloomy." "We missed the sense of being in the hub of things: but for those who want solitude and quiet this place is excellent; there are plenty of nooks and crannies to sit inside, and the staff are charming." No restaurant: lots in town. (*Andrew Meyn, Philippa Herbert, Angela and David Stewart, and others*)

Open All year.
Rooms 2 suites, 22 double – 21 with bath and shower, 3 with shower, all with telephone, radio, TV, mini-bar and air-conditioning; some doubles have terrace or balcony.
Facilities Hall, 2 lounges, bar, restaurant (for breakfast and snacks), games room. Large garden with terraces and swimming pool. 50 metres to sandy beach (cable car down).
Location Central, near Greek theatre, but quiet. Garage (5,000 L).
Restrictions Not suitable for ♿. No children under 10.
Credit cards Amex, Visa.
Terms [1989 rates] Rooms 74,000 L. Breakfast 6,500 L. Reduced rates for children sharing parents' room. (No restaurant.)

Please write and confirm an entry when it is deserved. If you think that a hotel is not as good as we say, write and tell us.

TELLARO DI LERICI 19030 La Spezia — Map 16

Il Nido di Fiascherino — *Tel* (0187) 967426
Via Fiascherino 75

A bright and airy modern hotel in a splendid location: set above a cove in a village near Lerici, on the Gulf of Spezia, it has fine views over beach, rocks and pine trees. Our readers are appreciative, "A tremendous welcome from the staff, and excellent food, with fish better than meat," say recently returning devotees. Others have written: "The coast is as idyllic now as it must have been when Shelley drowned here. The beach facilities have room for improvement, but the dining room is cool, white and spacious with lovely views of the bay, and food was good and plentiful – salads from a self-service buffet. Breakfast is also self-service, with cheese and ham: sybarites who opt for breakfast in bed do less well on packaged toast." "Our room with balcony overlooked the bay where waves crashed thrillingly day and night over the rocks below." *Warning*: there are 140 steps down to the small private beach which is crowded in high summer. Air-conditioning has just been added to almost all bedrooms. More reports please.

Open Mar–Nov and Christmas and New Year.
Rooms 1 suite, 34 double, 4 single – 2 with bath, 35 with shower, all with telephone, TV and baby-listening; some with balcony. 30 with air-conditioning. 22 in annexe across road.
Facilities TV room, bar, 2 dining rooms; terraces. Garden. Small private beach.
Location 2 km SE of Lerici; follow signs for Lerici and Tellaro. Parking.
Restriction Not suitable for ♿.
Credit cards All major cards accepted.
Terms B&B: single 66,000–73,000 L, double 113,000–124,000 L. Dinner, B&B 92,000–115,000 L per person. Set lunch/dinner 38,000 L; full alc 49,000 L. Reduced rates for children; special meals.

TORGIANO 06089 Perugia — Map 16

Le Tre Vaselle — *Tel* (075) 982447
Via Garibaldi 48 — *Fax* (075) 985214
Telex 564028 TREVAS

This "elegant country residence" is set quietly in a side street of a charming Umbrian village south of Perugia; it is owned by the ambitious Lungarotti wine firm, which also runs a wine museum in Torgiano. More praise this year: "We enjoyed the undeniable style, the refined yet honest food, the attentive and friendly staff. The interior has thick white walls, archways, wooden beams, terracotta tiles, comfortable sofas. Rooms are tranquil and simple, in very good Italian pared-down style (but bathrooms are small: heaven help the obese). Cooking is regional, gently modernised, using first-rate local ingredients, and flavours are fresh and uncluttered – try insalata di rucola (rocket with sliced mushrooms and cheese), home-made papardelle with truffles, pink filet of beef or sturgeon from nearby Lake Trasimeno. Breakfast is buffet-style, with fruit, ham, sausages. The admirable Lungarotti firm, much concerned with self-promotion, runs wine courses locally, and their hotel gets much custom from groups." (*David Wooff*)

Report forms (Freepost in UK) will be found at the end of the Guide.

Open 15 Jan–15 Nov.
Rooms 1 suite, 47 double – all with bath and/or shower and telephone.
Facilities Reading room, piano bar (music every evening), TV room, breakfast room, restaurant; conference facilities. Terrace where meals are served.
Location 15 km S of Perugia, just E of *autostrada.*
Restriction Not suitable for ♿.
Credit cards All major cards accepted.
Terms B&B: single 180,000 L, double 260,000 L, suite 360,000 L. Full alc 60,000 L. Children under 8 free of charge; special meals on request.

TORNO 22020 Como — Map 16

Villa Flora — *Tel* (031) 419222

Superbly located on a stone platform sticking out into Lake Como, this big pink villa is now a lively but modest hotel, again admired by several readers this year – especially for its cuisine, so good that many locals use the place for wedding parties. "Food wonderful, location terrific, rooms small." "An attractive terrace ablaze with flowers; the best rooms have balconies and all are quiet, save for the sound of lapping water." Breakfast is remarkable. However, some visitors have found the beds too soft, and the rooms are really quite basic: one reader this year thought them downright dreary, and considered the food no more than "OK". Another complained of inadequate heating during a cold spell in April. The hotel is run by an engaging male duo: one cooks, the other does the waiting in a multitude of languages, English included. (*Ellen and John Buchanan, H and B Shames, Stefan and Cosima Sethe, and others*)

Open Mar–Oct. Restaurant closed Tue.
Rooms 20 double – all with shower, and telephone.
Facilities Lounge with TV, bar, restaurant; conference facilities; terrace, where meals are served. Garden with private beach on lake, bathing.
Location 6 km N of Como. Take road to Bellagio: hotel is down road on left just past centre of Torno. Private parking.
Restriction Not suitable for ♿.
Credit cards Access, Visa.
Terms Rooms: single 45,000 L, double 70,000 L. Breakfast 8,000 L. Full alc 25,000–30,000 L. Children sharing parents' room free of charge; special meals.

TORRI DEL BENACO 37010 Verona — Map 16

Hotel Gardesana — *Tel* (045) 7225005
Piazza Calderini 20 — *Fax* (045) 7225771

A small resort with a 14th-century castle on the eastern shore of Lake Garda, crowded in summer, especially with German tourists. The *Gardesana* faces the little harbour, a traditional hotel with arcades and orange-brown stucco walls, but modernised inside; many rooms have a balcony with views across the lake. "A delightful hotel," runs a recent report; "the beds are comfortable, the welcome friendly, the staff courteous; hors d'oeuvre buffet every night, and excellent buffet breakfast." An earlier view: "An ideal honeymoon-style hotel. We spent a delightful week, enjoying the very comfortable rooms, above-average food and friendly service." The dining room has an outdoor terrace facing the harbour. Some rooms are small and simple, and noise can be a hazard: one reader this year complained of thin party walls, while another has written that the groups of musicians who play outside in the evenings till 11.30 may well consist of "a loud band with a Frank Sinatra impersonator singing Italian favourites such as *My Old Kentucky Home*" – perhaps not be quite what honeymooners would want.

Open 26 Dec–10 Nov. Restaurant closed lunch and 10 Oct–28 Apr.
Rooms 31 double, 3 single – 4 with bath and shower, 30 with shower, all with telephone and air-conditioning; some with balcony.
Facilities Lift. TV lounge, bar, dining room with outdoor terrace; conference room; portico with dancing in summer. Private cabins at lido 150 metres from hotel.
Location In traffic-free centre of Torri del Benaco which is 47 km NW of Verona. Private parking.
Credit cards All major cards accepted.
Terms B&B: single 50,000–65,000 L, double 80,000–140,000 L. Dinner, B&B: single 65,000–85,000 L, double 110,000–170,000 L. Set meals 35,000 L; full alc 45,000 L. Reduced rates and special meals for children.

TRICESIMO 33019 Udine — Map 16

Hotel Ristorante Boschetti — *Tel* (0432) 851230 and 851531
Piazza Mazzini 10

In a small town just north of delightful Udine, this old inn has been much enlarged and modernised, with a new wing, and is now a smart hotel well known for its food (*Michelin* rosette). It is family-owned and run, and well kept. Lack of up-to-date reports pushed it out of the 1989 Guide, but one admirer has now returned: "The staff were kind and thoughtful, my room was comfortable, and the food and wine are fantastic, a combination of regional and traditional recipes with a modern approach." This reader found the place much quieter, now that a newly opened motorway is diverting much heavy traffic: but another visitor still found the rooms noisy (as well as small). We'd be glad of further reports. (*Jeremy Temple*)

Open All year except 5–20 Aug. Restaurant closed Mon.
Rooms 32 double – all with bath or shower and telephone; 16 with TV.
Facilities Lift. 3 salons, bar, restaurant.
Location 12 km N of Udine.
Credit cards Amex, Diners, Visa.
Terms [1989 rates] (Excluding 12% tax) Rooms 70,000–100,000 L. Breakfast 10,000 L. Full board 120,000 L per person. Alc meals 42,000–61,000 L.

TRIESTE — Map 16

Hotel Riviera e Maximilian's — *Tel* (040) 224136 and 224300
Strada Costiera 22 — *Telex* 460297
34014 Trieste

Our only entry for the Trieste area, again approved in 1989 by its nominator last year: "It is on an attractive stretch of the coast road running north-west from Trieste along a wooded hillside, with fine views of the sea. It is in two buildings on either side of the road, close to the castle of Miramare in its romantic park and the busy little fishing and pleasure port of Grignano. A lift goes down to its seaside bar and bathing places. The rooms are furnished differently in the two buildings: ours was in the *Riviera*, and had elegant comfortable modern furnishings and a good bathroom. The outstanding experience is to dine on the flowery terrace as the sun sets over the sea and the lights come up around the bay. The food is simple, with much emphasis on local fish and pasta dishes, but carefully cooked and well served. The house wines are notable. One hazard: the main road has a high accident rate. Another: large and lengthy wedding parties at weekends." (*Prof. Sir Alan and Lady Cook*)

Open All year.
Rooms 57 – all with bath and/or shower. Rooms in two separate buildings.
Facilities Lift. Salon, restaurant; conference facilities; terrace. Garden with swimming pool. Lift to seaside bar and bathing.
Location NW of Trieste on coastal road S14.
Terms On application.

TURIN — Map 16

Hotel Conte Biancamano — *Tel* (011) 546058 and 513281
73 Corso Vittorio Emanuele II
Turin 10128

A small family-owned hotel in an arcaded *corso*, five minutes' stroll from the 17th-century Piazza San Carlo. "Unlike many of Turin's 'best' hotels," says its inspector, "it does preserve something of the atmosphere of faded grandeur that is so much part of the city. The narrow and quaint lift to the entrance on the second floor, and the elegant sitting room, give it something of the ambience of a private residence. Bedrooms are unexciting but comfortable and well equipped (those at the front are noisy). The cheerful breakfast room with its white bentwood chairs is a brave attempt to compete with the fine old *Café Platti* opposite. The hotel's owners favour a literary and artistic clientele. No restaurant, but I recommend the expensive *Vecchia Lanterna* round the corner."

Open All year except Aug.
Rooms 3 suites, 15 double, 7 single – 2 with bath, 23 with shower, all with telephone, radio and TV; 3 with tea-making facilities.
Facilities Lift. Lounge, bar, breakfast room; meeting room.
Location Near main station (windows double-glazed). Garage nearby.
Credit cards All major cards accepted.
Terms [1989 rates] Rooms: single 66,000 L, double 95,000 L, suite 110,000 L. Breakfast 10,000 L. Reduced rates for children. (No restaurant.)

VAGGIO-REGGELLO 50066 Firenze — Map 16

Villa Rigacci — *Tel* (055) 865.67.18 and 865.65.62
Fax (055) 8656537

A graceful 15th-century villa-farmhouse in the mellow Tuscan countryside, "What a find! A farmhouse in the hills half-an-hour's drive from Florence, full of character and warmth, run with style by a French-Italian family, the Pierazzi. Lots of antiques. Our room was enormous, overlooking the picturesque pool. Horse riding is available. The food was excellent and copious, and fresh flowers were on each table." A large shady garden, a library, beautiful country furniture; excellent Tuscan and French cuisine and reasonable prices for the area. (*Mrs JA Patterson*) More feedback welcome.

Open All year. Restaurant closed to non residents Tue.
Rooms 1 suite, 13 double, 4 single – all with bath and/or shower, telephone, radio, TV.
Facilities Bar/lounge, library, 4 salons, 2 dining rooms. Garden with swimming pool and golf practice.
Location 1 km N of Viaggio which is 30 km SE of Florence. Take exit Incisa off Autostrada del Sole.
Restriction Not suitable for ♿.
Credit cards All major cards accepted.
Terms B&B: single 85,000–110,000 L, double 133,000–210,000 L. Dinner, B&B 105,000–150,000 L per person; full board 130,000–195,000 L. Full alc 50,000 L. Reduced rates and special meals for children.

VARENNA 22050 Como — Map 16

Hotel du Lac — *Tel* (0341) 830238
Via del Prestino 4 — *Fax* (0341) 801081

Set charmingly by the water's edge in an unspoilt fishing-village on the east side of Lake Como, a clean and pleasant holiday hotel with good food, helpful signora *and fine views. Some rooms are small. Open 1 Mar–15 Dec. 19 rooms, all with bath and/or shower. B&B double 139,000–149,000 L. Set menu 38,000 L. Re-nominated. More reports please.*

VENICE — Map 16

Pensione Accademia — *Tel* (041) 5237846 and 5210188
Fondamenta Maravegie
Dorsoduro 1058-1060
Venice 30123

An admired bed-and-breakfast *pensione*, housed in a delightful 17th-century villa facing a side canal (sometimes a bit noisy) only a few yards from the Grand Canal at the Accademia bridge. In its patio garden you can take breakfast, tea or drinks, or even bring your snacks and picnics for which they will supply plates and cutlery at no charge. Rooms vary in size, some being fairly small, and in past years we have had complaints about poor housekeeping. More recently, however, the comfort and cleanliness are stressed; and most readers, but not all, find the staff helpful. You do need to book well ahead. (*Patricia Corbett*)

Open All year.
Rooms 20 double, 6 single – 8 with bath, 13 with shower, all with telephone.
Facilities 2 lounges, TV room, breakfast room; terrace. Garden.
Location Central, near Grand Canal.
Restriction Not suitable for ♿.
Credit cards All major cards accepted.
Terms [1989 rates] B&B: single 40,000--83,000 L, double 74,000–145,000 L. Reduced rates for children. (No restaurant.)

> Hotels often book you into their most expensive rooms or suites unless you specify otherwise. Even if all room prices are the same, hotels may give you a less good room in the hope of selling their better rooms to late customers. It always pays to discuss accommodation in detail when making a reservation.

Hotel Flora
Calle larga 22 Marzo 2283/a
Venice 30124

Tel (041) 5205844
Fax (041) 5228217
Telex 410401 FLORA

A quiet and friendly little hotel just west of St Mark's, "full of baroque mahogany and blue velvet" and laurelled with red print by *Michelin* for special charm and quality. It remains as popular as ever with readers: "We had a lovely large room with baroque decor, overlooking the courtyard/garden, blissfully quiet. Obliging staff, charming management." "Our spacious room was nicely decorated with antiques and Venetian glass, and had a fine view of the walled garden, beautifully landscaped with vines and flowers, an oasis amid the bustle of the big city. Service was the best we had in Italy." Bedrooms vary, some large and sumptuous, others much smaller and simpler. Most rooms face the garden; those that overlook the front can be noisy. Air-conditioning costs extra and one reader found that noisy. The Art Buchwald of regular Guide correspondents chips in, "The beds are the sort that Habitat sold for £39.95 before it owned Mothercare, but they are comfortable and do not squeak. The bathroom proves that Italian plumbing has long defied the laws of physics, but is beautifully appointed. In sum, a delightful place, where the laughing, smiling desk staff are a scream. The rolls are fresh and the coffee divine." (*Paul Palmer; NM Mackintosh, Mary Hanson and others*)

Open 1 Feb–20 Nov.
Rooms 38 double, 6 single – all with bath or shower and telephone. 2 on ground floor.
Facilities Lift. Lounge, TV room, bar, small breakfast room; air-conditioning. Courtyard/garden where breakfast and drinks are served.
Location Central, near St Mark's Square.
Credit cards All major cards accepted.
Terms B&B: single 118,000 L, double 180,000 L. (No restaurant.)

Hotel Gritti Palace
Campo Santa Maria del Giglio
2467
Venice 30124

Tel (041) 794611
Telex 410125 GRITTI

This famous *palazzo* on the Grand Canal is one of the great hotels of Venice. Some readers feel that it rests too readily on its laurels and that its quality does not match its prices. But recent visitors have mainly enjoyed it: "The food is delicious and the service perfection. We had a side room, which was beautiful and later a huge corner room which was marred by a lumpy mattress." "On the plus side, a superb position, exquisite lounge, breakfast on the terrace by the canal a joy, staff aesthetically efficient [*sic*], lovely luxurious bathroom. The minuses: dreary bedroom decor, and an atmosphere of mass-produced impersonal conveyor-belt luxury (it's a CIGA hotel)" – perhaps the mood was different in the good old days, when Somerset Maugham and his ilk were regulars. The quietest rooms are said to be the side ones, and the small attic rooms with four-posters.

Open All year.
Rooms 9 suites, 66 double, 13 single – all with bath and shower, telephone, radio and TV. Some ground-floor rooms.

Facilities Lift. 3 salons, TV room, bar, restaurants; terrace-restaurant overlooking the Grand Canal; conference facilities; beauty parlour. Free shuttle to Lido in summer.
Location On Grand Canal, 500 metres W of St Mark's.
Credit cards All major cards accepted.
Terms B&B: single 375,000 L, double 450,000–550,000 L, suite 950,000–1,350,000 L. Full alc 100,000 L. Children under 6 free; special meals.

Hotel Monaco & Grand Canal | *Tel* (041) 5200211
Calle Vallaresso, 1325 San Marco | *Fax* (041) 5200501
Venice 30124 | *Telex* 410450 MONACO

This elegant hotel on the Grand Canal, near San Marco, would make a slightly cheaper (but still expensive) alternative to the *Gritti*. It has a leafy courtyard, the public rooms are impeccable and the staff friendly. "A thrilling restaurant on the waterfront, with almost *too* much bustle and activity," says one recent visitor, who thought the food "average", whereas another spoke of "best food we had in Venice, with some local dishes". Breakfasts are only so-so, says a reader this year. (*Diane and Keith Moss*)

Open All year.
Rooms 3 suites, 53 double, 19 single – all with bath and shower, telephone, radio.
Facilities Lift. Lounges, piano bar, restaurant; conference room; terrace. Garden.
Location Central, near Piazza San Marco. Quietest rooms overlook garden.
Credit cards Access, Amex, Visa.
Terms B&B: single 140,000–220,000 L, double 185,000–330,000 L, suite 550,000–750,000 L. Dinner, B&B 70.000 L per person. Alc meals 70,000–100,000 L. Reduced rates and special meals for children on request.

Hotel Saturnia e International | *Tel* (041) 5208377
Calle larga 22 Marzo 2398 | *Fax* (041) 5207131
Venice 30124 | *Telex* 410355 SATURN

"A cool haven after hot sightseeing. We had a huge room with huge bed and attractive carved and gilded ceiling. Staff helpful and courteous" – a recent plaudit for this comfortable and unpretentious 14th-century *palazzo*-cum-hotel about three minutes' walk from St Mark's. The reception area makes quite an impact: a Gothic patio with an elaborate inlaid ceiling. "We liked the ambience, the friendly staff and, in particular, our room – on a back canal with two large windows and a huge Venetian glass chandelier." "Our room was smallish but adequate, and the bathroom's modern decor a bit alarming at first", says a reader this year. The hotel has two restaurants: the *Michelin*-rosetted *Caravella*, described this year as "excellent", though sometimes criticised in the past, and the slightly cheaper, but still expensive, *Cortile* (much liked by readers) where you can eat outdoors in summer. (*David and Patricia Hawkins*)

Open All year. Restaurants closed Wed.
Rooms 79 double, 16 single – 87 with bath, 8 with shower, all with telephone and TV; baby-listening on request.
Facilities Lifts. 2 lounges, bar, TV room, 2 restaurants; conference facilities.
Location Central, W of Piazza San Marco.
Restriction Not suitable for ♿.
Credit cards All major cards accepted.

Terms B&B: single 150,000–220,000 L, double 200,000–350,000 L; dinner, B&B 60,000 L added per person. Full alc 70,000–85,000 L. Special meals for children on request.

Pensione Seguso *Tel* (041) 5222340
Dorsoduro, Zattere 779
Venice 30123

The superb view of the Giudecca canal from front-facing windows is one main attraction of this modest and amiable *pensione* on the Zattere; side rooms overlook a small canal. It's a refined, old-fashioned establishment, somewhat shabby, with fine old Venetian furniture, and embroidered silk wall-coverings in the dining room. "It's the imperfections of the place that make it so charming," writes one reader this year; "our room was clean and peaceful. The decor throughout is quietly elegant and the dining-room has a relaxed, refined air. But meals are served at rigidly set times, and the food is no more than adequate, with poor breakfasts." Others have relished "Madame's gracious welcome"; one found the place "comfortable and quaint, full of character and of characters. I enjoyed the quiet, the Venetian glass windows and chandeliers, the heating, the service, and the position." (*Francis Durham*)

Open 1 Mar–30 Nov. Restaurant closed Wed.
Rooms 31 double, 5 single – 9 with bath, 9 with shower, all with telephone.
Facilities Lift. Lounge, restaurant; breakfast terrace.
Location 15 mins from the centre, overlooking the Giudecca canal.
Credit cards Access, Amex, Visa.
Terms On application.

VERONA 37121 — Map 16

Hotel Colomba d'Oro *Tel* (045) 595300
Via Cattaneo 10 *Telex* 480872 COLOMB

A dignified and serviceable hostelry, very central, on a side street near the Arena in a traffic-restricted zone. The interior has a club-like atmosphere with lots of polished wood and comfortable armchairs. A reader this year had a large room and found the staff pleasant and helpful, while others recently have enjoyed the quiet, comfort and good service: some rooms, however, are small. (*Mary Ann Meanwell*)

Open All year.
Rooms 2 suites, 30 double, 17 single – 36 with bath, 13 with shower, all with telephone and TV.
Facilities 3 lounges, bar; conference room.
Location Central, in pedestrian zone near Arena. Garage nearby.
Credit cards All major cards accepted.
Terms [1989 rates] Rooms: single 101,000 L, double 137,000 L. Breakfast 14,500 L. No restaurant.

Hotel Torcolo *Tel* (045) 8007512
Vicolo Listone 3

A small bed-and-breakfast hotel in a side street near the Arena, very centrally located but not noisy by Italian standards – and rooms are air-conditioned. Readers this year have again commented on the good breakfasts, and on the charm of Signora Pomari and her staff. Some rooms are large, and furnished with antiques: but others are more modern, and some have been judged a little basic, with pillows too hard. (*Anita Taylor, Michael and Margaret Crick*)

Open All year except 10 days in Jan. Restaurant closed Mon.
Rooms 15 double, 4 single – all with bath and shower, telephone and TV.
Facilities Lift. Breakfast room, TV room; terrace.
Location Central, off Piazza Bra, near Arena. Parking for 10 cars.
Credit cards None accepted.
Terms B&B: single 47,000–67,000 L, double 74,000–93,500 L. (No restaurant.)

VICENZA 36100 — Map 16

Hotel Campo Marzio
Viale Roma 21

Tel (0444) 545700
Fax (0444) 320495
Telex 341138 EUROHOT

A good practical modern hotel, very spruce, and usefully situated between the station and the wonderful centre of this old city, beside a canal and facing a park. Small but comfortable modern-style, air-conditioned rooms with excellent bathrooms. Good service and quite good food: for a superb meal, try the Cinzia e Valerio. *35 rooms, all with bath and shower. B&B double 132,000 L. Full alc 25,000–41,000 L [1989]. Endorsed this year, but further reports welcome.*

ZERMAN 31020 Treviso — Map 16

Villa Condulmer
Zerman, Mogliano Veneto

Tel (041) 457100

A beautiful 18th-century Venetian villa, in a pleasant rural setting on the misty plain between Venice and Treviso. Ronald and Nancy Reagan chose to stay here during the 1987 Venice summit; their autographed photo is displayed in the foyer. The hotel is much approved again this year, especially for its palatial public rooms in rococo style: "A lovely old building, elegantly furnished, with a dining terrace overlooking the attractive grounds where comfortable loungers surround the swimming pool. We had a delightful large room in the new wing, which has been skilfully integrated into the old part. The restaurant nicely presents good food at fair prices." "Food a bit on the *nouvelle* side in portions. All staff helpful save the receptionist." The rooms in the old part are not yet air-conditioned: but the newer ones are, and this year were called "the only truly cool and comfortable rooms we found in all Italy". (*Betsy C Maestro*)

Open 15 Mar–15 Nov.
Rooms 45 – all with bath and/or shower; most with telephone; 8 with radio. Some in annexe. Some ground-floor rooms.
Facilities Salon, reading room, TV room, bar (with piano), 3 restaurants; conference room. Park with unheated swimming pool, tennis court, 18-hole golf course and riding.
Location Outside village; 4 km NE of Mogliano Veneto and 22 km N of Venice.
Credit cards All major cards accepted.
Terms [1989 rates] Rooms: single 70,000 L, double 200,000 L. Breakfast 14,000 L. Full board 160,000–200,000 L. Alc meals 40,000–60,000 L plus 10% service.

Luxembourg

HÔTEL BEL-AIR, ECHTERNACH

ECHTERNACH 6409 **Map 9**

Hôtel Bel-Air *Tel* 729383
Route de Berdorf 1 *Telex* 2640 BELAIR

A rather grand country house hotel, newly renovated, on the edge of the attractive and popular resort town of Echternach, in the wooded and hilly "Luxembourg Suisse" near the German frontier. It is a palatial kind of place, with extensive and imposing gardens full of pools, flowering shrubs and Doric columns: pity that the facade facing the gardens is so ugly, in such a jumble of styles. Most of the bedrooms are in the modern part, each with a balcony where you can take breakfast: here Americans this year enjoyed their spacious room and also liked the food in the panoramic dining-room (*Michelin* rosette for such dishes as loup de mer en croûte). (*Geo F Outland*)

Open All year except 4 Jan–10 Feb.
Rooms 10 suites, 21 double, 2 single – all with bath and shower, telephone, radio and TV.

Facilities Bar, 2 salons, TV room, 2 dining rooms; conference facilities. 1½-acre grounds with tennis court and children's playground. Fishing nearby.
Location On W side of Echternach, off Diekirch road; follow river Sure to Berdorf turn-off. 35 km NE of Luxembourg city. Parking.
Credit cards All major cards accepted.
Terms [1989 rates] B&B: single 2,200–2,900 Lfrs, double 3,000–4,000 Lfrs, suite 4,000–5,000 Lfrs; dinner, B&B 3,100–3,700 Lfrs per person; full board 3,300–4,000 Lfrs. Set lunch/dinner 1,350–2,300 Lfrs; full alc 1,500–3,000 Lfrs. Reduced rates and special meals for children.

EHNEN 5416 — Map 9

Hôtel Bamberg — *Tel* 76022 and 76717
131 Route du Vin

Formerly known as the Hôtel de la Moselle *but still owned and run by the Bamberg family, this neat modern hostelry lies across a busy road from the Moselle river. Hospitable owners, comfortable rooms (some with balconies), and excellent food in the restaurant with its river views. Some night noises from traffic and striking clocks. Closed 1 Dec–mid-Jan and Tuesday. 15 rooms, all with bath and shower. B&B double 1,800–2,200 Lfrs. Set meals 1,500–1,900 Lfrs. More reports welcome.*

Hôtel Simmer — *Tel* 76030
117 route du Vin

The quality of the bedrooms, also the excellent food (*Michelin* rosette) and the friendly welcome, have again this year been commended at the venerable little family-run hotel facing the river. It has a 15th-century dining room (with soft lighting and quiet recorded music), much frequented by locals and by EC officials. "Wonderfully fresh asparagus and fish, and a superb rhubarb tart." "Our comfortable room was sombrely furnished but met our needs: there was even a chamber-pot. A homely atmosphere and good local wines." "Our room at the back was very quiet." (*Diana Cooper, Stephen Ruell*)

Open 12 Mar–31 Dec. Closed Tue in low season.
Rooms 19 double, 4 single – 18 with bath (14 also have shower), all with telephone.
Facilities Salon with TV, bar, dining room, banqueting facilities; terrace. Garden.
Location 10 km N of Remich. Central, parking.
Restrictions Not suitable for ♿.
Credit cards Access, Amex, Visa.
Terms B&B: single 1,650 Lfrs, double 2,300 Lfrs; dinner, B&B 2,150–2,300 Lfrs per person; full board 2,350–2,500 Lfrs. *Menu de Dégustation* 1,950 Lfrs. Reduced rates for children under 8.

ETTELBRÜCK 9010 — Map 9

Hôtel Central et Restaurant Taste-Vin — *Tel* 82116
25 rue de Bastogne

In a small town where two rivers meet, the Central *is no beauty from the outside but has inner virtues, such as pleasant owners, faultless service, large*

German-style breakfasts, and an elegant dining room with food fully worthy of its Michelin *rosette. Comfortable rooms – upper ones have the best views and are quietest (some noise on the street side). Closed 31 July–31 Aug, 24 Dec–4 Jan. 16 rooms, all with bath or shower. B&B double 1,900–2,600 Lfrs. Set menus 950–1,400 Lfrs. No recent reports. More please.*

LUXEMBOURG 1453 **Map 9**

Hostellerie du Grünewald *Tel* 431882
10–16 Route d'Echternach *Telex* 60543 HGRWD
Luxembourg–Dommeldange

The Queen of Sweden is said to have stayed at this sedate country hostelry in the northern outskirts; it is stronger on comfort and opulence than on personal charm, but staff are helpful. Elegant dining room with very good food (Michelin *rosette); pleasant garden. Restaurant closed 1–23 Jan, Sat midday and Sun. 28 rooms, all with bath or shower. B&B double 2,900–3,900 Lfrs. Full alc 2,000–2,500 Lfrs. Endorsed this year but further reports welcome.*

Traveller's tale *Among the brilliant throng that frequented the* Savoy *were some – not so brilliant. Ritz had induced the best society to dine there, but if these others, chiefly ladies of doubtful reputation and uncertain revenue, were allowed to frequent the place too much, what then? Yet how to avoid offending some of these "ladies" who brought along their princely partners of the moment? They were too ornamental, too influential, to turn away. But the others! Decidedly, something must be done!*
Ritz ordained that evening dress was de rigueur *in the dining rooms. Ladies without hats or ladies unaccompanied by gentlemen could not be admitted (another Ritz precedent that has since been always followed). The effect was magical.*
"You can lay down the law now," said Liane de Pougy, laughing airily. "For you have reached the height of your career in your profession – as I have in mine!"
"Alas," said Ritz, "I am afraid with far less pleasure and far more trouble than you have experienced, mademoiselle."
Mari Louise Ritz (César Ritz, 1938)

SANNAT Gozo **Map 16**

Hotel Ta' Cenc *Tel* (00356) 55.68.19 and 55.68.30
Telex 1479 REFINZ

Beautifully located on a high promontory, on a little island off the north-east coast of Malta, this long-admired single-storey hotel is cunningly terraced to blend into the hillside, and is built in the local honey-coloured limestone. Some rooms are bungalows, most with their own small patio. They are ranged round a central pool, with plenty of space between for oleanders, fig trees and cacti. The pool itself offers a breath-taking view of the sea and Malta beyond, and many guests are content to brown and browse there all day. There is also plenty of good rock bathing all round the island (but only one first-class sandy beach, ten kilometres away). The hotel has been criticised in recent years, but it now has an efficient new manager who is busily refurbishing the hitherto drab decor, and 1988/9 reports are nearly all favourable. "So much better than the average modern hotel. The staff were faultless and the food delicious." "Food and amenities are first-class and the staff all friendly." One reader this year thought the food erratic – some dinners superb, but breakfasts and poolside lunches disappointing. Lack of air-conditioning is a drawback, in torrid Malta. (*Michael Rubinstein, P Russell, Martin A Batteslieu, Alasdair and Moira Brown*)

Open 1 Mar–30 Nov.
Rooms 10 suites, 34 double (also let as singles) – all with bath and shower, telephone, radio, TV and patio or garden. All on ground floor. Some self-contained family bungalows.
Facilities Lounge, TV lounge, bar, snack bar, games room, restaurant; conference facilities. 3-acre garden with terraces, heated swimming pool, bar, 2 tennis courts (small charge). Disco; music in bar in season. Chauffeur service, car and motorbike hire. Hotel's rock beach with bar 2½ km (free transport by hotel bus 3 times a day), water-skiing, boats for hire, boat excursions.
Location 5 mins' walk from village (hotel provides free transport), on southern part of Gozo island, near Ta' Cenc cliffs.
Credit cards All major cards accepted.
Terms B&B £M14–£M32; dinner, B&B £M17–£M35. Set lunch/dinner £M7; full alc £M12. 1-night bookings may be refused in high season. Reduced rates and special meals for children.

XAGHRA Gozo — Map 16

Cornucopia Hotel — *Tel* (0356) 55.64.86 and 55.38.66
10 Gnien Imrik Street — *Telex* 1467 VJB

This cheerful family-run hotel, two miles inland, is a converted farmhouse with modern extensions in white stone, set attractively beside its swimming pool. It has again been liked this year: "Relaxed and informal, with plentiful, well cooked and imaginative food (poolside barbecues most enjoyable). Well-run, without being regimented; staff all friendly." A report last year was on similar lines, adding: "The new bedrooms, all well appointed and maintained, either overlook the pool or have a stunning view over the valley. A splendid honeymoon suite with jacuzzi is being completed." (*Fiona Mutch*)

Open All year.
Rooms 5 suites, 35 double – all with bath and shower, telephone; baby-listening on request. Some (with self-catering facilities) in annexe. Some ground-floor rooms.
Facilities Lounge, bar, TV room, restaurant. Garden. 2 swimming pools; 1 children's pool.
Location Outside village of Xaghra: follow signs to Xerri's Grotto.
Credit cards All major cards accepted.
Terms [1989 rates] B&B £M6–£M11.50; dinner, B&B £M7.25–£M13.50; full board £M8.75–£M14.75 per person. Set lunch/dinner £M2.75; full alc £M6.00. Reduced rates and special meals for children.

Morocco

LA ROSERAIE, OUIRGANE

FES **Map 19**

Hôtel Palais Jamai
Bab El Guissa

Tel (06) 343.31
Telex 51974

The spiritual capital of Morocco, which was founded in 808, lies in a bowl north of the Middle Atlas; in summer the lower part of the city is oppressively hot. Its grandest buildings are in Fes el-Jedid (new Fes), above Fes el-Bali (old Fes); one of these is the *Palais Jamai*, built in the 18th century by Sidi Mohamed Ben Arib El Jami, Grand Vizier to the Sultan. It now is a large and luxurious hotel in a magnificent Andalusian garden with panoramic views of the city. The bedrooms are decorated in traditional Moroccan style; the most luxurious are in the old building. "Most attractively furnished. Rooms in the new wing have breath-taking views of the old town. It is efficiently run, but a little cold and impersonal. It has an international restaurant and a traditional Moroccan one; the food is entirely satisfactory, but not memorable – the Moroccan restaurant is worth visiting for the decor, but the food and atmosphere in similar restaurants in the old town are to be preferred." "Lovely breakfasts with fresh orange juice. Good service in the Moroccan restaurant." (*PR Glazebrook, Joan Williamson*) More reports please.

Open All year.
Rooms 12 suites, 120 rooms, all with bath, telephone, radio, TV. Some on ground floor.
Facilities Lift, bar, 2 restaurants, night-club. Garden with swimming pool and tennis court.
Location North of Fes el-Bali.
Credit cards All major cards accepted.
Terms Rooms: single 650–900 Dhs, double 800–1,050 Dhs, suite 2,400 Dhs.

MARRAKECH — Map 19

Es Saadi — *Tel* (4) 488.11
Avenue Quadissia — *Telex* 72042

This old-established privately-owned hotel, built in the 1960s, set in attractive gardens with good views to the Atlas mountains and less than ten minutes' walk from the old town, has pleased readers this year: "We were made very welcome on arrival. Our bedroom had all the facilities you would expect of a five-star hotel; all rooms have a small balcony with table and seating arrangements. There is a beautiful large swimming pool with a small island; lunch by the pool offered a choice of simple and more elaborate dishes. We breakfasted outside (in March). Evening meals excellent; service efficient. Nothing Moroccan about the decor, just typical large hotel arrangements." "We could find no fault; extremely well run, with very friendly staff. Food is quite simple, but beautifully cooked and presented." (*B Ollendorff, PR Glazebrook*) The rooms in the main block are preferable to the poolside rooms. As we go to press we learn that the hotel may be up for sale.

Open All year.
Rooms 147 – all with bath and/or shower and balcony.
Facilities Salon, restaurant; boutique, hairdresser. Garden with terrace and swimming pool.
Location Central.
Credit cards All major cards accepted.
Terms [1989 rates] Rooms: single £55, double £80–£85. Breakfast from £3.50. Set meals from £5.

Hôtel Tichka — *Tel* (4) 48710
Route de Casablanca, Semlalia BP 894 — *Telex* 74855

Although *La Mamounia* (see p. 634), with its 180 rooms, 50 suites, six bars and six restaurants, remains *hors de concours* Marrakech's grandest hotel, with prices to match, and the *Es Saadi* (above) is a reasonable luxury alternative, the recently opened *Tichka* is also highly recommendable – and its tariff is a quarter that of the former. Its one shortcoming is that it is in the new city, a mile or two from the Medina and the amazing souk, in an area full of look-alike multi-storey package hotels. But the *Tichka* eschews group tourism, and is an architectural and designer's treat. Dusky rose from the outside, like most buildings in the city, its windows and balconies are chocolate-brown and turquoise; and the interior decor (by the American designer Bill Willis) is equally striking in its colour contrasts, as well as in the quality of the materials; the rooms are a pleasure to behold, besides being as comfortable as one could wish – no sign of cheese-paring anywhere. There is a large pool surrounded by palms, willows and orange trees and a well-kept substantial garden. "Best rooms are those with a pool view. Breakfast, lunches and evening drinks are taken poolside. The hotel is run with *brio* and charm. The buffet lunch was excellent." The hotel recently built a Moroccan restaurant, on which we'd be glad to have reports. Alternatively you can dine at *Stilia* or the *Yacout* in the old city – expensive but outstanding introductions to Morocco's distinctive *haute cuisine*.

Open All year.
Rooms 140 – all with bath, telephone and air-conditioning.
Facilities Lounges, bar, restaurant; night-club; health centre. Garden with swimming pool.
Location In new part of city, 3 km from the Medina.
Credit cards All major cards accepted.
Terms [1989 rates] (Excluding 5% tax) Rooms: single 280 Dhs, double 358 Dhs. Breakfast 31 Dhs. Set meals 109 Dhs.

OUIRGANE — Map 19

La Roseraie
Val d'Ouirgane
BP 769 Marrakech

Tel Ouirgane 4 and 5 (via Marrakech)

A charming small hotel outside a very simple mountain village, with bedrooms in rustic-style bungalows, each with a private bathroom and individual patio, set in a fragrant rose garden, with the High Atlas Mountains as a backdrop. It is fairly remote, being an hour or more by car from Marrakech, and the latter part of the drive is on fairly primitive mountain roads, so it is not a good base for touring. But there is plenty to do at *La Roseraie* – it has two immaculately maintained tennis courts, a large swimming pool, a newly built health centre with saunas, hammam, exercise room, and salt-water baths, and an equestrian centre where you can ride by the hour or from which you can go on treks of several days into the mountains, staying with Berber families. There are lovely walks in the grounds and in the surrounding mountains. Coach parties may stop for lunch, but are accommodated out of ear and eyeshot of the residents. Staff are friendly, the atmosphere is relaxed and peaceful. Breakfast is somewhat variable, lunch and dinner are cheerful occasions though the menu, with few options on each course, changes little from day to day, and the cooking is adequate rather than inspired. But the lunch-time table of hors d'oeuvre make an excellent meal and there are good grilled dishes. A more interesting alternative (but not recommended to those allergic to cats) is to eat at the *Auberge au Sanglier Qui Fume* in the nearby village. If you go in winter ask for a central-heated room; although the sun is bright by day, the nights can be very cold; and be warned – the water is not hot throughout the day and housekeeping can be somewhat erratic. (*CR, Joan Williamson*)

Open All year.
Rooms 15 suites (5 2-bedroomed, 10 1-bedroomed), 6 double, 3 single – all with bath and/or shower, telephone and patio. All in bungalows.
Facilities 4 salons, TV room, 2 bars, 3 restaurants. Health centre; terraces. 25-acre grounds with garden, swimming pool, 2 tennis courts, riding centre.
Location 10 mins' walk from village which is 60 km S of Marrakech.

Restrictions Not suitable for ♿.
Credit cards All major cards accepted.
Terms Rooms: single 280 Dhs, double 358 Dhs, Breakfast 31 Dhs. Set meals 109 Dhs.

TANGIER — Map 19

Hôtel El Minzah
85 rue de la Liberté

Tel 358.85
Fax 345.46
Telex 33775

A long-established and luxurious hotel, built by the Marquess of Bute in the centre of the cosmopolitan port (it is essential to ask for "superior" rooms, those on the road are noisy), set in exotic gardens, with extensive views of the harbour and the Straits of Gibraltar. "One of the best hotels we have ever visited. Splendid Moorish decor, with a feeling of space. Pleasant, friendly staff. Front room a bit noisy but spacious, with international standard of fittings combined with genuine local style. Nice choice of restaurants, though food in the main European one was rather ordinary and the Moroccan one was rather touristy (a contrast to the elegance elsewhere). We liked the small bar/restaurant best. The garden, its seating and pool were also good of their sort." (*R and J Freeman*)

Open All year.
Rooms 8 suites, 83 doubles – all with bath and shower, telephone, radio, TV and mini-bar.
Facilities 4 lounges, 2 bars, 2 restaurants, snack bar, tea-room. Courtyard. Large garden with swimming pool.
Location Central, near French consulate.
Credit cards All major cards accepted.
Terms [1989 rates] Rooms: single 460–640 Dhs, double 600–820 Dhs, suite 1,200–2,400 Dhs. Set meals 210 Dhs; full alc 260 Dhs. Special meals for children on request.

TAROUDANT — Map 19

La Gazelle d'Or
BP 260 Taroudant

Tel Taroudant 20.39 and 20.48
Telex 81902 GAZELOR

Readers often ask us to recommend a small hotel of character, well away from the bustle of a city or tourist crowds, where they can be shamelessly pampered and recuperate from the frenzy of their working lives. *La Gazelle d'Or* fulfils these needs. Classed as a 5-star establishment, it is expensive for Morocco, but not at all by the standards of Western Europe. Two kilometres from the ancient walled city of Taroudant, and an hour by a fast road from Agadir, *La Gazelle d'Or* is in a different world from either. It was once the home of a French baron, who built handsome bungalows in the grounds for his guests. There are now 30 of these small individual villas scattered round a large garden, with the High Atlas Mountains framing the horizon. Each has its own private terrace where they bring you breakfast. There are first-class tennis courts and riding stables, but life at the hotel tends to centre round the large pool, heated in the winter, where a decent buffet lunch is served. The evening meal takes place in an elegant tented dining-room. The hotel is managed with relaxed professional assurance by Bruno Hill, late of the *Savoy*. A high proportion of the clientele is English-speaking. Rooms are often booked months ahead. It is in no sense a Moroccan experience, but for those who want to get away from it all in sybaritic comfort and can afford its prices, the *Gazelle d'Or* offers a taste of one sort of earthly paradise; but be warned, the location is remote, and there are no distractions apart from what the hotel has to offer.

Open All year except August.
Rooms 2 suites, 28 double, all with bath (1 also has shower), telephone, TV, baby-listening and terrace. All in cottages.
Facilities Lounge, TV room, bar, 2 restaurants; conference facilities. Gardens with heated swimming pool, tennis and stables.
Location 2 km from Taroudant.
Credit cards All major cards accepted.
Terms Half board rates only: single occupancy 1,253 Dhs, double 1,708 Dhs, suite 3,076 Dhs. Full alc 250 Dhs.

Hôtel Palais Salam *Tel* (085) 21.30 and 25.01

A romantic palace built into the impressive red-earth walls of the city, now converted into a well-run hotel, with rooms scattered higgledy-piggledy around the premises. "The ones to ask for", we said last year, "are in the original palace facing banana groves, or the more modern suites and duplexes – designed and furnished in simple good taste, spacious and comfortable. The ones to avoid are the twin rooms on the first floor largely used for the in-and-out coach parties." But a regular visitor says: "We always *choose* the twin rooms on the first floor; in winter they are sunnier and warmer than the more sumptuous ones in the new wing – and excellent value". Another had a "charming, quiet room on an old courtyard, split level, with a sort of minstrels' gallery, nice bathroom and sitting room below; comfortable beds, best pillows yet." There is a key-shaped pool on the ground-floor, enclosed by great palms and the city walls, and a smaller rectangular one on a higher level for residents only. There are two restaurants as well – one serving bland international fare, often crowded with tourists, and another, in Moroccan style with low banquettes instead of chairs, serving specialities of the national cuisine – "very good food and lovely pâtisserie; excellent and witty head waiter. The hotel is a popular lunch or drinks stop for coach-parties from Agadir, but the coaching crowds are contained in the public rooms and swimming pool on the ground floor. Upstairs, the hotel is a peaceful and sympathetic haven. Taroudant has a good souk, with prices cheaper than in the great Marrakech one, but is not otherwise of much touristic interest. The *Palais Salam* makes an agreeable base for a stay of a night or two, but its attractions might pall on a longer visit. (*Lesley Goodden, Joan Williamson*)

Open All year.
Rooms 38 suites, 95 double – all with bath and/or shower, and telephone.
Facilities Lounge, 2 bars, TV room, 2 restaurants; conference facilities; health centre. Garden with 2 swimming pools; tennis nearby; bicycles available.
Location In town centre, within the old walls. Parking.
Credit cards All major cards accepted.
Terms [1989 rates] (Excluding 5% tax) Rooms: single 280 Dhs, double 358 Dhs. Breakfast 31 Dhs. Meals 109 Dhs.

We depend on detailed fresh reports to keep our entries up-to-date.

This selection of short listings is generously contributed by Annie Austin of Creative Leisure Management in London. We should be glad to get feedback from readers who have visited any of these hotels recently, or who can add fresh deserving names.

CASABLANCA **Hôtel Riad Salam Meridien** (5-star) *Tel* 363535 and 367922 *Telex* 24692. On beachside corniche of Casablanca. 100 rooms, 12 superb suites and 50 bungalows. Also an excellent and unique (to Morocco) Health Institute of Sea-water Therapy. Recommended for those who wish to avoid a nervous breakdown.

EL JADIDA **Club Salam des Doukkala** (4-star B) Avenue El Jamaiaa Al Arabia. *Tel* (34) 3622 and 2575 *Telex* 78014. Well-equipped club hotel with many sporting facilities and 82 rooms. Right on beach; about ten minutes' walk from centre of town. Ideal in summer for those who want a social sporting holiday on the beach in an unspoilt Moroccan town.

EL JADIDA **Hôtel de Provence** (1-star) 42 Avenue Fkih Rafy *Tel* (34) 2347. In centre of El Jadida with its own restaurant. 16 rooms, 14 with bath – good food and excellent value.

ESSAOUIRA **Hôtel des Iles** (4-star A) *Tel* (47) 2329 *Telex* 31907. Essaouira is a charming unspoilt fishing village. The *Hôtel des Iles*, with 77 rooms, belongs to the ONCF chain. Well-run and popular with British tourists.

IMMOUZER, Nr Agadir **Hôtel des Cascades** (3-star B) *Tel* 14. A lovely small (14-room) hotel recently refurbished. Next to the eponymous cascades and with superb views – a perfect place for a break. An hour's picturesque drive up from Agadir.

LAYOUNE **Hôtel Parador** *Tel* 2245 and 2200 *Telex* 28800. A beautifully decorated 31-room modern hotel in the far south run by Club Mediterranée. New on the Morocco tourist map and well worth a visit.

MARRAKECH **Hôtel Semiramis Meridien** (5-star) Route de Casablanca *Tel* (4) 313.77 *Telex* 72906. Attractive and well-run hotel in the new part of town. 186 rooms and a spectacular swimming pool – the best we have seen anywhere – set in spacious gardens.

MARRAKECH **Hôtel la Mamounia** (5-star) Avenue Bab J'did. *Tel* (4) 489.81 *Telex* 72018. Marrakech's most luxurious hotel – Winston Churchill's favourite – recently restored in lavish style. 180 rooms and 50 suites, a far cry from the original old pasha's palace. Service is excellent – and the gardens with their views towards the snow-capped Atlas Mountains superb. Accommodation and meals very expensive, even by European standards.

MARRAKECH **Hôtel Tafilalet** (4-star) Route de Casablanca. *Tel* (4) 345.18 *Telex* 72955. Immaculately run hotel with 84 rooms personally supervised by its owner, Madame Lamon.

MARRAKECH **Hôtel Imilchil** (3-star) Avenue Echouhada. *Tel* (4) 476.53 *Telex* 72018. A relatively small hotel – 86 rooms – with charming Moroccan decor but no bar serving alcohol. Well-run and excellent value.

MIDELT **Hôtel Ayachi** (3-star A) Route d'Agadir. *Tel* 21.61. 28-room *pension* hotel, owned and run by a resident family, useful as a stop-over.

MIDELT **Dayet Aoua** (2-star) Route de Fes, Ifrane. *Tel* 0. A simple small hotel with 26 rooms but one of the best French restaurants in Morocco. Set on a lovely lake with good fishing and shooting. Hotel has boats for hire.

OUALIDIA **Hôtel Hippocamp** (2-star A) *Tel* 111. On road from El Jadida to Safi overlooking the lagoon. A simple establishment, with 20 rooms. Excellent fish meals at reasonable cost.

RABAT **La Tour Hassan** (5-star) *Tel* (7) 21401 and 33814 *Telex* 31914. First opened its doors to guests in 1914 and can be considered one of the best traditional hotels in Morocco. 150 bedrooms, decorated in the latest modern pastel shades. Facilities include an authentic Chinese restaurant- and an excellent Moroccan room. Centrally situated and built around a pretty Andalusian garden.

TAFRAOUT **Hôtel Les Amandiers** (4-star B) *Tel* 8. A rather run-down 60-room hotel (the pool has not been filled for years), but friendly and a good base for anyone wishing to visit this spectacularly picturesque area.

ZAGORA **Hôtel Tinsouline** (3-star A) *Tel* 22 An unpretentious pleasant 90-room hotel at the edge of the desert in exotic, rugged surroundings. Plain but comfortable rooms and a swimming pool. Very French – many French tourists including children – and interesting food in restaurant.

Traveller's tale *It is the boast of* Barribault's Hotel, *which caters principally to American millionaires and visiting maharajahs, that it can make the wrong sort of client feel more like a piece of cheese – and a cheap yellow piece of cheese at that – than any other similar establishment in the world. The personnel of its staff are selected primarily for their ability to curl the upper lip and raise the eyebrows just that extra quarter of an inch which makes all the difference.*
PG Wodehouse (Full Moon, 1947)

The Netherlands

ALMEN 7218 AH Gelderland **Map 9**

De Hoofdige Boer *Tel* (05751) 1744
Dorpsstraat 38

Almen is a village in eastern Holland, close to the charming old town of Zutphen and not far from Arnhem and the Kröller-Müller museum (splendid Van Goghs). Here this old-established hotel, with tea-garden, comfortable lounge and unusual beamed decor, has again been liked in 1989: "An excellent place. The bedrooms are quite modern in decor, spacious and well lit, with lots of attention to homey detail – in our room, sewing and shoe-shine kit, and fresh fruit. The food is good substantial Dutch fare, and the ever-present staff are full of good cheer." Others have also enjoyed the cooking and the "friendly informality". At the back is a pleasant garden giving on to open fields. (*Lynne and David Allen*)

Open All year except New Year's Day.
Rooms 18 double, 2 single – all with bath and/or shower, and TV; 12 with telephone; baby-listening arranged. 2 ground-floor rooms.

Facilities Bar, lounge, TV room, restaurants; functions room; table tennis. Garden with tea-garden and dinner terrace. 5 mins' walk to heated swimming pool.
Location Central, near the church. Parking.
Credit cards Access, Amex, Diners.
Terms B&B: single 75 glds, double 115 glds; full board: single 115 glds, double 195 glds. Full alc 55 glds. Off-season and Christmas packages. Reduced rates for children sharing parents' room; special meals.

AMSTERDAM Noord-Holland — Map 9

Hotel Ambassade
Herengracht 341
Amsterdam 1016 AZ

Tel (020) 262333
Fax (020) 245321
Telex 10158 AMBAS

No other hotel on the Continent receives more reports, and more enthusiastic ones, than the bed-and-breakfast *Ambassade* – and that's truer than ever in 1988/89: "A treasure", "we were thrilled to bits", "the best small hotel in Amsterdam", "a wonderful greeting", are some of the enthusiastic reports we have received on this elegant bed and breakfast hotel. The secret of this success lies above all with Mr van der Velden, the manager, "always there, courteous, friendly, running the whole show without effort or tension", and with his team – "the most charming and polite hotel staff I've ever come across" and "extremely good-looking". But much depends, too, on the building and its location: seven adjoining 17th-century patrician houses on the Herengracht, Amsterdam's grandest canal. Rooms, varying in size according to their altitude in these tall buildings, are furnished in period or modern Dutch style and each has a bathroom. The public rooms have many items from the owner's personal collection of antiques – old china, clocks, paintings. Room service is amazing: "No charge for baby-sitting – one night the bell-boy rocked our son back to sleep." A feature of the hotel is the very steep steps to upper floors (normal in these old Amsterdam houses) and the spiral staircases, "hard to climb if you've been knocking back the Heineken". One reader saw all this as "an integral part of the charm". Now a lift has just been installed in a newly acquired house which connects with two of the others; there are seven rooms on the ground floor. (*John Clabaugh Leitch, Susan Chait, Patrick MacNamee, David Wurtzel, Georgene Smith, and many others*)

Open All year.
Rooms 5 suites, 39 double, 3 single – all with bath and/or shower, telephone, radio and TV; baby-sitters available. 15 in annexe. 7 ground-floor rooms.
Facilities Lift. 2 lounges, breakfast room. 24 hour room service.
Location Central, but quietly situated on Herengracht canal. Meter parking; public garage 5 mins' walk.
Credit cards All major cards accepted.
Terms B&B: single 170 glds, double 195 glds, suite 245–350 glds. Reduced rates for children sharing parents' room. (No restaurant, but drinks and light refreshments available 24 hours a day.)

> In all continental European and Scandinavian countries except Denmark, France, Hungary, Malta, Spain and Turkey, the dialling codes begin with a 0. Omit this when dialling from outside the country in question. Spanish codes begin with a 9, which should also be omitted.

Hotel Bodeman *Tel* (20) 201558
Rokin 154–6
Amsterdam 1012 LE

Centrally situated near the Rembrandtsplein, a recently opened B&B hotel in an old building, with antique furniture and a bar. Friendly owners; some rooms are large and overlook a canal. Open 1 Mar–10 Jan. 17 rooms, all with shower. B&B double 125–175 glds. New nomination. More reports welcome.

Het Canal House *Tel* (020) 225182
Keizersgracht 148 *Fax* (020) 241317
Amsterdam 1015 CX *Telex* 10412

This 17th-century merchant's house, rather elegant, stands quietly on a canal close to the Anne Frank House and five minutes' walk from the city centre. It has an attractive enclosed garden, illuminated at night. Visitors this year have again warmed to its American owners, Jane and Len Irwin, and their friendly staff; they have also liked the cosy bar, and the other public rooms. These, furnished with antiques, "have an air of faded elegance that we enjoyed". "The hall opens onto a high-ceilinged breakfast room with huge mirrors, a grand piano and white lilies everywhere. But the bedroom furnishings are ordinary." However, all rooms are comfortable and some double ones overlook the canal: the small single attic rooms are less admired. Stairs are steep, as in most canal houses of this type, but a lift has just been installed. Not all visitors admire the breakfasts. (*Dr Madeleine Montefiore, WR Halstead, Michael and Eloise Hulse, and others*) No restaurant: lots nearby.

Open All year.
Rooms 24 double, 3 single – all with bath and/or shower and telephone.
Facilities Lift. Lounge, bar, breakfast room. Garden.
Location Central. Street parking.
Restriction Not suitable for ♿. No children under 12.
Credit cards All major cards accepted.
Terms B&B: single 110–125 glds, double 145–200 glds. (No restaurant.)

Hotel de l'Europe *Tel* (020) 234836
Nieuwe Doelenstraat 2-8 *Fax* (020) 242962
Amsterdam 1012 CP *Telex* 12081

Built on the Amstel in 1895, this is one of the city's grander hotels. It has beautiful rooms and pleasant service, and this year was liked as much as ever by visitors endorsing their earlier account: "Our room was not so very spacious, but prettily decorated in cream and blue. All the public rooms are attractive, but breakfast for 15 florins is very basic." However, an inspector enjoyed a New Year's brunch that was anything but basic, "A huge variety of spectacular seafoods, and many delicious desserts. This was served in a restaurant of the highest elegance, overlooking the Amstel. The whole place had an air of ineffable grand-hotel superiority without being disdainful or snobbish." Bedrooms at the back, facing the river, are quietest. (*Kate and Stephan Murray-Sykes,*)

All inspections are carried out anonymously.

Open All year. Restaurant closed Sat midday.
Rooms 12 suites, 62 double, 40 single – 103 with bath and shower, 11 with shower, all with telephone, radio and TV. Baby-listening on request. 24-hour room service.
Facilities Lift. Lounge, bar, 2 restaurants; banqueting and conference facilities; indoor heated swimming pool, sauna, solarium; terrace overlooking Amstel where meals and drinks are served in summer.
Location Central, opposite the Mint Tower and Flowermarket (rooms double-glazed: quietest ones at back). Parking, public garage nearby.
Credit cards All major cards accepted.
Terms Rooms: single 305–405 glds, double 405–505 glds, suite 955 glds. Breakfast 20 and 30 glds. Set lunch from 52.50 glds, dinner from 65 glds; full alc 100 glds. Reduced rates for children; special meals on request.

Hotel Pulitzer *Tel* (020) 228333
Prinsengracht 315-331 *Telex* 16508
Amsterdam 1016 GZ

One of the largest hotels in our book, a sophisticated place that straddles a terrace of nine 17th-century houses, some facing the Prinsengracht and some the neighbouring canal, the Keizersgracht. "Despite its size (over 200 rooms), it feels intimate and friendly rather than impersonal. The rooms are a decent blend of old and new – original beams, exposed brickwork, slightly rustic furnishings. There is a pleasant glass-covered walkway through the gardens, with modern pictures on its walls and sculptures in the courtyards." Garden-facing rooms are quieter. The others enjoy the prospect over the canal.

Open All year. Restaurant closed in Aug.
Rooms 7 suites, 178 double, 44 single – all with bath and shower, telephone, radio, TV and mini-bar; baby-listening arranged. 25 ground-floor rooms.
Facilities Lifts. 2 lounges, bar, 2 restaurants; conference facilities; art gallery; gift shop; terrace for light meals, drinks, concerts in summer. Large garden. Private landing stage and canal boat.
Location Central, near Wester Church; garden rooms best for light sleepers. Garage 8 mins' walk; valet parking.
Credit cards All major cards accepted.
Terms Rooms: single 290–340 glds, double 340–390 glds, suite 775 glds. Breakfast 25 glds. Set lunch/dinner 35–60 glds; full alc 100 glds. Reduced rates for children; special meals for children on request.

BLOKZIJL 8356 DV Overijssel — Map 9

Kaatje bij de Sluis *Tel* (05272) 833
Brouwerstraat 20 *Fax* (05272) 836

Blokzijl used to be a prosperous Hanseatic port on the Zuiderzee and has many fine 17th-century houses; today it's an attractive yachting centre. This restaurant-with-rooms, "Katie by the canal lock", is named after a local 17th-century heroine who became an expert cook – and today the cooking is still stylish enough to earn a *Michelin* rosette, as our nominator attests: "The food is exceptional, far removed from the deservedly stodgy image that Dutch food has. The style is French-influenced, but Dutch ingredients are used intelligently, and the dishes are beautifully presented. The staff are helpful and attentive. The bedrooms, created more recently, are in a building across the bridge: our large double room was elegantly furnished and had a profusion of potted plants, typically Dutch.

Breakfast – also typically Dutch, with five types of bread – is served on the terrace or in the garden room, with a good view of the small but pretty garden and the boating manoeuvres." (*Diana Cooper*) The hotel and restaurant are in two separate buildings, one on either side of a drawbridge.

Open All year except Feb. Closed Mon and Tue. Restaurant closed for lunch on Sat.
Rooms 8 double – all with bath and shower, telephone, radio, TV and tea-making facilities. 4 ground-floor rooms. All in separate building from restaurant.
Facilities Lounge, restaurant, breakfast room. Garden, 2 terraces.
Location Blokzijl is 33 km N of Zwolle. Hotel is central (rooms double-glazed). Parking.
Credit cards All major cards accepted.
Terms B&B: single 160 glds, double 250–300 glds; dinner B&B: single 235 glds, double 400 glds. Set lunch 55 glds, dinner 75 glds; full alc 90 glds.

DELFT 2611 EE Zuid-Holland — Map 9

Hotel Leeuwenbrug
Koornmarkt 16
Delft 2611 EE

Tel (015) 147741
Fax (015) 159759
Telex 33756 ref no 013

A visitor this year found the buffet breakfast "sumptuous" and enjoyed his front room facing the canal, at this reasonably priced and friendly little B&B hotel in one of the best parts of Delft. Opposite, across the canal, are a picturesque foot-bridge and gabled houses – "the loveliest view from a hotel bedroom that I've ever had" (and at least one room has a flower-decked balcony). Some rooms are small. Only limited space in the lounge but a pleasant little bar. (*Geo F Outland*)

Open 1 Jan–25 Dec.
Rooms 30 double, 8 single – all with bath and/or shower, telephone, radio and TV. 6 ground-floor rooms.
Facilities Lift. Lounge, bar, TV room, conference facilities.
Location Take Delft Zuid turning off Rotterdam–Amsterdam highway, and follow signs to Centre West. Paid parking next to hotel.
Credit cards All major cards accepted.
Terms B&B: single 95 glds, double 135-175 glds. Reduced rates for children. (No restaurant.)

Museumhotel
Oude Delft 189
Delft 2611 HD

Tel (015) 140930
Fax (015) 140935
Telex 38026 MUSHL

Two 17th-century canal houses have recently been converted into a friendly and well-modernised hotel, set in the heart of Delft's old quarter, next to the Prinsenhofmuseum and opposite the Oude Jan church tower. Visitors this year found the staff courteous, and breakfast quite good. An earlier view: "It is run by an enthusiastic and efficient young team. The bedrooms have all amenities." Recently the hotel opened a restaurant, but we have no reports on this. (*Kathleen and Jack Beal*)

Open All year except Christmas and New Year. Restaurant closed to non-residents.
Rooms 2 suites, 26 double, 2 single – all with bath and/or shower, telephone, radio, TV and mini-bar. 4 ground-floor rooms.

Facilities Lift. Lounge, breakfast room, bar, restaurant; conference/functions room. Car and bicycle hire.
Location Next to Prinsenhofmuseum and opposite Oude Jan church. Parking.
Credit cards All major cards accepted.
Terms [1989 rates] B&B: single 118–178 glds, double 162–198 glds. Full alc 35–50 glds. Reduced rates for children sharing parents' room.

THE HAGUE (DEN HAAG) 2514 EG Zuid-Holland — Map 9

Hotel des Indes — *Tel* (070) 632932
Lange Voorhout 54-56 — *Fax* (070) 451721
Telex 31196

Situated opposite the Lange Voorhout Palace in the city centre, and facing a large tree-lined square, the elegant and expensive *Indes* was built in 1856 as a baron's residence and is now British-owned (Crest). "An excellent hotel where old-fashioned values of courtesy and good service are allied with efficiency and good food (presented prettily in the modern manner)." "The more sumptuous ground and first-floor bedrooms are better than the smaller ones higher up. But all are well equipped, with extras such as potions and fluffy bathrobes. Twin beds were narrow. Impressive flower-filled public rooms and pretty furniture. Service willing, but sometimes slow. Excellent breakfast, wonderful afternoon tea." (*Endorsed this year by Kate and Stephan Murray-Sykes*)

Open All year.
Rooms 5 suites, 55 double, 20 single – all with bath and shower, telephone, radio and TV. 24-hour room service. Ground-floor rooms.
Facilities Lift. Lounge, bar, restaurant; conference facilities. Park opposite.
Location Central, near palace. Private parking.
Credit cards All major cards accepted.
Terms B&B: single 369.50 glds, double 499 glds, suite 871 glds. Dinner, B&B: single 424,50 glds, double 609 glds, suite 981 glds. Set lunch/dinner 55–89 glds; full alc 70 glds. Reduced rates and special meals for children.

HEEZE 5591 HE Noord-Brabant — Map 9

Hostellerie du Château — *Tel* (04907) 3515
Kapelstraat 48 — *Fax* (04907) 3876)
Telex 59355

This ambitious restaurant-with-rooms (one rosette in *Michelin*) is in a pretty little town with an impressive castle in pleasant wooded country to the south-east of the big, ugly industrial town of Eindhoven, headquarters of Philips, "an attractive long two-storey yellow building with a Mediterranean touch: dark green shutters, flower-boxes, and lots of tables for outside eating and drinking". It was redecorated in 1987 and two visitors in 1989 have pronounced the accommodation quite as good as the food: "Decor and furnishings excellent and housekeeping perfect. Suite in 'attic' well worth the extra money. Dinner superb – *nouvelle* but with a local touch. Service excellent throughout." "Food and bedrooms both of a very high standard. Our double room was very attractive and large with lobby, large modern bathroom, separate loo, comfortable sleeping area divided from the sitting area by the fitted wardrobes and TV table (rotating TV so that it could be watched from the bed or the sofa). The colour scheme was pastel and soothing. Lots of windows and mirrors added to the light spacious feel. Dinner was excellent and the staff helpful and unpretentious despite the *Michelin* rosette. All in all a very pleasant experience." (*Cyril and Joyce Baily, Kate and Stephan Murray-Sykes*) One warning: "The steep stairs to the bedrooms make them inaccessible to anyone with a walking problem."

Open All year except New Year. Restaurant closed Sat midday.
Rooms 4 suites, 8 double, 2 single – all with bath and shower, telephone, radio, TV, mini-bar and baby-listening.
Facilities Lounge, bar, 2 restaurants; conference/functions facilities; covered terrace. Large garden. Golf, tennis, riding, walking and cycling nearby.
Location 10 km SE of Eindhoven, between E34 and E25 motorways.
Restriction Not suitable for ♿.
Credit cards All major cards accepted.
Terms [1989 rates] B&B: single 160–190 glds, double 210–240 glds, suite 280 glds. Set meals 52.50–115 glds; full alc 75 glds. Reduced rates and special meals for children.

HILVERSUM 1200 AP Noord-Holland — Map 9

Hotel Lapershoek
Utrechtseweg 16, Postbus 609
Tel (035) 231341
Fax (035) 284360
Telex 73068 LAPH

Near the Amsterdam-Utrecht motorway, on the edge of a city that houses the main Dutch TV and radio stations, a newly opened modern hotel, quite smart, with attentive and enthusiastic staff. Rooms vary in size but all are well furnished, some have water-beds. Very good nouvelle-*ish food. 39 rooms, all with bath and/or shower. B&B double 195 glds. Set menus 37–55 glds. New nomination. More reports please.*

LAGE VUURSCHE 3749 AJ Utrecht — Map 9

De Kastanjehof
Kloosterlaan 1
Tel (02156) 248
Fax (02156) 444

In a village north-east of Utrecht, near Baarn, a delightful white-walled restaurant-with-rooms in a large garden beside a stream, amid wooded countryside. Bright and airy rooms, a warm welcome, good sophisticated cooking. Closed 31 Dec–5 Jan. 12 rooms, all with bath or shower. B&B: single 130 glds, double 160 glds. New nomination. More reports welcome.

LEEUWARDEN 8911 AG Friesland — Map 9

Oranje Hotel
Stationsweg 4
Tel (058) 126241
Fax (058) 121441
Telex 46528

Our only entry for northern Holland is in that region's second largest city, an attractive place of canals and gabled houses. Here the *Oranje* is a sizeable and very spruce modern hotel, across a busy road from the station: rooms, however, are quiet, as well as spacious and well equipped.

"Benign owner, friendly and relaxed atmosphere, an outstanding restaurant with *nouvelle*-ish dishes, and breakfast the best I've had in Holland", says a reader this year. (*Imogen Cooper*)

Open All year except Christmas.
Rooms 78 – all with bath and shower, telephone and radio; some with TV. 1 room suitable for ♿.
Facilities Lift. Lounge, bar, 2 restaurants; conference facilities.
Location Opposite central station. Parking.
Credit cards All major cards accepted.
Terms B&B: single 140 glds, double 180 glds, suite 220–295 glds. Dinner B&B: single 165 glds, double 250 glds. Set lunch 30–45 glds, dinner 30–75 glds; full alc 40–70 glds. Reduced rates for children sharing parents' room; special meals.

LEUSDEN 3832 RS Utrecht — Map 9

Hotel Huize den Treek — *Tel* (03498) 1425
Trekerweg 23

A 17th-century mansion in a lovely wooded lakeside setting near Amersfoort, a good base for cyclists. Elegant public rooms; some bedrooms have antiques and gold brocade bedspreads and face the lake. French cuisine, possibly too ambitious; breakfast in the library. Closed 20 Dec–2 Jan. 18 rooms, all with bath and/or shower. B&B double 115–145 glds. Set menus 39–90 glds. Some criticisms of room upkeep this year. More reports welcome.

OISTERWIJK 5061 HT Noord-Brabant — Map 9

Hotel-Restaurant De Swaen — *Tel* (04242) 19006
De Lind 47 — *Telex* 52617

A very elegant and sophisticated little hostelry on the tree-lined main street of the pleasant shady town of Oisterwijk. "Superb accommodation and a wonderful meal", runs a report this year (in *Michelin*, this is one of the three restaurants in the whole country with as many as two rosettes). Other delights include a terrace in the front and a beautiful formal garden at the back; bedrooms are modern and comfortable, each with a small balcony. One reader, on her sixth visit, praised especially the breakfasts and maid service, and the availability of free bicycles. "Recently converted by a local furniture-maker, from the outside it looks like many other pleasant Dutch provincial hotels. But inside it's a veritable Aladdin's cave." "The bathrooms have gold-plated fittings!" "An exquisite and memorable meal, and the staff were most solicitous and efficient." (*Mrs V Walker-Dendle, and others*)

Open All year except 10–15 June.
Rooms 1 suite, 17 double – all with bath, shower, telephone, radio and TV.
Facilities Lift. Bar, lounge, restaurant; 2 conference rooms. Garden, terrace.
Location Central. Oisterwijk is 10 km NE of Tilberg. Parking.
Credit cards All major cards accepted.
Terms B&B: single 225 glds, double 275 glds, suite 345 glds. Set lunch 50–100 glds, dinner 110–165 glds; full alc 150 glds. Weekend rates. Special meals for children.

We are particularly keen to have reports on italicised entries.

OOTMARSUM 7631 HX Overijssel — Map 9

De Wiemsel
Winhofflaan 2

Tel (05419) 2155
Fax (05419) 3295
Telex 44667

Leading Dutch politicians and businessmen often come to relax at this spacious and sophisticated ranch-style hotel, which lies in gentle pastoral country near the German border, just east of the pretty little town of Ootmarsum. Set quietly in its own grounds, it is a number of low bungalow-style apartments attached to the main block which houses the restaurant; the modern decor is light and attractive. "Superbly luxurious, with excellent food and impeccable service", is a comment this year. Others have written: "Our room was lovely with a view over fields, and its bathroom luxurious." (*Dr GM Chapman*) One correspondent considers the food to be even better at *De Wanne* which is down in the town and under the same management. The hotel has a stable of horses for the use of guests, as well as a floodlit tennis court and a big indoor pool. It is 20 minutes' drive to the German casino across the border at Bad Bentheim.

Open All year.
Rooms 42 suites, 5 double (all also let as single) – all with bath, shower, telephone, radio, TV, tea-making facilities and baby-listening; many with terrace. 3 in villa, 50 metres from main building. Some ground-floor rooms with bathrooms equipped for ♿.
Facilities Hall, lounge, bar, restaurant; conference facilities; indoor heated swimming pool, sauna, solarium, billiard room. Large garden with terrace, tennis court and stables. Bicycles for hire.
Location 1 km E of Ootmarsum, which is 28 km N of Enschede.
Credit cards All major cards accepted.
Terms B&B 176 glds, suite 264.50 glds. Set lunch 52.50 glds, dinner 75 glds. Christmas, New Year, Easter, Whitsun packages. Reduced rates and special meals for children.

ROOSTEREN 6116 AW Limburg — Map 9

Hotel De Roosterhoeve
Hoekstraat 29

Tel (04499) 3131
Fax (04499) 4400

On the edge of a quiet village beside the Belgian border, north of Maastricht, a nicely converted farmhouse with plenty of rustic touches (beamed ceilings, log fire, painted furniture) but large modern bedrooms. Indoor and outdoor swimming pools, sauna; garden, patio; friendly staff, quite good simple food. 44 rooms (10 in annexe), most with bath and shower. B&B double 110–135 glds. Alc meals (excluding wine) 40–72 glds. New nomination. More reports welcome.

> We asked hotels to quote 1990 prices. Not all were able to predict them in the late spring of 1989. Some of our terms will be inaccurate. Do check latest tariffs at the time of booking.

> We get less feedback from smaller and more remote hotels. But we need feedback on all hotels: big and small, far and near, famous and first-timers.

VALKENBURG 6301 HV Limburg — Map 9

Hotel Prinses Juliana
Broekhem 11

Tel (04406) 12244
Fax (04406) 14405
Telex 56351 JULIA

Set in pretty countryside east of Maastricht, the charming and historic old town of Valkenburg has a ruined castle, Roman catacombs and countless grottoes, and is now a flourishing summer resort. Its best hotel, though not its largest, is the very superior *Prinses Juliana*, with cool modern decor. It has a garden, and a delightful shady terrace for summer eating, and the food, mainly traditional, wins two rosettes in *Michelin*. Recent visitors were impressed: "In the big restaurant with its well-spaced tables and silver candelabra, we tried the *menu gastronomique*, including smoked duck with foie gras, grilled fish with a herb sauce, and lamb with spinach and truffles – all excellent. Service was friendly and unstuffy. The hotel is nicely decorated in soft colours, with subdued lighting, and an open fire in the lounge. Our room also had pleasing colours, and was provided with trouser-press, hair-drier and fresh fruit. Good breakfast." Annexe rooms are cheaper, but this year one reader found them "uninspiring". We'd welcome more reports.

Open All year. Restaurant closed Sat midday.
Rooms 24 double, 3 single – all with bath, shower, telephone, radio, TV and baby-listening. 10 in annexe across road.
Facilities Lounge, TV room in annexe, bar, 2 restaurants; conference facilities. Garden, terrace.
Location Central. Garage and open parking.
Restriction Not suitable for ♿.
Credit cards All major cards accepted.
Terms Rooms: single 100–175 glds, double 120–210 glds. Breakfast 20 glds. Dinner, B&B 110–200 glds per person. Set lunch 55 glds, dinner 75 glds; full alc 75 glds. Special meals for children.

VLIJMEN 5251 EC Noord-Brabant — Map 9

Hotel Prinsen
Julianastraat 21

Tel (04108) 9131

Down a quiet road in a small town just west of 's-Hertogenbosch, and convenient for the motorway, an old family-run inn has been given a new wing of comfortable bedrooms overlooking an enclosed garden, where tables, chairs and pink parasols are set neatly on the lawn. Top-quality design and maintenance; friendly ambience; good cooking, well patronised locally. 29 rooms, all with bath and/or shower. B&B double 120 glds. Set meals 15–30 glds [1989]. Recent nomination. More reports please.

WELLERLOOI 5856 CL Limburg — Map 9

Hostellerie de Hamert

Tel (04703) 1260
Fax (04703) 2503

A fairly expensive restaurant-with-rooms (*Michelin* rosette), well suited for a self-indulgent stopover: it stands pleasantly amid lawns and tall trees by the banks of the wide Meuse (Maas), near the German frontier in northern Limburg. "It's in the middle of nowhere, between the river and a nature reserve, and close to a busy main road (but the traffic did not bother us at night, as the bedrooms do not face the road). The people of this little-known part of the Netherlands are more voluble and convivial than most Dutch, and perhaps this contributes to the dining-room's relaxed and pleasant atmosphere and its excellent service from owner and staff. People come here to eat, preferably on a fine day when you can dine on the terrace and watch the river flow past. The food is very rich, and I found it good but not exceptional – lots of high-quality expense-account ingredients such as salmon, quail, and the local asparagus for which they are famous. The cooking is old-fashioned, with lots of creamy vague-tasting sauces: none of your *nouvelle* plating in the kitchen, but carving at table. Wine list stuffy on the whole, but with a few local wines. The place does not have the feel or amenities of a hotel (no lounge) and is deserted in the morning: breakfast was poor and its service brusque. The bedrooms are comfortable, clean and neat, with some nice furniture, but have an air of faded gentility." A reader this year had no complaints: "Excellent hotel, magnificent staff, a beautifully served menu."

Open All year, but closed Tue and Wed 1 Nov–31 Mar.
Rooms 4 double – 2 with bath, all with radio.
Facilities Lounge, restaurant; 2 conference/function rooms; 2 terraces (meals served outdoors in fine weather). Garden leading to river.
Location 15 km N of Venlo on road to Nijmegen. Parking.
Credit cards All major cards accepted.
Terms B&B [1989 rates] single 70–90 glds, double 115–150 glds. Alc meals (excluding wine) 89–123 glds. Reduced rates and special meals for children.

DE WIJK 7957 NV Drenthe — Map 9

Havesathe de Havixhorst — *Tel* (05224) 1487
Schiphorsterweg 34–36 — *Fax* (05224) 1489

In a little-known part of the Netherlands, De Wijk is a village north-east of Zwolle, just off the motorway to Groningen – and here a reader this year has discovered this small 18th-century moated castle: "The red carpet leading to the front door gives way to marble inside. High ceilings, large windows - pity about the musak. Our room was clean and comfortable but not remarkable: the rooms are due to be refurbished within the next two years. The staff are young, friendly and very professional. We opted for no-meat meals and enjoyed fried quail egg, red pepper soup, herb soufflé, amid much else: all was thoughtfully conceived, and breakfast was the usual robust Dutch affair. I would recommend *Havesathe* for the food and welcome." (*Diana Cooper*) More reports welcome.

Open All year.
Rooms 8 double, 1 single – all with bath and/or shower, telephone, radio and mono TV.
Facilities Lounge, 2 bars, restaurant; conference/functions facilities. Garden; terrace. Golf nearby.
Location 6 km SE of Meppel and 25 km NE of Zwolle. Parking.
Restrictions Not suitable for ♿.
Credit cards All major cards accepted.

Terms [1989 rates] B&B 72, 50–95 glds. Dinner B&B 110–137.50 glds. Set lunch/dinner 45.50–111 glds; full alc 65 glds. Reduced rates and special meals for children.

WITTEM 6286 AA Limburg — Map 9

Kasteel Wittem
Wittemerallee 3

Tel (04450) 1208
Fax (04450) 1260
Telex 56287 KAWIT

This grey-walled 15th-century castle east of Maastricht was renovated in the 19th century in neo-Gothic style, and is now an elegant restaurant-with-rooms, surrounded by a flower garden and ancient trees, and a pond with black swans. In 1988/9, praise has again poured in, led by this report: "A real treat. The welcome was friendly and genuine. The bar area is cosy and intimate, the dining-room more grand. Here the food is superlative (*Michelin* rosette), especially ravioli filled with scallops, duck with honey, and grilled goats' cheese with quince sauce. Breakfast comes with strawberries, cherries, pumpernickel, three fruit breads, eggs, tomatoes, 'a real castle breakfast' said my daughter. A royal red carpet leads to the rooms: we had a round one, with suitably heavy furniture, wallpaper that can best be described as 'very busy'. But the bath-taps dripped, and one shelf was made of acrid yellow plastic 'enhanced' with cigarette burns. Apart from these small faults, the place is perfection." "Utterly charming." "Europe's best breakfast. Superb food, excellent service, and the twinkling eyes of the cordial owner always in evidence." One reader took the turret suite, with window seats overlooking the moat, and found the sitting-room and the grounds all "gorgeous". (*Diana Cooper; also John W Behle, Bettye Chambers, Geo Outland and others*)

Open All year.
Rooms 12 double – all with bath and shower, telephone, radio and TV.
Facilities Lounge, bar, breakfast room, restaurant; conference/banqueting facilities; terrace. Park with garden, river. Golf, cycling, walking, tennis and trout-fishing nearby.
Location Between Maastricht (17 km) and Aachen (15 km). 2 km SW of Gulpen on Maastricht road.
Restriction Not suitable for ♿.
Credit cards All major cards accepted.
Terms Rooms double 175,00 glds. Breakfast 20 glds. Set lunch 52.50–75 glds, dinner 75–110 glds; full alc 90–110 glds. Reduced rates and special meals for children.

Norway

HOTEL MUNDAL, FJÆRLAND

ÅNDALSNES 6301 — Map 7

Grand Hotel Bellevue — *Tel* (072) 21 011
PO Box 184

Mountain walking, rowing, and sea, lake and river fishing (trout and salmon, etc) are among the attractions of this resort at the head of the Romsdal fjord, south-west of Trondheim. The *Bellevue* is outwardly a rather graceless white block, but inside bright and cheerful: "A superbly friendly hotel with attentive and very obliging staff. Large modern rooms (ours overlooked the mountains) and an excellent bar and restaurant: superb local specialities such as reindeer prepared several ways, and good wine list." (*James M Lamont*)

Open All year except Christmas, New Year and Easter.
Rooms 42 double, 4 single – some with bath and/or shower, all with telephone; 22 with radio and TV. 2 ground-floor rooms.
Facilities Salon, TV room, bar, dining-room, bistro; disco. Grounds with tennis court; bicycles available; fishing nearby.
Location Central. Town is 160 km SW of Trondheim.

Credit cards All major cards accepted.
Terms [1989 rates] B&B: single 380–630 Nkr, double 500–785 Nkr. Set lunch 115 Nkr, dinner 140 Nkr. Reduced rates and special meals for children.

ASKIM 1800 — Map 7

Granheim Hotell — *Tel* (02) 88.15.30
Vammaveien 6

Attractive small inn, recently renovated, with new bedroom wing, in town 50 kilometres east of Oslo, near Swedish border, on road to Stockholm. Recommended as good overnight stop. Comfortable bedrooms with modern decor, relaxing and enjoyable atmosphere, good à la carte meals. Gentle hills, meadows, forests and inland lakes nearby; good cycling country. 25 rooms, all with private facilities. B&B double 560 Nkr. New nomination. More reports please.

BERGEN — Map 7

Augustin Hotel — *Tel* (05) 23.00.25
C. Sundtsgt. 24 — *Fax* (05) 23.31.30
5004 Bergen — *Telex* 40923 AUGUS

A dapper small hotel centrally located near the harbour in a busy fjord-girt city. "The bedrooms are small but clean and neat, and the additional facilities – large parlour and TV room, delightfully decorated breakfast room, and adjoining restaurant owned by the same management – make the hotel feel spacious. The staff are pleasant and helpful. The central location, minutes from the wharf and popular old Bryggen, made it easy to explore the city on foot." (*JT Simon; also Lizbeth and Craig Anderson*)

Open All year except Christmas.
Rooms 28 double, 10 single – all with shower, telephone, radio, and TV. 2 rooms suitable for ♿.
Facilities Lounge, TV room, breakfast room, café.
Location Central, near harbour. Public parking.
Credit cards All major cards accepted.
Terms B&B: single 395–575 Nkr, double 540–720 Nkr; Dinner, B&B: single 475–655 Nkr, double 700–880 Nkr. Set lunch/dinner 90 Nkr, full alc 175 Nkr. Reduced rates for children under 12; special meals.

Myklebust Pensjonat — *Tel* (05) 31.13.28
Rosenbergsgt. 19
5015 Bergen

"Deserves as many stars as possible," says a recent visitor of the unpretentious *Myklebust*, which occupies the upper floor of a block of flats, in a quiet but very steep street fairly near the centre. Another view, "Friendly and efficient family owners, who speak excellent English. Large, airy, comfortable, clean rooms and a good location, not too noisy." And a third, "Wonderful breakfast – every item one could think of from a Norwegian selection, brought to our room. Excellent value at half the price of some Bergen hotels." (*Rev. AG Mursell, DR Ritchie, and others*)

Open All year except Christmas, New Year and Easter.
Rooms 1 family, 4 double, 2 single – 2 with bath and shower; all with TV.
Facilities No public rooms or restaurant.
Location Central. Street parking.
Restriction Not suitable for ♿.
Credit cards None accepted.
Terms [1989 rates] B&B: single 295–480 Nkr, double 500–635 Nkr.

Hotell Neptun *Tel* (05) 32.60.00
Walckendorffsgt. 8 *Fax* (05) 23.32.02
5012 Bergen *Telex* 40040

Modern hotel, centrally situated overlooking harbour and old market, well equipped, quiet at night. Attractive restaurant offers some of the best food in Bergen – "elegant and delicious". Generous buffet breakfasts. 122 rooms, most with private facilities. B&B double 1,150 Nkr [1989]. Was in earlier editions of the Guide, but dropped for lack of feedback. Re-nominated this year. More reports please.

Park Pensjonat *Tel* (05) 32 09 60
Harald Hårfagresgt. 35 *Fax* (05) 31 03 34
5007 Bergen *Telex* 40365

Established as a bed-and-breakfast hotel for over 25 years, the *Park Pensjonat* comprises two old houses two minutes' walk apart, in a quiet residential district near the university and an attractive park. 15 minutes' walk *down* to the centre of the city (but considerably *more* to climb the steep hill back. Public rooms are slightly fussily furnished, but with some pleasant antiques. Our inspector's bedroom on the top of four floors was small, but comfortable; rooms on the lower floors, including two on the ground floor, are more spacious. Reception was friendly and helpful. Breakfast was the customary Norwegian self-help cold buffet, with good coffee and bread. The hotel caters primarily for foreign tourists and one-nighters joining or returning from cruises. Verdict: a reasonably priced, family-run, unpretentious hotel, acceptable for a two-or-three day stay.

Open All year except Easter and Christmas.
Rooms 14 double, 6 single – all with shower, telephone, radio and TV.
Facilities Breakfast room, meeting room.
Location 10–15 mins' walk from station. Parking.
Restrictions Not suitable for ♿. No smoking in breakfast room.
Credit cards Access, Visa.
Terms B&B single 360–450 Nkr, double 470–550 Nkr. Reduced rates for children.

Hotel Victoria *Tel* (05) 31.50.30
Kong Oscarsgt. 29 *Fax* (05) 32.81.78
5017 Bergen *Telex* 42190

Attractive white bow-windowed building, central and extremely comfortable. Bedrooms "with everything one could desire including umbrella (necessary) and mini-bar; conventional bedding available as alternative to duvets. Splendid buffet breakfast. Friendly, helpful staff speak excellent English." 43 rooms, all with bath/shower. B&B: single 690–740 Nkr, double 840–890 Nkr. New nomination. More reports please.

EIDFJORD 5783 — Map 7

Vøringfoss Hotel — *Tel* (054) 65184

Comfortable and welcoming white-washed hotel in lovely position at water's edge, in small village at head of Eidfjord, a branch of the great Hardangerfjord. Well situated for exploring Hardangervidda national park. Warm welcome from owner. Pleasant sitting room and bar, with old photographs, interesting pictures. Bedrooms in modern block at rear. Pretty, well-appointed dining-room overlooking water; evening meals available until 10 o'clock (unlike many Norwegian hotels, which serve promptly at 7). Recommended for a brief visit, but unexciting menu and criticisms of the cooking. 57 rooms, most with bath and shower. Dinner, B&B double 580–780 Nkr. New nomination. More reports welcome.

FJÆRLAND 5855 — Map 7

Hotel Mundal — *Tel* (056) 93101
Telex 74745 POLAR attn ORHEIM

Fjærland lies at the head of an arm of Sognefjord, Norway's longest and deepest fjord. The trim white clapboard-fronted *Mundal* sits by the water, in the shadow of Norway's largest glacier, the Jostedalsbreen. It has been run by the same family since it was built in 1891. The present owner's wife is English. A regular returning this year found the owners as kind and charming as ever, and says that the hotel is even better, thanks to continuing improvements. "The bedrooms are all different and all Norwegian in atmosphere. There is a library with English books, a billiard room and a music room with a piano. The food is plentiful and very good – for example fjord trout with butter sauce and cucumber salad – and served punctually at 7 pm. Many of the old traditions are carried on here – even breakfast butter balls fashioned by the kitchen ladies. There are antiques and beautiful furnishings made by past members of the family. Even the stair carpet is hand-woven." An inspector this year found the hotel "thoroughly congenial, and would happily return", but warned that service from some of the older staff was "kindly but slow", and that a request for a double bed resulted in "two wooden-sided beds placed next to each other". He appreciated the friendly information about nearby walks, and the electric driers for walking boots (for which no extra charge is made). Olav Orheim, a grandson of the hotel's founder and a glaciologist who has led three Norwegian expeditions to Antarctica, will take guests to visit the glacier at some 5,000 feet. (*Elizabeth Sandham, and others*)

Open Apr–end Nov.
Rooms 2 suites, 24 double, 11 single – 31 with bath and shower, 4 with shower, all with telephone.

Facilities Hall, lounge, TV room, music room, library/billiard room, bar, 2 restaurants. Garden on fjord; rowing boat free of charge; fishing (equipment can be borrowed); swimming possible, but very cold.
Location 180 km NE of Bergen. Reached by express boat service, ferry and bus.
Restriction Not suitable for ♿.
Credit cards None accepted.
Terms B&B 335–550 Nkr; dinner, B&B 510–725 Nkr. Set dinner 175 Nkr; full alc 250 Nkr. Reduced rates on special meals for children.

LOEN 6878 — Map 7

Alexandra Hotel

Tel (057) 77 660
Fax (057) 77 770
Telex 42665 ALEX

A luxurious large modern six-storey hotel "with a touch of luxury", in a valley surrounded by majestic mountains and fjords, waterfalls and glaciers, in an area good for summer skiing, mountain climbing and fishing. Not a typical Guide hotel, but readers have appreciated the beautiful situation, spacious and well-equipped bedrooms and public rooms, the friendly and helpful staff, the facilities offered for both parents and children including "endless activities" (see below), and the good food. More reports please.

Open All year.
Rooms 210 – all with bath and shower, telephone and radio.
Facilities Lift. 3 bars, 4 lounges, children's playroom, café, restaurant; conference facilities; hairdresser; indoor heated swimming pool, sun terrace, saunas, solarium, gym; dancing nightly in bar. Garden with tennis and mini-golf. Near sea with fishing and water sports.
Location 10 km E of Olden. Nearest station at Otta (200 km); bus connection.
Credit cards All major cards accepted.
Terms [1989 rates] B&B: single 540–1,190 Nkr, double 640–1,880 Nkr. Set lunch 115 Nkr, dinner 200 Nkr. Reduced rates and special meals for children.

LOM 2686 — Map 7

Røisheim Hotell
Bøverdalen

Tel (062) 12031

High above sea-level on the ancient Sognefjell road, a cluster of picturesque turf-roofed 18th-century farm buildings, a hotel since 1858. Bedrooms in romantic old annexes, some with private bath. Nominators' room was old-Norwegian in appearance, with painted wooden walls, wooden floor with a rug and little furniture apart from beds. Recommended for warmth, comfort, charming decor, good food, attractive public rooms, welcoming hosts. Open Apr–Oct. 25 rooms, 9 with bath and/or shower. B&B double 441–725 Nkr. Set dinner 200 Nkr. New nomination. More reports please.

> Hotels often book you into their most expensive rooms or suites unless you specify otherwise. Even if all room prices are the same, hotels may give you a less good room in the hope of selling their better rooms to late customers. It always pays to discuss accommodation in detail when making a reservation.

NORDFJORDEID 6771 Map 7

Nordfjord Hotell
POB 144

Tel (057) 60 433
Fax (057) 60 680
Telex 42971 EIDRB N

Near fjord and not far from west coast and mountains, well-placed for tours of the region. Modern Scandinavian in style with sleek, warm furnishings; open plan sitting rooms, spacious dining-room; discos, billiards, sauna, large garden with tennis; fishing, excellent walks nearby. Recommended for friendly staff, well-equipped bedrooms, unexpectedly high standard of cooking. Closed 22 Dec–4 Jan. 55 rooms, all with bath and/or shower. B&B 350–670 Nkr. Set dinner 170 Nkr. New nomination. More reports please.

OSLO Map 7

Hotel Continental
Stortingsgt. 24-26
0161 Oslo 1

Tel (02) 41.90.60
Fax (02) 42.96.89
Telex 71012 CONTI

Opposite the National Theatre, this large solid building, dated *c.* 1900, has been in the same family for four generations and is in the grand old style. Over 100 of its bedrooms have recently been renovated and the windows are now triple-glazed against street noise. But the dining-room remains classically formal, with chandeliers and serious waiters. "Oslo has, more than any other European capital, preserved the traditions and atmosphere of the 19th century. The *Continental* retains the grave dignity, courtesy and friendly warmth which visitors to Norway so much appreciate. I could wax even more lyrical over the breakfast's cold table." And of the hotel's famous *Theatercaféen*, another correspondent writes, "The last really Viennese-style restaurant in Scandinavia – a large room, with stained wood, mirrors and a stuccoed ceiling supported by tall white columns with decorated capitals. Food was super and people were having a good time, including us." We would welcome more reports.

Open All year except Easter.
Rooms 12 suites, 124 double, 43 single – all with bath, shower, telephone, radio, TV with video.
Facilities 2 lifts. Lounge, bar, restaurant, grill, café; conference/banqueting facilities; discothèque daily except Sun and Mon; terrace.
Location Central, between Royal Palace and National Theatre. Underground carpark.
Restriction Not suitable for ♿.
Credit cards All major cards accepted.
Terms B&B weekday rates: single 1,190 Nkr, double 1,450–1,530 Nkr, suite 2,100–3,400 Nkr; weekend rates: single 515 Nkr, double 830 Nkr. Extra bed 100 Nkr (cots free).

Gabelshus Hotell
Gabelsgt. 16
0272 Oslo 2

Tel (02) 55.22.60
Telex 74073 GABEL

A quiet, comfortable and friendly hotel on a tree-lined residential street not far from the centre of Oslo, with the city's excellent public transport only three minutes' walk away. Considerably cheaper than the large city-centre hotels – booking is usually essential. The lobby, decorated in dark wood, is reminiscent of a hunting lodge in the country. Bedrooms are clean and comfortable with an "understated and very restful decor. We had an early train to catch so the staff prepared a continental breakfast for us at 6.30 am." The restaurant offers good (but not gourmet) reasonably priced meals. (*Lizbeth and Craig Anderson, Martha Swartz*)

Open All year except July.
Rooms 32 double, 14 single – all with bath and shower, telephone, radio and TV.
Facilities Lift. Lounge, TV room, bar, dining-room; conference facilities. Garden.
Location Between Bygdøy alle and Drammensv. 15 mins' walk from city centre; bus and tram nearby. Parking.
Restriction Not suitable for ♿.
Credit cards All major cards accepted.
Terms [1989 rates] B&B: single 750 Nkr, double 950 Nkr. Full alc from 250 Nkr. Special meals for children.

ØVRE EIDFJORD 5754 — Map 7

Bessåa Touristhytta — *Tel* Hardangervidda west 88938
(via operator – 0104)
Off season (054) 65927

By a substantial margin, our most way-out entry! The Hardangervidda is a vast high plateau east of Bergen, dotted with lakes; vast herds of reindeer graze on its pastures. There are no roads, or settlements of any size. It is "a walkers' paradise", with an extensive system of paths usually running from one lake to another and linking the mountain huts, one of which is nominated this year by intrepid walkers: "Bessåa is a single-storey wooden building 29 kilometres from the nearest road; walking boots are necessary for crossing the rough terrain. There are only 30 beds, but all who turn up are guaranteed accommodation. The reception was homely and efficient. Our twin-bedded room (others have four to six beds) had pine walls and furniture, table, mirror, chair, jug and bowl for washing – hot water came from an urn near the kitchen. The lights above the firm and comfortable beds were adequate for reading and we were given candles for when the generator stopped working at 9.15 pm. There was floor space for luggage. Take your own sheets or sleeping bag; pillows, blankets and duvets are supplied. There is a large cold shower room, the earth closet, clean and throne-like, is a short walk across the yard. The sitting-room is well furnished with comfortable chairs, tables for route-planning and open fires. The dining room is light and airy, waitress service prompt and efficient. The three-course meal was excellent, everything home-made – soup, beef stew, three vegetables – and served very hot; pudding was fruit salad with huge helpings of fresh cream. The breakfast was the best we had in Norway: home-smoked salmon, fresh salmon, huge plate of home-made butter, cheeses and ham all served with good hot coffee. (*Susan and John Aglionby*)

Open Easter and April, 1 July–10 Sept.
Rooms 7 double, 5 4-bedded; 3 in annexe.
Facilities Lounge, dining room. Lake with fishing and swimming 15 metres.
Location In the Hardangervidda, S of Eidfjord, 5 hrs' walk from nearest road.
Terms [1989 rates] Per person: In 4-bedded room 75 Nkr, in double 110 Nkr. 55 Nkr for bedlinen. Breakfast 48 Nkr. Set dinner 90 Nkr.

SKJOLDEN 5833 — Map 7

Skjolden Hotel

Tel (056) 86 606
Fax (056) 86 720
Telex 40654 SOGTU

Situated at the end of the Lusterfjord (a branch of the long Sognefjord), this square flat-roofed hotel, owned by the Galde family for 75 years, is popular as a base for hiking, fishing and other sports. The surrounding countryside is magnificent for touring as well. The hotel offers large sitting-rooms furnished in a modern style, an open terrace, a fairly big garden, and a "very large and light restaurant serving plain but adequate food, well cooked, in substantial portions". Bedrooms are simply but comfortably furnished with light wood furniture and feathered duvets, though with poor insulation. Recommended for its beautiful situation and good value, acceptable for a three-to-four day stay. More reports welcome.

Open May–Sept.
Rooms 38 double, 16 single – 50 with bath and shower.
Facilities Lift. Lounges, restaurant. Large garden, badminton. Fjord 20 metres, free rowing boats.
Location In the western fjords north-east of Bergen, 75 km from Sogndal airport.
Credit cards Visa.
Terms B&B 255–360 Nkr. Set meals 130 Nkr. 50% reduction for children up to 15.

TRONDHEIM 7011 — Map 7

Neptun Hotel and Bistro

Tel (07) 51.21.33

Ths Angellsgt. 12b

Newly renovated, a modern hotel centrally situated in the historic cathedral city, on the site of a seamen's hostel, rebuilt in the early 1980s to a high standard. "Our spacious bedroom was remarkable. It had four windows facing the street; the double bed which had a firm and comfortable mattress in a creaking old bedframe, was in a curtained alcove. The furniture had been rescued from a Norwegian cruise ship built in 1908. More modern facilities included TV, mini-bar and telephone. The bath was deep and there was a good supply of towels. Most of the double rooms look over the street which is noisy; singles face the rear. The reception area is part of the bistro/restaurant and there is a lounge. We did not dine in the hotel but the à la carte meals appeared to be reasonably priced and adequate. The breakfast buffet offered a good choice including fresh fruit. Our fellow guests were mainly Norwegian." (*Susan, Francis and John Aglionby*) More reports please. Visitors in search of more luxurious accommodation could try the nearby 177-roomed *Britannia*, Dronningensgt. 5, *Tel* (07) 53.00.40, *Fax* (07) 51.09.00, *Telex* 55451.

Open All year. Bistro/restaurant closed Sun evening.
Rooms 36 – all with bath/shower, telephone, radio, mini-bar.
Facilities Lounge, bistro/restaurant; banqueting room.
Location Central.
Credit cards Probably some accepted.
Terms [1989 rates] B&B: single 365–665 Nkr, double 540–825 Nkr.

ULVIK 5730 — Map 7

Ulvik Fjord Pensjonat

Tel (05) 526170
Fax (05) 526170

A small guest house, new to the Guide this year, on the edge of an attractive village, now a popular resort, in western Norway on an arm of the Hardangerfjord, sheltered on three sides by impressive mountains. It has been run by for the past 16 years by Lilly and Odd Hammer, who speak excellent English. It has a white weatherboarded exterior and is separated from the road by a small garden. Lounges are pleasantly furnished, there is a spacious dining-room; dinner, announced by a bell, is served punctually at 7 pm – "beautifully cooked by Odd Hammer, and served by Lilly with the help of a young girl, in a friendly unhurried manner. No choice but it included fresh sea trout, and second helpings were offered. Breakfast was the usual generous self-help buffet. Our bedroom was small but adequate, though lighting, except for the bedside lights rather poor. Comfortable bed. The private shower/loo had been cut out of the long side of the room and was really too small, but the baths for general use were excellent. All the other guests were British; it is well situated for walking holidays." (*Francis and Susan Aglionby*) More reports please.

Open 1 May–20 Sept.
Rooms 18 double, 2 single – 17 with shower. 7 in annexe.
Facilities 3 sitting/TV rooms, dining-room. Garden.
Location 500 metres from centre. 44 km E of Voss.
Restriction Not suitable for ♿.
Credit card Visa.
Terms B&B 225–375 Nkr. Set meals 135 Nkr. 5-day rates.

UTNE 5797 — Map 7

Romantik Utne Hotel

Tel (054) 66 983

Warmly admired for many years, this delightful little hotel on the Hardangerfjord, east of Bergen, is Norway's oldest (founded 1722) and has been run by the same family since 1787. It is a white clapboard building, lovingly maintained, with flowers in all the public rooms, embroidered cushions, lace curtains, and lots of old painted Norwegian furniture. "Its setting is splendid, at the foot of a steep promontory where the Hardanger branches into two small fjords; high blue mountains across the water; sheer cliffs above it; a waterfall plunging down the cliff face and rushing through the village; apple orchards on each side. There are fine walks along the fjord in both directions or you can climb paths to the high pastures. The village is small and tranquil; the *Utne* stands in its centre opposite the boat landing. Behind it, on the hillside, is a small modern annexe. Meals (taken communally) are hearty and excellent. Fru Aga Blokhus and her staff, wearing the Hardanger costume, look after you with grace and enthusiasm." "We were made to feel as house guests in a gracious and charming country house." An inspector this year confirmed these accounts, "A comfortable, charmingly furnished room. The food was delicious and there was an interesting wine list with prices moderate by Norwegian standards." (*Elizabeth Sandham, Mrs J Gould, and others*)

Open All year except Christmas and New Year.
Rooms 20 double, 4 single – 4 with bath, 15 with shower. 7 in nearby annexe.
Facilities 3 sitting-rooms, basement café, dining-room; some off-season conference facilities; games room, badminton. Garden and terrace; sailing, fishing, boating, cycling and good walks.
Location At tip of Folgefonn Peninsula; at Odda cross bridge on to peninsula, or take ferry from Kvanndal or Kinsarvik.
Restriction Not suitable for ♿.
Credit cards All major cards accepted.
Terms B&B 275–460 Nkr. Set lunch 125 Nkr, dinner 170 Nkr. Reductions for long stays. 50%–70% reduction for children under 12 in parents' room.

VOSS 5700 — Map 7

Park Hotell Voss — *Tel* (05) 51.13.22
Boks 190 — *Fax* (05) 51.00.39
Telex 42587

Voss is a well-known resort at east end of the Vangsvatn, in the heart of beautiful fjord country – Sognefjord to the north, Hardangerfjord to the south – a region of orchards, waterfalls, glaciers, winter sports. The Park *is central; well run, with attractive public rooms and bedrooms, "magnificent" buffet dinner including four hot dishes, good breakfasts. Coffee bar always open. Bedrooms "nice but small". 106 beds. B&B double 850–2,100 Nkr. Set meals 175 Nkr. New nomination. More reports please.*

> There is inevitably less feedback from Scandinavia than from other more touristy parts of Europe. If you have been to Scandinavia and stayed in a good hotel, whether in the present Guide or not, please write and tell us.

Portugal

ESTALAGEM QUINTA DA CAPELA, SINTRA

AMARANTE 4600 Porto **Map 12**

Zé de Calçada *Tel* (055) 42.20.23
Rue 31 de Janeiro

Amarante is a picturesque small town, its 16th-, 17th- and 18th-century houses with wooden balconies and wrought-iron grilles are built in tiers up a hillside overlooking the river Tâmega. It is well-known for its pastries and its vinho verde, and now appears in the Guide for the first time with this nomination: "Just by the old bridge in the centre stands the *Zé de Calçada* restaurant with a rustic decor, where you eat well and prettily on the riverside terrace. It has a house across the narrow cobbled street containing seven bedrooms, each with a bath, one with a kitchen too. All are refurbished, with a touch of the Laura Ashleys. Mount, if you can, the four flights of gleaming wooden steps to the topmost room which has a tiny terrace and a three-star view of the Italianate front of the church of San Gonçalo, the patron of conjugal love – on his day the town celebrates by baking properly priapic pastries. Amarante's finest residence is being converted into a spectacular *pousada*, but we shall return to the *Zé de Calçada*." (*Christine and Stephen Wright*)

Open Probably all year.
Rooms 7 double – all with bath, 1 with kitchen. All in building opposite restaurant.
Facilities Restaurant; terrace.
Location In centre of town 64 km E of Oporto.
Credit cards Possibly some accepted.
Terms Double room 6,150 esc. Set dinner 1,500 esc.

ARMAÇÃO DE PERA 8365 Faro — Map 12

Hotel do Levante — *Tel* (082) 323.22
Telex 57478 LEVANT

Eight miles west of Albufeira, on the Algarve coast, a modern family-run holiday hotel, functional but attractively so, set on a cliff above a lovely sandy beach. Large swimming pool, lido and garden; fine views. Service good and cooking well above average, especially fish. 41 rooms, all with bath and shower. B&B: single 4,300–11,500 esc, double 6,050–16,500 esc. Set menu 2,500 esc [1989]. Recent nomination. More reports please.

AZEITÃO 2925 Setúbal — Map 12

Estalagem da Quinta das Torres — *Tel* (065) 208.00.01

Azeitão, on the old Lisbon–Setubal road, consists of two small adjacent villages set amid vineyards and olive orchards. It is a good base for touring the Arrabida peninsula with its beautiful coastline and fine beaches. The *Quinta das Torres* – "a poetic retreat" – is a beautiful rather shabby old house, said to have been an elegant social venue for the wealthy residents of Lisbon before the 1974 Revolution, in its own grounds, with a small ornamental lake. It is finely furnished with family antiques, portraits and prints (including, oddly, some of Scotland). Readers enjoy its "old-world charm, tinged with gentle melancholy" and the high-ceilinged bedrooms. One is in a tower wing overlooking the courtyard with its Renaissance fountain and orange trees, and has a four-poster bed "worthy of Catherine of Braganza". "Dinner was excellent and exquisitely served; breakfast is taken in the bedroom." "Wholeheartedly endorse your report. It is one of the most atmospheric places to stay in Portugal." (*ATW Liddell*)

Open All year.
Rooms 2 suites, 6 double, 2 single – all with bath, shower and tea-making facilities. 2 bungalows in grounds with kitchenette and lounge. Some ground-floor rooms.
Facilities Lounge, bar, restaurant; terrace. 30-acre grounds. Sandy beaches 15 km.
Location 27 km W of Setúbal off N10; in village centre. Parking.
Credit cards None accepted.
Terms On application.

Report forms (Freepost in UK) will be found at the end of the Guide.

BOM JESUS DO MONTE 4700 Braga — Map 12

Hotel do Elevador *Tel* (053) 250.11
Parque do Bom Jesus do Monte

Bom Jesus is a 19th-century religious shrine on a mountain-top just outside the old town of Braga, in the "tender green vinho-verde country of the Minho, glorious to drive through, with some interesting old towns and villages". The old-style *Elevador* is inside the park surrounding the shrine. It is a small hotel, "the best at Bom Jesus, with an old-fashioned elegance and fantastic views, more a place for the Portuguese than foreign tourists, so it has not been gussied up and spoiled". A recent visitor praised her large and comfortable room with lovely views and found the staff very friendly. The food has been described as "standard hotel type", but there's a good selection of local wines. More reports please, especially on the food.

Open All year.
Rooms 25 double – all with bath.
Facilities Salon, restaurant. Garden.
Location 50 km NE of Oporto, 6 km SE of Braga.
Credit cards All major cards accepted.
Terms [1989 rates] B&B double 8,500 esc. Full board 7,450–10,700 esc. Set meals 1,700 esc.

BUÇACO 3050 Aveiro — Map 12

Palace Hotel do Buçaco *Tel* (031) 931.01
Floresta do Buçaco *Fax* (031) 936.09
Telex 53049 BUCACO

Readers continue to disagree about the merits of this 19th-century royal hunting lodge situated in the middle of the ancient oak and cypress forest on the ridge of Buçaco, described by Wellington as "a damned long hill". Wellington prepared for battle against Masséna in the Carmelite convent next to the hotel. The *Palace Hotel* itself is decorated with faïence and paintings illustrating both the battle and Portuguese maritime journeys. "It's difficult not to succumb to its cake-frosting architecture – like a wealthy dowager, who has piled on the rouge and ruffles and yet is fun to be around. I highly recommend this hotel. Even with its rough edges and excesses, it is a wonderful stop." (*Suzanne Carmichael*) But also, "Wins the prize of the decade as the hotel we least wish to return to." Or, "The charm of the place is its run-down old maple furniture, its quaint plumbing, and its period atmosphere – a bit like a Portuguese version of *Raffles* in Singapore"; and, "Bathrooms are ghastly – worn enamel, stained loos, and tatty decoration – untouched for thirty or forty years." Now much frequented by coach parties, it is praised for its good wine list. The owners tell us that the hotel is being completely renovated this year. More contributions to the debate welcome.

Open All year.
Rooms 4 suites, 56 double – all with bath and telephone. Some ground-floor rooms.
Facilities Lifts. Salon, TV room, bar, restaurant; conference facilities. Garden and large park; tennis courts.
Location 22 km N of Coimbra on N234.

Credit cards All major cards accepted.
Terms B&B: single 17,300 esc, double 18,150 esc. Set lunch/dinner 3,100 esc. Reduced rates and special meals for children.

CASCAIS 2750 Lisbon **Map 12**

Hotel Albatroz *Tel* (01) 28.28.21
Rua Frederico Arouca 100 *Fax* 284.48.27
Telex 16052 ALTROZ

A trim classical villa, built for the Portuguese royal family in the mid-19th century, now a hotel with a modern wing, and "highly recommended for understated luxury". It is set on a rocky headland by the sea, in a relatively unspoiled fishing-port west of Lisbon; most rooms have panoramic views over the Bay of Cascais and the adjacent coastline. Recent reports praise the locally popular restaurant, the immaculate linen and towels, the comfortable beds, and the service; a writer who has known the hotel for years now finds it "quite restored to its former excellence". (*Suzanne Carmichael, Ralph Dubery, and others*) Some readers, however, have had reservations: poor reading lights in the bedroom, variable housekeeping, and discourtesy from the staff at reception.

Open All year.
Rooms 3 suites, 36 double, 1 single – all with bath and shower, telephone, radio and TV; most with air-conditioning and balcony. 2 ground-floor rooms.
Facilities Lift. Salon, bar, TV room, dining room; conference facilities; terrace. Music evenings. Unheated saltwater swimming pool.
Location On bay, near station. Parking.
Restriction Not suitable for ♿.
Credit cards All major cards accepted.
Terms B&B: single 13,000–26,500 esc, double 15,000–31,000 esc, suite 21,000–45,000 esc. Full alc 5,500 esc. Reduced rates for children; special meals on request.

Estalagem Senhora da Guia *Tel* (01) 28.92.39 and 28.97.85
Estrado do Guincho *Telex* 42111 GUIA

"Two families – two adults and two children each – were made to feel *so* welcome. Every request was answered and the children were treated like royalty. Breakfasts out of this world, including fresh fruit, as much as we wanted to eat, and we were never hurried. Our bedrooms were spotless, clean towels all the time, beds turned down at night." "Food good and clientele civilised." "Pleasant atmosphere, still something of a private house." This enticing white-walled holiday hotel on a promontory amid trees, about ten minutes' drive from Cascais, was once a villa built by a brewer. Some of the rooms have been converted from the stables, others have terracotta-tiled balconies with coastal views, where one can breakfast or have drinks. The large, comfortable lounge/bar and restaurant are "beautifully kept"; drinks and meals are also served on the terraces in the garden by the ample but unheated sea-water swimming pool. (*Susan Haskell, HR, and others*) A drawback is the hotel's position – "it is on the main road, with the constant noise of traffic passing along the coast, and is in a very windy spot". And one reader this year considered the meals "not wonderful, and rather pricey", but concluded, "we would certainly recommend this hotel to our friends".

Open All year.
Rooms 4 suites, 24 double – all with bath and shower, telephone, baby-listening; TV on request. 12 in 2 annexes. Some ground-floor rooms.
Facilities Lounge/bar with fireplace and balcony, restaurant. *Fado* singers once a week. Garden with swimming pool, children's pool, bar/restaurant. Beach 3 km (bus from hotel). Golf, tennis and riding nearby.
Location 2 km W of Cascais on road to Guincho.
Restriction Not suitable for ♿.
Credit cards All major cards accepted.
Terms B&B: single 6,500–20,500 esc, double 7,000–21,000 esc, suite 12,000–25,000 esc; dinner, B&B: single 9,000–23,000 esc, double 12,000–26,000 esc, suite 17,000–30,000 esc. Set lunch/dinner 2,500 esc. Children under 8 half price; special meals on request.

ESTOI 8000 Faro — Map 12

Monte do Casal
Cerro do Lobo
Estoi, Nr Faro

Tel (089) 91503 and 91341
Telex 56682 MONTCA

Converted farmhouse with swimming pool, and one-acre garden, run by English couple, Bill and Carol Hawkins. Twenty minutes by car from Algarve coast. Recommended – "if you have to be near this overdeveloped area" – for tranquil setting, informal atmosphere, simple, clean bedrooms, reasonable food. No children under 16. Open 2 Mar–4 Jan. Limited menu on Mon. 3 suites, 4 double rooms, all with bath and shower; 4 more planned for 1990. Double room £30–£53, suite £39–£70. Set lunch £8.75, dinner £12.75. New nomination. More reports please.

FUNCHAL 9000 Madeira — Map 12

Quinta Penha de França
Rua da Penha de França 2

Tel (091) 290.87

This small hotel of real character, "an astonishing green oasis, not far from the centre of busy Funchal" is exceptional in Madeira's sadly overdeveloped capital, now crammed with many large and impersonal hotels. It is an old building in a charming garden and several readers have written this year in praise of "the peace and comfort among the high-rise horrors", the friendly, hard-working staff, the "very leisurely, elegant" breakfasts on the terrace, and the "nicely furnished, very comfortable" bedrooms, particularly the studios in the grounds, and the rooms in the handsome new annexe. "The sea-water swimming pool is spotless; there are several restaurants within walking distance, but if you are unambitious you can survive pleasantly on the *quinta*'s simple but tasty and nicely presented meals – soups, salads, omelettes, dish of the day and fruit – served on the terrace. Recent visitors have not been bothered by evidence of package trade; the building works in the neighbourhood are now completed, but during the day there can be some noise from the harbour below. (*Mrs A Colbatch Clark, Isabel and John Brasier, Dr and Mrs IM Ingram, and others*)

Open All year.
Rooms 35 double – all with bath and/or shower, and telephone. Some in annexe, some in garden studios.

Facilities Lounge, snack bar, terrace. Large garden with sea-water swimming pool; near sea and rock beach.
Location Central.
Restriction Not suitable for ♿.
Credit cards All major cards accepted.
Terms [1989 rates] B&B double 12,000 esc. (No restaurant, but light meals served.)

Reid's Hotel — *Tel* (091) 230.01
Estrada Monumental 139 — *Fax* (091) 304.99
Telex 72139

A large, grand and very famous 19th-century hotel on the outskirts of Madeira's capital, set gracefully apart on a cliff above Funchal Bay with magnificent semi-tropical gardens and numerous impressive and high-ceilinged public rooms, including a "superb pre-war style billiard room". There are two swimming pools on the level of the hotel, where a buffet lunch is served, and you can walk down through the gardens to swim in the sea or in a rock pool. *Reid's* has over the last few years been extensively renovated, and all the sea-facing rooms now have a balcony, but it keeps up the old traditions such as afternoon tea on a terrace and formal dress at dinner, where a pianist plays "the tunes of yesteryear". It has many devotees who return year after year. "After a break of three years, nothing seemed to have changed – that is why so many visitors go back. We recognised many old faces, both staff and guests. An ideal place for total rest. We had a quiet, spacious bedroom in the main building; rooms are not luxurious but very clean and comfortable, with excellent housekeeping and the most charming and discreet chambermaids. Service could not be faulted. In the dining-room there is a set menu with a reasonable amount of choice; the Grill Room has more choice, on an à la carte menu; it is more expensive, but not necessarily better. *Reid's* reminds me of one of those traditional hotels in India, but with the the benefit of Madeira's equable climate, high standards of cleanliness and expertise of service and management." (*Alan Greenwood; also Isabel and John Brasier*) The hotel tells us that a new road will take much transit traffic away from the rear of the building. A new manager arrived early in 1989 so we'd be glad of more reports.

Open All year.
Rooms 15 suites, 145 double, 21 single – all with bath and/or shower, telephone, radio and baby-listening. Suites have TV. Room service.
Facilities Lifts. 3 lounges, 2 bars, TV room, card room, restaurant, grill room; tea terrace. Large garden with 2 heated swimming pools, 2 tennis courts; lift and 3 flights of stairs down to sea with swimming pool, changing rooms and bathing platform; windsurfing, sailing, fishing etc.
Location 1 km from town centre.
Restriction Not suitable for severely ♿.
Credit cards Access, Amex.
Terms [1989 rates] B&B: single £61–£91, double £88–£141, suite £140–£500. Half board £19 added to room rate, full board £34 added. 1-night bookings sometimes refused over Christmas/New Year. Reduced rates and special meals for children.

> In Portugal, reservations for pousadas can be made direct or through Enatur, Avenida Santa Joana Princesa, 10-A, 1700 Lisbon.Tel (01) 88.12.21. Telex 63475.

GUIMARÃES 4800 Braga — Map 12

Pousada da Santa Marinha — *Tel* (053) 41.84.53
Estrada da Penha — *Telex* 32686

This ancient town at the foot of the mountains north-east of Oporto was the birthplace in 1109 of Portugal's first king, Alfonso Henriques, and is now a prosperous commercial city. It has two *pousadas*, the centrally situated *Santa Maria da Oliveira*, a quite small, remodelled 17th-century castle, which is omitted this year for lack of feedback, and the *Santa Marinha*, newly opened and luxurious, and recommended to the Guide this year. It is a former monastery, set above Guimarães, overlooking the surrounding hills, with beautiful cloisters with fountains, formal gardens "and lots of fascinating nooks and crannies". The original church next door still operates. Some bedrooms are in a lower wing, modern, luxurious, but impersonal; the most attractive ones are in the former cells. "This was one of the most spacious, well-furnished *pousadas* we visited. It is discreetly grand, with enormous reception rooms filled with antiques, oil paintings, luxurious carpets, hand-painted wall tiles. The cells are off a vast hall, and are comfortably furnished, each with private bath; ours had an unusual small double window with a prayer stool. They look over the garden or the town (we recommend the town view)." "The dining room is a somewhat cavernous refectory with high ceilings, many archways. Food typically *pousada*, i.e. acceptable but not noteworthy. Probably the best *pousada* in Portugal; prices are high as it is in the de luxe range." "Service efficient and unobtrusive, room quiet and comfortable, gardens and woods to wander in. Peace and tranquillity." (*Nigel and Sarah Walker, Suzanne Carmichael, ATW Liddell, RM Rowan*)

Open All year.
Rooms 51 – all with bath and shower.
Facilities Lift, salons, bars, dining-room; conference facilities; courtyard, terrace, garden.
Location 2.5 km E of Guimarães on road to Penha.
Credit cards All major cards accepted.
Terms [1989 rates] B&B: single 7,500–12,600 esc, double 10,000–14,400 esc. Set meals 2,500 esc.

LAMEGO 5100 Viseu — Map 12

Villa Hostilina — *Tel* (054) 623.94

A former farmhouse on a hill overlooking the attractive old town of Lamego, in a wine-growing area near the Douro Valley. "A beautiful location. There always seems to be a festival going on. From the little tiled terrace that leads off your bedroom, gentle vine-covered hills roll into the blue distance. Immediately below is the house's own vineyard where, if you're up early enough, you can watch the workers tend the vines. It is the most peaceful prospect imaginable. Downstairs a breakfast awaits you, both generous and gorgeous to behold – figs, peaches, quince jelly." Other readers add: "Breakfast was the best we had in Portugal, especially the caramelised plums and freshly made pineapple cake." "The service was cheerful." The villa is comfortable and up-to-date, with its own health centre and gym, and the welcome is warm. Guests may find themselves invited to eat with the Senhor in his private dining-room.

"Happily I was able to praise all the food – which *was* delicious. Our host was delightful, but conversation (in my laborious pidgin Portuguese and English) was a bit of a strain." Others have found communication easiest in French. There is no restaurant, but there are places to eat nearby. Don't miss the amazing staircase of over 600 steps leading up to the shrine of Our Lady of the Cures, a flowering of the Baroque concept, surrounded by lush woodland. (*Deborah Loveluck, and others*) A July 1989 report tells of major building work close by seriously impairing "the beautiful location".

Open All year.
Rooms 7 double – all with bath, shower, telephone, radio; TV on request.
Facilities Lounge, TV room, bar, dining room; health centre with gymnasium, massage, sauna etc. Garden with swimming pool (unheated) and tennis courts. River with fishing rights nearby.
Location 1,000 metres from war memorial; private parking.
Credit cards None accepted.
Restriction Not suitable for ♿.
Terms [1989 rates] B&B: single 6,000 esc, double 8,500 esc. Extra bed 3,000 esc. Meals by arrangement.

LISBON — Map 12

Hotel Principe Real

Rua da Alegria 53, Lisbon 1200 — *Tel* (01) 346.01.16 — *Telex* 44571 PREAL

Clean and comfortable, centrally located near Botanical Gardens, Avenida da Liberdade and the Bairro Alto, known for its restaurants and casas de fado. *Comfortable lounge. Rooms vary: some have balcony, about half are air-conditioned, but some are said to be small and dull. Staff friendly. Top-floor breakfast room with panoramic views over Lisbon. 24 rooms, all with private facilities. B&B: single 8,000–13,000 esc, double 10,000–16,500 esc. Set menu 1,200–1,500 esc. More reports please.*

Albergaria da Senhora do Monte

Calcada do Monte 39 — *Tel* (01) 86.28.46
Lisbon 1100

In residential area with colourful tile-faced houses, small shops and cafés, few tourists. Slightly awkward to find, the exterior is more like a house than a hotel. Inexpensive simple accommodation – clean, comfortable bedrooms with modern bathrooms; some, on ground floor, have terrace, others have marvellous views over Lisbon. "We felt someone had placed the city at our feet." Basement bar, continental breakfasts, no restaurant. 27 rooms, all with bath and shower. B&B single 6,000–6,500 esc, double 7,000–7,800 esc, suite 8,500–9,500 esc. More reports please.

Hotel Tivoli Jardim

Rua Julio Cesar Machado 7 — *Tel* (01) 53.99.71 — *Telex* 12172 JARDIM
Lisbon 1200

A useful modern establishment, centrally located just off the city's main avenue, and catering for the business and package trade as well as the individual traveller. Readers enjoy the comfort, good food, quiet location down a side street, and general value for money. "Nothing fancy, but adequate facilities, friendly staff and pleasant atmosphere". It should not be confused with its sister hotel, the *Tivoli*, next door, with which it shares "a very pleasant swimming pool surrounded by a lawn". More reports please.

Open All year.
Rooms 69 double, 50 single – all with bath and shower, telephone, radio, TV, air-conditioning and mini-bar.
Facilities Lift. Hall, bar, restaurant. Gardens with Tivoli club, heated swimming pool, tennis.
Location 10 mins from town centre, off Avenida da Liberdade, NE of Botanical Gardens. Garage and carpark.
Restriction Not suitable for ♿.
Credit cards All major cards accepted.
Terms [1988 rates] B&B: single 9,000–10,000 esc, double 11,000–12,500 esc. Full alc 1,550–2,780 esc. Reduced rates for children sharing parents' room.

York House (Residencia Inglesia) *Tel* (01) 66.24.35
Rua das Janelas Verdes 32 *Telex* 16791
Lisbon 1200

In a somewhat inconvenient location two kilometres from the city centre, but near the National Art Museum, embassies, and the Tower of Belem, a converted 17th-century convent with an annexe across the street (the latter recently redecorated in contemporary style). Its great attraction is its shady courtyard for drinks and snacks – "an oasis of calm". Front rooms overlooking a tram route are noisy; courtyard ones are quieter. Staff friendly. Meals in a charmingly tiled old refectory are not recommended. 48 rooms, all with bath or shower. B&B: single 13,500 esc, double 15,700 esc. Set meals 2,500 esc. More reports please.

MANTEIGAS 6260 Guarda **Map 12**

Pousada de São Lourenço *Tel* (075) 981.50 and 981.73
Telex 53992 PSLOUR

"The views are splendid, the surrounding scenery is spectacular, the location very peaceful." High on the Serra da Estrela, this pousada is 13 kilometres up the mountain from the old town of Manteigas. It is well placed for exploring this highest part of Portugal. "We were made very welcome", runs one recent report. "The hotel has a family feel and the cooking is homely and generous to match." "The charming and locally costumed restaurant staff could not have been nicer. After finishing a gargantuan dinner (we had forgotten that the fish and meat courses would both come with substantial vegetable accompaniment), we were presented with *pousada* port 'on the house'. The breakfast included fruit juice, fresh fruit, local mountain cheese, ham, rolls, toast, madeira cake, butter, jams and good coffee and tea." (*WK Reid*) Rooms are pleasantly furnished, and there's a terrace where you can sit gazing down over the valley. Best for a summer visit: it can be bleak in winter and the snow can be nine feet deep. The local lake, near Penhas Douadas, has a small beach surrounded by wooded slopes, "and the water is clear and like warm milk to bathe in". (*J Hillas, and others*)

Open All year.
Rooms 23 double – all with bath and shower; some with balcony. 7 ground-floor rooms.
Facilities Bar, TV room, restaurant. Garden. Lake with beach and safe bathing 4 km.
Location 13 km N of Manteigas on estrada de Gouveia.
Credit cards All major cards accepted.
Terms B&B: single 4,000–7,700 esc, double 5,300–8,800 esc. Set lunch/dinner 2,250–2,400 esc. Reduced rates for children sharing parents' room.

MARVÃO 7330 Portalegre — Map 12

Pousada de Santa Maria

Tel (045) 932.01
Telex 42360 PMARIA

A simple, small and charming *pousada,* built of stone with tile floors, in an equally small and charming village on a rocky escarpment near the Spanish border, four miles north of the main Lisbon–Madrid road, thus useful for a stopover. The white houses and narrow cobbled streets are entirely inside the walls of a castle over which the keep stands guard. You can walk round the ramparts, looking within at the roofs, gardens, chicken runs, kitchens and television sets, or without over the Sierra de Torrico in Spain and the valleys below in Portugal. Its entry is warmly endorsed again this year: "A wonderful place to stay, and very accommodating. When we checked in they showed us to one of their newer rooms – perhaps assuming that being American we would prefer it; it was nice but not special. We asked if there was anything in the older section and were given a small but pretty room with a balcony from which you could see hills, farms, and Spain." Other readers, however, have been enthusiastic about the "very attractive new rooms, with air-conditioning". "The staff are young, enthusiastic and eager to help." "Bedrooms comfortable, public rooms well-furnished, good local food and vinho verde at dinner; breakfast excellent." (*Suzanne Carmichael, Mrs JE Lyes, and others*) One reader, while agreeing about the breakfast is less enthusiastic about the dinner.

Open All year.
Rooms 1 suite, 12 double – all with bath and telephone, baby-listening on request. Some ground-floor rooms.
Facilities Lounge, bar, TV room, restaurant. Garden.
Location 27 km N of Portalegre on N521.
Credit cards All major cards accepted.
Terms [1989 rates] B&B: single 5,000–9,400 esc, double 6,500–10,600 esc, suite 9,000–14,300 esc. Set lunch/dinner from 2,100 esc. Reduced rates for children under 10 sharing parents' room; special meals on request.

MIRANDA DO DOURO 5210 Bragança — Map 12

Pousada de Santa Catarina

Tel (073 422.55
Telex 22388

Miranda do Douro is a small town in north-east Portugal, dramatically perched above the Douro valley where it divides Portugal from Spain. It is a timeless place, with its own special dialect, rather similar to low Latin; on special holidays the local men, wearing white kilts and black, colourfully embroidered shirts, perform the Pauliteiros Dance, a rhythmic stick dance, reminiscent of sword-fighting. The *pousada*, new to the Guide this year, is small, purpose-built, not aesthetically pleasing, but bright and airy. The bedrooms, with balcony, and the "very pleasant dining-room and lounge" overlook the splendid view. "Our room was well-furnished and had plenty of drawers and wardrobe space, the bathroom, also spacious, was one of the best we had in three weeks in Portugal. The staff were welcoming and meals *much* better than those we had in higher-priced *pousadas* elsewhere." "Upholstery in the lounge needed repair, rugs needed cleaning, but we learned that money was not forthcoming owing to the *pousada*'s out-of-the way situation. However, the charming and friendly manager and dramatic setting made this a pleasant place to stay." (*John Hillas, Suzanne Carmichael*)

Open All year.
Rooms 12 – all with bath/shower, telephone.
Facilities Lounge, dining room.
Location 83 km SE of Bragança, near Spanish border.
Credit cards All major cards accepted.
Terms [1989 rates] B&B: single 4,000–7,000 esc, double 5,300–8,100 esc. Set meals 1,950 esc.

MONCHIQUE 8550 Faro — Map 12

Estalagem Abrigo da Montanha — *Tel* (082) 921.31
Corte Pereira/Estrada de Foia

"The warmth of welcome was most endearing, they are all so anxious to please", writes a visitor this year to this small family-owned restaurant-with-rooms, a pretty building in a flower-filled garden. The surrounding forests of cork, chestnut and eucalyptus trees are lovely, and the inn, which is halfway between the Algarve hill-town of Monchique and the peak of Foia, has fine views over green hills, lush valleys and the coastline. There is a main building and, at the other end of a pretty garden, a tier of separate apartments which readers have approved. "Breakfasts are memorable, with freshly squeezed orange juice, and local honey; given notice they are willing to arrange any requested dish for dinner." Lunch on the terrace under the chestnut trees with the sweeping view of the valley below is also described as "memorable". The peacefulness of the surroundings is only slightly marred by the rock quarry down the hillside. Prices are very modest. (*Mrs RB Richards*)
Warning: It can be cold and wet in Monchique even when blazing on the coast, and the peace can be shattered when coach parties arrive for lunch.

Open All year.
Rooms 3 suites, 5 double – all with bath, shower and telephone. 2 suites in annexe.
Facilities Lounge, bar with TV, dining room; terrace. Garden.
Location About 25 km inland from Portimão. Hotel is 2 km from Monchique on road to Foia.
Restriction Not suitable for ♿.
Credit cards All major cards accepted.
Terms B&B: single 7,700 esc, double 8,000 esc. Alc meals (excluding wine) 1,500–2,400 esc.

> When hotels have failed to return their questionnaire, we have quoted 1989 prices, with a note to that effect.

MONSARAZ 7200 Évora — Map 12

Estalagem de Monsaraz — *Tel* (066) 551.12
Largo de S. Bartolomeu

Modest little inn, charming in a simple, rural way, in old fortified town on a hilltop near the Guadiana Valley on the border with Spain, much visited by tours by day, but totally quiet at night. Overhanging beams, tiny stairs, rooms and bathrooms at different levels. Tiny dining-room serving acceptable fare, handkerchief-size garden with mini swimming pool. Very cheap – rates on application. New nomination. More reports please.

ÓBIDOS 2510 Leiria — Map 12

Pousada do Castelo — *Tel* (062) 951.05
Paço Real — *Telex* 15540 POSOBI

A 15th-century castle, now a small, fairly expensive pousada, *above little walled medieval hilltop town, rather spoiled by tourism, near coast north of Lisbon. Well-restored "maintaining the ambience of an old castle without too many of the discomforts", but little in the way of public rooms. Most bedrooms overlook the delightful courtyard, not the view; the tower bedroom, supposedly the best, is poorly ventilated. "Good regional food at dinner, staff pleasant and helpful, but breakfast variable." 9 rooms, all with bath and shower, and air-conditioning. B&B double 10,000–14,400 esc. Alc meals (excluding wine) 2,300–3,100 esc. More reports please.*

Estalagem do Convento — *Tel* (062) 952.17 and 952.14
Rua Dom João de Ornelas — *Telex* 44906

Part ancient, part modern, this hotel lies just outside the walls of a medieval town full of cobbled alleys and flower-girt piazzas. Readers last year took a room in the new annexe: "Beautifully designed to blend with the older existing house and the garden. We had a very pretty room with balcony looking over to the countryside and city walls. Nice staff, and the best hotel food we had in Portugal." A frequent visitor this year concurs: "I have always found the rooms comfortable (if somewhat tiny), the decor stylish, and the food very good indeed. The building has a lot of character, and I'd be surprised if anyone failed to be enchanted." (*ATW Liddell, also Julia Mallach, and others*)

Open All year.
Rooms 6 suites, 21 double – all with bath and shower, telephone and radio; suites have TV.
Facilities 2 lounges, 2 bars (1 with TV), dining room. Garden.
Location In town centre. Parking.
Restriction Not suitable for ♿.
Credit cards Access, Visa.
Terms [1989 rates] B&B 3,000–8,000 esc. Half board 1,900–1,950 per person added.

> Don't keep your favourite hotel to yourself. The Guide supports: it doesn't spoil.

OPORTO Map 12

Hotel Infante de Sagres
Praça D. Filipa de Lencastre 62
Oporto 4000

Tel (02) 281.01
Fax (02) 31.49.37
Telex 26880 SAGRES

"A splendid old-style Anglo-Portuguese hotel", the grandest in town, "where the British connection is still appreciated, and where you can find superb ports and the best vinho verde outside the Tras es Montes". Many visitors this year have confirmed this previous verdict. "We endorse all praise for this most serious of hotels. Service is extraordinarily attentive, both indoors and out; and you can forget all parking problems (how Oporto has them!) once the doorman has taken over your car keys. The rooms, public and private, are luxuriously furnished in keeping with another era. Dornford Yates would have loved it." (*Christine and Stephen Wright; Roger Bennett, Brian L Davis*) The hotel was originally built by a textile magnate to accommodate his clients. The restaurant specialises in French and Portuguese dishes, but also grilled salmon and roast beef "English style".

Open All year.
Rooms 4 suites, 70 double, 10 single – all with bath and shower, telephone, radio and TV.
Facilities Lift. Lounges, bar, restaurant. Garden. Sandy beach with safe bathing 15 km.
Location In city centre, near Avenida dos Aliados. Parking arranged.
Credit cards All major cards accepted.
Terms B&B: single 16,500–20,000 esc, double 19,000–25,000 esc, suite 40,000–50,000 esc. Set lunch/dinner 3,900 esc; full alc 7,500 esc. 50% reduction for children under 8 sharing parents' room; special meals.

Hotel Malaposta
Rua da Conceição 80,
Oporto 4000

Tel (02) 262.78
Telex 20898

Modest hotel, central, near main station, but very quiet, simple but comfortable, staff friendly and helpful. No restaurant, but there are plenty a short walk away. 37 rooms, some with bath. B&B single 4,300 esc, double 5,300 esc. No recent feedback. More reports please.

PALMELA 2950 Setúbal Map 12

Pousada do Castelo de Palmela

Tel (01) 235.12.26
Telex 42290

This small and pretty white-walled town stands in tiers on the northern slopes of a hillside, 43 kilometres south of Lisbon. Here a convent, built in 1423, has been transformed into a state-run *pousada*, liked by readers especially for its setting and its location. "High above the beautiful town with its houses cascading down the slopes, surrounded by the plains and olive groves, and in the distance the coastline in clear view. Our room afforded splendid views over the plains towards Évora. The standard of furnishings and comfort was about the best we encountered. The swimming pool, open during the summer months, is in a delightful location, in a low walled courtyard. The cloisters are wonderful, full of the most exotic and vivid array of plants." This year two readers report happy visits: "Beautifully maintained, marvellous flowers, very clean, unbelievable view! Excellent food (all eight of our meals very tasty), helpful and friendly waiter, large elegant room (we had four people in ours). A wonderful experience." "Breakfast (in our room) almost the best anywhere ever – offering the choice of two honeys, one mild and runny, the other dark and aromatic. Food average, with a representative selection of local dishes such as cabbage soup and ocean fish dishes, but not the hotel's strong point. But worth its entry for the position alone." (*Susan Haskell, Charles A Quest-Ritson*)

Open All year.
Rooms 2 suites, 25 double – all with bath, telephone, radio and TV. Some ground-floor rooms.
Facilities Lift. Lounge, bar, TV room, dining-room; conference room; art gallery. Large grounds with unheated swimming pool and children's play area. Sandy beaches with safe bathing and life-guard nearby.
Location 7 km from Setúbal in centre of village; signposted. Parking for 40 cars.
Credit cards All major cards accepted.
Terms [1989 rates] B&B: single 10,800–13,900 esc, double 12,500–15,600 esc. Set lunch/dinner 2,300 esc; full alc 3,350 esc. Reduced rates for children.

PONTA DELGADA Azores — Map 12

Hotel de São Pedro — *Tel* (096) 22223
Ponta Delgada, São Miguel — *Telex* 82602 BENS

Our first hotel in the Azores, on the island of São Miguel "which is like a lush, giant garden. Rows of hydrangeas separate the fields, blue-green lakes dot the volcanic countryside; there are mineral-spring spas, pineapple and tea plantations. The pavements of Ponta Delgada are made from squares of white marble and black lava arranged in artistic patterns. The hotel, a 19th-century building, is set across the street from the inner harbour; like so many others in town it is white with black volcanic stones on the edges, around windows and doors. Originally the town house of a wealthy orange importer, it is filled with antiques, comfortable furniture and warm wood tones. Our bedroom was comfortable, but not special, with a nice view to the quay. The dining room had white-clothed tables, each with a fresh bird of paradise centre-piece. Service was excellent, the food fair, the fresh pineapple for dessert exquisite. The staff was friendly; we communicated in a smattering of English and French." (*Suzanne Carmichael*) More reports please.

Open All year.
Rooms 6 suites, 17 double, 3 single – all with bath or shower, telephone and TV.
Facilities Lounge, bar, 2 restaurants. Garden. Beach 10 mins by car.
Location 5 mins from centre, opposite inner harbour.
Credit cards Probably all major cards accepted.
Terms [1989 rates] B&B: single 5,700–7,250 esc, double 6,900–11,500 esc, suite 14,000–17,500 esc. Extra bed 1,500 esc. Set lunch/dinner 1,500–2,000 esc. No charge for children under 3.

In Portugal, reservations for pousadas can be made direct or through Enatur, Avenida Santa Joana Princesa, 10-A, 1700 Lisbon. Tel (01) 88.12.21. Telex 63475.

SAGRES 8650 Faro — Map 12

Pousada do Infante

Tel (082) 642.22
Telex 57491 PINFA

"What a joy it is to be in a civilised place like this! The meals are not at all bad, and are served to perfection. We were struck by the quality of the staff." "Ideal for rest and relaxation. Hotel very clean, staff very pleasant and helpful." With those endorsements this modern purpose-built *pousada*, a short walk from the centre of a small village, returns to the Guide, having been absent only for lack of feedback. It is on the south-western tip of Europe, the point from which the great Portuguese navigators set sail in the 15th century. There are long sandy beaches nearby, though "a car is needed as the *pousada* is isolated". An earlier report described "the stunning views" and recommended Sagres as a good base from which to explore the Algarve, "though the early or late season could be chilly with strong Atlantic winds." Fish is landed daily at the port of Sagres, and *À Tasca* and *Mar à Vista* are recommended as good seafood restaurants nearby. (*HR, NR Measey*)

Open All year.
Rooms 2 suites, 21 double – all with bath and shower, telephone, radio, TV and balcony.
Facilities Lounge, bar, restaurant. Garden with terrace and swimming pool. Sandy beach 100 metres, safe bathing and fishing.
Location 35 km W of Lagos. Follow *pousada* signs in Sagres.
Credit cards All major cards accepted.
Terms B&B: single 10,800–13,900 esc, double 12,500–15,600 esc, suite 16,400–20,700 esc. Set meals 2,550–3,500 esc; full alc 5,300 esc. Reduced rates for children; special meals by arrangement.

SÃO BRÁS DE ALPORTEL 8150 Faro — Map 12

Pousada de São Brás

Tel (089) 423.05
Telex 56945

About 12 miles north of the coast town of Faro in the Algarve, this *pousada*, in a small town of Moorish origin, is on a hill with beautiful views all round. Some rooms are large, with a balcony. Readers praise "the comfort, warmth, superb service, smiling friendliness and attention, and the simple food done in the regional style, their local fish dishes are excellent." The entry is endorsed this year by *JA Matheson*: "Excellently situated. Reception was cheerful and efficient. Our room was very small, but adequate, and had been recently decorated. But it had no view, being on the ground floor. The dinner was very good and I sympathise with *Drew Smith* who complained last year that he missed the caldeirada de borrego (stewed lamb) – it was delicious. Breakfast was good value." Other readers are equally positive about the cooking: "Breakfasts probably the best we had in three weeks' touring. Delicious bread soup at dinner." (*P and M Horswell*) One correspondent, however, while liking the quiet situation and swimming pool and agreeing about good value for money, writes: "Typical *pousada* restricted menu and poor preparation and presentation." More reports please.

Open All year.
Rooms 23 – most with bath/shower and telephone.

Facilities Salon, restaurant. Garden with swimming pool.
Location 2 km N of São Brás de Alportel on the Lisbon road.
Credit cards All major cards accepted.
Terms [1989 rates] B&B: single 4,000–7,000 esc, double 5,300–8,100 esc. Set lunch/dinner 1,950 esc.

SÃO TIAGO DA GEMIEIRA 4990 Ponte de Lima — Map 12

Casa do Barreiro — *Tel* (058) 941937

A new nomination, one of the Turismo de Habitação (tourism in private homes) group. "A guest house on a gentle slope, looking down over its own vineyards to the Lima valley. It is a rectangular building surrounding a central court. Painted tiles abound, including a tiled description of the history going back to 1643 and erected when it was restored in 1928. Furnishings are rustic and antique and the house has a delightfully rural character with a very agreeable swimming pool next to the hen-run. The front rooms overlooking the vines are the nicest, though they have basins and loos, but not bath or shower – but there is a large and well-equipped bathroom serving them; they also overlook the road, but it is not busy. The back rooms are self-catering duplexes, which might be a godsend for a young family, but to my mind are lacking in atmosphere. No restaurant, but snacks are available." (*AWT Liddell*)

Open All year.
Rooms 1 suite, 6 double, 2 single – 6 with bath and shower. 2 with WC.
Facilities Salon, TV room, bar, games room. Garden with unheated swimming pool.
Location 4.5 km from Ponte de Lima.
Credit cards None accepted.
Terms B&B: single 6,100 esc, double 7,200 esc. (No restaurant.)

SINTRA 2710 Lisbon — Map 12

Estalagem Quinta dos Lobos — *Tel* (01) 923.0210
Estalagem Quinta da Capela — *Tel* (01) 929.01.70
Monserrate

Both the *Quinta dos Lobos* and its sister the *Quinta da Capela* (four kilometres down the road to Colares, past Monserrate), manor houses rebuilt after the 1755 earthquake, have been tastefully restored. An inspector last year liked them both, "At the *Lobos* I had a large bedroom with antique furniture and paintings. It was very quiet. You help yourself to drinks in the bar and sign for them. A big log fire in the candle-lit lounge, with peaceful classical music and big comfy armchairs. The *Capela*, too, is lovely – light and airy public rooms, very clean, pretty little pink breakfast room, smallish bedrooms (but not poky), and fantail doves in a garden with a pond and orange grove. Friendly staff in both places." We asked for more reports, and have two this year on the *Capela*: "Superlative, and good value. On the edge of a wooded hill, with lovely views. Magical peace: breakfast from 8 am up to noon, and it's the only hotel I've ever been in without a single admonitory notice. A big and beautiful garden and the absence of formality make one feel one is staying in a friendly Cotswold manor house." "The decor is a judicious mixture of ancient and modern, done with unerring taste. There is no restaurant, but omelettes and sandwiches are readily produced. Impeccably clean and civilised; I would rather stay here than at the *Palacio de Seteais* (q.v.) at twice the price. It's a real find." (*Ben Whitaker, ATW Liddell*). We would welcome reports on the *Lobos*.

Estalagem Quinta dos Lobos

Open All year.
Rooms 8 double – all with bath and shower, telephone and baby-listening.
Facilities 2 lounges, bar. 8-acre grounds with woods, gardens, small unheated swimming pool; near sandy beaches with fishing.
Location From National Palace of Sintra take road to Seteais, *Quinta* is on right.
Credit cards None accepted.
Terms On application. (No restaurant but use of kitchen.)

Estalagem Quinta da Capela

Open All year except Christmas.
Rooms 3 suites, 10 double – all with bath and/or shower (not all *en suite*) and telephone. 3 cottages in the garden. Some ground-floor rooms.
Facilities 2 lounges, bar; gym and sauna. Large garden with small unheated swimming pool; sandy beaches, fishing nearby.
Location 3 km W of Sintra on Colares road, next to Palace of Monserrate.
Credit card Visa.
Terms [1989 rates] B&B: single 9,000 esc, double 11,000–13,000 esc, suite 15,000 esc. Reduced rates for children sharing parents' room. (No restaurant.)

Quinta São Thiago *Tel* (01) 923.29.23

"Not for the faint-hearted," writes a recent visitor, describing both the long rough private access road and also the *en famille* dinner arrangements and other characteristics of this 16th-century manor guest house. The *quinta* is owned and run by Tereza Braddell – Portuguese, Spanish and American by birth and English by marriage. Her establishment is mildly eccentric – utterly acceptable, indeed wonderful to some, a bit over the top to others. "The approach road is horrendous to the newcomer, but supremely worth traversing. Hospitality is generous and imaginative, and Mrs Braddell's enthusiasm for her guests' comfort is remarkable." "Once or twice a week Mrs Braddell organises a home-cooked dinner, which often ends with music and dancing. At other times she advises on restaurants in the area." "Evening meals are like successful dinner parties, eaten at a huge refectory table loaded with candles and flowers. Music figures largely." "Whether a snack or a full blown dinner, the food is superb." Bedrooms are individually furnished with antiques, and the bathrooms are decorated with hand-painted tiles. Nearby are lovely walks with plenty of bird life and wild-flowers. "Most beautiful house and setting." (*Mark Gerson, Mrs P Rowe-Evans, WA Howard, A Wheeler*) Criticisms have included an arbitrary style requiring that everyone participate in after-dinner entertainments (charades, dancing etc), an unfilled swimming pool, a poorly maintained tennis court, fitful and uneven housekeeping. The "ayes" have it, just. More reports please.

Open All year.
Rooms 1 suite, 8 double – 7 with bath, 1 with shower. 2 ground-floor rooms.
Facilities Drawing rooms, library, music room, bar. Patio, garden with swimming pool and tennis court. Sea and sandy beaches nearby.

Location 4 km W of Sintra, off road to Colares. Watch for green sign on right after *Hotel Seteais*.
Credit cards None accepted.
Terms [1989 rates] B&B double 10,000–12,000 esc. Set dinner 3,500 esc. Special meals for children.

Hotel Palácio de Seteais *Tel* (01) 923.32.00
Rua Barbosa do Bocage 8 *Fax* (01) 923.42.77
Telex 14410 HOPASE

Immortalised by Byron in *Childe Harold*, this famous hill town is set dramatically against the north face of the *serra*. The *Palace of Seteais*, built a year before the poet's birth, sits regally about a mile away up the Colares road. It is one of the few de luxe country houses in Portugal – "a beautifully proportioned classical mansion with an elegant formal garden on one side and a series of terraces, lemon groves and wilder gardens spilling down the hillside on the other. Everything is spotless. The staff are friendly and considerate, yet discreet. The salons have fine tapestries and exceptional murals and, like the bedrooms, are carefully furnished with antiques." A report in 1989 praised the well-equipped bedrooms ("big bowls of fresh fruit, towelling gowns, even a safe") and the food – international hotel fare, but – "particularly good soups, a traditional Portuguese dish in each course, delicious Portuguese white wine, and excellent pastries. The swimming pool is heated all year and there are fine walks, to the Monserrate gardens, and in the hills around. Views from the front of the hotel up to the Pena Palace, "flood-lit at night, very romantic"; from the back, down over farmland and little hamlets to the sea. (*HMW, Alisdair Aird*)

Open All year.
Rooms 1 suite, 17 double – all with bath and shower, and telephone. Some ground-floor rooms.
Facilities Lift. Salons, bar, TV room, restaurant; terrace. Garden. Heated swimming pool, tennis courts and riding centre. Beach 10 km.
Location 1 km W of Sintra on Colares road. Parking.
Credit cards All major cards accepted.
Terms [1989 rates] B&B: single 20,500 esc, double 22,000 esc. Set lunch/dinner 4,100 esc. Special meals for children on request.

Vila das Rosas *Tel* (01) 923.42.16
Rua António Cunha, 2-4

19th-century architecturally interesting guest-house a kilometre from centre on road to Ericeira. Recommended for beautifully furnished bedrooms – "period furniture yet modern as well" – and "excellent, friendly service". Pleasant garden, tennis court. Breakfasts taken communally with other guests. Owners enjoy helping guests plan visits to nearby beaches, villages, restaurants, and will serve dinner given one day's notice. 7 rooms, all with bath or shower, 3 in garden apartment with kitchen. B&B double 7,500–10,000 esc. Set meals 3,000 esc. New nomination. More reports please.

> Italicised entries are for hotels on which we need more feedback – either because we are short of reports or because we have had mixed or inadequate reports.

VALENÇA DO MINHO 4930 Viana do Castelo — Map 12

Pousada de São Teotónio — *Tel* (051) 222.52 and 222.42
Telex 32837 PSTEOT

This welcoming *pousada* is built on the 17th-century ramparts of a Vaubanesque frontier fortress; it commands a fine view of the Minho river border with Spain and the Spanish cathedral citadel of Tuy. The pleasant modern bedrooms, the airy and comfortable lounge and restaurant all share this view. "Comfortable and clean public rooms. Great views", wrote a reader this year. Another, writing several years ago, caught the flavour: "In the Portuguese tradition, everything starts late in the morning – the hot water as well as the 8 o'clock breakfast – but we can heartily recommend this beautifully located and well-managed *pousada.* I especially recommend the Minho river salmon, and broa, the local bread made with cornmeal." Valença itself (the *pousada* lies within its walls) is trippery, but the Minho valley offers gentle classical landscapes. Readers continue to recommend the inn, even though meals have disappointed, and one reader mentions "amateurish service, e.g. wrong wine presented already opened".

Open All year.
Rooms 15 double – all with bath and shower, and telephone. 3 in nearby annexe.
Facilities Lounge, TV room, bar, restaurant. Garden. River 1 km; fishing. Sea 30 km.
Location On Portuguese/Spanish frontier, 37 km NE of Viana do Castelo, on E50.
Restriction Not suitable for ♿.
Credit cards All major cards accepted.
Terms [1989 rates] B&B: single 5,000–10,300 esc, double 6,500–11,500 esc. Set lunch and/or dinner 1,950 esc; full alc 5,600 esc. Reduced rates and special meals for children.

VILA NOVA DE CERVEIRA Vian do Castelo — Map 12

Estalagem da Boega — *Tel* (051) 952.31
Quinta do Outeiral, Gondarem
Vila Nova de Cerveira 4920

Four kilometres south-west of Vila Nova de Cerveira, near the Spanish border, overlooking the river Minho. Purpose-built bedrooms in bungalows, basic but clean, surrounding old quinta with reception/lounge area. Interesting, generally very good Portuguese food. Portuguese, not international clientele; staff very helpful and friendly. Swimming pool, tennis. "Amazingly cheap; not without fault, but interesting." 30 rooms, most with private facilities. B&B double 6,000 esc. Set meals 1,500 esc [1989]. New nomination. More reports please.

Pousada de Dom Diniz — *Tel* (051) 956.01
Praça da Liberdade — *Telex* 32821
Vila Nova de Cerveira 4920

An unusually atmospheric *pousada* is brought to the Guide by an enthusiastic recommendation from an American travel writer: "Vila Nova de Cerveira, at the foot of a mountain, on the bank of the Rio Minho which divides Portugal from Spain, and not far from the sea, is a quiet little town centred on a small square. We registered at a small office facing the square then walked up a cobbled path through a double walled gate to the interior of the walled city which, except for the church, is entirely owned by the *pousada*. Our bedroom, No 6, was part of a series of rooms built directly out from the ancient fortress wall. It was large, with a bathroom, separate sitting room, well-stocked refrigerator and private courtyard. The dining area was in a large modern building with views of the river, the sea, and Spain; other public rooms are in a converted old building. On Christmas Day we were the only couple in the *pousada* and it was perfect. We walked along the top of the wall and wandered the narrow streets. We were served dinner by a waiter and waitress who doubtless would rather have been elsewhere, but were charming and friendly, and the food was grand. The waiter invited us to join the staff Christmas party, but we declined, feeling this might put a damper on their fun." (*Suzanne Carmichael*)

Open All year.
Rooms 3 suites, 26 double – all with bath/shower and telephone.
Facilities Lounge, 2 bars, library, dining room, banqueting room; terraces, patios.
Location In town centre.
Credit cards Probably all major cards accepted.
Terms [1989 rates] B&B: single 7,500–12,600 esc, double 10,000–14,400 esc. Set meals 3,100 esc.

Traveller's tale *At 9.45 pm we emerged from the dining room and decided to take a stroll before turning in. Madame's husband enquired, apprehensively, when we were going to return but declined to give us a key. When we got back, at 10.15 prompt, the hotel was in darkness and the front door locked. We had to rouse one of the waiters to get in. Hoteliers may like their beds but they had no right to inflict an early night on a group of people who had just spent well nigh £200 on dinner and were destined to be the sole occupants of the £40 rooms.*

Spain

HOTEL LA BOBADILLA, LOJA

ALCALÁ DE GUADAIRA 41500 Seville — Map 12

Hotel Oromana — *Tel* (954) 70.08.04
Avenida de Portugal

Plenty of red print in *Michelin*, including three red gables for attractiveness and a red rocking-chair for peaceful seclusion, endorses our own nominator's liking for this small hotel south-east of Seville, by the main N334 road to Granada: "It is situated above the town of Alcalá de Guadaira, by a pine forest where you can take lovely walks down to and along the river below it. The verandas give a fine view, and the outdoor pool is set in pleasant gardens. Privately owned by Sr Ramirez, who carefully renovated the original building some five years ago, it's a hotel with a very traditional Spanish feel. All rooms are large, clean and well furnished and have balconies with views. A comfortable lounge and bar, and simple but good food (best gazpacho ever). Management helpful and service good." (*Angela Langdon*) Recent visitors were less enchanted with the food and management and tell of creeping industrialisation spoiling the views. We'd welcome more reports.

Open All year.
Rooms 30 – all with bath and/or shower, telephone and air-conditioning.
Facilities Lounge, bar, restaurant; conference facilities. Garden with swimming pool.
Location Town is 14 km SE of Seville, on N 334.
Credit cards All major cards accepted.
Terms [1989 rates] (Excluding tax) Double room 6,000–7,000 pts. Breakfast 500 pts, set lunch/dinner 2,000 pts.

ALCÁZAR DE SAN JUAN 13600 Ciudad Real — Map 12

Hotel Don Quijote y Restaurante Sancho — *Tel* (926) 54.38.00
Av. de Criptana 5

This clean modern hotel is in a market town south-east of Toledo on the wide plain of La Mancha (hence its Cervantesian name). Though no beauty, it has large airy rooms with good bathrooms, an amiable and efficient staff, and serves excellent food. A useful stopover travelling south from Madrid. Restaurant closed Sun and holiday nights. 44 rooms, all with bath and shower. Rooms double 5,000–6,500 pts. Breakfast 350 pts. Set lunch 1,000 pts; alc dinner 3,000 pts. Recent nomination. More reports please.

ALMAGRO 13270 Ciudad Real — Map 12

Parador de Almagro — *Tel* (926) 86.01.00
Ronda de San Francisco — *Fax* (926) 86.01.50

A converted 16th-century convent in a small town on the open plain of *La Mancha* 190 kilometres south of Madrid – a short detour off the main road south to Granada, and an important milestone on the route taken by Don Quixote in Cervantes' epic. Readers continue to endorse the entry: "The town has many fine 16th-century buildings in a heavenly reddish stone, and a splendid main square. The *parador* is a delightful calm oasis, beautifully furnished in the public areas with handsome dark chests and tables, lots of attractive pottery about, and pleasing pictures and tapestries on the walls. Our room was large, extremely comfortable and well equipped. We chose regional specialities for dinner, enjoying a vivid roast sweet red pepper salad and roast (baby) lamb Manchego style. Breakfast was an excellent buffet – tortillas, bacon, chorizos, eggs, cold meats and toast." (*Mrs KE Rawes; Martin L Dodd*)

Open All year.
Rooms 1 suite, 48 double, 6 single – all with bath and/or shower and telephone; some with air-conditioning. 5 ground-floor rooms.
Facilities Bar, salon with TV, 2 restaurants; conference rooms. Garden with swimming pool.
Location Central (*parador* is sign-posted). Parking.
Credit cards All major cards accepted.
Terms [1989 rates] (Excluding 12% tax) Rooms: single 4,435–6,800 pts, double 7,000–8,500 pts, suite 10,500–12,855 pts. Breakfast 800 pts, lunch/dinner 2,500 pts, full pension 4,930 pts. Special meals for children.

> We are particularly keen to have reports on italicised entries.

ANTEQUERA 29200 Málaga — Map 12

Parador de Antequera
Paseo Garcia del Olmo

Tel (952) 84.02.61
Fax (952) 84.09.91

A little more than an hour by car from Málaga airport, this modern *parador*, somewhat unprepossessing in appearance, is on the outskirts of an old white-walled town – "a living, noisy place, but genuine Andalusia" – up in the hills behind Málaga and useful for exploring the Andalusian countryside away from the frenzy of the coast. It is designed rather in Swedish style with split-level reception areas and first-class furnishings; the bedrooms are large, even by *parador* standards; the interior courtyards and public rooms have decent modern furniture and antiques. "The dining room is beautiful, with flowers and well-spaced tables. The breakfast buffet was a work of art." "All the staff delightful – I couldn't believe I wasn't staying in a de luxe hotel at double or treble the price." (*Charles A Quest-Ritson, David and Angela Stewart, A and J Sennet, M and R Milner, Mrs EH Prodgers*) Some readers, while praising the rooms, report unkempt grounds, impersonal service and disappointing food. We'd welcome more reports.

Open All year.
Rooms 55 double – all with bath, shower, telephone and air-conditioning.
Facilities 3 lounges, TV room, bar, dining room; conference room. Garden with swimming pool.
Location Off N342 between Granada and Jerez de la Frontera. Hotel is on the outskirts of town. Parking.
Credit cards All major cards accepted.
Terms [1989 rates] (Excluding tax) Rooms: single 5,200–6,400 pts, double 6,500–8,000 pts. Breakfast 800 pts, set lunch/dinner 2,500 pts.

ARCOS DE LA FRONTERA Cádiz — Map 12

Parador Casa del Corregidor
Plaza del Cabildo

Tel (956) 70.05.00

A welcome return to the Guide of a *parador* that was in earlier editions until it closed some years back for extensive redecoration. "The town of Arcos is perched on a vertical outcrop of rock overlooking the Guadalete river with spectacular Andalucian views of castles and rolling countryside. The *parador* is a former magistrate's mansion in the Renaissance style, its front facing the plaza and the rear the edge of the cliff face. The interiors have been restored and, in typical Moorish style, there is a central open patio surrounded by public rooms. Ask for bedrooms overlooking the cliff – they have private patios with magnificent views. Service was especially good at reception, but only average in the restaurant, as was the food, which was expensive. Overall the setting and the hotel interiors are outstanding. It was one of the few *paradors* which were full during our trip." (*David Ball*)

Open All year.
Rooms 20 double, 4 single – all with bath and shower.
Facilities Salon with TV, bar, restaurant.
Location Central.
Credit cards All major cards accepted.
Terms B&B: single 7,450 pts, double 11,100 pts. Set meals 2,800 pts; full alc 3,100 pts.

BAGUR 17255 Gerona — Map 12

Hotel Aigua Blava
Playa de Fornells, Aigua Blava

Tel (972) 62.20.58
Telex 56000 HABIT

Built in the style of a typical Catalan village round a small fishing beach and harbour, *Aigua Blava* has delighted readers since it first appeared in the Guide in 1979. "The best hotel on the Costa Brava", "one of the best-run hotels in Spain". Its charm is due partly to its setting, amid trees and rocks, on various levels, on a specially lovely stretch of coast. "It has been extended in such a way that you never see the whole place at one go – and everything is in the best design and possible taste. Nothing kitsch – all fresh, spotless and loved." But the "excellent" food and "friendly and helpful" staff also play a big role in its success story – "the waiters and waitresses are obviously paid well and seem extremely happy in their job; most have been working here for years." A report written some years ago still holds good, "The *Aigua Blava* (which is Catalan for Blue Water) has literally grown from a fisherman's hut. Xiquet (pronounced Chickee) Sabater, who owns it, is quarter-Japanese, quarter-French, half-Spanish, and married to a local woman. He is a great charmer. Some of his first guests are still coming back after more than 30 years." (*AS*) Sr Sabater is an anglophile and his hotel is something of a traditional British stronghold, but "less encroachingly anglophilic" than one recent visitor had feared. "The wine list is well worth exploring – there are some wonderful, good-value Riojas." (*Minda Alexander, Dave Watts*)

Open 1 Apr–22 Oct.
Rooms 14 suites, 67 double, 8 single – all with bath and/or shower, telephone and air-conditioning; 4 with TV; some with balcony. All in 5 different buildings.
Facilities 4 lounges, 2 bars, 4 restaurants, TV room; conference and banquet rooms; boutique, hairdresser. Gardens with tennis (floodlit after dark), volleyball, paddling pool, swimming pool (disco by pool every night); children's play area. Sand and rock beach with safe bathing and water sports. Golf 7 km.
Location 4 km SE of Bagur, 8 km E of Palafrugell. Garage and parking.
Restriction Not suitable for ♿.
Credit cards Access, Amex, Visa.
Terms (Excluding 12% tax) B&B: single 5,100–6,500 pts, double 7,400–10,900 pts, suite 9,700–14,900 pts; half board: single 6,400–7,900 pts, double 10,800–15,800 pts, suite 15,600–19,600 pts. Set lunch/dinner 2,500 pts; full alc 4,000 pts. Reduced rates for children under 7; special meals.

Parador Costa Brava
Aigua Blava

Tel (972) 62.21.62
Fax (972) 62.21.66

Nominations from two regular Guide correspondents introduce Bagur's *parador*: "Aigua Blava is one of the gems of the Costa Brava, and we spent a long weekend here in warm November sunshine. It must run the *Aigua Blava,* which is closed in the winter, a very close second. It is a large, ugly flat-roofed white concrete building in a fabulous setting opposite the tiny harbour, with trees, surf, sea and sky all around you. A smiling welcome was combined with an irresistible offer of an exceptional room with a circular whirlpool bath big enough for 12, separate sunken shower room, two wash basins – all in pale coffee-coloured marble. Acres of space, enough wardrobes for a small army, large balcony." "Every outlook is entrancing. There's a walk down through pine-woods to a sandy cove for sea bathing. Rather cosmopolitan – no GB cars parked in rows outside the hotel (British visitors mustn't expect fluent English at reception or in the dining room). Bedrooms are elegant. Huge squidgy chairs in the lounge. Ferocious modern paintings in soft lime greens, lemon yellow and terra cotta. The breakfast buffet is stupendous: champagne, of course, at no extra charge. Chilled melon, cherries, strawberries, grapes and plums, six different kind of juice. Baskets piled high with sugared fairy sponge cakes – croissants and bread which you toast at a revolving grill. Cold table of cheese, hams, salami, hot tray with eggs. Dinner doesn't quite match this perfection, but the fish is fresh and the meat very good." (*Angela and David Stewart, Eileen Broadbent*)

Open All year.
Rooms 72 double, 8 single – all with bath and shower, telephone, air-conditioning, balcony.
Facilities Lift. Lounge, bar, restaurant; conference facilities. Garden, swimming pool; cove for sea bathing.
Location In Aigua Blava, 3½ km from Bagur.
Credit cards All major cards accepted.
Terms [1989 rates] (Excluding 12% tax) B&B double 8,000–11,000 pts. Breakfast 800 pts. Set lunch/dinner 2,700 pts.

BAÑALBUFAR Mallorca — Map 12

Hotel Mar I Vent — *Tel* (971) 61.00.25 and 61.80.00
José Antonio 47-49

New plaudits for this small, inexpensive hotel in a fishing village on the rugged west coast of Mallorca, popular with readers since our first edition. There are fine views of the sea and cliffs from the hotel and its swimming pool.You can also bathe from a tiny cove about 15 minutes' stroll away by taking the winding paths through the terraced tomato fields; the hills behind the hotel offer exhilarating walking, too. Run by a brother and sister, Tony and Juanita Vives, it has been in the same family for four generations. It still retains some older features, in spite of considerable modernisation. There is antique furniture; the comfortable lounges have English books (the Vives speak excellent English) and many of the guests are British. Bedrooms are furnished in local style: some are small, but all are bright and airy. "The balconies are delightful and the bathing cove uncrowded and beautiful. We enjoyed a very good breakfast, with juicy sweet melon, served on the terrace – and dinner was a pleasant experience with good wine and straightforward home-cooking." "Don't expect luxury – but the hospitality is great and the ambience enchanting." "The two Vives work very hard and were much in evidence in the dining room in the evening. There is no beach to speak of, but the sea was beautifully warm, warmer in autumn than the swimming pool which is unheated and gets little sun owing to the hotel's north-facing position." (*A and C Herxheimer, Gabriele Berneck, and others*) One guest comments on our mention last year of the Vives' house rule of up-to-bed-by-11.30, "Some friends who were there in April report Juanita firmly urging them bedwards at *10:30*, and when Juanita urges – you go!" The dining room is closed for lunch except on Sunday, but there is a nice café down the road.

Open 1 Feb–end Nov. Restaurant closed for lunch except Sun.
Rooms 16 double, 3 single – all with bath, telephone and balcony. 8 in adjoining annexe. Some ground-floor rooms.

Facilities 2 salons (1 with TV), bar/restaurant. Terrace with swimming pool. Sea bathing.
Location 24 km NW of Palma, at entrance to village. Parking.
Restriction Not really suitable for ♿.
Credit cards None accepted.
Terms B&B: single 3,830 pts, double 5,170 pts; dinner, B&B: single 5,440 pts, double 8,390 pts. Set lunch/dinner 1,650 pts. 10% reduction for children sharing parents' room.

BAYONA 36300 Pontevedra — Map 12

Parador Conde de Gondomar
Carretera de Bayona

Tel (986) 35.50.00
Fax (986) 35.50.76
Telex 83424 RRPP

Bayona is famous as the Atlantic port, south of Vigo, that first received, in 1493, the news of Columbus' discovery of the New World. The white-walled *Conde de Gondomar* stands in a splendid setting high above the sea, a mock *pazo* in the public grounds of the old Monte Real fortress and governor's palace; the old walls and tower remain, but the hotel itself is thoroughly modern. A report last year: "Beautiful pool, service friendly, rooms good (you must ask for one with a view)." This year the *parador* wins praise for its food: "The most imaginative of the holiday"; "Breakfast of a high standard and dinners magnificent, with a daily change of menu – Paella Valenciana, broad beans and clams, and crêpes with cream recommended." The hotel is large, on two floors only, necessitating a lot of walking along corridors. Huge tapestries and suits of armour adorn the main staircase. The bedrooms have traditional furnishings, good lighting, comfortable beds, and well-equipped bathrooms, though hot water isn't quite constant. "The romantic sandy beach viewed from our bedroom on closer acquaintance turned out to be shingle covered with tar and infested seaweed – but the sound of the waves breaking on the rocks more than compensated for the reality". (*C and M Dehn; M and R Milne-Day, and others*)

Open All year.
Rooms 2 suites, 106 double, 20 single – all with bath and shower, telephone, radio and baby-listening. 20 with TV. Some ground-floor rooms.
Facilities 4 salons, TV room, bar, 2 restaurants; conference facilities. Park with swimming pool, tennis court and children's play area. Beach nearby with bathing and fishing.
Location On coast, 18 km SW of Vigo by C550. Garage and parking.
Credit cards All major cards accepted.
Terms [1989 rates] (Excluding 12% tax) Rooms: single 5,800–6,850 pts, double 8,000–11,000 pts. Breakfast 800 pts; set lunch/dinner 2,700 pts. Reduced rates and special meals for children.

BENAOJAN 29370 Málaga — Map 12

Molino del Santo
Bda. Estacion s/n.

Tel (952) 167151
In UK Bury St Edmunds
(0284) 750512

British-owned and managed small hotel high in mountains two hours from coast. Old watermill set in flower-filled gardens beside mountain stream. Recommended for "breath-taking scenery, interesting excursions, warm and friendly welcome". Bird-watching, walks along river or on goat and mule tracks, cycling. "Excellent, imaginative" local and regional cooking. Three minutes' walk from Benaojan railway station. Open 17 Mar–17 Nov. 10 rooms – all with shower. B&B double 3,500–7,000 pts, family suite 4,500–9,000 pts. Set lunch 1,200 pts, dinner 1,500 pts. New nomination. More reports please.

CALA RATJADA 07590 Mallorca — Map 12

Hotel Ses Rotges — *Tel* (971) 56.31.08 and 56.43.45
Calle Rafael Blanes 21

A newcomer to the Guide last year, and now warmly endorsed, this hotel is in a small fishing resort on the north-east coast of Mallorca, near the mighty Artá caves and adjoining clean sandy beaches. It is an old stone mansion of some character, gracefully converted with attention to detail. The *patron*, Gérard Tétard, is French and his food has earned a *Michelin* rosette. "We can truthfully say that we could find no fault. Arriving at 1 am, we found the tone was set by Madame Tétard's being there to greet us and a cold meal being served in our room. The bedroom was spacious and furnished in the Spanish style; the bathroom had been equipped to a very high standard, the heating/air-conditioning unit was a welcome addition on cool April evenings. The food, as expected, was of the highest standard. In the summer one eats out in a lovely courtyard. A highly efficient small hotel run by a hard-working dedicated and delightful young couple." (*Alasdair and Moira Brown, also Ann and Sidney Carpenter*)

Open 1 Apr–30 Oct. Restaurant closed Wed morning in Oct.
Rooms 2 suites, 20 double, 2 single – all with bath and shower, and telephone.
Facilities 2 salons (1 with TV), bar, restaurant. Terrace for summer meals.
Location Fourth street to the right after the sign "Calaratjada".
Restrictions Not suitable for ♿.
Credit cards All major cards accepted.
Terms B&B: single 6,020 pts, double 7,490 pts, suite 10,465 pts, dinner, B&B: single 7,775 pts, double 11,000 pts, suite 13,975 pts. Set menu 2,035 pts. Full alc 3,500–5,000 pts.

CAMBADOS 36630 Pontevedra — Map 12

Parador del Albariño — *Tel* (986) 54.22.50
Paseo de Cervantes — *Fax* (986) 54.20.68

On the indented west coast of Galicia, not far from Pontevedra and the white sandy beaches of La Toja, here in the small modern port of Cambados is an attractive *parador*: "It has been converted from a beautiful aristocratic manor house set within a large walled and tree-shaded garden, and has been furnished with taste: the bedrooms have polished pine floors and luxurious bathrooms. The central courtyard with its sunshades captures the cooling breezes off the sea. Service is good, and so is the seafood. Some traffic noise at night." Endorsed recently by two readers, but more reports welcome.

Open All year.
Rooms 51 double, 12 single – all with bath and shower, and telephone; some with TV. Ground-floor rooms.

Facilities Lift. 2 salons with TV, bar, restaurant, games room. Garden.
Location Central; parking. Town is 53 km S of Santiago.
Credit cards All major cards accepted.
Terms [1989 rates] (Excluding 6% tax) B&B: single 4,800–6,800 pts, double 6,000–8,500 pts. Breakfast 800 pts; set lunch/dinner 2,500 pts. Special meals for children.

CARMONA 41410 Seville — Map 12

Parador Alcázar del Rey Don Pedro

Tel (954) 14.10.10
Fax (954) 14.17.12
Telex 72992

"Here's a *parador* about which I can't eulogise enough," writes one correspondent, and he speaks for nearly all our readers. Opened by the King and Queen of Spain in 1976, it is built inside the massive walls of the ancient Moorish *alcázar* on the top of a hill, from which there are marvellous views over the wide green plain of the Guadalquivir valley, with mountains on the horizon. Moorish influences prevail in the decor – pierced wooden shutters and doors in the public rooms, a patio with a fountain in the middle. The interior walls, white-washed or of honey-coloured brick, are complemented by black or brown wooden-and-leather furniture. The swimming pool is "a model of good taste, with natural brick and grass surrounds, arcades to protect you from the sun, white-painted garden furniture and colourful flowers". In the baronial dining hall with its high beams, the food generally receives good reports – as does the service. But only the top-floor rooms have a balcony with views; there is some traffic noise if windows are opened; poor insulation between rooms and between floors continues to be mentioned this year, and one reader thought his bathroom "showed distinct signs of wear and tear". (*David Ball, and many others*) *A helpful tip*: Driving in Seville is difficult. Stay here and use the good bus service instead.

Open All year.
Rooms 51 double, 8 single – all with bath and/or shower, and telephone; 25 with radio and TV; some with balcony, 6 ground-floor rooms.
Facilities Lifts. Hall, sitting room with TV, bar, dining room; room for functions and banquets; air-conditioning. Patio and garden with swimming pool.
Location In town centre (hotel is signposted). Parking.
Credit cards All major cards accepted.
Terms [1989 rates] (Excluding 12% tax) Rooms: single 7,600–8,400 pts, double 9,500 pts–10,500 pts. Breakfast 800 pts, set lunch/dinner 2,700 pts. Reduced rates and special meals for children.

CAZORLA Jaén — Map 12

Parador El Adelantado
Cazorla 23470

Tel (953) 72.10.75 and 72.13.03
Fax (953) 72.10.75

New to the Guide this year, a *parador* built 25 years ago, 27 kilometres from the pretty village of Cazorla (shady squares, winding narrow streets, balconies cascading with flowers, towering mountains all around). "The distance seems much more because the road through the glorious national park winds up and up, and the *parador* is sited at around 4,000 feet with mountains still climbing up behind it." It has a rather austere monastic feel about it. There is a large lounge with a huge wood fire and a pleasant dining room serving excellent cold soups and traditional main courses. Our bedroom was spacious and adequate, but a little dark. It is worth asking for one with a view. The place would be heaven for the serious walker – wild goats with huge curly horns reputed to be nearby." (*Ray and Angela Evans*)

Open All year except Feb.
Rooms 33 double – all with bath and shower, telephone and TV.
12 in annexe. 4 on ground floor.
Facilities Bar, lounge with TV, restaurant. Garden, children's play area.
Location 27 km from Cazorla, in the mountains.
Credit cards All major cards accepted.
Terms [1989 rates] (Excluding 6% tax) B&B single 6,400–7,600 pts. Double 8,600–10,100 pts. Half board 2,500 pts added, full board 4,930 pts per person. No charge for child in cot.

Hotel Sierra de Cazorla *Tel* (953) 72.00.15
Carretera de la Sierra
La Iruela 23476

A modern box-like hotel, far from expensive, and popular with Spanish families, set in lovely open country just outside the town of Cazorla. It entered the Guide last year: "It's in a fine position at the foot of the mountains of two of Spain's most dramatic National Parks, the Sierra de Cazorla and the Guadalquivir. It faces into the sun, all rooms have terraces with sweeping views. Because the ground is so steep, in the pool one has the pleasant feeling of swimming beside the treetops. The large bar – facing the view and furnished with old-fashioned armchairs with thick, thick cushions – is nice to relax in over a drink and watch the sun go down. The rooms are spacious, with a third bed in each for a child. The food, well cooked, slants towards the Spanish: local salmon and fat rainbow trout at prices that will bring a smile." "The staff are all helpful, though few speak English. The food only fair, but good for the price." (*Madeleine Polland; JR Lloyd*) A dissenter, while agreeing about the lovely setting, comments: "Service so-so, much used by coach parties, very thin walls and fittings are cheap and rather dilapidated." More reports please.

Open All year.
Rooms 30 rooms – most with bath and shower, all with balcony, telephone.
Facilities Lounge, bar, TV room, restaurant, café; solarium. Garden with swimming pool.
Location 2 km W of Cazorla, 101 km E of Jaén, in La Iruela. Parking.
Credit card All major cards accepted.
Terms B&B: [1989 rates] (Excluding tax) single 2,950 pts, double 4,700 pts. Breakfast 300 pts; set lunch/dinner 1,100 pts. Reduced rates and special meals for children.

COSGAYA 39539 Cantabria — Map 12

Hotel Del Oso *Tel* (942) 73.04.18

In the Picos de Europa National Park in northern Spain, an area renowned for winter sports, mountaineering, horseback riding, trout and salmon fishing. Handsome stone hotel in spectacular setting, with inviting public rooms, lovely swimming pool, good tennis court, spotlessly clean modern bedrooms (some with balcony). Helpful and attentive staff. Recommended "for lovers of mountain scenery, bird-watching, and comfort in out of the way places". Closed 1 week Christmas. 36 rooms, all with bath and shower. B&B double 5,550–6,550 pts. Alc dinner 3,000 pts (1989 rates, excluding 6% tax). New nomination. More reports please.

DEYÁ Mallorca — Map 12

Hotel Es Moli — *Tel* (971) 63.90.00 and 63.90.50
Carretera de Valldemossa — *Fax* (971) 63.93.33
Telex 69007 SMOLI

This village, at the foot of the Teix mountains on the rugged coast of north-west Mallorca, has one of the loveliest settings in the Mediterranean, close to a beautiful coastline, with sunny valleys of oranges and lemons. And it is this setting above all that draws many readers back again and again to the *Es Moli*. "Luxurious. The gardens, dazzling with blossom and fruit, fragrant with scents galore, huge colourful butterflies, and the cheerful gossipy frogs shouting across the lily ponds. The stunning views to the sea and the marvellous meandering walk through olive, orange and lemon groves down to the rocky cove of Port Deyá." "For people who enjoy shade, as well as sun, the gardens are superb." Meals in summer are served on the terrace overlooking the gardens. The swimming pool is "bedazzling in its beauty"; the hotel also provides a mini-bus to its small private beach at Muleta, 20 minutes' drive away, for deep-water bathing from a rocky platform, rather than for sunbathing. (There is no nearby sandy beach.) Another reader delighted in a morning walk led by "Pepe, the mainstay at reception: he takes guests over the mountains or along the coast. We had a memorable day that ended at 5.30 pm with lunch under the trees." Other readers have referred to "the courtesy of Mr and Mrs Peters and their staff" – everyone "friendly and helpful". The hotel has been fully redecorated recently; a reader reports that the lighter, more modern rooms in the annexe "have the highest and therefore the best view of the sea". A weak point in recent years has been the food, "made of fresh and plentiful ingredients", but often unimaginative. There are still gripes, but also compliments. Service is speedier, twice a week there are numerous "delectable" hors d'oeuvre, once a week there's a "Mallorcan evening", and the menu is altogether "more adventuresome". (*Alice and John Sennett, Tim Brown; also Dr R Wise, and others*)

Open 6 Apr–29 Oct.
Rooms 1 suite, 61 double, 11 single – all with bath and shower, telephone, radio and air-conditioning; most with terrace (300 pts supplement). Annexe with 15 additional rooms 50 metres from main buildings.
Facilities Lift. 2 lounges, TV room, 2 bars, card and writing room; dining terrace, dancing by the pool weekly in summer. Large gardens with swimming pool, tennis court, pétanque. Free mini-bus to rock beach with bar; restaurant (not hotel's) 6 km away.
Location ½ km from Deyá; Palma 29 km.
Credit cards All major cards accepted.
Terms B&B: single 7,500–10,000 pts, double 13,800–18,000 pts, suite 24,000–30,000 pts; dinner, B&B: single 9,000–11,500 pts, double 16,000–21,000 pts, suite 27,000–33,000 pts. Set lunch/dinner 3,000 pts; full alc 4,500 pts. Reduced rates for children sharing parents' room; special meals on request.

La Residencia *Tel* (34.71) 63.90.11
Telex 69570 DEYA

Smaller, more exclusive, and pricier than the *Es Moli* above, *La Residencia* also causes its admirers to reach for their superlatives: "Absolute magic – just what we needed. Peace, tranquillity, and beautiful surroundings." "Without a doubt the best hotel on the island." "Lovely place. Can't wait to get back." Two adjacent manor houses in the heart of the village have been converted most elegantly, and this setting plus the "welcoming staff" and "surprisingly good restaurant" have again pleased visitors to this visually stunning hotel, "It is in the style of a Spanish grandee's house, cool, spacious and a bit dark, the swimming pool lined with elegant cypresses and silver birches, against a magnificent backdrop of mountains and forests, and grounds of orange and lemon trees, lawns and bright flowers. Our room was a charming mixture of elegance and austerity, with antique furniture including a four-poster bed, and original modern paintings. A superb breakfast was brought punctually by smiling waiters; luxurious towels and bed-linen were changed daily. The restaurant was a beautiful evocation of a stately banqueting hall, with its minstrels' galleries and intimate alcoves, lit by white candles in silver and wrought-iron sticks and candelabra. The *nouvelle cuisine* was delicious." "Fantastic wines are delightfully served by a marvellous team of girls who have been superbly trained." (*Brian and Jan Goodenough, L Morley, and others*) There are now 15 new bedrooms in an extension by the swimming pool.

Open Easter–6 Jan.
Rooms 14 suites, 26 double, 9 single – all with bath and/or shower and telephone; baby-listening on request. 15 in new extension by pool.
Facilities 5 salons, 3 bars, 2 restaurants (1 by pool); conference room; concerts, poetry readings, fashion shows etc. in summer. 32-acre grounds with gardens, tennis court, swimming pool 15 mins from sea – private beach, snack bar, sailing, windsurfing.
Location On edge of village, on road to Sóller.
Restriction Not suitable for ♿.
Credit cards None accepted.
Terms (Excluding 12% tax) B&B: single 8,000–12,000 pts, double 14,000–20,000 pts, suite 23,000–25,000 pts. Set meals 4,000 pts; full alc 5,000 pts. Reduced rates for children; special meals on request.

FORMENTOR 07470 Mallorca — Map 12

Formentor *Tel* (971) 53.13.00
Playa de Formentor *Fax* (971) 53.11.55
Telex 68523

"A dream spot – swimming first-class, about the best on the island – and so also the service and food. More expensive than the Es Moli, *(q.v.), but there is no comparison." In splendid setting amidst pine trees and flowers, large established hotel with air-conditioned public rooms and bedrooms, two restaurants (terrace and beach), heated swimming pool, children's pool and play area, tennis, riding and miniature golf. 127 rooms – all with bath, some suites. Single room 14,250 pts, double 22,000 pts. Breakfast 1,500 pts. Set lunch/dinner 4,950 pts* [1989]. (*Tax added.*) *New nomination. More reports please.*

GIBRALTAR — Map 12

The Rock Hotel
3 Europa Road

Tel (350) 73000
Fax (350) 73513
Telex 2238

Our first in Gibraltar. Large, old-fashioned British hotel in terraced gardens with fine views across bay to Algeciras. Sea-water swimming pool, open-air grill in summer, afternoon teas. "Like a Trust House hotel of ten years ago – a mixture of English custom and a Spanish setting, familiar yet strange. Superb lounge where most locals seem to meet; dining-room serving traditional British food rarely found now in the UK. Useful stop between the Costa del Sol and Cadiz, now that the frontier with Spain is open." 8 suites, 120 double, 32 single – all with bath and shower. B&B single £45; double £75–£85, suite £160–£210. Set dinner £15, full alc £20–£25. New nomination. More reports please.

GOMERA 38800 Canary Islands — Map 12

Parador Conde de la Gomera
Orilla del Llano de la Villa 5
San Sebastián de la Gomera

Tel (922) 87.11.00
Fax (922) 87.11.16

"If you have come this far, go just a bit further, an hour and a half by ferry, to the tiny island of Gomera." So begin, in one way or another, virtually all of our reports on this aristocratic island *parador*. The island of Gomera, neglected by the tourist hordes, is a far cry from its extrovert sister, Tenerife. It has a mountain, valleys and forests, and hidden beaches along the coast. In the capital port of San Sebastián, Christopher Columbus prepared his ships to sail for the New World (arrival nowadays is by roll-on–roll-off ferry). On a cliff above the town sits the *parador*, a long, low-built stone-and-tile mansion surrounded by a garden of date palms. "A splendid situation overlooking the harbour with attractive scented gardens." "Our main memory is of abundant birdsong and tropical trees." "It's hard to believe it's a new building. Utterly timeless and harmonious, with cool leafy courtyards and lots of lovely places to sit indoors and in the garden. The pool is sparkling. The staff, especially the receptionists, are pleasant and helpful." "Bedrooms are beautifully appointed and furnished (even the reading lamps are good) and the public rooms are magnificent." "Our bedroom was lofty and spacious; the bathroom had two large wash-basins and good plumbing." "Excellent breakfasts, efficient laundry service, and the unheated swimming pool – in a magnificent setting – was clean." (*Wendy Whelan; JS and F Waters, and others*) Only flaw in this paradise is the food: portions are "enormous" but the set menu "is uninspiring – based on tinned tuna, tinned asparagus, tinned sweetcorn. The à la carte menu (local specialities) was a much better bet, and little more expensive."

Open All year.
Rooms 1 suite, 40 double, 1 single – all with bath, shower, telephone, radio and TV.
Facilities 3 salons (1 with TV), bar, restaurant (air-conditioned). Large garden with unheated swimming pool, bar. Black sand beach 15 mins' walk.
Location 700 metres from centre of San Sebastián, overlooking the port. Parking.
Restriction Not suitable for ♿.

Credit cards All major cards accepted.
Terms (Excluding 4% tax) Rooms: single 8,800 pts, double 11,000 pts, suite 13,200 pts. Breakfast 800 pts. Set lunch/dinner 2,700 pts. Full alc 3,600 pts. Children under 2 free; special meals on request.

GRANADA 18009 — Map 12

Hostal América — *Tel* (958) 22.74.71
Real de la Alhambra 53

More praise again for this civilised small hotel of character, splendidly situated on the hill of the Alhambra, right next to the palace. "It is in an enviable location from which you can take evening strolls around the Alhambra grounds after the tourists have left. The colourful architecture immediately attracted us. Geraniums drip from glazed pots around the windows and doors; dinner was served in an *al fresco* setting in the central courtyard." "Solid comfort amidst a treasury of art; the food isn't all that bad either, and the wines are fairly priced." "The staff were friendly and the convivial atmosphere encouraged conversations between the guests. The food was plain, but substantial and good – our vegetarian tastes catered for at a moment's notice. Our room was tiny, but this was more than compensated for by being the only one with a balcony overlooking the gardens of the *Generalife*. It was simply furnished with Moorish curtains and bedspreads and lemon-scented sheets." (*Mark and Sue Rubinstein, J Michael Morrison, Clayton Blackburn, and others*) The hotel insists on half board terms; one reader found the food too lacking in choice for other than a short stay.

Open Mar–9 Nov.
Rooms 1 suite, 8 double, 4 single – all with bath and/or shower, and telephone.
Facilities Lounge, dining room. Patio.
Location On Alhambra hill. Parking, guarded by day.
Restriction Not suitable for ♿.
Credit cards None accepted.
Terms Dinner, B&B: single 5,355 pts, double 9,000 pts.

Parador de San Francisco — *Tel* (958) 22.14.40
Alhambra — *Fax* (958) 22.22.64
Telex 78792

Often regarded as a flagship among *paradors*, and certainly one of the most expensive, the *San Francisco* is splendidly situated on the Alhambra hill. It has modern extensions, and has been much renovated, but its core is an old Franciscan monastery. "Such a marvellous setting," wrote an inspector last year; "the delights of sitting in the lovely patio, and walking round the garden and exquisite Moorish courtyard, outweigh most failings." Readers last year criticised front desk "hostility", but this year "our welcome was cordial and our car safely parked". "Reception was courteous and helpful despite being very busy." Bedrooms are comfortable and well furnished, with good lights. The rooms to go for are in the 200s and 300s (the 400s are downstairs and lack a view). Food continues to be a cause for grumbles – "unadventurous" – and service can be slow when the *parador* is full (which is most of the time). (*M and R Milner, A and J Sennett, Nancy Raphael, JA Matheson, and others*)

Open All year.
Rooms 39 – all with bath and/or shower, telephone and TV; air-conditioning.
Facilities Salons, bar, breakfast room, restaurant; patio, garden.
Location On Alhambra hill, 3 km from city centre. Parking.
Credit cards All major cards accepted.
Terms [1989 rates] (Excluding 12% tax) Rooms: single 10,400–11,600 pts, double 13,000–14,500 pts. Breakfast 800 pts, set lunch/dinner 2,700 pts.

GUADALUPE 10140 Cáceres — Map 12

Parador Zurbarán — *Tel* (927) 36.70.75
Marqués de la Romana 10 — *Fax* (927) 36.70.76

Named after famous 17th-century artist, some of whose paintings can be seen at nearby monastery, beautiful restored convent with courtyards full of orange trees. Many bedrooms are luxurious and have good bathroom and balcony. Lavish breakfasts, with cakes and biscuits; staff friendly. A recent visitor reports the swimming pool out of commission in June, and poor insulation between rooms, but hotel otherwise satisfactory. 40 rooms, most with bath, double 6,000–8,000 pts. Breakfast 800 pts. Set lunch/dinner 2,500 pts [1989]. (Tax added.) More reports please.

GUALCHOS 18614 Granada — Map 12

La Posada — *Tel* (958) 64.60.34
Plaza Constitucion 9 — *Reservations* in UK (0223) 323618

Just out of reach of the madding crowds of the Costa del Sol, Gualchos is a still unexploited inland village in the foothills of the Sierra de Lujar, in a region of almond groves. Here two adjacent 18th-century houses in the main square have been restored to create this "absolute gem" of a *posada* (inn), with terraced gardens and a minute swimming pool. Gualchos is unspoilt Spain – the square outside the hotel (almost inaccessible by car) is alive with children playing, old men talking, others drinking at the bar till 1 am. Yet the coast and Granada are only short drives away. "We endorse all aspects of your 1989 entry", wrote a reader who spent ten days at *La Posada* this year. "We must add the heavenly perfume of jasmine filling our room at night. An idyllic haven in the Spanish hills." "The restoration of the old houses is exemplary – a maze of inner courtyards and gardens on many levels provides enchanting private rooms: ours had its own large balcony/terrace and a view of mountains and Med from the bed." The owner-chef José Gonzalez trained in France and Switzerland and spent 20 years in London. His cooking is warmly commended in all our reports; many dishes have a Spanish accent, but the cuisine is essentially French. (*Lesley Heal, Kenneth Richards, and others*) But a few readers have not been so happy: "We had an inner room which was dark and airless; the small garden was pleasant but infested with flies so I had nowhere to sit and read; the food was good, but ruined by electronic music." "Extremely well restored and the food excellent, but the menu was exactly the same for lunch and dinner the whole seven days we were there – and we were not made to feel welcome."

Open All year except June, July and Aug. Closed 28–30 Sept. Restaurant closed Mon.
Rooms 8 double, 1 single – all with bath and shower.
Facilities Lounge, bar, restaurant; patio. Small garden with pergola, tiny swimming pool. Pebble beach 20 mins' drive.
Location 9 km inland from coast at Castell de Ferro which is E of Motril. Hotel is in village centre; leave your car at edge of village and walk; hotel will collect and park it.
Restrictions Not suitable for ♿. No children under 12.
Credit cards None accepted.
Terms Dinner, B&B 7,500 pts. Full alc 7,250 pts.

JAÉN 23000 — Map 12

Parador Castillo de Santa Catalina — *Tel* (953) 26.44.11, *Fax* (953) 26.44.11
Carretera del Castillo

Many readers continue to praise the *Santa Catalina*: "An exquisite *parador*, the interior a fine example of creative architecture, stylish and at times breathtaking." It is a colossal eagle's nest of a castle perched precariously on a mountain above the town of Jaén, with dizzying views. Only south-facing rooms have a balcony, but all have remarkable vistas. "Lovely large rooms, cool tiled interiors, new swimming pool, good food," wrote a visitor last year. Most have been equally enthusiastic: "The ante-room to the dining room has an arch springing from each of the four corners of the room to meet 60 or 70 feet above your head, and is worthy of a cathedral. The dining room itself, with its priceless tapestries, is only slightly less grand." Since that report, dining-room and ante-room have been transposed: but no one has tinkered with the "friendly ambience" and "well-appointed rooms", nor with the "wide range of local specialities and international cuisine". (*JA Matheson, A and J Sennett*) But one reader had a different impression: the public rooms with small barred windows recalled dungeons, he found the food unimaginative or unsuccessful, the prevailing mood one of gloom. . .

Open All year.
Rooms 45 rooms – all with bath and shower, and telephone; some with balcony. 11 ground-floor rooms.
Facilities Lift. 2 lounges, chess and card room, TV room, bar, 2 restaurants; air-conditioning. Large garden with trees; swimming pool.
Location 3 km SW of Jaén.
Credit cards All major cards accepted.
Terms [1989 rates] (Excluding 12% tax) Rooms: single 6,800–7,200 pts, double 8,500–9,000 pts. Breakfast 800 pts, set lunch/dinner 2,500 pts.

LAGUARDIA 01300 Álava — Map 12

Marixa — *Tel* (94) 10.01.65
Sáncho Abarca 8

High on a hill, overlooking Riojan plain, restaurant with "truly breathtaking views" and bedrooms "well furnished with lots of cupboard space and nice bathrooms". Bar, terrace. Recommended for good food and friendly staff: "they were especially kind to my bicycle, bringing it into the entrance hall at night, after the last guest had retired." Closed 23 Dec–Jan. 10 rooms – all with bath, telephone, TV: *single 2,900 pts, double 3,950 pts. Breakfast 490 pts. Alc meals (excluding wine) 1,825–2,950 pts [1989]. (Tax added.) New nomination. More reports please.*

LEÓN 24001 **Map 12**

Parador Hostal de San Marcos *Tel* (987) 23.73.00
Plaza de San Marcos 7 *Telex* 89809 HSML

The glory of the proud city of León is its huge Gothic cathedral, one of Europe's finest. Its second glory is the former 16th-century monastery of San Marcos, with a splendid Renaissance facade: today part of it is an archaeological museum, and part is a very grand hotel (five red *Michelin* gables), recently nationalised and now a *parador,* and again admired this year. There are three-quarters of a mile of carpeted corridors, lined on both sides with exquisite reproductions of Spanish furniture through the ages. Large paintings and tapestries soften the cool stone walls; the furnishings are understated, restrained, elegant. Stone staircases are carpeted; there are fast, efficient lifts. The restaurant – "surprisingly modern in style" gives on to a summer terrace, with the river beyond; "the entrance provides guests with reassuring glimpses of chefs at work in a sparklingly clean kitchen." One recent visitor preferred the *San Marcos* to other *paradores,* "As you know, they mostly lack the personal touch, whereas this is a proper hotel and its staff are prepared to put themselves out for guests." Another, however, disagreed: "The service was offhand and the food indifferent." Another criticism: the rooms in the modern extension, while "still on the grand scale", enabled "our neighbours' (regrettably uninteresting) conversation in their bathroom to be audible in our own."

Open All year.
Rooms 13 suites, 245 double – all with bath, shower, telephone, radio, TV.
Facilities Lift. Salons, TV room, bar, restaurant, breakfast room; conference facilities; hairdresser, beauty parlour. Archaeological museum. Garden.
Location On river. Parking.
Credit cards All major cards accepted.
Terms [1989 rates] (Excluding 12% tax) Rooms: double 10,000–11,500 pts, suites 16,000–33,000 pts. Breakfast 800 pts. Set lunch/dinner 2,700 pts.

LOJA 18300 Granada **Map 12**

Hotel La Bobadilla *Tel* (958) 32.18.61
Finca la Bobadilla, Apartado 52 *Fax* (58) 32.18.10
Telex 78732 BOBA

"It must be one of the great hotels of Europe" writes a reader this year of *La Bobadilla,* a modern Swiss-owned luxury hotel of striking originality and character. Set in open rolling country just off the Granada–Málaga road, it entered our pages a year ago after an inspector's report: "We were enchanted. It is not so much a building as an assembly of 35 suites, brilliantly designed; the building style is *cortijo* – that of an old country

Please make a habit of sending a report if you stay at a Guide hotel.

house. Once past a foyer of breathtaking beauty, you enter a quiet, almost austere world: the finest traditional materials have been used, and it is hard to believe it is all new. There is much carved wood and tile, and small patios where fountains bubble. The furniture in the suites is plain and exquisite – heavy silk curtains, dark carved woodwork, bathroom walls of plain red brick. The five-star luxury here is very subtle. Sherry greets you at lunchtime, and champagne before dinner, where the food in the charming *La Finca* restaurant is memorable (*Michelin* rosette e.g. for duck with truffles). Another correspondent adds a few more awesome details: "There is a fully equipped 'gym' for men and women, two large saunas, the most up-to-date exercise equipment, an indoor pool and a beauty salon for all treatments – with good operators. Outdoors is an enormous pool, horse riding from their own stables, and tennis courts. The cost of the suite includes riding." The grounds are extensive and "there are splendid walks in the surrounding area". It is possible to have a room, but "the suites cost only 30% more, and not to have one is to escape the special flavour and atmosphere of the hotel" – including "an open fire which was lit every evening". (*Paul M Jackson*)

Open All year.
Rooms 7 suites, 24 double, 4 single – all with bath and shower, telephone and TV.
Facilities Salons, TV room, bar, 2 restaurants; conference rooms; terraces. Garden. Indoor and outdoor swimming pool. Tennis, sauna, jacuzzi, fitness centre. Concerts weekends.
Location At Km 502 marker on N342 Granada–Málaga road, turn off towards Rute: hotel, down its own 3 km drive, is signposted.
Restriction Not suitable for ♿.
Credit cards All major cards accepted.
Terms [1989 rates] (Excluding tax) B&B: single 19,000–20,300 pts, double 26,000–28,700 pts, suite 36,300–38,900 pts. Set lunch/dinner 6,500 pts. Reduced rates for children.

MÁLAGA 29016 — Map 12

Parador de Gibralfaro — *Tel* (925) 22.19.03
Apartado de Correos 274 — *Fax* (952) 22.19.02

A *parador* of stone arcades and terraces on a hill above Málaga, with magnificent views of city, coast and mountains from bedroom balconies and public rooms. "As a blood-red sun sinks behind the Sierra Mijas, the city turns pink and the lights twinkle on – magical. Even the hideous high-rise modern blocks acquire a certain grandeur at this distance." The bedrooms (only 12, so it is essential to book) are in predictable Spanish style, with heavy carved wooden furniture and large bathrooms. A regular visitor last year noted a great improvement in the cooking. This year his report is highly critical: "Alas, little remains to be said in favour of this once outstanding *parador*, other than its magnificent views. The food very indifferent, the service poor and unfriendly, the whole place noisy, with festoons of loudspeakers in the public rooms and restaurant. A year or two ago it was difficult to get a table; now we had the place almost to ourselves." Could we have more reports, please?

Open All year.
Rooms 12 double – all with bath and/or shower, and telephone.
Facilities Lounge, bar with TV, restaurant. Terrace.
Location 3 km from town centre, on Almeria side of city, in large park.

Credit cards All major cards accepted.
Terms [1989 rates] (Excluding 12% tax) Rooms: single 6,800–7,200 pts, double 8,500–9,000 pts. Breakfast 800 pts, set lunch/dinner 2,500 pts.

MOJÁCAR 04638 Almería — Map 12

Parador Reyes Católicos
Playa de Mojácar
Tel (951) 47.82.50
Fax (951) 47.81.83

A modern white-walled *parador*, just outside a small ancient town on a rocky hill, above the coast and plain between Almería and Murcia. "From the road the building looks rather like a sanatorium, but inside it proves a peaceful haven from the once lovely, but now increasingly garish and touristy Mojácar. The reception area is spacious, and there are many lounges with soft leather sofas, lovely pottery, and good modern prints on the walls. Everything is built for coolness – corridors to the bedrooms are open to the sky and the bedrooms are large, forty feet from the door to the terrace. Below are terraces on different levels, a good-sized pool with palm trees, and the sea beyond. Breakfast is a vast array of meats, cheese, bacon, eggs, cakes, buns, croissants, toast, yoghurt, fruit etc. Room service is quick and efficient. This would be a good place for a complete rest or as a base to visit the many pleasant and interesting small villages nearby." (*Ray and Angela Evans; Lesley Heal*) One reader found the welcome at the *parador* "efficient, but not particularly friendly", and another mentioned "horrid muzak".

Open All year.
Rooms 98 double – all with bath and shower, telephone, and TV; some with balcony. Some ground-floor rooms.
Facilities 2 salons, bar, TV room, restaurant; terrace. Garden with swimming pool.
Location 2.5 km SE of Mojácar on N340 coastal road. Parking.
Credit cards All major cards accepted.
Terms [1989 rates] (Excluding 12% tax) Single 5,200–7,200 pts, double 6,500–9,000 pts. Breakfast 800 pts. Set lunch/dinner 2,500 pts.

MONZÓN DE CAMPOS 34410 Palencia — Map 12

Hotel Castillo de Mónzon
Tel (988) 80.80.75

On road to Santander, good overnight stop en route to ferry. Comfortable modern hotel inside restored 10th-century castle on a hill. Medieval, but light in feeling; rooms pleasantly furnished, opening onto central courtyard. Quiet setting, acceptable food. Closed Nov. 10 rooms, all with bath and shower, telephone. B&B double 6,500–12,000 pts. Set lunch/dinner 2,000 pts (excluding tax). New nomination. More reports please.

> In Spain, reservations for state-run establishments can be made direct or through their central booking office: Central de Reservas de los Paradores de España,Calle Velazquez 25, Madrid 28001. Tel (91) 435.97.00.

NERJA 29780 Málaga — Map 12

Parador de Nerja — *Tel* (952) 52.00.50
Playa de Burriana — *Fax* (952) 52.19.97

A modern parador *splendidly situated high on a cliff above the beach, at the eastern edge of one of the largest resorts on the Costa del Sol. Large well-furnished rooms with good bathrooms and sea or mountain views from their balconies. Swimming pool in a shady garden. Average* parador *food in a restaurant with sea views. 73 rooms, all with bath and shower, double 9,500–11,000 pts. Breakfast 800 pts. Set lunch/dinner 2,700 pts [1989]. (Tax added) Reinstated in Guide after period of rebuilding: recent visitor reports new garden, and interior looking beautiful. More reports please.*

NUÉVALOS 50210 Zaragoza — Map 12

Hotel Monasterio de Piedra — *Tel* (976) 84.90.11 and 84.90.42
Fax (976) 84.90.54

This "unique" hotel between Madrid and Zaragoza, dropped last year for lack of feedback, returns to the Guide with recommendations from two readers. It began life in the 12th century as a Cistercian monastery; part of it is open to the public as an ancient monument, the other part is a hotel. Surrounding the monastery are "magnificent gardens full of waterfalls – some very dramatic, and all amazing considering the miles of arid countryside around". The hotel is also impressive – the vestibule has a beautiful romanesque ceiling with paintings and gilded rib-vaulting. "There are large grand hallways and staircases and an enormous dining room, but the general atmosphere is relatively informal rather than luxurious." Bedrooms vary – "the best are roomy with a sitting-room and balcony"; others are in the former monks' cells, "most with balcony, but the rooms themselves are fairly small and plain (our bath could have done with some retiling, but the shower packed a lot of power)". An à la carte dinner was "very fresh, well prepared and enormous". Readers are cautioned that the park is a major tourist attraction; while the hotel itself remains tranquil, there are full parking lots, souvenir stands and cafés nearby. (*Stephan and Kate Murray-Sykes, Myrna Malec*)

Open All year.
Rooms 7 suites, 45 double, 9 single – all with bath, shower, and telephone. Ground floor rooms.
Facilities 2 lounges with TV, 2 cafeterias, 2 restaurants. Large park with gardens, swimming pool, tennis court. Fishing and shooting nearby.
Location Turn off main Zaragoza–Madrid road at Catalayud; hotel is 28 km S.
Credit cards All major cards accepted.
Terms [1989 rates] (Excluding tax) Rooms: single 2,700–4,500 pts, double 3,400–6,500 pts. Breakfast 375 pts. Set lunch/dinner 1,500 pts.

> Many hotels put up their prices in the spring. Tariffs quoted in the text may be more accurate before April/May 1990 than after.

> We need feedback on all entries. Often people fail to report on the best-known hotels, assuming that "someone else is sure to".

OJEN 29610 Málaga — Map 12

Refugio de Juanar — *Tel* (952) 88.10.00
Sierra Blanca — *Fax* (952) 88.10.00

In a state nature reserve in the foothills of the Sierra Blanca, just inland from Marbella, this attractive little white-walled hotel is a converted hunting-lodge, new to the Guide last year, "This is where the Spanish come. When it's busy, you can only stay two nights. Our bedroom was small but adequate, with a large bathroom. Comfortable public areas with sofas and a log fire. You can find yourself legless over the generous gins in the bar. Specialities are the superb game casseroles – we watched wild deer on the lawn eating chestnuts. Walk up to the viewpoint for sunsets over Marbella." This year another reader reports, "The atmosphere is relaxing and friendly, the staff are local young ladies, the lack of skill made up for by their charm. The food is uncomplicated but freshly cooked and hot. The surroundings are pine forests, away from the cosmopolitan coast line. The bedrooms are rustic, but with all amenities; everything works, very cosy." (*David Ball*)

Open All year.
Rooms 1 suite for 6–8, 4 smaller suites, 14 double, 1 single – all with bath, shower, telephone and TV. Ground-floor rooms.
Facilities 3 salons, 2 bars, TV room, restaurant; functions room. Garden with swimming pool and table tennis.
Location 20 km N of Marbella, 10 km W of Ojen. Hotel is signposted.
Credit cards All major cards accepted.
Terms (Excluding 6% tax) Rooms: single 5,100 pts, double 6,200 pts, suite 8,600–13,200 pts. Breakfast 600 pts. Set lunch/dinner 1,980 pts. Full alc 2,500 pts. Reduced rates for stays of 3 or more nights.

ORIENT 07110 Mallorca — Map 12

Hotel L'Hermitage — *Tel* (971) 61.33.00
Carretera de Alaró

Orient is "a Shangri-La hidden valley of orchards hemmed in by mountains, and for that reason alone lovely to stay in." Up in the wooded hills near the rugged north-west coast of Mallorca, and just outside the old village of Orient, *L'Hermitage* has been converted from a 17th-century country mansion whose former guests included King Farouk of Egypt and the King of Bulgaria. There is a swimming pool amongst pine trees, and two tennis courts. Our nominator found an enormous range of delights, including "the main house with a reading room and games room, a small bar with interesting Mallorcan watercolours, plenty of German and UK/US magazines, and large bowls of splendid fresh flowers. The dining-room, in the old olive mill, has an olive press as its focal point, and the grinding-stone is now used as a table where a lavish breakfast buffet is laid out, including the island's delicious specialty, ensaimadas. Bedroom comfortable, with European cable TV programmes, and modern bathroom. Four rooms are in the older building, the rest in a chalet-like block; ours had easy chairs, a wall safe, a large balcony." This year readers report "adventurous food – fresh, and soundly cooked" – "the consistently best hotel food we experienced anywhere in Spain." One reader warns that there is no public transport in Orient, so a car is essential: "the scenic, climbing shorter route to Palma is 28 kilometres; the faster, 35 kilometres, is via Alaró and Consell." (*LH, JR Lloyd, David Ball*)

Open All year.
Rooms 20 double – all with bath, telephone, TV and terrace. 4 in annexe.
Facilities Lounge, salons, bar, TV room, games room, restaurant. Garden with 2 tennis courts, swimming pool, sauna.
Location 1.3 km NE of village of Orient, 25 km N of Palma.
Credit cards Access, Diners, Visa.
Terms [1989 rates] (Excluding 12% tax) Double room 15,800 pts. Breakfast 1,075 pts. Alc meals (excluding wine) 2,500 pts.

PORT MAHÓN 07700 Menorca — Map 12

Hotel Port Mahón
Avenida Fort de l'Eau, 12

Tel (971) 36.26.00
Fax (971) 36.43.62
Telex 69473 PORME

Our first entry for the smaller, less touristy Balearic island of Menorca: "A comfortable, old-fashioned four-star hotel in best position in Mahón, near harbour. Bedrooms overlooking water recommended for view; breakfast served on balconies. Excellent service from maids and waiters (staff in reception and bar less welcoming). Average food, well cooked, with good buffet of desserts. Swimming pool and terrace. Close to harbour walk, where there are lots of little cafés." 74 rooms – all with bath or shower, single 4,900–7,100 pts, double 6,050–10,000 pts. Breakfast 750 pts. Set lunch/dinner 2,300 pts [1989]. (Tax added.) More reports please.

RIBADEO 27700 Lugo — Map 12

Parador de Ribadeo — *Tel* (982) 11.08.25

A relatively modern *parador*, overlooking a magnificent deep inlet on the Galician coast, just outside Ribadeo, a town of faded elegance. There's an unusual feature: you go down by lift from the ground floor to the bedrooms below – the most expensive have fine views over the estuary. "From the outside this is a small and unimpressive building, though with obvious charm and a pretty garden. Inside all is clean and comfortable. Our bedroom was well appointed and adequate in size; it had a big bathroom and large walled balcony overlooking the water and the little town beyond." (*C and M Dehn*) Other visitors were equally pleased: "Lovely position, extremely comfortable, with good food and helpful staff. It was our first visit to Galicia, where there are miles of empty beaches, lots of ancient churches, and friendly people. We certainly recommend this *parador*." (*M and R Milne-Day*) The Bay of Ribadeo and the magnificent river valley make this an attractive stop on the long north coast.

Open All year.
Rooms 41 double, 6 single, all with bath and shower, and TV.
Facilities Lift. 2 salons, restaurant, bar, terrace. Beach 200 metres.
Location On outskirts of town. Parking.
Credit cards All major cards accepted.
Terms (Excluding 6% tax) B&B 4,050–7,600 pts. Set lunch/dinner 2,500 pts. Full alc 2,000–3,000 pts.

SANTIAGO DE COMPOSTELA La Coruña **Map 12**

Hotel de los Reyes Católicos
Plaza de España 1
Santiago de Compostela 15705

Tel (981) 58.22.00 and 58.23.00
Fax (981) 56.30.94
Telex 86004 HRCS

This *very* large, grand and famous hotel stands in the heart of medieval Santiago and was built by Ferdinand and Isabella in the 15th century as a hostel for pilgrims to the shrine of St-James. ("Imagine staying at a cross between Hampton Court and All Souls, furnished with the best pieces from the Victoria and Albert Museum", wrote one reader.) It forms one side of the *plaza* on which the cathedral sits. Some reports this year: "We were escorted to our room through a series of small, cloistered courtyards, containing either a fountain, ornamental flower beds, or miniature topiary. During our journey we heard evocative music which – blended with the romanesque arches and stone staircases – was reminiscent of a scene from *Brideshead*." "We had a four-poster, and I wrote my postcards in a huge armchair overlooking a beautiful courtyard, with a piano playing in the background." Rooms vary greatly in size and style, but at least some have canopied beds, very high ceilings and period Spanish furniture. "Expensive but worth it", has been one recent comment, although another reader suggests that if you eat in the elegant cafeteria, and take a room with a shower, not a bath, the expense need not be so great. The dining room is an enormous gracefully vaulted crypt, but the food – and the room's decor – get mixed reports: "The cod with almonds on Saturday was particularly good, but on Sunday it was reheated." "The banquette seats in the dining room were remarkably uncomfortable – but the food quite good." "Breakfast was superb, both for choice and presentation – set out like a harvest festival." Don't expect impeccable room maintenance; the plumbing is "noisy and not always efficient". But readers still support an earlier report: "For a knock-out hotel experience (honeymoon or something), you really couldn't do much better in Spain."

Open All year.
Rooms 3 suites, 114 double, 13 single – all with bath and/or shower, telephone, radio, TV, and baby-listening. Some ground-floor rooms.
Facilities Lifts. Reception hall, salons, TV room, bars, dining-room, cafeteria; conference facilities; hairdressing salon, boutiques; Chapel Royal with occasional concerts. Gardens.
Location In town centre, by cathedral. Garage parking nearby. Special bus to station.
Credit cards All major cards accepted.
Terms (Excluding 12% tax) Rooms: single 9,600–12,000 pts, double 12,000–15,000 pts, suite 27,000–31,200 pts. Breakfast 800 pts. Set lunch/dinner 2,700 pts; full alc 4,000–5,000 pts. Reduced rates and special meals for children.

Hostal Windsor
República de El Salvador 16
Santiago de Compostela 15701

Tel (981) 59.29.39

Useful for short stay; half the price of Reyes Católicos, *above. B&B in newer part of town, five minutes' walk from historic quarter. Recent visitors found rooms clean, and Italian manager and staff helpful; though one complained of plumbing and other noises at night. "Though modern, it has been attractively decorated in traditional Spanish style, using wood, glass and brasswork to great effect. Our bedroom was attractive, quiet and comfortable, though the bathroom was tiny." 50 rooms, all with bath and/or shower, double 3,700–4,700 pts. Breakfast 350 pts [1989]. (Tax added.) No recent reports. More needed.*

SANTO DOMINGO DE LA CALZADA 26250 La Rioja — Map 12

Parador Santo Domingo de la Calzada
Plaza del Santo 3

Tel (941) 34.03.00
Fax (941) 34.03.25

In heart of the Rioja wine country, a "serviceable" parador, converted from what was once a hostel for pilgrims en route for Santiago – though little now remains of the old building but the facade and an imposing main hall. Commended in the past for its food, service, and its 27 smallish but clean and comfortable rooms, all with bath and shower. B&B 4,300–7,600 pts. Set meals 2,500 pts [1989]. Little recent feedback. More reports please.

SEGOVIA 40001 — Map 12

Parador de Segovia
Apartado de Correos 106
Carretera de Valladolid

Tel (911) 43.04.62 and 43.07.50
Fax (911) 43.73.62
Telex 47913 RRPP

An elegant, modern hotel perched on a hill above the town, with fine views of the golden cathedral and the romantic *alcázar*. Praise in earlier editions has been endorsed again: "With its two pools and grassy lawn, this is a great place to relax in. Every room has a view, the lobby is vast with glass from floor to ceiling; the food is very good." "It should be ugly since it is only concrete beams and brick walls. But lines in every direction give pleasure to the eye, and the place is full of small gardens." "It is palatial, stylishly designed and sumptuously furnished. Bedrooms are ultra-modern, excellently equipped." A reader this year adds, "The large comfortable bedrooms have refrigerators and balconies, and the garden/pool area is lovely. The handsomely decorated public rooms are cavernous, however, and the general tone is impersonal." Some readers have found the food uninspiring, and have recommended venturing into the more atmospheric restaurants in the town.

Open All year.
Rooms 5 suites, 70 double, 5 single – all with bath and shower, telephone, radio and TV; air-conditioning. Some ground-floor rooms.
Facilities Salons, library, TV room, bar, restaurant; conference facilities; indoor swimming pool, sauna. Garden with swimming pool.
Restriction Not suitable for ♿.
Location 2 km N of Segovia on N601.
Credit cards All major cards accepted.
Terms [1989 rates] (Excluding 12% tax) Rooms: single 7,200–8,000 pts, double 9,000–10,000 pts, suite 12,150–13,500 pts; dinner, B&B: single 10,700–11,500 pts, double 16,000–17,000 pts. Breakfast 800 pts. Set lunch/dinner 2,700 pts; full alc 4,000 pts. Special meals for children.

> Hotels are dropped if we lack positive feedback. If you can endorse an entry, please do so.

LA SEU D'URGELL 25700 Lerida — Map 12

Hotel El Castell — *Tel* (973) 35.07.04 and 35.10.41
Apt. Correos 53 — *Telex* 93610 CSEU

20 kilometres south of Andorra, a modern single-storey luxury hotel on a hillside with beautiful views over the valley below, well situated for exploring the Pyrenees, with fishing, river canoeing and golf nearby. It enters the Guide this year with the following report: "In a very pleasant small town, *El Castell* has previously been classified as a motel, but is now 'three-turret red' in *Michelin*, with a rosette. It lies one kilometre south of the town on the side of a ruined castle. Towards the castle, and surrounded by a rose garden, is an attractive swimming pool. All the bedrooms are off a long corridor, well appointed with private bathrooms, small fridge and TV. Balconies have pleasant views. The dining-room is restful and pleasant, and the owners (or managers) very much in evidence (also at breakfast!) speak excellent English. Food superb as one might expect from the *Michelin* rosette. I had a perfectly cooked roast kid and my wife an equally perfect duck. Hot puff pastry sweets – which I can still taste! Presentation modern without being excessively *nouvelle*. (*Dr Ian Anderson*)

Open All year. Restaurant closed Christmas.
Rooms 2 suites, 38 double – all with bath and shower, telephone, TV, mini-bar, baby-listening by arrangement. Ground floor rooms.
Facilities Salon, TV room, reading room, bar, 2 dining rooms; conference/functions rooms. Garden with unheated swimming pool, badminton. Fishing (permits arranged); Nordic and Alpine skiing nearby.
Location On edge of village 20 km S of Andorra la Vella, on Lerida road.
Credit cards All major cards accepted.
Terms (Excluding 12% tax) Room: single 8,500 pts, double 11,000 pts, suite 21,000 pts. Breakfast 1,200 pts. Lunch and dinner alc 3,500–5,000 pts.

SIGÜENZA 19250 Guadalajara — Map 12

Parador Castillo de Sigüenza — *Tel* (911) 39.01.00
Plaza del Castillo — *Fax* (911) 39.13.64
Telex 22517

130 kilometres north-east of Madrid, Sigüenza is a historic old town, with a castle and a fine cathedral. The *parador* is set in a medieval fortress, with splendid views from the ramparts. "Well worth a journey just for the opulence of the setting," writes a correspondent this year, who also appreciated its warmth when it was snowing outside. Usual "traditional" *parador* furnishings (e.g. suits of armour in the lounge), plus well-furnished bedrooms and "quite good" cooking. (*Martin L Dodd*)

Open All year.
Rooms 5 suites, 68 double, 3 single – all with bath and shower, telephone and TV.
Facilities Lifts. Restaurant, bar, TV room. Small gardens.
Location 200 metres from town.
Credit cards All major cards accepted.
Terms (Excluding tax) Rooms: single 6,000–6,800 pts, double 7,500–8,500 pts, suite 9,500–10,500 pts. Breakfast 800 pts. Set lunch/dinner 2,500 pts.

We depend on detailed fresh reports to keep our entries up-to-date.

SOLDEU Andorra — Map 12

Hostal Sant Pere — *Tel* (9738) 510.87
El Tarter — *Telex* 234

One of our two entries for the principality of Andorra, this restaurant-with-rooms on the main road from the capital to the French border was nominated last year by a distinguished British restaurateur, now retired: "I must have had between 50 and 100 dinners here over the past two years and stayed on several occasions, and in my experience it is by far the best hotel and restaurant in Andorra, where nearly all the others are either cheap for skiers or overdone Pyrenean style. The restaurant, not expensive, is very professionally staffed in the Spanish manner and has a limited menu of good quality." (*Kenneth Bell*) Endorsed this year: "Location – excellent! At the foot of a ski trail, ten miles from very noisy downtown Andorra. Room very nice, appropriately alpine, but not rustic. A wonderful shower room. Only the skiers were noisy and awoke before I did – soundproofing was sparse. Food – excellent! Catalan-inspired and very expertly presented. Service was equal to the food. One of my all time top dozen meals." (*Paul A Hoffstein*)

Open All year.
Rooms 6 double – all with shower and telephone. Also 11 studio apartments nearby.
Facilities 2 salons with TV, restaurant; terrace.
Location At El Tarter, 3 km W of Soldeu on main road to Andorra la Vieja. Parking.
Credit cards All major cards accepted.
Terms [1989 rates] B&B double 7,500–9,000 pts. Full alc 3,500–4,500 pts. Special menus for children.

TOLEDO — Map 12

Hostal del Cardenal — *Tel* (925) 22.49.00
Paseo de Recaredo 24 — *Fax* (925) 22.29.91
Toledo 45004

This "true Toledan palace", home of the local archbishop in the 18th century, adjoins the city walls. It is well known for its excellent restaurant, and offers good hotel accommodation as well; some of its rooms overlook the terraced garden which extends to the city gates. A report last year, "A magical setting and a lovely hotel. Bedroom *very* adequate with a fab view of the gardens. Public rooms furnished with Spanish antiques. Ate well at dinner, with heavenly view of floodlit city gates. Service was both polite and patient. Bottled orange juice at breakfast was the only jarring note." "The distinguished furnishings are in total keeping with the surroundings. The walk through the gardens and along the inner walls is a delight – a haven from the crowded streets outside." Endorsed again this year: "Memorable. Proof that excellence doesn't have to cost a fortune. (Minor grievance: Why, in a palace with so many spectacular rooms, must breakfast be offered in a cramped and sunless chamber?)" (*J Michael Morrison; also Ray and Angela Evans*)

Open All year.
Rooms 2 suites, 22 double, 3 single – all with bath and shower, and telephone.
Facilities Lounges, TV room, dining room. Garden, patios and courtyards.

Location 10–15 mins' walk from centre; by the old walls at Puerta de Bisagra. Parking.
Restriction Not suitable for ♿.
Credit cards All major cards accepted.
Terms [1989 rates] (Excluding 6% tax) Rooms: single 4,200 pts, double 6,900 pts, suite 10,000 pts. Breakfast 400 pts. Set meals 1,800 pts.

Parador Conde de Orgaz — *Tel* (925) 22.18.50
Paseo de los Cigarrales — *Fax* (925) 22.51.66
Toledo 45002 — *Telex* 47998 RRPT

"For the view alone, this is *the* place to stay in Toledo," wrote a visitor last year of this showpiece *parador*, often crowded with coach parties. First impressions are of 16th-century Spain at its most baronial – coats of arms, shields and antique weapons forged from Toledo steel in the halls and corridors, and banners and portraits of grave-faced bearded grandees. In fact the hotel was built in 1968, and the rooms, although furnished in the old style, have every modern amenity including a fridge. It is on the site where El Greco executed his famous painting of Toledo, high on a hill to the north. A room with a view of the city is well worth the extra money. "Ours was in the most expensive range, but worth it for the stupendous sight of the floodlit cathedral at night and the sandy pinks of the buildings contrasting with dark cypresses by day. Splendid furnishings – heavily fringed woollen curtains and bed covers to match. Plentiful lighting. Pretty rugs on the tiled floor: 45 feet from the door to the balcony." Alas, other aspects of the hotel are less satisfactory: "Breakfast excellent, but dinner almost inedible: half-emptied plates collected by waiters, and strong complaints from fellow guests. We had flavourless soup, bitter-tasting scrambled eggs with shrimp, dry fresh tuna with undercooked boiled potatoes. Luckily there are good restaurants in Toledo, but what a pity the *paradores* don't take more pride in their food." Another reader found reception unhelpful, and the service indifferent. More reports welcome.

Open All year.
Rooms 71 double, 6 single – all with bath and shower, telephone, radio and TV.
Facilities Lift. 3 salons, TV room, bar, restaurant – all with air-conditioning. Extensive landscaped grounds with terraces and unheated swimming pool. Hunting and fishing nearby.
Location 3 km S of town centre; well signposted.
Restriction Not suitable for ♿.
Credit cards All major cards accepted.
Terms (Excluding 12% tax) B&B: single 10,500 pts, double 13,800 pts. Set lunch/dinner 2,900 pts.

Hotel Maria Cristina — *Tel* (925) 21.32.02
Marqués de Mendigorria 1 — *Telex* 42827 HMCT
Toledo 45003

Just outside city walls 100 metres from Puerta de Bisagra, modern hotel with traditional Spanish interior. Spacious cool dining-room with blue painted ceiling, red tiled floors, soft muslin curtains. Recommended for well-appointed bedrooms, comfortable beds, spotless bathrooms, friendly staff. "Service in dining room impeccable – though food not spectacular." Air-conditioned. Used by tour groups, it has extensive business and conference facilities. 66 rooms, all with bath and shower; single 3,900–4,125 pts, double 5,800–6,250 pts. Breakfast 395 pts, lunch/dinner 1,800 pts [1989]. New nomination. More reports please.

TORTOSA 43500 Tarragona — Map 12

Parador Castillo de la Zuda

Tel (977) 44.44.50
Fax (977) 44.44.58

On a hilltop dominating this historic town on the banks of the Ebro, a massive feudal castle dating from Moorish times, now much restored in true *parador* style, and warmly endorsed by several readers: "An attractive building in a lovely setting overlooking Tortosa; the views from all sides are interesting (river, mountains, rooftops, the cathedral, the old town), and it is well worth wandering round the perimeter walls and looking out from each vantage point. The public rooms are well kept and attractive (except the bar) and there are three fireplaces preserved from the 13th century. The bedrooms (twin beds only) are pleasantly furnished in traditional Spanish style – terracotta tiled floors with patterned cotton rugs, dark wooden furniture, iron lamps, heavy wooden doors, shutters. Good lighting, modern and clean bathroom, good plumbing and ventilation. All the staff were pleasant and hardworking." "The hotel has been renovated from a ruin with much care and feeling. Everything sparkles with polish and love. All the staff are fantastic." "The restaurant is a baronial hall, with a tiled ceiling between wooden beams. Helpful staff, and good, simple authentic local food: the fried fish platter was particularly tasty." (*JK Baker, S Croft, and others*) Not everyone agrees about the food, except for the "excellent" breakfast. "Avoid the set menu," was the advice of one reader.

Open All year.
Rooms 3 suites, 71 double, 8 single – all with bath and shower, telephone and TV.
Facilities Lift. Salon, bar, restaurant. Garden with swimming pool.
Location 500 metres from centre, sign-posted.
Restrictions Not suitable for ♿.
Credit cards All major cards accepted.
Terms [1989 rates] Dinner, B&B: single 6,375 pts, double 9,800 pts.

TRUJILLO 10200 Cáceres — Map 12

Parador de Trujillo
Plaza de Santa Clara

Tel (927) 32.13.50
Fax (927) 32.13.66

Trujillo is the birthplace of Pizarro, whose magnificent statue stands in the town square. On a hilltop in its ancient citadel is this new *parador* (opened 1985), built within the ancient convent of Santa Clara. Rooms in the old part have been tastefully modernised and have good bathrooms, but remain in keeping with the character of the rambling old building with courtyards; there is also a modern annexe. Recent comments: "A very pleasant hotel with a tranquil atmosphere. The staff were helpful; the dinner menu was interesting and the food most attractively presented." "We happened to arrive on a day of fiesta when 90,000 people from all over Extremadura descended on the small town, and the fireworks and bands in the streets made us dubious about our location.

We need not have worried: the bedrooms were peaceful, the swimming pool clean, and the bar gave good service despite the influx of local politicians. The food was superb. The selection of cold fish for starters included a generous serving of smoked salmon on a bed of red cabbage, decorated with radishes *en rosette*, and hot aubergines with ham and salami. The main course included roast suckling pig and half a cold partridge. The puddings were less exciting, but very good. An '81 Extremaduran red wine at 850 pesetas was excellent in value and flavour." (*WK Reid; Diane Sumner*)

Open All year.
Rooms 1 suite, 41 double, 4 single – all with bath, telephone and mini-bar. Some in annexe.
Facilities TV room, bar, dining room; conference facilities. Garden with swimming pool.
Location 47 km E of Cáceres. Hotel is central. Garage.
Restrictions Not suitable for ♿.
Credit cards All major cards accepted.
Terms [1989 rates] (Excluding 12% tax) Rooms: single 6,400–6,800 pts, double 8,000–8,500 pts. Breakfast 800 pts; set lunch/dinner 2,500 pts.

UBEDA 23400 Jaén — Map 12

Parador Condestable Dávalos — *Tel* (953) 75.03.45
Plaza Vazquez de Molina 1 — *Fax* (953) 75.12.59

Ubeda, in north-eastern Andalusia, is an exceptionally beautiful old town with some fine churches (notably San Pablo and El Salvador), and many Renaissance buildings. In its historic main square is this "lovely 16th-century stone palace with a wonderful internal patio, surrounded by tiled corridors leading to cool rooms; the best ones look onto the square or small courtyards." "Antiques add to a sense of nobility, though our room was not entirely in keeping with this style, having bright and modern furnishings. It was, however, spacious, and had a cavernous bathroom." Readers this year have been enthusiastic about the food, especially the *tapas*, and "the most delicious olives – Ubeda is surrounded by miles of olive groves". Service is by "rather taciturn ladies, attired in national costume". (*Marion and David Fanthorpe, A and J Sennett, and others*) One warning: "there is no public room other than the rather gloomy and uncomfortable bar; with dinner not served until 9.30 pm, the wait during darker months of the year can be a trial."

Open All year.
Rooms 1 suite, 25 double – all with bath and shower, telephone, radio and TV.
Facilities Bar, TV room, restaurant; air-conditioning. Garden.
Location Central. Ubeda is 57 km NE of Jaén.
Restriction Not suitable for ♿.
Credit cards All major cards accepted.
Terms [1989 rates] (Excluding 6% tax) Rooms: single 7,200–8,000 pts, double 9,000–10,000 pts. Breakfast 800 pts; set lunch/dinner 2,500 pts.

> Our italicised entries indicate hotels which are worth considering, but which, for various reasons – inadequate information, lack of feedback, ambivalent reports – do not at the moment warrant a full entry. We should particularly welcome comments on these hotels.

VALENCIA DE DON JUAN 24200 León — Map 12

Hotel Villegas II — *Tel* (987) 75.01.61
Calle el Palacio 21

Small hotel in small market town 38 kilometres south of León, "quiet, cheap, unpretentious, agreeably managed, comfortable and charmingly decorated", with garden and, in season, swimming pool. The rather simpler 24-roomed Villegas *nearby is under the same management. 12 rooms, all with bath, single 2,000–2,500 pts, double 3,500–4,500 pts. Breakfast 250 pts; set lunch/dinner 1,200 pts [1989]. (Tax added.) New nomination. More reports please.*

VALVERDE 38900 Hierro, Canary Islands — Map 12

Parador de El Hierro — *Tel* (922) 55.80.86 and 55.80.36
Las Playas

A pleasant modern parador *in quiet and beautiful countryside on the east coast of the small island of Hierro, the smallest and most remote of the Canaries. 20 km from Valverde and 15 from the airport. Attractive rooms, each with balcony, overlook the garden and the sea. Large well-kept pool; friendly service; food above* parador *average; excellent breakfasts. Open all year. 47 rooms, all with bath and shower. B&B double 8,960–9,600 pts. Set menu 2,500 pts [1989]. Recent nomination. More reports please.*

VERÍN 32600 Orense — Map 12

Parador de Monterrey — *Tel* (988) 41.00.75
Fax (988) 41.20.17

Verín lies just a few kilometres north of the Portuguese border. It is a well-preserved medieval town, with narrow streets and attractive old houses, and fine views of burnt Castilian countryside all around – "the most perfect site for a hotel we have ever seen". There is a pear-shaped swimming pool, surrounded by lawn and variegated trees, which must be welcome on hot days. The hotel is modern, with two storeys, clean and light outside, in the style of an old Spanish manor house, cool and dark inside. The staircase is wide and shallow and the corridors long; the bedroom was well appointed. The food was good, with plenty of choice, though the menu did not change. The place was, however, less efficient than other *paradores*; no one spoke English, no forms were signed on arrival, and the system of charging for extras was casual and led to duplication and disquiet." (*LH, Conrad and Marilyn Dehn*)

Open All year.
Rooms 1 suite, 22 double – all with bath, and telephone. 8 in annexe.
Facilities Lounge with TV, bar, dining room. Garden with swimming pool.
Location 71 km SE of Orense on N525. *Parador* is 4 km NW of Verín.
Restrictions Not suitable for ♿.
Credit cards All major cards accepted.
Terms [1989 rates] (Excluding tax) Rooms: single 4,800–6,000 pts, double 6,000–7,500 pts. Breakfast 800 pts; set lunch/dinner 2,500 pts.

VICH 08500 Barcelona — Map 12

Parador de Vich — *Tel* (93) 888.72.11
Fax (93) 888.73.77

Off the Barcelona-Andorra road, 14 kilometres north-east of Vich, an austere stone Catalan *parador* with views over the lake and distant Pyrenees. "As in other *paradores*, the room was large and clean, the beds large and comfortable, the furniture generally large and ornate, the bathroom large and the managers nicely assuming you will need at least ten towels. The water was abundant and always hot. The mini-bar was overpriced. Dinner was acceptable and very reasonably priced: artichokes stuffed with cod, and quail and bean casseroles followed by lamb cutlets. After dinner came the first highlight of our stay – we drank wine on the balcony until about midnight. It was peaceful and our conversation was accompanied by the croaking of what sounded like thousands of frogs, calling and answering back and forth down the valley. In the morning we saw our view – we overlooked the swimming pool, which in turn overlooked a lake which stretched away into the distance between the hills. We ate breakfast on the balcony accompanied by our second highlight – our first cuckoos of the year, not just one or two, but maybe ten or twenty calling down the valley in the same manner as the frogs the night before. This *parador* was not the prettiest we have stayed in, but it was certainly in an extremely attractive setting. There are plenty of public rooms laid out for billiards, cards, television or just conversation. The bar was large and well stocked." (*Elizabeth Jones*)

Open All year.
Rooms 1 suite, 31 double, 4 single – all with bath and shower, telephone and TV.
Facilities Lift. 3 lounges, bar, TV salon, restaurant. Garden with swimming pool, tennis court. Large artificial lake nearby, accessible on foot.
Location 14 km NE of Vich, well signposted.
Credit cards All major cards accepted.
Terms [1989 rates] (Excluding 12% tax) B&B: single 6,000–8,000 pts, double 8,100–10,600 pts. Set meals 2,500 pts. Full alc 2,000–6,500 pts. Special meals for children on request.

VILLALBA 27800 Lugo — Map 12

Parador Condes de Villalba — *Tel* (982) 51.00.11
Valeriano Valdesuso — *Fax* (982) 51.00.90

In a town on the Galician plain in north-west Spain, and a possible staging post between Gijon and Santiago, this small *parador* is a converted medieval bastion with a drawbridge and an octagonal tower – "a delight, and quite astonishing", a reader wrote this year. "We had a huge room, with magnificent antique furniture, a vast bathroom, and a curtained alcove with loopholes for shooting at pedestrians below." Traditional high-quality furnishings, comfortable beds, "service nice, but amateur". There is no bar and few interesting drinks – e.g. "no dry Amontillado or Oloroso (unheard of)". The restaurant is in the dungeon: the food is good according to one report, "pretty ordinary" according to another. More reports welcome.

Open All year.
Rooms 6 double – all with bath and shower, telephone and TV.

Facilities Lift. Salon with TV, cafeteria, dining room. Garden.
Location 36 Km N of Lugo. Hotel is central. Parking.
Restrictions Not suitable for ♿.
Credit cards All major cards accepted.
Terms [1989 rates] (Excluding 6% tax) Rooms: single 7,200–8,000 pts, double 9,000–10,000 pts. Breakfast 800 pts; set lunch/dinner 2,500 pts.

VITORIA-GASTEIZ 01192 Álava — Map 12

Parador de Argomániz — *Tel* (945) 28.22.00
Apartado 601 Vitoria — *Fax* (945) 28.22.00

A converted 18th-century country mansion in a peaceful setting amid the Navarre hills of the Basque country, just off the Pamplona–Vitoria road. Vitoria, capital of the largest of the Basque provinces, lies 12 kilometres to the west. The *parador* is comfortable, clean and attractive, with many public rooms, ancient stone floors, modern wooden floors, and a raftered, barn-like restaurant, where "good wine and *very* good food" are served. "Friendly service" is reported by one reader, "little personal charm" by another. Recommended as a useful overnight stop. (*Elizabeth Jones, PW Arnold*)

Open All year.
Rooms 54 double – all with bath and shower, telephone.
Facilities Lift. Salon, TV room, bar, restaurant. Garden.
Location 12 km E of Vitoria by N1 to Irun.
Restrictions Not suitable for ♿.
Credit cards All major cards accepted.
Terms [1989 rates] (Excluding 6% tax) Double room 6,000–7,000 pts. Breakfast 800 pts; set lunch/dinner 2,500 pts.

ZAFRA 06300 Badajoz — Map 12

Parador Hernán Cortés — *Tel* (924) 55.02.00
Plaza Corazón María 7 — *Fax* (924) 55.10.18

In a small town just off the Badajoz–Seville road, this *parador*, like so many others, is a converted castle. It has massive grey walls and is austere from the outside, but cool and inviting inside: "An inspired conversion, modern enough for convenience but retaining the best of the period (tapestries everywhere)", wrote a reader last year. This year a regular correspondent writes: "The only *parador* I have encountered which I think is splendid. Distinguished architecture, a humane and well-furnished interior, exceptionally well-furnished bedroom and the best-appointed bathroom I have found in Spain. My one reservation: the food is mediocre, in the standard *parador* way." (*ATW Liddell*) One reader this year found the pool closed in June, and didn't like his bottled water *sin gaz* arriving *sin stopper* too. Poor insulation between rooms has also been mentioned; upper rooms or those not facing the town square are quietest.

Open All year.
Rooms 22 double, 6 single – most with bath or shower, all with telephone.
Facilities Salon, bar, dining room. Garden with swimming pool.
Location Central; parking. Town is 76 km SE of Badajoz.
Credit cards All major cards accepted.
Terms [1989 rates] (Excluding 6% tax) Rooms: single 5,200–6,400 pts, double 6,500–8,000 pts. Breakfast 800 pts; set lunch/dinner 2,500 pts.

ZAMORA 49001 **Map 12**

Parador Condes de Alba y Aliste
Plaza de Viriato 5

Tel (988) 51.44.97
Fax (988) 53.00.63

By the banks of the upper Duero, in the heart of an old city north of Salamanca, this beautiful 15th-century palace with an inner court has been carefully restored. Recommended for friendly service and its fine restaurant: "the best food we have had at a parador – cuisine bourgeoise *with a strong regional accent, and interesting puddings." Large bedrooms, antiques, modern well-lit bathrooms. Swimming pool with fine view. 27 rooms, all with bath and shower. B&B double 8,600–10,600 pts. Set lunch/dinner 2,500 pts (Excluding 12% tax). A recent visitor encountered "unhoovered carpets, waterstained table, less than splendidly clean bedspreads". Just an off-day? More reports please.*

Traveller's tale *The brochure stipulates 'No dogs'. This augurs well for those who object to animals in public rooms. But the proprietors have two dogs and at least three cats. These are allowed access to all the public rooms and have occasionally to be ejected from the bedrooms if doors are left open. In the lounges, cats' claws have caused some damage to clothing, but more serious is their presence in the dining room and – unbelievably – the kitchen. In the bar one of the dogs was seen to be eating crisps out of a bowl and attempting to drink the beer of one of the guests; and we were cheerfully informed one evening that there was a shortage of cheese biscuits because one of the dogs had eaten them in the kitchen.*

Sweden

TIDBLOMS HOTEL, GOTHENBURG

BORGHOLM 387 00 Öland **Map 7**

Hotell Guntorps Herrgård *Tel* (0485) 13 000
Guntorpsgatan

A four-mile bridge, Europe's longest, links the mainland to Öland, Sweden's second largest island (87 miles by 10 miles). Rich in wildlife, it is a breeding ground for many different varieties of land and sea birds, and has an abundance of protected wildflowers (30 species of orchid, 15 of violet); there are also Viking rune-stones and prehistoric burial chambers. Our previous entry for Borgholm was *Halltorps Gästgiveri*, a 17th-century royal stables, now dropped for want of feedback. We'd welcome more reports. *Guntorps Herrgård* is a picturesque manor house, converted from a family home six years ago, with self-contained suites in one wing, ten-minutes' walk from the village centre. "We found this hotel was sheer paradise. We had only planned to stay a day or two but enjoyed it so much we spent the rest of our vacation here. It was wonderfully peaceful and relaxing. We chose one of the suites, furnished in warm light pinks and creams with typically Scandinavian furniture.

Breakfast was a pure delight. The owner and manager treated us like family rather than guests." (*Capt Richard M Seitz*) The hotel serves only breakfast, but has an arrangement with restaurants in the area and will reserve tables and sometimes drive guests in the hotel's car. More reports please.

Open All year.
Rooms 14 suites, 6 double, 1 single – all with bath and shower, telephone, radio and TV. Suites, in separate wing, have fridge and kitchenette.
Facilities Ramps to suites. Salon, breakfast room; conference room. Garden with heated swimming pool, children's pool, croquet. Sandy beaches 1 km.
Location 800 metres from centre; 50 metres N of traffic lights.
Credit cards All major cards accepted.
Terms B&B: single 400–450 Skr, double 470–550 Skr, suite 570–650 Skr. (No restaurant but snacks available).

GOTHENBURG 416 66 — Map 7

Tidbloms Hotel
Olskroksgt. 23

Tel (031) 19.20.70
Fax (031) 19.78.35
Telex 27369 TIDBLO

"We were pleasantly surprised by Gothenburg, a pretty, walled city with an interesting waterfront and a fabulous new amusement park, Liseborg, which our children thoroughly enjoyed. We did notice, however, that most of the hotels looked pretty institutional, and were glad we were at *Tidbloms*. It was extremely comfortable. We had two adjoining rooms, one of them under the turret, very pretty, especially the 'master' which was decorated in lovely soft colours." "We were charmed by the very helpful staff in both the hotel and the restaurant. The place felt Swedish rather than international, but our strangeness as foreigners was swept away by the staff who made us feel at home." *Tidbloms* is a turn-of-the-century, turreted, red-brick house, close to the centre of Sweden's second city, well situated, with bedrooms comfortably furnished in modern contract style. The restaurant and bar, "dark and cosy", are built into the rocky hillside and have a cavernous feel, softened by hand-woven rugs, real oil lamps and rustic furniture. There is a good selection of Swedish specialities (including snow goose and reindeer fillet) with carefully prepared sauces. "The food was outstanding; we had an excellent dinner and wonderful buffet breakfasts." (*Mary Hanson, AP Baxter*)

Open All year except 23 Dec–2 Jan.
Rooms 28 double, 14 single – all with bath and shower, telephone, radio and TV.
Facilities Lift. Cocktail bar, restaurant; conference facilities. Rock and sand beach 20 mins.
Location In E part of Gothenburg, within a pedestrian housing area (take small access road behind filling station). Parking.
Credit cards All major cards accepted.
Terms [1989 rates] B&B: single 350–660 Skr, double 480–785 Skr. Dinner, B&B 550–785 Skr per person.

We get little feedback from Scandinavia. Please help if you can.

Don't let old favourites down. Entries are dropped when there is no endorsement.

GRYTHYTTAN 710 60 Västmanland — Map 7

Grythyttans Gästgivaregård — *Tel* (0591) 147.00
Prästgt. 2 — *Fax* (0591) 141.24

The village of Grythyttan is in "a peaceful corner of old Sweden", off the beaten track some 270 kilometres west of Stockholm, in a region of small lakes just north of huge Lake Vanern. This unusual and sophisticated hotel is run with showmanlike *brio* by Carl-Jan Granqvist who restored the 17th-century house and converted the surrounding old shops and cottages to give additional bedrooms – many are "lavish and furnished with the Swedish sense of colour"; others are much simpler – and cheaper. The popular restaurant, a series of connecting rooms, is well known in Sweden for its French-influenced cuisine. Breakfast is generous and "impeccable"; "service by the dedicated young staff is outstanding, wines marvellous". Some of the plumbing is said to be idiosyncratic. We'd be glad of more reports.

Open All year.
Rooms 9 suites, 53 double, 18 single – 26 with bath, 52 with shower, all with telephone and radio. 52 in cottages and houses in grounds; 18 in annexe *Saxa Mansion* (15 mins' drive away). Some ground-floor rooms.
Facilities Lounges, bars, TV room, restaurant; conference facilities. Dancing on Sat. 2-acre grounds with tennis, children's playground. 150 lakes in area; boating, bathing, fishing and golf nearby.
Location 70 km W of Orebro. In centre of village. Parking.
Restriction Not suitable for ♿.
Credit cards All major cards accepted.
Terms [1989 rates] B&B: single 590–690 Skr, double 690–1,070 Skr; dinner, B&B 630 Skr per person. Budget rooms: single 475 Skr, double 600 Skr. Reduced rates and special meals for children.

LUND Skåne 221 04 — Map 7

Hotel Lundia — *Tel* (046) 12.41.40
Knut den Stores Gata 2 — *Fax* (046) 14.19.95
Telex 32761

Comfortable modern hotel in centre of old university town 20 km north of the large port of Malmö, with fine Romanesque cathedral. Attractive, well-provided bedrooms with desk space and good lighting. Excellent Swedish buffet breakfast and popular, reasonably priced self-service lunch. Closed 24–26 Dec. 97 rooms, all with bath/shower. B&B double 990 Skr. An alternative is the Lundia's *sister hotel, the much older, aptly named* Grand. *New nomination. More reports please.*

SIGTUNA 193 00 Uppland — Map 7

Stadshotellet-Mälarens Pärla — *Tel* (0760) 501.00
Stora Nygt. 3 — *Fax* (0760) 51.587

Sigtuna, between Stockholm and Uppsala, is a picturesque little town, one of the oldest in Sweden, on Lake Skarven. It has wooden 18th-century houses and the ruins of very early Christian churches. The *Stadshotellet-Mälarens Pärla* stands on an embankment at the end of the main street, with phenomenal views from the restaurant and upper back rooms. Bedrooms, in pastel shades, are very pleasant; some have an adjoining sitting room. The attractive restaurant, separately managed, is very well known and people drive out to it from Stockholm. The food is "very good, with spectacular sweets. Breakfast adequate. Everyone speaks good English." More reports please.

Open All year.
Rooms 4 suites, 13 double, 9 single - 25 with bath and shower, all with telephone, radio and TV.
Facilities Bar, restaurant; sauna, solarium.
Location About 45 km NW of Stockholm. Parking.
Credit cards All major cards accepted.
Terms [1989 rates] B&B: single 470–825 Skr, double 560–980 Skr, suite 750–1,150 Skr (lowest prices at weekend). Alc meals 80–200 Skr.

SIMRISHAMN Skåne 272 31 — Map 7

Hotell Svea
Strandv. 3

Tel (0414) 117.20
Fax (0414) 143 41
Telex 33473

A new nomination in a quiet seaside town east of Malmö in Skåne, an area of gently rolling countryside with sandy beaches and wooded dunes. "Built in 1936, and overlooking the Baltic Sea, it has the charm of an old hotel, with the advantage of having recently been completely renovated. Every inch is new, fresh and very Swedish – contemporary, but not stark. Nice prints on draperies and bedspreads. Spotless hardwood floors, lots of white and lots of light. The dining room was large, comfortable and restful; Wonderful meals and good breakfasts. Staff extremely friendly and helpful. (*Lizbeth and Craig Anderson*) More reports please.

Open All year.
Rooms 38 double, 23 single – all with bath/shower.
Facilities Lounge, bar, dining room. Garden.
Location On seafront.
Credit cards All major cards accepted.
Terms [1989 rates] B&B: single 440–630 Skr, double 540–740 Skr. Set lunch 43 Skr, dinner 90 Skr.

STOCKHOLM — Map 7

Clas på Hörnet
Surbrunnsgatan 20
Stockholm 113 48

Tel (08) 16.51.30
Fax (08) 33.53.15
Telex 14619 CPH

This elegant little restaurant-with-rooms was first opened as an inn in 1731, then became successively a smart ballroom, hospital, apartment block and garage, but has now reverted to its original vocation. 15 minutes walk' from the centre of Stockholm, it is known more by locals for its excellent restaurant – but there are lovely bedrooms on the upper floor. 18th-century furnishings, modern office conveniences (telex, etc). Open all year, except Christmas, New Year, mid-summer. 10 rooms – all with shower. B&B double 695–1,400 Skr. Set menus 210 Skr. Recent nomination. More reports please.

Hotel Diplomat
Strandvägen 7C
Stockholm 104 40

Tel (08) 663.58.00
Fax (08) 783.66.34
Telex 17119

The Diplomat is an expensive, fashionable and comfortable hotel which enjoys a fine central position by the waterfront. Its attractive ground-floor tea-house, with potted plants, white chairs and check tablecloths, is a smart local rendezvous, as well as serving lavish buffet breakfasts, and is praised this year, as is the "unusually attractive and helpful staff". Bedrooms vary in price; the better ones face the harbour, front ones can be noisy in warm weather. "The pleasantest Stockholm hotel we have yet stayed in," writes *John Woolsey* this year. More reports please.

Open All year except Christmas.
Rooms 5 suites, 70 double, 55 single – 98 with bath, 34 with shower, all with telephone, radio, TV.
Facilities Lounges, TV room, bar, tea room, restaurant, open-air café, sauna; conference facilities.
Location 5 mins' walk from centre. Parking.
Credit cards All major cards accepted.
Terms [1989 rates] B&B: single 750–1,300 Skr, double 1,200–2,200 Skr. Full alc 280 Skr.

Lady Hamilton Hotel
Storkyrkobrinken 5
Stockholm 111 28

Tel (08) 23.46.80

Lord Nelson Hotel
Västerlånggt. 22
Stockholm 111 29

Tel (08) 23.23.90
Telex 10434 NELSHAM
(*for both hotels*)

Readers continue to be pleased with this "two hotels in one" enterprise in the old-town area of Stockholm. "My first stay, although I've stayed in Stockholm previously. Will definitely use the hotel again. Excellent housekeeping, friendly helpful staff, simple but more than adequate Swedish breakfast." Each hotel carefully portrays its historical theme: there are models of ships, nautical pictures and items taken from boats, such as figure-heads and brass rails. The bedrooms are modern and attractive, but not large; some are positively poky. "If you can pretend that the very small rooms are cabins, it helps." Other parts of the hotel reflect the older origins of the buildings: the basement plunge pool at the *Lady Hamilton* was a well in the 15th century. The *Lord Nelson* is on a pedestrian street that can be lively until the small hours; but despite the possibility of noise, some readers prefer its location to that of the *Lady Hamilton*: "It's in an area of fascinating cobbled streets and little shops – with an open-air rooftop for a drink while viewing the city skyline." (*Mrs A Rooker*)

Lady Hamilton Hotel
Open All year.
Rooms 3 triple, 18 double, 13 single – all with bath and/or shower, telephone, radio and TV.
Facilities Bar/breakfast room/tea-room; conference facilities; sauna, plunge pool.
Location Central, in pedestrian zone, near royal palace. (Front rooms might be noisy.) Street parking.
Credit cards All major cards accepted.

Terms [1989 rates] B&B: single 1,090–1,200 Skr, double 1,100–1,400 Skr. (Light meals only, no restaurant.)

Lord Nelson Hotel
Open All year.
Rooms 9 double, 22 single – all with shower, telephone, radio and TV.
Facilities Small lift. Bar/breakfast-room/tea-room; conference facilities; rooftop terrace; sauna.
Location Central, in pedestrian zone, near royal palace. Street parking.
Credit cards All major cards accepted.
Terms [1989 rates] B&B: single 825–910 Skr, double 1,050–1,200 Skr. (Light meals only, no restaurant.)

TÄLLBERG 793 03 Dalarna — Map 7

Hotell Åkerblads

Tel (0247) 508.00
Fax (0247) 506.52

"A remarkable place for a rural holiday", praised for many years by our readers. Halfway between Leksand and Rättvik on Lake Siljan, the hotel, the oldest part of which is a 17th-century farmhouse, is comfortable and spacious in the old style. Bedrooms are pleasantly furnished, hardly any two being alike. "A first-class hotel, classically Swedish in style, warmth and comfort. Our suite had views over the beautiful lake and forests. Staff friendly and efficient." This supports an earlier report, "We had a delightful bedroom with verandas. It felt very Swedish, painted in different shades of green and orange. The atmosphere in the hotel is easy and informal. We loved the meals too. Lunch seemed to be the main one – often with several kinds of fish and potatoes with dill. It always ended with cake and excellent coffee in the upper hall. Local parties coming for meals often included men and women in national costume." Christina and Arne Åkerblad, the owners, and their sons are the 19th and 20th generations of the founders – probably the oldest reigning hotel family in Europe. Few recent reports, more welcome.

Open All year except Christmas.
Rooms 15 suites, 29 double, 15 single – all with bath and/or shower, telephone, radio, TV. 39 in 3 annexes in garden, some on ground floor (4 steps to main building).
Facilities 2 sitting rooms, bar, 2 TV rooms, coffee/dancing room, restaurant; functions facilities; sauna, whirlpool. Large garden with tennis, badminton, table tennis, skating rink; bicycles; Winter sports; lake with beach, bathing, fishing, boating nearby.
Location 12 km from Leksand; on road between Leksand and Rättvik. Parking.
Credit cards All major cards accepted.
Terms [1989 rates] B&B 320–460 Skr; dinner, B&B 470–630 Skr. Set lunch 135 Skr, dinner 145 Skr. 1-night bookings sometimes refused. Reduced weekend rates in low season. Reduced rates and special meals for children.

TROLLHÄTTAN 461 27 Västergötland — Map 7

Hotel Swania

Storgatan 47

Tel (0520) 125.70
Fax (0520) 397.02
Telex 42225

Some 80 kilometres north of Gothenburg, this industrial town on the Götaälv, has Saab and Volvo connections, but areas by the river are idyllic and here the

Swania *has pleasant views. It's a sizeable and urbane hotel in international style, with rather over-insistent decor (lots of potted palms). Breakfast copious, staff friendly. 143 very pleasant and well-equipped bedrooms, all with bath/shower. B&B double 885–915 Skr [1989]. Recent nomination. More reports welcome.*

Traveller's tale *John and Amanda Booth found something unexpected in their hotel bed on the first night of their honeymoon. . .the manager. Blushing bride Amanda, 23, said: "We were given the key to the suite but when we opened the door a man rushed to block us from coming in." The newlyweds stormed out of the country hotel and went back to the reception where they had said goodbye to relatives and friends a few minutes earlier. A guest said: "The party was going with a swing but we were surprised to see the couple back so soon. It must have been one of the quickest honeymoons on record." The apologetic manager of the hotel said later that there had been "a terrible mix-up". He explained: "I was taking my rest in the hotel room when the couple, covered in confetti, came in. I said the honeymoon suite was the room below but they said they had booked Number 14. They were immediately offered another room but they refused it and left."* The Daily Mirror

Switzerland

AMSTEG AM GOTTHARD 6474 Uri **Map 14**

Romantik Hotel Stern und Post

Tel (044) 6.44.40
Fax (044) 6.32.61
Telex 866 385 STEPO

An old coaching inn, useful as a stopover, in a village south of Altdorf on the way to the St-Gotthard pass: "A charming place. The village has been by-passed by the motorway and the principal noise is the rushing torrent right by the hotel. Mr Tresch and all his staff gave us warm and friendly service. We had the choice between enchantingly atmospheric period rooms with no bathroom and much more expensive modern ones. All was spotlessly clean. Food was well cooked and copious (excellent trout); breakfast, served in the old pine-panelled dining room, was a very good buffet. There are two small and picturesque lounges, straight out of a romantic novel."

Open All year. Closed Tue and Wed in winter.
Rooms 25 double, 15 single – 20 with bath and shower, all with telephone.

Facilities Lift. 2 lounges, bar, 3 restaurants; conference room. Garden with direct access to two rivers; fishing.
Location In centre of village, 14 km S of Altdorf, off N2 motorway. Parking.
Restriction Not suitable for ♿.
Credit cards All major cards accepted.
Terms [1989 rates] B&B 27.50–80 Sfrs. Dinner, B&B 57.50–110 Sfrs. Set lunch/dinner 30–50 Sfrs; full alc 50–70 Sfrs. Reduced rates and special meals for children.

APPENZELL 9050 Appenzell — Map 14

Romantik Hotel Säntis
Landsgemeindeplatz

Tel (071) 87.87.22
Fax (071) 87.48.42
Telex 883733

In an attractive little mountain town south of Lake Constance, not far from Austria, the Säntis, *owned and run by the Heeb family, is a highly traditional chalet-style inn, with painted facade and antique wood furnishings. Recently renovated, the light and airy rooms are a blend of the old and the high-tech new, with lots of mirrors. A warm welcome, and very good food including buffet breakfast. 35 rooms, all with bath or shower, some equipped for the disabled. B&B: double 130–180 Sfrs. Set menus 30–48 Sfrs. Complaints this year of noise from nocturnal gatherings such as wedding parties. More reports welcome.*

AROSA 7050 Graubünden — Map 14

Hotel Hof Maran

Tel (01) 31.01.85
Telex 851629

"Superb hospitality", say devotees revisiting this fairly large and very well-equipped modern hotel that has been grafted on to an old chalet: it has a fine mountain setting, high above Arosa, beside the golf cum cross-country ski course. Other regular fans report it better than ever – especially the food, both in the main restaurant and in the atmospheric little *Stübl*. "Half board is almost inevitable," they wrote earlier, "as it is a long way down to the town. The bedroom door was nearly a foot thick and totally soundproof; the bedroom furniture in honey-gold wood veneer was superbly finished. The beds were wonderfully hard, the bathroom fitted with all the latest gadgets. Dinner at 7 pm – ushered in and out with Swiss efficiency – did mean rather a long evening, but on some nights the lounge fairly rocked with music and dancing. Surprisingly, the only thing missing was a swimming pool."

Open Mid-Jun–mid-Oct, mid-Dec–mid-Apr.
Rooms 44 double, 15 single – 50 with bath, 9 with shower, all with telephone, radio, TV and baby-listening.
Facilities Lift. Lounge, TV room, bar (dancing), 3 restaurants; conference room; games room with ping-pong; sun terrace on roof. Large grounds with 2 tennis courts (pro available), children's play area; skating rink in winter, 4 curling rinks. Sauna, solarium, fitness-room. Ski-lift and ski school behind hotel; 9-hole golf course nearby.
Location 1 km from Arosa near Maran golf course. Bus service every 20 mins. Parking.
Restriction Not suitable for ♿.
Credit cards All major cards accepted.

Terms Dinner, B&B: single 80–190 Sfrs, double 160–400 Sfrs; full board 20 Sfrs per person added. Reduced rates and special meals for children.

ASCONA 6612 Ticino — Map 14

Hotel Casa Berno — *Tel* (093) 35.32.32 *Telex* 846167

This modern four-star hotel stands on a hillside above Lago Maggiore, between Monte Verità and Ronco: it's about 30 minutes' walk up a steep winding road from the centre of smart, animated Ascona, so a car is an asset. The views from its terraces and heated swimming-pool are stunning; all rooms face south over the lake and have a balcony. Readers again have especially praised the charming managers, the Goetschis, and their staff. "A very well-run hotel, full of courtesy, with breath-taking vistas of the lake from the beautiful rooms. The food is excellent. But we cared less for the hotel's utter formality – guests dress for dinner." Another reader, too, has found the style "rather tired 'sixties". But others continue to extol the bedrooms, breakfast buffet, and "delicious" Franco-Helvetico-Ticinese cuisine, including the pension meals. (*H and B Shames, Ellen and John Buchanan*)

Open Mar–Oct inclusive.
Rooms 11 suites, 43 double, 7 single – all with telephone, radio, balcony/terrace.
Facilities Lift. Lounges (1 with TV), bar on roof-garden, grill room, restaurant with terrace; sauna, massage, solarium, fitness room, ladies' hairdresser. Garden with heated swimming pool. Golf, tennis nearby.
Location Between Monte Verità and Ronco; about 20–30 minutes' walk from Ascona. Parking.
Credit cards Access, Amex, Visa.
Terms B&B 125–155 Sfrs; half board 145–185 Sfrs; full board 165–195 Sfrs. Reduced rates for children sharing parents' room; special meals. Weekly package in spring.

BASLE 4001 — Map 14

Hotel Drei Könige — *Tel* (061) 25.52.52
Blumenrain 8 — *Fax* (061) 25.21.53 *Telex* 962937

Basle's grandest hotel, and one of Europe's oldest (royalty have stayed often). A bit old-fashioned, but comfortable, with a fine Rhineside position: some room balconies face the river, as does the dining-room terrace (food is good). 90 rooms, all with bath and shower. B&B double 275–405 Sfrs. Meals 17–92 Sfrs [1989]. Restored to Guide. More reports please.

BERN 3001 — Map 14

Hotel Bären — *Tel* (031) 22.33.67
Schauplatzgasse 4 — *Fax* (031) 22.01.01 *Telex* 912819

The hotel is named after the city's mascot, and it is full of emblems of the black teddy rampant; but the service, happily, is more bullish than Bär-ish. This, our first-ever entry for Switzerland's charming capital, is four-star and usefully central, very near the station and main square; but also quiet (rooms are double-glazed, most face the inner courtyard). A modern interior, and plenty of modern facilities. Excellent food in a stylish restaurant. 91 beds, all with bath and shower. B&B double 145–185 Sfrs. Meals 20–45 Sfrs [1989]. Endorsed this year. Further reports welcome.

BRAUNWALD 8784 Glarus — Map 14

Hotel Bellevue — *Tel* (058) 84.38.43

Ideal for families with children, and the kind of classic holiday hotel that the Swiss do so very well. It is a big white turn-of-the-century building, no great beauty but with many other virtues, and peacefully set amid meadows and woodlands at the top of a mountain railway above Linthal, between the Klausenpass and Glarus. "The large rooms and high ceilings give a feeling of spaciousness, and the views are stunning. The hotel is superbly well run by its ubiquitous young owners, the Vogels – she charming her guests in her many stunning fashionable outfits, and he every evening before dinner telling fairy-tales to the children grouped around him, as he sits in a high-backed cane armchair. Children are especially welcome and have their own dining room and playroom. Our large and comfortable bedroom had a wrought-iron balcony facing the superb view. The food is always good. The sitting-room is a real one, and the large indoor pool looks out on the view. The staff are a happy selection; and one token of the hotel's good value is that it changes travellers' cheques at the same rate as a bank." More reports would be welcome.

Open Jun–Oct, Dec–Apr.
Rooms 100 beds – most rooms with bath and/or shower, telephone and balcony.
Facilities Lift. Lounge, sitting room, TV/video room, children's playroom, bar (with dancing), restaurant; conference facilities; indoor swimming pool, whirlpool, fitness room, sauna, solarium; table tennis. Garden with terrace, 2 tennis courts. Winter sports nearby.
Location 4 km by railway from Linthal which is 17 km S of Glarus. No access by car.
Credit cards None accepted.
Terms [1989 rates] Dinner, B&B: single 55–137 Sfrs, double 110–274 Sfrs; full board 15 Sfrs added per person. Reduced rates and special meals for children.

CHÂTEAU-D'OEX 1837 Vaud — Map 14

Hostellerie Bon Accueil — *Tel* (029) 4.63.20

A converted 18th-century chalet, up a steep road from the wide and sunny Alpine village of Château-d'Oex, ten minutes west of Gstaad. Regulars in 1989 liked it as much as ever. Last year they attended a New Year's Eve dinner that was "more like a private house party than being in a hotel" and they got on well with the "hard-working and friendly" English manager. "Our bedroom was wood-panelled, with rustic but comfortable furnishings and a glorious view over meadows and snowy peaks. The public rooms are attractive, and tables and chairs were set out in the pleasant gardens. Dinner in another wood-panelled room with a log fire was very enjoyable."

Open Dec–Apr.
Rooms 1 suite, 16 double, 2 single – 19 with bath, 1 with shower, all with telephone. 8 in annexe.
Facilities Lounge, cellar bar, dining room. Garden. Winter sports.
Location 1 km from centre of village which is 15 km SW of Gstaad.
Credit cards Amex, Diners, Visa.
Terms [1989 rates] B&B: single 65–90 Sfrs, double 100–160 Sfrs; half board 30 Sfrs added per person; full board 40 Sfrs added. Reduced rates and special meals for children.

DAVOS DORF 7260 Graubünden — Map 14

Hotel Flüela
Bahnhofstrasse 5

Tel (083) 6.12.21
Fax (083) 5.44.01
Telex 853100 FLUA

"Outstanding food and service", "exceptional value for money", run two recent reports on this sizeable ski-hotel, owned and managed by the Gredig family for over a century, and now much modernised. Open only in the winter, it is close to the Parsenn Bahn, the largest ski-lift in this big and bustling resort. "Five- or six-course dinners, a mixture of *nouvelle* and traditional cuisine, with second helpings encouraged." "Super lounges, with pianist every evening, open log fire, indoor swimming pool, sauna, solarium; and quite outstanding breakfast and dinner." The staff tidy the bedrooms twice a day, and will even clean your boots. This year, a reader admired the food, but criticised the decor and "boring" ambience.

Open 25 Nov–18 Apr.
Rooms 10 suites, 55 double, 25 single – 75 with bath and shower, 5 with shower, all with telephone, radio and TV.
Facilities Bar lounge (with pianist), sitting rooms, restaurants; function rooms; games room. Indoor swimming pool, sauna, solarium, massage, fitness-room; ski boutique, barber, hairdresser; bank.
Location In town centre. A few roadside rooms may be noisy. Parking.
Restriction Not suitable for ♿.
Credit cards All major cards accepted.
Terms B&B 115–405 Sfrs; dinner, B&B 160–450 Sfrs; full board 185–475 Sfrs. Set lunch 35 Sfrs, dinner 50–70 Sfrs; full alc 70–100 Sfrs. Reduced rates and special meals for children.

DAVOS PLATZ 7270 Graubünden — Map 14

Hotel National
Obere Strasse 31

Tel (083) 3.60.46
Fax (083) 3.86.50
Telex 853103

On the edge of Davos Platz, the lower part of this straggling resort, this great white modern cube of a hotel might not be to every taste, but its nominator this year was well pleased, "Isolated from all but the noise of church bells, it has rooms with balconies that look along the valley, while others look back along the the town. The staff all seemed enthusiastic and interested. Over ten days we had the best half-board evening food I've ever encountered, generally in the *minceur* style, invariably interesting, and attractively served. Wines are moderately priced. Occasionally a piano player entertained – preferable to the Swiss night when a poor accordionist did his worst and an alpenhorn blasted nearby. Breakfast was the usual spread. A small games room with table tennis, and a lounge with a fire. Warmly recommended." (*TH Nash*)

Open 2 Dec–17 Apr, 2 Jun–30 Sept
Rooms 4 suites, 40 double, 24 single – all with bath and/or shower, telephone and radio; TV on request.
Facilities Lift. Lounge, 2 bars, TV room, 2 restaurants; Piano player, dancing, entertainment. 2 games rooms for children. Garden.
Location 400 metres from town centre.
Credit cards All major cards accepted.
Terms B&B: summer 52–108 Sfrs per person, winter 137–192 Sfrs. Dinner, B&B 60–200 Sfrs, full board 75–215 Sfrs. Set lunch 15–30 Sfrs, dinner 25–45 Sfrs; full alc 35 Sfrs. Reduced rates for children; special meals on request.

LES DIABLERETS 1865 Vaud — Map 14

Hôtel Les Lilas — *Tel* (025) 53.11.34

"Our children were sure that Heidi would appear at any minute and must live somewhere in the village" – that new report sets the tone for this "charming and homely" little chalet-like roadside hotel, run by Jean-Pierre Matti and his "delightful" wife, in an unspoilt village between Aigle and Gstaad. "Our room was small and rustic, and its balcony gave a marvellous view of the mountains", runs another letter this year, "in the candlelit restaurant the food was excellent, if expensive; the breakfast rolls were delicious." Specialities include such dishes as poulet à la bière and filet de boeuf aux morilles. One possible snag: a new hotel is being built opposite. (*R Maxwell-Gumbleton, H and B Shames, Stephen Ruell*)

Open All year.
Rooms 10 double, 5 single – 11 with bath and/or shower.
Facilities Bar, TV room, 2 restaurants. Garden.
Location In village 20 km E of Aigle on road to Gstaad.
Credit cards Access, Amex, Visa.
Terms B&B: single 50–60 Sfrs, double 90–100 Sfrs; dinner, B&B: single 75–90 Sfrs, double 140–160 Sfrs. Set lunch 15–25 Sfrs, dinner 35–60 Sfrs; full alc 35–65 Sfrs. Reduced rates and special meals for children.

ENGELBERG 6390 Unterwalden — Map 14

Hotel Eden — *Tel* (041) 94.32.94

Just rebuilt and modernised, this friendly little *restaurant-mit-Zimmer* stands in a well-known resort high up in a lovely isolated mountain valley south of Lucerne. "Our lasting memory is of the superb food and warm hospitality provided by Sybille and Thomas Reinhardt-Waser", runs one report this year; "our bathroom was small, but everything functioned perfectly". Others have enjoyed the mountain views from those rooms that have a balcony, and the good food, such as vegetable mousse with basil sauce and fresh lake perch. "The homely gentle ambience created by Sibylle in the restaurant is so fitting for the food that Thomas prepares. Both find time to spend talking with their guests." "Yes, a real Eden, this *Eden* – delightful public rooms, atmosphere, rocking-chairs, a nursery which would keep any child quiet on a wet day." (*GL Turner, Leonard and Lora Moss*) One reader this year regretted the lack of choice on the menus. More to the point, the hotel has just added a lift and other facilities, so that all rooms now have bath or shower: prices have risen somewhat, but we are reassured by recent visitors that the improvements have not been to the detriment of the hotel's simple friendly charm.

Open Dec–Oct.
Rooms 3 suites, 7 double, 2 single – 9 with bath, 3 with shower, all with telephone, radio and TV, some with balcony.
Facilities Lift, bar, TV room, library, bistro, restaurant, conference room, children's games room, sauna, solarium. Garden, terrace for meals in summer.
Location Central, near station. Garage and outdoor parking.
Restriction Not suitable for ♿.
Credit cards All major cards accepted.
Terms B&B: single 80–100 Sfrs, double 130–180 Sfrs, suite 170–210 Sfrs; dinner, B&B: single 110–130 Sfrs, double 190–270 Sfrs. Set lunch/dinner 18–60 Sfrs; full alc 45–65 Sfrs. Reduced rates and special meals for children.

FLIMS-WALDHAUS 7018 Graubünden — Map 14

Hotel Adula

Tel (081) 39.01.61
Fax (081) 39.43.15
Telex 851960 ADUL

Flims is a popular medium-height (1,100 metre) summer and winter resort in the Grisons, west of Chur. The pinewoods of the Waldhaus offer miles of easy walking, and there are plenty of mountain hiking-paths for the more energetic. The large chalet-style *Adula* has this recent adula-tor: "The service, quality of food, and the friendly spirit of owners and staff have, if anything, improved. A new extension, *Soldanella*, has very comfortable rooms." The hotel has a huge range of facilities; in summer it also organises conducted walks, and has barbecues outside the large indoor pool. But one guest was depressed to find that dinner started at 6.45 and the place was dead quiet by 9.30. It might be best suited to older citizens.

Open All year except mid-Oct–mid-Dec.
Rooms 10 suites, 67 double, 22 single – most with bath and/or shower, all with telephone and radio, some with TV. 39 in new annexe with underground connection to main building.
Facilities Lift. Salon, TV room, bar with pianist, 3 restaurants; children's playroom; conference facilities; indoor swimming pool, sauna, steam bath. Garden with terrace, 3 tennis courts.
Location Flims-Waldhaus is about 15 km W of Chur. Follow main road to Laax; hotel is signposted. Parking.
Credit cards All major cards accepted.
Terms B&B: single 115–175 Sfrs, double 190–310 Sfrs, suite 270–390 Sfrs. Dinner, B&B 20 Sfrs added per person. Set lunch 25 Sfrs, dinner 40–55 Sfrs. Reduced rates for children sharing parents' room; special meals. Walking tours in summer, ski packages in winter.

> Set dinner refers to a fixed price meal (which may have ample, limited or no choice on the menu). Full alc is the hotel's own estimated price per person of a three-course meal taken à la carte, with a half-bottle of house wine.

FTAN 7551 Graubünden — Map 14

Hotel Haus Paradies — *Tel* (084) 9.13.25
Telex 854154

Most Alpine hotels, even the new smart ones, tend to be in the traditional chalet style. This one, extremely elegant and far from cheap, was built in the 1920s in a mode closer to Le Corbusier, and its decor is original and pleasing, with Scandinavian touches. It is in the lovely country of the Upper Engadin just west of Scuol (Schuls), with views towards the Lischana peaks and the hilltop castle of Tarasp, "The setting is maybe the most spectacular of any hotel we know. All the rooms, spacious and luxuriously furnished, have large picture windows and balconies looking across this dramatic valley, and it is a lovely base for walking or skiing. Managers are Brigitte and Roland Jöhri: she is very sweet and runs the service team efficiently, he is one of the rising young chefs of Switzerland. His menu is perhaps too complicated, but his local dishes are excellent." Very *soigné* dining room and salons; sleek, well-stocked classical library; lovely panoramic terrace. The hotel's brochure is one of the most civilised we have ever seen. More reports please.

Open 15 Jun–15 Oct, 22 Dec–17 Apr.
Rooms 8 suites, 13 double – all with bath, telephone, radio, mini-bar, and balcony or terrace; TV on request.
Facilities Lounge, library, bridge room, dining-room, restaurant. Sauna, solarium, massage.
Location 3 km W of Scuol.
Credit cards None accepted.
Terms B&B: single 160–180 Sfrs, double 320–350 Sfrs, suite 390–440 Sfrs. Dinner, B&B: single 200–220 Sfrs, double 360–420 Sfrs, suite 490–520 Sfrs. Reduced rates and special meals for children.

GENEVA 1204 — Map 14

Hôtel L'Arbalète — *Tel* (022) 28.41.55
3 rue de la Tour Maîtresse — *Telex* 427293 ARBA

Well located near the lake, museums and best shops, a small de luxe hotel that this year has again won approval: "Reception charming and helpful, food and service very good. A spacious, comfortable room, but decor a bit heavy ('arbalète' means crossbow)." Earlier comments: "The staff were marvellous, serving us a special breakfast when we overslept." "A homely feel, and quiet, because windows are double-glazed; good food." "Nice touches like an umbrella in the bedroom to help with Geneva rain." The ground-floor brasserie is cheaper than the main first-floor restaurant. (*NPD & J Levine*)

Open All year.
Rooms 20 double, 12 single – all with bath and shower, telephone, radio, TV, mini-bar and baby-listening.
Facilities Lift. Hall, 2 bars, pub with pianist, 3 restaurants. Lake Geneva 2 mins' walk, with sandy beach, safe bathing, fishing.
Location Central; near Mont Blanc bridge. Windows double-glazed. Garage and parking.
Credit cards All major cards accepted.

Terms B&B: single 210–240 Sfrs, double 270–300 Sfrs. Set lunch 25 Sfrs, dinner 40 Sfrs; full alc 40–50 Sfrs. Reduced rates for children sharing parents' room; special meals on request.

Hôtel Les Armures *Tel* (022) 28.91.72
1 rue du Puits St-Pierre *Telex* 421129

In a small square near the cathedral, up in the old town, this elegant small hotel makes a pleasant contrast to the grand, impersonal places down by the lake; like them it is not cheap – but in Geneva, what is? It is an old stone building dating mainly from the 17th century, when it was extended to accommodate Huguenots fleeing from France. A recent visitor enjoyed the hotel and the location, but thought the prices charged for breakfast extras were excessive. The quietest rooms are on the interior court, where one reader had one "beautifully furnished, with a small roof-garden outside its window". The cosy *stüberl* restaurant is noted for its local dishes, including raclette.

Open All year. Restaurant closed Easter, Christmas and New Year.
Rooms 4 suites, 20 double, 4 single – all with bath and shower, telephone, radio, TV, tea-making facilities and baby-listening.
Facilities Lift. Lobby, salon, breakfast room, bar, lounge, restaurant, *Stüberl* (rustic bar/restaurant).
Location Central, near St-Pierre Cathedral. No special parking facilities.
Restriction Not suitable for ♿.
Credit cards All major cards accepted.
Terms B&B: single 195–230 Sfrs, double 315 Sfrs, suite 305–390 Sfrs. Full alc 50–60 Sfrs.

GSTAAD 3780 Bern Map 14

Hotel Christiania *Tel* (030) 4.51.21
Hauptstrasse *Fax* (030) 4.71.09
Telex 922250

In the main street of fashionable Gstaad, a small, spruce hotel with a four-star rating. Dropped from last year's Guide for lack of new reports, it is now re-nominated by two readers: "A warm greeting, wonderful breakfasts, and good food in their cosy restaurant. Our bedroom had a balcony, writing desk, easy chairs. Very quiet"; "The public rooms are small and cosy, and have a lived-in feel. In the rustic-style restaurant we had a good lunch. Many bedrooms overlook a pleasant garden." The owner's daughter is chef and her son-in-law head waiter – a true family affair. (*Ellen and John Buchanan, Kate and Stephan Murray-Sykes*)

Open All year.
Rooms 3 suites for 4 to 6 people with bath and shower, salon, dining-room; 15 double with bath – all with telephone, radio, TV; most with balcony.
Facilities Lift. Salon with TV, bar, restaurant (pianist in high season). Garden with restaurant. Free use of outdoor swimming pool at nearby *Palace Hotel* in summer.
Location Central, near station; street-facing rooms can be noisy. Garage (16 Sfrs).
Credit cards Diners, Visa.
Terms [1989 rates] B&B: (low season) single 60–150 Sfrs, double 120–220 Sfrs; (high season) single 90–200 Sfrs, double 230–350 Sfrs. Dinner, B&B 45 Sfrs per person added. Special meals for children.

ISELTWALD 3807 Bern — Map 14

Hotel Bellevue

Tel (036) 45.11.10
Fax (036) 45.12.77

Iseltwald is a picturesque hamlet and summer resort on a peninsula beside the lake of Brienz, east of Interlaken. You can sail or water-ski, or go for mountain walks or climbs; the beautiful Giessback falls are worth a visit. The chalet-style *Bellevue* has a good position close to the lake, with two terraced gardens for drinks and light meals: but woods rise steeply just behind and some visitors have found this setting sombre, especially if you have a back room (front ones with a balcony are best). The food served in its two restaurants is the hotel's strongest feature, especially local fish, but it's not cheap: fish soup, salmon trout in pernod, pike charcoal-grilled or poached, have all been enjoyed this year, but one visitor found the service very slow. The breakfast buffet is lavish. The design of the hotel is "typically Swiss", with much use of wood and folkweave fabrics; bedrooms are not large, but they have been provided with new, improved lighting (this was formerly criticised by readers). A motorway has just been completed high behind the hotel, but its status as a *Relais du Silence* is unaffected, for the traffic is out of earshot. (*Eileen Broadbent, Mike and Judi Taylor-Evans, Padi and John Howard, and others*)

Open 15 Feb–4 Jan. Closed Tue.
Rooms 9 double, 2 single – all with bath and/or shower; telephone, radio and TV, many with balcony.
Facilities Salon, bar, restaurant. Terrace garden. On lake shore with beach and sailing.
Location On S shore of Lake Brienz, 10 km E of Interlaken.
Restriction Not suitable for ♿.
Terms B&B 40–60 Sfrs. Half board 22 Sfrs added. Full alc 19–28 Sfrs. Special meals for children.

Hotel Chalet du Lac

Tel (036) 45.11.12

Our second entry for this pretty fishing village is an authentic lakeside chalet remodelled as a spotless small hotel, with modern wood furnishings and good but informal service. Some rooms face the mountain, others have a balcony above the lake. Meals on a lakeside terrace or indoors; food and service commended this year. Closed Nov. 12 rooms, all with shower (2 also have bath). B&B: double 80–134 Sfrs. Set menu 20 Sfrs [*1988 rates*]. *Recent nomination. More reports please.*

KANDERSTEG 3718 Bern — Map 14

Hotel Ermitage

Tel (033) 75.15.12

Run by the friendly Hirschi family, the *Ermitage* stands amid meadows and trees on the edge of this big resort, near to a chairlift and a carpark. It has just installed a lounge for guests, and several readers this year speak well of this, also of the cheerful service, relaxed atmosphere and good food: "The evening meal was a delight, but it took a long time because each dish is specially prepared"; "the food was delicious, astonishingly sophisticated, but with rather too much cream"; "good buffet breakfast".

Rooms vary: those at the front have balconies, but rear ones can be cramped. A returning devotee confirms earlier praise, "If you love the sound of rushing water to go to sleep by, several waterfalls and a steep brook provide that. Rooms are beautifully furnished, and some have a fully equipped kitchenette. Lovely garden restaurant." (*Mr and Mrs BW Boyd, E Goldby, Richard Pinner*)

Open 22 Dec–15 Apr, 26 May–28 Oct. Restaurant closed Mon in low season.
Rooms 2 suites, 11 double – 9 with bath and shower, 4 with shower, all with telephone, radio, TV and mini-bar; many with balcony; 6 with kitchenette.
Facilities Lounge with TV, restaurant, grill room, breakfast room; sun terrace. Garden with restaurant and children's play area. Winter sports, heated swimming pool, tennis, walking, climbing, fishing nearby.
Location Turn left off road from Spiez and Thun, near the Oeschinensee chairlift. Hotel is quietly situated. Parking.
Restriction Not suitable for ♿.
Credit cards Access, Diners, Visa.
Terms B&B 55–85 Sfrs; dinner, B&B 75–105 Sfrs. Set lunch 10–30 Sfrs, dinner 20–40 Sfrs; full alc 40 Sfrs. Reduced rates and special meals for children.

KLOSTERS 7250 Graubünden — Map 14

Romantik Hotel Chesa Grischuna
Bahnhofstrasse 9

Tel (083) 4.22.22
Fax (083) 4.16.82
Telex 853348 CHESA

In the centre of this busy resort, a very *gemütlich* traditional hotel with flowery balconies and lots of character, but also well modernised. "Very friendly staff, food and service excellent" is this year's endorsement of previous panegyrics: "Lots of antiques, pretty dining room (excellent fresh vegetables), front desk kind and pleasant. We had a nice large room with pretty balcony in the chalet-annexe." "An ancient timber door unlatches into a bright interior modernised with honey-coloured wood, set off with furnishings in the traditional Swiss green, white and scarlet. The bright reception area is new, but the rest of the hotel is delightfully old and mellow, made of wood dark with age. Our room on the fourth floor of the main building (no lift) was not large, but had bright rugs on the polished floor and hand-woven bedspreads. Everything was shiningly clean. The food is good, pleasantly served by girls in Klosters costume. The cellar-bar is where the young locals and the après-skiers meet: wonderful lively friendly atmosphere." (*David Thibodeau*)

Open Early Jun–mid-Apr.
Rooms 16 double, 10 single – 17 with bath and/or shower, all with telephone and radio. 11 in annexe opposite.
Facilities Lounge with TV, restaurant; cellar bar with pianist in high season; bowling. Sun terrace, small garden.
Location In centre of Klosters Platz, near the station.
Restriction Not suitable for ♿.
Credit cards All major cards accepted.
Terms Dinner, B&B: single 90–190 Sfrs, double 160–380 Sfrs; full board 20 Sfrs per person added. Set lunch 15–28 Sfrs, dinner 41–61 Sfrs; full alc 79 Sfrs. Special meals for children on request.

We asked hotels to estimate their 1990 tariffs some time before publication so the rates given are often arbitrary. Please always check terms with hotels when making bookings.

LAUSANNE 1006 Vaud — Map 14

Hôtel Le Château d'Ouchy
2 place du Port, Ouchy
Lausanne 6

Tel (021) 26.74.51
Telex 455402
Fax (021) 275137

Two kilometres from the city centre, an old castle in a splendid lakeside setting at Ouchy, converted into an expensive classic hotel. Furnishings, many in period style, are somewhat heavy, but rooms are comfortable and spacious, with fine views of the Alps. Helpful staff; good food, served on a terrace above the lake. 44 rooms (some subject to traffic noise), all with bath and/or shower. B&B double 160–210 Sfrs [1989]. Recent nomination. More reports please.

LENK 3775 Bern — Map 14

Hotel Wildstrubel

Tel (030) 6.31.11
Telex 922258

A sizeable modern chalet-style hotel, opposite the railway station (but quiet), in a mountain resort (walking and skiing) up a valley in the Bernese Oberland. Large comfortable rooms with balconies and views, big heated swimming pool, food good and varied. Open June–mid-Oct, mid-Dec–mid-Apr. 45 rooms, all with bath and shower. B&B: single 74–95 Sfrs, double 143–189 Sfrs. Full alc 60–80 Sfrs. Recent nomination. More reports please.

MEGGEN 6045 Lucerne — Map 14

Hotel Sonnegg
Hauptstrasse 37

Tel (041) 37.21.64

A popular family hotel just east of Lucerne, up a hill above its lovely lake. "Simple, unpretentious and comfortable, with meticulous housekeeping", runs a report this year; "the seafood restaurant is superlative, with a friendly, informal ambience." Others agree that the fish and seafood dishes are excellent, if expensive (but there's also a cheaper coffee-shop, serving pizzas, etc). "A good hotel, with good service and modern comfort combined with Swiss rustic touches. The helpful staff will baby-listen and even supervised our teenage sons. There is a small park on the lake's edge." (*H and B Shames, J Michael Morrison*) However, some bedrooms have this year been found noisy, either from traffic or owing to thin party-walls. And a muddle has been reported over a room booking.

Open All year. Restaurant closed Sun, and Mon lunch.
Rooms 18 double – 9 with bath and shower, all with TV.
Facilities Lift. Bar, restaurant.
Location On lake Lucerne, 5 km E of Lucerne towards Rigi, Gotthard on old road.
Credit cards All major cards accepted.
Terms [1989 rates] B&B: single 55–60 Sfrs, double 85–90 Sfrs; half board 30 Sfrs per person added.

> If you think we have over-praised a hotel or done it an injustice, please let us know.

MONTREUX 1820 Vaud — Map 14

Hôtel Eden au Lac
11 rue du Théâtre

Tel (021) 963.55.51
Fax (021) 963.18.13
Telex 453151

Montreux, with its backcloth of Lac Léman and mountains, its beautifully manicured flower walk by the waterfront, and its many elegant Edwardian Victorian villas, is a delightful town. The *Eden*, one of its larger hotels, is set right by the lake and has recently been restored to its turn-of-the-century glory. "The glorious pink-and-white first-floor dining-room makes a romantic setting for dinner, looking out on the lake. The food is excellent (there is an à la carte restaurant downstairs and another in the garden in the summer) and breakfasts are buffet affairs, with wonderful muesli. Service combines style with friendliness. Bedrooms well equipped, bathrooms large but old-fashioned." All lake-facing rooms have a balcony with awning.

Open All year except Jan.
Rooms 10 suites, 76 double, 18 single – all with bath, shower, telephone and TV. Baby-sitting on request.
Facilities Hall, 2 salons, TV room, bar, 2 restaurants; 3 conference rooms. Garden; terrace for meals. Swimming pool nearby.
Location Central, on lake. Parking.
Credit cards All major cards accepted.
Terms [1988 rates] B&B: single 150–200 Sfrs, double 200–250 Sfrs, suite 350–480 Sfrs; dinner, B&B 35 Sfrs added.

MÖREL 3893 Valais — Map 14

Hôtel Relais Walker

Tel (028) 27.24.45
Fax (028) 27.17.16
Telex 473355

Just east of Brig up the Rhône valley, Walter Walker's modern hotel makes a good base for climbers and skiers as well as for his more eponymous guests. "Mörel used to be familiar to many of the British upper classes as the starting point for the 4,000-ft climb to the Villa Cassel, the surprising mock-Tudor mansion built for Sir Ernest Cassel, the father of Lady Edwina Mountbatten; today nearly all that climb can be done in a cable car. The *Relais* has comfortable rooms, but no real lounge, though the bar provides a meeting and eating place for locals. The grill room serves excellent meat and fish dishes, and in autumn some delicious game specialities such as back of roe deer served with cooked fruits. Drawing sheets and colouring pencils are provided to keep younger guests happy. Good local wines. Herr Walker trained in Cornwall and speaks good English." More reports please.

Open All year.
Rooms 22 – all with shower, telephone and radio.
Facilities Lift. Bar, grill room, restaurant.
Location Village is 7 km E of Brig. Parking.
Credit cards All major cards accepted.
Terms [1989 rates] B&B 45–68 Sfrs; dinner, B&B 20 Sfrs per person added.

Report forms (Freepost in UK) will be found at the end of the Guide.

MURTEN 3280 Fribourg — Map 14

Le Vieux Manoir Au Lac
Meyriez

Tel (037) 71.12.83
Fax (037) 71.31.88
Telex 942026

Murten (Morat in French) is an attractive medieval ramparted city built by the Zähringers. In its outskirts, by the shores of Lac Morat, the stylish *Vieux Manoir* – "expensive but worth it" – has pleasant views across the lake to the vineyards opposite. The rooms, most overlooking the lake, are large and tastefully decorated, well furnished in period style. The staff are pleasant, friendly and professional. The good Swiss breakfasts include freshly squeezed and peeled fruit, proper muesli, real jams and excellent coffee served in a nicely decorated room overlooking the lake. Cooking, presentation and service at dinner have all been commended. But we'd welcome further reports.

Open Mid-Feb–mid-Dec.
Rooms 5 suites, 15 double, 4 single – all with bath and/or shower, telephone, radio and TV.
Facilities Lift. 2 lounges, restaurant, veranda, terrace restaurant; conference facilities. Lakeside garden, beach, swimming, sailing and fishing. Public indoor and outdoor swimming pool 200 metres.
Location 1 km SE of Murten right on road to Lausanne.
Credit cards All major cards accepted.
Terms B&B single from 100 Sfrs, double from 180 Sfrs, suite 380 Sfrs. Full alc 75 Sfrs. Reduced rates for children sharing parents' room; special meals.

NEUHAUSEN 8212 Schaffhausen — Map 14

Hotel Bellevue
Bad Bahnhofstrasse 17

Tel (053) 22.21.21

Just two kilometres from the attractive medieval town of Schaffhausen are the Rhine Falls, not the highest waterfalls in Europe but the most powerful, and 500 feet wide. Here the *Bellevue,* aptly named, has a breath-taking situation: most bedrooms, and some bathrooms, overlook the falls. "From my bed, I had a fine view of the falls, in my splendid double room," says a reader this year; "the food was excellent, especially the game (huge helpings), and the service was *svelte.*" Another visitor had "an interesting room with the structural beams appearing out of the floor". The spectacular views extend also to the "splendid lofty dining-room" where there is lots of choice and breakfast includes cooked dishes. Hotel staff pleasant. "The hotel's exterior is ordinary; without the Guide we'd have passed it by." (*Trevor Lockwood*)

Open All year, except 24 Dec–26 Jan.
Rooms 24 double, 3 single – 13 with bath, 7 with shower, all with telephone, radio and mini-bar.
Facilities Lift. Lounge, restaurants; functions room. Large garden with terrace.
Location By the Rhine on outskirts of Neuhausen, 2 km SW of Schaffhausen. Parking.
Credit cards All major cards accepted.
Terms [1989 rates] B&B: single 42–98 Sfrs, double 80–170 Sfrs.

Give the Guide positive support. Don't just leave feedback to others.

NYON 1260 Vaud — Map 14

Hôtel du Clos de Sadex *Tel* (022) 61.28.31

A dignified creeper-covered house on Lac Léman, formerly the home of Major and Madame Louis de Tscharner. They now run it as a hotel, seeking to preserve its patrician atmosphere as well as its elegant furnishings. And they appear to succeed. "What a delight", runs a recent report, "to be welcomed as if to a private house. Our beautiful bedroom had pretty butterfly wallpaper and a view on to the delightful gardens which run down to the lake. Our meal was reasonable but not remarkable." A visitor this year thought highly of the staff, but was less impressed by the food – "The plat du jour did not change during the three days of my visit." In fine weather, breakfast and lunch are served on the terrace overlooking the lake and mountains. One reader stayed in the annexe, on the ground floor, "I lived like a princess, in a huge beautifully furnished room with its own entrance hall. First-floor rooms are smaller." Bedrooms are expensive – but less so than in exorbitant Geneva, not far away.

Open All year except mid-Jan–mid-Feb.
Rooms 13 double, 5 single – 12 with bath and shower, 2 with shower, all with telephone and baby-listening. 5 in annexe 10 metres away. 2 ground-floor rooms.
Facilities Hall, salon with TV, restaurant; conference room. Gardens with terrace for meals, leading directly to lake (hotel has small harbour); swimming, boating, water-skiing.
Location 1 km from Nyon towards Lausanne on lake road; hotel is on right. Parking.
Credit cards All major cards accepted.
Terms B&B: single 65–160 Sfrs, double 110–230 Sfrs. Set lunch 40 Sfrs, dinner 60 Sfrs; full alc 60 Sfrs. Reduced rates for children sharing parents' room; special meals on request.

PONTRESINA 7504 Graubünden — Map 14

Hotel Garni Chesa Mulin *Tel* (082) 6.75.75
Via Mulin *Fax* (082) 6.70.40

Pontresina is an anagram of "inane sport", non-skiers may be relieved to hear. This is a smaller and quieter resort than its flashy neighbour, St-Moritz, but it still gets its fill of athletes. Here the modern white-walled *Chesa Mulin* has its admirers. "A warm personal welcome from the Schmid family, who work hard. Rooms are attractively furnished, and the excellent and varied buffet breakfast is served in a bright Alpine-style room." "Bedrooms have comfortable beds and armchairs. Lights are sensibly arranged and you can read in bed. There is a lovely garden with a fine view. Led by Mr and Mrs Schmid, the staff are most polite, friendly and helpful." In summer there are walks in woods and across meadows and glaciers. No restaurant, but good ones nearby. (*R Pinner*)

Open Dec–Apr, June–Oct.
Rooms 23 double, 4 single – all with bath and/or shower, telephone, radio, mini-bar and TV. 1 specially designed for ♿.
Facilities Lift. Lounge, bar, TV room, breakfast room; sauna, solarium; terrace. Garden.
Location Central; turn off main road towards station. Garage and parking.
Credit cards All major cards accepted.

Terms [1989 rates] B&B: single 72–98 Sfrs, double 124–176 Sfrs. 1-week bookings (Sat–Sat) preferred in winter; ski packages in winter low season. Reduced rates for children sharing parents' room; special meals on request. (No restaurant, but snacks available.)

ROUGEMONT 1838 Vaud — Map 14

Hôtel Valrose

Tel (029) 48146
Fax (029) 48854

Set on the edge of a pretty village west of Gstaad, here is a simple modern chalet-style hotel without frills or graces: but it is clean and welcoming, and offers good value to those on a budget holiday in an expensive country. "The owner is pleasant and humorous, the food is plentiful, and nearly every room has a view of the mountains. The railway station is close by, but Swiss trains are quiet, and after 10 pm the only sound was the tinkling of cow bells." (*Esler Crawford; Stephan and Kate Murray-Sykes*)

Open All year except Nov. Restaurant closed Tue.
Rooms 12 double, 3 single – 7 with shower, all with mini-bar; TV on request.
Facilities Salon with TV, bar/cafe, 2 dining-rooms. Terrace, garden.
Location Rougemont is 4 km W of Saanen. Parking.
Restriction Not suitable for ♿.
Credit cards All major cards accepted.
Terms [1989 rates] B&B 33–46 Sfrs; dinner B&B 16 Sfrs added per person; full board 28 Sfrs added. Set lunch/dinner 18–20 Sfrs; full alc 40–45 Sfrs. Reduced rates for children; special meals on request.

SAANENMÖSER 3777 Bern — Map 14

Hotel Hornberg

Tel (030) 4.44.40
Fax (030) 4.62.79

"Situation lovely, food excellent, owners and staff warm and genuine" – a new plaudit for a typical family-run chalet-style hotel which stands alone at the foot of the Hornberg and looks out over the valley near Gstaad. "The bedrooms are extremely comfortable and well equipped. The food is imaginative, artistically presented and *hausgemacht*. The breakfast buffet is the best I've ever seen. Children are made welcome and are well provided for. The owners, the von Siebenthals, run excursions at no extra charge: the trip may be to the family cheese-making hut high up in the mountains, a mountain lake or some remote local beauty spot." (*Confirmed this year by K and SM–S*)

Open Jun–Oct, Dec–Apr.
Rooms 7 suites, 20 double, 6 single – 27 with bath, 6 with shower, all with telephone and radio; some with balcony.
Facilities Lounge, bar with TV, children's playroom, restaurant, dining-room; terrace. Large garden, indoor and outdoor swimming pool, sauna. Winter sports. Trips, barbecues, picnics organised for guests.
Location 20 km N of Gstaad.
Restriction Not suitable for ♿.
Credit cards All major cards accepted (but only in restaurant).
Terms Half board: single 80–135 Sfrs, double 148–320 Sfrs. Set lunch 20–25 Sfrs, dinner 40–60 Sfrs; full alc 40 Sfrs. Reduced rates for children; special meals.

Please make a habit of sending a report if you stay at a Guide hotel.

ST MORITZ 7500 Graubünden — Map 14

Hotel Chesa sur l'En

Tel (082) 3.31.44
Fax (082) 3.64.74

A romantic and unusual hotel, probably not to all tastes, and very different from most others in swanky St-Moritz. It is a huge 19th-century chalet, set amid pines on a hillside just outside the town, and its old-style decor is lavish: the massive front door opens onto a richly panelled and ornately carved main hall. The warm personal touch of the ever-present owners, the Schwarzenbachs, is admired: but the rooms are defiantly old-fashioned (few have private baths), and it was this above all that took the *Chesa* out of last year's Guide. But it has many devotees who return affectionately year after year – such as the American couple who sent this year's report: "A jewel of Swiss belle époque architecture, with an enveloping ambience – a wonderful experience. The Schwarzenbachs have been running the inn for 30 years. Eliane is in front organising glühwein parties and making little favours for the ladies; Dieter is preparing delicious four-course meals. This is not a place for those who want mod cons. Many of the rooms would be ruined if *en suite* bathrooms were installed. In fact, with a little imagination one can imagine oneself back in the 1880s: to get a bath you ring a bell, soon there's a soft knock on the door and clean towels are presented. But it's a very dreary bathroom." Upper rooms have fine views over the mountains. The central heating has been described as "of venerable age and infirmity". Four rooms *do* now have baths *en suite*. (*Lynne and David Allen*) More reports would be appreciated.

Open 15 Dec–30 Apr, 10 Jul–6 Nov.
Rooms 12 double, 2 single – 4 with bath and shower, 3 with shower; 5 with radio, 7 with TV.
Facilities Hall, salon with TV, dining-room, functions room. Sun terraces.
Location In St Moritz Bad, 5 mins by bus to St Moritz. Parking.
Restrictions Not suitable for ♿.
Credit cards All major cards accepted.
Terms B&B 35–99 Sfrs; dinner B&B 58–127 Sfrs. Set dinner 32 Sfrs; full alc 42–49 Sfrs. 50% reduction for children sharing parents' room.

SCHAFFHAUSEN 8200 — Map 14

Rheinhotel Fischerzunft
Rheinquai 8

Tel (053) 25.32.81
Fax (053) 24.32.85
Telex 897162 FZFT

A very picturesque medieval town on the upper Rhine, close to Europe's most powerful waterfall, the Rhine Falls – that is the suitable setting for this former fishermen's guild house, now converted into an exceptionally brilliant and stylish restaurant (three red *Gault Millau toques*), with glorious bedrooms and bathrooms to match. The owner-chef André Jaeger met his Chinese wife Doreen in Hong Kong, and their inspired partnership continues to draw superlatives from readers. "Cooking with a decidedly oriental accent, served with great style by the glamorous Doreen and her team in a beautiful dining-room; she runs her busy restaurant with discipline *and* style. The food is served on clear glass plates which are placed on black lacquer trays decorated with flower petals. My favourite dishes were sautéed foie gras coated with sesame, and crisply fried duck breast with shitake mushrooms in oyster sauce. There are spectacular large flower arrangements in the restaurant and in the bedrooms. Our room had every mod con imaginable, including beds which adjust so that either your head or your feet can be elevated." Most reports also comment on the Closomat machines attached to the loos, with "a warm water jet if you press one lever, a warm air jet if you press another". "Dinner was one of the best we have ever had; I am told that the dishes have a 'Celestial Empire' taste. Breakfast was a buffet affair. We felt the hotel fell apart a bit in the morning, as the owners were not there and the whole place was being hoovered and polished – it is a restaurant-with-rooms, rather than a hotel." (*Minda Alexander*)

Open All year, except last week Jan, first 2 weeks Feb, 23/24 Dec.
Rooms 3 suites, 8 double – all with bath and/or shower, telephone, radio, TV and mini-bar.
Facilities 2 lounges, card room, restaurant; conference facilities. Terrace for alfresco dining in summer.
Location On banks of Rhine, 5 mins' walk from centre (all windows triple-glazed). Parking.
Restriction Not suitable for ♿.
Credit cards All major cards accepted.
Terms [1989 rates] B&B: single occupancy 110–160 Sfrs, double 150–220 Sfrs, suite 260–305 Sfrs. Children under 6 sharing parents' room free; special meals on request.

SCHÖNRIED-GSTAAD 3778 Bern — Map 14

Hotel Ermitage-Golf

Tel (030) 4.27.27
Fax (030) 4.71.95
Telex 922213

Surrounded by pinewoods and upland meadows, smooth with snow in winter, the village of Schönried stands 180 metres higher than Gstaad and is now a reputed resort with superb skiing facilities. The smartest and largest of its hotels is the *Ermitage-Golf*, two big connecting chalets, magnificently equipped, recently refurbished and enlarged. "The new rooms are of high quality," says a reader this year; "the young staff are pleasant and attentive, and the food is interesting, varied and plentiful, much of it buffet style. The breakfast buffet is enormous, and can be taken out on the terrace facing the pretty garden." Others have written: "There are now four restaurants – a charcoal grill, two French restaurants, and an intimate *Stübli* for modest fare. Dishes are finely prepared and elegantly served. Tucked well away in the basement is a disco, and a 'sauna park' with steam baths and bio-sauna. The garden provides beautiful views." A prime attraction is the *Solbad*, a large indoor swimming pool fitted with briny water heated to 35°C. This indoor pool opens to an outdoor one heated similarly: "It was a sensational experience in December to swim outside, the body most comfortably warmed, but the head in the nippy night air of -10°C, the steam of the water rising to reveal the high surrounding snow banks." (*Kenneth Bishop*)

Open Mid-Dec–Easter; mid-May–end Oct.
Rooms 28 suites, 28 double, 15 single – all with bath and/or shower, telephone, radio and TV.

Facilities Lift. Hall, salon, TV room, 2 bars, snack bar, 2 restaurants, café, terrace restaurant; conference facilities. Billiards, table tennis, squash, indoor and outdoor swimming pool, sauna, fitness room. Garden with tennis, squash. Ski lifts, cable cars opposite hotel.
Location On N11, 8 km E of Gstaad. Underground parking.
Credit cards All major cards accepted.
Terms [1989 rates] Dinner, B&B: single 105–2,420 Sfrs, double 190–560 Sfrs. Full board 20 Sfrs per person added. Reduced rates and special meals for children.

SCHWANDEN 3657 Bern — Map 14

Gasthof-Restaurant Rothorn — *Tel* (033) 51.11.86

This "authentic Swiss mountain village", full of yodelling and creamy milk, stands high above Gunten, facing across the lovely lake of Thun to the Bernese Alps. Here the *Rothorn*, a big brown chalet amid meadows, backed by pinewoods, has evoked four new plaudits this year for its genuine local character and rural charm – and for the "friendly and gracious hospitality" of the owners, Werner and Trudi Amstutz-Rentsch. "The place is a social centre for the village – pensioners sit smoking, gossiping, playing cards, and spontaneous singing comes and goes. And the warmth and professionalism of the whole operation are augmented by the breathtaking views. Our room was simple but tasteful and spacious." "The food was wholesome, plentiful, local in style: fresh wild fruit (bilberries, etc) were often the basis of delicious puddings. An outstandingly pleasant hotel." Others, too, have admired the "delightful" Amstutzes, the friendly staff, the rooms, the good and copious food – and the yodelling in the bar. Rooms at the back look out onto the hillside and are very quiet. Those at the front are larger and have balconies, but suffer from some noise from traffic and from the bar around midnight. (*David and Hanna Rampton, AD and JE Stokes, Ellen Buchanan, R Barratt*) One reader filed a disgruntled minority report, complaining of poor room and bathroom maintenance, and a spartan breakfast.

Open All year except 3 weeks in Nov and 3 weeks after Easter. Restaurant closed Mon.
Rooms 13 double – 10 with bath and/or shower; some with balcony. 4 in annexe.
Facilities Lounge, TV room, dining-room, restaurant with occasional folk music.
Location 30 mins' drive NW of Interlaken, 15 mins NE of Thun.
Credit cards None accepted.
Terms B&B: single 38–50 Sfrs, double 64–94 Sfrs; dinner, B&B: single 55–67 Sfrs, double 98–128 Sfrs; full board: single 67–78 Sfrs, double 120–150 Sfrs. Set lunch/dinner 12–26 Sfrs. Children under 6 sharing parents' room half price, 6–12 30% reduction.

SILS-MARIA 7514 Graubünden — Map 14

Edelweiss Hotel — *Tel* (082) 4.55.51
Dorfstrasse — *Fax* (082) 4.55.22
Telex 852235

In a smart village resort of the upper Engadin valley, between two lakes, this sedate hotel dating from 1875 has been properly modernised and is well run, with friendly staff and good food. But it's a bit impersonal and lacks cosiness. 74 rooms, all with bath and shower. B&B double 180–320 Sfrs. Set menus 25–40 Sfrs. Little recent feedback. More reports welcome.

SOGLIO 7610 Graubünden — Map 14

Pension La Soglina — *Tel* (082) 4.16.08

Hitherto in the Guide under the name of *Stüa Granda*, this hotel has now rechristened itself *La Soglina*, the name of its main annexe. It's an unpretentious, appealing and very well-run place, in a high mountain village above the main valley highway from St-Moritz to Chiavenna in Italy. It continues to be popular, "We were met off the bus by the courteous owner, Roland Nass, and taken to a lovely room with a balcony and fine view down the valley. The food was delicious, and though the set menus offered little choice, they varied daily. Staff were efficient, serving breakfast at 6.30 am when we needed it." An earlier view, "Chestnut trees surround the village and the air is unusually crisp. The sunny terrace restaurant is a favourite meeting place for hikers and the fare is hearty and fresh. Guest rooms (some small) have high-beamed ceilings and lace curtains. The aroma of fresh bread and local specialities such as bundner gerstensuppe fill the air. A romantic hotel for those who love out-of-the-way places in beautiful settings." More reports would be welcome.

Open All year. Restaurant closed in Nov.
Rooms 31 double – all with bath, shower, telephone and radio; some with balcony. Ground-floor rooms.
Facilities 2 sitting rooms, restaurant. Garden terrace. Sauna, turkish bath, whirlpool, solarium and fitness room.
Location On edge of village, just N of route N3 between Chiavenna (to W) and Maloja pass (to E). Nearby parking.
Credit cards None accepted.
Terms [1989 rates] B&B 43–50 Sfrs per person; dinner, B&B 68–73 Sfrs. Special meals for children on request.

SPORZ 7078 Graubünden — Map 14

Hotel Guarda Val — *Tel* (081) 34.22.14, *Fax* (081) 34.46.45, *Telex* 851776

Near Lenzerheide on the Chur–St-Moritz road, the alpine village of Sporz offers indeed plenty of sports (skiing, tennis, golf), as well as this stylish, very attractive and somewhat unusual holiday hotel, its bedrooms in eight old wooden buildings scattered on a hillside: "A 'picture postcard' hotel, the rooms being converted from original barns and cowsheds in a most tasteful manner. Ours also had a lounge and settee, thus providing a room for our teenage son, separated from the main bedroom by a small kitchenette. The view from the window took in mountain streams, alpine meadows and Swiss cows with bells. Lunch was an excellent buffet affair, with mountain cured ham. Not a cheap place, but idyllic." Plenty of old beams, and a handsome candle-lit dining-room.

Open 15 Dec–15 Apr, 10 June–30 Oct.
Rooms 12 suites, 21 double, 2 single – 25 with bath, 10 with shower, all with telephone and radio. Some with kitchenette. Rooms in 8 different buildings.
Facilities TV room, bar, 2 restaurants; functions room. Sauna.
Location 2 km from Lenzerheide, 16 km S of Chur.
Restriction Not suitable for ♿.
Credit cards All major cards accepted.

Terms B&B: single 100–155 Sfrs, double 180–270 Sfrs, suite 270–380 Sfrs; dinner, B&B: single 130–185 Sfrs, double 240–330 Sfrs, suite 330–440 Sfrs. Reduced rates for children; special meals on request.

VADUZ 9490 Liechtenstein — Map 14

Park-Hotel Sonnenhof — *Tel* (075) 21192
Mareestrasse 29, — *Telex* 889329 soho fl

In a glorious mountain-backed parkland setting just outside Liechtenstein's tiny capital, a luxurious and elegant villa-style hotel, run by the warmly welcoming Real family. Large, well-fitted bedrooms, spacious gardens and lounges, indoor heated pool, excellent food. Closed 23–27 Dec. 29 rooms, all with bath and shower. B&B double 240–330 Sfrs. Set menu 45 Sfrs. New nomination. More reports welcome.

VEVEY 1800 Vaud — Map 14

Les Trois Couronnes — *Tel* (021) 921.30.05
49 rue d'Italie — *Fax* (021) 922.72.80
Telex 4511489

A five-star late-Victorian hotel in the grand tradition, right on the lakeside promenade in one of the smartest of Lac Léman resorts, well known for its exclusive girls' finishing-schools. Rooms have large french windows and balconies facing the lake. Dropped from the 1989 Guide for lack of reports, it is restored by a visitor this year: "Indeed a great hotel! Our 4th-floor room had a wonderful lake view and its embroidered bed-linens were wonderful. Breakfast the best on our tour." Others have praised the efficient and courteous service, and the food in the beautiful Louis XV-style dining room. Public rooms have an abundance of carved, gilded and marbled decor, with much fine furniture. There are fountains and flowers on the terrace. (*NPD and J Levine*)

Open All year.
Rooms 7 suites, 41 double, 27 single – all with bath and shower, telephone, radio and TV; baby-listening on request.
Facilities Lift. Salons, TV room, bar, restaurant; conference facilities; large terrace with open restaurant. Pianist several evenings a week.
Location Central, but quietly situated. Parking in courtyard.
Restrictions Not suitable for ♿.
Credit cards All major cards accepted.
Terms [1989 rates] B&B: single 150–250 Sfrs, double 250–350 Sfrs; dinner, B&B: 45 Sfrs added per person; full board 90 Sfrs added. Set lunch/dinner 50–60 Sfrs. Reduced rates and special meals for children.

VITZNAU 6354 Lucerne — Map 14

Hotel Floralpina — *Tel* (041) 83.13.86
PO Box 77

For a really stunning view, take Europe's oldest mountain rack-railway (1871) up to the Rigi-Kulm, which towers above Vitznau, one of the more elegant resorts on Lake Lucerne. Just outside the village, in a glorious lakeside setting backed by steep wooded hills, is this handsome modern hotel, praised again this year for its comfort, fine views and "simple but tasty" meals (good solid Swiss fare from a limited menu). It has huge grounds, direct access to swimming in the lake (private beach), and unbeatable views from the dining terrace. "Some of the largest double bedrooms one can find these days in Europe, and it's well worth paying extra for a lakeview room. Good cheese-board." (*WG Francis*) One reader criticised the food and its presentation and felt the hotel was too closely geared to package holidays and conferences.

Open 12 Apr–19 Oct.
Rooms 6 suites, 49 double, 9 single – all with shower, telephone, radio; TV on request.
Facilities Lift, ramps. Lounge, TV room, bar, restaurant, room; whirlpool, sauna, solarium. Terrace, park with children's playground, private beach.
Location 2 km S of Vitznau on Brunnen road.
Credit cards All major cards accepted.
Terms B&B 48–60 Sfrs. Set lunch/dinner 16 Sfrs; full alc 30 Sfrs. Reduced rates and special meals for children.

WEGGIS 6353 Lucerne — Map 14

Hotel Beau Rivage

Tel (041) 93.14.22
Fax (041) 93.19.81
Telex 862982

Weggis is a delightful resort some 30 minutes by road or 45 by steamer from Lucerne; other lake pleasures are easily accessible, as are the heights of Rigi, served by Weggis's funicular. The ever-popular *Beau Rivage* has a choice position right by the water, a few minutes' walk from the quay, with its own garden and swimming pool. "Charming and well appointed," runs a report this year; "food good, but not extraordinary." Previous verdicts: "The delightful hard-working Geering family make this an outstanding hotel, and it keeps on improving. The bedrooms are now superb and we can never fault the food." "The rooms are lovely with pleasant lake views and the staff were friendly and very helpful." (*Aaron W Esman, RS McNeill*) Some package tours, out of season only.

Open Early Apr–mid-Oct.
Rooms 4 suites, 31 double, 9 single – all with bath and/or shower, telephone, radio and TV.
Facilities Lift. Hall, lounges, TV room, bar, garden room, restaurant; lakeside terrace; band twice a week. Garden with swimming pool, beach, fishing.
Location 20 km E of Lucerne; on lake, near quay. Garages and parking.
Credit cards All major cards accepted.
Terms B&B: single 80–130 Sfrs, double 136–234 Sfrs, suite 240–270 Sfrs; half board: single 110–160 Sfrs, double 196–294 Sfrs, suite 300–330 Sfrs. Set lunch/dinner 40–45 Sfrs; full alc 60 Sfrs. Reduced rates for children sharing parents' room; special meals.

> There are many expensive hotels in the Guide. We are keen to increase our coverage at the other end of the scale. If you know of a simple place giving simple satisfaction, please write and tell us.

> Always let a hotel know if you have to cancel a booking, whether you have paid a deposit or not. Hotels lose thousands of pounds and dollars from "no-shows".

WENGEN 3823 Bern — Map 14

Hotel Eiger

Tel (036) 55.11.31
Fax (036) 55.10.30
Telex 923296

Family-run by the Fuchses for generations, but rebuilt in 1980 in traditional style (neat balconies, masses of stripped pine), here's a typical ski-hotel in a leading resort of the Bernese Oberland. Two nominations this year: "Very comfortable. The rooms are large, and the beds, duvets, etc, are pushed away each morning to create a sitting room, reinstated as a bedroom at 7 pm. The well-designed balconies look onto a marvellous view of the Jungfrau. Breakfast buffets were excellent (muesli with blackcurrants and bilberries); dinner was not so good, but adequate." "Warm and welcoming. Next door to station, so convenient for skiers. The charming staff join in the fun of your being on holiday. The small Eiger bar is the focal point of Wengen après-ski." (*M Scott Russell, and others*)

Open All year except 29 Apr–17 June. Grill Room closed Mon.
Rooms 9 suites, 20 double, 4 single – 31 with bath, 2 with shower – all with telephone and radio; TV on request.
Facilities Lift. Lounge, TV room, 2 restaurants, bar (in winter).
Location Central. No cars in Wengen. Park in Lauterbrunnen and take train.
Credit cards All major cards accepted.
Terms B&B: single 60–98 Sfrs, double 60–108 Sfrs, suite 75–118 Sfrs. Set lunch 13–22 Sfrs; dinner 35 Sfrs; full alc 35–65 Sfrs. Reduced rates and special meals for children.

WORB 3076 Bern — Map 14

Romantik Hotel Löwen

Enggisteinstrasse 3

Tel (031) 83.23.03
Fax (031) 83.58.77

In a village four miles from Bern, this small traditional hotel of character has been run by the same family for over 300 years,and has a solid local reputation for its good food. Lack of news forced it out of last year's Guide, but Americans now restore it: "A fine, elegant hostelry whose staff are courteous beyond courtesy, helpful to a fault. The rooms are spacious: ours had an armoire whose door hinges and locks were sensuously magnificent. Dinner was beautifully served and the atmosphere was relaxed." (*H and B Shames*)

Open All year. Restaurant closed Wed, Thur midday, 4 weeks Jul/Aug.
Rooms 14 – all with bath, shower, telephone and radio; 7 with TV.
Facilities Lounge, bar, TV room, restaurant, functions room. Garden with restaurant, children's playground, bowling alleys. Tennis, swimming nearby in summer, skating in winter.
Location Central, by church; parking. Worb is 10 km E of Bern on Lucerne road.
Restriction Not suitable for ♿.
Credit cards All major cards accepted.
Terms [1989 rates] B&B: single 70–85 Sfrs, double 130–145 Sfrs. Set lunch/dinner 10 and 30 Sfrs; full alc 55 Sfrs. Reduced rates and special meals for children.

> Please make a habit of sending in a report as soon as possible after a visit when details are still fresh in your mind.

ZERMATT 3920 Valais — Map 14

Hôtel-Garni Metropol

Tel (028) 67.32.31
Fax (028) 67.23.42
Telex 472137

More affectionate plaudits in 1988/9 for this unpretentious little hotel beside a river in the town centre, run tirelessly by the friendly Taugwalder family. The views of the Matterhorn, from the bedrooms with balconies on the south side, are a star feature: "The sight of this peak from your window each morning, so close you could almost touch it, is an exhilarating experience. Wonderful little hotel, reasonably priced." Another new report: "Good and clean as ever, everyone so friendly, Frau Taugwalder's cooking is really good and the helpings enormous, while the buffet breakfast seems to improve each year." One devotee, after a new two-week stay, regards it as "still my favourite hotel anywhere, and I'd like to take it with me on my travels". He wrote earlier: "Zermatt with its 107 hotels has developed in such an ugly way that almost every bit of green is replaced by grey concrete. But the Taugwalders bought a meadow in front of their hotel, so you have a clear view to the south. The rooms have sensible beds, spacious cupboards and well-equipped bathrooms. The constant rush of the river is soothing at night." There is no full-scale restaurant, but snacks are available in the evening, and more substantial dishes can be ordered specially in advance. (*Karen and David Bashkin, Alex and Beryl Boyd, D and J Morris, Richard Pinner*)

Open 1 Dec–10 May, 10 June–20 Oct.
Rooms 20 double, 4 single – 16 with bath and shower, 4 with shower, all with telephone, radio, TV and baby-listening.
Facilities Lift. Lounge, bar, TV room, dining-room. Garden and terrace.
Location Central; near station. Hotel porter will fetch you (no cars in Zermatt).
Credit cards All major cards accepted.
Terms B&B: single 55–94 Sfrs, double 100–188 Sfrs. Reduced rates for children.

ZÜRICH — Map 14

Hotel Florhof

Florhofgasse 4, Zurich 8001

Tel (01) 47.44.70
Telex 817364

A converted 16th-century patrician house with a small garden, in a residential street near the *Kunsthaus* and university, and next to the music conservatoire. This year, praise has flowed in more than ever – above all for the friendly staff, also for the pleasant rooms and good food. "If you don't turn up by the time breakfast ends, you get a call asking if they may bring it up to you (free of charge). Most hotels don't care a bit whether you have had your breakfast. We also had an oustandingly good lunch in the garden." The restaurant is closed at weekends. (*Dr TJ David; also Shelley B Andrews, Mrs PA Godden, EM Jacob, and others*)

Open All year. Restaurant closed Sat and Sun.
Rooms 23 double, 10 single – 22 with bath, 11 with shower, all with telephone, radio, TV and mini-bar.
Facilities Lift. Salon, restaurant. Garden with restaurant.
Location Near *Kunsthaus* and university. Parking.
Restriction Not suitable for ♿.
Credit cards All major cards accepted.

Terms B&B: single 115–155 Sfrs, double 160–220 Sfrs. Set lunch 25–35 Sfrs, dinner 30–50 Sfrs; full alc 55–70 Sfrs. Reduced rates/special meals for children.

Hotel zum Storchen *Tel* (01) 211.55.10
Am Weinplatz, Zurich 22 *Fax* (01) 211.64.51
Zürich 8001 *Telex* 813354

A pleasant riverside hotel, in the heart of old Zürich. Half the bedrooms, also the restaurant and terrace, face the river Limmat and have the classic view of the cathedral and the Baroque town hall. Those not facing the river overlook the charming Weinplatz, now a pedestrian precinct. The hotel is in a fairly new building, but its history dates back 600 years: past guests have included Paracelsus and Richard Wagner. "Really civilised", says one old admirer. "The cuisine is distinguished, international with a Swiss touch, service is courteous and regulars are greeted like old friends." "The panelled restaurant, with the atmosphere of one of Zurich's old guild-halls, is good", runs one report this year; "in summer drinks and light meals are served on the lovely canopied terrace facing the river. My room was simple but cosy." Another 1989 visitor commended the "reliable, efficient" staff, but a third thought the place rather characterless and found his riverside room a bit noisy and his breakfast uninspiring. (*Dr AJ Pearce, FR; also Arnold Horwell*)

Open All year.
Rooms 37 double, 40 single – all with bath and shower, telephone, radio and TV; baby-listening on request.
Facilities Lift. Bar, restaurant. Conference and banqueting facilities. Terrace.
Location Central, on river; no private parking.
Restriction Not suitable for ♿.
Credit cards All major cards accepted.
Terms B&B: single 160–240 Sfrs, double 240–360 Sfrs. Set lunch /dinner 50 Sfrs; full alc 75 Sfrs. Reduced rates for children; special meals on request.

Hotel Tiefenau *Tel* (01) 251.24.09
Steinwiesstrasse 8–10 *Fax* (01) 251.24.76
Zürich 8032 *Telex* 816395

This well-located family-run hotel, gracefully furnished in period style, makes a useful addition this year to our still modest selection for Switzerland's largest city. "Cosy without being Swiss-stuffy. It's in a tiny quiet street very close to the Kunsthaus (with its wonderful Munchs, Impressionist and post-Impressionist collections) and the tram terminus which will get you in ten minutes to the Bahnhofstrasse. There's a terrace where you can eat or drink under huge shady trees and the food is quite good. You can walk to any number of good restaurants, including the *Krönenhalle*, James Joyce's favourite. The rooms are very comfortable, prettily furnished, and the service friendly." (*Nadine Gordimer, KA*)

Open All year except 2 or 3 weeks over Christmas/New Year.
Rooms 5 suites, 14 double, 11 single – all with bath, shower, telephone, radio, TV.
Facilities Lift. Salon, restaurant; conference facilities. Garden; terrace.
Location Fairly central, by Schauspielhaus. Free parking.
Credit cards All major cards accepted.
Terms [1989 rates] B&B: single 145–190 Sfrs, double 220–290 Sfrs, suite 340–410 Sfrs. Set lunch 25 Sfrs, dinner 30 Sfr; full alc 47.50 Sfrs. Reduced rates and special meals for children.

Turkey

TURBAN ADALYA OTELI, ANTALYA

ANAMUR Akdeniż **Map 18**

Otel Anahan *Tel* (7571) 3511
Tahsin Soylu Cad. 109 *Fax* (0751) 1005

On the long beach outside this south coast town, a newly opened hotel with clean, simple rooms, eager service and a large restaurant. 30 rooms, all with bath and shower. B&B double US$47. Set menus US$8. No recent reports. More welcome.

ANKARA **Map 18**

Bulvar Palas Oteli *Tel* (4) 117.50.20
Atatürk Bulvari 141 *Telex* 42613 BLVD

"Good value: the rooms are airy, and though the plumbing creaks, it works," says a recent visitor. An earlier comment: "The rest of Ankara may try to impress with its modernity, but the *Bulvar Palas* sails through still in the fifties, with its big bedrooms, solid plumbing and comfortable beds. Staff are efficient and abundant, meals are reasonably priced and of fair quality, but it is the atmosphere that is the thing: a 'B' movie remake of Istanbul's *Pera Palas*."

Open All year.
Rooms 177 – 167 with bath or shower, all with telephone, radio, TV, mini-bar and air-conditioning.
Facilities Lift. Lounge, restaurant; conference facilities; hairdressing salon.
Location Central. Next door to Belgian Ministry in area called "Ministries". Parking.
Credit cards All major cards accepted.
Terms On application.

ANTALYA — Map 18

Turban Adalya Oteli
Kaleiçi Yat Limani

Tel (31) 11.80.66 and 17.69.05
Fax (31) 123679
Telex 56241 TBA

Antalya's famous harbour has recently been much restored, and it is now a showplace resort. "Sleek yachts", we are told, "are moored alongside beautifully preserved Turkish houses with their dark wooden balconies and colourful tiled roofs. The *Turban Adalya*, originally a bank and then a warehouse, has been converted into a most individual small luxury hotel. The refreshing sound of running water from the fountains in the atrium-patio greets you as you walk into its welcome coolness; the charmingly decorated bedrooms lead off from upstairs galleries. There is a small bar-terrace at the back overlooking the harbour, with another bar and an excellent restaurant on the top floor." Endorsing that account, one visitor this year had a spacious, clean and quiet room with efficient air-conditioning, and found breakfast "a feast". Others agree that the rooms are charming, but point out that they have no view and there is no lounge; the hotel might be better for a stopover than for a long stay. A new "Presidential Suite" has just been opened in an old house nearby, with all modern facilities, balconies and harbour views. (*Mr and Mrs SC Jones-Parry*)

Open All year.
Rooms 2 suites, 26 double – all with shower, telephone, radio, TV, air-conditioning and mini-bar. "Presidential Suite", in building 15 metres away.
Facilities Lounge, 2 bars, restaurant; terrace. Garden. Swimming pool nearby.
Location Central, near citadel and harbour; parking.
Credit cards Possibly some accepted.
Terms [1989 rates] B&B: single US$49–US$66.50, double US$63–US$85.50, suite US$91–US$170. Reduced rates for children sharing parents' room.

ARSUZ Hatay — Map 18

Arsuz Turistik Oteli
Uluçinar,
Arsuz-Iskenderun

Tel (881) 217.82 and (8873) 1444
Telex 68676 SEDT

"Certainly the best resort-hotel on the eastern Mediterranean coast of Turkey. Its clean white block sits like a docked liner on the shore of this tiny fishing village, now officially renamed Uluçinar. The Mistikoglu family have made it the weekend seaside retreat of wealthy Alexandretta (Iskenderun) and Antioch (Antakya). Bedrooms are sparsely furnished but well maintained; public rooms have a relaxed Mediterranean style; the broad paved terrace – with its palms, flower-beds, globe lanterns, white wrought-iron balustrades and well-upholstered garden furniture – is worth the front cover of any tourist office hand-out. The brothers who host the operation are unforced charm itself and speak excellent English. Other staff are obliging and professional. Food in the restaurant is fine and unfussy. High season high jinks extend to an open-air disco – Turkish hotel discos are relatively dressy and sedate affairs. Potential hazards are the local mosquitoes and the village itself which has little to offer apart from a good back-drop of distant mountains." More reports please.

Open 15 Mar–31 Oct.
Rooms 20 suites, 74 double – all with bath or shower, telephone and radio.
Facilities Lift, ramps. 2 lounges, TV room, 2 bars, restaurant; banqueting room; Terrace with snack bar. Private beach.
Location 32 km S of Iskenderun.
Credit cards Diners, Visa.
Terms B&B: single US$31, double US$39, suite US$78; dinner, B&B: single US$38, double US$52, suite US$104. Set lunch/dinner US$9. Children under 5 free; special meals.

BODRUM Muğla — Map 18

Manzara Oteli — *Tel* (6141) 1719
Kumbahçe Mah, Meteoroloji Yani

A small hilltop hotel, some five minutes' walk from the seafront of an attractive resort town opposite the Greek island of Kos. Its position gives a stunning view of the bay and of the 'crusader castle', especially when illuminated at night. Rooms are in the style of small apartments, each with a terrace for outdoor eating, small sink unit and refrigerator. Enthusiasm again this year: "The most delightful discovery of our trip. Staff are very welcoming. We took dinner at sunset on the flower-decked poolside terrace, overlooking the castle and twin harbours: food was delicious, imaginative, served with friendly care. The bedrooms are small suites, artfully strewn down a steepish hill, linked by meandering whitewashed steps lined with pots of brilliant flowers. There are great swatches of bougainvillea, trumpet vine, morning glory, and other lovely climbing plants, creating privacy, providing shade, and framing spectacular views. I felt that I could understand at last what the Hanging Gardens of Babylon must have been like. We loved the hotel and the charming though touristy atmosphere of the busy yacht harbour. Only two small niggles: some mosquitoes, and an uncomfortable bed." There is a small heated swimming pool with an adjoining bar and small restaurant, with service throughout the day. (*Dr Suzanne L Martin*) The *Manzara* may now be insisting on half-board terms despite the self-catering facilities.

Open All year.
Rooms 20 double, including some suites – all with bath or shower, arranged in small apartments with living room, with sink unit and refrigerator, and terrace.
Facilities Restaurant. Terrace with swimming pool and bar.
Location On hill overlooking Bodrum.
Terms On application.

Hotel Myndos *Tel* (6141) 2591 and 3080
Eski Çeşme Cafer Paşa Caddesi 68 *Telex* 52802 AGSO

Brand new: 6 attractive white 2-storey villa-style blocks, set round a lovely central pool with loungers and chairs, all floodlit at night. 62 rooms, cool, elegantly simple, with marble floors, all with modern shower. Restaurant poor, but lots in town. Some teething troubles: e.g. hot water erratic. Double room with breakfast US$55, with half board US$75. Recent nomination. More reports please.

BURSA — Map 18

Çelik Palas Oteli *Tel* (24) 361900
Çekirge Caddesi 79 *Telex* 32121 CEPA

A large pre-war "grand hotel" in a smart suburb, overlooking the old town. Recently renovated and enlarged, it has large, clean comfortable rooms, some with balconies facing the mountains and valley. Marble hammam, indoor pool, disco; copious breakfasts, decent international restaurant with violinists and dance floor. 173 rooms, all with bath and shower. B&B double 150,000 Tl. Breakfast 10,000 Tl [1989]. No recent reports. More welcome.

ÇAVUŞIN Nevşehir — Map 18

Turbel Pansion Restaurant *Tel* (4861) 14.27

"Definitely the best place to stay in Cappadocia", writes this year's enthusiastic nominator; "Çavuşin is a village in the heart of the Göreme region with its 'fairy chimneys' of lava and ancient churches cut in the soft rock, many with fine frescos. Hence every tour seems to pass through here and every town boasts a host of tacky hotels. Çavuşin is the only unspoilt place in Göreme, and this small *pension* is its only hotel, set at the mouth of a beautiful valley where the locals grow grapes and vegetables between the strange rock chimneys. The pale rock cliffs lining the valley are a lovely pink which deepens beautifully at sunset. The *pension* itself is a fine converted farm, with an open-air restaurant in its ample courtyard. The lower bedrooms, once the stables, are cut in the rock; cool at all times of the day, they are downright musty at night. Upper rooms have lovely views and are less musty, but warm during the day. Each room has pretty blue striped sheets. The loos and showers, located across the courtyard, were clean. The best thing about the *pension* is the owner/manager Mustala Kaygisiz, extremely kind and pleasant, who worked in France for many years and is intent on making his hotel comfortable and attractive. He will take you for tours round the valley in his van. As for his food, the chicken and lamb are good, but the local fish is bony and tasteless. The local rosé wine is excellent." (*Claire Enders*) More reports eagerly awaited.

Open 1 Apr–15 Nov.
Rooms 3 double, 7 triple – some ground-floor rooms.
Facilities Salon, 2 bars, TV room; restaurant. Garden with children's play area. Occasional traditional music and dance evenings.
Location Çavuşin is 15 km E of Nevşehir, 3 km N of Göreme. Parking.

Restrictions Not suitable for ♿.
Credit cards Access, Visa.
Terms B&B: single 15,000 Tl, double 30,000 Tl; dinner, B&B: single 22,000 Tl, double 45,000 Tl; full-board single 28,000 Tl, double 55,000 Tl. Set dinner 10,000 Tl; full alc 13,000 Tl. Reduced rates and special meals for children.

ÇEŞME 35930 İzmīr — Map 18

Kanuni Kervansaray Oteli — *Tel* (549) 26490
Çeşme Kalesi Yani — *Telex* 51902 GOLD

This attractive Guide newcomer is a converted caravanserai (inn for travellers), with a massive arcaded courtyard and rooms of real Turkish character, set in a small town on the coast west of Izmir: "Çeşme is said to be destined to be *the* major Turkish resort and big hotels are shooting up outside it: but as yet it retains a lovely quiet village ambience. This atmospheric hotel looks up to the superb 15th-century walled castle, lit up at night. The garden courtyard itself is a wonderful place to sit of an evening. Rooms are fair sized with good bathrooms, and cool because of the thickness of the walls. The staff are charming and attentive. Food is twice the price of a Turkish restaurant but nicely prepared and less bland and 'international' than in many hotels: we enjoyed our meals by the beautiful old fountain in the courtyard. There's no pool, but guests can go 3 kilometres to the pool and beach of the *Golden Dolphin*, part of the same chain. Nearby beaches are sandy and pleasant." (*C and N Brooks-Matthew*)

Open Apr–Oct.
Rooms 2 suites, 30 double – 30 with bath, 2 with shower, all with telephone and radio. 9 ground-floor rooms.
Facilities Lounge, TV room, bar, restaurant. Garden, courtyard. Swimming pools 3 km.
Location Central, parking. Çeşme is 70 km W of İzmīr.
Credit cards All major cards accepted.
Terms [1989 rates] B&B: US$22–US$39, suite US$81–US$100. Set lunch/dinner US$12,50, full alc US$15. Reduced rates and special meals for children.

DATÇA Muğla — Map 18

Perīlī Köşk — *Tel* (081) 44027
PO Box 46 — *Fax* Istanbul (1) 345.36.25
Telex 29279 MRCC

Few hotels in this book are more beguilingly idiosyncratic than this "Fairies' Castle" (literal translation) on the coast opposite Rhodes. "From Marmaris after a tortuous 60-kilometre drive through the mountains, a neat sign on the left directs you along a rough track that you'd think only fit for a donkey. After about 700 metres, a lovely tiled roof and chimneys come into view, peering over cascades of oleander and bougainvillea. The hotel faces a beautiful crescent bay with no other building in sight (Datça village is 18 kilometres away). The design is impressive – a wealth of lovely natural pine, with balconies and latticed windows, and the rooms have stunning traditional framed panelled ceilings. We had a good-sized room – some are cramped, but all have bathrooms." That nominator's report has since been qualified by an inspector who was at once dazzled and infuriated: "That tortuous drive is spectacular, hair-raising, stunningly beautiful, past vistas of islands and bays. This part of Turkey is blessedly green. The *Köşk* is the fantasy of a rich Turk (seldom there) who regards it as his toy, which he delights to embellish. Tiled terraces at different levels, a blue-tiled fountained courtyard, a wrought-iron gateway leading to the beach, and a white wrought-iron pavilion like a Victorian bandstand. The interior is even more Turkish, its core being a windowless mosque-like dome. My husband thought it all a bit over-the-top, but I swallowed it delightedly, partly because it's the only hotel in Turkey outside Istanbul that we found to have any personal eccentricity. However, there are drawbacks. While most rooms have a balcony, those at the rear must be dark (though cool). It's a summer place, and in mid-October it was all a bit *triste*. Though breakfast was good, the main meals were poor. And the place is expensive, and remote from anywhere of interest." *Since receiving that report, we learn this year that the hotel has a new manager, and has added 17 bedrooms in pavilions in the grounds, almost doubling its size. Have these changes spoilt the wayward charm, or do they mean that bed and board are now improved? More reports badly needed.*

Open Apr–end Oct.
Rooms 37 double – all with shower. 23 in pavilions in grounds. Ground-floor rooms.
Facilities Lounge, bar, dining room; terrace. Garden with tennis court; beach with water sports.
Location 18 km E of Datça towards Marmaris.
Restriction Not suitable for ♿.
Credit card Visa.
Terms Dinner, B&B: double US$54–US$90. Full alc US$10–US$15. Reduced rates and special meals for children.

INCEKUM Antalya — Map 18

Alara Oteli — *Tel* (3237) 1146 and 1153
Yeşilköy, Bay of Incekum — *Telex* 56613 ALRA

Enjoyed for its tranquil setting and unspoilt beach, the *Alara* is 23 kilometres from the big popular resort of Alanya, but it runs a twice daily mini-bus service into town. "It is in a prime position high up at one end of the bay giving wide vistas over the surrounding area. Built in the Moorish style, it is made up of five separate buildings. The main one houses reception, lounge, bar and open-air dining-room and is ringed by a pleasant patio and pool overlooking the cliffs. The four bedroom blocks are set amid the well-tended gardens which run down to the sea. The rooms all have a sea view and are clean and fresh, though rather unsophisticated. All the staff are helpful, though only the manager spoke English. The food was palatable, if hardly a gastronomic experience. A pleasant and relaxing base for a most enjoyable holiday." More reports please.

Open 1 Apr–31 Oct.
Rooms 6 suites, 119 double – all with bath and shower and telephone; many with balcony. All in 4 separate buildings in grounds.
Facilities 2 bars, breakfast room, snack bar, restaurant; shops; belly dancing once a week. Garden with table tennis and swimming pool. Private beach, with water sports.
Location 23 km W of Alanya; mini-bus service twice a day.

Credit cards Amex, Visa.
Terms Dinner, B&B: single 50–88 DM, double 100–200 DM. Set meals 11 DM; full alc 15 DM. Reduced rates for children.

ISTANBUL — Map 18

Ayasofya Pansiyonlari

Soğukçeşme Sokaği
Sultanahmet

Tel (1) 513.36.60
Telex 23841 TSAP

An admirable work of restoration by the Touring Club of Turkey (see also *Hīdīv Kasri* and *Yeşil Ev*, below): it is a terrace of nine historic houses, with attractive pastel-coloured wooden exteriors, down a narrow lane between Topkapi Palace and Hagia Sophia. Two houses have ground-floor breakfast and tea rooms, one has been converted into a library, strong on books about Old Constantinople. The old Roman cistern in the same road has recently been converted into a good restaurant, whose food, service and atmosphere have all again been found "delightful" this year. Earlier accounts: "The location is amazing. Try to get front rooms with the view of Hagia Sophia, for back ones face a wall. The omnipresent musak of a good sort (such as Chopin) seems to symbolise the yearning to make westerners feel at home." "The buildings are modernised yet have kept the charm of the period; their decor is lovely, with Turkish rugs on every floor." "Rooms comfortable, but plumbing could be better." The sluggish service, it is suggested, might not appeal to businessmen in a hurry. (*Mrs JA Patterson, Claire W Enders, Dr Suzanne L Martin*)

Open All year.
Rooms 5 suites, 6 triple, 34 double, 12 single – all with bath and/or shower, telephone and radio. All in 9 different houses.
Facilities Library, breakfast room, tea-room, two restaurants. Garden where breakfast and snacks are served.
Location Central, near Hagia Sophia.
Credit cards Access, Amex, Visa.
Terms On application.

Hīdıv̄ Kasrī

Çubuklu-Kanlīca

Tel (1) 331.26.51
Fax (1) 32.34.34
Telex 23346

Of the three Istanbul hotels converted from Ottoman mansions (see also *Ayasofya Pansiyonlari* and *Yeşil Ev*), this is by far the most bizarre and spectacular – the old summer palace of the last Viceroy of Egypt, set on a wooded hill on the Asian side of the city above the Bosphorus-shore villages of Çubuklu and Kanlīca (famed for its yoghurt). The palace was built and originally furnished in a fabulous mixture of styles – stolid Middle-Eastern opulent, Tuscan villa and Belgian *Art Nouveau*. The restoration and refurbishment have kept many of the fittings, including regal mahogany-surrounded loos from a works in Lambeth, bronze cage-lifts from Munich and baths as big as boats with elaborate *fin-de-siècle* shower attachments surmounted by chrome crescent moons and stars. All the present furniture is fetchingly clumsy reproduction *Art Nouveau*. The master-mind of this enterprise, Çelik Gülersoy, decides on and designs everything according to how he sees the buildings in his dreams. His fantasy here includes features such as a vast marble fountain in the central hall, a wood-panelled salon hung with a riot of crystal and gilt chandeliers, a field of roses growing through grass outside a marble-floored tea-room lit by pastel-coloured blown glass flowers. A piano trio plays in the banana-shaped dining room at night – Mozart, Schubert, then *The Blue Danube*. Most rooms have views that it would be hard to better anywhere in the city. The superb Viceroy's suite has a long, wide terrace looking out over the trees to a sumptuous bend in the Bosphorus. On the same floor at the back, where the Tuscan eaves are most harmonious, the bedrooms overlook a rose field framed by cypresses. The cheaper rooms on the second floor are on a more human scale, but have no terrace. In order not to destroy the room plan of the palace, bathrooms and loos have not been knocked into the bedrooms – they are shared between two or three rooms but have the advantage of retaining their original impressive proportions. The grounds, with their wooden viewing-pavilions and a glass house selling local honey and preserves, are popular with day-trippers from all around. Getting to the hotel is not so easy. The infrequent boat all the way from the city centre to Kanlica takes up to two hours – although this is a trip worth taking on its own account; or take the ferry to Uskudar, then bus, dolmuş (shared taxi) or taxi along the Asian shore of the Bosphorus to Kanlica.

Open All year.
Rooms About 30 including 2 suites – all with telephone and radio.
Facilities 3 restaurants, tea-room; tavern, beer garden; terrace. Wooded grounds.
Location On Asian shore of the Bosphorus, 2 hours by boat from the city centre (45 mins by ferry and land transport).
Terms [1989 rates] B&B double US$143.

Kalyon Hotel
Sahil Yolu
Sultanahmet

Tel (1) 511.44.00
Fax (1) 526.62.51
Telex 23364 KLYN

A modern hotel on the edge of the Bosphorus, away from the crowds yet only ten minutes' walk from the Blue Mosque, Hagia Sophia and Topkapi Palace. A reader this year was delighted, "Our room looked out over the hotel lawn, past the fishermen who sit by the water to the constant, silent fascinating stream of ships moving through the Bosphorus: I was enchanted by the combination of the hotel's peaceful setting and the swirl of activity in the crowded, ancient streets just behind. Our rooms, though clean and pleasant, were nondescript: but the staff were pleasant, and we enjoyed our Turkish buffet breakfasts (with yoghurt, honey, fresh fruit, herb-scented breads, etc), taken facing the water." Others have reported that rooms at the back can be small; front ones are larger, with sea views, but lower floors would hear traffic noise. (*Dr Suzanne L Martin*) The hotel this year has been hugely enlarged, moving from 38 rooms to 110, and we'd be glad of reports on the impact of these changes.

Open All year.
Rooms 8 suites, 100 double, 2 single – all with bath and shower, telephone, radio and TV; many with balcony.
Facilities Lift. Lounges, bar, restaurant, cafeteria; conference room, meeting room.
Location Central; on the waterfront; near Blue Mosque. Parking.
Terms B&B: single US$71–US$89, double US$93–US$115, suite US$140–US$176. Set lunch US$12, dinner US$15; full alc US$18. Reduced rates and special meals for children.

Hotel Sokullu Paşa *Tel* (1) 512.37.53
Ishakpaşa Mah. Mehmetpaąsa
Sokak 10
Sultanahmet

Another splendid Ottoman conversion of a wooden house in the Old City, just round the corner from the superb Sokullu Paşa mosque, below the south end of the Hippodrome. Attractively decorated – small lobby with fountain; Turkish bath; garden at back, "a haven of peace". Staff exceptionally helpful and friendly. But some bedrooms very small, with awkwardly installed plumbing, and buffet breakfast, though generous, criticised for too many packaged items. 35 rooms, all with private facilities. B&B: single US$65, double US$85 [1989]. *New nomination. More reports please.*

Yeşil Ev Oteli *Tel* (1) 528.67.64
Kabasakal Sok 5, Sultanahmet *Telex* 30470

Located high up in the oldest part of the Old City, in an area of carpet shops between Hagia Sophia and the Blue Mosque, this charming hotel of character is a large wooden Ottoman mansion, painted a fresh apple green and white. Till recently it was derelict, but the Touring Club of Turkey has now restored it lovingly. An expert on Turkey gives his reactions: "The interiors are now in highest 19th-century Victorian-Ottoman taste, with velveteen chaises-longues, loving-bird table lamps, heavy flock drapes, ornate wooden pelmets and the like. The wooden floors creak; the light bulbs' wattage is low; a pianist at an upright accompanies afternoon tea in the cramped lobby; out back is a sheltered courtyard with marble fountain – the idea is that one should feel like a guest in an Ottoman household. It all worked perfectly for me, but I could understand some finding it precious and vulgar. The food is unimaginative, clumsy attempts at Turkish international. The dining rooms are small and low-ceilinged (the back one is best)." An earlier view: "Our ground-floor bedroom was almost more bed than room: the huge and well-sprung bed left just enough room to squeeze past an armchair, a polished mahogany wardrobe and a chest of drawers. The room was high and had tall sash windows hung with lace and brocade curtains, and fitted with latticed shutters giving what were basically light rooms a pleasantly secretive, Ottoman feeling. Communication with the outside world – and the present century – was via a brass 'candlestick' telephone made in Coventry in 1930. The walled, paved garden is the hotel's happiest asset. Water splashes down from a porphyry fountain; fig and plane trees are edged with pansies and stocks, wallflowers and marigolds; roses and vines climb the walls. On one side stands a pelargonium-filled conservatory, for cool evenings. The food is good, typically Turkish, with enough variety for a week's stay. And where better than here to take the last Turkish coffee of the day, turning one's gaze from the great dome of

Our italicised entries indicate hotels which are worth considering, but which, for various reasons – inadequate information, lack of feedback, ambivalent reports – do not at the moment warrant a full entry. We should particularly welcome comments on these hotels.

Hagia Sophia to the six slender minarets of the Blue Mosque?" But be prepared also for the muezzin at 5 am. A reader this year enjoyed the food and comfort, but found the Turkish ambience spoilt by the large numbers of tourists. (*Claire Enders*)

Open All year.
Rooms 1 suite, 19 double – 1 with bath, 18 with shower, all with telephone and radio; suite has TV and Turkish bath. Some ground-floor rooms.
Facilities Salon, coffee shop, bar, restaurant. Garden with restaurant.
Location In Old City, mid-way between Hagia Sophia and the Blue Mosque.
Credit card Access, Amex, Visa.
Terms On application.

KALKAN Antalya — Map 18

Kalkan Han Hotel — *Tel* (3215) 1151
Telex 56524 KLKH

In a fishing-village in a deep bay backed by mountains, on Turkey's south-west coast, a pleasant small hotel with good views. Friendly staff, simple but nicely furnished rooms, buffet breakfasts; terrace for meals. Open 1 May–31 Oct. 16 rooms, all with shower. B&B double US$ 39–49. Set menus US$ 10. Children discouraged. New nomination. More reports please.

KONYA — Map 18

Başak Palas Oteli — *Tel* (331) 111.338
Hükümet Meydani 3

In the centre of an ancient city between Ankara and the Taurus mountains, a clean and characterful hotel with outstanding service (e.g. breakfast with boiled eggs served at 5 am for an early start). No restaurant, but the staff will advise on good ones near by. 2-star. 40 rooms, some with bath. Prices on application. More reports please.

KÖYCEĞIZ Muğla — Map 18

Hotel Özay — *Tel* (6114) 1300 and 1361
Kordon Boyu 11

In a small town on the north side of Köyceğiz lake, just off the Izmir–Antalya main road, a family-run 2-star lakeside hotel on the promenade, with efficient plumbing, clean and airy bedrooms all with balcony and fine views. Attentive service, pleasant pool, food so-so. 22 rooms, all with shower. B&B double US$26–30. Full alc US$10. New nomination. More reports please.

> Detailed information about many Turkish hotels was not available in mid-1989 when we went to press.

> Our feedback on Turkish hotels is patchy. Please help if you can.

KUŞADASI Aydin — Map 18

Hotel Kismet — *Tel* (636) 12005
Akyar Mevkii — *Telex* 58556

This pleasant resort not too far from Ephesus has a fashionable marina; and high on a small peninsula just above it stands the white modern *Kismet*, surrounded by its pleasant palm and pine-shaded gardens. A recent report: "Quiet, relaxing and well run, in an understated way. All the staff were industrious and keen to help you enjoy yourself. Food was reliable and plentiful." Others have relished the sea breezes and the wide views (many rooms have a balcony). "The *Kismet* is far from the tavernas and carpet shops which make the evenings agreeable with colour, and loud with amiable huckstering. Its small paradise of a garden is liberally set with lounging chairs and with a tennis court for the energetic, niched above the Aegean into which you can plunge from a private, rocky 'beach'. The bedrooms are well maintained and offer remarkable value. The dining room is adequate, but we would not recommend full *pension*. However, the breakfast is self-service and there is a full vat of yoghurt on which to start the day. Nicely served afternoon teas remind one of what one is not missing in Britain, so to speak." Some noise from a disco round the bay; and a huge new hotel is being completed nearby. The *Kismet* itself has recently been enlarged. We'd welcome more reports.

Open 15 Mar–31 Oct.
Rooms 2 suites, 90 double, 6 single – 29 with bath, 69 with shower, all with telephone and radio; suites with TV. 10 in garden annexe.
Facilities Lift. Hall, salon, TV room, bars, restaurant. Garden with restaurant and tennis court. Private beach.
Location On peninsula in Kuşadasi bay.
Restriction Not suitable for ♿.
Credit cards Access, Amex, Visa.
Terms B&B: single US$66, double US$88, suite US$154; half board: single US$82.50, double US$121, suite US$187. Set lunch/dinner US$16.50; full alc US$20. Reduced rates for children.

OF Trabzon — Map 18

Hotel-Restaurant Çaykent — *Tel* (0441) 2424 and 1230
Cumhuriyet Cad.

In a town east of Trabzon on the Black Sea coast, at the mouth of a lovely valley with luxuriant vegetation and curious covered footbridges, a modern concrete hotel, no beauty, but clean, comfortable and efficient, with good plumbing and sea views; excellent if expensive restaurant, best for fish. 27 rooms, all with shower. B&B double 30,000 Tl [1989]. New nomination. More reports please.

PAMUKKALE Denizli — Map 18

Tusan Oteli — *Tel* (621) 1010

Set in a weird landscape high above the broad Meander valley, Pamukkale has been called "one of the seven wonders of Turkey", with its hot springs constantly adding to the petrified cascades of gleaming white marble. It is also the site of ancient Hierapolis, whose ruins are scattered over the hillside. Admired again recently, the "clean and well-kept" *Tusan* is the best hotel in the area: it has a helpful management, its own thermal pools on the lip of the escarpment, pleasant if fairly basic rooms in single-storey motel style, and cooking similarly adequate. We'd be glad of more reports.

Open All year.
Rooms 47 – all with bath or shower, and telephone.
Facilities Restaurant. Thermal pools.
Location 14 km N of Denizli.
Terms On application.

ÜRGÜP Nevşehir **Map 18**

Hotel Eyvan *Tel* (4868) 2424
Karagendere Mah. *Telex* 49686 EVYA

The surrealistic scenery of Cappadocia, with its caves and its strange white hills rising out of the plain, is one of the main attractions of southern inland Turkey. This new hotel offers a chance to savour it, with modern comforts too: it is in traditional stone style, literally carved out of a rock cliff near the centre of a town that makes a good base for exploring such cave cities as Göreme. "English-speaking staff offering good service and good breakfasts, plus that rarity in Turkey – hot water. We had dinner in town." More reports please, especially on the food.

Open Apr–Oct.
Rooms 1 suite, 26 double – all with shower and telephone.
Facilities Bar, TV room, restaurant. Swimming pool.
Location 5 mins' walk from centre. Ürgüp is about 50 km W of Kayseri.
Terms On application.

VAN Van **Map 18**

Hotel Akdamar *Tel* (061) 18100
Kâzimkarabekir Cad. 56 *Telex* 73164 ATOY

In the far east of Turkey, on the main street of a town near the shores of the beautiful mountain-girt Lake Van, "a last outpost of civilization between Trabzon on the Black Sea and Diyarbakir in the south". An outwardly characterless three-star hotel with somewhat cheerless 'East European' ambience and decor, but clean and quite comfortable, with plumbing that works. Good Turkish cooking, helpful staff. Back rooms are quietest. 75 rooms, all with bath. Single 25,000 Tl, double 36,900 Tl. New nomination. More reports please.

Yugoslavia

GRAND HOTEL TOPLICE, BLED

BLED 64260 **Map 17**

Grand Hotel Toplice *Tel* (064) 77.222
Telex 34588 TOPLIC

Set beside Yugoslavia's loveliest lake, in its smartest inland resort, this traditional 'grand hotel' was built soon after 1918 but has now been brought up to date, and is well run by a charming and efficient management who speak good English. Lots of praise this year and last: "We had a beautiful room facing the lake. The breakfasts were huge and sumptuous and the service exemplary." "Old-fashioned rooms with curtained sleeping alcoves. Food excellent for Yugoslavia, service friendly. The classic 'grand hotel' atmosphere is barely affected by the large number of English group tours." "Our quiet room on the third floor had excellent beds, comfortable furniture upholstered in gold velvet (with curtains to match) and a terrace with a splendid view. The chef creates magnificent things à la carte (e.g. roast sucking pig, rašniči, good soups). We admired the way the staff coped with the Great British Public, always smiling and anxious to please even though the Brits never said thank you, never gave any praise." Back rooms mostly lack views and can be small. (*S and E Holman, H and B Shames*) The covered colonnaded swimming pool has its own thermal spring.

Open All year.
Rooms 10 suites, 121 double or single – all with bath, telephone and balcony. Also 194 beds in 3 annexes.
Facilities Lift. Salon, reading room, TV room, bar, restaurant; conference facilities, reading room. Indoor swimming pool, sauna, solarium, fitness room. Lakeside terrace and bathing beach; boats, fishing available.
Location Central. Bled is 55 km NW of Ljubljana.
Credit cards Access, Amex, Diners.
Terms [1989 rates] B&B: single 68–115 DM, double 115–250 DM, suite 250–380 DM. Half board 20 DM per person added, full board 40 DM added. Reduced rates for children sharing parents' room.

Hotel Vila Bled — *Tel* (064) 77.436
Cesta Svobode 26 — *Telex* 34515 VILABL

This white palace above Lake Bled, Yugoslavia's most sumptuous hotel, was remodelled by President Tito after World War II and was used as his official summer residence: here he entertained Eden, Nehru, Brandt, and many other world leaders. The government in 1984 turned it into a luxury hotel, which stands in its own 13-acre park, overlooking Yugoslavia's leading inland resort: views of the lake and the Alps are spectacular. Prices for so much pampered splendour are amazingly low by Western standards, but quality is not skimped, as a recent visitor discovered: "A wonderful display of flowers just inside the big gates. Our taxi deposited us on to the red carpet (yes, a real red carpet), where the commissionaire greeted us warmly. The receptionist rushes to meet you, then you are handed over lovingly to under-manager, then to cocktail-lounge waiter. There's an awful lot of marble, white and black, and lots of chandeliers – all very thirties. A pianist tinkles. The dining room has wonderful white linen, good modern prints, good silver and candles – everything glistens. Large menu, too large (most of it must be frozen): but dinner was good (wonderful veal escalope and banana soufflé, good salad, which is unusual in Yugoslavia, but bad coffee, as it imports inferior stuff). The bedrooms are well modernised, with bathrooms of gleaming white marble. Flower arrangements dreadful. The rooms don't really have a lake view, I suppose for security reasons. On the top floor is a small concert hall, which Tito used for receptions." This year, three other readers were equally impressed by the gardens, the views and the general splendour; two thought that the food and service fully lived up to the setting ("refined taste. . .courteous and efficient staff. . .best dinner we had in Yugoslavia. . .food excellently presented"), but a third judged the food poor and the service "virtually non-existent". A fourth, visiting out of season, saw no red carpet, no rushing receptionist, no flowers; service was haphazard, the rooms with the lake view were closed for the winter and her husband's mattress had "little plastic needle-shaped things sticking out so that he had to wrap a towel round himself to try to sleep". (*Aileen Stone, Joe van der Sneppen*)

Open All year.
Rooms 21 suites, 10 double – all with bath and/or shower, telephone and radio; 21 with TV.

Facilities 3 lifts. Lounge, TV lounge, bar with piano music, 2 breakfast rooms, restaurant; concert hall, conference facilities; terrace. Garden with tennis, private beach on lake with café in summer, rowing boats. Golf, riding, hunting, fishing, gliding nearby.
Location 1 mile along the lake from Bled, towards Bohinj.
Restriction Not suitable for ♿.
Credit cards All major cards accepted.
Terms B&B: single US$71–US$91, double US$92–US$122. Dinner, B&B US$66–US$151 per person; full board US$86–US$171. Set lunch/dinner US$20; full alc US$35. Special meals for children on request.

DUBROVNIK 50000 — Map 17

Villa Dubrovnik

Tel (050) 22.933
Telex 27503

This is the smallest of the three smart hotels on the south side of Dubrovnik, and the one that readers continue to prefer ("I've seen only happy faces", says one this year). It is a modern building, terraced into a cliff, with lovely views of the old walled town and harbour, and the island of Lokrum opposite. Pine trees, flowers and blue awnings give a Riviera flavour. The bar and dining room both have superb views, and you can eat outdoors in fine weather. Most bedrooms face the front with a small balcony, and are well furnished; it's worth paying extra for a sea-facing room. The hotel has its own concrete "beach" with rock bathing in unpolluted water. A report this year: "A beautifully run hotel, with neat, clean rooms: ours had a lovely view from its private balcony. The food was ordinary, but the staff are exceptionally courteous and helpful." Others agree that the food is only average – but very cheap. "Our room was beautifully quiet save for the lapping of the waves below." A few minor gripes, such as bed-lights too dim, furnishings not perfect. There is no nightlife on the spot, but you can wander down to the city in about 20 minutes or take the hotel's own motor-boat, and it is easy to get a taxi back. A hotel not recommended for the elderly or infirm, as there are 66 steep steps up from the hotel to the road above. (*H and B Shames, Joe van der Sneppen*)

Open All year.
Rooms 54 – most with bath or shower, all with telephone; many with sea-facing balcony.
Facilities Lifts. Lounge, bar, restaurant. Sub-tropical gardens;
Location On S side of Dubrovnik. Garage parking.
Restriction Not suitable for ♿.
Credit card Amex.
Terms [1989 rates] Rooms: single US$32–US$100, double US$44–US$131.

HVAR 58450 — Map 17

Palace Hotel

Tel (058) 74.966
Telex 26235 HVAR

About an hour by hydrofoil from Split, this charming little port on Hvar island has a gentle winter climate, and is backed by pines, olives and vines. You can visit the remains of a Greek colony and a neolithic cave. Devotees this year have again enjoyed the *Palace*, a classic white-fronted hotel, centrally located just above the busy quay: "Another lovely holiday at a lovely hotel, Hvar's best. Rooms were clean, the food excellent, and service efficient and courteous, while the weekly cocktail party was enjoyed by everyone. Entertainment was provided several evenings." Front rooms are more attractive and have a view; back ones are duller but quieter. Best avoid high summer and its package tours. (*Noreen Redfern*)

Open All year.
Rooms 76 double – all with bath and shower, and telephone; some with TV.
Facilities Lifts. Lounge, salon, TV room, bar, restaurant; indoor swimming pool. Sun terrace overlooking harbour with music and dancing every night during summer.
Location Central.
Credit cards Access, Diners, Visa.
Terms [1989 rates] Rooms: single 35–72 DM, double 57–120 DM, Half board 36–90 DM per person.

LOVRAN 51415 — Map 17

Hotel Beograd — *Tel* (051) 731.022

A large *fin-de-siècle* hotel "with a calm 1920s flavour", in a quiet Slovene seaside resort just west of Opatija. "The rooms with bath and balcony are clean and spacious", says its nominator, "and some have superb views of the bay. Helpful staff. The large restaurant resembled a typical package-tour eatery and we did not try it: but we ate very well at the small *Hotel Belvedere* next door". (*Tony and Kathy Gillett*) Endorsed this year: "It was built in about 1900 for the Austrian aristocracy and still has a strong Hapsburg flavour (the Grand Duchess Stephanie did a lot along this coast). Friends who went recently said it was 'like staying in Buckingham Palace'. Our rooms were furnished in rich Venetian style, with beautiful woods all upholstered in gold velvet. Set in a pleasant garden facing the sea, the hotel has discreet creeper-covered booths where you can sit in the evenings listening. On our visit a three-piece Viennese-type orchestra played Strauss. There's no beach, but to swim you go down an iron ladder into a roped-off bit of sea, full of fish and very clear. The food was as good as any we have eaten in Yugoslavia, with the names of various Austrian royals used for puddings. The day we left, the other packagers had to vacate their rooms by noon, but our chambermaid let us remain until we had to leave for the airport at five. Could it have been because of my Christian name?" (*Stephanie Sowerby*)

Open 1 May–31 Oct.
Rooms 102 – all with bath and/or shower; many with balcony. Ground-floor rooms.
Facilities Lounge, restaurant; terrace. Garden with tables and chairs. Sea bathing.
Location Lovran is 16 km W of Rijeka. Parking.
Credit cards None accepted.
Terms [1989 rates] Dinner, B&B: single 41–74 DM, double 31–64 DM per person. Reduced rates for children sharing parents' room.

> In all continental European and Scandinavian countries except Denmark, France, Hungary, Malta, Spain and Turkey, the dialling codes begin with a 0. Omit this when dialling from outside the country in question. Spanish codes begin with a 9, which should also be omitted.

PLITVIČKA JEZERA 48231 Map 17

Hotel Jezero

Tel (048) 76.526
Fax (048) 76.310
Telex 23817 PLITVICE

The Plitvice National Park, in the wooded hills of western Croatia, is a place of "serene beauty", and its focal point is this huge and unusual holiday complex, again enjoyed this year for its pleasant staff, good food, comfort, and "wonderful ambience". An earlier account set the scene: "Sixteen lakes, linked by streams and waterfalls, are surrounded by lovely maple trees, firs and beeches which range in colour from blazing autumn crimson to a breathtaking variety of greens. A well-contrived system of paths, often built on stilts, makes walking easy. The forest is so tranquil that even chamois, deer and bear live at ease with the visitors. A few boats commute to hamlets on the largest lake: there is no machinery and no pollution.

Here the *Jezero* is a huge well-planned wooden chalet-type hotel, and no one looking at it would guess that it held 247 bedrooms, a big lounge with snug bar area, an attractive restaurant, and indoor swimming pool, ladies' hairdresser and souvenir shop. Plus a nightbar with dancing during the high season, and facilities for many sports. The hotel is mainly concealed by the forest, but there are glimpses of lakes from some bedrooms. On one day every year many young couples, usually wearing national dress, come to the hotel in preparation for their wedding, which is celebrated beside the highest of the many waterfalls. Staff are efficient; food is good, with lake trout among the specialities. Prices are moderate and cleanliness ideal." "Rooms are clean, quiet and spartan." (*H and B Shames*)

Open All year except 1 Feb–9 Mar.
Rooms 7 suites, 240 double or triple – all with bath and shower, telephone and radio; many with balcony. Some ground-floor rooms.
Facilities Large lounge with bar (dancing in high season), 2 bars, 3 restaurants; cinema and conference hall; heated indoor swimming pool, sauna, ladies' hairdresser. Adjoins sports and recreation centre with automatic 4-lane bowling alley. Near lake with safe bathing.
Location In National Park, 140 km SW of Zagreb.
Credit cards Access, Diners, Visa.
Terms [1989 rates] Rooms: single 36–86 DM, double 50–128 DM. Half board 30–103 DM per person, full board 35–111 DM.

SVETI STEFAN 85315 Map 16

Hotel Miločer
Hotel Maestral
Vila Miločer

Tel (all hotels) (086) 41.333
and 41.411
Telex 61188 SV STF

This is not one hotel but four, all state-run and close together on the lovely Montenegrin coast just south of the old walled city of Budva. The *Miločer* was built as a summer palace by Alexander I for his wife, and still retains an air of opulence. It is much smaller than the other hotels in the complex. The central block has a handsome vine-shaded terrace where meals are served. Most of the rooms are in annexes set discreetly in the grounds. Readers enjoy the *Miločer* for its privacy, its big gardens, and its fine, if pebbly, beach. One recent verdict: "Food good by Yugoslav standards. Breakfast under the vines, with toast, toast and more toast, and anything cooked that you want. Bedroom like a suite, with damask linen, fresh flowers, a fireplace." However, some have thought the main lounge unattractive and institutional in appearance, the food mediocre, and the service at meals rather sluggish. The second hotel, on the coast near the *Miločer*, is the *Maestral*, considerably larger and with a lot of group clients. A devotee this year enjoyed it as much as ever and confirms her earlier praise: "From the outside it is hideous, but inside it is beautifully furnished, with good-sized bedrooms, all now with TV and mini-bar, excellent reception rooms and restaurant, cool marble floors. It has a good private beach with a water-skiing school and a superb swimming pool. The food is a lot better than at the other hotels and the service much superior too." (*Stephanie Sowerby*) More recently opened is the *Vila Miločer*, between the *Miločer* and the *Maestral*, with its own beach. The fourth and much the most expensive hotel in the complex, *Sveti Stefan*, is on a small island joined to the mainland by a causeway. It has been liked in the past, but food and service have again been sharply criticised this year, and we are dropping it from the Guide ("It's fit only for oil kings and ageing film stars", says a reader this year). Even with the other three recommended hotels, there have been murmurs of discontent about food and service, and about dishonoured bookings, indicating that the centralised state management may be in need of some *perestroika*. So, please, send us more reports.

Hotel Miločer
Open May–end Oct.
Rooms 27 – most with bath or shower. Also cottages in grounds.
Facilities Bar, large terrace for meals. Large secluded wooded grounds and gardens; private beach; tennis.
Terms [1989 rates] Rooms: single 110–157 DM, double 120–220 DM.

Hotel Maestral
Open May–end Oct.
Rooms 156 – all with bath or shower, telephone, TV and mini-bar, most with terrace.
Facilities Lift. Bar, café, restaurant; indoor swimming pool, sauna. Grounds with swimming pool, tennis, private beach.
Terms [1989 rates] Rooms: single 75–149 DM, double 92–264 DM. Half board: single 85–149 DM, double 112–304 DM.

Vila Miločer
Open May–end Oct.
Rooms 4 villas, 55 double rooms – most with bath or shower and telephone.
Facilities Café, restaurant. Indoor swimming pool, sauna. Private beach.
Terms [1989 rates] Rooms: single 70–143 DM, double 86–350 DM.

Alphabetical list of hotels

England

Wales

Scotland

Channel Isles

Northern Ireland

Republic of Ireland

Austria

Belgium

Denmark

France

Germany

Greece

Italy

Luxembourg

Malta

Morocco

Netherlands

Norway

Portugal

Spain

Sweden

Switzerland

Turkey

Yugoslavia

Maps

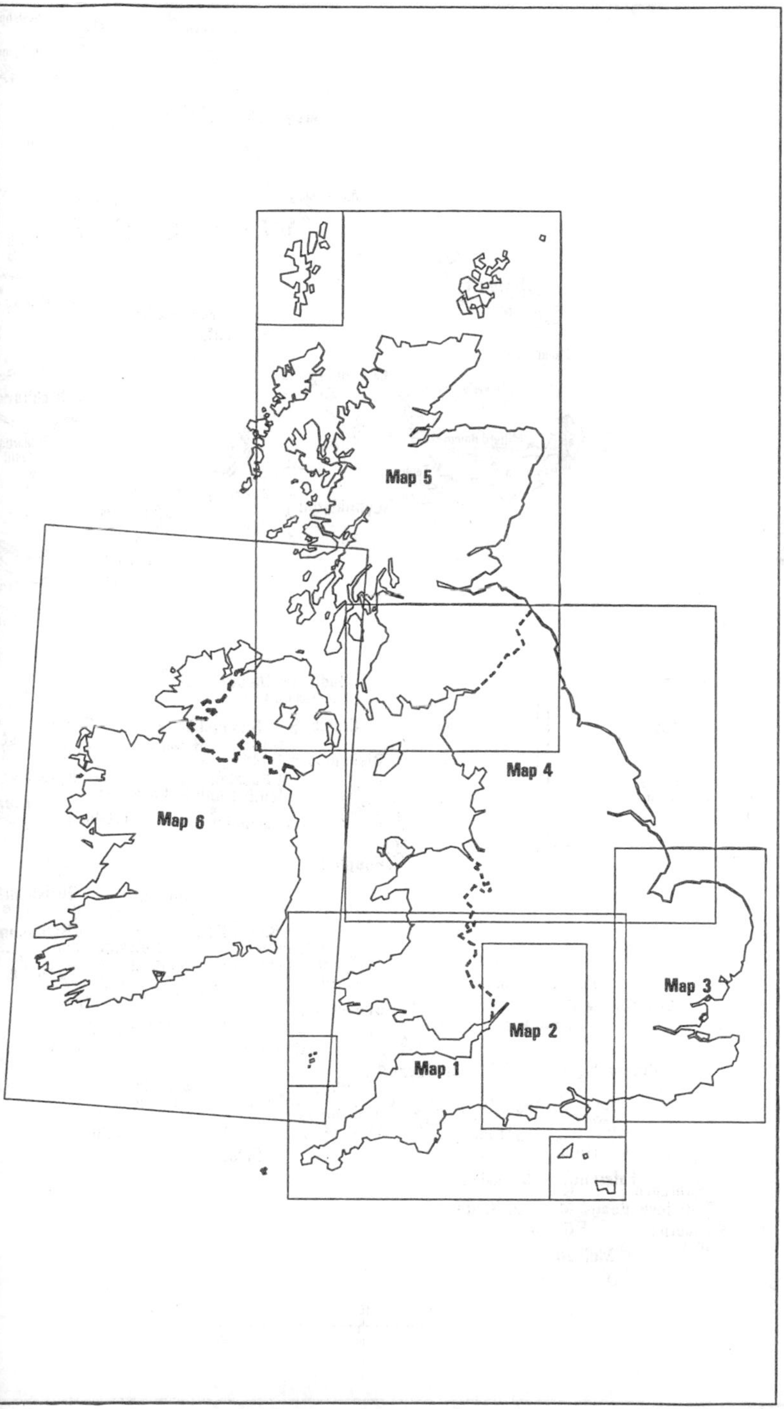
Map 5
Map 4
Map 6
Map 3
Map 2
Map 1

Map 1 South–West England and South Wales

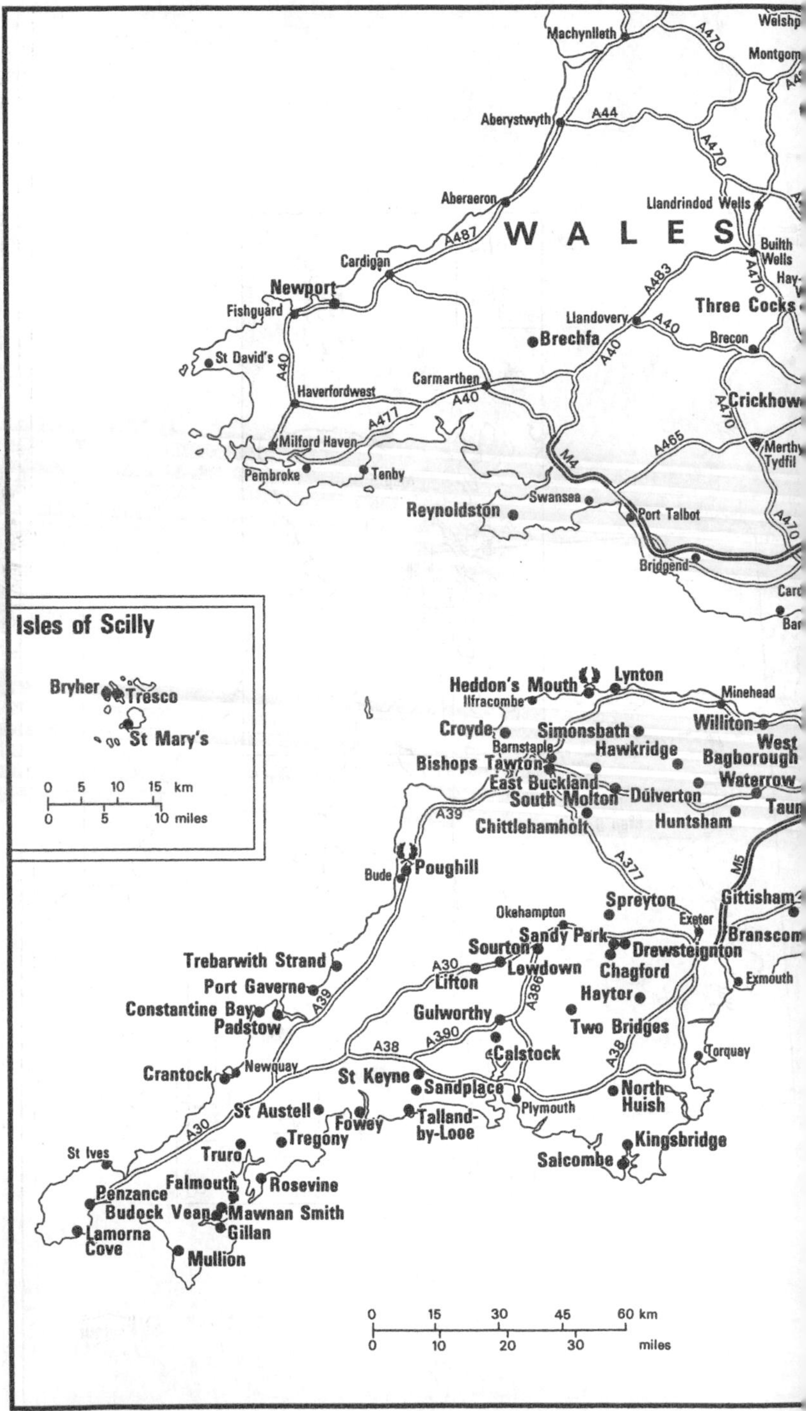

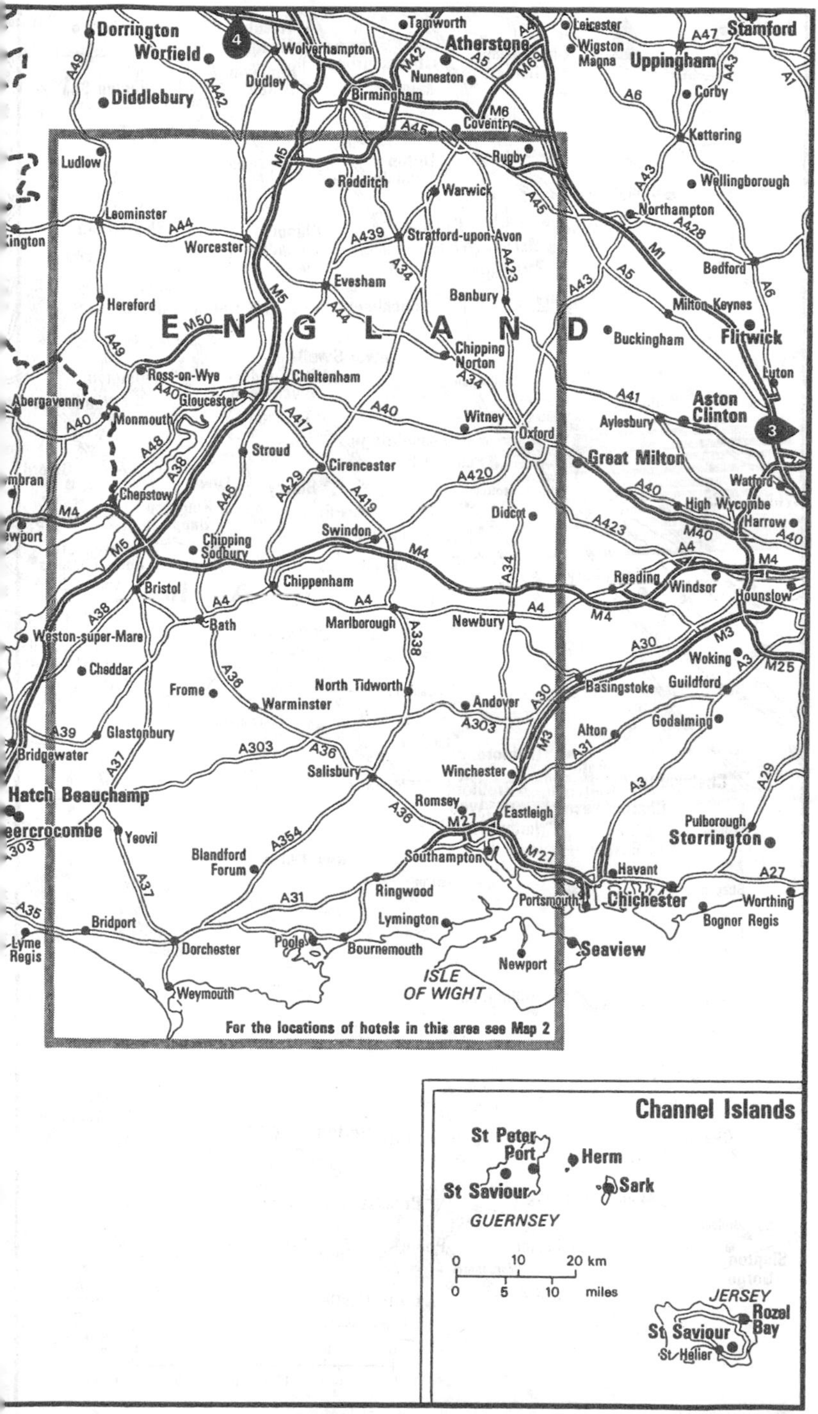
ENGLAND
Dorrington
Worfield
Diddlebury
Wolverhampton
Dudley
Tamworth
Atherstone
Nuneaton
Birmingham
Coventry
Leicester
Wigston Magna
Stamford
Uppingham
Corby
Kettering
Wellingborough
Northampton
Bedford
Milton Keynes
Flitwick
Buckingham
Luton
Aston Clinton
Aylesbury
Great Milton
Watford
High Wycombe
Harrow
Hounslow
Windsor
Reading
Woking
Guildford
Godalming
Basingstoke
Alton
Pulborough
Storrington
Havant
Chichester
Worthing
Bognor Regis
Seaview
Portsmouth
Ludlow
Leominster
Kington
Worcester
Redditch
Warwick
Rugby
Stratford-upon-Avon
Evesham
Banbury
Hereford
Ross-on-Wye
Chipping Norton
Cheltenham
Gloucester
Abergavenny
Monmouth
Witney
Oxford
Stroud
Cirencester
Chepstow
Didcot
Swindon
Chipping Sodbury
Newport
Chippenham
Bristol
Bath
Marlborough
Newbury
Weston-super-Mare
Cheddar
Frome
Warminster
North Tidworth
Andover
Glastonbury
Bridgewater
Salisbury
Winchester
Hatch Beauchamp
Beercrocombe
Yeovil
Romsey
Eastleigh
Southampton
Blandford Forum
Ringwood
Lymington
Bridport
Dorchester
Poole
Bournemouth
Newport
Lyme Regis
Weymouth
ISLE OF WIGHT
M5
M50
M4
M42
M6
M69
M1
M40
M25
M3
M27
A49
A442
A44
A45
A43
A428
A5
A6
A47
A1
A439
A34
A423
A41
A40
A417
A429
A419
A420
A48
A38
A46
A4
A338
A36
A303
A30
A31
A3
A29
A27
A39
A37
A354
A35
3
4
For the locations of hotels in this area see Map 2
Channel Islands
St Peter Port
St Saviour
Herm
Sark
GUERNSEY
0 10 20 km
0 5 10 miles
JERSEY
Rozel Bay
St Saviour
St Helier

Map 2 Wessex and the Cotswolds

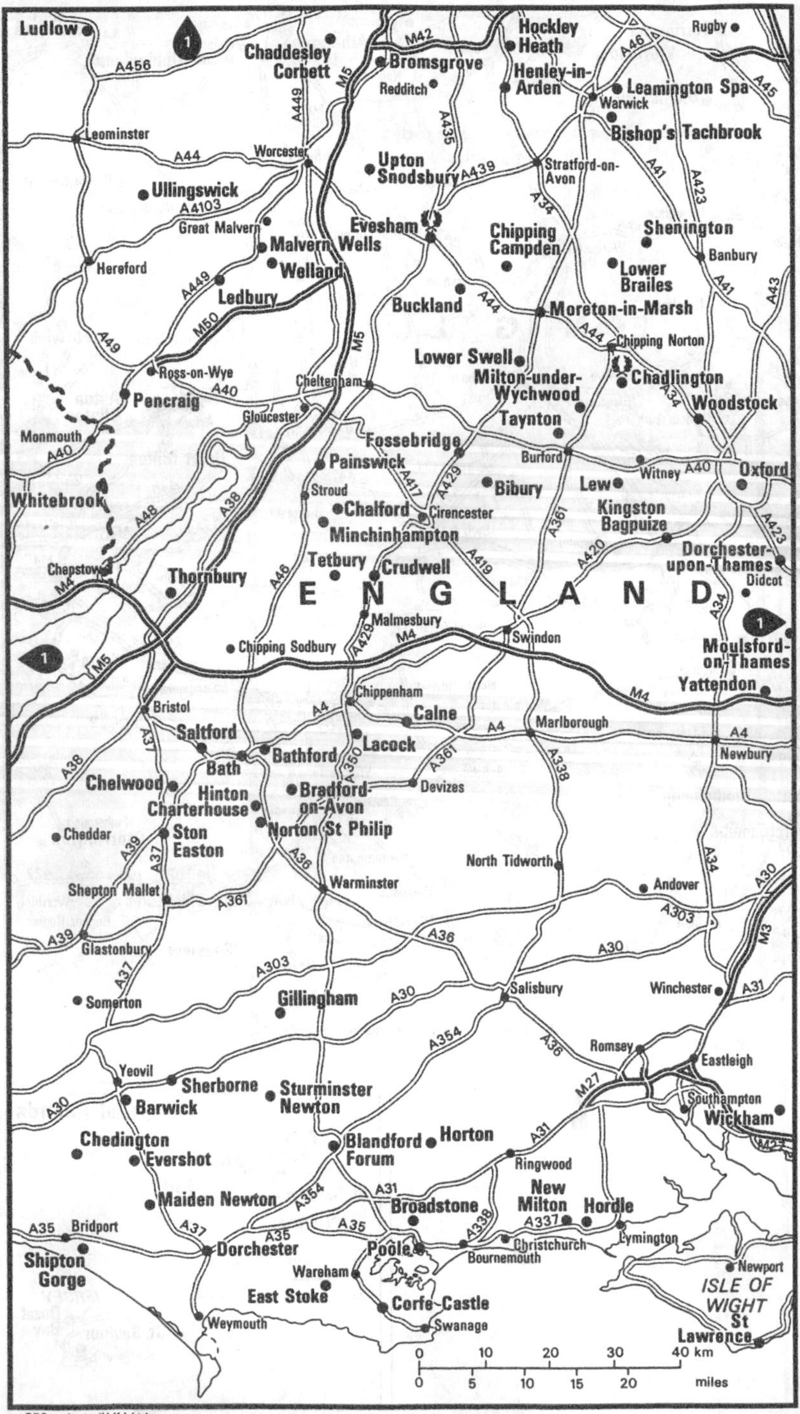

Map 3 South–East England

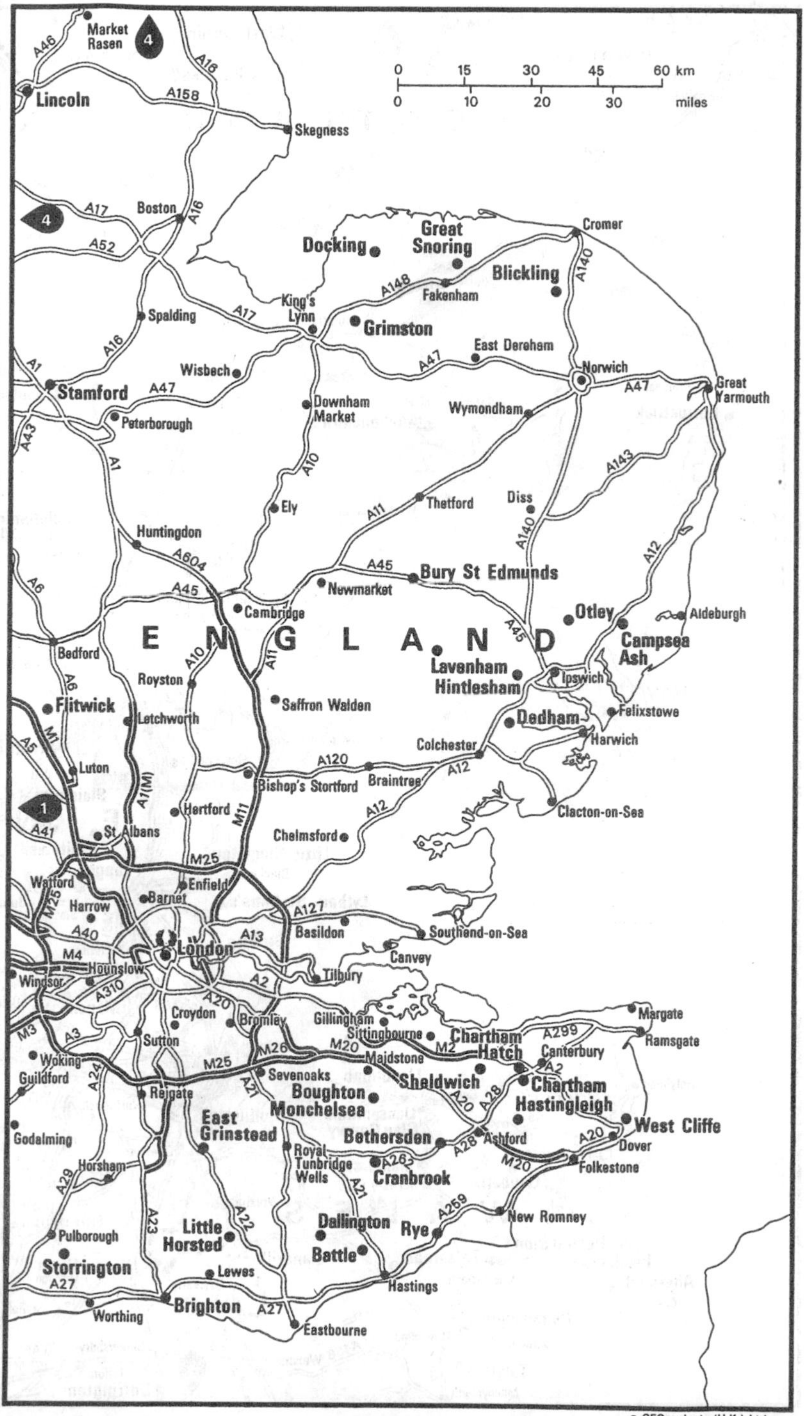

Map 4 North Wales, the Midlands and the North of England

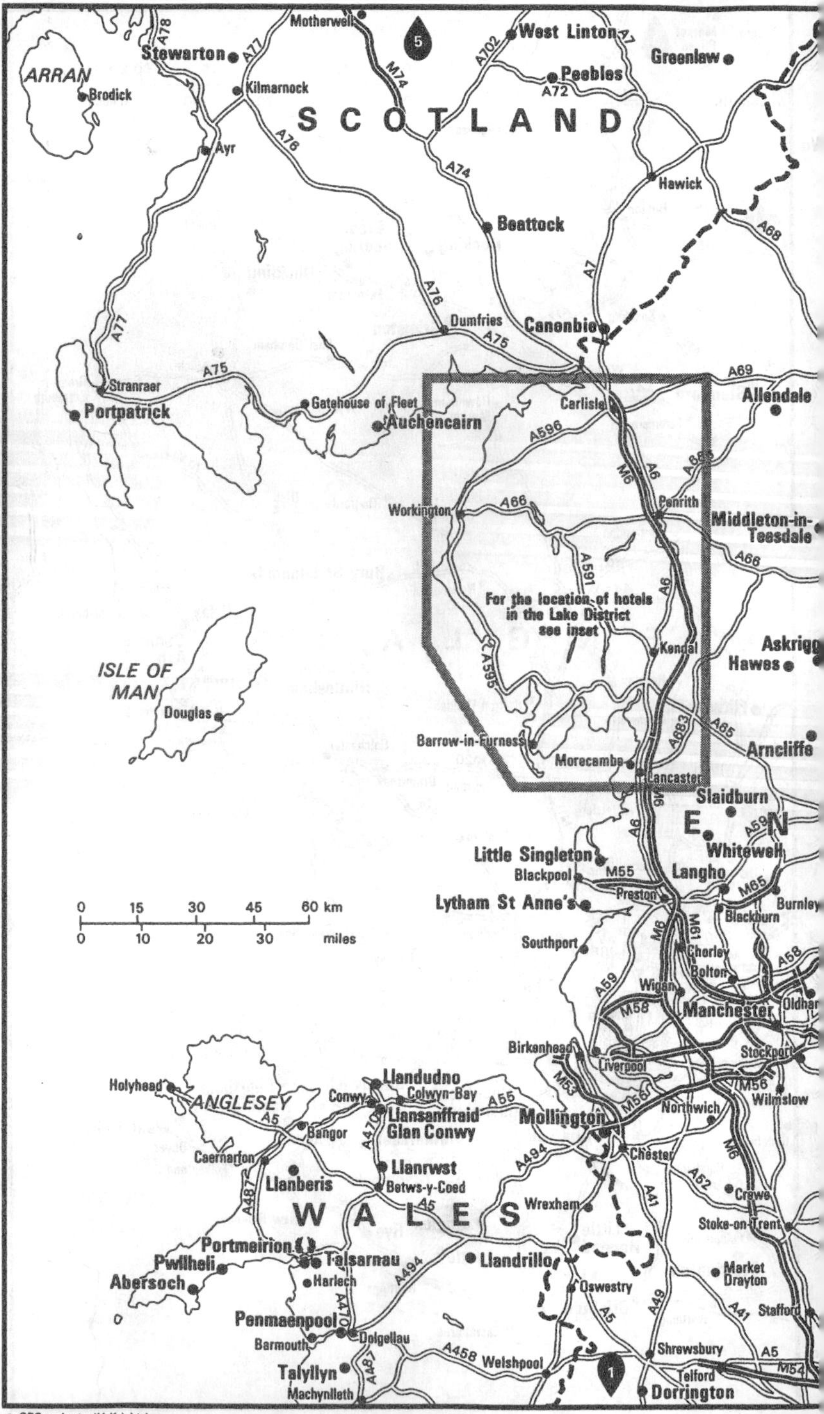

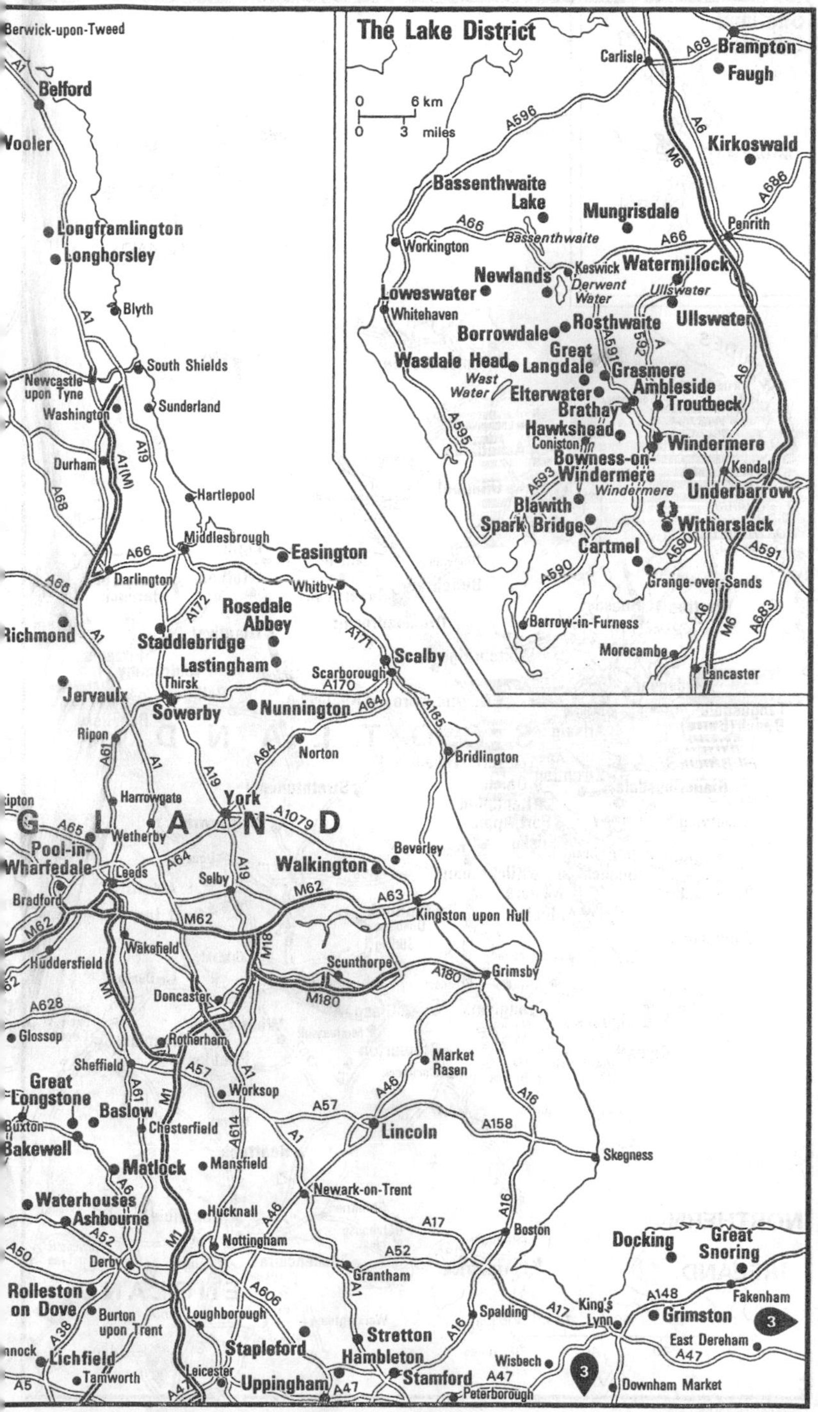
The Lake District
0 6 km
0 3 miles
Carlisle
A69
Brampton
Faugh
A596
A6
M6
Kirkoswald
A686
Bassenthwaite
Lake
Mungrisdale
Penrith
A66
Bassenthwaite
A66
Workington
Newlands
Keswick
Watermillock
Derwent
Water
Ullswater
Loweswater
Whitehaven
Rosthwaite
Ullswater
Borrowdale
A591
A592
Great
Langdale
Wasdale Head
Grasmere
West
Water
Ambleside
Elterwater
Troutbeck
Brathay
Hawkshead
Coniston
Windermere
A595
Bowness-on-
Windermere
Kendal
A593
Windermere
Underbarrow
Blawith
Spark Bridge
Witherslack
Cartmel
A590
A591
A590
Grange-over-Sands
Barrow-in-Furness
A6
M6
A683
Morecambe
Lancaster
Berwick-upon-Tweed
A1
Belford
Wooler
Longframlington
Longhorsley
Blyth
A1
South Shields
Newcastle
upon Tyne
Washington
Sunderland
A19
Durham
A1(M)
A68
Hartlepool
Middlesbrough
A66
Easington
Darlington
A66
Whitby
A172
Rosedale
Abbey
Richmond
A1
Staddlebridge
A171
Scalby
Lastingham
Scarborough
Thirsk
A170
Jervaulx
Sowerby
Nunnington
A64
A165
Ripon
A64
Norton
Bridlington
A61
A1
A19
Harrowgate
York
ENGLAND
A1079
Skipton
A65
Wetherby
Pool-in-
Wharfedale
A64
Leeds
Beverley
Walkington
Bradford
Selby
A19
M62
A63
M62
Kingston upon Hull
M62
M18
Wakefield
Huddersfield
Scunthorpe
A180
Grimsby
M1
Doncaster
M180
A628
Glossop
Rotherham
Market
Rasen
Sheffield
A57
A1
A61
M1
Great
Longstone
Worksop
A46
A16
Baslow
A57
Buxton
Chesterfield
A614
Lincoln
A158
Bakewell
A1
Matlock
Mansfield
Skegness
A6
Newark-on-Trent
Waterhouses
Ashbourne
Hucknall
A46
A16
A17
A52
Boston
M1
Nottingham
Docking
Great
Snoring
A50
A52
Derby
Grantham
A606
A1
Rolleston
on Dove
Fakenham
A148
A17
King's
Lynn
Burton
upon Trent
Loughborough
A16
Spalding
Grimston
3
A38
Stretton
East Dereham
Stapleford
A47
Lichfield
Hambleton
Tamworth
Wisbech
A5
Leicester
A47
Stamford
A47
3
Uppingham
A47
Downham Market
Peterborough

Map 5 Scotland

Map 6 Ireland

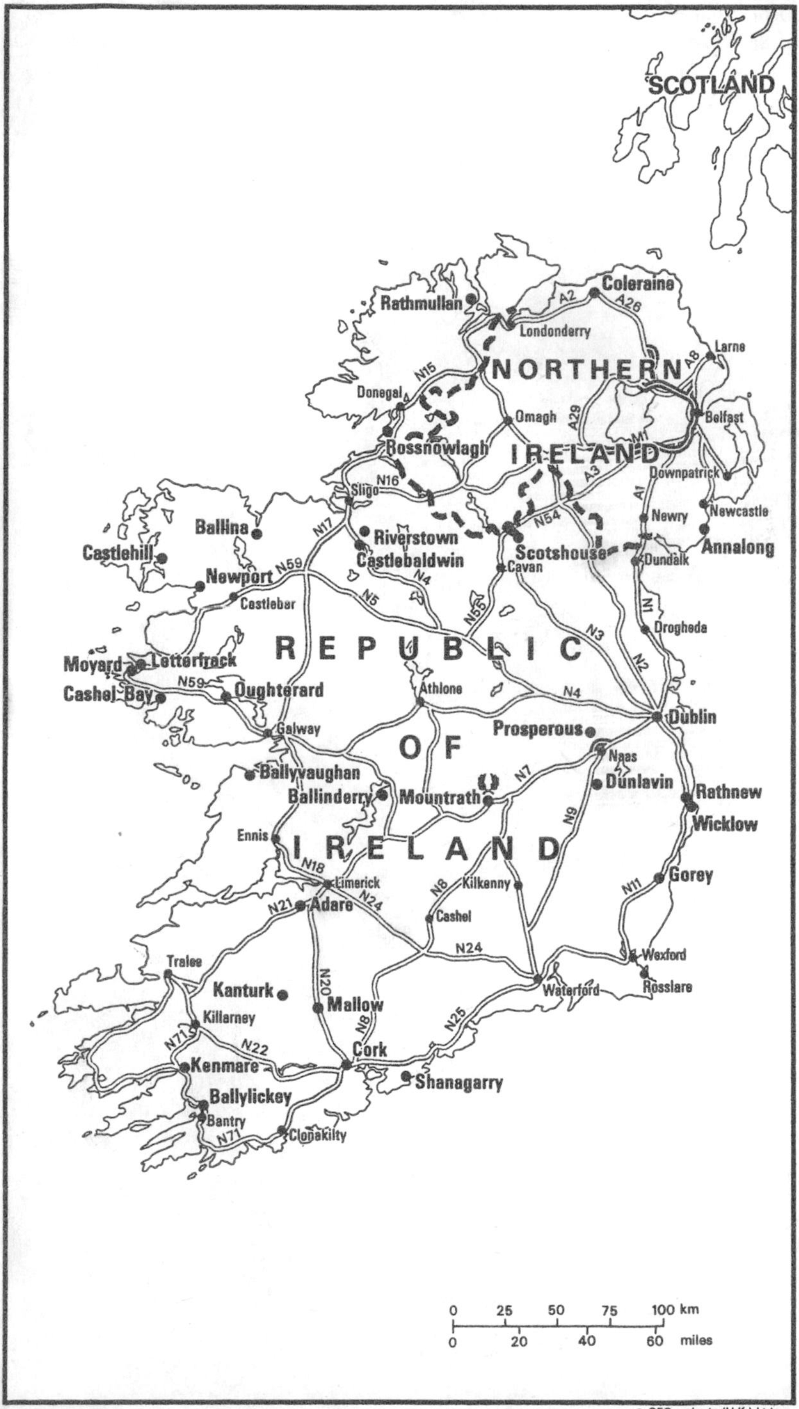

Europe Maps

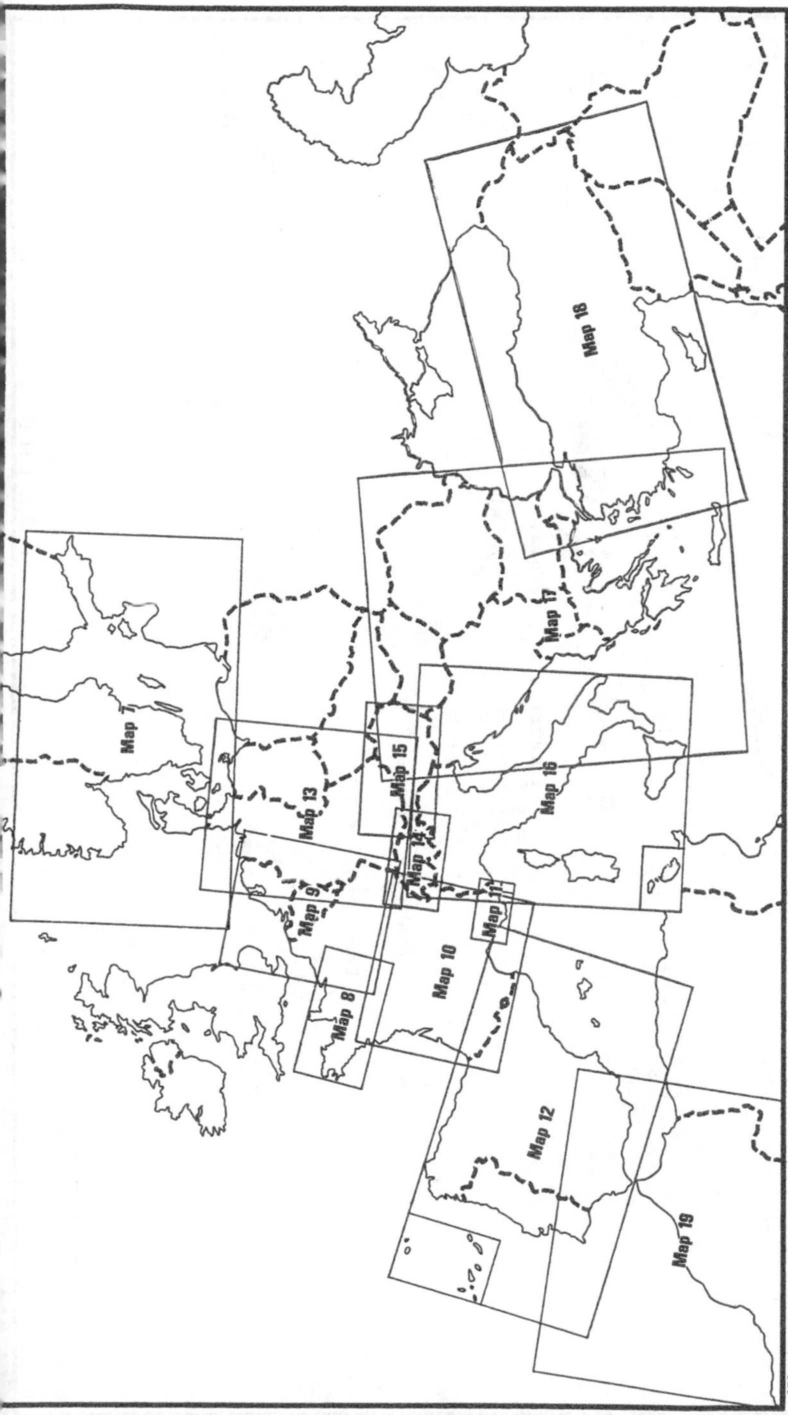
Map 7
Map 8
Map 9
Map 10
Map 11
Map 12
Map 13
Map 14
Map 15
Map 16
Map 17
Map 18
Map 19

Map 7 Southern Scandinavia

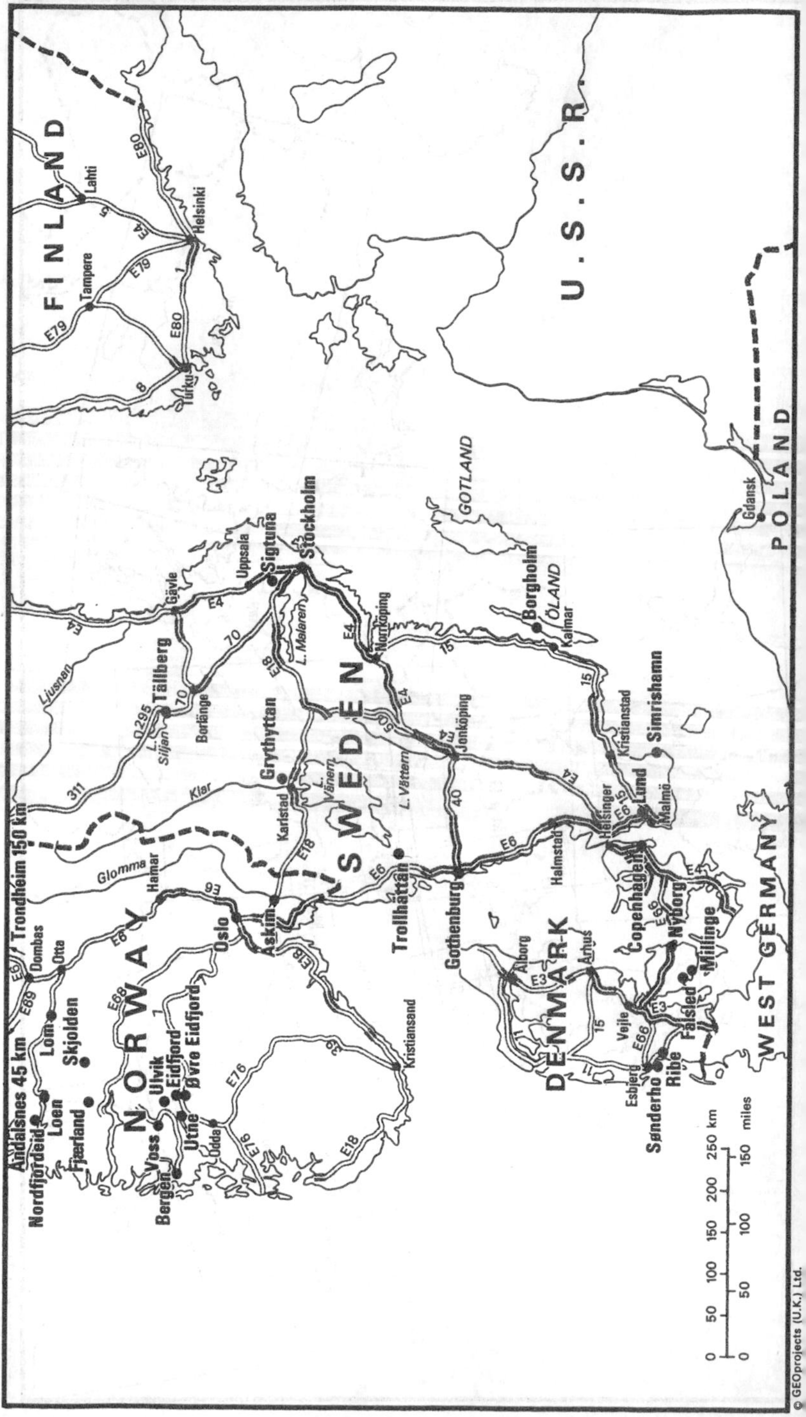

Map 8 North-West France

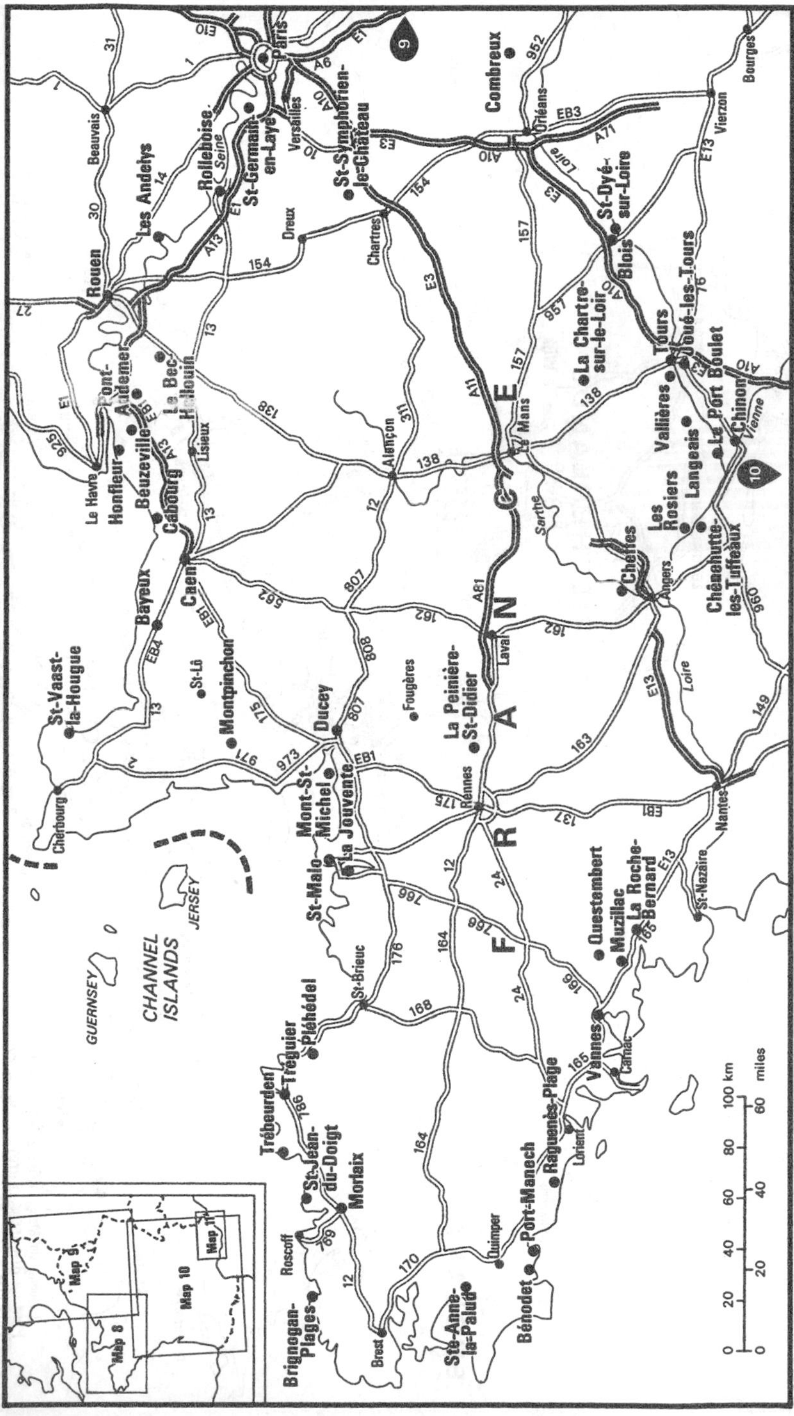

Map 9 Benelux and North-East France

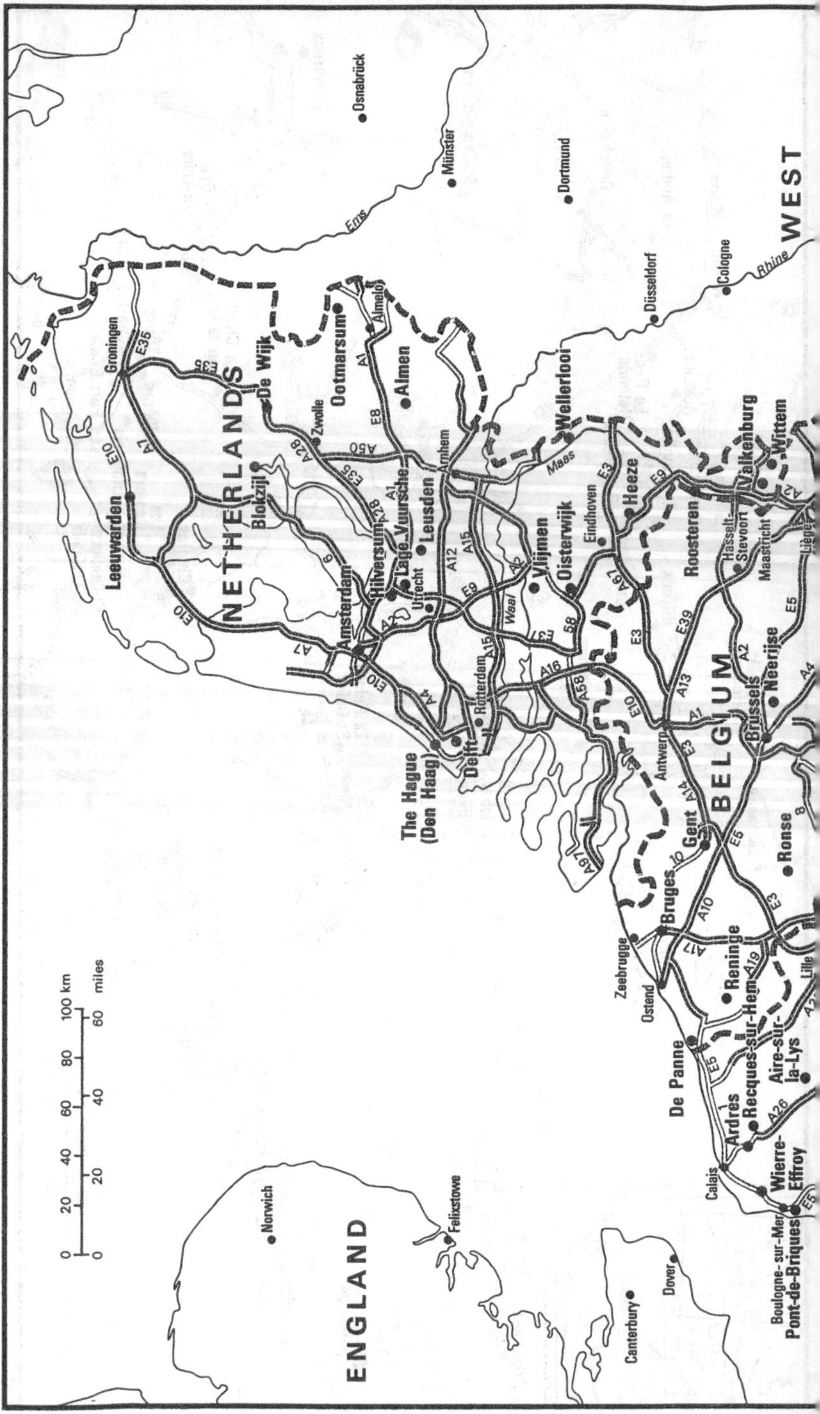

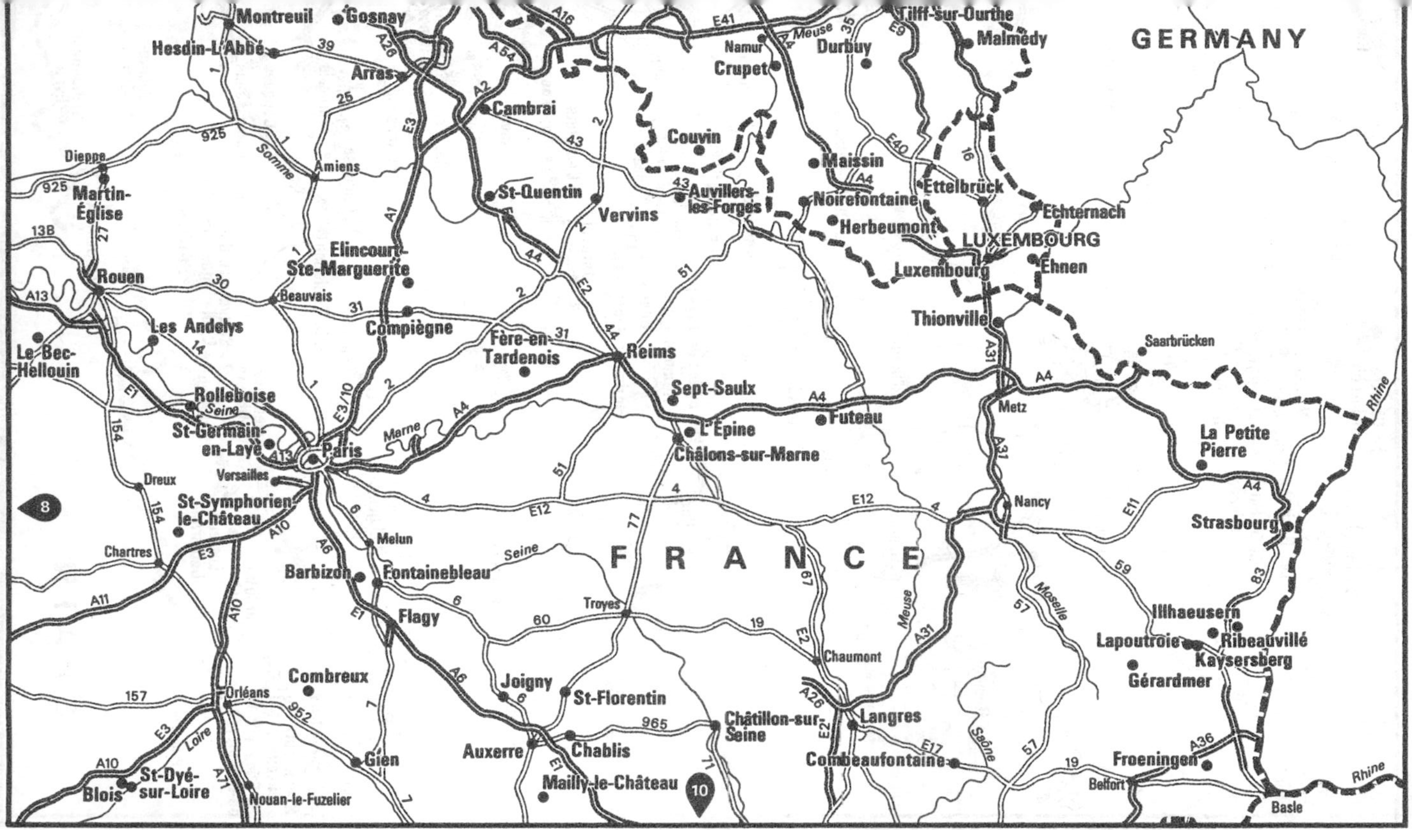
GERMANY
FRANCE
LUXEMBOURG
Montreuil
Gosnay
Hesdin-L'Abbé
Arras
Cambrai
Dieppe
Martin-Église
Amiens
Somme
St-Quentin
Vervins
Couvin
Auvillers-les-Forges
Crupet
Namur
Meuse
Durbuy
Maissin
Noirefontaine
Herbeumont
Ettelbrück
Echternach
Malmédy
Tilff-sur-Ourthe
Ehnen
Luxembourg
Thionville
Saarbrücken
Metz
Nancy
La Petite Pierre
Strasbourg
Rhine
Rouen
Le-Bec-Hellouin
Les Andelys
Elincourt-Ste-Marguerite
Beauvais
Compiègne
Fère-en-Tardenois
Reims
Sept-Saulx
L'Épine
Châlons-sur-Marne
Futeau
Rolleboise
Seine
St-Germain-en-Laye
Paris
Marne
Versailles
Dreux
St-Symphorien-le-Château
Chartres
Melun
Barbizon
Fontainebleau
Flagy
Troyes
Chaumont
Langres
Moselle
Illhaeusern
Ribeauvillé
Lapoutroie
Kaysersberg
Gérardmer
Combreux
Orléans
Joigny
St-Florentin
Châtillon-sur-Seine
Combeaufontaine
Saône
Froeningen
Belfort
Basle
Loire
Blois
St-Dyé-sur-Loire
Nouan-le-Fuzelier
Gien
Auxerre
Chablis
Mailly-le-Château
8
10

Map 10 Central and Southern France

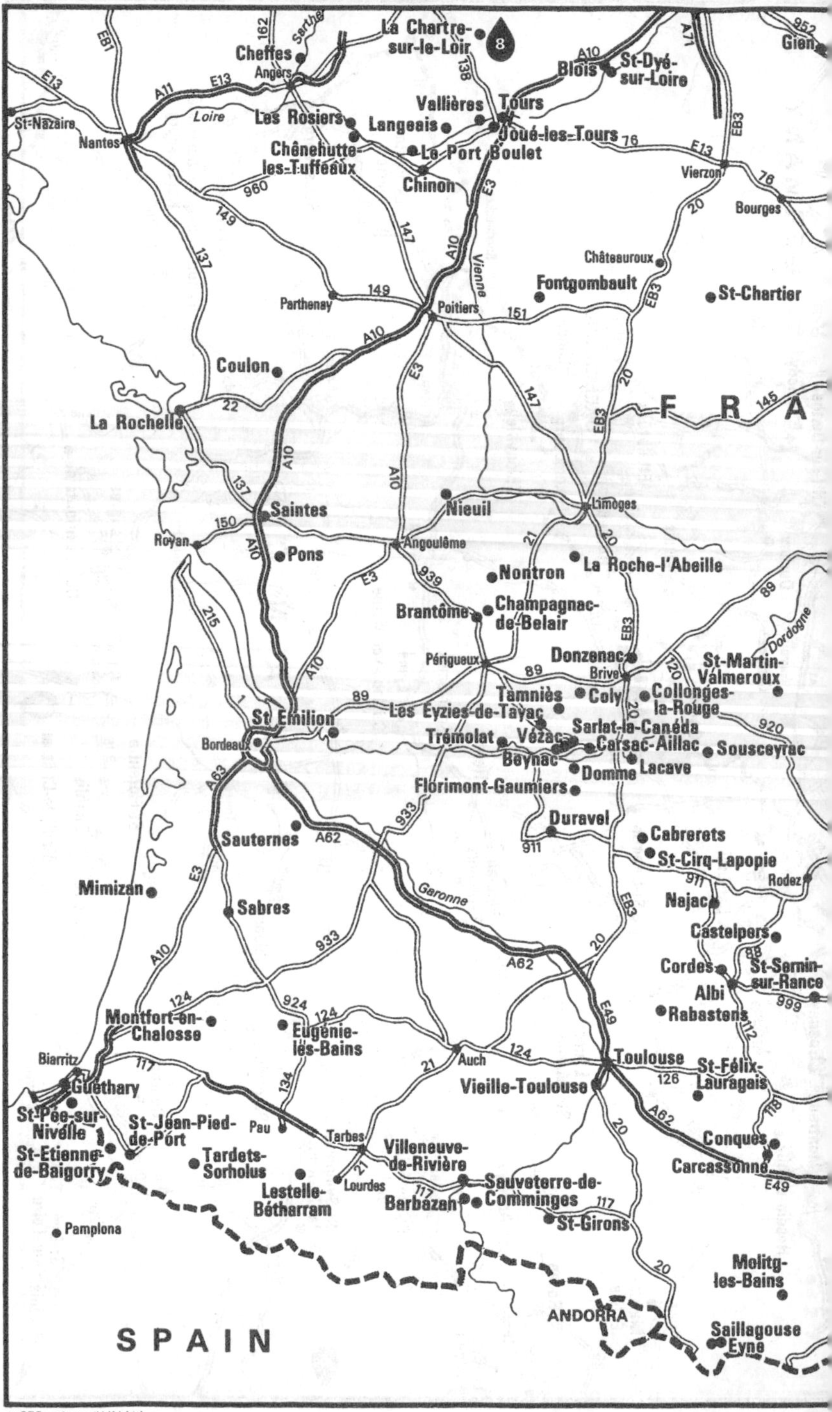

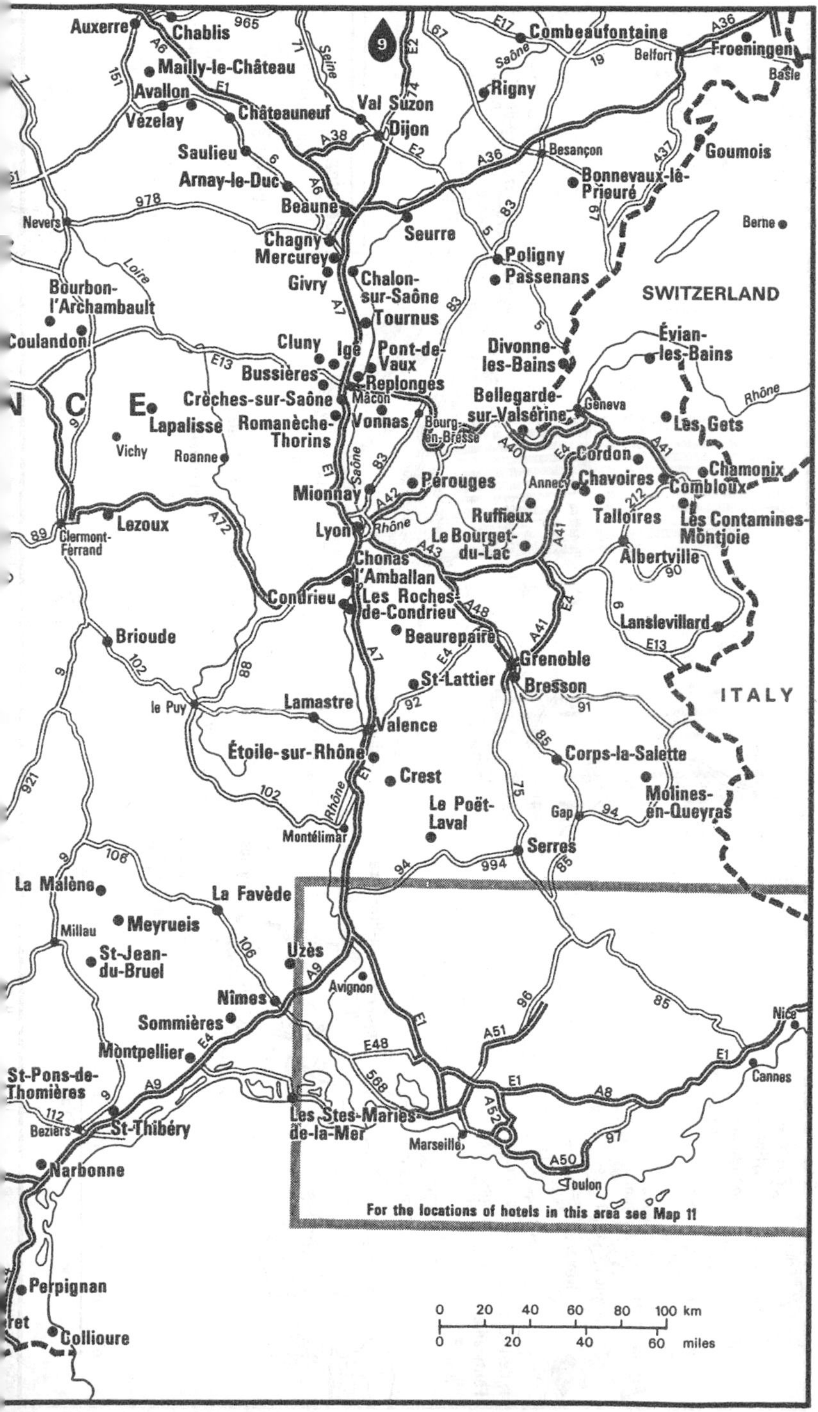

9
Auxerre
Chablis
Mailly-le-Château
Avallon
Vézelay
Châteauneuf
Saulieu
Arnay-le-Duc
Beaune
Val Suzon
Dijon
Combeaufontaine
Belfort
Froeningen
Basle
Rigny
Besançon
Goumois
Bonnevaux-le-Prieuré
Berne
Nevers
Seurre
Chagny
Mercurey
Givry
Chalon-sur-Saône
Poligny
Passenans
SWITZERLAND
Bourbon-l'Archambault
Coulandon
Tournus
Cluny
Igé
Pont-de-Vaux
Bussières
Replonges
Mâcon
Divonne-les-Bains
Évian-les-Bains
Crèches-sur-Saône
Bellegarde-sur-Valsérine
Geneva
N C E
Lapalisse
Vichy
Roanne
Romanèche-Thorins
Vonnas
Bourg-en-Bresse
Les Gets
Cordon
Chamonix
Annecy
Chavoires
Combloux
Mionnay
Pérouges
Talloires
Ruffieux
Les Contamines-Montjoie
Lezoux
Clermont-Ferrand
Lyon
Le Bourget-du-Lac
Albertville
Chonas l'Amballan
Condrieu
Les Roches-de-Condrieu
Lanslevillard
Beaurepaire
Brioude
Grenoble
Bresson
St-Lattier
ITALY
le Puy
Lamastre
Valence
Étoile-sur-Rhône
Crest
Corps-la-Salette
Molines-en-Queyras
Le Poët-Laval
Gap
Montélimar
Serres
La Malène
La Favède
Meyrueis
Millau
St-Jean-du-Bruel
Uzès
Avignon
Nîmes
Sommières
Nice
Montpellier
Cannes
St-Pons-de-Thomières
Les Stes-Maries-de-la-Mer
Marseille
Beziers
St-Thibéry
Toulon
Narbonne
For the locations of hotels in this area see Map 11
Perpignan
Collioure
0 20 40 60 80 100 km
0 20 40 60 miles
Loire
Saône
Seine
Rhône

Map 11 The South of France

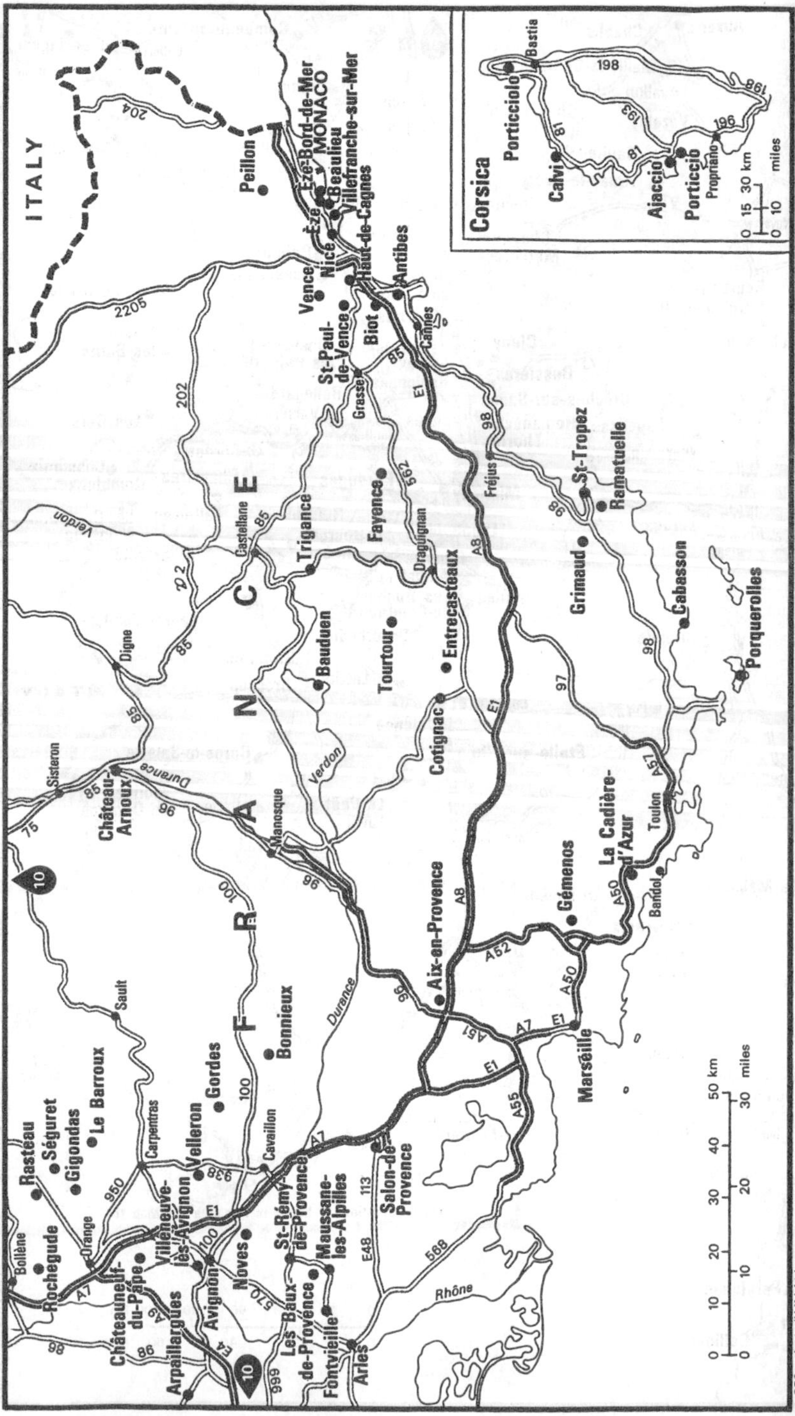

Map 12 Spain and Portugal

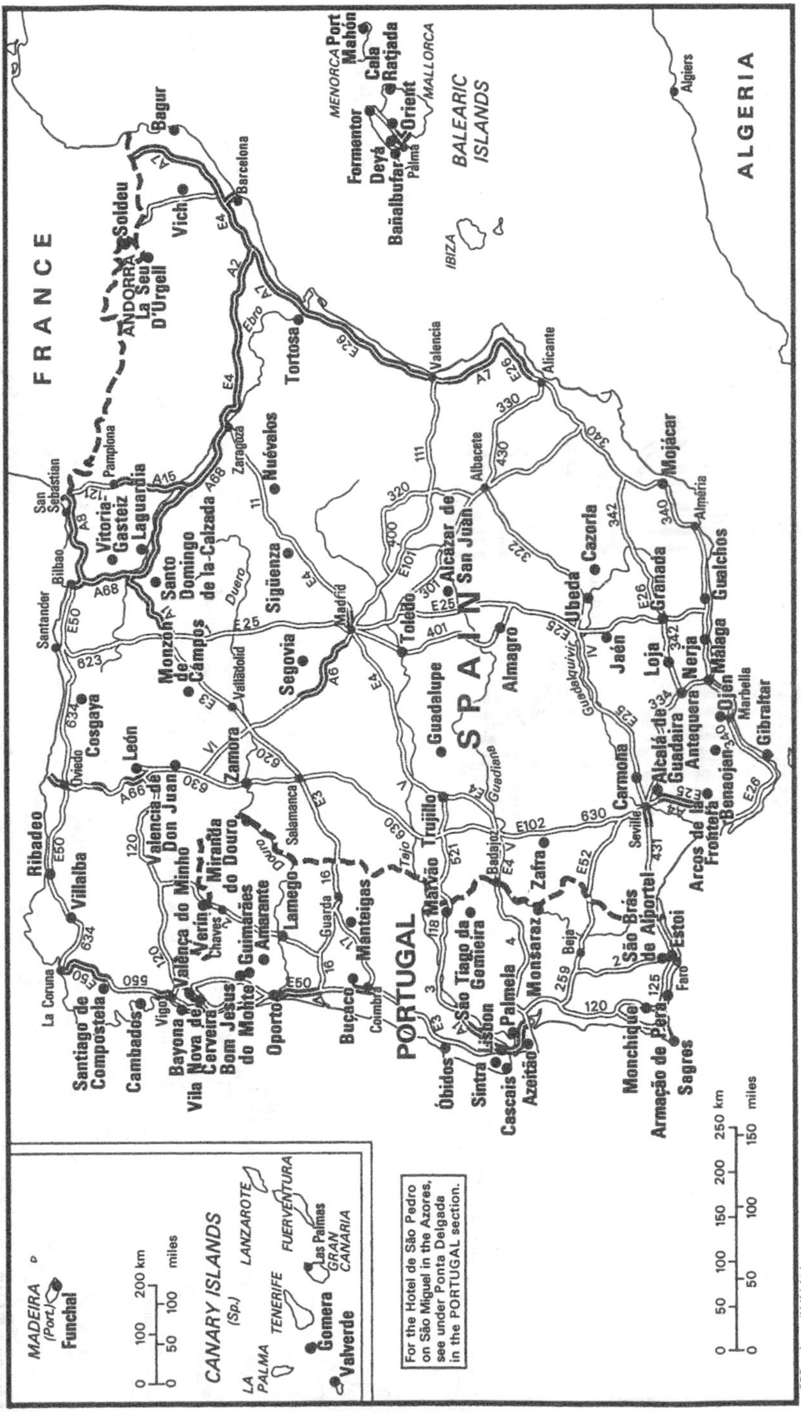

Map 13 Germany

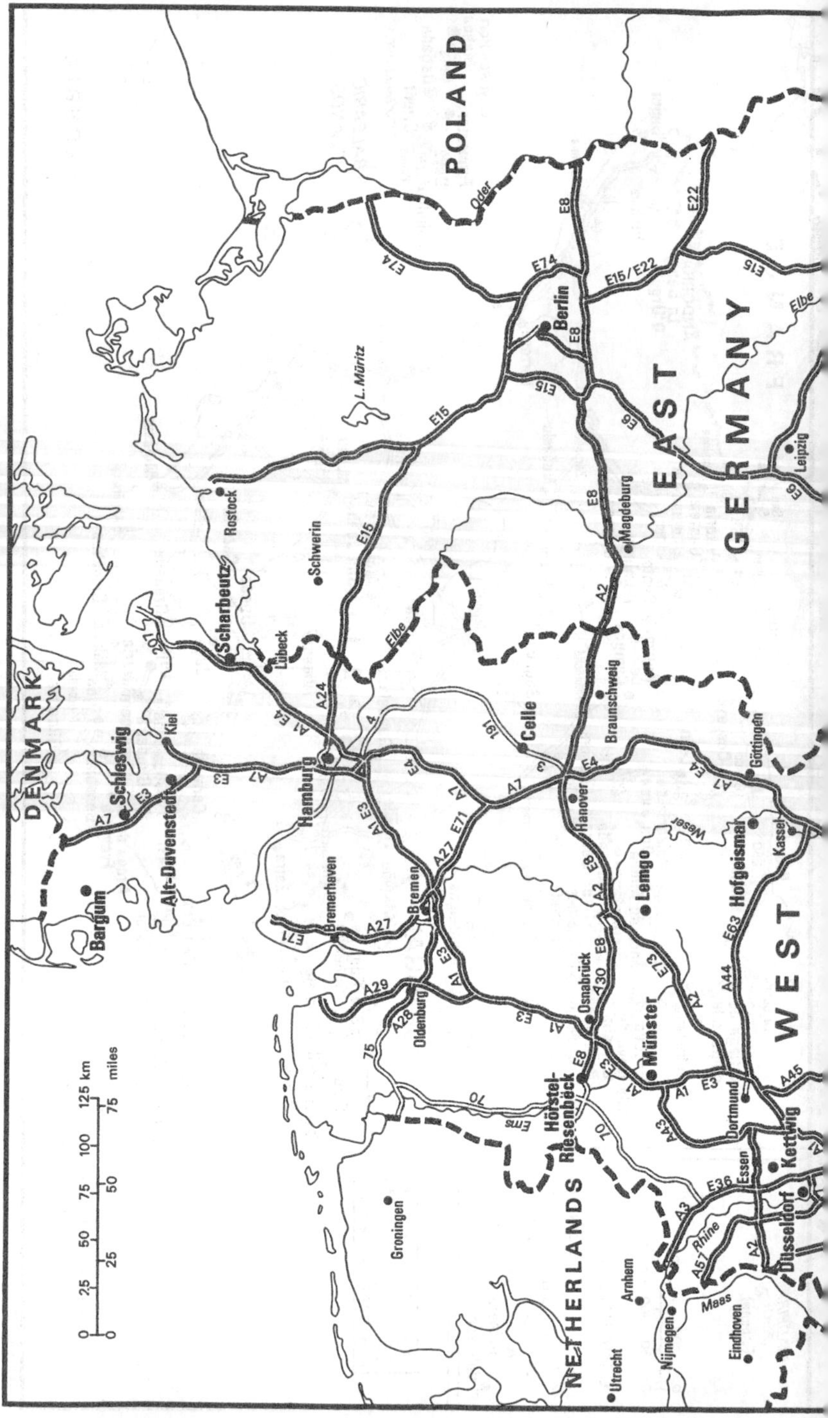

© GEOprojects (U.K.) Ltd.

Map 14 Switzerland

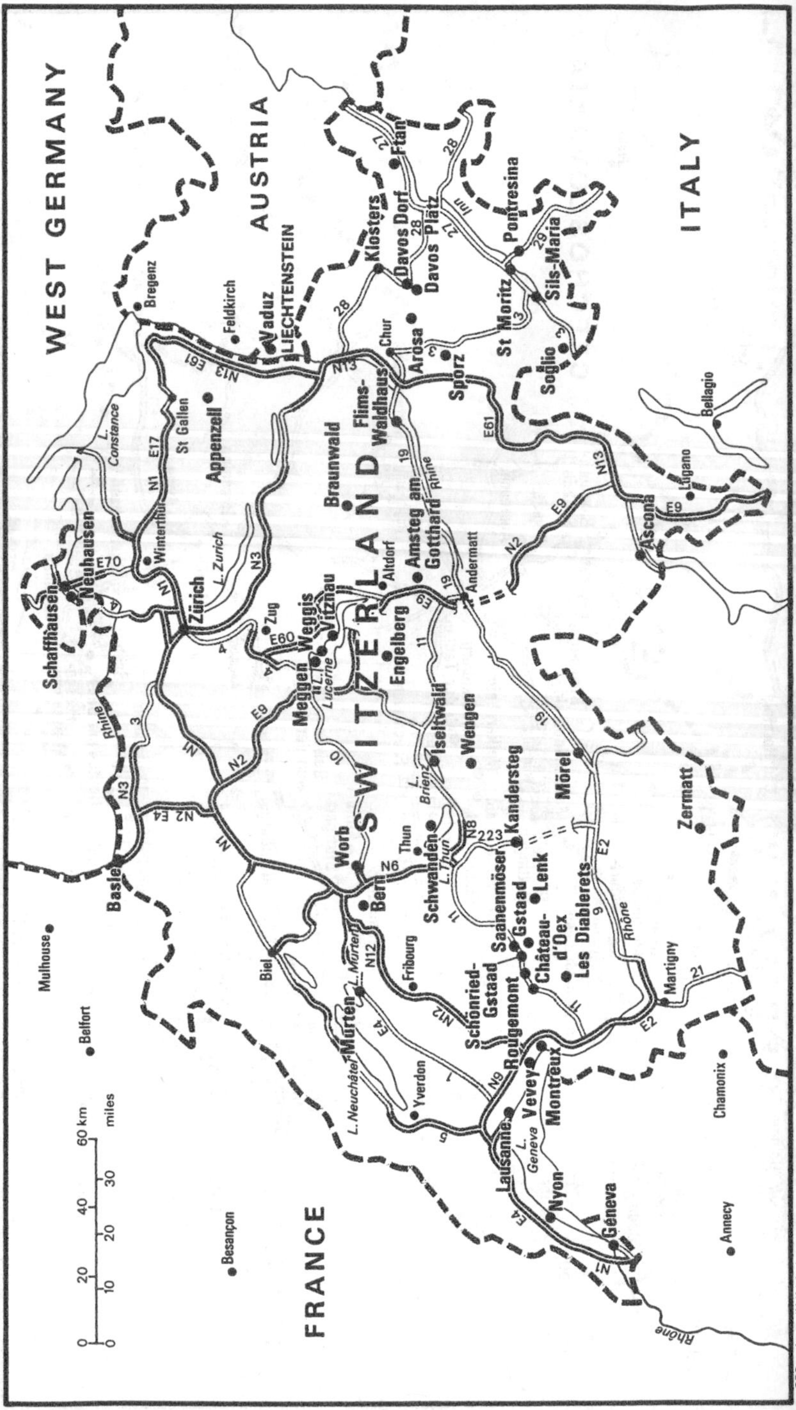

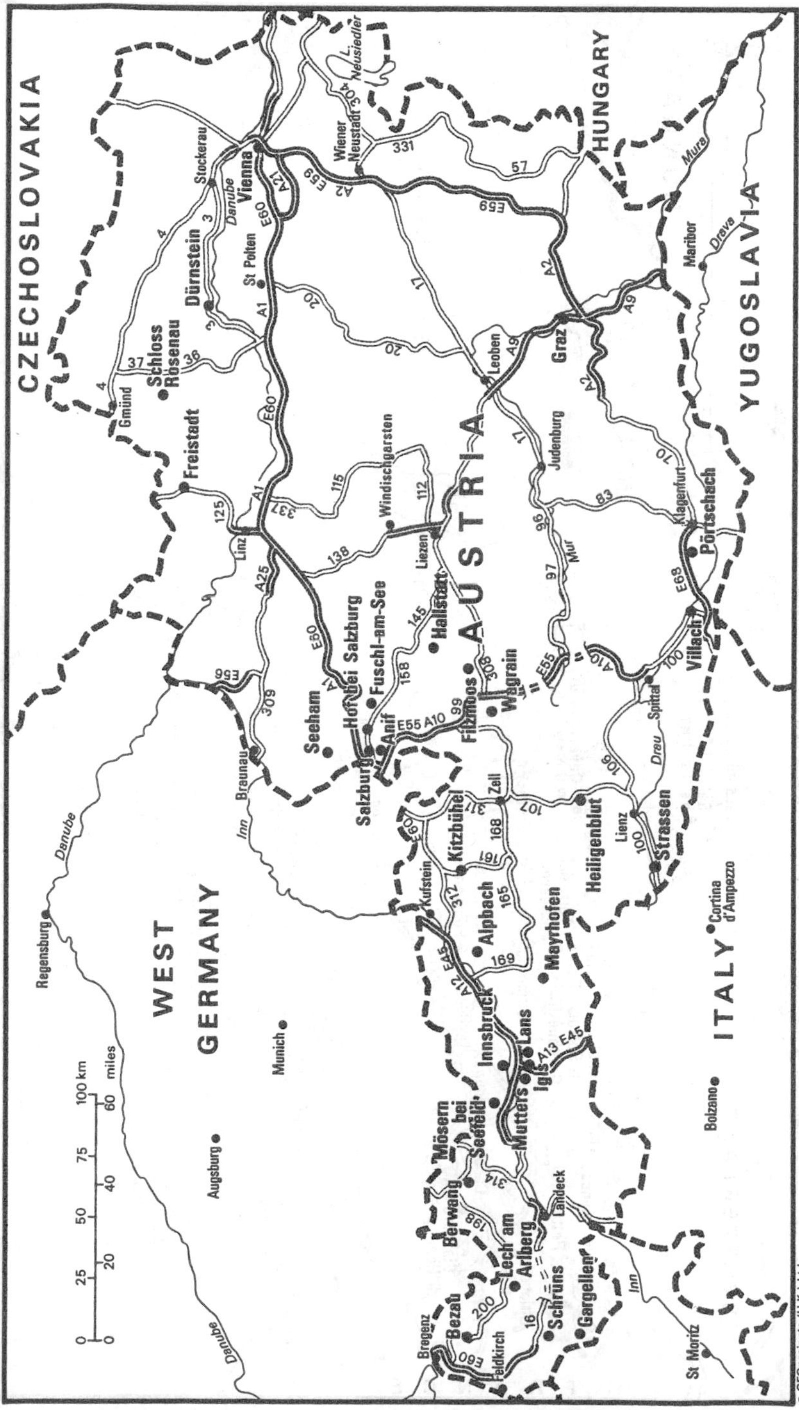
CZECHOSLOVAKIA
HUNGARY
YUGOSLAVIA
ITALY
WEST GERMANY
AUSTRIA
Vienna
Stockerau
Dürnstein
St Polten
Schloss Rosenau
Gmünd
Freistadt
Linz
Windischgarsten
Liezen
Hallstatt
Salzburg
Hof bei Salzburg
Fuschl-am-See
Seeham
Anif
Filzmoos
Wagrain
Braunau
Kitzbühel
Zell
Kufstein
Alpbach
Mayrhofen
Innsbruck
Lans
Igls
Mutters
Mösern bei Seefeld
Landeck
Berwang
Lech am Arlberg
Bezau
Schruns
Gargellen
Bregenz
Feldkirch
Leoben
Graz
Judenburg
Klagenfurt
Pörtschach
Villach
Spittal
Lienz
Strassen
Heiligenblut
Wiener Neustadt
L. Neusiedler
Maribor
Regensburg
Munich
Augsburg
Bolzano
Cortina d'Ampezzo
St Moritz
Danube
Inn
Mur
Mura
Drava
Drau
0 25 50 75 100 km
0 20 40 60 miles

Map 16 Italy and Malta

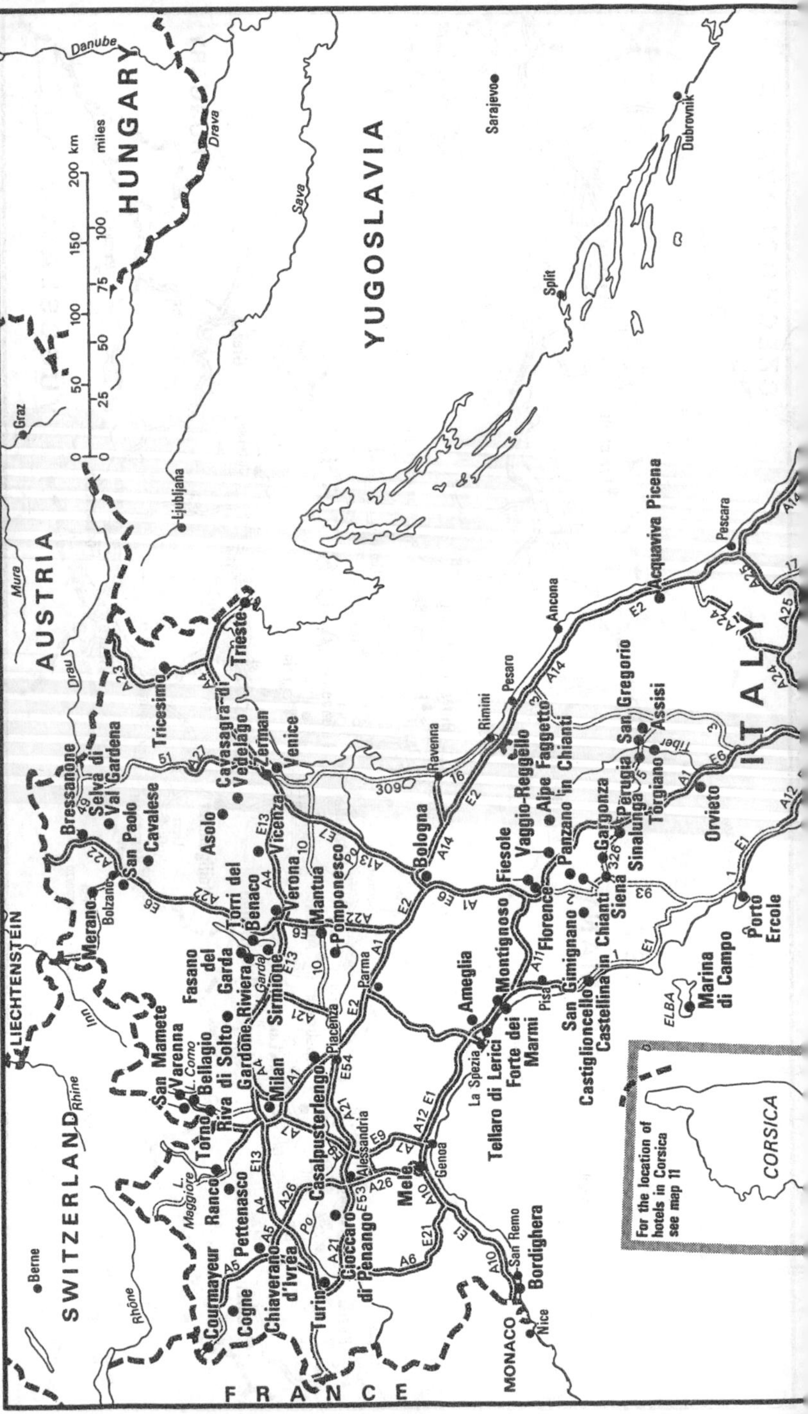

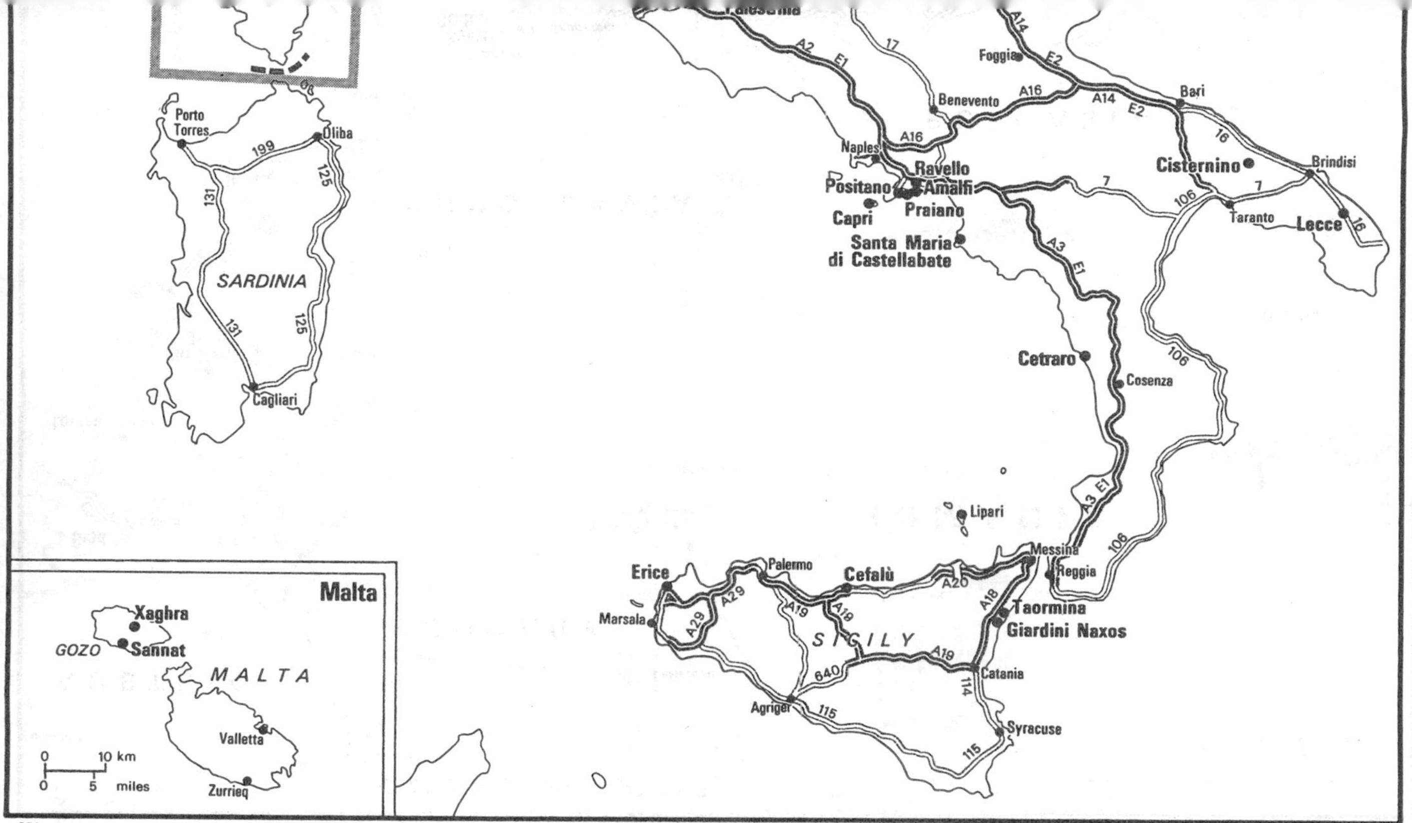
Foggia
Benevento
Bari
Naples
Ravello
Positano
Amalfi
Praiano
Capri
Santa Maria
di Castellabate
Cisternino
Brindisi
Taranto
Lecce
Cetraro
Cosenza
Lipari
Messina
Reggia
Taormina
Giardini Naxos
Erice
Palermo
Cefalù
Marsala
SICILY
Catania
Agrigen
Syracuse
Porto
Torres
Olibia
SARDINIA
Cagliari
Malta
Xaghra
Sannat
GOZO
MALTA
Valletta
Zurrieq
0
10 km
0
5
miles
A14
E2
A2
E1
A16
17
16
7
106
A3
114
115
640
A18
A19
A20
A29
199
131
125

Map 17 Greece and Yugoslavia

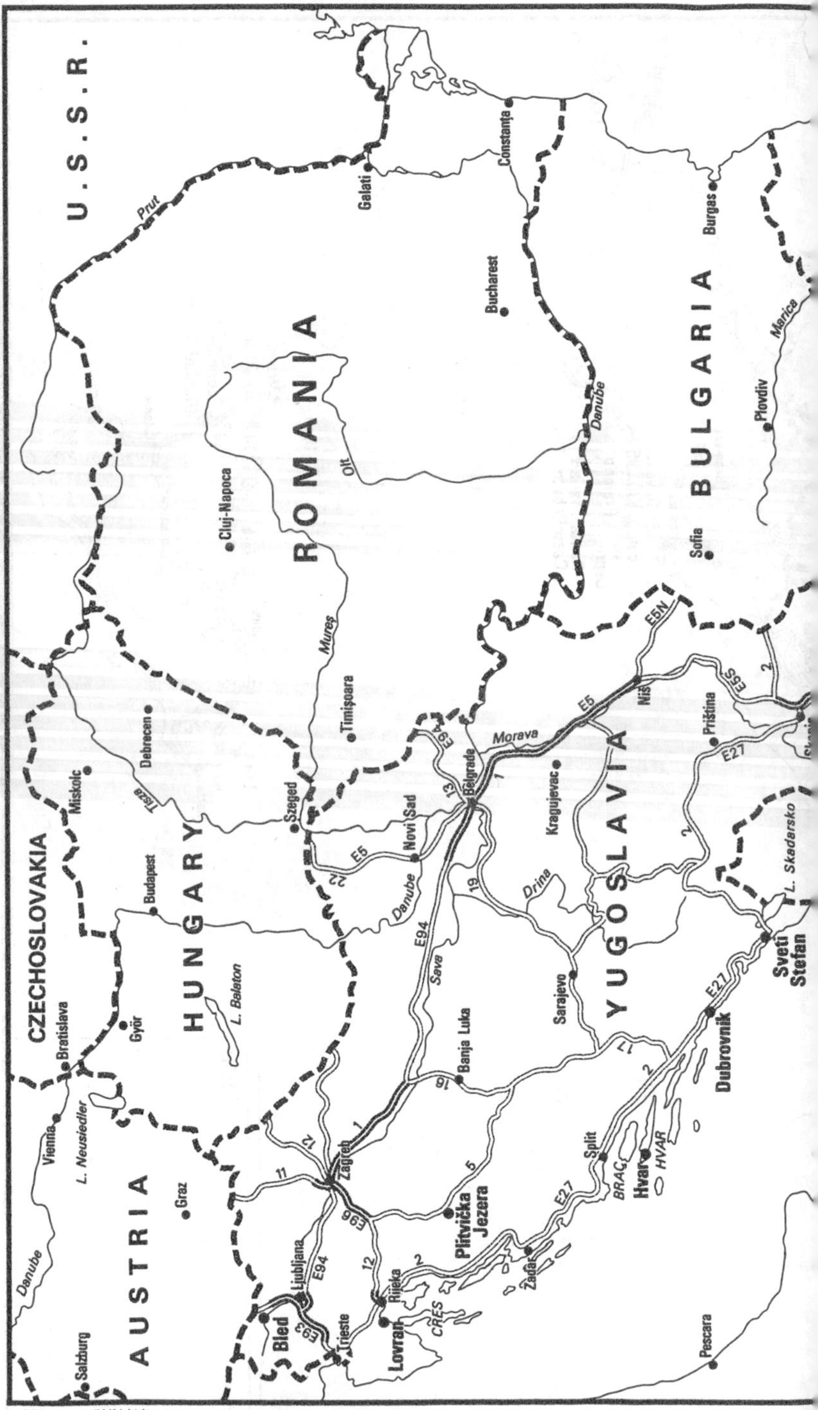

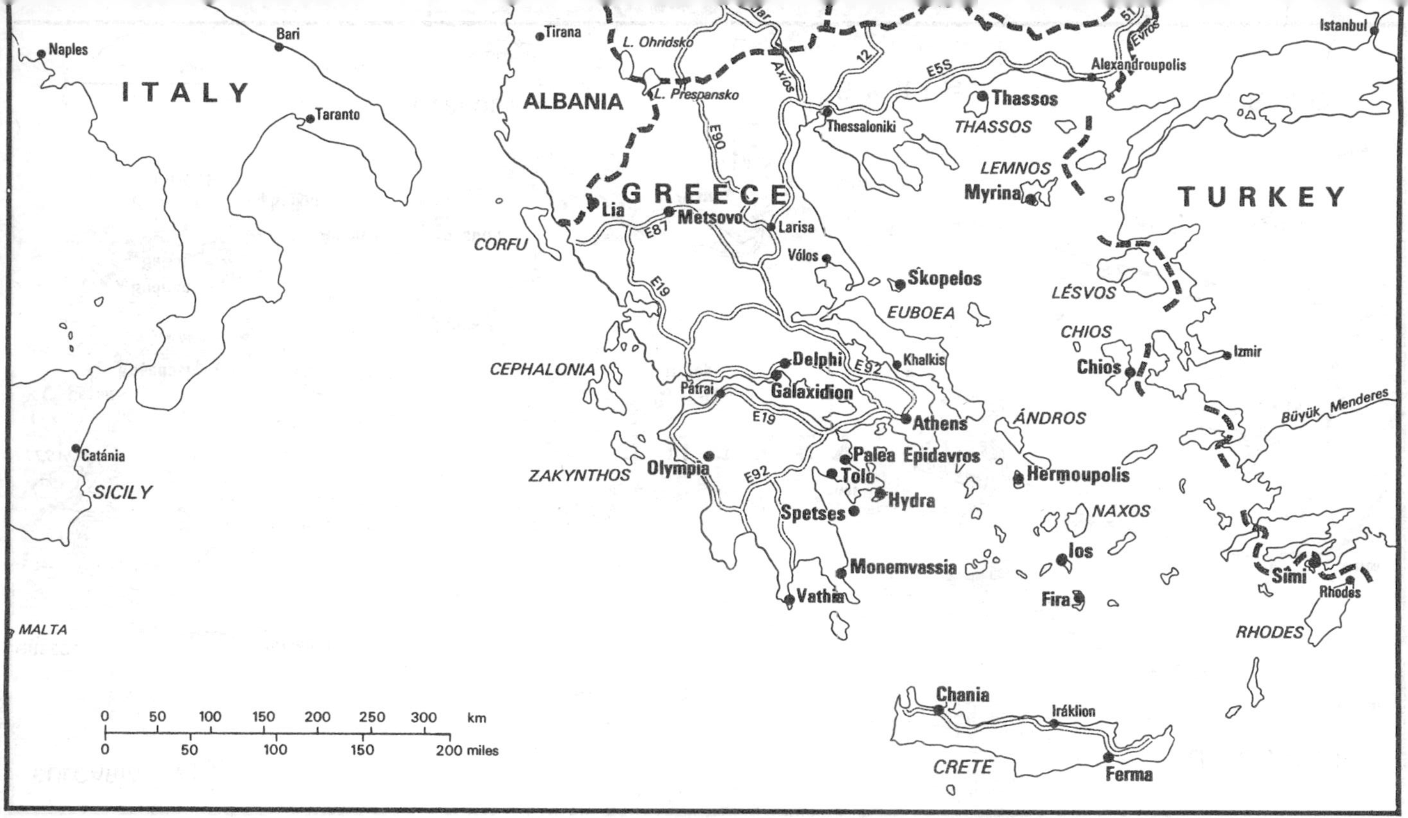
Naples
Bari
ITALY
Taranto
Catánia
SICILY
MALTA
Tirana
ALBANIA
L. Ohridsko
L. Prespansko
Axios
12
E90
E5S
51
Evros
GREECE
Lia
Metsovo
E87
CORFU
E19
Larisa
Vólos
Thessaloniki
Thassos
THASSOS
Alexandroupolis
Istanbul
LEMNOS
Myrina
TURKEY
Skopelos
EUBOEA
LÉSVOS
CHIOS
Chios
Izmir
Büyük Menderes
CEPHALONIA
Delphi
E92
Khalkis
Pátrai
Galaxidion
E19
Athens
ÁNDROS
Palea Epidavros
ZAKYNTHOS
Olympia
E92
Tolo
Hydra
Hermoupolis
Spetses
NAXOS
Monemvassia
Ios
Vathia
Fira
Sími
Rhodes
RHODES
Chania
Iráklion
CRETE
Ferma
0 50 100 150 200 250 300 km
0 50 100 150 200 miles

Map 18 Turkey

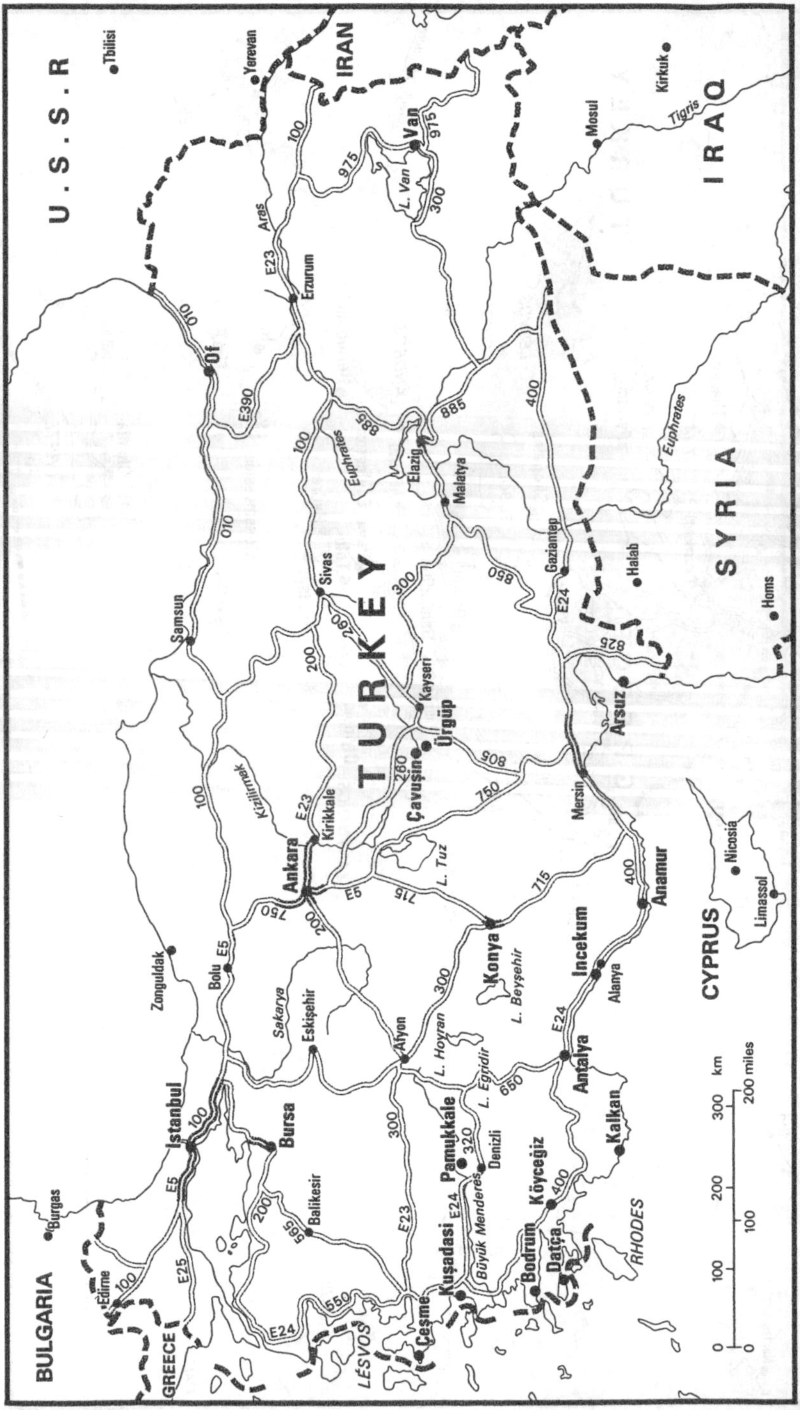

Map 19 Morocco

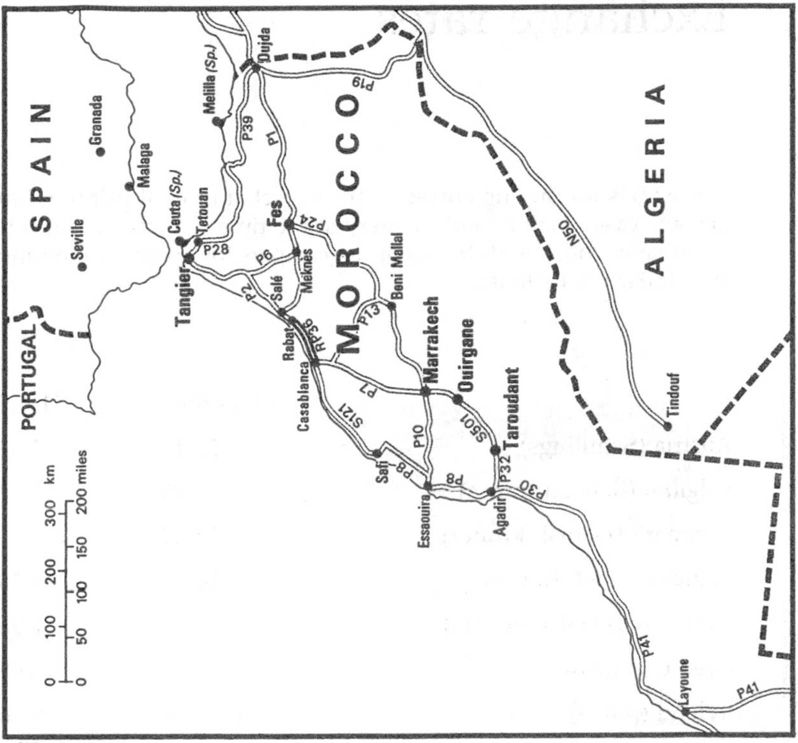

Exchange rates

These rates for buying currency are correct at time of printing but in some cases may be wildly awry at the time of publication. It is essential to check with banks or newspapers for up-to-date pound and dollar equivalents.

	£1 sterling	$1 US
Austria (Schillings)	22.10	13.83
Belgium (Belgian francs)	65.75	41.40
Denmark (Danish kroner)	12.22	7.70
France (French francs)	10.66	6.73
Germany (Deutschmarks)	3.15	1.98
Greece (drachmae)	266.30	168
Ireland (punts)	1.14	0.70
Italy (lire)	2,282	1,433
Luxembourg (Luxembourg francs)	65.80	41.40
Malta (Maltese cents)	0.55	0.33
Morocco (dirhams)	13.80	8.69
The Netherlands (guilders)	3.55	2.23
Norway (Norwegian kroner)	11.30	7.10
Portugal, Madeira (escudos)	260	163.45
Spain, Andorra, Balearics, Canaries (pesetas)	197.75	124.20
Sweden (Swedish kronor)	10.58	6.60
Switzerland (Swiss francs)	2.75	1.73
Turkey (lira)	3,415	2,076
Yugoslavia (dinars)	27,800	16,800

Hotel reports

The report forms on the following pages may be used to endorse or criticise an existing entry or to nominate a hotel that you feel deserves inclusion in next year's Guide. Either way, there is no need to use our forms or, if you do, to restrict yourself to the space available. All nominations (each on a separate piece of paper, please) should include your name and address, the name and location of the hotel, when you stayed there and for how long. Please nominate only hotels you have visited in the past 12 months unless you are sure from friends that standards have not fallen off since your stay. And please be as specific as possible, and critical where appropriate, about the character of the building, the public and bedrooms, the meals, the service, the night-life, the grounds. We should be glad if you would give some impression of the location as well as of the hotel itself, particularly in less familiar regions.

You should not feel embarrassed about writing at length. More than anything else, we want the Guide to convey the special flavour of its hotels; so the more time and trouble you can take in providing those small details which will help to make a description come alive, the more valuable to others will be the final published result. Many nominations just don't tell us enough. We mind having to pass up a potentially attractive hotel because the report is inadequate. There is no need to bother with prices or with routine information about number of rooms and facilities. We obtain such details direct from the hotels selected. What we are anxious to get from readers is information that is not accessible elsewhere. And we should be extremely grateful, in the case of foreign hotels and new nominations, to be sent brochures if you have them available. Nominations for the 1991 edition should reach us not later than 1 May 1990. The latest date for comments on existing entries is 1 June 1990.

We would ask you please never to let on to a hotel your intention to file a report. Anonymity is essential to objectivity. We would not have thought it necessary to say this, but we have heard that some readers have made a habit of telling hotel managers or owners that they would be reporting to us.

Please let us know if you would like more report forms. Our address is The Good Hotel Guide, Freepost, London W11 4BR, for UK correspondents (no stamp needed). Reports sent from outside the UK should be addressed to The Good Hotel Guide, 61 Clarendon Road, London W11 4JE, stamped normally.

These report forms may also be used, if you wish, to recommend good hotels in North America to our equivalent publication in the States, *America's Wonderful Little Hotels and Inns*. They should be sent adequately stamped (no Freepost to the United States), not to The Good Hotel Guide, but to America's Wonderful Little Hotels and Inns, PO Box 150, Riverside, Conn. 06878, USA.

Champagne winners

As usual we have awarded a dozen bottles of champagne for reports of the year. There is no overall winner; a bottle apiece will go to the following readers: Lynne and David Allen of Paris, Tim Brierly of Oxford, Chris and Dorothy Brining of West Kirby, Wirral, WH Bruton of Bristol, Philippa Herbert of Aldeborough St John, Yorkshire, Angela Lambert of London, Mary and Rodney Milne-Day of London, John and Connie Partridge of Naarden, the Netherlands, Charles and Helen Priday of London, JRF Seely of Terling, Essex, W Ian Stewart of Edinburgh, and Wende West of Beaulieu-sur-Mer, France. A further case will be on offer for 1990. No special entry form is required; everything we receive in the course of the year will qualify. A winner may be someone who nominates a new hotel or comments on an existing one. We award champagne to those whose reports are consistently useful as well as to individually brilliant examples of the art of hotel criticism.

To: *The Good Hotel Guide,* Freepost, London W11 4BR

NOTE: No stamps needed in UK, but letters posted outside the UK should be addressed to 61 Clarendon Road, London W11 4JE and stamped normally. Unless asked not to, we shall assume that we may publish your name if you are recommending a new hotel or supporting an existing entry. If you would like more report forms please tick ☐

Name of Hotel ______________________________

Address ______________________________

____

Date of most recent visit

Duration of visit

☐ New recommendation

☐ Comment on existing entry

Report:

I am not connected directly or indirectly with the management or proprietors
(Continue overleaf if you wish or use separate sheet)

Signed ______________________________

Name and address (capitals please) ______________________________

____

[1990]

To: *The Good Hotel Guide*, Freepost, London W11 4BR

NOTE: No stamps needed in UK, but letters posted outside the UK should be addressed to 61 Clarendon Road, London W11 4JE and stamped normally. Unless asked not to, we shall assume that we may publish your name if you are recommending a new hotel or supporting an existing entry. If you would like more report forms please tick ☐

Name of Hotel ______________________________

Address ______________________________

____

Date of most recent visit | Duration of visit

☐ New recommendation | ☐ Comment on existing entry

Report:

I am not connected directly or indirectly with the management or proprietors
(Continue overleaf if you wish or use separate sheet)

Signed ______________________________

Name and address (capitals please) ______________________________

____

To: *The Good Hotel Guide,* Freepost, London W11 4BR

NOTE: No stamps needed in UK, but letters posted outside the UK should be addressed to 61 Clarendon Road, London W11 4JE and stamped normally. Unless asked not to, we shall assume that we may publish your name if you are recommending a new hotel or supporting an existing entry. If you would like more report forms please tick ☐

Name of Hotel ________________________________

Address ________________________________

____

Date of most recent visit | Duration of visit

☐ New recommendation | ☐ Comment on existing entry

Report:

I am not connected directly or indirectly with the management or proprietors

(Continue overleaf if you wish or use separate sheet)

Signed ________________________________

Name and address (capitals please) ________________________________

____

[1990]

[illegible] The Good Hotel Guide, Freepost, London W11 4BR

[illegible] No stamps [illegible] in UK, but letters posted outside the UK should be [illegible] and stamped normally. Unless asked not to, we shall assume that we may publish your name if you are recommending a new hotel or supporting an existing entry. If you would like more report forms please tick [illegible]

Name of Hotel ______________________________

Address ______________________________

____

Date of most recent visit [illegible] Duration of visit [illegible]

[ ] New recommendation [ ] Comment on existing entry

Report:

[illegible]

Signed ______________________________

Name and address (Capitals please) ______________________________

____

To: *The Good Hotel Guide,* Freepost, London W11 4BR

NOTE: No stamps needed in UK, but letters posted outside the UK should be addressed to 61 Clarendon Road, London W11 4JE and stamped normally. Unless asked not to, we shall assume that we may publish your name if you are recommending a new hotel or supporting an existing entry. If you would like more report forms please tick ☐

Name of Hotel ____________________________________

Address ____

____

Date of most recent visit

Duration of visit

☐ New recommendation

☐ Comment on existing entry

Report:

I am not connected directly or indirectly with the management or proprietors
(Continue overleaf if you wish or use separate sheet)

Signed ____

Name and address (capitals please) ____________________

____

To: The Good Hotel Guide, Freepost, London W11 4BR

[illegible] No stamps needed in UK, but letters posted outside the UK should be addressed to 61 [illegible] Road, London W11 [illegible] and stamped normally. Unless asked not to, we shall assume that we may publish your name if you are recommending a new hotel or supporting an existing entry. If you would like more report forms please tick ☐

Name of Hotel ______________________________

Address ______________________________

____

Date of most recent visit ________ Duration of visit ________

☐ New recommendation ☐ Comment on existing entry

Report:

[illegible] with the management or [illegible] on a separate sheet)

____

[illegible] (capitals please) ______________________________

____